COURAGE
OFFICIAL
RUGBY UNION CLUB
DIRECTORY
1989–90

OFFICIAL

RUGBY UNION
CLUB DIRECTORY
1989–90

Edited by
TONY WILLIAMS
and
BILL MITCHELL

A

Daily Mail

PUBLICATION

Published by Harmsworth Publications Ltd,
for Associated Newspaper plc
London EC4Y 0JA

© 1989 Associated Newspaper plc

ISBN No. 0 85144 518 7

Distributed by: Biblios,
Glenside Industrial Estate,
Partridge Green, Horsham, Sussex RH13 8LD

Typeset by MC Typeset Ltd, Gillingham, Kent, and printed by Richard Clay Ltd, Bungay, Suffolk.

WHEN WILL WE SEE THE 800 PAGE DIRECTORY?

THE COURAGE CLUBS CHAMPIONSHIP has now settled down after two seasons in which the world's largest sporting league has proved an outstanding success.

All clubs who want to play in a well organized, progressive competition may now do so and as the seasons go by they will all find their correct level. Gone are the days when lively young clubs with good facilities and ever improving playing standards found their way to better matches continually blocked as there was little room within the fixtures lists of the more traditionally well known clubs.

We published this Directory last season to record the historic first year of the Courage Clubs Championship. With information requested late and club secretaries not really sure of our requirements it wasn't surprising that our first edition was published too late to be useful. However, in ten years time that first edition will be a collector's piece, as Rugby Union collects a new 'breed of statistician'. Thanks to Wisden, cricket has been well recorded for over a hundred years, I have personally been able to help Association Football to improve it's statistical records with a number of new annual publications and now we are determined to record the growth and success of 'The Courage Clubs Championship' as it develops season by season.

The progress of all clubs will be recorded. A running total of try scorers and penalty kickers will be listed. Record scores, record appearances, sequences of results and photographic records will help us increase the pages of this Directory every year.

Hopefully, club secretaries will ALL want their clubs to have a full entry in the Directory and they will also WANT us to include their photographs. (This year over 150 club secretaries failed to reply to our circular and although more photos were sent than last year, we would like to include a lot more).

We have enjoyed the helpful and cheerful co-operation of 'Michael Humphreys & Partners Ltd' who do such a great job for Courage and the R.F.U. with their excellent administration of the Championship and our special thanks go to Allison Walter and Sue Madge.

In semi-professional Football today a new phenomenon has emerged – 'The Groundhopper' – whose hobby is 'collecting' as many grounds as he can visit each season. As the Courage Clubs Championship develops and some clubs make their way right through the complicated 'pyramid' system of Leagues it is quite likely that Rugby Union will also find its extrovert band of followers who will travel the country watching their beloved sport from Aller to Ashington or Redruth to Rushmoor.

What a lovely hobby! I wonder who will be the first enthusiast to visit every member club. One thing is sure, by the time that achievement is accomplished 'The Courage Championship Rugby Club Directory' will be well established and will also probably contain at least 800 pages!

TONY WILLIAMS
Managing Editor

WELCOME

THE COURAGE CLUBS CHAMPIONSHIP has quickly established itself as a major part of the Rugby Union Football calendar in England. That it has done so in such a short space of time reflects the amount of work, skill and effort put into the organisation by all concerned.

There is no doubt that the introduction of these National leagues was timely and this can best be shown by the amount of interest generated by the clubs in the Championship and the media coverage which results.

Courage have played a full part in the success of this venture and I am pleased to have the opportunity to endorse the thanks of others for all the co-operation and assistance they offer to the Rugby Football Union.

I take this opportunity also to wish all the players and Officials of clubs in membership a very happy and enjoyable season. May it be one to remember and cherish on and off the field.

D.L. SANDERS
President,
The Rugby Football Union

THE PUBLICATION OF this Official Directory comes on the eve of the third season of the Courage Clubs Championship. In only two years the English game has come a long way, and we at Courage are proud to have played an important part.

To see the extent of the progress made, we can look with great satisfaction at the strength in depth now evident in the game in England. Bath may have taken the major honours – including the Courage Clubs title – but many other clubs have also demonstrated top form.

There is a resurgence in rugby shown not only by the commitment of players, but also by the enthusiasm of supporters. Ever larger crowds are backing the teams and are being rewarded by the sight of first-class rugby.

This new spirit is seen at all levels of the game, with fitness and determination clearly on parade from early season right through to the final matches. And sportsmanship is not forgotten, showing the real character of rugby.

We are now eagerly anticipating the new season and looking forward to the further success of the Courage Clubs Championship.

MICHAEL REYNOLDS
Executive Director Public Affairs,
Courage Ltd

CONTENTS

ACKNOWLEDGEMENTS

ONCE AGAIN it is our pleasure to acknowledge all the help we have been given in producing this second Directory – starting appropriately with Courage Ltd. and the Executive Director of Public Affairs, Michael Reynolds.

In our Editorial the tremendous efforts of Michael Humphreys and his company's team have been acknowledged, but the thanks can well be repeated, whilst we could not possibly have produced the book on time without the extraordinary dedication and energy shown by Ken and May Culver and their very efficient team at MC Typeset Ltd. From Harmsworth Publications there was the support and help of Sally Cartwright, the Managing Director, Ken Hole and their efficient staff.

Assembling a directory of this nature is a mammoth task and it can never be accomplished in a satisfactory manner wtihout the help of the clubs secretaries, whose task it is to send in information, all of which we try to print. As the years roll on not only will this process become much easier for all concerned, but also as clubs realise how potentially good the book must be for their own prestige and publicity they will themselves insist on supplying more and more information and pictures, which will go into each succeeding publication.

We are most grateful to all those secretaries and press officers, who replied to our requests for information (and this year they were in a vast majority), and we would suggest that next year you not only supply us with as much information and photographic material that you can, but also bombard us with constructive ideas which would help us to make this a better book. It is your directory and you have a right to the best.

FOREWORD

WELCOME TO THE second edition of the Daily Mail Rugby Club Directory, the only comprehensive guide to all the clubs involved in the Courage Clubs Championship.

There have been many marvellous rugby moments since the first issue appeared in the bookshops a year ago.

Who will easily forget the magnificent climax to the Five Nations Championship when the title permutations before the last-day programme would have given a computer problems?

France, of course, were the eventual winners – to the disappointment of Scotland and England, who had cause once again to rue their inevitable failure to slay the Dragon at Cardiff. And this in a season which started so promisingly with success against the Australians at Twickenham and ended with the astonishing record-shattering triumph in Romania.

At club level, the toast was undoubtedly Bath RFC as their dedication and hunger for success was doubly rewarded in the Courage Championship and Pilkington Cup.

And after all this, the Lions achieved the seemingly impossible in Australia by recovering from a disastrous performance in the first Test to win the series and bring a dawn chorus of delight from all those who rose early to watch the rousing recovery live on television.

Now for the new season . . . and you will enjoy it all the more with this directory as your guide. Articles to set you talking . . . information by the fact-load . . . and comprehensive statistics and fixtures.

Have a winning time!

PETER LEA
Sports Editor,
Daily Mail

THE COURAGE PUB –
GOOD COMPANY,
GOOD BEER, GOOD FOOD

ONE OF THE single most enduring institutions in the British Isles is the pub.

For centuries it has been a haven for those seeking good company, good beer and good food – and still remains one of our most popular leisure venues.

Essentially, the role of the pub has not changed. But the standard to which pubs now operate has risen immensely to match the expectations of a more affluent and discerning population.

Courage is leading the industry in the type and quality of outlets it operates and is constantly striving to improve its retailing standards.

The range of pubs operated by Courage – from no-nonsense locals, tucked away from the main thoroughfares, to the new modern showpiece sites is immense, with more than 4,600 tenant licensees and a further 400 directly managed outlets across the south of England.

But as any customer knows however attractive the pub itself may be, the man or woman behind the bar is probably the single most important factor to success. Courage has a very comprehensive and thorough selection process which seeks to make that very difficult match of the right licensee in the right pub; and a major investment in training to ensure the licensees are equipped for the job in hand.

With the company's first class reputation in the trade it is able to attract some of the most professional and hard working couples in the business.

With their skills and the support they receive from the company, many make great successes of their businesses and form a close partnership with Courage that often endures for many years.

With the 1988 legislation giving greater flexibility of opening hours the pub is set on another chapter of its unfolding story which has seen it develop and improve to meet the needs and wishes of its customers.

But of course not all outlets supplied by Courage are directly operated by the company.

A very important market for Courage is the many thousands of pubs, clubs and other leisure outlets operated by individuals, small companies or large groups.

Free trade salesmen based in the regional locations have regular contacts with individual outlets to explain the range of products and services on offer and to give valuable advice and assistance.

At national level Courage has a specialised team whose job it is to deal 'headquarters to headquarters' with some of the biggest names in the leisure business who may own chains of pubs, wine bars, hotels or holiday centres.

At all levels the same standard of dedication to providing only a first class service operates.

COURAGE – OFFERING WIDE CUSTOMER CHOICE

COURAGE RECOGNISES THAT choice for customers is an essential ingredient of success.

So a wide range of ales and lagers is produced from the company's three breweries – a range so wide that no outlet stocks every item. The success of its various individual brands is the key to maintaining the success of the whole organisation.

Courage brews three major draught, cask-conditioned ales – Best Bitter and Directors Bitter, both brewed in Bristol, and John Smith's Yorkshire Bitter, brewed in Tadcaster.

The Courage attack on the lager market is led by the flagship of the whole Elders IXL Group – Foster's, known as the amber nectar. Courage now brews Foster's in draught and canned form, not only for the home market but for export as well.

More than 80 countries now take Foster's Lager and the latest market to open up is among the foreign embassies in Moscow, making it a truly worldwide brand.

Paul Hogan's Australian humour in the Foster's TV advertising has long been a hit with British consumers and the overall marketing programme for Foster's lager is one of the biggest behind any beer brand in Britain.

Miller Lite is brewed at the Berkshire Brewery and was a major success following its launch in 1986. With strong television advertising and promotional support, Miller Lite became a highly successful 'national' brand within one year.

Television commercials for Foster's, Miller Lite, Hofmeister, Kronenbourg 1664 lagers plus Courage Best Bitter and the John Smith's Bitter series are not only acclaimed for being the best, but have proven records supporting the strong sale of their individual brands.

Among brewery-conditioned ales, Courage Best Bitter is again market leader as well as John Smith's Yorkshire Bitter and Magnet Ale, plus mild beers – Dark Mild from Courage and Chestnut Mild from John Smith's.

In order to keep the choice as wide as possible, Courage also sells other brewer's products, some imported.

COURAGE AND SPORT

COURAGE LTD HAVE a long tradition in supporting sporting and community activities throughout the country. The following are the major sports events supported by Courage and by the John Smith's brand.

JOHN SMITH'S ANGLING CHAMPIONSHIP

The John Smith's Angling Championship has grown into the angling world's top tournament with "minnows" competing on equal terms with the sport's "big fish".

The total £25,000 sponsorship package by Courage heralds the twelfth year of backing, making it the longest running sponsorship in domestic angling.

JOHN SMITH'S YORKSHIRE CUP

Sponsored by the brewery for three years initially from 1985/86 season but this has been renewed for 1989/90 season. Competition is open to all professional rugby league clubs in Yorkshire (as defined by the *old* county boundaries) plus one invited team Mansfield. They play a qualifying round and thereafter it is a knock out competition. John Smith's produce a Man of the Match award at the Final.

JOHN SMITH'S MAGNET CUP

First run in 1960 this is the oldest sponsored flat race in the country (30th anniversary this year). There has been one dead heat in 1987; on two occasions the same horse has won in consecutive years: 1971 & 1972 – Prominent. 1985 & 1986 – Chaumiere.

The Magnet Cup itself is a silver cup gilded and valued at £1500; it is given as part of the prize.

READING FOOTBALL CLUB

Courage initially signed a three-year sponsorship agreement with Reading FC in 1984. A new contract to extend the sponsorship for a further three years was signed in May 1987.

Second Division Reading won the Simod Cup in 1988.

STEVE DAVIS

The association between Steve Davis and Courage began in 1982 when an initial sponsorship deal was agreed. The 'partnership' proved so successful that two years later, in 1984, the company signed him for a further five-year contract.

The much-publicised deal made sporting history because it was the first time ever than any British sports star had been sponsored to the tune of £1 million.

A national programme of exhibition matches is held each year when Steve Davis meets opponents drawn from Courage and John Smith's pubs and other supplied outlets giving their customers the chance to take on the superstar on the snooker table.

IAC ATHLETICS

In 1986 Miller Lite began its sponsorship of the IAC International Athletics Meeting, the longest running 'spectacular' athletics event in Britain.

In 1988, the year of the Seoul Olympics, Miller Lite increased its sponsorship of the IAC International by helping athletes to prepare for the Olympics at "warm weather" training camps in places such as California, Florida, Portugal and Tenerife.

In the last twelve months, Miller Lite has engaged in a multi-event sponsorship of British athletics, in a package beginning last December with sponsorship of international cross-country races from Cardiff Castle and warm-weather training again this Spring.

This year's International has attracted athletes from no fewer than 28 countries including Said Aouita, Olympic 800 Metres champion Paul Ereng and Britain's own Linford Christie.

FOSTER'S SPONSORSHIPS – Foster's and Cricket

Foster's has come to the rescue of one of Britain's greatest sporting institutions – the Oval cricket ground – with a substantial package of aid to ensure the future of the ground including repainting of the stands and buildings to complement the new stand and sporting centre.

Foster's is also investing in perimeter advertising boards at all test and county cricket grounds, revenue from which is channelled to the individual clubs, and is giving awards to century scorers at grass-roots club grounds. More than 550 cricketers received such awards in the scheme's first season, 1988.

The Foster's Tennis Classic attracts the world's top tennis players and celebrities. This year's Tennis Classic was in aid of the British Deaf Association and last year's event raised £150,000 for the Great Ormond Street Wishing Well Appeal.

The Foster's Polo Challenge will take place for the second year at Cirencester, this year in aid of the British Paraplegic Sports Society.

Foster's also sponsored a major Australian Rules Football match at the Foster's Oval in October '88. This fast-moving, action-packed sport is gaining popularity in Britain.

COURAGE LTD – PROUD PAST, CONFIDENT FUTURE

COURAGE – A COMPANY proud of its past and confident of its future. For two centuries the company, its pubs and its people have been an integral part of the very fabric of the nation and have earned for themselves a reputation many envy.

Much of the company's success over the generations has been its ability to adapt to changing circumstances and in today's highly competitive environment this skill has never been more important.

It is a challenge that is being enthusiastically met throughout Courage where a culture of innovation and flexible thinking is encouraged, ensuring that the company remains one of the most successful, exciting and progressive in today's industry by seizing and developing opportunities where and when they arise.

Now part of the international Elders IXL group, Courage has also benefitted from the Elders philosophy of identifying and responding to change ahead of the rest of the market with a flair and style that constantly sees it in the headlines.

So the experience of the past has served the company well. The decades to come promise even greater challenges.

Courage accepts these challenges willingly and faces the future with the utmost confidence.

REVIEW OF 1988–89
AND FUTURE PROSPECTS
By Bill Mitchell

THERE IS EVERY reason why a continued note of optimism can be sung by the game in England after a second season of Courage Leagues during the course of which most problems were coming close to being solved in a satisfactory way and the process of teams finding their own levels of competence continued logically. Also, there were signs that the system was bringing its benefits for England international rugby and this was one of the main objectives sought when the idea of leagues was first advanced.

The England team has been in the doldrums throughout the eighties with only three good seasons to report and one which could be passed off as being moderate. The good seasons were those of 1980, when Bill Beaumont's men won a worthy Grand Slam, and in 1982 the side finished a satisfactory second with victory over the touring Wallabies as a bonus.

Then there followed a period of weak performances when the main feature of England's results was the number of record defeats suffered. By 1988 the situation was poor but the team did end the Five Nations campaign with a rare win away (at Murrayfield) and a massive home victory over Ireland, who where later beaten in a special match in Dublin. A trip to Australia and Fiji was a disappointment with two test defeats in Australia, but a good win in Fiji.

However, the 1988–89 season for England has been most promising with a fine win over Australia at Twickenham in November being a starting point. Scotland – never easy opponents nowadays – managed a draw in the next match at Twickenham, but victories over Ireland and France (at Twickenham) followed and there was a better chance than usual that Wales could be beaten in Cardiff for the first time since 1963 and bring home the championship. A dubious try and poor performance on the day denied England that success, but a visit to Bucharest saw an astonishing triumph over Romania (58–3), who had with almost the same team beaten Wales in Cardiff in December. Four wins and a draw out of six was a good record, although those who would say that it could have been better had a point and a lack of adventure in all matches except against Australia and Romania was the cause. However, there has been an improvement and the latest season could be described as good, which meant that the eighties ended as they began with the poor stuff being forgotten. Without the leagues could this have happened? It is a matter of opinion, but one doubts it.

The leagues have meant a much higher standard of fitness among all clubs allied to greater skills. A successful team must have a complete complement of athletes in every position and more clubs are now beginning to achieve this objective.

Bath in 1988–89 did the double by not only taking the Courage League Division One title but they also took the new Pilkington Cup, although Leicester made them fight all the way in an absorbing, but low-scoring final at Twickenham (10–6). A week earlier Leicester had also handed Bath their only league defeat of the season, but as the match was played between the clubs' shadow squads because Bath had already comfortably won the title.

Criticism apart it could be said that it was another good campaign if one allows for the fact that the two champions of the top leagues were known long before the programme was completed. In the top section the main question was the identity of the team to finish seconde and Gloucester eventually took that honour from Wasps, who lost out on points difference and again failed to live up to their own hopes fostered by the knowledge that they have a very talented squad. The relegation problems were also settled quite early in this Division.

Saracens won all their Division 2 games but the scramble for the second promotion spot had a bizarre result as all the teams with a chance of going up failed to win and Bedford's draw at Sale sent them up! London Welsh were always likely descenders and they duly went down with fellow exiles London Scottish.

Replacing them were Plymouth Albion and Rugby, who were promoted for a second successive season with Wakefield missing out again. Plymouth scored a massive 311 points in their 11 matches, all of which they won; they must be in with a chance of making a real impression in higher circles.

Elsewhere in the leagues the "shakeout" continued – as it will for several seasons to come – but ther were the usual high-scorers who deserved special attention. In the North, Wigan won North West Division 1 thanks to scoring 223 points in 10 matches and Kirkby Lonsdale managed an impressiv e 220 points from nine games to win the North West North Division 1. In the same part of the North Hoylake took the West Division 3 with 280 points from 11 matches, but were outscored in the same division by St Mary's Old Boys, who achieved 299 but failed to ascend. Rotherham won

North East Division 1 with ten victories and 273 points and Whitby, another side with a perfect record, won their ten Durham/Northumberland 2 matches with 255 points scored – four more than rivals Sunderland. Bramley (236 in Yorkshire 1), Bridlington 243 (in Yorkshire 2), Hessle (241 in Yorkshire 4) and Sheffield Oaks (236 in Yorkshire 5) all had prolific results from their ten games and won promotion to higher leagues.

The outstanding team in the Midlands was Walsall, who won the top division and all their ten matches for a total of 210 points and promotion to Area League North. Elsewhere defences had improved but Camp Hill (216 in North Midlands 1), Aston Old Edwardians (in North Midlands Division 2 - 258), West Midlands Police (278 in North Midlands Division 3), Tenbury and Birchfield (284 and 310 respectively in North Midlands Division 4) were all teams which used their ten games profitably. Coventry Welsh won all their games in Warwickshire Division 1 with 274 points and Old Newtonians of Leicestershire Division 2 achieved 211 points (38 conceded) in winning all seven games. Bedford Swifts won the tiny six-team East Midlands Division 3 with five games won and 147 points scored, whilst Cleethorpes in Notts., Lincs. and Derbys. Division 4 East managed 241 points and promotion from only eight games.

The South-West produced some stirring scoring deeds and leaky defences with Clifton's attack taking the Division 1 title and promotion to Area League South as a result of 237 points scored n 10 matches – to pip Hygh Wycombe on points. The winners of the three other major leagues in the division – Matson (South-West Division 2 – 244 ponts and four less than rivals Brixham), Gordon League (218 points and 10 wins in Western Counties League) and Banbury (242 points in Southern Counties League) – all needed strong attacks to advance, but top scorers here were Wiveliscombe (Somerset Division 3) who amassed 459 points in winning all their 11 games. Beside their efforts several other performances pale by comparison but good scoring efforts came from a number of teams, which we detail elswhere in the book, although Westbury's 258 points from six games in Berks., Dorset and Wilts Division 3 rate special attention.

Finally, in London Basingstoke's achievement in gaining promotion to Area League South from London League 1 was based on 240 points scored in 10 matches. Here there were astonishing scoring achievements from Eton Manor (369 from 10 games in London North East 3), Old Brightonians (326 points with only seven conceded in Sussex League 3 in six games), H.A.C. (347 points from eight matches in Middlesex League 5) and Bancrofts (412 points from their 10 Eastern Counties League 4 games).

Thrills and spills? Yes! It may be trite to say it, but the leagues mean that every player and every club does now have a yardstick by which they can assess respective abilities – very much like a national handicapping system similar to golf. At the top end of the scale there is the prospect of the England team being improved to possible World Cup winning standards. At the bottom there is the satisfaction of knowing that each club and player has reached a certain level of competence – whatever that may be. In this organisation everyone matters.

EXPANSIVE
By Terry O'Connor (Daily Mail Rugby Correspondent)

IN LAST YEAR'S annual I wrote that any home country with serious aspirations of winning the 1991 World Cup had to change course and play a more expansive game, like New Zealand and France who contested the 1987 final.

During the 1988–89 Five Nations Championship there were signs that this important message was getting through. In the end France, easily the best footballing country competing, emerged winners of the title and also scored more tries than any other team.

England, only team to beat France with a masterly forward display, had promised to play in a more adventurous style with a running performance against the touring Wallabies. It was exciting to see Englishmen attacking from their own half to create some superb scores.

They had been inspired during the build up Wallaby matches, starting with London, who were prepared to attack rather than confine themselves to a grinding forward encounter. This was due to the Harlequin coach Dick Best who had been strongly influenced by former All Black Earle Kirton.

When South-West and the North followed London's example by winning in a similar style it seemed that English rugby at last had been freed from the curse of a forward dominated game obsessed by set pieces and limited movement.

Sadly it proved a false dawn as seen when the championship unfolded. England missed out on the opening day while Scotland revealed their rucking skills and attacking flair to crush Wales 21–7 at Murrayfield. On the same Saturday in Dublin, France had a shattering opening hour falling 21–10 adrift to Ireland before a sparkling revival for a late 26–21 win.

England were odds on favourites to retain the Calcutta Cup but the Scots had not forgotten the spoiling tactics which had beaten them in Murrayfield the previous year. They adopted similar tactics and gave their opponents little room to move.

It was obvious in this game that the Welsh born scrum-half Dewi Morris who had excelled in games against Australia did not possess the speed of thought or pass to release his backs in the pressurised games – always a feature of the top European tournament. Unfortunately the selectors did not recognise this failure until the championship was over and they played an additional match with Rumania.

Therefore these brave hopes, born during the victory over Australia, were put on ice with England deciding on a power game when they arrived in Ireland to find themselves faced with a wet track at Lansdowne Road. It was a clinical performance but left thousands wondering whether winning was all that mattered. Did style not matter? Even when well on top, England were not prepared to bring the backs into the game.

Meanwhile Ireland won for the third successive occasion in Cardiff with Noel Mannion, the Irish No. 8, running 60 yards for a remarkable try. Wales complained Paul Dean's score came following a knock-on, but were later compensated when given an illegal try against England.

France cast aside their tight forward game and in Paris Serge Blanco proved once again that he is the world's finest attacking full back when he helped to demolish the once feared Welsh. The limitations of the Wales game was seen when they only managed to hold their own in the set pieces, but lacked their once native attacking flair or ability to win loose possession.

At this stage with three championship defeats Wales were experiencing one of the darkest periods of their rugby history. Defeat to France at Cardiff in 1988 had been followed by outright destruction in New Zealand when they conceded more than a hundred points in two test matches. During the autumn they were beaten at home by Romania, although managed a win over Western Samoa. Little wonder one wit commented that it was a good thing they did not play all of Samoa.

With the arrival of the third championship Saturday it was obvious the crunch match would be France's appearance at Twickenham. Even drizzling rain could not spoil the car park parties as anticipation was high. By now Blanco had attained Hollywood status following so much media space in England.

Sadly those valuable lessons were forgotten on the day as the English successfully decided to squeeze the life out of the French forwards. Even after they scored a brilliant try by accident the iron grip remained the tactical plan. Skipper Will Carling's first try for his country came about when he discovered the French had only eyes for wing Chris Oti which allowed him to exploit a gap which opened.

In this game No. 8 Dean Richards produced a fantastic performance creating a try for the fair haired flanker Andy Robinson who gave an exhibition of perpetual motion. Blanco seemed bemused as he watched his forwards badly mauled and therefore incapable of producing the ball which so often ensures him a leading role.

While this grim rugby affair was providing an 11–0 win, Murrayfield was ablaze with activity as the Scots and Irish scored 58 points with Scotland collecting the important 16 point margin. After falling badly behind Ireland staged a remarkable recovery but the Scots revelled in the open spaces and lack of tension which so often makes these encounters a delight.

As the triumphant England players left the field at Twickenham they felt certain that at last they would lay the bogey of Cardiff where they had not won since 1963. Even the bookmakers tipped them to win which is not surprising as Wales had lost three championship matches.

As the day approached the odds lessened, the skies opened to produce a typical Cardiff rugby day, and Arms Park still appeared a formidable fortress to the Englishmen. Whether England had any thoughts of reverting back to those running tactics which beat Australia is doubtful. The pouring rain ensured they had decided on trench warfare.

This was ideal for Wales as the only rugby where they had achieved any equality was in scrums and line-outs. On the day their superiority in both proved decisive. England's success at winning the loose ball gave them the edge for most of the first half until Rory Underwood made one of those mistakes which so often puts a black mark on his rugby career.

He seemed to have well covered a long diagonal kick but as so often he proved indecisive. Instead of running the ball into touch after slipping, he threw a suicide pass to Jon Webb and Arthur Emyr hacked through for Mike Hall to score a dubious try.

This put England in arrears soon after half-time but Carling was full of confidence that his men could still save the day. He might have been proved right if Morris had not again proved the Achilles heel by throwing out a wretched pass after the England forwards won three successive rucks.

That proved the end as for the final 20 minutes the rugby knowhow of the Welshmen took over. Scrum-half Robert Jones chipped into the box and Robert Norster won the ball. England never escaped from their own half for the final quarter.

Meanwhile the French showed how to play the Scots in Paris by winning 19–3 and Finlay Calder admitted they were a class way ahead of his team.

There are only two seasons left for a home country to develop the skills and tactical awareness for all conditions against the proven warriors of New Zealand and France who must be favourites at this stage.

British Lions hero Mike Teague and lovely Lorraine Hancock "take the plunge" with best man John Gadd (Gloucester flanker) on the right. The Australian now wishes he had married during the tour rather than after it. Photo: Gloucester Citizen

EXILES
By Huw Richards

TO READ J.B.G. Thomas's "Great Rugger Clubs", published in 1962, is to enter another age.

It isn't just the title – does anyone under 60 use the term "rugger" nowadays? that echoes another world. His selection of 23 English clubs makes strange reading today. No place for Bath – or for two of their closer rivals last season, Orrell and Nottingham. But he does include Guy's Hospital, Old Merchant Taylors and Old Millhillians.

The demise of the closed club has been one of the features of club rugby in the last quarter-century. As the senior game has become more committed and competitive and demanding teams drawn from small, closed groups had no chance of keeping pace. Only the Exiles clubs, drawing on a far wider catchment area than the products of a single school or hospital, have lasted the pace.

But as the arrival of leagues has intensified these trends, even their ability to survive has come into doubt. A few years ago Harlequins chairman John Currie said that in the future London would only be able to support three or four major clubs. No doubt his own club and Wasps would be two, and at the time the Exiles might also have been contenders.

They were the top three in the 1981–2 London Merit Table and all made final appearances in the John Player Cup. But their relative decline was reflected when all three started Courage League life in Division Two, and brutally rubbed in as Welsh and Scottish tumbled into Division Three at the end of last season. With the Third Division representing a transition zone between the senior and junior ranks, there is a fear that the Exiles are about to join the Old Boys and Hospitals as casualties of history.

Where other London clubs reflect the strength of the game in the capital, the Exiles are vulnerable to fluctuations in a more complex set of relationships. All three depend on supplies of players from their home countries. Talent may dry up or changes in the jobs and property markets stop the flow.

Nowhere are worries greater than at London Welsh. Memories of the great days of the late sixties and early seventies – when Welsh were as unstoppable as Bath today, receiving an endless torrent of talent from Wales and despatching a record seven players on the historic 1971 Lions tour of New Zealand – still burn brightly at Old Deer Park.

Their 1985 John Player Cup final appearance was hoped to be harbinger of a new tradition of success. Instead it looks to have been the last gasp of an old one. In an otherwise tightly-contested division Welsh were clearly doomed to the drop from early in the season, while their second successive cup exit at the hands of Berry Hill would only have justified "Cup Shock" headlines if the result had been reversed.

Where has all the talent gone? Aside from general worries about the state of the Welsh game, former Exiles chairman Geoff Evans, one of the magnificent seven Lions in his playing days, points out; "Welsh clubs will make a greater effort nowadays to keep a promising player in Wales – looking after them in the best sense of the word. So we don't get mature, experienced quality players in the numbers we used to", he says.

Students still come to London and join Welsh, but are often transients, moving back to Wales or elsewhere in England when their courses finish.

And with senior Welsh clubs only a couple of hours away by train, two high-class students studying in London have chosen to play in Wales: "Richard Wintle plays at Bridgend and Damian Griffiths at Newport, both wingers. You could argue that as wingers they don't think they'd get much chance with us, or that they'd strengthen us a great deal. There's probably a bit of both", says Geoff.

But without the mature player, your forwards will always struggle. And it isn't just the desire of Welsh clubs to hang on to players that is holding the Exiles back. The much wider social base the game enjoys in Wales means many players are in jobs where they simply can't afford the cost of living, and in particular of property, in the south-east. Many of the 1960s greats were teachers, but, with property prices and education cuts making London teaching jobs much less attractive, this particular Welsh export is following coal into decline.

The Welsh have always been hospitable towards other London exiles with no obvious home – a Norwegian sailor called Gunnar Poppe was an interwar stalwart and more recently a series of New Zealanders have appeared, not to mention England outside-half Neil Bennett.

An understandable response from some club members was to raise the possibility of going open, but this has been firmly rejected. Geoff Evans points out: "It is hard to see who might join us if we did go open". The ambitious English player is still far more likely to opt for near-neighbours like

Harlequins and Rosslyn Park. To become just another not very successful rugby club would be to sacrifice a unique identity.

London Scottish secretary Ross Luke, who points out that the debate on open status has not even been raised at his club, applauds the Welsh decision, arguing that closed status – making Scottish the magnet for all rugby-playing Scots in the south-east – is a positive advantage.

He holds that view in spite of their relegation; "We never got anything like our full side out, and we lost a number of matches we should have won", he says – a view backed by his Irish counterpart Pat Barragry who admits they were very fortunate to take the league points at the Richmond Athletic Ground.

Scottish are determined to bounce straight back. With Wakefield, desperately unlucky still to be in the third, opening opponents on September 9th they'll get an early idea of the likely competition. If ever an opener also looked a championship decider, this one does.

Ross Luke suggests that, so long as they don't get stuck in the Third, relegation might benefit them in the long run: "It has promoted a good hard look at ourselves and the way we run the club".

One change has been recognition that the club fulfils two functions – serious first-class rugby for the top players, social rugby for the rest: "The two have now been split completely with 30 or 40 players in the first squad and a separate set-up and committee for the rest of the club. The first squad will be reviewed every month", says Mr. Luke.

And with Gavin Hastings captain and Alistair McHarg nominated coach there'll be a determined dedicated attitude at top level: "The players have taken full responsibility for relegation, recognising that they didn't produce the goods. There'll be no ski-ing holidays in February this season", says Mr. Luke.

The social composition of the Scottish game makes them less vulnerable than Welsh: "There's a mix of the broader base in the borders and the professional classes in the big cities. A lot of professional people from Edinburgh or Glasgow move to London for career reasons", says Mr. Luke. Fewer problems with property prices here – nor is it practical to go home to play at weekends.

The same applies to Irish, still bemused by their spectacular last-match collapse at home to Blackheath, losing a 21–0 lead and promotion. They draw from only 12,000 players in all Ireland. The game is the province of a small but wealthy and well-educated business class, making finance workers such as Brendan Mullin or Hugo McNeill typical recent imports.

Ireland's extremely young population and high unemployment rates are likely to combine to send ever-larger groups of young people across the Irish Sea, and the Irish club – with a firm financial and playing base around their six acre wholly-owned site in Sunbury – stand to benefit. And with a huge population apparently able to claim Irish grandparents, Irish will continue, along with Jack Charlton, to make the use of their eligibility rules. Wing Conor Malucci, half-Italian, and full-back Jim Staples are among the rising young players qualified this way.

The Exiles clubs have contributed a rich and distinctive flavour to English, and in particular London, rugby. Their determination to retain those distinctive identities will be widely welcomed. But ability to compete with Bath, Leicester or Wasps has probably gone for good. Ability to retain senior status depends as much on events in Dublin, Llanelli and Glasgow as in London, but also on willingness to conduct the sort of ruthless self-examination that looks to be happening at Scottish.

THE NORTH – STRENGTH IN BREADTH
By Paul Stephens

WHEN THE ANNOUNCEMENT was made that the Courage leagues would start in September 1987, the loudest applause came from those most acutely aware of the democratic opportunity it presented. No longer would life for an enterprising club be a perpetual uphill struggle to improve its fixtures with only the occasional opportunity to face the footlights in The Pilkington Cup. To ape the pre-league rise to the top achieved by Orrell was, even for the most aspiring, little more than fantasy, until the advent of the Courage Clubs Championship laid down a path to the summit that all can hope to travel.

The introduction of leagues in Scotland in 1973 lit the beacons of ambition throughout the country. While the established clubs who had traditionally provided the bulk of the national team were initially secure, the brightest bonfires burned in the most unlikely places. In Inverness, Highland with a minimum round trip mileage of 200 for each away league match, swept through the fourth division undefeated. The following season they topped the third, losing only one match and in season 1975–77 put together another unbeaten sequence to burst into division one.

It didn't last, nor did it for Gordonians, the Aberdeen based club, who won promotion to the premier section in 1979–80 and it will be interesting to see if Stirling County, who took the division two title last term, can improve upon the record of the two northern clubs and establish themselves in the top flight. The message, like the example, has an undeniable clarity about it, especially for clubs in the north of England, who in my view are best placed to follow the example of Highland and Gordonians, though like the hopeful Scots they may find that reaching the elevated territory is one thing – holding it is altogether a different proposition.

Once the applause of the democrats had died away, a second ripple was detected from the clubs with the substance, support, skill and pedigree to substantiate their claims for advancement. Mostly they were clubs with a proud history, a loyal following, a high and established place in their community and in the game itself; with a record of having tasted some success and a clubhouse honours board with the names of some international players gold leafed upon it. Mostly they were northern clubs.

Not much that has happened since the launch of the leagues has persuaded me that the northern clubs are not more affluent in the components necessary to build as Orrell have done; though it is undeniable that the playing talent, vital to provide the cutting edge to avidity, is too thinly spread throughout the area. Nevertheless I remain doubtful of the ability or resources of the clubs from other regions to make much impression on National Division Three – the assembly point for all legitimate challengers.

A notable exception has already been provided by Rugby, who not only survived, but succeeded gloriously, to move straight into division two, along with Plymouth Albion who carry the banner for the far south west, which has seen such a sad decline in recent years. Otherwise, national three has six northern clubs; but of greater and more lasting significance, perhaps, is the support provided by the two regional divisions below it, from where the next challenger will appear.

Before the Courage tournament saw birth, we had merit tables. Unwieldy, complicated, in some cases unfair and not, for the most part, taken seriously by clubs, until given a national flavour by John Smith's, the Yorkshire brewers. Then in a 24 club, two division, competition that got under way in 1984, they were the model for the national divisions now seen in today's league arrangement.

The exception to the lack of gravity in clubs' approach to merit tables was in the north where, because of the numbers involved, there were two tables, one in which final positions determined places in the draw for John Player Special Cup, the other a qualifying table with promotion and relegation between each. Both were taken very seriously indeed and, with a background of several very competitive seasons in one table or the other, most of the better northern clubs have been given a head start over their brethren from other regions.

Area League North for instance looks altogether stronger than Area League South and North Division One is immeasurably more powerful than either Midlands Division One or London Division One. Of the four that support the two area leagues, only South West Division One looks to have the strength to match their northern counterparts, but below it South West Division Two looks comparatively lightweight against North Division Two.

In sheer playing terms, the north's great strength is the broad spread of quality players throughout the region. At the same time it is it's greatest weakness, for far too few of them are concentrated in clubs most likely to benefit in the national divisions.

Sale were first winners of John Smith's Table A in 1985, but in the first season of Courage leagues were relegated from Division One to be replaced by Liverpool St. Helens. The Mersey club lasted just one term and rejoin, with neighbours Waterloo, three other northern clubs in the lower section. Now that there is free passage between National Two and National Three, I expect the movement between them to be equally as volatile as between the top two, but recognise the down side to club leagues that brings into question player loyalty to his club – the priceless adhesive that has bound the game together for all these years and been the foundation for affection, friendship and help, that is the cornerstone of rugby union football.

Nowadays we have covert recruitment campaigns and an unseemly scramble for players, that makes the end of season chase for seats in motor racing's Formula One contractual merry-go-round, seem positively well mannered.

The mercenary rarely does as well as the enlisted man – he is not imbued with the same sense of national pride. English county cricket has that message emblazoned all over its sweaters. The same applies in club rugby and, until loyalty regains the high regard that it deserves from player and club alike, I see no probability that another northern club will establish itself in the top flight.

Equally, with the region awash with quality players spread over as many as twenty clubs, the likelihood is that National Division Three will become packed with northern challengers supported by the broad strength of the apsirants immediately below – all hoping to emulate Orrell.

Paul Stephens

NATIONAL DIVISIONS

MEMBER CLUBS 1989–90

National Division One
Bath
Bedford
Bristol
Gloucester
Harlequins
Leicester
Moseley
Nottingham
Orrell
Rosslyn Park
Saracens
Wasps

National Division Two
Blackheath
Coventry
Gosforth
Headingley
Liverpool St. Helens
London Irish
Northampton
Plymouth Albion
Richmond
Rugby
Sale
Waterloo

National Division Three
Askeans
Exeter
Fylde
London Scottish
London Welsh
Lydney
Nuneaton
Roundhay
Sheffield
Vale of Lune
Wakefield
West Hartlepool

NATIONAL DIVISIONS AND IMMEDIATE SUPPORTING LEAGUES

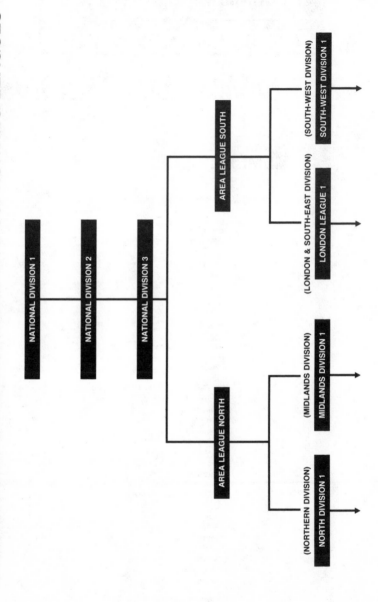

THE COURAGE CLUBS
CHAMPIONSHIP

NOW ENTERING ITS third season, the Courage Clubs Championship – believed to be the largest structure in the world, encompassing 1184 clubs in 114 leagues – epitomises the strength and popularity of club rugby in England.

From the National Divisions to the lowest leagues in this huge structure, Rugby Union is enjoyed in a competitive but sportsmanlike way enabling ambitious and successful players and clubs to reach, in time, the highest levels of the game and for those less ambitious and talented within the game to find their own level.

The Courage Clubs Championship forms the very foundation for the growth and development of a national side of which we can be proud.

The first season of the Championship was received warmly by players, officials and the public alike. Courage, in addition to the sponsorship fee paid to the Rugby Football Union, put considerable funds into building good communications amongst the large number of clubs and officials within the Championship. This first season saw Leicester emerge as National Division One Champions but every league within every Division – London and South East, South West, Midlands and the North – had a winner.

Last season, 1988/89, saw Bath achieve the double as Courage Club Champions and Pilkington Cup Champions, thus ensuring their reputation as the strongest club in England. Many clubs have seen their own teams grow in stature during the last two seasons – not only in terms of quality of play but in the numbers of teams each club is able to field on a Saturday afternoon.

The Courage Clubs Championship creates that opportunity for clubs to compete and enjoy competition against others of similar standard.

Celebrations as Bath are officially the new National Division 1 champions. Photo: Chris Raphael, All-Sport Photographic

COURAGE CLUBS CHAMPIONSHIP 1989

National Divisions; RFU Senior Clubs Association (Executive Committee):

CHAIRMAN:

Ken Phillips
8 Rhineland Way
Bedford   (H) 0234 42801
MK41 7YP   (O) 0234 46101

DEPUTY CHAIRMAN:

Neil Hannah
62 Beeston Fields Drive
Beeston   (H) 0602 254798
Nottingham NG9 3DD   (O) 0509 674848

SECRETARY:

Peter Jackson
147 Chester Road
Castle Bromwich
Birmingham B36 0AB   (H) 021 747 2498

TREASURER:

Brian Baister
The Cedars
3 Kidderton Close
Brindley,
Nantwich   (H) 0270 74465
Cheshire CW5 8JU   (O) 0244 350000 ext 2092

MEMBERS:

Colin Bosley
21 Ellesmere Avenue
Mill Hill
London NW7   (H) 01-906 0799

Ray Ellis
31 Russell Avenue
Hartley
Plymouth   (H) 0752 771237
Devon, PL3 5RB   (O) 0752 773521

Roy Fawden
36 Bisham Gardens
Highgate   (H) 01-348 4753
London N6 6DD   (O) 01-348 4254

Frank Gibbon
12 The Green
Bishopton
Stockton-on-Tees   (H) 0740 30410
Cleveland   (O) 0642 602221

Tom Mahoney
2 Raymend Walk
Victoria Park
Bristol BS3 5AP   (H) 0272 664782

Nigel Morris
5 Station Avenue
Edgbaston   (H) 021 429 7926
Birmingham B16 9SZ   (O) 021 765 4039

John Winterbottom
5 Church Gate
Bramhope   (H) 0532 842066
Leeds LS16 9BN   (O) 0532 452251

John Roberts
Grove House
Ashley
Box, Corsham
Wiltshire SN14 9AJ   (H) 0225 742251

Eric Smith
20 Vicarage Road
Orrell
Nr Wigan
Lancashire WN5 7AX   (H) 0695 622040

Howell Thomas
Flat A
20a Molyneux Park Road
Tunbridge Wells   (H) 0892 543233
Kent TN4 8DT   (O) 0892 511172 (am only)

COURAGE CLUBS CHAMPIONSHIP GENERAL CONTACTS

NATIONAL ADMINISTRATION OFFICE

Michael Humphreys & Partners Ltd
Thames House, 18 Park Street,
London SE1 9EL.
Tel: 01 407 4433, Fax: 01 403 6797, Telex:
8950995

Administration Director: Allison Walter
Administration Manager: Sue Madge

Michael Humphreys & Partners Ltd (MH&P)
is responsible to the Rugby Football Union
for the administration of fixtures, results and
league tables for National Divisions and Area
Leagues.
　　MH&P also represents the R.F.U. in liaison
with the Committee of each R.F.U. Division
of the Championship. The company is
responsible for ensuring that all necessary
fixtures have been made and that all
promotions and relegations are arranged.

Media Relations Director: Teresa Cash
Media Relations Manager: Jacquie Leavy
Media Relations Executive: Sara Douglas

MH&P is responsible for the overall
promotion and press relations with regard to
the Courage Clubs Championship. All
information regarding fixtures, results and
tables for the National Divisions and Area
Leagues is co-ordinated from MH&P. MH&P
will also hold the results and the tables for all
other leagues in the Championship. All media
information regarding the overall
Championship is released from MH&P and all
enquiries should be directed to MH&P for any
regional information not available from the
regional contact.

THE RUGBY FOOTBALL UNION

Roger Godfrey Esq
The Administrative Secretary, The Rugby
Football Union,Rugby Road,
Twickenham,Middlesex,TW1 1DZ.
Tel: 01 892 8161

RFU COMPETITION SUB-COMMITTEE

*The Committee will act as a final arbiter in case
of all disputes:*

Chariman:
W J Bishop Esq, Lafrowda, 43 Tregolis Road,
Truro, Cornwall TR1 1LE.
Tel: (H) 0872 76144
　　　(O) 0209 714914

COURAGE LTD

East Region:
The Manager, Trade Marketing, Courage Ltd,
Brooklands Industrial Park, Oyster Lane,
Weybridge, Surrey KT13 0YU.
Tel: 09323 54100

West Region:
The Manager, Trade Marketing Courage Ltd,
C.I.B.C., Temple Way,
Bristol, Avon BS1 6ED
Tel: 0272 299888

North Region:
The Manager, Trade Marketing John Smith's
(Courage) Ltd, The Brewery, Tadcaster,
North Yorkshire LS24 9SA
Tel: 0937 832091

Head Office:
Courage Ltd, Ashby House, 1 Bridge Street,
Staines, Middlesex TW18 4TP
Tel: 0784 466199

THE COURAGE CLUBS
CHAMPIONSHIP REGULATIONS

1.   **Description and Form**

The Competition shall be called 'The English Clubs Rugby Union Championship' (hereinafter referred to as 'the Competition') and shall be open to Clubs in membership with the Rugby Football Union (hereinafter called 'the R.F.U.'). All matches in the Competition shall be played under the Laws of Rugby Union Football and shall comply with the Bye-Laws Rules and Regulations of the R.F.U.

2.   **Organising Committee**

The Competition will be organised by the Competition Sub-Committee of the R.F.U. (hereinafter referred to as 'the Committee') whose decision shall be binding and final on any matter not provided for in and on the interpretation of these Regulations.

3.   **Delegation of Administration**

(a)   The Committee appoints the R.F.U. Senior Clubs Association Committee as the Organising Committee of National Divisions 1, 2, and 3.

(b)   The R.F.U. Divisions shall be responsible for the administration of all Leagues within their Divisions.

(c)   The Committee (in respect of Area Leagues North and South) and the R.F.U. Senior Clubs Association and the R.F.U. Divisions shall, subject to Regulation 18 (a) of these Regulations, deal with all disputes, transgressions, and complaints as laid down by Regulation 19.

4.   **Structure**

(a)   National
There shall be three National Divisions 1, 2 and 3 comprising twelve clubs each.

(b)   Areas
      (i)   The North and Midland R.F.U. Divisions shall combine to provide one North Area League and the London and South East and South West R.F.U. Divisions shall combine to provide one South Area League each comprised of eleven clubs.
      (ii)   Promotion from the North Area and South Area Leagues shall be to National Division 3.

(c)   R.F.U. Divisions
      (i)   Each of the R.F.U. Divisions shall have a first League.
      (ii)   Promotion from the North Division League I and the Midland Division League I shall be to the North Area League and from the London and South East Division League I and the South-West Division League I shall be to the South Area League.
      (iii)   The Divisional league structure below Division League I in each Division shall be such as shall with the approval of the Committee be determined by that Division.
      (iv)   Each League shall be comprised of eleven clubs, except that the lowest leagues may with the consent of the appropriate Divisional Committee consist of more or less.

(d)   General
      (i)   Not more than two lower Leagues may support a higher League.
      (ii)   Only Club First XV's may enter the Competition.
      (iii)   A club may only play in any Area or Divisional League according to its R.F.U. Constituent Body allocation.

5.   **Club Positions**

The position of a club in a league shall be established by awarding two points for a win and one point for a draw. In the case of equality positions shall be determined on the basis of match points scored. A club with a larger difference between match points for and match points against shall be placed higher in a League than a club with a smaller difference between match points for and match points against. Should two clubs have the same number of competition points and the same match points difference the club having scored more match points for shall be placed higher in the League than the club having a lesser number of match points for. In the event of the match points for still being unable to establish the position of two clubs and if the winning of the Competition or promotion or relegation is involved a play-off on a neutral ground shall be necessary to decide the position between them.

6. **Promotion and Relegation**

(a) The winner of National Division 1 shall be the English Clubs Rugby Union Champion in the year concerned.

(b) There will be promotion and relegation at all levels.

(c) Where one League supports one League promotion and relegation will be on a two up and two down basis.

(d) Where two Leagues support one League the winners of each of the two supporting Leagues shall be promoted and the two bottom clubs of the single league shall be relegated.

(e) Where two Leagues support one League and two clubs from the single League must both be relegated on a geographical basis to one of the supporting Leagues, then the winners of the two supporting Leagues are promoted in any event and the necessary number of clubs are relegated in lower Leagues (involving the movement of one or more clubs as necessary) to ensure that all Leagues continue to be comprised of eleven clubs in the following season, except National Divisions 1, 2 and 3 which shall continue to be comprised of twelve Clubs each.

7. **Fixtures**

(a) All league matches shall be played as directed by the Committee on Saturdays 2, 4, 6, 8, 10, 11, 12, 18, 26, X7 and 32.

(b) All league fixtures lists shall be prepared by the Organising Committee of the League concerned and submitted to the clubs comprising the League by the 31st May in each year. A copy shall be sent to the Secretary of the RFU by the same date.

(c) Where a club has a home match on Saturday 2, 30 or 32 then such club may apply to the Secretary of the Organising Committee of the League in which the club is playing for permission to re-arrange the match. When such permission is granted the match shall be played on Saturday 20, 22 or 24 as agreed by the two clubs concerned and notified in writing to the Secretary of the League concerned, or failing such agreement on such of those dates as the Organising Committee of the League concerned shall direct.

(d) Every club in all league fixtures shall play its bona fide first XV.

8. **Eligibility**

(a) Clubs

    (i) Any Club in membership with the R.F.U. may enter the Competition subject to the approval of the Committee and of the appropriate R.F.U. Division according to its R.F.U. Constituent Body allocation.

    (ii) Any Club applying to join the Competition shall only be permitted to do so by being placed in the bottom League in its R.F.U. Division.

(b) Players

    (i) No players may represent a Club in the Competition unless he is and is to be a bona fide regular playing member of that Club and was born in or has resided for the preceding two years in the United Kingdom or Republic of Ireland save in as much as he qualifies by virtue of clause *(b)*(ii) below. For the purpose of these regulations the United Kingdom shall include the Isle of Man and the Channel Islands.

    (ii) No player who was born outside and has not resided for the preceding two years in the United Kingdom or Republic of Ireland may represent a Club in the Competition until he has been a bona fide regular playing member for a period of twelve weeks (exclusive of the close season) immediately preceding his first Competition match.

    (iii) For the purposes of the Competition a player cannot be a bona fide regular playing member of two or more Clubs and if he is a member of more than one Club he must elect by the 1st September which is his Club for the purposes of the Competition for that Season and such election shall be in writing and be held by the Club which he has elected. If he fails to elect by the 1st September then he shall be deemed to have elected the Club for which he first plays in that season whether it be in a Competition match or otherwise. For the purposes of this clause the word Club shall be construed as including any Club in the United Kingdom and Republic of Ireland which is participating in the Competition or any similar league or Merit table Competition in the United Kingdom and Republic of Ireland. Subject to Clause *(b)*(ii) above this regulation shall not apply to any player who is a member only of a Club which is not participating in the Competition or any similar league or merit table competition in the United Kingdom and Republic of Ireland.

(iv) Subject to clause *(b)*(ii) above a player is deemed to be a bona fide regular playing member for the purposes of the Competition in a season if he is a member of that Club and plays regularly for it.

(v) Subject to Clause *(b)*(iii) above where a player becomes a bona fide regular playing member of a Club after Saturday No. 1 and before Saturday No. 24 in a particular season whether or not he terminates his membership of another Club in so doing he may not play for his new Club in a league match in the Competition until that Club shall have played two league matches in the Competition after the date of his joining and he shall have played at least two games for his new Club in the three weeks preceding his first league game for that Club.

(vi) Subject to Clause *(b)*(iii) above where a player joins his new Club after Saturday 24 in the season concerned he may not play for that club in the Competition during that season.

(vii) For the purpose of determining the date of joining a new Club the date shall be the date upon which he is elected to the Club and his subscription shall have been paid or the date on which he first plays for his new Club whichever shall be the later.

(viii) A player who joins a Club subject to the provisions of the last sub-clause and then resumes playing for his previous Club then the provisions of sub-clauses (i) (ii) (v) and (vi) above shall apply as if this were a further change of membership.

(ix) Where a player has become eligible to play for a Club in the Competition under the provisions of clause *(b)*(ii) above his eligibility shall terminate if he ceases to reside in the United Kingdom or Republic of Ireland for a period of twelve weeks (inclusive of the close season) and if he wishes to continue playing for that Club in the Competition on his return after such an absence it will be necessary for him to re-establish his eligibility again under the provisions of that clause.

(x) No Club may select for and thereafter play in a league match in the Competition whether as a player or replacement more than one member who has become eligible as a bona fide regular playing member under the provisions of clause *(b)*(ii) above.

(xi) Any Club with any doubt concerning the eligibility of a player shall apply to the Organising Committee of the League concerned for a decision.

9. Players in Representative Matches

Where an English representative match involving a visiting National team is played on a date fixed for a League match any Club which is affected by three or more players or replacements taking part in such representative match may require the League match to be rearranged for a later date. Such re-arranged match will be fixed by the Clubs concerned or failing agreement between them by the Organising Committee of the League concerned. The Clubs concerned must notify in writing such Committee of the re-arranged date within fourteen days of the original match date.

10. Replacements

In all matches in the Competition replacements are permitted in accordance with the R.F.U. Resolutions relating to use of replacements.

11. Unplayed, Postponed and Abandoned Matches

(a) If weather conditions prevent a match being played or a match is abandoned because of such conditions with less than sixty minutes having been played, the match shall be played or replayed on a date to be agreed between the two clubs concerned (when the Clubs concerned must notify in writing the Organising Committee of the rearranged date within fourteen days of the original match date) or failing agreement as directed by the Organising Committee of the League concerned. If a match is abandoned because of weather conditions when sixty or more minutes have been played, then the score at the moment of abandonment shall stand and be deemed the final score in the match. The Referee's

decision as to the necessity for abandonment and the number of minutes played at the moment of abandonment shall be final.

(b) If the Referee finds it necessary to abandon a match for any reason other than weather conditions, then, irrespective of the number of minutes played, the result of that match may be determined by the Organising Committee of the League concerned or that Committee may order the match to be replayed.

(c) In the event of a Competition match not being played the Organising Committee of the League concerned shall have power to award the competition points but no match points will be awarded to either side.

(d) In the event of a Competition match not being played whether or not Championship points are awarded to a Club under this regulation, if that Club be a contender for promotion or relegation at the end of the season, the difference between the match points for and against of all Clubs (other than the offending Club) in the League shall be adjusted to exclude all match points scored in matches played against the offending Club before establishing the final position of each Club in the League in accordance with regulation 5.

12.   Notification of Results

Each Club shall within 48 hours notify the appropriate officer of the League concerned of the result of each match played, with the score.

13.   Referees and Touch Judges

(a) The referee for each match shall be appointed or provided by the Referee's Society to which the home Club pay a Referees' Society subscription, subject to any appointments made by the R.F.U.

(b) Each Club shall provide a competent touch judge who shall not be a replacement.

(c) If the referee is unable to officiate for the whole of a match for any reason and a replacement referee is available the Captains of the two clubs concerned may agree that the replacement referee can officiate and the result shall count in the Competition. Such agreement shall be binding upon the clubs. If there is no agreement then the match shall not count in the Competition and it must be replayed in accordance with the provisions of Regulation 11*(a)*.

14.   Kick-Offs and Late Arrivals

Matches shall be played during normal daylight hours unless two clubs mutually agree to play under floodlights. All shall start at the agreed time and any delay may be reported by the non-offending club to the Organising Committee of the League concerned and may lead to the match being awarded to the non-offending club.

15.   Clash of Colours

In the event of Clubs having similar or clashing colours the home Club will be responsible for changing its colours, subject to the satisfaction of the appointed referee.

16.   Grounds

(a) A home club is responsible for correctly and clearly marking its pitch and it must make proper provision to ensure that (with the exception of the touch judges) all spectators, replacements and officials are kept at a reasonable distance from the field of play.

(b) When a late decision as to the fitness of the ground for the playing of a match is necessary it shall be made by the respective captains of the clubs involved but if the captains are not able to agree the decision shall be made by the appointed referee.

17.   Finance

(a) Any monies provided for the 1987/88 Competition and all Competitions thereafter (until otherwise agreed) shall belong to the clubs in the League or Leagues or National Division for whom the monies have been provided and

shall be distributed in such manner as the R.F.U. shall determine.

(b)   Any proposal involving an offer of sponsorship, financial assistance or gift for a League or combination of Leagues must be submitted to the R.F.U. for approval.

(c)   Gate receipts at a match shall belong to the home club.

(d)   The home club shall be responsible for all match expenses.

(e)   The away club shall be responsible for its own travelling and accommodation expenses.

(f)   Such membership fee may be charged to each participating club as may from time to time be determined by the Organising Committee of the League concerned with the approval of the Committee.

18.   Disciplinary Powers

(a)   Without prejudice to the powers of the R.F.U. or the delegation of powers to Constituent Bodies under Bye-Law 13 (d) the Committee shall have the power to expel or suspend any Club from membership of the Competition or impose such other penalty as is considered appropriate on any Club for a breach of these Regulations.

(b)   The Committee shall have the right to delegate disciplinary powers (other than the power to expel or suspend from membership of the Competition) for any breach of these Regulations to an Organising Committee of a League or National Division subject to the rights of appeal as hereinafter provided.

19.   **Complaints and appeals**

(a)   Any complaint shall be referred to the Secretary of the Organising Committee of the League concerned by telephone within 48 hours of knowledge of the occurence giving rise to the complaint and thereafter submitted by the complaining Club to the Secretary of the Organising Committee in writing within a further 48 hours. The complaining Club shall also send a copy of such complaint in writing within such 48 hours to the other party to the complaint. The Secretary on receipt of the written complaint shall give a ruling within 7 days. If either party to the complaint is dissatisfied with such ruling there shall be a right of appeal to the Organising Committee of the League concerned to be given in writing within 7 days of receipt of the Secretary's decision.

(b)   If either the complaining Club or the other party to the complaint or the Club against whom the complaint is made requires an oral hearing, it shall be requested in writing and the Organising Committee responsible for the League concerned shall within 48 hours of receiving notice of such request appoint a time, date and place for the hearing of such complaint.

(c)   Any party aggrieved at the decision of the Organising Committee may appeal to an Appeal Committee appointed by the Officers of the R.F.U. Notice of such appeal must be in writing and must be received by the Secretary of the R.F.U. within 7 days of the date of the decision appealed against. The decision of the R.F.U. Appeal Committee shall be final and binding.

20.   **Medical Safety**

Whenever possible the home team should ensure that a doctor or other medically qualified person is in attendance throughout the match.

21.   **Copyright**

The copyright in the fixture lists of the Competition shall vest in the R.F.U. and must not be reproduced in whole or in part except with the written consent of the R.F.U.

NATIONAL MEDIA CONTACTS

DAILY EXPRESS:

Ludgate House
245 Blackfriars Road
London SE1 9UX   01 928 8000

DAILY MAIL:

Northcliffe House
2 Derry Street
London W8 5EE   01 938 6000

DAILY MIRROR:

Holborn Circus
London EC1P 1DQ   01 353 9246

THE DAILY TELEGRAPH:

181 Marsh Wall,
Isle of Dogs
London E14 9SR   01-538 5000

THE GUARDIAN:

119 Farringdon Road
London EC1R 3ER   01 278 2332

THE INDEPENDENT:

40 City Road
London EC1Y 2DB   01 2534 1222

EVENING STANDARD:

Northcliffe House
2 Derry Street
London W8 5EE   01 938 6000

THE STAR:

121 Fleet Street
London Ec4P 4JT   01 928 8000

THE SUN:

PO Box 481
Virginia Street
London E1 9BD   01 782 4000

THE TIMES:

1 Pennington Street
London E1 9XN   01 782 5000

TODAY:

Allen House
70 Vauxhall Bridge Road
Pimlico
London SW1V 2RP   01 630 1300

MAIL ON SUNDAY:

Northcliffe House
2 Derry Street
London W8 5EE   01 938 6000

NEWS OF THE WORLD:

1 Virginia Street
London EC1 9XR   01 782 4000

THE OBSERVER:

Chelsea Bridge House
Queenstown Road
London SW8 4NN   01 627 0700

SUNDAY EXPRESS:

Ludgate House
245 Blackfriars Road
London SE1 9UX   01 928 8000

SUNDAY MIRROR:

Holborn Circus
London EC1 1DQ   01 353 0246

SUNDAY TELEGRAPH:

181 Marsh Wall
Isle of Dogs
London E14 9SR   01 538 5000

SUNDAY TIMES:

1 Pennington Street
London E1 9XW   01 782 5000

BBC RADIO TWO:

Broadcasting House
London W1A 1AA   01 580 4468

I.R.N.:

Communications House
Gough Square
London EC4P 4DP   01 353 1010

BBC TELEVISION NEWS:

TV Centre
Wood Lane
London W12 7RJ   01 743 8000

CEEFAX:

BBC Television Centre
Wood Lane
London W12 7RJ   01 743 8000

CHANNEL FOUR NEWS:

ITN House
48 Wells Street
London W1P 4DE   01 637 2424

CHANNEL FOUR TELEVISION:

60 Charlotte Street
London W1P 2AX   01 637 4444

INDEPENDENT TELEVISION NEWS:

48 Wells Street
London W1P 4DE   01 637 2424

ORACLE:

Craven House
25-32 Marshall Street
London W1V 1LL   01 434 3121

TV-AM:

Breakfast TV Centre
Hawley Crescent
London NW1 8EF   01 267 4300

BREAKFAST TIME TV:

Lime Grove
Shepherd's Bush
London W12   01 576 7201

NATIONAL DIVISIONS FIXTURES 1989/90

SATURDAY 9TH SEPTEMBER 1989. (WEEK 2)

DIVISION I.

Orrell	vs	Bristol
Moseley	vs	Gloucester
Bath	vs	Harlequins
Wasps	vs	Leicester
Nottingham	vs	Rosslyn Park
Bedford	vs	Saracens

DIVISION II.

Liverpool St. Helens	vs	Gosforth
Waterloo	vs	Headingley
Coventry	vs	London Irish
Northampton	vs	Plymouth Albion
Blackheath	vs	Rugby
Richmond	vs	Sale

DIVISION III.

Sheffield	vs	Exeter
Askeans	vs	Fylde
Nuneaton	vs	Roundhay
West Hartlepool	vs	Lydney
Wakefield	vs	London Scottish
Vale of Lune	vs	London Welsh

SATURDAY 23RD SEPTEMBER 1989. (WEEK 4)

DIVISION I.

Gloucester	vs	Bath
Leicester	vs	Bedford
Rosslyn Park	vs	Moseley
Bristol	vs	Nottingham
Harlequins	vs	Wasps
Saracens	vs	Orrell

DIVISION II.

Plymouth Albion	vs	Liverpool St. Helens
Gosforth	vs	Blackheath
Sale	vs	Coventry
Headingley	vs	Northampton
Rugby	vs	Richmond
London Irish	vs	Waterloo

DIVISION III.

Exeter	vs	Askeans
Fylde	vs	Nuneaton
London Welsh	vs	Sheffield
London Scottish	vs	Vale of Lune
Lydney	vs	Wakefield
Roundhay	vs	West Hartlepool

SATURDAY 4TH OCTOBER 1989. (WEEK 6)

DIVISION I.

Moseley	vs	Bristol
Wasps	vs	Gloucester
Bedford	vs	Harlequins
Orrell	vs	Leicester
Bath	vs	Rosslyn Park
Nottingham	vs	Saracens

DIVISION II.

Richmond	vs	Gosforth
Liverpool St. Helens	vs	Headingley
Northampton	vs	London Irish
Blackheath	vs	Plymouth Albion
Coventry	vs	Rugby
Waterloo	vs	Sale

DIVISION III.

Nuneaton	vs	Exeter
West Hartlepool	vs	Fylde
Wakefield	vs	Roundhay
Vale of Lune	vs	Lydney
Sheffield	vs	London Scottish
Askeans	vs	London Welsh

SATURDAY 28TH OCTOBER 1989. (WEEK 8)

DIVISION I.

Bristol	vs	Bath
Gloucester	vs	Bedford
Saracens	vs	Moseley
Leicester	vs	Nottingham
Harlequins	vs	Orrell
Rosslyn Park	vs	Wasps

DIVISION II.

London Irish	vs	Liverpool St. Helens
Headingley	vs	Blackheath
Gosforth	vs	Coventry
Sale	vs	Northampton
Plymouth Albion	vs	Richmond
Rugby	vs	Waterloo

LEAGUE DIVISION III.

London Scottish	vs	Askeans
London Welsh	vs	Nuneaton
Lydney	vs	Sheffield
Roundhay	vs	Vale of Lune
Fylde	vs	Wakefield
Exeter	vs	West Hartlepool

NATIONAL DIVISIONS FIXTURES 1989/90

SATURDAY 11TH NOVEMBER 1989.
(WEEK 10)

DIVISION I.
Harlequins	vs	Bristol
Bath	vs	Moseley
Wasps	vs	Nottingham
Bedford	vs	Orrell
Gloucester	vs	Rosslyn Park
Leicester	vs	Saracens

DIVISION II.
Coventry	vs	Liverpool St. Helens
Richmond*	vs	Blackheath
Rugby	vs	Gosforth
London Irish	vs	Headingley
Sale	vs	Plymouth Albion
Waterloo	vs	Northampton

DIVISION III.
Wakefield	vs	Askeans
Lydney	vs	Exeter
Roundhay	vs	Fylde
West Hartlepool	vs	Nuneaton
London Scottish*	vs	London Welsh
Vale of Lune	vs	Sheffield

SATURDAY 18TH NOVEMBER 1989.
(WEEK 11)

DIVISION I.
Orrell	vs	Bath
Bristol	vs	Gloucester
Saracens	vs	Harlequins
Rosslyn Park	vs	Leicester
Nottingham	vs	Bedford
Moseley	vs	Wasps

DIVISION II.
Blackheath	vs	Coventry
Gosforth	vs	London Irish
Plymouth Albion	vs	Rugby
Northampton	vs	Richmond
Headingley	vs	Sale
Liverpool St. Helens	vs	Waterloo

DIVISION III.
Exeter	vs	Roundhay
London Welsh	vs	Lydney
Fylde	vs	London Scottish
Askeans	vs	Vale of Lune
Nuneaton	vs	Wakefield
Sheffield	vs	West Hartlepool

SATURDAY 25TH NOVEMBER 1989.
(WEEK 12)

DIVISION I.
Wasps	vs	Bath
Harlequins	vs	Leicester
Bedford	vs	Moseley
Nottingham	vs	Orrell
Bristol	vs	Rosslyn Park
Gloucester	vs	Saracens

DIVISION II.
Waterloo	vs	Blackheath
Plymouth Albion	vs	Gosforth
Rugby	vs	Headingley
Sale	vs	London Irish
Liverpool St. Helens	vs	Northampton
Coventry	vs	Richmond

DIVISION III.
Exeter	vs	Fylde
Vale of Lune	vs	Nuneaton
Roundhay	vs	London Welsh
Askeans	vs	Sheffield
Lydney	vs	London Scottish
Wakefield	vs	West Hartlepool

SATURDAY 13TH JANUARY 1990.
(WEEK 18)

DIVISION I.
Saracens	vs	Bristol
Leicester	vs	Gloucester
Bath	vs	Bedford
Moseley	vs	Nottingham
Wasps	vs	Orrell
Harlequins	vs	Rosslyn Park

DIVISION II.
Richmond*	vs	Liverpool St. Helens
Headingley	vs	Gosforth
London Irish	vs	Plymouth Albion
Sale	vs	Rugby
Blackheath	vs	Northampton
Coventry	vs	Waterloo

DIVISION III.
West Hartlepool	vs	Askeans
London Scottish*	vs	Exeter
London Welsh	vs	Fylde
Lydney	vs	Roundhay
Nuneaton	vs	Sheffield
Wakefield	vs	Vale of Lune

*Date and venue subject to confirmation.

NATIONAL DIVISIONS FIXTURES 1989/90

SATURDAY 10TH MARCH 1990. (WEEK 26)

DIVISION I.

Nottingham	vs	Bath
Gloucester	vs	Harlequins
Bristol	vs	Leicester
Orrell	vs	Moseley
Bedford	vs	Wasps
Rosslyn Park	vs	Saracens

DIVISION II.

Liverpool St. Helens	vs	Blackheath
Northampton	vs	Coventry
Plymouth Albion	vs	Headingley
Rugby	vs	London Irish
Waterloo	vs	Richmond
Gosforth	vs	Sale

DIVISION III.

Fylde	vs	Lydney
Askeans	vs	Nuneaton
Roundhay	vs	London Scottish
Exeter	vs	London Welsh
Sheffield	vs	Wakefield
Vale of Lune	vs	West Hartlepool

SATURDAY 28TH APRIL 1990. (WEEK 32)

DIVISION I.

Bedford	vs	Bristol
Nottingham	vs	Gloucester
Moseley	vs	Harlequins
Bath	vs	Leicester
Orrell	vs	Rosslyn Park
Wasps	vs	Saracens

DIVISION II.

Waterloo	vs	Gosforth
Richmond	vs	Headingley
Blackheath	vs	London Irish
Coventry	vs	Plymouth Albion
Northampton	vs	Rugby
Liverpool St. Helens	vs	Sale

DIVISION III.

Vale of Lune	vs	Exeter
Sheffield	vs	Fylde
Askeans	vs	Roundhay
Nuneaton	vs	Lydney
West Hartlepool	vs	London Scottish
Wakefield	vs	London Welsh

SATURDAY 31ST MARCH 1990. (WEEK X7)

DIVISION I.

Saracens	vs	Bath
Rosslyn Park	vs	Bedford
Leicester	vs	Moseley
Harlequins	vs	Nottingham
Gloucester	vs	Orrell
Bristol	vs	Wasps

DIVISION II.

Rugby	vs	Liverpool St. Helens
Sale	vs	Blackheath
Headingley	vs	Coventry
Gosforth	vs	Northampton
London Irish	vs	Richmond
Plymouth Albion	vs	Waterloo

DIVISION III.

Lydney	vs	Askeans
London Scottish	vs	Nuneaton
Roundhay	vs	Sheffield
Fylde	vs	Vale of Lune
Exeter	vs	Wakefield
London Welsh	vs	West Hartlepool

NATIONAL DIVISION ONE

ONE HORSE RACES are never those which can sustain interest for any great length of time and the top title race for 1988–89 fell into this category. Bath won all but their final game and by then the question was a simple one – 'Who finishes second?' The answer was Gloucester, who won their final home game against one of their main rivals – Nottingham – and thus pipped Wasps for the honour.

Bath were the winners long before the final two rounds of matches were played in April and along with their Final opponents Leicester could afford the luxury of playing an Extra 'A' strength side in their last league game at Welford Road after the competitions committee of the R.F.U. had turned down the request of both sides to allow the Cup Final a week later to double up as a cup and league game. Bath lost the "reserves" match narrowly and then did the double by taking the Cup – also in a close fought game. With the talent at their disposal they frequently used a reserve team for some of their "friendlies" – and still won most of them against strong opposition! Not for nothing were they awarded the Whitbread-Rugby World & Post Club of the Year award. How many clubs could go into a cup final with international players like Nigel Redman and Paul Simpson on the bench with another dozen on the field?

Gloucester were probably the country's second best team, although international cap rewards were few thanks to Bath's dominant form and selection concentration looking for the gaps to be filled by the successful London Division side. But they only lost three of their league games and narrowly succumbed to Bath in a Pilkington Cup semi-final. Their star for the season was the revived and most admirable back-row man Mike Teague, whose come-back from obscurity was well rewarded by a British Lions tour place where he became the Player of the Series..

Wasps for all their array of star names did well enough to finish third, but they will have been disappointed by their overall showing for the season which could have been better and showed a slight decline from previous high standards. Nottingham and Orrell should however be well pleased with their efforts as they do not have the same resources as some of the teams above them but still manage to put up a creditable performance.

Leicester, the first champions, never looked like mounting a serious challenge but their cup form was something of a consolation, something which could not be said for either Bristol or the cup-holders Harlequins, who both had enough talent (on paper, at least) to have achieved better results. Rosslyn Park – promoted the previous season – had a shaky start to the campaign but finished strongly to escape a return to the lower division with something to spare and they did this with a side mostly brought together from their own youth policy and recruits of lesser glamour than those captured by near neighbours Harlequins and Wasps.

For Moseley it was a struggle and a late win over Leicester was enough to see them through to another nail-biting (?) season at the top. Defeat in the Cup by juniors Aspatria did nothing to raise their morale.

By the time the last games of the campaign were being played the relegation fates of Waterloo and Liverpool-St. Helens were known. Waterloo had been in decline for some 18 months after a tremendous start to the 1987–88 campaign, but Liverpool-St. Helens had only just been promoted and despite the presence of new England scrum-half Dewi Morris were just not good enough for the top flight. Is it a coincidence that the two descending clubs are from the same area – Merseyside? Is there really room there for two clubs ambitious for top level rugby? How can it be resolved? They must find a solution or else the North-West could become a rugby back-water.

Who can bet against Bath winning again this coming season? A good question! But everyone will hope for a more sustained campaign and they will be watching Gloucester – at least – with some anxiety.

TABLES 1987–88

DIVISION ONE

	P	W	D	L	F	A	PTS
Leicester	10	9	0	1	225	133	37
Wasps	11	8	1	2	218	136	36
Harlequins	11	6	1	4	261	128	30
Bath	11	6	1	4	197	156	30
Gloucester	10	6	1	3	206	121	29
Orrell	11	5	1	5	192	153	27
Moseley	11	5	0	6	167	170	26
Nottingham	11	4	1	6	146	170	24
Bristol	10	4	1	5	171	145	23
Waterloo	10	4	0	6	123	208	22
Coventry	11	3	1	7	133	246	21
Sale	11	0	0	11	95	374	11

Coventry and Sale relegated to Division Two and replaced by Rosslyn Park and Liverpool-St. Helens.

TABLES 1988–89

DIVISION ONE

	P	W	D	L	F	A	PTS
Bath	11	10	0	1	263	98	20
Gloucester	11	7	1	3	215	112	15
Wasps	11	7	1	3	206	138	15
Nottingham	11	6	1	4	142	122	13
Orrell	11	6	1	4	148	157	13
Leicester	11	6	1	4	189	199	13
Bristol	11	6	0	5	188	117	12
Harlequins	11	5	0	6	194	184	10
Rosslyn Park	11	5	0	6	172	208	10
Moseley	11	3	0	8	113	242	6
Waterloo	11	1	1	9	120	235	3
Liverpool-St-Helens	11	1	0	10	116	254	2

Waterloo and Liverpool-St-Helens relegated to Division Two and replaced by Saracens and Bedford.

COURAGE NATIONAL DIVISION ONE
Results Season 1987–88

	1	2	3	4	5	6	7	8	9	10	11	12
1 Bath		15-9			21-9		14-0		23-18			10-17
2 Bristol				16-21			21-10			378-3	12-12	N/P
3 Coventry	9-9	235-3			12-15			15-20	11-24	24-19		15-10
4 Gloucester	9-16	39-3				18-12	17-9		61-7	13-24		
5 Harlequins		28-22		9-9		9-12		34-8	6-12	66-0		37-4
6 Leicester	24-13	15-10	32-16	N/P						42-15	12-9	39-15
7 Moseley			26-3		11-32	3-21			28-10		19-12	27-3
8 Nottingham	25-15	3-16				13-22	21-12		12-12			
9 Orrell		13-25		9-13		30-6				19-0		30-6
10 Sale	17-46						15-19	3-17			6-14	
11 Wasps	19-15		20-4		17-16			17-9	23-15			
12 Waterloo				16-6				10-9		29-13	13-22	

Results Season 1988–89

	1	2	3	4	5	6	7	8	9	10	11	12
1 Bath		16–9	19–9					22–16	36–12		16–6	38–9
2 Bristol				18–6		50–14	18–0		15–6			14–3
3 Gloucester		10–11			28–0		37–9	13–6			19–3	
4 Harlequins	9–26		26–11			15–6	38–15					23–24
5 Leicester	15–12	13–12		21–31					15–27	28–15	15–6	
6 L'pool St Helens	7–21		9–31			15–22		12–32				
7 Moseley	0–38				22–13	18–15			10–12	7–13		13–6
8 Nottingham	10–6		12–0	12–12		13–9			9–15			
9 Orrell			6–16	16–15		20–24		12–6			9–9	15–12
10 Rosslyn Park	6–19	18–16	8–26	12–16				9–18	17–13			
11 Wasps		21–19		23–15		16–10	39–10			39–16		
12 Waterloo			15–15		22–34	6–12		9–18		14–24	0–29	

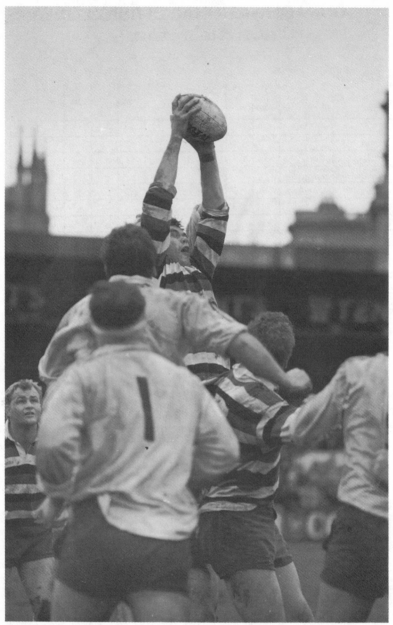

The Bath pack wins line-out ball in the vital match against Nottingham. Photo: Chris Raphael, All-Sport Photographic

TANDEM COMPUTERS RUGBY UNION STATISTICS

		Total	*(Tries, Cons, Pens, Drop G)*
1.	Dusty Hare (Leicester)	399	(12t, 60c, 76p, 1dg)
2.	Tim Smith (Gloucester)	343	(11t, 58c, 61p)
3.	Simon Hodgkinson (Nottm)	298	(6t, 32c, 62p, 8dg)
4.	Andy Kennedy (Saracens)	297	(10t, 34c, 63p)
5.	Stuart Barnes (Bath)	284	(7t, 53c, 47p, 3dg)
6.	Carl Arntzen (Moseley)	261	(2t, 53c, 49p)
7.	Brian Mullen (Lon Irish)	245	(3t, 34c, 48p, 7dg)
8.	David Pears (Sale)	239	(7t, 14c, 54p, 7dg)
9.	Chris Howard (Rugby)	237	(10t, 34c, 43p)
10.	Rob Andrew (Wasps)	221	(3t, 37c, 42p, 3dg)
11.	Simon Irving (Headingley)	219	(10t, 43c, 31p)
12.	Colin Parker (Blackheath)	215	(8t, 30c, 41p)
13.	Stuart Thresher (Quins)	211	(7t, 33c, 39p)
14.	Ian Aitchison (Waterloo)	193	(4t, 18c, 42p, 5dg)
15.	Jon Webb (Bristol)	173	(6t, 22c, 35p)
16.	Andy Finnie (Bedford)	170	(13c, 41p, 7dg)
16.	Martin Livesey (Richmond)	170	(16c, 39p, 7dg)
18.	John Graves (Ross Park)	165	(2t, 29c, 33p)
19.	Simon Hogg (Bristol)	162	(5t, 23c, 25p, 7dg)
20.	Steve Burnage (Fylde)	159	(12c, 44p, 1dg)

Tandem Top Try Table

1.	Jeremy Guscott (Bath)	25
2.	Tony Swift (Bath)	21
3.	Audley Lumsden (Bath)	20
3.	Frank Packman (Northampton)	20
4.	Nick Price (Gloucester)	19
4.	Barry Evans (Leicester)	19

Tandem Top Kickers (Tries Excluded)

1.	Dusty Hare (Leicester)	351
2.	Tim Smith (Gloucester)	299
3.	Simon Hodgkinson (Nottm)	274
4.	Andy Kennedy (Saracens)	257
5.	Stuart Barnes (Bath)	256
6.	Carl Arntzen (Moseley)	253
7.	Brian Mullen (Lon Irish)	233
8.	David Pears (Sale)	211
9.	Rob Andrew (Wasps)	209
10.	Chris Howard (Rugby)	197

Tandem Top Drop Kickers

1.	Les Cusworth (Leicester)	10
1.	John King (Blackheath)	10
2.	Simon Hodgkinson (Nottm)	8
3.	Andy Finnie (Bedford)	7
3.	Martin Livesey (Richmond)	7
3.	Brian Mullen (Lon Irish)	7
4.	David Pears (Sale)	7
3.	Simon Hogg (Bristol)	7

COURAGE

The proud sponsors
of the English Clubs Championship.

BATH

Recreation Ground, Bath. Tel: 0225 25192

COLOURS Blue, black and white hoops, black shorts
(Change colours: all white)

Back-room staff join the full squad before the double was achieved at Twickenham. Standing (l to r): B. Jenkins (coach), R. Quittenton (touch-judge), F. Howard (referee), G. George (physio), P. Simpson (rep), V. Ubogu (rep), N. Redman (rep), J. Morrison, D. Egerton, J. Rowell (coach), D. Cronin, M. Lee, G. Dawe, S. Knight (rep) A. Robinson, T. Hudson (coach), A. Swift, N. Halse (President), A. Lumsden (injured fullback), D. Robson (coach), Julie Bardner (physio), I. Bullerwell (touch-judge). Sitting: R. Hill, S. Halliday, J. Palmer, S. Barnes (captain), J. Hall, J. Guscott, J. Deane (rep), G. Chilcott, F. Sagoe, P. Pothecary (baggage man).

REVIEW OF SEASON

Bath were unbeaten for their first 30 matches and became the first club to do the league and cup double. So strong is the club in terms of personnel that they can field a team of players capped whilst playing for the club in every position and they also had three players (Gareth Chilcott, Jeremy Guscott and Andy Robinson) picked for the British Lions tour of Australia, whilst the team did another double with the awards of the Whitbread-Rugby World & Post Club of the Year and Player of the Year (Andy Robinson) also going to Bath. Their second string were strong enough to fill in for the first team when representative demands took players away and the only defeat in the league – at Leicester in the final match – happened when both clubs were resting their full first team squads for the Pilkington Cup final a week later! The club player of the year was Jeremy Guscott.

RESULTS

Date	Opponents	Venue	Points		Date	Opponents	Venue	Points	
Sept. 1988					**Jan. 1989**				
3	Pontypool	A	50	9	Wed 4	Cheltenham	A	31	6
10	Harlequins	*A	26	9	7	Cardiff	H	35	4
17	London Welsh	H	40	3	14	Liverpool St. Helens	*A	21	7
24	Gloucester	*H	19	9	Wed18	Metropolitan Police	A	64	21
Wed28	Clifton	A	22	6	28	Oxford (All Pay)	†H	82	9
Oct 1	Aberavon	H	24	13	**Feb-**				
8	Rosslyn Park	*A	19	6	.Fri 3	Llanelli	A	20	4
Wed12	Public School				11	Hereford (All Pay)	†H	48	0
	Wanderers	H	54	44	Fri17	Gloucester	A	12	18
15	Bedford	A	16	10	25	Bristol	†H	14	12
22	Bristol	*H	16	9	**Mar.** 4	Swansea	H	13	15
29	Toulouse	H	24	24	11	Nottingham	*H	22	16
Nov. Wed	Combined Services	H	20	3	Tues14	Bristol	A	Cancelled	
5	Llanelli	A	25	12	Fri 17	Ebbw Vale	H	55	0
12	Moseley	*A	38	0	25	Gloucester	†A	6	3
19	Orrell	*H	36	12	Mon27	Richmond	H	Cancelled	
26	Wasps	*H	16	6	Wed 29	Plymouth	A	32	19
Wed30	Exeter University	H	30	4	**Apr.**				
Dec. 3	London Scottish	**A	27	19	1	Bridgend	A	3	23
10	Newport	**A	21	21	Wed 5	Newport	H	13	17
17	Saracens	**H	24	6	8	Waterloo	*H	38	9
Fri23	Newbridge	A	22	18	Wed12	S.W. Police	A	4	37
Mon26	Clifton	H	57	6	15	Llanelli	H	43	25
31	Northampton	H	58	3	22	Leicester	*A	12	15
					29	Leicester	†A	10	6

*Courage Clubs Championship   †Pilkington Cup Round   **Divisional Championship Dates

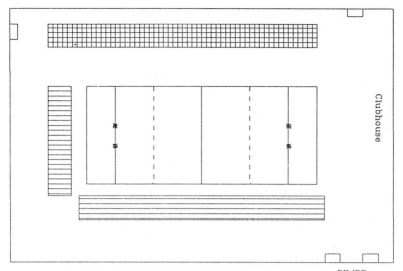

Clubhouse

PE/PR

KEY TO GROUND PLANS

OPEN TERRACE	OPEN SEATS	TURNSTILE	PE PLAYERS'/OFFICIALS' ENTRANCE
COVERED TERRACE	COVERED SEATS	MAIN ENTRANCE/EXIT	PR PRESS ENTRANCE

Jeremy Guscott makes a typical break for Bath against Liverpool St. Hellens.
Photo: K.B. Riding, Bolton

BATH R.U.F.C.

Founded: 1865
President: Alec. O. Lewis
Chairman: Brendan Perry
Secretary: Clive D. Howard, Horseshoe Cottage, Faulkland, Bath BA3 5XA. Tel: 0373 87501 (H), 0225 462827 (W)
Fixtures Secretary: Geoff W. Hancock, 191 Ringswell Gardens, Bath. Tel: 0225 20532
Press Officer: As Secretary
Coach: Jack Rowell
Club captain (1988–89): Stuart Barnes
Club captain (1989–90): Stuart Barnes
No. of teams: Senior 3, Youth 4, Minis 7
Directions to ground: Entrance at end of William Street, off Pulteney Street, near to city centre
Ground capacity: Seating 1000, Standing 7300
Clubhouse facilities: 3 bars plus sponsors area with own bar
Floodlights: Yes
Membership fees: T.B.D.
Ground admission: T.B.D.
Programme: No. of editorial pages 24; No. of advertising pages 16; Price T.B.D.
Programme editor: As Press Officer
Local newspaper: Bath & West Evening Chronicle
League: National League Division 1
League position (1988–89): 1st
League playing record (1988–89): P 11, W 10, D 0, L 1, F 263, A 98
Competitions won: Courage League National Division 1, Pilkington Cup
Most capped players (including British Lions appearances): J.P. Hall (19), G.J. Chilcott (14), S.J. Halliday (13), D.F. Cronin (9), R.J. Hill (9), S. Barnes (8), R.A. Robinson (7), A.H. Swift (6), R.G.R. Dawe (4), D.W. Egerton (4), N.C. Redman (4)
Players' appearances (1988–89): M.R. Leg 31, A. Lumsden 28, C.J. Chilcott 27, J. Guscott 27, R.G.R. Dawe 26
Leading scorers (1988–89): S. Barnes 275 (5 t, 60 cons, 42 pens, 3 d.g.), P. Cue 111 (1 t, 22 cons, 19 pens, 2 d.g.), J. Guscott 110 (25 t, 5 cons), A. Lumsden 80 (20 t)

Simon Halliday – Watch out, here I come

The Future of Bath?

The next Gareth Chilcott? Nicholas Cartwright hopes so!

The under 12 front row – Nicholas Cartwirght, Malcolm Bond and Richard Fletcher (nearest to camera).

"Facing" the camera 1. Paul Runacles (right) still eating his lunch?

"Facing" the camera 2. Paul Runacles and Nicholas Cartwright seen to be jeering the ball at a line-out.

BEDFORD

Goldington Road, Bedford. Tel: Bedford 47511

COLOURS Oxford/Cambridge blue hoops, blue shorts.
(*Change colours*: White shirts, blue shorts)

Bedford's John Francombe outjumps everyone against Sale at Brooklands last season. Photo: Peter Baston.

REVIEW OF SEASON

Secured promotion to Division One on the last day of the campaign as a result of a draw at Sale when all the other contenders lost! Although there were no international caps won the club enjoyed seeing several players gain representative honours with Brian Gabriel, the scrum-half, and Mark Howe, being in the Midlands squad, whilst Mark Upex played for England's students. Andy Finnie became the second highest points scorer in the club's history and Mark Howe reached 361 career appearances for the club and he is now third in the club's all-time list.

RESULTS

Date	Opponents	Venue	Points		Date	Opponents	Venue	Points	
Sept. 1988					**Jan.**				
3	Leicester	A	10	40	**1989** 7	Wakefield	H	17	13
10	Gosforth	*A	17	16	14	Richmond	*H	15	3
17	Arbertillery	H	25	14	20	Leicester	H	3	16
24	London Scottish	*H	9	6	28	Nottingham	†H	3	6
Oct 1	Gloucester	A	16	25	**Feb.** 2	Fylde	H	22	16
8	Headingley	*A	7	7	11	Liverpool/St. Helens	A	6	24
12	Cambridge Univ.	A	9	7	18	Orrell	H	22	31
15	Bath	H	10	16	25	Coventry	A	3	6
22	London Irish	*H	15	21	**Mar.** 4	Waterloo	H	12	15
26	Rugby	A	21	13	11	Blackheath	*A	13	12
29	Loughborough St.	A	16	7	18	Nottingham	A	0	55
Nov. 1	Oxford Univ.	A	12	6	25	Morley	A	48	22
5	Nuneaton	†H	16	0	27	Northampton	H	7	18
12	Coventry	*H	19	9	**Apr.** 1	Wasps	H	14	26
19	Saracens	*A	10	50	8	London Welsh	*H	18	6
26	Northampton	*A	3	42	15	Sheffield	A	Cancelled	
30	Bedfordshire	**H	30	3	22	Sale	*A	15	15
Dec. 3	Rosslyn Park	A	12	30	29	Eastern Counties	H	40	8
7	Royal Air Force	H	18	26					
10	Harlequins	H	25	4					
17	Moseley	A	19	24					
21	Metropolitan Police	H	Cancelled						
26	Old Paulines	H	68	4					
30	Bristol	A	4	34					

*Courage Clubs Championship   †Pilkington Cup Round   **Alan Lovell Memorial

BEDFORD R.U.F.C.

Founded: 1886
President: Kenneth W. Phillips
Chairman: Tony P. Goodman
Secretary: Tony D. Mills, 7 Sandy Road, Bedford. Tel: Bedford 47796 (H), 64351 (W)
Fixtures Secretary: John Saunders, College Farm, Oakley, Bedfordshire. Tel: Oakley 2328 (H)
Press Officer: As Fixtures Secretary
Coach: T.B.A.
Club captain (1988–89): John Orwin
Club captain (1989–90): Mark Howe
No. of teams: Senior 5, Youth 6, Minis 5
Directions to ground: Follow A428 road towards Cambridge. Ground is approximately mile from town centre on left-hand side
Ground capacity: Seating 900, Standing 4000
Clubhouse facilities: Two clubhouses, one open lunchtimes and evenings all week except Sundays
Nickname: Blues
Floodlights: Yes
Membership fees: T.B.D.
Ground admission: £2.50
Programme: No. of editorial pages 6; No. of advertising pages 10; Price 30p
Programme editor: Roger Forsyth, Pear Tree Cottage, Pavenham, Bedfordshire. Tel: Oakley 2669
Local newspapers: Bedfordshire Times, Bedford Herald, Beds-on-Sunday
League: National League Division 1
League position (1988–89): 2nd
League playing record (1988–89): P 40, W 19, D 2, L 19, F 649, A 696
Competitions won: Runners-Up Courage League National Division 1
Most capped players (including British Lions appearances): D.P. Rogers (Eng – 34) (2), W.C. Steele (Scot – 23) (2), D.G. Perry (Eng – 15), J.P.A.G. Janion (Eng – 11), A.M. Jorden (Eng – 7), W.N. Bennett (Eng – 7)
Players' appearances (1988–89): Mark Upex 34, Glyn Wood 32, Andy Finnie 31, Brian Gabriel 30, John Orwin 30, Ian Swingsley 30
Leading scorers (1988–89): Andy Finnie 221 (1 t, 29 cons, 44 pens, 9 d.g.), Stuart Vaudin 86 (5 t, 9 cons, 11 pens, 5 d.g.), Steve Cunningham 44 (5 t, 9 cons, 1 pen, 1 d.g.), Kevin Canning 36 (9 t)

(Cambridge)   Goldington Road   (Bedford Town Centre)
(A. 428)

BRISTOL

Memorial Ground, Filton Avenue, Horfield,
Bristol BS7 0AQ. Tel: 0272 514448
COLOURS Blue/white.
(*Change colours*: Slate/yellow/brown, white)

Bristol – 1988–89.

REVIEW OF SEASON

This was an interim season for Bristol with no international honours apart from Jon Webb at full-back coming their way, no cups and seventh place in Division One – albeit they won more matches than they lost. However, they were an attractive side to watch and were unlucky that their Pilkington Cup campaign ended in impossible playing conditions at Bath in the quarter-finals. With promising young players coming through they can only improve and could soon challenge for top honours.

RESULTS

Date	Opponents	Venue	Points		Date	Opponents	Venue	Points	
Sept. 1988						18	Plymouth	A	31	4
1	Stroud	H	42	0	21	Cardiff	H	20	12
3	Cardiff	A	23	17	25	New Brighton	H	92	10
10	Orrell	H	15	6	27	Glamorgan Wands.	H	18	16
17	Swansea	H	22	21	**Apr. 1**	Harlequins	A	7	7
24	Nottingham	A	6	10	8	Wasps	A	19	21
28	Metropolitan Police	H	29	10	12	Exeter	H	45	3
Oct. 1	London Irish	A	43	8	15	Newport	A	19	28
8	Mosely	H	18	0	22	Liverpool	H	50	14
12	Newbridge	A	9	24	29	Waterloo	A	32	23
15	Northampton	A	20	16					
22	Bath	A	9	16	*Pilkington Cup Round				
25	Glamorgan Wands.	A	18	10					
29	Coventry	H	51	9					
Nov. 1	Weston-super-Mare	A	46	15					
5	Bridgend	A	23	19					
12	Harlequins	H	18	6					
19	Gloucester	A	11	10					
26	Rosslyn Park	A	16	18					
Dec. 3	Newport	H	15	22					
7	Mosely	A	10	18					
17	Nottingham	H	10	0					
24	Llanelli	A	3	48					
26	Weston-super-Mare	H	73	6					
30	Bedford	H	34	4					
Jan. 1989									
2	Clifton	A	31	15					
7	London Welsh	H	48	8					
14	Waterloo	H	14	3					
21	Taunton	A	41	3					
28	Orrell	*H	13	7					
Feb. 3	Gloucester	H	13	15					
11	London Irish	*H	45	16					
17	Begles	A	9	9					
25	Bath	A	12	14					
Mar. 3	Pontypridd	H	3	12					
11	Leicester	A	12	13					

Appearances: 37, Blackmore, Hogg; 36, Doubleday; 34, Dun, Knibbs; 32, Colings, Palmer, 29, Woodman; 26, Sharp; 23(1) STiff; 23, Carr, Hone; 22, Eves; ;29, Harding, Thomas; 19(1), Painter, 18(1), Davis; 18, Webb, Duggan; 16, G Crane; 14(1), Hodges; 14, Phillips; 13, Skuse; 11, Essien, Adams; 10(1), Jeffery; 10, Watson; 9(1), Tainton; 9, Smith; 8, Hull; 7(2) Cotton; 7 Pollendri, Whitehead; 6(1) Mann; 5, Lear, Sorrelli; 3, Hickey; 2, Wring; 1(1), Edbrook; 1, Famer, Perkins, M. Crane, Bennett, de Glanville, Sheppard; (1), Biggins, Lander

Tries: 18, Collings; 13, Woodman; 12, Knibbs; 11, Hodges; 10, Carr, 9, Eves, Essien, Davis; 8, Hogg, Dun; 7, Stiff, Whitehead, Smith; 6, G Crane, Webb; 5, Hone, Harding; 4, Jeffery, Duggan; 3, Blackmore, Polledri; 2, Painter, Phillips, Edbrfooke, Palmer, Thomas; 1, Hull, Cotton, Skuse, Wring, Doubleday.

Conversions: 44, Hogg; 20, Webb; 17, Tainton; 4, Someli.

Penalties: 30, Webb; 29, Hogg 7, Tainton; 6, Sorrell; 3 Hull.

Dropped goals: 7, Hogg 1, Tainton, Sorrell.

Car Park

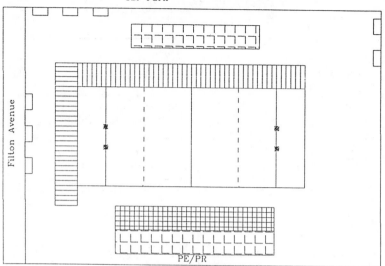

Filton Avenue

PE/PR

BRISTOL R.U.F.C.

Founded: 1888
President: T.A.B. Mahoney
Chairman: E.J. Blackman
Secretary: T. Wynne Jones, 31 Bromley Heath Road, Downend, Bristol BS16 6HY. Tel: 0272 569161
Fixtures Secretary: B.W. Redwood, 205 Stoke Lane, Westbury on Trym, Bristol BS9 3RX. Tel: 0272 684342 (H), 424473 (W)
Coach: R. Hesford
Club captain (1988–89): A.F. Dun
Club captain (1989–90): A.F. Dun
No. of teams: Senior 3, Youth 1
Directions to ground: Exit 2 M32, follow signs for Horfield
Ground capacity: Seating 1600, Standing 6900
Clubhouse facilities: Bristol Football Social Club. Tel: 0272 514134
Floodlights: Yes
Membership fees: Full Stand £50/Ground £25, Playing £15, Social £3.50, Youth Stand £30/ Ground £15, OAP Stand £30/Ground £15
Ground admission: £2.50, Stand £5, Scholars OAPs £1/Stand £2
Programme: No. of editorial pages 7; No. of advertising pages 22; Price 30p
Programme editor: (Advertising): R. Brookes, Memorial Ground, Horfield, Bristol BS7 0AQ. Tel: 0272 514134
Local newspapers: Western Daily Press, Evening Post
League: National League Division 1
League position (1988–89): 7th
League playing record (1988–89): P 45, W 30, D 2, L 13, F 1138, A 556
Competitions won: Bournemouth Sevens, Moseley Invitation Sevens
Most capped players (including British Lions appearances): J.V. Pullin 42 + 2 British Isles, J.S. Tucker, 27, M. Rafter 17, J.M. Webb 16, I.J. Corbett 16, W.R. Johnston 16, G.G. Gregory 13, R.M. Harding 12, D.M. Rollitt 11, R. Hesford 10
Players' appearances (1988–89): A. Blackmore 37, S. Hogg 37, J. Doubleday 36, A. Dun 34, R. Knibbs 34
Leading scorers (1988–89): S. Hogg 228 (8 t, 44 cons, 29 pens, 7 d.g.), J. Webb 154 (6 t, 20 cons, 30 pens), P. Collings (18 t), D. Woodman (13 t), R. Knibbs (12 t)

No luck at Twickenham 1988 – Bristol go down gallantly to Harlequins in the last John Player Cup Final

GLOUCESTER

Kingsholm, Worcester Street, Gloucester. Tel: 0452 20901/28385

COLOURS Cherry and white hoops, black shorts. (*Change colours*: Yellow)

Gloucester Rugby Club's front-row Richard Pascall, Kevin Dunn and Malcolm Preedy. Photograph courtesy of The Citizen, Gloucester

Founded: 1973
President: Canon H.M. Hughes, B.A.
Chairman: P.J. Ford
Secretary: T.R. Tandy, 48 Cotteswold Road, Gloucester GL4 9RQ. Tel: 0452 23049 (H), 28641 (W)
Fixtures Secretary: M.J. Nicholls, 90 Kingsholm Road, Gloucester. Tel: 0452 301879
Press Officer: As Secretary
Coach: Keith Richardson
Club captain (1988–89): Marcus Hannaford
Club captain (1989–90): Mike Hamlin
No. of teams: Senior 2, Colts 1
Directions to ground: Use inner ring road. Kingsholm is signposted
Ground capacity: Seating 1100, Standing 9000
Clubhouse facilities: Dressing rooms, dining room, bars and sponsors room
Floodlights: Yes
Membership fees: Full 20, Playing £1.50, Social £1, Youth £4, Student £11, OAP £11
Ground admission: £2

Programme: No. of editorial pages 4; No. of advertising pages 15; Price 40p
Programme editor: P.J. Arnold, 83 Brookfield Road, Hucclescote, Gloucester. Tel: 0452 618726
Local newspapers: Citizen
League: National League Division 1
League position (1988–89): 2nd
League playing record (1988–89): P 44, W 34, D 1, L 9, F 1028, A 525
Competitions won: Courage National League Division 1 Runners-up
Most capped players (including British Lions appearances): A.T. Voyce, 29 (2), D. Rutherford 15 (1), G.W.D. Hastings 13
Leading scorers (1988–89): Tim Smith 345 (31 t, 59 cons, 61 pens), Nick Marment 116 (5 t, 21 cons, 18 pens), Nick Price 76 (19 t), Jim Breeze 68 (17 t)
Season's review: Good season. Runner-up National League Div. 1, Semi-finalist losing narrowly to Bath in Pilkington Cup

RESULTS

FIRST XV FIXTURES

1988

Date		Opponents	Venue	Points	
Sep	3	Swansea	H	35	13
	6	Stroud	A	34	0
	10	*Moseley	H	37	9
	17	Pontypridd	A	25	18
	24	*Bath	A	9	19
	27	Exeter	A	14	18
Oct	1	Bedford	H	25	16
	8	*Wasps	H	19	3
	12	Ebbw Vale	H	21	10
	15	Newport	A	19	15
	22	*Liverpool	A	31	9
	29	Newbridge	A	10	17
Nov	2	South Wales Police	H	45	7
	5	Rugby	H	Cancelled	
	9	Cheltenham	H	48	3
	12	*Rosslyn Park	A	26	8
	19	*Bristol	H	10	18
	26	*Waterloo	A	15	15
Dec	3	Leicester	A	13	19
	10	Plymouth	H	28	12
	17	Coventry	A	30	14
	19	Newport	H	42	6
	26	Lydney	H	21	10
	31	Bridgend	H	17	12
1989					
Jan	2	Moseley	A	3	23
	7	London Scottish	H	20	12
	14	*Leicester	H	28	0
	18	Pontypool	A	23	13
	21	Blackheath	H	37	0
	28	Brixham (P.C.)	A	28	4
Feb	3	Bristol	A	15	13
	11	Waterloo (P.C.)	H	19	16
	17	Bath	H	18	12
	25	Wakefield	A	28	13
Mar	3	Northampton	H	29	12
	11	Harlequins	A	11	26
	15	Cheltenham	A	16	19
	18	London Irish	A	32	19
	23	Lydney	A	Cancelled	
	25	Bath (P.C.)	H	3	6
	27	Fylde	H	42	15
Apr	1	Headingley	A	12	9
	8	*Orrell	A	16	6
	15	Sale	A	19	7
	22	*Nottingham	H	13	6

UNITED XV FIXTURES

1988

Date		Opponents	Venue	Points	
Sep	3	Swansea	A		
	10	Coventry	A	28	13
	13	Cheltenham	A	30	6
	17	Pontypool	H	24	10
	24	Moseley	H	44	16
	28	Glamorgan Wander's	H	6	6
Oct	1	Bedford	A	6	9
	3	Cinderford	H	13	9
	8	Richmond	A	3	13
	15	Newport	H	21	17
	29	Saracens	H	17	7
Nov	5	Crediton	A	40	12
	12	Bath	H	30	18
	19	Bristol	A	12	26
	21	St. Pauls College	H	42	0
	26	London Irish	H	15	12
Dec	3	Leicester	H	36	6
	10	Glamorgan Wander's	A	18	6
	17	Coventry	H	41	3
	24	Newport	A	20	19
	31	Moseley	A	18	15
1989					
Jan	7	Wasps	A	22	22
	14	Leicester	A	9	16
	21	Cleve	A	18	14
	28	Newport H.S.O.B.	H	15	6
Feb	4	Bristol	H	6	15
	11	Plymouth	H	25	7
	18	Bath	A	12	9
	25	Rosslyn Park	H	29	12
	28	Cheltenham	H		
Mar	4	Northampton	A	16	23
	11	Harlequins	H	10	24
	19	Orrell	A	15	8
	25	Pontypool	A	Cancelled	
Apr	1	Abergavanny	H	23	9
	15	Sale	H	21	24
	22	Nottingham	A		

*Courage League Fixture
P.C. Pilkington Cup

HARLEQUINS

Stoop Memorial Ground, Craneford Way, Twickenham. Tel: 01–892 1222

COLOURS L blue, magenta, chocolate, Fr. grey black and light green

Harlequins 7 Leicester 16: A gallant cup defence ends as the Tigers' pack takes charge.

REVIEW

Harlequins are an enigma. They only seem to come into their own in the second half of any season, which explains their modest league position. That was improved by a gallant defence of their knock-out cup success in 1988, but eventually they were forced to concede their position there to Leicester in a semi-final at the Stoop Memorial Ground. Only when interest in 15-a-side competitions was over for them did they start to win things and four important sevens victories were registered at Old Belvedere, Headingley, the first Wang National Sevens and the Middlesex event (for a fourth consecutive year). In the Wang event they scored a massive 54–0 win over Wasps in the final! If they could transfer their sevens form to the full game they would be absolutely irresistible. On the international scene they provided the England captain Will Carling, the lock Paul Ackford and, in Bucharest against Romania, Peter Winterbottom.

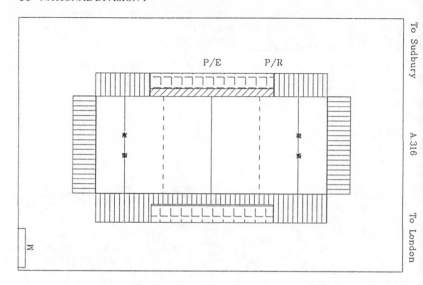

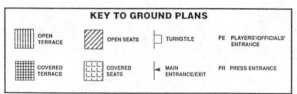

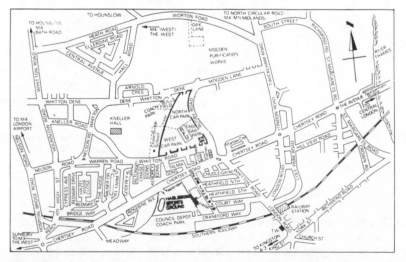

Directions to ground: A316 from London to Twickenham, turn into Egerton Road and then right to Craneford Way. Ground at end of road

HARLEQUINS R.U.F.C.

Founded: 1866
President: Kenneth H. Chapman
Chairman: Roger F. Looker
Secretary: Colin M. Herridge, 11 Langley Avenue, Surbiton, Surrey KT6 9QN. Tel: 01–390 0201 (H), 0932 569166 (W)
Fixtures Secretary: Robert F. Read, Brookside, Lodge Lane, Salfords, Redhill, Surrey. Tel: 0293 783711 (H), 01–661 5107 (W)
Press Officer: Alex Saward, 152 Woodseer Street, London E1 5HQ. Tel: 01 377 1151
Coach: Robert Hiller
Club captain (1988–89): John Olver
Club captain (1989–90): John Olver
No. of teams: Senior 4, Youth 2
Ground capacity: Seating 2000, Standing 7000
Clubhouse facilities: 4 changing rooms, weights room, 3 bars, refreshments
Floodlights: Yes
Membership fees: Full £40, Playing £25, Youth £10, Student £10, OAP £15
Ground admission: £3
Programme: No. of editorial pages 4; No. of advertising pages 20+; Price 50p
Programme editor: As Secretary
Local newspaper: Richmond & Twickenham Times

League: National League Division 1
League position (1988–89): 8th
League playing record (1988–89): P 11, W 5, D 0, L 6
Competitions won: Sevens: Wang National, Middlesex, Old Belvedere and Headingley
Most capped players (For England unless otherwise stated): W.W. Wakefield 31, P.T. Winterbottom 30 + 4 for British Isles, J.D. Currie 25, C.B. Stevens 25, R.W.D. Marques 23, W.J.A. Davies 22 + 3 for British Isles, R.J. Dixon 22 + 3 for British Isles, J.G.G. Birkett 21, R.H. Hiller 19; W. Cuthbertson 20 for Scotland; R.C.C. Thomas 26 for Wales + 2 for British Isles
Players' appearances (1988–89): David Thresher 23, Paul Curtis 23, Everton Davis 23, John Eagle 20, Andrew Mullins 19
Leading scorers (1988–89): Stuart Thresher 139 (3 t, 20 cons, 29 pens), Marcus Rose 61 (3 t, 5 cons, 13 pens), Jamie Salmon 45 (5 t, 5 cons, 4 pens)

England caps Rory Underwood (left) and Quins' Jamie Salmon collide as the ball runs loose. Leicester emerge on top.

Leicester control this line-out as they beat Quins in the Pilkington Cup Semi-final at the Stoop Memorial Ground (16–7)

Gloucester's new skipper – fly-half Mike Hamlin. Photo: Gloucester Citizen

LEICESTER

Aylestone Road, Leicester LE2 7LF. Tel: 0533 541607

COLOURS Scarlet green and white. (*Change colours*: Red with green and white hoop across middle)

Scrum-half Aadel Kardooni of Leicester gets his line away against Moseley, whose Simon Robson waits to pounce. Photo: Chris Dennis, Leicester.

REVIEW OF SEASON

After the heady days of success the previous season there was the expected reaction and with Bath in such dominating form there was little chance of the title being retained. In fact with six matches won out of the 11 scheduled a final position of sixth was satisfactory but not flattering. In the top division there are some seven elite clubs and the rest struggle, but the Tigers are not one of the strugglers and should once again be challengers for honours next season. The consolation was another Cup Final appearance at Twickenham and a narrow defeat by Bath, whose unbeaten league record had gone at Welford Road a week earlier – albeit both sides were selected from outside the first team squads so as to rest players for the final. The feature of the season was the continued superb form of Dusty Hare, who finally announced his retirement from the game (who will really believe that?), the usual consistency of Les Cusworth, likewise Paul Dodge, also new scrum-half Aadel Kardooni, again Barry Evans, promising form by another Underwood (Tony) and some brave work by the pack. Dean Richards and Rory Underwood played in all England's matches and both went on tour with the British Isles and appeared effectively in the Tests in Australia. There was much to cheer.

RESULTS

Date	Opponents	Venue	Points		Date	Opponents	Venue	Points	
Sept. 1988					**Jan. 1989**				
3	Bedford	H	40	10	7	Headingley	H	53	7
10	Wasps†	H	15	6	14	Gloucester†	A	0	28
17	Northampton*	A	30	19	20	Bedford	A	16	3
24	Liverpool St. Helens†	A	23	12	28	Liverpool St. Helens*	A	37	6
Oct 1	Coventry	A	45	7	**Feb.** 4	Northampton	H	42	8
8	Orrell†	H	15	27	11	Rosslyn Park*	A	23	9
15	Swansea	A	16	35	14	R.A.F.	H	34	12
18	Oxford Univ.	H	24	6	18	Moseley	H	27	10
22	Nottingham†	A	12	12	25	Wasps*	H	22	18
30	Llanelli	H	15	29	**Mar.** 4	Saracens	H	25	6
Nov. 5	Cardiff*	A	24	26	11	Bristol†	H	13	12
8	Cambridge Univ.	A	23	21	25	Harlequins*	A	16	7
12	Waterloo†	A	34	22	27	Ballymena	H	21	17
19	Rosslyn Park†	H	28	15	**Apr.** 1	London Scottish	A	20	15
26	Harlequins†	H	21	31	8	Moseley†	A	13	22
Dec. 3	Gloucester	H	19	13	15	Gosforth	A	47	14
10	Blackheath	H	22	12	22	Bath†	H	15	12
17	Richmond	A	16	7	29	Bath (Final)*		6	10
28	Barbarians	H	19	36	*Pilkington Glass Cup Round				
31	Nuneaton	A	39	13	†League matches				

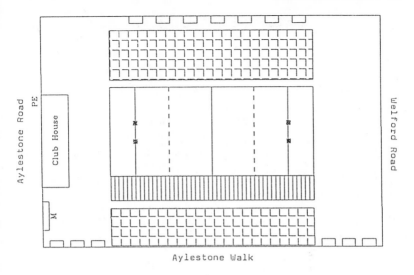

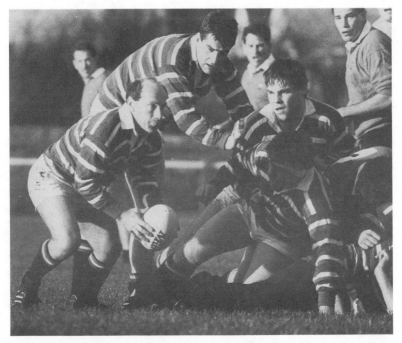

Old Faithful Les Cusworth stands in at scrum-half with deft handling. Photo: Chris Dennis, Leicester.

LEICESTER R.U.F.C.

Founded: 1880
President: Brian Small
Chairman: Brian Small
Secretary: John Allen, The Clubhouse, Aylestone Road, Leicester LE2 7LF. Tel: 0533 858407 (H), 0533 471234 (W)
Fixtures Secretary: John Berry, Bunnystone Cottage, Bunnison Lane, Colston Bassett, Notts. Tel: 0949 81258 (H), 81428 (W)
Press Officer: As Secretary
Coach: David Matthews/Allan Foster
Club captain (1988–89): Paul Dodge
Club captain (1989–90): Dean Richards
No. of teams: Senior 3, Youth 1
Directions to ground: Exit 21 of M1 – A46 towards Leicester. 1 mile turn right at traffic lights (Post House Hotel on corner), after 1 mile T-junction, turn left. 2 miles towards city. On entry into one-way system ground on right
Ground capacity: Seating 9200, Standing 6000
Clubhouse facilities: Open matchdays and training evenings

Appearances: S. Redfern 35, M. Foulkes-Arnold 34, W. Hare 32, J. Bates 29, C. Bridge 29, I. Smith 28, A. Kardooni 28, L. Cusworth 26, W. Richardson 26, B. Evans 25, T. Smith 24, J. Well 22, C. Tressler 22, T. Thacker 16, D. Richards 15, R. Underwood 125, M. Grant 15, T. Underwood 14, A. Masrriott 14, J. Harris 14, C. Gerald, 13, M. Reid, 13, C. Dextger 10, A. Warwood 10.

Tries: B. Evans 19, W. Hare 12, D. Richards 8, T. Underwood 8, M. Grant 7, A. Kardooni 6, I. Smith 5, R. Underwood 4, C. Gerald 4,

Club colours: Scarlet green and white. (*Change colours*: Red with green and white hoop across middle)
Nickname: Tigers
Floodlights: Yes
Membership fees: Full £24, Playing £24, Youth £12, Student £12, OAP £12
Ground admission: £2
Programme: No. of editorial pages 7; No. of advertising pages 25; Price 40p
Programme editor: Bob Barker, 335 Uppingham Road, Leicester LE5 4DN. Tel: 0533 766712
Local newspaper: Leicester Mercury
League: National League Division 1
League position (1988–89): 6th
League playing record (1988–89): P 11, W 6, D 1, L 4, F 189, A 199
Most capped players (including British Lions appearances – for England unless stated): P.J. Wheeler 41, R. Underwood 33, P.W. Dodge 32, W.H. Hare 25, C. Wood 21, D. Richards 20, R.V. Stirling 19, G.R. Beamish (Ire) 12

I. Bates 4, L. Cusworth 3, A. Warwood 3, T. Smith 3, S. Redfern 2, N. Youngs 2, J. Wells 2, P. Dodge 2, P. Thornley 2, S. Kenny 2, K. MacDonald 2, Pentry 2, C. Dexter 2, A. Marriott 1, D. West 1, J. Harris 1, M. Reid 1, M. Poole 1, T. Thacker 1.

Points: W. Hare 438 (Club record), B. Evans 76, J. Harris 45, L. Cusworth 42, D. Richards 32, T. Underwood 32.

Drop goals: L. Cusworth 11, J. Harris 3.

MOSELEY

The Reddings, Reddings Road, Moseley, Birmingham B13 8LW. Tel: 021 449 2149

COLOURS Red and black hoops. (*Change colours*: White shirt with red and black hoops)

Entertaining and beating Leicester at The Reddings. A man of letters Dean Richards ("G") joins in with gusto. Photo: Chris Dennis, Leicester

REVIEW OF SEASON

The main achievement of 1988–89 was to reach ninth place in Division One and thus avoid relegation, but in other respects it was a season to forget. The Pilkington Cup campaign ended abruptly in Round 3 with defeat at the junior club Aspatria and the main hope for the future is that the younger players will come through and produce better form, but there will have to be an improvement if the coming season is not going to be a bitter battle against relegation. If Robson (the captain) and Linnett can recover the form which made them England candidates the rest of the team might respond and bring the desired results. On the credit side Moseley won 11 successive home matches from 26th November to 3rd March and there were four tries by Herd against Maesteg with additional hat-tricks by Shillingford, Parsons and Denhardt. Also on the credit side Coventry were beaten twice and other victims were Gloucester, Bristol, Bedford, Bridgend and Northampton. It was not all gloom and doom.

RESULTS

Date	Opponents	Venue	Points		Date	Opponents	Venue	Points	
Sept. 1988					**Jan. 1989**				
1	Wakefield	H	24	17	2	Gloucester	H	23	3
3	London Welsh	H	32	18	7	West Hartlepool	H	31	16
10	Gloucester (L)	A	9	37	14	Nottingham (L)	A	9	13
13	Coventry	A	41	21	20	Northampton	H	13	11
17	Maesteg	A	26	39	28	Aspatria	A	3	6
24	Rosslyn Park (L)	H	7	13	**Feb. 4**	Richmond	H	29	10
27	Ebbw Vale	H	22	12	11	Saracens	A	7	23
Oct 1	Sale	H	33	14	18	Leicester	A	10	27
8	Bristol (L)	A	0	18	25	Headingley	A	11	19
11	Loughborough Studs.	H	7	11	**Mar. 3**	London Irish	H	40	8
15	Aberavon	H	41	23	11	Orrell (L)	H	10	12
22	Waterloo (L)	H	13	6	17	Northampton	A	3	12
29	Cardiff	H	20	20	25	Nottingham	H	12	6
Nov. 1	Sheffield	H	49	10	**Apr. 1**	Newport	H	9	35
5	Newport	A	15	37	8	Leicester (L)	H	22	13
12	Bath (L)	H	0	38	11	Glamorgan Wands.	A	6	51
19	Wasps	A	10	39	18	Wasps	H	26	24
26	Liverpool/St. Helens	H	18	15	25	Harlequins (L)	A	15	38
Dec. 3	Bridgend	A	6	16					
6	Rugby	H	21	13					
10	Bristol	H	18	10					
13	Nuneaton	H	19	10					
17	Bedford	H	24	19					
23	Swansea	A	10	29					
26	Coventry	H	12	9					
30	Newbridge	A	10	16					

(L) = League.

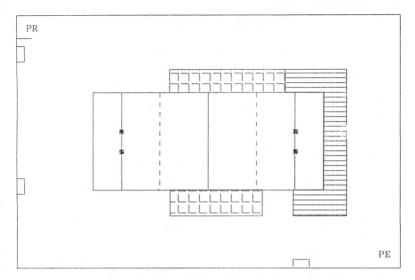

Moseley 1988–89: (Standing l to r): K. Davies (Chairman of playing), I. Metcalfe (coach), D. Nutt (coach), P. Suckling, I. Day, M. Bishop, S. Lloyd, J. Pullinger, R. Denhardt, S. Masters, P. Shillingford, C. Allen, R. Cook (touch judge), K. Birrell (match secretary), D. Protherough (coach). (Seated): C. Arntzen, A. Johnson, M. Linnett, A. James, S. Robson (captain), M. Morris (President), G. Smith (vice-capt), A. Parsons, R. Barr, B. Fenley, Gareth Smith.

MOSELEY R.U.F.C.

Founded: 1873
President: Nigel R.E. Morris
Chairman: John C. White
Secretary: Bernard J. Malin, The Reddings, Reddings Road, Moseley, Birmingham B13 8LW. Tel: 021 476 6890 (H), 021 449 2149 (W)
Fixtures Secretary: D.A.E. Evans, 22 Brooks Road, Wylde Green, Sutton Coldfield, West Midlands B72 1HP. Tel: 021 354 5076 (H), 021 742 8751 (W)
Coach: Derek Nutt
Club captain (1988–89): Simon Robson
Club captain (1989–90): Robert David Barr
No. of teams: Senior 6, Youth 1, Minis (U8–U17) 10
Directions to ground: South Birmingham A38. Take Priory Road traffic lights County Cricket Ground on left island right into Russell Road 100 yds left into Moorcroft Road into Reddings Road
Ground capacity: Seating 1800, Standing 8199
Clubhouse facilities: Two members bars, public bar, two players bars and portercabin shop
Floodlights: Yes
Nickname: 'Mose'
Membership fees: Full £37 (pre 1 Sept.)/£42 after, Playing £24, Youth £7, Student £7.50

Ground admission: £2.50, Juniors & OAPs £1
Programme: No. of editorial pages 8; No. of advertising pages 40; Price 50p
Programme editor: Peter Woodroofe, 14 Stanley Road, Kings Heath, Birmingham B14 7NB
Local newspapers: Birmingham Post, Daily News
League: National League Division 1
League position (1988–89): 9th
League playing record (1988–89): P 11, W 3, D 0 L 8, F 113, A 242
Most capped players (including British Lions appearances): Nigel Horton 20, P.G.D. Robbins 19, Peter Cranmer 16, Nick Jeavons 14, John Finlan 13, J.F. Byrne 13, Jan Webster 11, Martin Cooper 11, C.W. McFadyean 11, K.J. Fielding 10 (all Eng)
Players' appearances (1988–89): Carl Arntzen 39, Adrian James 37, Richard Denhardt 37, P. Shilingford 33, Adrian Parsons 32
Leading scorers (1988–89): Carl Arntzen 258 (8 t, 106 cons, 144 pens), P. Shillingford 60 (15 t), Simon Robson 48 (12 t), Murray Jones 44 (4 cons, 12 pens)

Rosslyn Park srum-half Alex Woodhouse spins out a neat pass against London Scottish.

NOTTINGHAM

Ireland Avenue, Dovecote Lane, Beeston,
Nottingham NG9 1JD. Tel: 0602
254238/224920

COLOURS Green and white.
(*Change colours*: Yellow and green)

Lions hooker Brian Moore (right) as his locks command a line-out.

REVIEW OF SEASON

Nottingham report an excellent season though not a record one. They finished fourth in Division One and reached the last eight of the Pilkington Cup, losing in shocking conditions at the Stoop Memorial Ground. Other highlights included a draw against Leicester and a close run at Bath, where the points were badly needed by the home team. Four players won international caps – Brian Moore (England and British Lions tour), Gary Rees, Simon Hodgkinson (both England) and Chris Gray (Scotland) the latter is the new club captain. The club also had excellent representation at other levels – England 'B', England Under-21 and the Barbarians. On a "Round the World Tour" covering Honolulu, Sydney, Brisbane and Bangkok four matches were won and two lost. The Midlands Division called generously on Nottingham players – 13 of them!

RESULTS

Date	Opponents	Venue	Points	Date	Opponents	Venue	Points
Sept. 1988							**Jan. 1989**
3	Hawick	15	21	3	Rugby	17	21
10	Rosslyn Park (L)	18	9	7	London Irish	21	15
17	Sale	6	13	14	Moseley (L)	13	9
24	Bristol (L)	10	6	21	Fylde	18	0
Oct 1	Northampton	25	12	28	Bedford (P.C.)	6	3
8	Waterloo (L)	18	9	**Feb.** 4	Wasps	43	10
15	London Scottish	30	3	11	Richmond (P.C.)	12	9
22	Leicester (L)	12	12	14	Nuneaton	29	17
29	Ebbw Vale	7	20	18	Gosforth	25	13
Nov. 2	Lichfield	65	15	25	Harlequins (P.C.)	9	15
5	Maesteg	42	0	**Mar.** 4	Aberavon	6	9
12	Wasps	9	15	11	Bath (L)	16	22
19	Liverpool St.			18	Bedford	55	0
	Helens (L)	22	15	25	Moseley	6	12
26	Orrell (L)	6	12	27	Rosslyn Park	15	30
29	Loughborough Colls.	26	6	**Apr.** 1	Cardiff	18	12
Dec. 3	Richmond	27	3	8	Harlequins (L)	12	0
10	Saracens	4	14	11	Coventry	34	11
13	RAF	26	16	15	Northampton	22	19
17	Bristol	0	10	22	Gloucester (L)	6	13
24	Headingley	24	6	23	Wang Sevens	2nd round loser	
31	Newport	21	36	29	Newbridge	16	16

(L) = League   (P.C.) = Pilkington Cup

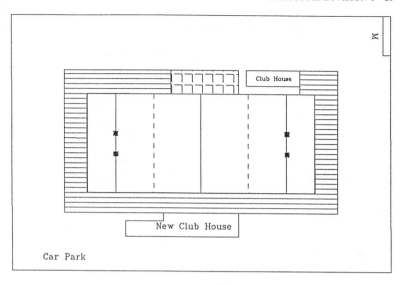

NOTTINGHAM R.U.F.C.

Founded: 1877
President: David W. Roberts
Chairman: James B. Bourke, FRCS
Secretary: T.B.A., c/o Nottingham R.F.C.
Fixtures Secretary: J.H. Addison, Wycliffe Mills, High Church Street, New Basford, Nottingham NG7 7JP. Tel: Plumtree 4780 (H), 0602 785466 (W)
Coach: Alan B.C. Davies/Jim Robinson
Club captain (1988–89): Brian Moore
Club captain (1989–90): Chris Gray
No. of teams: Senior 4, Youth 1, Minis 10 (inc. Junior 5)
Directions to ground: M1 (Junc. 25). Dir. Nottm. 1st rndabt exit 3 B6003, at T-junc. turn L onto A6005, pass dual carriageway, Barton's bus depot (L) turn R at next crossroad into Dovecote Lane, imm. turn R into Ireland Ave. Ground at end of road
Ground capacity: Seating 586, Standing 5000
Clubhouse facilities: New clubhouse and old clubhouse, 2 bars all open to members and spectators
Nickname: Green and Whites
Floodlights: Yes
Membership fees: Full £25, Playing £37, Social £5, VPs £37, Youth £18.50, Student £18.50, OAP £12.50

Ground admission: £3 (L) £2
Programme: No. of editorial pages 10–12; No. of advertising pages 0–28; Price T.B.A.
Local newspaper: Nottingham Evening Post
League: National League Division 1
League position (1988–89): 4th
League playing record (1988–89): P 43, W 25, D 3, L 15, F 822, A 519
Most capped players (including British Lions appearances): G.W. Rees 18 (Eng), B.C. Moore 17 (Eng), V.H. Cartwright 12 (Eng), C.R. Andrew 5 (Eng), J. Pallant 3 (Eng), H.A. Hodges 2 (Eng), C. Oti 2 (Eng), W.H. Hare 1 (Eng), S.D. Hodgkinson 1 (Eng), C.A. Gray 1 (Scot)
Players' appearances (1988–89): Richard Byrom 39, Glynn Mosses 32, Gary Hartley 26, Peter Cook 25, Simon Hodgkinson 24
Leading scorers (1988–89): S. Hodgkinson 257 (5 t, 30 cons, 50 pens, 9 d.g.), Kevin Stiles 63 (8 t, 8 cons, 5 pens), Gary Hartley 59 (6 t, 4 cons, 9 pens), Richard Byrom 48 (12 t), Andy Sutton 47 (4 t, cons 11, 3 pens), Neil Back 32 (8 t)

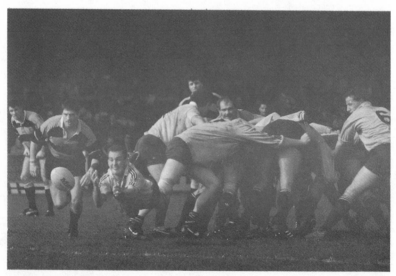

Nottingham 1988–89. Another attack is launched.

ORRELL

Edgehall Road, Orrell, Wigan WN5 8TL.
Tel: Up Holland 623193
COLOURS Black and amber.
(*Change colours*: Amber or red/white)

*Big game at Orrell! North win their Divisional match against the attacking South-West
(14–12). Photo: K.B. Riding, Bolton.*

REVIEW OF SEASON

Orrell is the kind of club the others would like to avoid as their fifth position in Division One proves. They can beat the best and are doughty cup fighters as Bath found out a few seasons ago when they only survived at Edgehall Road by scoring more tries than the home team in a drawn game. This season they were not so lucky in the Pilkington Cup, losing at Bristol in the Third Round, but they did win the Lancashire Cup by thrashing Broughton Park in the final (48–6). They have no current international players at the moment, but top scorer Gerry Ainscough, if he escapes injury, could make up for that one day and their speedy wing Nigel Heslop is another, who must be close to honours. Fullback Simon Langford is another who has come close and may be lucky one day.

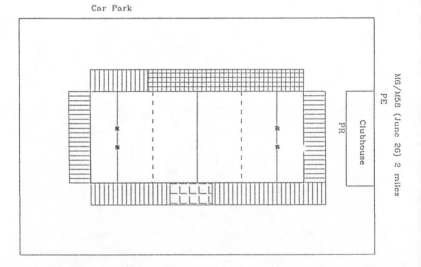

KEY TO GROUND PLANS

OPEN TERRACE	OPEN SEATS	TURNSTILE	PE PLAYERS'/OFFICIALS' ENTRANCE
COVERED TERRACE	COVERED SEATS	MAIN ENTRANCE/EXIT	PR PRESS ENTRANCE

ORRELL R.U.F.C.

Founded: 1927
President: George Southworth
Chairman: Ron J. Pimblett
Secretary: John Arrowsmith, 1 Fisher Drive, Orrell, Wigan. Tel: 0942 216879 (H), 0772 264221 (W)
Fixtures Secretary: Barry Cooper, 81 Crab Tree Lane, Burscough, Ormskirk. Tel: Burscough 893239 (H), 051 236 9231 ext. 6 (W)
Coach: Bill Lyon
Club captain (1988–89): Simon Langford
Club captain (1989–90): David (Sammy) Southern
No. of teams: Senior 4, Youth 6
Ground capacity: Seating 300, Standing 5000
Clubhouse facilities: Members' lounge, president's lounge, sponsors' lounge, clubroom
Floodlights: Yes
Membership fees: Full £29, Jnt. Husband/Wife £33, Playing £29, Female/Social £10, Youth £10, Student £10, OAP £8/Jnt. Husband/Wife £12
Ground admission: £2.50

Programme: No. of editorial pages 10; No. of advertising pages 14; Price 50p
Programme editor: As Press Officer
Local newspapers: Wigan Observer, Wigan Reporter, MCR Evening News, Liverpool Post
League: National League Division 1
League position (1988–89): 5th
League playing record (1988–89): P 11, W 6, D 1, L 4, F 148, A 157
Competitions won: Lancashire Cup
Most capped players (including British Lions appearances): Frank Anderson 1, John Carleton 26, Fran Clough 3, Dave Cusani 1, Peter Williams 4 (all for England)
Players' appearances (1988–89): David Cleary 35, David Fell 32, Steven Taberner 32, Michael Glynn 31, David (Sammy) Southern 29
Leading scorers (1988–89): Gerry Ainscough 148 (4 t, 24 cons, 26 pens, 2 d.g.), Martin Strett 107 (6 t, 28 cons, 7 pens, 2 d.g.), Simon Clanford 98 (5 t, 12 cons, 18 pens), Nigel Heslop 80 (20 t)

Tony Brooks, Rosslyn Park's captain and no. 8 (with headband), leads this charge against London Scottish with scrum-half Woodhouse (9 – left) in support.

Wasps Mark Rose tidies up loose ball as his side prepares to attack yet again.

ROSSLYN PARK

Priory Lane, Roehampton, London SW15.
Tel: 01–876 1879

COLOURS Red and white hoops.
(*Change colours*: Dark blue with red band)

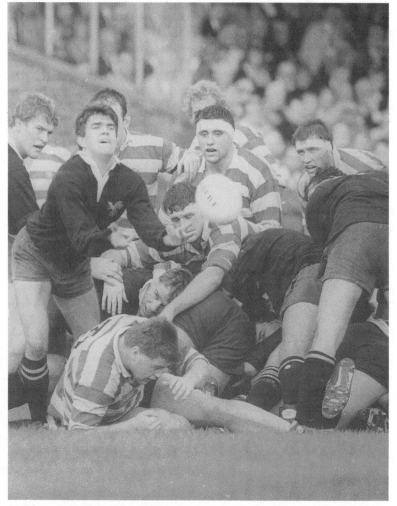

Park lose possession and the match against Wasps (16–39). Scrum-half Steve Bates sets his backs in motion for the Sudbury club.

REVIEW OF SEASON

Just by finishing ninth in Division One Rosslyn Park survived and this on its own must have given a great deal of satisfaction to the hard-working officials and players of a most friendly club, which in many ways lives in the shadows of its more glamorous neighbours – Harlequins and Wasps. It was a struggle, but late wins (three in succession) against Waterloo, Liverpool/St. Helens and Orrell made sure that the first two would go down and that "Park" would stay up. The club has a sound youth policy and is well coached by Hugh McHardy. There are no "name" players at the moment, but consistency is maintained by Graves, the leading points scorer yet again, scrum-half Woodhouse, wing Hunter and the huge lock Dear. Proof of the strength of the youth team is shown by the fact that they were voted Whitbread-Rugby World & Post Colts Team of the Year, which was achieved by winning all their matches. Once again, however, at the top level there was no real joy in the main cup competition as victory at home against Plymouth Albion was followed by the now almost customary defeat at the hands of Leicester.

RESULTS

Date	Opponents	Venue	Points		Date	Opponents	Venue	Points	
Sept. 1988					**Jan. 1989**				
3	Birkenhead Park		53	4	2	Richmond		9	26
10	Nottingham (L)		9	18	7	Glamorgan Wands.		17	18
17	London Scottish		9	29	14	Harlequins (L)		12	16
24	Moseley (L)		13	7	21	Cross Keys		51	0
Oct 1	London Welsh		15	6	28	Plymouth Albion		18	0
8	Bath (L)		6	19	**Feb.** 3	Selkirk		41	7
15	Cambridge Univ.		6	7	11	Leicester		9	23
22	Wasps (L)		16	39	17	London Irish		25	22
26	Metropolitan Police		9	37	22	Northampton		29	15
29	Abertillery		6	12	25	Pontypridd		Cancelled	
Nov. 5					**Mar.** 3	Blackheath		15	3
12	Gloucester (L)		8	26	11	Waterloo (L)		24	14
19	Leicester (L)		15	28	18				
26	Bristol (L)		18	16	24	Portugal		18	4
Dec. 3	Bedford		30	12	27	Nottingham		30	15
10	Exeter Univ.		36	12	**Apr.** 2	Public School Wands.		32	15
17	Llandovery		22	18	8	Liverpool/St.			
24	Wasps		16	15		Helens (L)		32	12
31	Llanelli		24	44	15	Bridgend		17	19
					22	Orrell (L)		19	13

(L) = Courage League Division One

Rosslyn Park (in change colours) contest a line-out in the Pilkington Cup in their "annual" tie against Leicester – with its routine result of another defeat.

ROSSLYN PARK R.U.F.C.

Founded: 1879
President: Geoffrey Dodds
Chairman: Alan Taylor
Secretary: David E. Whittam, FRCS, 37 Queens Road, Kingston-upon-Thames, Surrey KT2 7SL. Tel: 01–549 4209 (H), 01–672 1255 ext. 52052 (W)
Fixtures Secretary: Colin Horgan, 96 Thames Street, Sunbury-on-Thames TW16 6AG. Tel: 0932 785012
Press Officer: As Fixtures Secretary
Coach: Hugh McHardy
Club captain (1988–89): Tony Brooks
Club captain (1989–90): Tony Brooks
No. of teams: Senior 9, Youth 1, Minis 5
Directions to ground: Ground situated at the junction of Upper Richmond Road (South Circular Road) and Roehampton Lane, London SW15
Ground capacity: Seating 630, Standing 2870
Clubhouse facilities: Large public bar, members bar, presidents bar, kit. and souvenir shop
Nickname: The Park
Floodlights: Yes

Membership fees: Full £34.50, Playing £34.50, Social £17.25, Youth £23, Student £23
Ground admission: £2
Programme: No. of editorial pages 2; Price 50p
Programme editor: As Secretary
Local newspapers: Richmond & Twickenham Times, Surrey Times
League: National League Division 1
League position (1988–89): 9th
League playing record (1988–89): P 11, W 5, D 0, L 6, F 172, A 208
Competitions won: Surrey Sevens, April 1989
Most capped players (including British Lions appearances): J.P. Scott 34, M.J. Colclough 25, A.G. Ripley 24, C.E. Winn 8, P.J. Warfield 6, C.P. Kent 5, T.C. Wintle 5, A. Obolensky 4 (for England)
Players' appearances (1988–89): S. Dear 32, A. Woodhouse 28, T. Hyde 26, S. Hunter 24, J. Graves 24
Leading scorers (1988–89): J. Graves 212 (5 t, 42 cons, 36 pens), R. Crawford 79 (7 t, 12 cons, 9 pens), S. Hunter 60 (15 t)

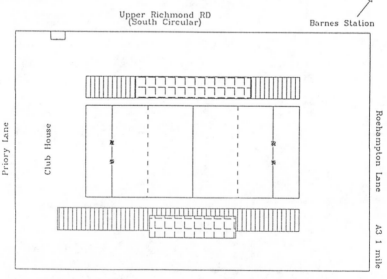

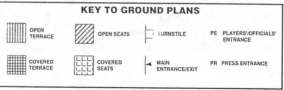

SARACENS

Bramley Road Sports Ground, Green Road,
Chase Side, Southgate, London N14. Tel:
01–449 3770

COLOURS Black with red star and crescent.
(*Change colours*: Black/white/red hoops)

Saracens 1988–89 – Division Two champions.

REVIEW OF SEASON

After difficult early away wins at Headingley and Sale, Saracens, under the captaincy of Floyd Steadman and coached by Tony Russ, never looked back with particularly impressive wins against Northampton and Bedford but defeat from London Scottish in the Pilkington Cup was a rare setback in their best ever season.

RESULTS

Date	Opponents	Venue	Points		Date	Opponents	Venue	Points	
Sept. 1988					**Jan. 1989**				
3	West Hartlepool	W	25	10	7	Rugby	W	24	7
10	Headingley*	W	7	3	14	Coventry*	W	13	6
17	Bridgend	W	28	22	21	Harlequins	W	12	14
24	London Irish*	W	20	3	28	London Scottish†	L	0	16
Oct 2	Newbridge	L	7	41	**Feb.** 4	Metropolitan Police	W	16	14
8	Sale*	W	12	10	11	Moseley	W	23	7
15	Exeter	W	33	0	18	Waterloo	L	14	31
22	London Welsh*	W	37	4	25	Swansea	L	6	19
29	Nuneaton	W	40	8	**Mar.** 4	Leicester	L	6	25
Nov. 5	North Walsham†	W	31	3	11	Richmond*	W	27	10
12	Northampton*	W	32	4	18	Orrell	W	12	7
19	Bedford*	W	50	10	25	Vale of Lune	W	49	7
26	Blackheath*	W	24	12	**Apr.** 1	Abertillery	W	24	10
Dec. 3	Wakefield	W	26	3	8	London Scottish*	W	19	9
10	Nottingham	W	14	4	15	Liverpool St. Helens	W	31	16
17	Bath	L	6	24	22	Gosforth*	W	47	9
26	Northampton	L	4	56	29	Middlesex 7s Prelims			
31	Wasps	L	3	24					

* = Courage Clubs Championship Division 2
† = Pilkington Cup

Saracens attack against London Scottish with skipper Floyd Steadman about to receive the ball and take on Gavin Hastings (no. 15).

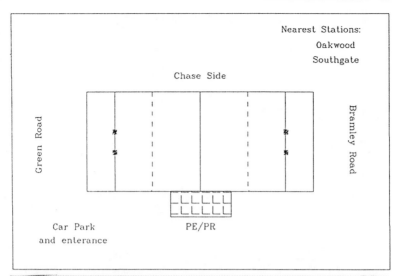

Nearest Stations:
Oakwood
Southgate

Chase Side

Green Road

Bramley Road

Car Park
and enterance

PE/PR

Saracens turn on the style against London Scottish at Southgate on their way to their Division Two triumph.

SARACENS R.U.F.C.

Founded: 1876
President: George Sherriff
Chairman: John How
Secretary: Barney Richards, 36 Stone Hall Road, Winchmore Hill, London N21 1LP. Tel: 01–360 4061 (H), 01–262 5055 (W)
Fixtures Secretary: David Grammer, 75 Roundwood Lane, Harpenden, Herts AL5 3EX. Tel: 05827 62356
Press Officer: Chris Johnson, 36 Orchard Way, Knebworth, Herts. Tel: 0438 811345 (H), 0462 420939 (W)
Coach: Tony Russ
Club captain (1988–89): Floyd Steadman
Club captain (1989–90): Floyd Steadman
No. of teams: Senior 7, Youth (U19) 2, Minis (All ages up to 16)
Directions to ground: From Junction 24 on M25 follow A111 to Cockfosters (2 miles), pass Cockfosters Tube Station on left, through shops to roundabout (mile), straight on towards Southgate. Saracens is on your left
Ground capacity: Seating 400, Standing 2000
Clubhouse facilities: Bar, tea bar, shop, ladies and gents toilets. Car parking in Middx. Polytechnic

Nickname: Sarries
Floodlights: No
Membership fees: Playing £26, Non-Playing £16, Youth £10
Ground admission: £3
Programme: No. of editorial pages 2+; No. of advertising pages 28; Price (included in admission)
Programme editor: As Press Officer
Local newspapers: Enfield Gazette, Barnet Press
League: National League Division 2
League position (1988–89): 1st
League playing record (1988–89): P 11, W 11, D 0, L 0, F 288, A 70
Competitions won: Courage Clubs Championship Division 2
Most capped players (including British Lions appearances): V. Harding 6
Players' appearances (1988–89): Sean Robinson 31, John McFarland 30, Peter Lindley 29, Floyd Steadman 28
Leading scorers (1988–89): Andy Kennedy 297 (10 t, 34 cons, 63 pens), Sean Robinson (15 t), Dave McLagen (15 t)

FIXTURES

Date	Opponents	Time	Venue	Date	Opponents	Time	Venue
		Sept. 1989		**Jan. 1990**			
2	Richmond	3 pm	H	6	Rugby		A
9	Bedford*		A	13	Bristol*	2.30 pm	H
16	Bridgend		A	21	Harlequins		A
23	Orrell*	3 pm	H	27	Pilkington Cup	(3rd Round)	
30	Exeter		A	**Feb.** 3	Metropolitan Police	3 pm	H
Oct 7	Newbridge	3 pm	H	10	London Scottish		A
14	Nottingham*		A	17	Waterloo	3 pm	H
21	Ebbw Vale	3 pm	H	24	Swansea		A
28	Moseley*	3 pm	H	**Mar.** 3	London Welsh		A
Nov. 4	Vale of Lune		A	10	Rosslyn Park*		A
11	Leicester*		A	17	Blackheath	3 pm	H
18	Harlequins*	2.30 pm	H	24	Fylde	3 pm	H
25	Gloucester*		A	31	Bath*	3 pm	H
Dec. 2	Abertillery		A	**Apr.** 7	West Hartlepool	3 pm	H
9	Nuneaton	2.15 pm	H	14	Bradford & Bingley	3 pm	H
16	Wakefield		A	21	Liverpool St. Helens	3 pm	H
23	Sale	2.15 pm	H	28	Wasps*		A
30	London Irish		A				

* = Courage League Division One

WASPS

Repton Avenue, Sudbury, Wembley,
Middlesex. Tel: 01–902 4220

COLOURS Black with gold wasp on left
breast.
(*Change colours*: Black and gold hoops)

*Rob Andrew (Wasps, England and British Lions). Photo: Picturesport Associates,
Wembley, Middlesex.*

REVIEW OF SEASON

During May 1989 Wasps provided the captains for England against Romania (Rob Andrew), for England 'B' in Spain (David Pegler) and for England Under-21 against Romania Under-21 (Steve Pilgrim) – a record other clubs will have envied. In fact, the team's representatives at the top level start with Andrew and Chris Oti chosen for the Lions tour of Australia (Andrew as a replacement), with the same two players playing six and five times respectively for England, with Paul Rendall (six times), Jeff Probyn (four times) and Steve Bates (against Romania) also playing for England, with David Pegler (as captain), Mark Bailey (once as captain), Sean O'Leary, Kevin Simms and Rob Lozowski appearing for England 'B' and with Pilgrim, Hopley, Simms and O'Leary turning out for England Under-21. Another Hopley was an England colt and Bailey, Bates, Oti, Probyn and Rendall were all honoured with Barbarian matches. However, top honours for the players were not translated into trophies for the team, which did well to finish third in Division One and reached the quarter-finals of the Pilkington Cup. However, doing well and winning are two different things, but with all the first class talent available how long can they be denied? The cub would like to know and perhaps the new season will provide the answers.

RESULTS

Date	Opponents	Venue	Points	
Sept.				
1988 3	Maesteg	A	29	29
4	Metropolitan Police	H	11	23
10	Leicester*	A	6	15
17	Liverpool St. Helens	A	28	13
24	Harlequins*	H	23	15
28	London Irish	H	14	22
Oct 1	Blackheath	A	20	12
8	Gloucester*	A	3	19
15	Rugby	A	17	18
22	Rosslyn Park*	H	39	6
29	Gosforth	A	19	15
Nov. 5				
12	Nottingham*	A	15	9
19	Moseley*	H	39	10
26	Bath*	A	6	16
Dec. 3	Torquay	H	29	16
10	Headingley	H	19	9
17	Northampton	A	14	28
24	Rosslyn Park	A	15	16
31	Saracens	A	24	3

Date	Opponents	Venue	Points	
Jan.				
1989 7	Harlequins	A	10	29
14	Orrell*	A	9	9
21	Richmond	H	41	16
28	Durham C. (P.C.)	H	33	3
Feb. 4	Nottingham	H	10	43
11	Aspatria (P.C.)	H	39	7
18	London Welsh	H	9	9
25	Leicester (P.C.)	A	18	22
Mar. 4	Coventry	A	31	14
11	Liverpool St. Helens*	H	16	10
17	Neath	A	34	6
27	Birkenhead Park	H	92	12
Apr. 1	Bedford	A	26	14
8	Bristol*	H	21	19
15	Moseley	A	24	26
22	Waterloo*	A	29	0
29	P. Final & Middlesex 7s Prelims Twickenham			
May 6	Twickenham			

* = Courage Clubs Championship Division 1 (P.C.) = Pilkington Cup

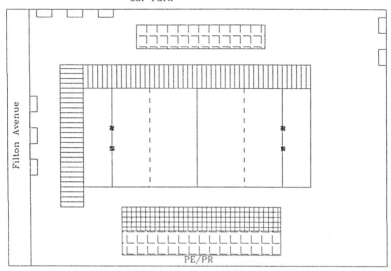

Chris Oti (Wasps, England and British Lions) against Richmond. Photo: Picturesport Associates, Wembley, Middlesex.

WASPS R.U.F.C.

Founded: 1867
President: Michael J. Cutter
Chairman: Peter G. Yarranton
Secretary: Ivor A. Montlake, Nash House, 25 Mount Sion, Tunbridge Wells, Kent. Tel: 0892 35857 (H), 034282 2980 (W)
Fixtures Secretary: Don Wills, 25 Woodlands Gardens, Isleworth, Middlesex TW7 6LN. Tel: 01–560 7594 (H), 01–481 9892 (W)
Press Officer: John Gasson, The Manor, Willington, Beds MK44 3PX. Tel: 0234 838314 (H), 01–409 3455 (W)
Coach: Mark Taylor
Club captain (1988–89): Rob Lozowski
Club captain (1989–90): Rob Andrews
No. of teams: Senior 10, Youth 2, Ladies 1
Directions to ground: Piccadilly Line to Sudbury Town or B.R. to North Wembley. Ground marked in London A-Z (see attached map)
Ground capacity: Seating 900, Standing 3100
Clubhouse facilities: Bars, medical suite, gym, changing, offices, press room, shop, sponsors' suite, trophy room, disabled wc's
Floodlights: Yes

Membership fees: Full £30, Playing £12, Social £30, Youth £5, Student £2, OAP £15
Ground admission: £2
Programme: No. of editorial pages 6–8; No. of advertising pages 20; Price 50p
Programme editor: Kevin O'Shea. Tel: 01–892 7224
Local newspapers: Wembley & Harrow Observer, Willesden Chronicle
League: National League Division 1
League position (1988–89): 3rd
League playing record (1988–89): P 35, W 20, D 2, L 13, F 791, A 560
Most capped players (including British Lions appearances – England if not stated): C.R. Andrew 26, M.J. Colclough 25, R.M. Uttley 23, P.A.G. Rendall 23, G.H. Davies 21, N.H. Horton 20, D.J. O'Brien (Ire) 20, G.J. Fay (Aus) 20, R.V. Stirling 18, K.G. Simms 15
Players' appearances: (1988–89): Rob Lozowski, Alan Simmons, Steve Pilgrim, Mark Rigby, Mark Rose
Leading scorers (1988–89): Rob Andrew 176 (2 t, 28 cons, 35 pens, 2 d.g.), Steve Pilgrim 114 (9 t, 21 cons, 12 pens), Mark Bailey (15 t), John Ellison (14 t), Chris Oti (12 t)

Steve Bates breaks through a tackle from Harlequins' Moon at Sudbury – 24.9.88. Roger Quittenton, the manel referee, looks on with interest. Photo: Picturesport Associates, Wembley, Middlesex.

NATIONAL DIVISION TWO

AGAIN WE HAVE to report a dominant team as Saracens ran away with the title and were never threatened, winning all their 11 matches with a points difference of 208 in their favour. This they did with a team almost bereft of stars and their potentially best player – the Army and England 'B' no. 8 Dean Ryan – was out of the picture for more than half the season with a broken arm. With no stars they relied on good teamwork and the sound kicking of wing Andy Kennedy, who put over most awards to keep his side's noses well in front. Even with the loyal and enthusiastic captain – scrum-half Floyd Steadman – continuing for another season can Saracens maintain a realistic challenge in the top division or even survive? Only time will tell.

The main excitement in the division was over the second promotion place and on the last day five sides were in with a chance – and none of them managed to win! Thus Bedford's scrambled draw at Sale gave them the promotion place leaving the others to wonder what had happened. Bedford will find life at the top difficult particularly as they have lost their fine scrum-half Brian Gabriel to Nottingham. The others who missed out are probably relieved that they did so as none would have been reasonably expected not to struggle at the top level.

Northampton (who were in a "relegation" spot at the end of the previous season but were reprieved by the lack of such a penalty) did much better to take third place, but the two relegated clubs from 1987–88 were just not good enough to return. Sale in fact had a sticky time before rising to the upper reaches of the table and Coventry were well and truly thrashed in their final match at London Scottish, who were unluckily relegated.

London Irish somehow managed to throw away a 21–0 lead in their concluding match against Blackheath to rob themselves of promotion and Headingley's promotion challenge – never too convincing – foundered on their final game when their defeat at home to Richmond meant survival for the latter, which their improved form over the season just about deserved.

Gosforth just about kept North-Eastern prestige together but by the narrowest of margins and the two teams to fall were the exile clubs – London Scottish and London Welsh. The former had injury problems right through the season and lost at least one match by courtesy of quaint refereeing decisions. However, with Gavin Hasting staying to lead them and the arrival of Derek White they should mount a good challenge for promotion.

The same cannot be said of the Welsh who suffer from the lack of good recruits from a formerly traditional rich source – the Valleys. The players are just not going to London and the only – most unacceptable – alternative is for them to "go open". They learned the hard way that great fitness is just not enough, since all teams enjoyed that same virtue. There was a lack of skill and technique – Mark Douglas excepted – and the future is bleak if they cannot repair their defects.

With the leagues becoming gradually polarised the time has almost arrived where the Second Division will not provide teams who can challenge the best, but it will be interesting to see how promoted Plymouth Albion and Rugby fare and whether one or both of them can break the mould. For the rest, unless they can hang on to their best players – a tall order – their present status must become the summit of their ambitions.

TABLES 1987–88

DIVISION TWO

	P	W	D	L	F	A	PTS
Rosslyn Park	11	8	2	1	155	83	37
Liverpool-St Helens	11	8	1	2	154	97	36
Saracens	11	7	2	2	228	86	34
Headingley	11	6	2	3	202	104	31
Bedford	11	6	2	3	152	139	31
Richmond	11	6	0	5	140	156	29
London Scottish	11	4	1	6	141	158	24
London Irish	11	4	1	6	120	177	24
London Welsh	11	3	2	6	153	185	22
Gosforth	10	2	1	7	99	129	17
Blackheath	11	2	0	9	102	187	17
Northampton	11	1	0	9	81	226	13

Gosforth had three points and one win deducted for fielding an ineligible player against Bedford.

TABLES 1988–89

DIVISION TWO

	P	W	D	L	F	A	PTS
Saracens	11	11	0	0	288	80	22
Bedford	11	6	2	3	141	187	14
Northampton	11	5	2	4	195	152	12
Sale	11	6	0	5	150	143	12
Coventry	11	6	0	5	150	143	12
London Irish	11	5	2	4	194	222	12
Headingley	11	5	1	5	179	136	11
Blackheath	11	4	1	6	181	144	9
Richmond	11	4	1	6	112	216	9
London Scottish	11	4	0	7	176	246	8
London Welsh	11	3	1	7	146	160	7
	11	1	1	9	125	235	3

COURAGE NATIONAL DIVISION TWO
Results Season 1987–88

	1	2	3	4	5	6	7	8	9	10	11	12
1 Bedford		6-0	16-25		33-25		21-9	6-6	17-16		15-3	
2 Blackheath						12-16		22-7	19-12	3-4		12-48
3 Gosforth		26-8				14-22		12-14	N/P	12-10		
4 Headingley	7-13	21-9	26-7						38-3		12-12	3-12
5 L'Pl St Helens		15-0	15-12	6-6		14-0	10-3				3-13	
6 London Irish	12-12			12-32			3-6			17-15		9-27
7 London Scottish		18-9	13-8	6-22					50-3			
8 London Welsh				10-18	10-27	6-13	24-24			22-26		
9 Northampton						9-13	15-13		14-16	3-16	0-22	
10 Richmond	28-25			14-13	3-13		9-6					3-22
11 Rosslyn Park		14-8	14-3			20-3	15-6	16-15		20-12		
12 Saracens	33-4		7-7		10-13		34-0	7-25	22-6		6-6	

Results Season 1988–89

	1	2	3	4	5	6	7	8	9	10	11	12
1 Bedford			19-99			15-2	9-6	18-6		15-3		
2 Blackheath	12-13			34-10	21-3					31-3	12-6	12-24
3 Coventry		18-2		19-12	7-18				22-10		7-3	
4 Gosforth	16-17				29-14		16-14	34-26		16-4		9-27
5 Headingley	7-7					48-9	22-10	24-0		9-12		3-7
6 London Irish		21-6	6-29	32-7				24-19	18-10		18-18	
7 London Scottish		6-3	224-9			16-21			3-3		16-17	
8 London Welsh		15-15	14-21				29-10		0-22		9-16	
9 Northampton	42-3	15-7		13-12	19-7						15-12	4-32
10 Richmond		12-3				18-18	12-32	14-3	15-12			10-27
11 Sale	15-15		23-15	15-24					50-9		10-12	
12 Saracens	50-10		13-6			20-3	19-9	37-4				

BLACKHEATH

Rectory Field, Charlton Road, SE3. Tel:
01–858 1578
COLOURS Red/black.
Change colours: Black

REVIEW OF SEASON

On the last day of the season "Club" needed to win at London Irish to make sure of escaping relegation and at one stage they were 21–0 down before they made a miraculous recovery to win 22–21 thanks to a late dropped-goal by King. So, London Scottish, who had crushed Coventry the same afternoon descended instead. This was an improvement on the previous season's efforts, when they would have been relegated if such a fate had existed for them, and their final position of eighth was satisfactory – if flattering. In the cups they survived a round at Swindon (13–3), but failed to repel the challenge at the Rectory Field of Waterloo (13–6) and to do better in the coming season that is the kind of team they will need to beat. They do have an excellent coach in Alex Keay and some good young players, but they are not unique in this respect so no-one will be surprised if they struggle again.

BLACKHEATH R.U.F.C.

Founded: 1858
President: J.B. Williamson
Chairman: F. McCarthy
Secretary: P. Rossiter-Marvell, Flat 2, 157 Victoria Way, London SE7 7NX. Tel: 01–858 0646 (H), 01–485 4100 ext. 258 (W)
Fixtures Secretary: R. Pearce, 2 Robin Hood Cottages, St. Pauls Wood Hill, Chislehurst, Kent. Tel: 0689 70205 (H), 01–930 5454
Press Officer: T.B.A.
Coach: A. Keay
Club captain (1988–89): T. Fenby
Club captain (1989–90): T.B.A.
No. of teams: Senior 6, Youth 4, Minis 6

Directions to ground: S.R. to Blackheath bus 54 or 75, or S.R. to Charlton then short walk. Bus 53 from Oxford Street direct to ground
Nickname: Club
Floodlights: No
Membership fees: Playing £35, Non-Playing £25, Minis & Youth £5, Student £15
Ground admission: £2.50
League: National League Division 2
League position (1988–89): 8th
League playing record (1988–89): P 11, W 4, D 1, L 6
Most capped players (including British Lions appearances): N.S. Bruce 31 (Scot), C.N. Lowe 25, A.L. Horton 7, T.P. Wright 13 (for Eng)

Plymouth Albion wins this line-out ball as they win their Division Three match at Rugby. Sean Stevens and Ian Russell (right) are the men in charge. Photo: Mike Cox.

Plymouth Albion right-wint Eddie Gibbs kicks ahead at –Rugby. Photo: Mike Cox

COVENTRY

Barker Butts Lane, Coundon, Coventry
Tel: 0203 591274 and 593399
COLOURS Navy blue and white hoops, navy shorts.
(*Change colours*: Dark blue

"Cov" have plenty of bodies in action against visitors Leicester, but Dean Richards has the ball. Enough said! Photo: Coventry Evening Telegraph.

REVIEW OF SEASON

For "Cov" this was a dreadful season by their own high standards and their final position in Courage League Division Two of fourth was false, although a victory at London Scottish in their final game of the season would have brought promotion. Instead, the team was comprehensively thrashed, which was probably just as well as the side at the moment is just not good enough for Division One rugby. An overall First XV record of only 13 wins in 40 games with one draw and 26 defeats (points differential – 528–817) bears testimony to that. The colts did well, however, with 26 wins from 36 game s and a 793–492 points differential and that does give hope for the future. In the Pilkington Cup there was more humiliation as Plymouth Albion came to Coundon Road and won (12–7). Consistency amongst players was not too obvious, although prop Steve Wilkes did appear in 35 games with Leroy McKenzie playing one less game and scoring 125 tries. Skipper Martin Fairn scored 136 points from 34 games, but he now steps down and the captaincy passes on to Steve Thomas. The good old days seem like a distant memory.

RESULTS

Date		Opponents	Venue	Points		Date		Opponents	Venue	Points	
Sept	3	Newport	A	15	13	Jan	7	Llanelli	H	6	29
	10	London Irish	*A	29	6		14	Saracens	*A	6	13
	13	Moseley	H	21	41		22	Newbridge	H	13	30
	17	Cardiff	A	10	17		28	Vale of Lune	H	13	12
	24	Sale	*H	7	3	Feb	4	Waterloo	A	3	16
	28	Nuneaton	H	15	9		11	Morley	H	44	3
Oct	1	Leicester	H	7	45		17	Northampton	A	Canc.	
	8	London Welsh	*A	21	14		25	Bedford	H	6	3
	15	Bridgend	A	24	31	Mar	4	Wasps	H	14	31
	22	Gosforth	*H	19	12		11	Northampton	*H	22	10
	29	Bristol	A	9	51		18	Harlequins	A	Canc.	
Nov	5	Plym Alb	CupH	7	12		22	Nuneaton	A	12	10
	12	Bedford	*A	9	19		25	Neath	H	9	42
	19	Blackheath	*H	18	12		27	Headingley	A	13	18
	26	Richmond	*A	3	12	Apr	1	Maesteg	H	16	21
Dec	3	Wanderers	H	11	22		8	Headingley	*H	7	18
	10	Pontypool	A	13	25		11	Nottingham	A	11	34
	17	Gloucester	H	14	30		15	S.Wales Pol.	A	4	27
	23	Ebbw Vale	H	18	19		22	London Scottish	*A	9	24
	26	Moseley	A	9	12		26	Rugby	H	12	12
	31	Cheltenham	A	16	10		29	Sale	A	14	49

* = Courage National Division 2 match.

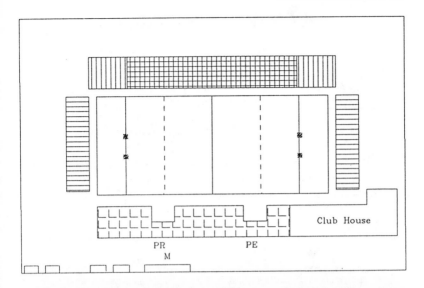

A rare "Cov" attack is halted as Leicester come to Coundon Road and win a "friendly" (45–7). Photo: Coventry Evening Telegraph.

COVENTRY R.U.F.C.

Founded: 1874
President: Harry Walker
Chairman: Eric Blackburn
Secretary: Peter Jackson, 147 Chester Road, Castle Bromwich, Birmingham B36 0AE Tel: 021 474 2498 (H)
Fixtures Secretary: John Butler, 62 Spring Lane, Whittington, Nr Lichfield. Tel: 0543 432654 (H) 0827 289999 0827 289999 (B)
Club captain (1988–89): Martin Fairn
Club captain (1989–90): Steve Thomas
No. of teams: Senior 3, Youth 1, Minis 0
Directions to ground: Leaving Coventry on the A4114 take the first right fork (at traffic lights) and follow the road round, crossing railway lines, the ground is on your left. Entering Coventry by the A4114 turn left at the Holyhead public house, turn right at next set of traffic lights. Ground is on your right.
Ground capacity: Seating 1100, Standing 8900
Clubhouse facilities: General bar, cocktail bar, sponsors bar, dining room.
Floodlights: Yes
Nickname: 'Cov'

Membership fees: Vice President Full £35 (pre 1 Sept.)/£42 after, Playing £24, Youth £7, Student £7.50
Ground admission: £2.20, Stand £3.30
Programme: No. of editorial pages 5; No. of advertising pages 12; Price 40p
Programme editor: Mr John Butler. As above.
Local newspapers: Coventry Evening Telegraph
League: National League Division 2
League position (1988–89): 4th
League playing record (1988–89): P 11, W 5, D 2 L 4, F 195, A 152
Most capped players D.J. Duckahm 36, S.E. Brain 14, R.E. Webb 12, F.E. Cotton 31, J.F. Finaln 13, P.B. Jackson 20, K.E. Fairbrother 12, P.G.D. Robbins 19, I. Preece 12, J.E. Owen 14, P.S. Preece 12.
Players' appearances (1988–89): Steve Wilkes Prop Forward 35, Leroy McKenzie Wing threequarter 34, Martin Fairn Full Back 34, Clive Medford Centre Threequarter 30, Jim Graham Centre Threequarter 29.
Leading scorers (1988–89): Martin Fairn 136 points, Leroy McKenzie 60 points (15 tries)

Coventry 1988–89. Photo: Coventry Evening Telegraph.

GOSFORTH

North Road, Gosforth, Newcastle upon Tyne
NE3 2DT. Tel: 091 2856915
COLOURS Green and white.
(*Change colours*: Blue)

GOSFORTH R.U.F.C.

President: John H. Gray
Chairman: R.W. Wood
Secretary: Tom Farrell, 1 Parklands, Darras Hall, Ponteland, Newcastle upon Tyne NE20 9LL. Tel: 0661 24557 (H), 091 2646464 (W)
Fixtures Secretary: T.L. Hall, 7 Roseworth Crescent, Gosforth, Newcastle upon Tyne NE3 1NR. Tel: 091 2856565 (H), 2815711 (W)
Press Officer: Duncan M. Carson, 31 Harwood Close, Whitelea Grange, Cramlington NE23 6AW. Tel: 0670 733896 (H), 091 2810678 (W)
Coach: J.S. (Steve) Gustard
Club captain (1988–89): G.G. Smallwood
Club captain (1989–90): D. Briggs
No. of teams: Senior 6, Youth & Minis 9
Directions to ground: 3 miles north of Newcastle upon Tyne along the Great North Road A6125
Ground capacity: Seating 2000, Standing 400
Clubhouse facilities: 3 bars, players and sponsors. Open matchdays and evenings
Nickname: Gos
Floodlights: No

Membership fees: Full £30, Social £10, Youth £6, Student £16
Ground admission: £1.50
Programme: No. of editorial pages 2; No. of advertising pages 20; Price 20p
Programme editor: W.M.H. Dix, 41 Ingram Drive, Chapel Park, Newcastle upon Tyne NE5 1T6.. Tel: 091 2676342 (H), 4820033 (W)
League: National League Division 2
League position (1988–89): 10th
League playing record (1988–89): P 40, W 21, D 1, L18
Most capped players (including British Lions appearances – for England unless stated): R.J. McLoughlin (Ire) 40, A. Smith (Scot) 33, R.M. Uttley 23, P.J. Dixon 22, S. Bainbridge 16, D.F. Madsen (SAcot) 14, M. Young 10
Players' appearances (1988–89): Derek Briggs 38, Ross Wilkinson 31, Neil Frankland 31, Peter Clark 30, David Walker 30
Leading scorers (1988–89): Peter Clark 201 (1 t, 40 cons, 34 pens, 5 d.g.), David Walker 68 (17 t), Derek Briggs 52 (13 t), David Ogilvie 32 (8 t)

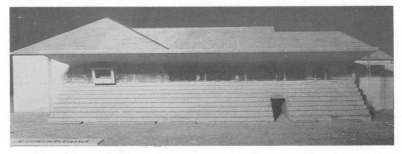

A model of the new Gosforth clubhouse

REVIEW OF SEASON

In a season plagued by injuries Gosforth were perhaps lucky to survive in Division 2. By finishing 10th they were only one place above the two exile clubs – Scottish and Welsh – and the latter two were the ones to go down. An early season victory over London Welsh in fact proved decisive and they had to rely on the losers' poor goal-kicking for ultimate victory. Naturally, the club hopes for better in the new season and is well prepared for that, but it can be assumed that every rival has the same attitude. The new captain is fullback or wing Derek Briggs, scorer of 14 tries last season, and he has the job of keeping the team motivated. He will be looking for continued good form from leading scorer Peter Clark, scrum-half Derek Walker, flanker Neil Frankland and centre Ross Wilkinson, but it will be a tough season for Gos and they may need to rely on a lot of luck to survive. Perhaps, that will come with the projected ground move, which is due to take place in 1990.

FIXTURES 1989–90

Date	Opponents	Time	Venue	Date	Opponents	Venue	Points
Sept. 1989				**Jan. 1990**			
2	Roundhay		H	1	Novos		A
3	Northern Sevens			6	Kendal		A
5	Gateshead Fell		H	13	Headingley		*A
9	Liverpool		*A	20	Hawick		H
16	Headingley		H	27	London Welsh		A
23	Blackheath		*H	**Feb. 3**	West Hartlepool		A
30	Durham City		A	10	Sheffield		A
Oct 7	Broughton Park		H	17	Nottingham		H
14	Richmond		*A	24	Vale of Lune		A
21	Orrell		H	**Mar. 3**	Harlequins		H
28	Coventry		*H	10	Sale		*H
Nov. 4	Pilkington Cup Rd. 2			17	Bedford		A
11	Rugby		*A	24	Edin. Academicals		A
18	London Irish		*H	31	Northampton		*H
25	Plymouth		*A	**Apr. 7**	Wasps		A
Dec. 2	Tynedale		H	14	Fylde		H
9	Wakefield		H	16	Morpeth		H
16	Gala		A	21	Leicester		A
23	Middlesbrough		H	28	Waterloo		*A
26	Northern		A				
30	Boroughmuir		H				

* = Courage League Division 2

PLAYING SECTION REPORT

The results for the season were as follows:

	P	W	D	L	F	A	1989	1988
1st XV	42	22	1	19	761	669	52.38%	60.98%
Greyhounds	33	22	1	10	842	370	66.67%	71.43%
2nd XV	35	20	–	15	505	420	57.14%	53.12%
Falcons	29	23	–	6	720	161	79.30%	35.48%
3rd XV	10	5	–	5	100	241	50.00%	70.00%
Nomads	16	9	1	6	217	167	56.25%	86.96%
Colts	25	18	–	7	585	239	72.00%	53.85%
Total	190	119	3	68	3730	2267	62.63%	59.69%

Plymouth Albion's heavy try-scoring winger Steve Walklin is halted in full stride by Exeter fly-half, Andy Green (right). Photo: Nigel Chanter, Broadclyst, Devon.

Dewi Morris tries a break for Liverpool St. Helens against Leicester at Moss Lane, but to no avail. His team loses and later on is relegated. Photo: Graham Taylor

Exeter hooker hooked! Rob Pugsley about to have his collar felt by Plymouth Albion prop Chris Hocking, although Graham Bess (left) tries to prevent the indignity. Photo: Nigel Chanter, Broadclyst, Devon

HEADINGLEY

Clarence Field, Bridge Road, Kirkstall, Leeds
Tel: 0532 755029
COLOURS Green, black and white.
(*Change colours*: Red, white and blue)

HEADINGLEY R.U.F.C.

Founded: 1878
President: J.D.H. Kitchen
Chairman: E.P.S. Arundel
Secretary: J.H. Winterbottom, 5 Churchgate, Bramhope, Leeds LS16 9BN. Tel: 0532 842066 (H) 452251 (W)
Fixtures Secretary: P.A.W. Stephens, Hobberend House, Main Street, Shadwell, Leeds LS17 8JG. Tel: 0532 651214 (H)
Club captain (1988–89): P. Huntsman
Club captain (1989–90): P. Huntsman
No. of teams: Senior 5, Youth 1
Directions to ground: A65 to Ilkley out of the centre of Leeds. Two miles out of centre turn left at traffic lights, immediately on left
Ground capacity: Seating 750, Standing 8000
Clubhouse facilities: Main bar and tea facilities downstairs. Sponsors bar upstairs. Squash club with three courts attached to clubhouse
Floodlights: Yes
Membership fees: Full £25, Playing £20, Youth £7, Student £12, OAP £7
Ground admission: £2

Programme: No. of editorial pages 4; No. of advertising pages 24; Price 30p
Programme editor: P.A.W. Stephens, as Fixtures Secretary
Local newspapers: Yorkshire Post, Yorkshire Evening News, Bradford Telegraph and Argus
League: National Division 2
League position (1988–89): 7th
League playing record (1988–89): P 11, W 5, D 1, L 5, F 179, A 136
Most capped players: I.R. McGeechan (Scotland) 32, P.J. Winterbottom 29, P.H. Thompson 17, J.S. Spencer 14, J.A. King 12, F. Williams (Wales) 11, P.J. Winterbottom 1983 N.Z, I.R. McGeechan, 1974 S.A, 1977 N.Z, J.S. Spencer 1971 NZ & A, C.W.W. Rea 1971 NZ & A.
Players' appearances (1988–89): N. Hargreaves Flanker 38, N. Summers Scrum Half 37, A. Machell Prop 36, S. Irving Centre 34, P. Sellar Hooker 33
Leading scorers (1988–89): S. Irving 313 (13T, 72C, 39P), N. Summers 120 (30T), D. Kennell 88 (22T), M. Appleson 51 (4T, 7C, 7P)

YORKSHIRE CUP

Round 1 v Pontefract (H)
Thursday 30 March W 42–9
Round 2 v Middlesborough (A)
Tuesday 4 April W 20–9
Round 3 v Rotherham (A)
Tuesday 11 April W 37–9

Semi v Wakefield (H)
Wednesday 19 April W 74–0
Final v Otley at Morley
Tuesday 25 April W 48–9

REVIEW OF SEASON

Headingley will mainly remember the season for a good parochial reason – they won the Yorkshire Cup in style without being extended in any of their five ties and they ended the campaign against Wakefield's reserves in the semi-final (74–0!) and a brave Otley side, which went down in the final (48–9). In the Courage League Division Two they broke even with five wins, a draw and five defeats, but this would have looked much better if they had won their final home match against Richmond, who needed a win to be sure of survival and gained it narrowly. In their only Pilkington Cup game they were at home in Round Two against Wakefield and went out narrowly (10–7). Still, any silverware is better than none at all and the club had a sturdy performer in centre Irving, who scored more than 300 points in 34 games. Scrum-half Summers crossed for 30 tries, another fine effort in his 37 appearances, which were only one less than those of flanker Hargreaves. Obviously, there is talent at the club and it might well bring rewards this coming season if some consistency can be found. The overall record was quite good with 28 of the 44 games played being won, two drawn and another 14 lost. The points balance of 1009 against 548 also suggests a good potential for the future.

RESULTS

Date		Opponents	Venue	Points		Date		Opponents	Venue	Points	
Sep	1	Rotherham	H	26	3	Jan	2	Otley	H	22	9
	3	Winnington Park	A	10	3		7	Leicester	A	7	53
	10	Saracens	†H	3	7		14	Gosforth	†A	14	29
	17	Gosforth	H	28	12		21	Harrogate	H	20	19
	24	Northampton	†A	7	19		28	Huddersfield	A	45	4
Oct	1	Morley	H	58	3	Feb	4	Vale of Lune	H	25	3
	8	Bedford	†H	7	7		11	Northern	H	47	18
	15	West Hartlepool	H	44	13		18	Harlequin	H	16	20
	22	Blackheath	†A	3	21		25	Moseley	H	19	11
	26	Roundhay	H	30	0	Mar	4	Orrell	A	3	22
	29	Bradford & Bingley	H	10	10		11	London Scottish	†H	22	10
Nov	5	Wakefield	*H	7	10		18	Wakefield	A	3	10
	12	London Irish	†H	48	9		25	Liverpool St. Helens	H	33	12
	19	Sale	†A	24	15		27	Coventry	H	18	13
	26	London Welsh	†H	24	0	Apr	1	Gloucester	H	9	12
Dec	3	Waterloo	H	22	15		8	Coventry	†A	18	7
	10	Wasps	A	9	19		15	Fylde	A	18	32
	17	Sale	H	14	3		22	Richmond	†H	9	12
	24	Nottingham	A	6	24		29	Rugby	H	29	19
	31	Wakefield	H	31	18						

† Courage Clubs Championship Division Two League Match   * Pilkington Cup

LIVERPOOL-ST. HELENS

Moss Lane, Windle, St. Helens, Merseyside.
Tel: 0744 25708

COLOURS Red/black/white/blue hoops.
Change colours: White

Liverpool-St. Helens – 1988–89.

REVIEW OF SEASON

Hopes of a successful spell in the top division were never fulfilled and after a season of traumas Liverpool-St. Helens returned to Division Two after ending up in bottom place. To add insult to injury the Pilkington Cup campaign ended in Round Three at home with a comprehensive thrashing at the hands of Leicester (37–6). The main consolations were the England selections for new scrum-half Dewi Morris, vast improvements to the ground at Moss Lane (including a new stand, drainage system and multi-gym) and a tour to North America. There is enough will and determination in the club for an early return to the top and apart from Morris there are good players in leading scorer Tosh Askew and top try-scorer Brendan Hanavan.

Dewi Morris (the England scrum-half) passes despite the attentions of Bath's Richard Hill. Photo: Graham Taylor.

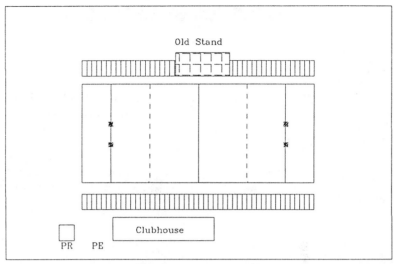

Moss Lane

Liverpool-St. Helens 7, Bath 21. The Moss Lane team is almost doomed and Bath are almost there. Photo: K.B. Riding, Bolton.

LIVERPOOL-ST. HELENS R.U.F.C.

Founded: 1857
President: Graham Twist
Chairman: Terry Ryan
Secretary: Bernard Cragg, 9 Mulberry Avenue, St. Helens WA10 4OA. Tel: 0744 59345 (H), 54221 (W)
Fixtures Secretary: Richard McCullagh, 9 Fullwood Park, Liverpool L17. Tel: 051–727 4190
Press Officer: John Hetherington, 162 Broadway, Eccleston, St. Helens. Tel: 0744 54812 (H), 051 2362755 (W)
Coach: Mike Slemen
Club captain (1988–89): Brian Wellens
Club captain (1989–90): Keiron Rabbitt
No. of teams: Senior 6, Youth 1
Directions to ground: No change
Ground capacity: Seating 120, Standing 4000
Clubhouse facilities: Clubroom, lounge, sponsors suite
Nickname: L.S.H.
Floodlights: Yes

Membership fees: Full £33, Playing £28, Youth £5, Student £14
Ground admission: £2
Programme: No. of editorial pages 12; No. of advertising pages 22; Price 50p
Programme editor: Geoff Duckworth, 64 Crawford Village, Upholland, Lancashire. Tel: 0744 882202
Local newspapers: St. Helens Reporter, St. Helens Star, L'pool Daily Post
League: National League Division 2
League position (1988–89): 12th (relegated)
League playing record (1988–89): P 37, W 13, D 3, L 21
Most capped players (including British Lions appearances): No change
Players' appearances: (1988–89): Keiron Rabbitt 31, Brendan Hanavan 29, Mark Davies 29, John Shinwell 28, Brian Wellens 26
Leading scorers (1988–89): Tosh Askew 138 (1 t, 19 cons, 32 pens), Brendan Hanavan (14 t), Mike Mallalieu (5 t)

Liverpool-St. Helens' Paul Hamer on the burst against Leicester's Les Cusworth (left).

LONDON IRISH

The Avenue, Sunbury-on-Thames, Middx.
Tel: 0932 783034
COLOURS Green and white

REVIEW

AFTER an up-and-down season London Irish arrived at their last league match with a chance of promotion to Division One and all went well at first with 21 points being chalked up against Blackheath, who showed few signs of putting up a fight. At the same time elsewhere the other contenders for the top were either losing or drawing so the prize was theirs for the taking. However, it was here that the team seemed to freeze and Blackheath fought back incredibly to win and save themselves from relegation, which was quite astonishing. Will there ever be a better chance to play at the top level? Would the Irish have been good enough in any case? Those are imponderables, but the heavy Pilkington Cup defeat at Bristol in the Fourth Round would suggest that the team would probably have struggled. On the representative front Neil Francis earned himself a regular international place in the Ireland team and must have been close to Lions selection. The main question for the new season is "Can Irish pick themselves up after the late and bitter disappointment suffered?" If they cannot there might be a fight against relegation on the cards.

LONDON IRISH R.U.F.C.

Founded: 1898
President: Hugh Brady
Chairman: Air Comm. J.R. Forsyth
Secretary: Pat Barrangry, 155 Hemmingford Road, Islington, N1. Tel: 01–607 394 (H), 01–631 1355 (W)
Fixtures Secretary: Mike Tewksbury, 48 Bingley Road, Sunbury-on-Thames, Middx. Tel: 0932 780278
Press Officer: Michael Flatley. Tel: 01–607 3941 (H), 01–631 1355 (W)
Coach: L. Flye
Club captain (1988–89): David Fitzgerald
No. of teams: Senior 10, Youth & Minis 7
Directions to ground: trains from Waterloo to Sunbury-on-Thames at 04 and 34 mins past the hour

Ground capacity: Seating 400
Nickname: The Irish
Floodlights: No
Membership fees: Playing £30, Non-playing £35, Life £2
Ground admission: £2
Programme: 50p
Programme editor: Brendon Quirke
League: National League Division 2
Most capped players (including British Lions appearances): K. Kennedy, J. O'Driscoll, M. Molloy, J. Richie, A. Mulligan, M. Gibson, H. McNeill, R. Roe, J. Daly, T. Reid, H. Francis, B. Mullin

NORTHAMPTON

Franklins Gardens, Weedon Road, St. James, Northampton. Tel: 0604 51543

COLOURS Black/green/gold hoops.
(*Change colours*: White)

The Saints back on the move – 1988–89.

REVIEW OF SEASON

This season has been on of change, both on and off the field. On the playing side, a process of rebuilding has led to a number of promising new players wearing the Saints shirt. The results overall reflect a lack of consistency of performance and an inability to win games away from home.

In the league the Saints moved from last position the previous year to third place this season, missing out on promotion by one point. It is worth noting that the only league win away from the Gardens was at London Welsh in our last league game.

Notable performances during the season were in beating the Harlequins at Twickenham on the first Saturday in September, completing the double over Bedford, including our best league performance of the season, and Aberavon, part of a notable Easter triumph which included winning at Llanelli for the first time for a number of years. The three away wins at Easter during a run of seven consecutive victories gave a glimpse of the potential within the side.

Gary Pearce in his first season as captain suffered unduly with injuries before Christmas. His influence on the side is reflected in the improved results on his return to regular duty. In Gary's absence David Elkington, Paul Alston and Rob Tebbutt have shared the captaincy of the side, for which the club is extremely grateful. Gary and David are continuing next season as captain and vice captain and we wish them every success.

Top points scorer for the season was John Steele in his first season with the club. John scored 154 points in a season badly disrupted by injury and Army calls. Frank Packman with 22 tries was leading try scorer and scored his 100th try for the club during the season. Frank also represented the Midland Division for the first time, a just reward for one of the country's leading try scorers. Frank was also voted player of the year by the supporters.

The coaching responsibilities have been shared by Terry Burwell and Paul Bryant. They are both thanked for their hard work and commitment to a most demanding job. Paul will continue as club coach for next season, assisted by Peter Bodily.

Bunny Ingram was once again a most hepful and efficient team secretary, while John Raphael chaired the selection committee throughout the season.

At the end of the season the club undertook a two match tour of Italy to play the Italian National Squad.

Castle Station 1 mile

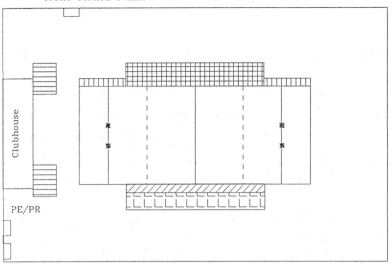

Clubhouse

PE/PR

FIXTURES 1989–90

Date	Opponents	Venue			Date	Opponents	Venue	Points
Sept. 1988					**Jan. 1990**			
2	Harlequins	H			6	Bective Rangers	H	
9	Plymouth Albion*	H			13	Blackheath*	A	
13	Bedford	A			20	Moseley	H	
16	Leicester	A			27	(P.C.)		
23	Headingley*	A			**Feb.** 3	Leicester	H	
Oct 7	Nottingham	H			11	South Wales Police.	T.B.A.	
14	London Irish*	H			16	Coventry	A	
21	Bristol	A			24	Fylde	H	
28	Sale*	A			**Mar.** 3	Gloucester	H	
31	Oxford Univ.	H			10	Coventry*	H	
29	Cambridge Univ.	H	21	28	13	Met. Police	H	
Nov. 4	(P.C.)				16	Moseley	A	
11	Waterloo*	A			24	Bath	H	
18	Richmond*	H			31	Gosforth*	A	
25	Liverpool St. Helens*	A			**Apr.** 7	Rosslyn Park	A	
Dec. 2	Llanelli	H			14	Llanelli	A	
9	Aberavon	H			16	Bedford	H	
16	Wasps	A			21	Nottingham	A	
22	Nuneaton	H			28	Rugby*	H	
30	Cheltenham	H						

* = Courage Clubs Championship
(P.C.) = Pilkington Cup

NORTHAMPTON R.U.F.C.

Founded: 1880
President: Geoff Allen
Secretary: Roger Horwood, Sturtridge Pavilion, Franklins Gardens, Weedon Road, Northampton. Tel: 0604 410326 (H), 790777 (W)
Fixtures Secretary: Bob Taylor, 82 Bridgewater Drive, Northampton. Tel: 0604 38626
Press Officer: Barrie Corless, Sturtridge Pavilion, Franklins Gardens, Weedon Road, Northampton.. Tel: 0604 55149
Club captain (1988–89): Gary Pearce
Club captain (1989–90): Gary Pearce
No. of teams: Senior 3, Youth 1
Directions to ground: From Junction 16 from M1 (A45) to Northampton, Weedon Road
Ground capacity: Seating 2000, Standing 6000
Clubhouse facilities: 2 bars, function room, 4 hospitality boxes
Nickname: Saints
Floodlights: Yes
Membership fees: Full £25, Playing £15, Youth £8, OAP £12

Ground admission: £2.50, U18/OAP £1.20, Stands £3/£1.50
League: National League Division 2
League position (1988–89): 3rd
League playing record (1988–89): P 40, W 19, D 1, L20, F 733, A 637
Honours during 1988–89: Congratulations to Gary Pearce on being a member of the England squad and playing for England "B" v Italy. John Steele was a replacement for England "B", and captained the Combined Services against Australia. Frank Packman and Harvey Thorneycroft represented the Midland Division against Ulster. Tim Rodber and Harvey Thorneycroft represented England U21 v Romania. Michael Ord played for England Colts. Richard Still has been awarded his Club cap
Players' appearances (1988–89): Mark Charles 35, Rob Tebbutt 32, John Thame 32 (1), David Elkington 31 (1), Frank Packmsn 30 (1)
Leading scorers (1988–89): John Steele 154, Frank Packman (22 t), Harvey Thorneycroft (11 t)

RESULTS

Date		Opponents	Venue	Points		Date		Opponents	Venue	Points	
			Sept. 1988			**Jan.**					
	3	Harlequins	A	22	13	**1989**	7	Bective Rangers	A	15	20
	10	London Scottish (C)	A	3	3		14	Blackheath (C)	A	15	7
	17	Leicester	H	19	30		21	Moseley	A	11	13
	24	Headingley (C)	H	19	7		28	Richmond PC 3	A	0	6
Oct	1	Nottingham	A	12	25	**Feb.**	4	Leicester	A	8	42
	8	London Irish (C)	A	10	18		11	South Wales Police.	H	29	17
	15	Bristol	H	16	20		17	Coventry	H	Cancelled	
	22	Sale (C)	H	15	12		25	Fylde	A	11	12
	26	Oxford Univ.	A	18	26	**Mar.**	3	Gloucester	A	12	29
	29	Cambridge Univ.	H	21	28		11	Coventry (C)	A	10	22
Nov.	5	Winnington Park	H	37	4		14	Met. Police	H	23	6
	12	Saracens (C)	H	4	32		17	Moseley	H	12	3
	19	Richmond (C)	A	12	15		24	Aberavon	A	13	9
	26	Bedford (C)	H	42	3		25	Llanelli	A	24	16
Dec.	3	Llanelli	H	0	8		27	Bedford	A	18	7
	10	Aberavon	H	20	13	**Apr.**	1	Vale of Lune	H	48	0
	17	Wasps	H	28	14		8	Gosforth (C)	H	13	12
	26	Saracens	H	56	4		11	Rugby	A	13	19
	31	Bath	A	3	58		15	Nottingham	H	19	22
							22	London Welsh (C)	A	22	0
							29	Cheltenham	A	44	12

(C) = Courage Leagues

PLYMOUTH ALBION

Beacon Park, Plymouth
Tel: 0752 772924
COLOURS Cherry, white and red. (*Change colours*: Red)

Plymouth Albion skipper Kevin Norris celebrates after receiving the Courage Division Three trophy. Photo: Mike Cox.

REVIEW OF SEASON

Although Albion eventually finished the season with a 100 per cent record in Division Three their top place was not actually confirmed until the last game of the season, since defeat by West Hartlepool might have meant promotion but no championship title. Elevation had been confirmed by a win at Nuneaton two weeks earlier. Since the earliest stages of the campaign they were favoured to be promoted but could not afford any slips because at various stages Rugby, Wakefield and West Hartlepool had been hot on their heels, but the final table shows just how good a side they have been and they will obviously hope to make a strong impact on Division Two. Much of their success can be attributed to the fine kicking of Cundy and Slade – well served by centre Leonard – and the strong running of the wings Walklin (22 tries) and Penfold (14 tries). Kevin Norris, a flanker who led the side, was another consistent performer. The cups were a bit disappointing. In the Pilkington Cup Stoke Old Boys were no challenge in the First Round at Beacon Park (60–3) and a fine win at Coventry followed (12–7), but in the Third Round at Rosslyn Park form deserted the side and they lost badly (18–0). In the county cup an easy win at home to Brixham (34–6) was followed by a narrow victory over Okehampton (11–10), before Devon dethroned them in the semi-finals (6–0). Still it had been a great season with a tour of Canada to follow.

RESULTS

Date	Opponents	Venue	Points		Date	Opponents	Venue	Points	
Sept 3	South Wales Police	A	6	3	Jan 7	Newbridge	A	10	30
5	Public School				14	Exeter	A	21	6
	Wanderers	H	32	11	17	Royal Air Force	H	20	12
10	Wakefield	H	21	12	21	Weston-s-Mare	H	20	4
17	Stoke Old Boys	*H60	3		22	Okehampton	†	11	10
24	Vale of Lune	A	20	6	28	Rosslyn Park	*A	0	18
Oct 1	Abertillery	H	12	7	Feb 1	Exeter University	H	Canc.	
8	Sheffield	H	34	13	3	Devonport Services	A	39	6
12	Exeter University	H	11	18	11	Tredegar	H	23	0
15	Maesteg	A	0	34	18	Glamorgan Wand's	A	Canc.	
22	Askeans	A	28	12	25	Camborne	A	10	11
29	Clifton	H	23	9	Mar 3	Exeter	‡A	0	6
Nov 5	Coventry	*A	12	7	11	Maidstone	H	20	6
12	Rugby	A	26	10	18	Bristol	H	4	31
19	Fylde	H	43	6	27	Torquay	A	39	9
26	Metropolitan Police	H	57	3	29	Bath	H	19	32
Dec 3	Tredegar	Aban.			Apr 1	Cheltenham	H	14	30
10	Gloucester	A	22	28	8	Nuneaton	A	21	3
11	Brixham	†H	34	6	15	Birmingham	H	Canc.	
17	Exeter	H	42	3	22	West Hartlepool	H	20	12
23	Bridgwater	H	Canc.		29	Glamorgan Wand's	H	30	33
27	Chairman's XV	H	0	20					

* = Pilkington Cup   † = Devon Cup   ‡ = Devon Cup Semi Final

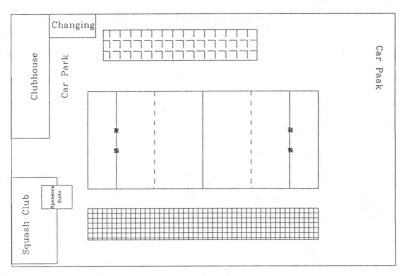

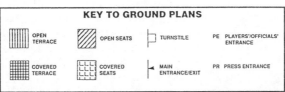

KEY TO GROUND PLANS

OPEN TERRACE

OPEN SEATS

TURNSTILE

PE PLAYERS'/OFFICIALS' ENTRANCE

COVERED TERRACE

COVERED SEATS

MAIN ENTRANCE/EXIT

PR PRESS ENTRANCE

Plymouth Albion – 1988–89.

PLYMOUTH ALBION R.U.F.C.

Founded: 1876
President: D.J.L. Gabbitass FCI Arb
Chairman: V.T. Pinches
Secretary: W.J. Foster, Tooleys, Horsham Lane, Tamerton Foliot, Plymouth. Tel: 0752 768111 (H) 221312 or 265728 Ext. 5705 (W)
Fixtures Secretary: R.J. Evans, 4 Brynmoor Walk, Higher Comptom, Plymouth. Tel: 0752 771825 (H). 93 42398 (W)
Club captain (1988–89): Kevin Norris
Club captain (1989–90): Kevin Norris
No. of teams: Senior 4, Youth 4, Minis 5
Ground capacity: Seating 450, Standing 4,000
Clubhouse facilities: 5 bars, 6 court squash club, sports injuries clinic. Open match days and all day
Floodlights: Yes
Membership fees: Full £5, Social £5
Ground admission: £2
Programme: No. of editorial pages 4; Price 50p

Programme editor: W. Pearce, Tel: 0752 844500
Local newspapers: Western Evening Herald, Western Morning News
League: National Division League 2
League position (1988–89): Winners National Division League 3
League playing record (1988–89): P 11, W 11, D 0, L 0, F 311, A 89
Most capped players: E. Stanbury 16, W.A. Mills 11, R.H. Sparks 9, S.G. William 7, R.A. Jago 5, J. Peters 5
Players' appearances (1988–89): Russell Forward 36, Walklin Wing 33+1, Norris Flanker 32, Saunders Forward 31, Leonard Centre 31, Penfold Wing 31
Leading scorers (1988–89): Cundy 1 Try, 4 Dropped-Goals, 31 Pens, 37 Cons = 183 pts. Slade 5 Tries, 14 Pens, 36 Cons = 122 pts. Walklin 22 Tries = 88 pts. Leonard 14 Tries = 56 pts.

The Albion front-row led by Nigel Saunders (with ball), hooker Bruce Privary (left) and Ian Davies (rear) take off. Photo: M. Cox.

RICHMOND

The Athletic Ground, Kew Foot Road,
Richmond, Surrey TW9 2SS.
Tel: 01 940 0397
COLOURS Old gold, red and black hoops.

REVIEW OF SEASON

The 1988–89 season for Richmond could have been a great deal
worse – in fact it could have been seen as a disaster if the final league
game at Headingley had not been won. A loss there and they would
have dropped into Division Three instead of co-tenants London
Scottish. On the other hand two more victories would have secured
promotion, but a look at the league results will reveal no hard luck
stories for people to talk about "might-have-beens". The club was
just happy to have survived with hopes for a better time in 1989–90.
The form in the Pilkington Cup showed the club in a reasonable light
with a good Second Round win at Finchley (40–6) followed by a
Third Round win on a waterlogged Athletic Ground against
Northampton (6–0). This brought another home tie against
Nottingham, who won after a tough struggle (12–9). In other fixtures
there were some good performances, which included good home
results against Pontypridd (19–3) and Rosslyn Park (26–9), but in the
latter game the lock Maren was dismissed for misuse of the boot and
the same fate befell the no. 8 Catt in the home game against Oxford
University, who scored all the game's three tries in a 16–12 win. The
team's outstanding players were the flanker David Sole (not of
Scotland) with 30 appearances, the wing Ricky Forde (27
appearances), the centre Rob Rydon, the outside-half Martin
Livesey (182 points with his trusty boot) and the veteran scrum-half
John Cullen, who led the side and now hands over to Doug Cooper.
An overall record of 13 wins in 31 games with two draws and 16
defeats is modest, but there have been worse seasons and an
improvement might well be on the way.

RICHMOND R.U.F.C.

Founded: 1861
President: Graham M. deP. Tardif
Chairman: Robert B. Rakison
Secretary: Keith G. Cresswell, The Athletic Ground, Kew Foot Road, Richmond, Surrey TW9 2SS. Tel: 01 878 4401 (H)
Fixtures Secretary: Dr Tom E. Roberts, 7 Homestead Road, Basingstoke, Hants. Tel: 0256 464999 (H) 484771 (W)
Club captain (1988–89): John Cullen
Club captain (1989–90): Doug Cooper
No. of teams: Senior 4, Youth 5, Minis 5
Directions to ground: The athletic ground is situated in Old Deer Park on the A316 Twickenham Road and is two minutes walk from Network SE and District Line services at Richmond Street
Ground capacity: Seating 1300, Standing 6–8,000
Clubhouse facilities: 7 pitches (2 Floodlit) 2 bars, restaurant and club shop
Floodlights: On training pitches only
Membership fees: Full £35, Family £45, Youth £15, Student £15, Associate £25

Ground admission: £2
Programme: TBA
Programme editor: TBA
Local newspapers: Richmond and Twickenham Times
League: National Division League 2
League position (1988–89): 9th
League playing record (1988–89): P 11, W 4, D 1, L 6, F 112, A 216
Most capped players: A.S. Gould (Eng) 27, T.P. Bedford (SA) 25, P.W. Kininmonth (Sco) 21, C.W. Ralston (Eng) 21, N.M. Hall (Eng) 17, E.T. Gurdon (Eng) 16, P. Cranmer (Eng) 16, C. Gurdon (Eng) 14, F.M. Stout (Eng) 14, W.E. Bromet (Eng) 12
Players' appearances (1988–89): David Sole Flanker 30, Ricky forde Wing 27, Rob Rydon Centre 26, Martin Livesey Outside Half 24, John Cullen Scrum Half 24
Leading scorers (1988–89): Martin Livesey 19 Conv, 41 PG, 7 DG = 182 pts. Martin Breddy 1 Try, 7 Conv, 8 PG, 1 DG = 45 pts. Rob Rydon 6 Tries = 24 pts. Chris Morrish 5 Tries = 20 pts.

RESULTS

Date	Opponents	Venue	Points		Date	Opponents	Venue	Points	
	Waterloo	H	16	17		Rosslyn Park	H	26	9
	Sale	*A	9	50		S. Wales Police	H	25	19
	Clontarf	H	19	16		Bedford	*A	3	15
	L. Welsh	*H	14	3		Wasps	A	16	41
	Pontypridd	H	19	3		Northampton	**H	6	0
	Gosforth	*A	4	16		Moseley	A	10	29
	Oxford University	H	12	16		Nottingham	**H	9	12
	L. Scottish	*H	12	32		Bristol		Canc.	
	Orrell	A	23	10		Maesteg		Canc.	
	Finchley	**A	40	6		L. Scottish	H	16	6
	Blackheath	*A	3	31		Saracens	*H	10	27
	Northhampton	*H	15	12		Liverpool St. Helens	A	0	0
	Coventry	*H	12	3		Bath		Canc.	
	Nottingham	A	3	27		Neath	A	4	50
	Metropolitan Police	H	34	14		L. Irish	*H	18	18
	Leicester	H	7	16		Newbridge	H	15	25
	Harlequins	H	7	21		Headingley	*A	12	9

* = Courage League   ** = Pilkington Cup

RUGBY

Webb Ellis Road, off Bilton Road, Rugby.
Tel: 0788 544907 (matchdays only), 0788
542252 (other days)
COLOURS Orange/black/white.
Change colours: White/red yoke or navy blue

Rugby celebrate promotion from Division Three.

REVIEW OF SEASON

Rugby concluded another successful league campaign when securing promotion to Division 2 following an injury time win against Wakefield in the final league game of the season. The outcome of the second place promotion battle could not have been closer as Rugby won a cracking game by 14 points to 13 with Chris Howard's try two minutes into injury time deciding the result.

It was Howard's second try of the match and with two penalties, he accounted for all of Rugby's points.

For unlucky Wakefield it was doubly disappointing. Last season they were champions of Division 3 but promotion did not apply. On this occasion, like Rugby, having only previously lost to champions, Plymouth, they went down by a solitary point. Even the points differential amounted to only one point.

However, for Rugby it was champagne time and, for the second year running, promotion. Last season they were Area League North champions and secured promotion to Division 3. Overall, the season was highly successful with only ten games lost from the forty played. Notable victories outside the League included Wasps (18–17) repeating a win the previous season, Nottingham (21–17), Cambridge University (24–12), Oxford University (19–7) and Northampton (19–13).

The Club also reached the third round of the Pilkington Cup beating Vale of Lune (27–6) and West Hartlepool (30–9) before losing to the 87/88 cup holders, Harlequins (3–25) in a televised tie at Webb Ellis Road.

A final honour in an exciting season was Rugby's appearance as one of the guest sides on finals day of the Middlesex Sevens at Twickenham. They lost their only match to London Scottish by (6–26), but they, however, went on to the semi-final where they lost to holders and eventual winners, Harlequins.

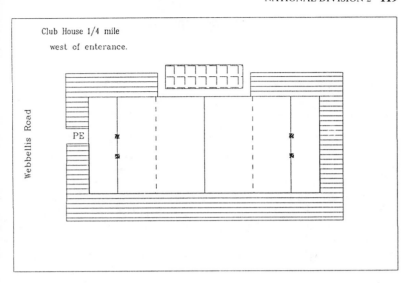

Club House 1/4 mile west of enterance.

Webbellis Road

PE

Rugby's leading try scorer Eddie Saunders, who also heads the England list with 28. Photo: Ray Andrews

Rugby's leading points scorer Chris Howard and the new club record holder – he beat his own figure of 345 points in 1987–88 by scoring 395 last season. Photo: Ray Andrews

RUGBY R.U.F.C.

Founded: 1873
President: Peter Galliford, O.B.E.
Chairman: David Rees
Secretary: John W. Llewellyn, 11 Rokeby Street, Rugby. Tel: 0788 72287
Fixtures Secretary: Malcolm W.T. Palmer, Virginia Cottage, High Street, Grandborough, Rugby CV23 8DQ. Tel: 0788 812326
Press Officer: Roy William Batchelor, 36 Barton Road, Rugby CV22 7PT. Tel: 0788 810573 (H), 0203 688694 (W)
Coach: Andy Johnson
Club captain (1988–89): Steve Brain
Club captain (1989–90): Steve Brain
No. of teams: Senior 3, Youth 1, Minis 6
Directions to ground: South west of town centre take A4071 (Bilton Road), within 500 yds Webb Ellis Road is second turning on right
Ground capacity: Seating 200, Standing 3000–4000
Clubhouse facilities: Changing rooms, bath, shower facilities, gymnasium, squash bar, function room, conference room. Meals and snacks
Nickname: Lions

Floodlights: Yes
Membership fees: T.B.D.
Ground admission: T.B.D.
Programme: No. of editorial pages 12; No. of advertising pages 24; Price 30p
Programme editor: As Press Officer
Local newspapers: Rugby Advertiser, Rugby & Coventry Evening Telegraph
League: National League Division 2
League position (1988–89): 2nd (promoted)
League playing record (1988–89): P 40, W 27, D 3, L 10, F 943, A 507
Competitions won: Division 3 Runners-Up
Most capped players (including British Lions appearances): Steve Brain (Eng) 13
Players' appearances: (1988–89): Ian Heywood 39, Chris Howard 37, Martin Fleetwood 36, Richard Pell 35, David Bishop 34, Trevor Revan 34
Leading scorers (1988–89): Chris Howard 395 (17 t, 69 cons, 63 pens), Eddie Saunders 112 (28 t), Richard Pell 50 (8 t, 3 cons, 1 pen, 3 d.g.), David Bishop 40 (10 t)

RESULTS

Date	Opponents	Venue	Points		Date	Opponents	Venue	Points	
			Sept. 1988		**Jan. 1989**				
3	Manchester	H	71	12	3	Nottingham	A	21	17
10	Vale of Lune*	H	28	9	7	Saracens	A	7	24
17	Vale of Lune (P.C.)	H	27	6	14	Fylde*	A	17	12
24	Sheffield*	A	22	6	21	Lough'ro St.	H	30	8
Oct 1	London Scottish	H	10	10	28	Harlequins (P.C.)	H	3	25
8	Askeans*	H	41	3	Feb. 5	Blackheath	A	9	29
15	Wasps	H	18	17	7	R.A.F.	H	24	11
22	Nuneaton*	A	18	15	11	Birkenhead Park	A	38	3
26	Bedford	H	13	21	18	Middlesbrough	H	30	7
29	Bridgewater & Alb.	H	59	21	25	Cambridge Univ.	A	24	12
Nov. 5	W. Hartlepool (P.C.)	A	30	9	Mar. 3	Oxford Univ.	H	19	7
12	Plymouth*	H	10	26	11	Exeter*	H	23	3
19	Met. Police*	A	36	6	18	Preston Grasshoppers	H	38	11
26	Maidstone*	H	44	3	27	Swansea	A	10	17
Dec. 3	Broughton Park	H	16	3	Apr. 1	Halifax	H	42	8
6	Moseley	A	13	21	8	W. Hartlepool*	A	15	3
10	Harrogate	A	23	23	11	Northampton	H	19	13
17	Harlequins	A	9	13	22	Wakefield*	H	14	13
23	Solihull	H	34	10	26	Coventry	A	12	12
26	Nuneaton	H	7	9	29	Headingley	A	19	29

* = Courage League   (P.C.) = Pilkington Cup

Rugby prop Ian Heywood – player of the year, most appearances for the second season running (39 games out of 40) and scorer of a try in the club's first win over Nottingham for 20 years (his only one so far for the team).

Double promotion. Rugby celebrate their second rise up the pecking order in two seasons as they move upwards to Division Two.

SALE

Heywood Road, Brooklands, Sale, Cheshire
Tel: 061 973 6348

COLOURS Royal blue and white hoops.
(*Change colours*: Plain dark blue or white
with royal collar and cuffs)

Mark Hamilton (Sale) surges at the Winnington Park defence. Photo: Pete Barton.

REVIEW OF SEASON

Having been relegated at the end of the first season of the league Sale were obviously keen to return immediately but this was not to be. In fact, for a time the team struggled against possible further relegation before there was a general recovery and a satisfactory fourth place in Division Two. This was just as well since in the Pilkington Cup there was an embarrassing defeat in the Second Round, to which the club had a bye, against Durham City – no consolations there. There was solace however in the form of several players notably the prop Martin Whitcombe, who picked up an England 'B' cap as did the fly-half David Pears. So did scrum-half Doggart, but he returned to Aspatria for the second half of the season. Player of the Year was flanker Simon Morrison and the most appearances were made by the centre-cum-wing Stansfield. Top scorer was Pears with 171 points overall, but the leading try-scorer, Jeff Powell, only managed 11 touch-downs. Other consistent scorers were Jee (107 points) and Graham Jenion who managed 99 in only 13 appearances (a most creditable effort). The overall record for the season was useful with 20 of the 39 matches played being won, four drawn and only 15 lost.

With Fran Cotton and Steve Smith now reinstated as amateurs they can both officially coach – and will do so. Steve will take the backs and Fran the pack and it will be most interesting to see how far the side can progress. One suspects that in an inconsistent division Sale could be strong promotion candidates.

Sale's Dave Baldwin scraggs ex-England Skipper John Orwin of Bedford. Photo: Peter Baston

SALE R.U.F.C.

Founded: 1861
President: Eric Tootill
Chairman: David Craven
Secretary: Peter Tsker, 26 Alcester Road, Sale, Cheshire M33 3QP. Tel: 061 973 8423 (H)
Fixtures Secretary: Andy Lawson, 1 Oakenrod Villas, Bury Road, Rochdale, Lancs. Tel: 0706 525440 (H) 061 832 4986 (W)
Press Officer: David Craven, Apostle Cottage, Henbury, Macclesfield. Tel: 0260 204350 (H) 061 205 2274 (W)
Club captain (1988–89): Andrew Simpson
Club captain (1989–90): Howard Fitton
No. of teams: Senior 4, Under 21s 1, Colts 1
Directions to ground: Off the A56 between Manchester and Altrincham. Railway – Brooklands Station 4 minutes walk between Manchester and Altrincham
Ground capacity: Seating 500, Standing 3,500
Clubhouse facilities: 2 bars, large function room
Floodlights: Yes
Membership fees: Full £33, Playing £25, Social £16.50, Youth £12, Student £12, OAP £16.50
Ground admission: £2 adult, £1 boys and OAPs

Programme: No. of editorial pages 4; No. of advertising pages 10; Price 30p
Programme editor: Ed Cook, 20 Kirkby Avenue, Sale, Cheshire. Tel: 061 973 5114
Local newspapers: Sale and Stratford Guardian
League: National Division League 2
League position (1988–89): 4th
League playing record (1988–89): P 39, W 20, D 4, L 15, F 784, A 560
Most capped players: F.E. Cotton (Eng) 31 (7 B.Lions), E. Evans (Eng) 30, S.J. Smith (Eng) 28, E.C. Davey (Wales) 23, W. Wooler (Eng) 18, P.K. Stagg (Sco) 28 (3 B.Lions), A.M. bond (Eng) 6, V.S.J. Harding (Eng) 6, W.M. Patterson (Eng) 2 (1 B.Lions), K.C. Fyfe (Sco) 10
Players' appearances (1988–89): P. Stansfield Centre/Wing 37, A. MacFarlane No.8 27, S. Burnhill Centre 26, P. Jee Utility 26, J. Howe 2nd Row 25
Leading scorers (1988–89): David Pears 4 T, 40 P, 13 Con, 4 DG = 171 pts. Phil Jee 6 T, 13 P, 19 Con, 2 DG = 107 pts. Graham Jenion 2 T, 15 P, 23 Con = 99 pts (only 13 appearances). Leading Try scorer Jeff Powell – 11 Tries.

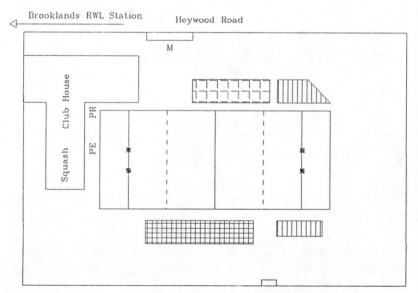

WATERLOO

St. Anthony's Road, Blundellsands,
Liverpool L23 8TW
Tel: 051 924 4552

COLOURS Myrtle, scarlet and white hoops.
(*Change colours*: Red and white collar)

Waterloo 6, Livekrpool-St Helens 12. Early season and they meet again this new campaign in Division Two! Photo: K.B. Riding, Bolton.

REVIEW OF SEASON

Waterloo had been in the doldrums since the New Year of 1988 and after just surviving in Division One in 1988–89 they must have been most people's favourites to go down to Division Two; they did not disappoint the pessimists. From a very early stage they looked doomed and were assured of relegation long before the end of the season. In the Pilkington Cup the club survived the Third Round and then earned a great deal of credit for a brave fight at Gloucester before going out (19–16), but that was one of the few rays of sunshine in a depressing season, in which their poor form meant few representative honours for the team. Regrouping will now be done in the lower division with the hope springing eternal that if and when promotion is achieved the club will be better placed to deal with the situation.

RESULTS

Date	Opponents	Venue	Points		Date	Opponents	Venue	Points	
Sept 3	Richmond	A	17	16	**Jan.**				
6	Merseyside Police	A	27	9		Sale	A	15	6
10	Liverpool St. Helens	H	6	12	14	Bristol	A	3	14
17	Blackheath	H	12	28	21	Northern	H	23	10
24	Orrell	A	12	15	28	Blackheath	A	13	6
Oct 1	Wanderers	A	15	23	**Feb** 4	Coventry	H	16	3
8	Nottingham	H	6	18	11	Gloucester	A	16	19
15	Pontypool	A	6	30	18	Saracens	H	31	14
22	Moseley	A	6	13	25	Merseyside Police	H	39	3
29	Vale of Lune	H	40	7	**Mar** 4	Bedford	A	15	12
Nov 5	Preston				11	Rosslyn Park	H	14	24
	Grasshoppers	H	39	16	18	Gosforth	A	16	11
12	Leicester	h	22	34	25	Wakefield	H	25	15
19	Harlequins	A	24	23	27	Orrell	H	27	9
26	Gloucester	H	15	15	**Apr** 1	Morley	A	48	21
Dec 3	Headingley	A	15	22	5	Kersall	H	13	10
10	London Irish	H	32	25	8	Bath	A	9	38
17	Fylde	H	37	10	5	Vale of Lune	H	74	0
24	Sheffield	A	19	13	19	Broughton Park	H	19	22
26	Birkenhead Park	H	61	0	22	Wasps	H	0	29
31	Broughton Park	A	64	3	29	Bristol	H	23	32

WATERLOO R.U.F.C.

Founded: 1882
President: Denis Bowman
Secretary: Keith Anderson, 66 St. Michaels Road, Blundellsands, Liverpool L23 7UW. Tel: 051 924 1168 (H) 0925 34283 (W)
Fixtures Secretary: Ged Poynton, 19 Lakeside Gardens, Rainford, St. Helens, Merseyside WA1 18HH. Tel: 074488 4128
Press officer: Ian Pazey, 8 Beachlawn, Waterloo, Liverpool L22 8GA. Tel: 051 928 3441 (H) 061 834 9381 (W)
Club captain (1988–89): Shaun Gallagher
Club captain (1989–90): Shaun Gallagher
No. of teams: Senior 5, Youth 5, Minis 5
Directions to ground: End of M57 – follow signs for Crosby, then signs Waterloo FC to ground
Ground capacity: 10,000. Stand 950
Clubhouse facilities: Two large bars, function room, gym, hospitality lounge, changing rooms, bathing area
Floodlights: No
Membership fees: Full £34, Playing £34, Social £34, Youth £12, Student £12, OAP £34
Ground admission: £2

Programme: No. of editorial pages varies; No. of advertising pages approx. 14; Price 30p
Programme editor: David Smallshaw, 22 Harwich road, Blundellsands, Liverpool 23. Tel: 051 924 2036
Local newspapers: Crosby Herald/Liverpool Echo/Daily Post
League: National Division League 1
League position (1988–89): 11th
League playing record (1988–89): P 11, W 1, D 1, L 9, F 116, A 254
Most capped players: (for England unless otherwise stated): Joe Periton 14, Jack Heaton, H. "Bert" Toft, Alan Ashcroft, Gordon Rimmer, Reg Bazley. (for Wales): Watcyn Thomas 14
Players' appearances (1988–89): Shaun Gallager Wing Forward 35, Nigel Wilkinson Second Row 33, Jeff Tickle Full Back 31, Chris Crane Second Row 28, Dave Carfoot Scrum Half 27, Laurie Connor No.8 27
Leading scorers (1988–89): Ian Aitcheson 5 Tries, 35 Conv, 48 Pens, 6 DG = 252 pts. Peter Cooley 20 Tries = 80 pts. Dave Carfoot 7 Tries, 2 Conv, 8 Pens, 3 DG = 65 pts. Richard Angel 4 Tries, 13 Conv, 5 Pens = 60 pts.

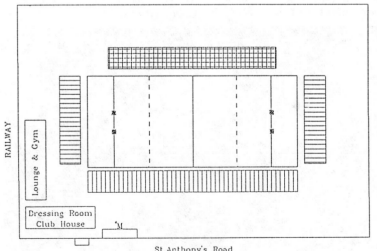

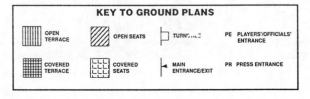

*We are the champions! The campaign is over and Plymouth Albion's skipper Kevin
Norris hitches a ride as he caries the Courage Division Three Trophy*

*Plymouth Albion's scrum-half Bruce Fairgrieve kicks for position against Rugby.
Photo: Mike Cox*

NATIONAL DIVISION THREE

THIS division provided easily the most exciting title race and even though Plymouth Albion ended with a perfect record to take top place with 311 points scored in the process for only 89 conceded they only actually clinched promotion in their penultimate match with the title coming their way as a result of a final win at Nuneaton, who had themselves been early season pace-setters before they slumped to a mid-table position, although the Midlanders were one of the greatly improved sides of the season.

The real competition in this division was for the second promotion place, which eventually depended on the last day at Rugby, where last season's champions Wakefield were the visitors. In a match seen on Rugby Special the Yorkshire team led until injury time, but the loss through dismissal of their flanker Hill in the first half took its toll on their pack and they were unable to hold a late Rugby rally, which brought a decisive try by Chris Howard who scored all his side's points in a 14–13 win. Thus Rugby were promoted for a second successive season and Wakefield were denied again.

The rest of the division was decidedly mediocre with West Hartlepool the best of them. Sheffield and Vale of Lune escaped possible relegation with last game wins at the already-safe Fylde and Exeter respectively, but all four teams had their moments with the Devon team doing well to improve greatly on recent seasons and also relieve Plymouth Albion of the County Cup. Fylde were everyone's favourites for relegation when the campaign started after a number of team losses, but they bravely hung on, whilst Sheffield were a better team than their struggles would have suggested. The same judgement could be made about the Lancaster team, but all will have problems this coming season if squads are not strengthened.

This left Metropolitan Police and Maidstone to go down to Area League South and the former were the unlucky ones with their last-ditch demolition of Nuneaton at their superb Imber Court ground being too little and too late. Maidstone were out of their class, but in their final game they only narrowly lost at home to Askeans, who thus also survived in Division 3 with a point to spare after they had also struggled for much of the season only to escape with a better second half than first series of games. They would expect to do much better after their initial season in improved company.

This division should be a most interesting competition in 1989–90 with the two exile clubs to provide a yardstick as to abilities and ambitious promoted sides in Roundhay – formerly a great side and now back in the "big time" – and Lydney, who would like to show that Gloucestershire does not end at Bristol and the "Cherry & Whites".

TABLES 1987–88

DIVISION THREE

	P	W	D	L	F	A	PTS
Wakefield	11	10	0	1	308	90	41
West Hartlepool	11	10	0	1	249	105	41
Plymouth	11	8	0	3	276	125	35
Sheffield	11	7	1	3	134	161	33
Vale of Lune	11	7	0	4	183	149	32
Fylde	11	6	0	5	269	170	29
Met Police	11	5	0	6	130	128	26
Maidstone	11	4	0	7	134	162	23
Exeter	11	3	2	6	128	197	22
Nuneaton	11	2	1	8	94	157	18
Morley	11	1	1	9	109	235	15
Birmingham	11	0	1	10	46	381	12

TABLES 1988–89

DIVISION THREE

	P	W	D	L	F	A	PTS
Plymouth Albion	11	11	0	0	311	89	22
Rugby	11	10	0	1	268	99	20
Wakefield	11	9	0	2	282	114	18
West Hartlepool	11	5	1	5	164	133	11
Nuneaton	11	5	0	6	178	214	10
Sheffield	11	4	1	6	170	182	9
Vale of Lune	11	4	1	6	120	145	9
Askeans	11	4	1	6	141	215	9
Exeter	11	4	0	7	142	180	8
Fylde	11	4	0	7	136	181	8
Metropolitan Police	11	4	0	7	130	275	8
Maidstone	11	0	0	11	74	289	0

COURAGE NATIONAL DIVISION THREE
Results Season 1988–89

	1	2	3	4	5	6	7	8	9	10	11	12
1 Askeans					3–22		3–33	3–46		15–42	3–50	6–43
2 Exeter	32–0				4–3			9–18	12–12		19–29	6–18
3 Fylde	68–6	48–13								12–14	3–33	12–17
4 Maidstone	18–3	23–9	16–18			15–0	9–3			14–16		
5 Met Police			9–23	9–6		26–12		25–18			6–7	6–22
6 Nuneaton	23–3	10–10	13–38						7-12		7–38	
7 Plym. Albion		9–11	13–18		7–12	21–6		9–7				
8 Rugby			33–17	45–11		24–0			43–7		16–12	
9 Sheffield	34–0		13–12	10–3	13–6		15–9			8–3		
10 Vale of Lune		27–3			13–6	25–19	6–3	13–16				12–21
11 Wakefield				23–9		33–3		41–0	37–12			16–12
12 W. Hartlepool				12–10		23–3	37–14	19–10	25–10			

Results Season 1987–88

	1	2	3	4	5	6	7	8	9	10	11	12
1 Birmingham					3-22		3-3	3-46		15-42	3-50	6-43
2 Exeter	32-0				4-3			9-18	12-12		19-29	6-18
3 Fylde	68-7	48-13								12-14	3-23	12-17
4 Maidstone	18-3	23-9	16-18			15-0	9-3			14-16		
5 Met Police			9-23	9-6		26-12		25-18			6-7	6-22
6 Morley	23-3	10-10	13-38						7-12		7-38	
7 Nuneaton		9-11	13-18		7-12	21-6		9-7				
8 Plym. Alb			33-17	45-11		24-0			43-9		16-12	
9 Sheffield	34-0		13-12	10-3	13-6		15-9			8-3		
10 Vale of Lune		27-3			13-6	25-19	6-3	13-16				12-21
11 Wakefield				23-9		33-3		41-0	32-12			16-12
12 W. Hartlepool				12-10		23-3	37-14	19-10	25-10			

ASKEANS

60A Broad Walk, Kidbrooke SE3. Tel:
01–856 1025

COLOURS Blue, black and white.
Change colours: Red

Askeans – 1988–89.

REVIEW OF SEASON

After losing their first six Division Three games Askeans were most people's favourites to descend to Area League South, but once there the losing habit ended and the last five matches produced a draw and four victories (the last three in succession) for safety, but it was a close run thing and without all those nine points they would not have survived. The Pilkington Cup was not a success story, but other teams have lost at Berry Hill in the competition (ask London Welsh) and the 18–7 defeat should be seen in that context. The Kent Cup was won, so the cupboard was far from bare. John Field (169 points) was the top scorer and it was good to see the veteran centre Tony Bond appearing regularly. For the record the league wins were gained against Sheffield (27–17), Nuneaton (19–12), Metropolitan Police (21–10) and Maidstone (15–12). The drawn match was against West Hartlepool (10–10) and those early six straight losses came against Fylde (6–13) and Vale of Lune (12–29). The club hopes that later form is the most reliable guide to their capabilities and, if it is, there should be a much better season in store for them.

ASKEANS R.U.F.C.

Founded: 1929
President: R.E. Bonner
Chairman: Dr. K.P. Walker, O.B.E.
Secretary: A.L.M. Eastick, 97 Heathleg Road, Blackheath SE3 9HJ. Tel: 01–852 8596 (H), 01–901 3333 (W)
Fixtures Secretary: G. Terry, End Waye, Brookhurst Gardens, Southborough, Kent TN4 0VA. Tel: 0892 28996 (H), 01–387 9366 (W)
Press Officer: J. Ratcliffe, Boughtons, Leafy Grove, Keston, Kent. Tel: 0689 51846 (H), 01–631 4474 (W)
Coach: Stewart McKinney
Club captain (1988–89): Tony Bond
Club captain (1989–90): Tony Bond
No. of teams: Senior 5, Youth 4
Directions to ground: Off A2 between Blackheath and Eltham
Ground capacity: Seating 300, Standing 1200
Clubhouse facilities: Open all week
Floodlights: Yes

Membership fees: Full £40, Playing £40, Social £10, Youth £5, Student £5
Ground admission: £2
Programme: No. of editorial pages 3; No. of advertising pages 13; Price £2 (includes admission)
Programme editor: M. Blake, P.O. Box 276, Blackheath SE3. Tel: 01–852 3001
Local newspapers: Kentish Times, South East London Mercury
League: National League Division 3
League position (1988–89): 8th
League playing record (1988–89): P 38, W 21, D 1, L 16, F 587, A 597
Competitions won: Kent Cup Winners
Most capped players (including British Lions appearances): Tony Bond 6 (whilst with Sale)
Players' appearances: (1988–89): Haydn Corliss 31, Tony Bond 29, Peter Greenway 27, Peter Rauh 26, Gary Potter 25
Leading scorers (1988–89): John Field 169 (4 t, 21 cons, 37 pens), Peter Greenway 85 (5 t, 16 cons, 11 pens)

EXETER

The County Ground Stadium, St. Thomas, Exeter. Tel: 0392 78759

COLOURS All black with white collar and badge. *Change colours*: White

EXETER R.U.F.C.

Founded: 1872
President: L.J.B. Challenger
Chairman: A.R. Cole
Secretary: D.W.K. Crudge, 'Oystese', Orchard Close, Upton Pine, Exeter. Tel: 0392 841847 (H), 215471 (W)
Fixtures Secretary: R. Huxtable, 21 Somerset Avenue, St. Thomas, Exeter. Tel: Stoke Canon 847 (H), 0392 215471 (W)
Press Officer: W.J. Baxter, Exwick Barton, Exwick, Exeter. Tel: 0392 73496
Coach: R.C. Staddon
Club captain (1988–89): Dave Hartland
Club captain (1989–90): Dave Hartland
No. of teams: Senior 4, Youth 2, Minis 4
Directions to ground: M5 motorway to end, follow road signposted Okehampton, turn off signposted Exeter (Marsh Barton). Follow signs to city centre to Sainsbury's, left-hand lane under railway. St. Thomas Station, first left, first right
Ground capacity: Seating 750, Standing 5000
Clubhouse facilities: Yes
Floodlights: Yes
Membership fees: Full £22, Playing £15, Social £18, Youth £2, Colts £5, OAP £8

Ground admission: £2
Programme: No. of editorial pages 4; No. of advertising pages 32; Price 30p
Programme editor: T.G. Turner, April House, Sandford, Crediton, nr. Exeter. Tel: 922 2044
Local newspapers: Express & Echo, Western Morning News
League: National League Division 3
League position (1988–89): 9th
League playing record (1988–89): P 11, W 4, D 0, L 7, F 142, A 180
Competitions won: The Bass Devon Cup, April '89
Most capped players (including British Lions appearances): M.A. Underwood 5, R.J.P. Madge 4, D.C. Manley 4, P.L. Nicholas 3, A.A. Brown 1 (all for Eng), J.R. Buchanan 16 (Scot)
Players' appearances: (1988–89): M. Collins 40, G. Bess 38, H. Langley 36, M. Cathery 34, I. Stewart 34
Leading scorers (1988–89): I. Stewart (18 t), A, Maunder (16 t), A. Green (10 t), D. Hartland and M. Cathery (7 t). Kickers points: M. Collins 243 (+2 t), A. Green 71 (+10 t), D. Russell 13

RESULTS

Opponents	Venue	Result	Points	
Sheffield	H	W	19	12
Askeans	A	W	20	6
Nuneaton	H	L	12	25
West Hartlepool	A	L	3	16
Maidstone	A	W	21	0
Fylde	A	L	14	16
Plymouth	H	L	6	21
Met. Police	H	W	14	6
Rugby	A	L	3	23

	Venue	Result	Points	
Vale of Lune	H	L	12	26
Pilkington Cup				
Sudbury	H	W	40	12
Redruth	H	W	18	3
Havant	A	L	3	9
Bass Devon Cup				
Totnes	A	W	42	0
Tiverton	A	W	10	4
Plymouth	H	W	6	0
Barnstaple	A	W	17	9

Exeter – 1988–89.

Exeter win this early season game at home to Sheffield (19–12) and flanker Graham Bess looks unstoppable. Photo: Nigel Chanter, Broadclyst, Devon

FYLDE

The Woodlands Memorial Ground, Blackpool
Road, Ansdell, Lytham St. Annes,
Lancashire. Tel: 0253 734733
COLOURS Claret, gold and white

REVIEW OF SEASON

For Fylde this was a season of mixed fortunes and the final playing
record in the league showed just how close they were to becoming an
Area League North club. For a team of their former strengths and
traditions this would have been a disaster. Four wins in 11 league
matches was just not good enough and the Pilkington cup fortunes
were little better; a win at home against Wolverhampton (17–6) was
followed by heavy defeat at Gosforth (31–10) and this meant that
there were no games against top clubs to provide something tasty for
the club's supporters. With Bill Beaumont reinstated as an amateur
there is a new name as club coach and his influence could make a big
difference to the club's fortunes in the new season.

FYLDE R.U.F.C.

Founded: 1919
President: Tom Windridge, V.R.D.
Chairman: Ray Woolley
Secretary: Peter Makin, 5 Ribblesdale Place, Preston PR1 8BZ. Tel: 0253 722713 (H), 0772 59625 (W)
Fixtures Secretary: Ken Scragg, 30 Howick Cross Lane, Penwortham, Preston. Tel: 0772 747572 (H), 716543 (W)
Press Officer: Stewart Brown, 179 Hardhorn Road, Poulton le Fylde. Tel: 0253 883100
Coach: Bill Beaumont
Club captain (1988–89): Mark Hesketh
Club captain (1989–90): Mike Dixon
No. of teams: Senior 5, Youth 1, Minis 9
Directions to ground: Leave M55 (Exit 4) on to A583 (Preston Kirkham) to traffic lights and turn right into Whitehill Road to next set of lights. Then turn left on to Queensway Ground about 3 miles on left (after Blossoms pub and R.C. Church on right)
Ground capacity: Seating 900, Standing 7000
Clubhouse facilities: Clubroom, tea bar, lounge bars, sponsors room
Floodlights: No
Membership fees: Full £38, Playing £38, Social £8, Youth £8, Student £8
Ground admission: £1.20
Programme: No. of editorial pages 4; No. of advertising pages 8; Price 20p
Programme editor: L.B. Jones. Tel: 0253 735610
Local newspaper: Evening Gazette (Blackpool)
League: National League Division 3
League position (1988–89): 10th
League playing record (1988–89): P 11, W 4, D 0, L 7, F 136, A 181
Most capped players (including British Lions appearances): Bill Beamont 34 (7), Malcolm Phillips 25
Players' appearances: (1988–89): M.J. Weir 39, S. Walker 38, M. Jackson 36, P. Faulkner 36, S. Burnage 34, D. Young 34
Leading scorers (1988–89): S. Burnage 267 (4 t, 31 cons, 62 pens, 1 d.g.), P. Greenwood (14 t), M. Hesketh (12 t)

LONDON SCOTTISH

Kew Foot Road, Richmond, Surrey. Tel: 01–940 0397

COLOURS Blue shirts, white shorts, red socks.
(*Change colours*: White)

REVIEW

London Scottish struggled throughout the season in the League and their main problem was that they were never able to field their strongest side. In their final match they thrashed Coventry – so depriving the Midlands side of promotion – but their nearest rivals (Blackheath and Richmond) also won, so relegation to Division Three was their fate. In the cup they had a shock win over Saracens, but that was as far as they went, whilst in the sevens competitions they had a particularly satisfactory series with a Middlesex semi-final and victory at Rosslyn Park amongst their best efforts.

LONDON SCOTTISH R.U.F.C.

Founded: 1878
President: Robin I. Marshall
Secretary: William Ross Luke, 105 Palewell Park, London SW14 8JJ. Tel: 01–876 9228 (H), 01–748 9020 (W)
Fixtures Secretary: Neil R.H. Stanners, 70 Farningham Road, Caterham, Surrey. Tel: 0883 43658 (H),, 01–948 5351 (W)
Press Officer: As Fixtures Secretary
Coach: Alastair F. McHarg
Club captain (1988–89): Charles B.S. Richardson
Club captain (1989–90): Gavin Hastings
No. of teams: Senior 10, Youth 3, Minis 6
Directions to ground: London Transport (District Line), British Rail (Southern Region) from Waterloo or British Rail (North London Line) from Broad Street
Ground capacity: Seating 500, Standing 2000
Clubhouse facilities: Extensive
Nickname: The Scottish
Floodlights: No
Membership fees: Playing £35, Social £30, Youth £10
Ground admission: £2
Programme: Price with admission

Local newspaper: Richmond and Twickenham Times
League: National League Division 2
League position (1988–89): 11th (relegated)
League playing record (1988–89): P 11, W 3, D 1, L 7
Competitions won: Sevens tournaments won: Sevenoaks, Worthing, Glasgow Academicals, Oxford, London Floodlit Sevens. Runners-up: Esher, Stirling County
Most capped players (including British Lions appearances): A.F. McHarg 44, I.H.P. Laughland 31, J.P. Fisher 25, M.A. Biggar 24, M.J. Campbell-Lamerton 23 (8), W.C.C. Steele 23 (2), S. Wilson 27 (5), A.G. Hastings 24 (3), R.G. McMillan 21, A.J. Hinshelwood 21 (4)
Players' appearances (1988–89): N. Grecian 24, A. Buchanan-Smith 21, D. Caskie 21, D. Denham 21, C. Richardson 21
Leading scorers (1988–89): G. Hastings 95 (2 t, 12 cons, 21 pens), N. Grecian 75 (8 t, 2 cons, 12 pens, 1 d.g.), A. Mitchell 44 (7 cons, 9 pens, 1 d.g.), A. Campbell 28 (7 t), D. Millard 28 (7 t)
Season's review: Unbeaten results against Scottish clubs and a number of sevens titles did not balance the relegation to Division III

LONDON WELSH

Old Deer Park, Kew Road, Richmond,
Surrey
Tel: 01 940 2520
COLOURS Scarlet. (*Change colours*: Green)

REVIEW OF SEASON

London Welsh had their worst season since 1922 – and there are few people around who will have any clear recollection of that. Of 35 matches played only eight were won and another two drawn with the rest all lost for a dreadful points against total of 898. In the Courage League Division Two there was a solitary win – at home to fellow exiles London Scottish – but for the most part the club's first fifteen was a chopping block for its opponents. Club members were surprised at the decline citing the excellent fitness of their players as a reasons for expecting better, but in these days when the leagues are so important all teams are becoming super-fit and an absence of class and experience can be fatal for any team's prospects. "Welsh" lacked class players (Mark Douglas and Wintle apart) and with the former supply of good players coming to London from the Valleys apparently drying up there seems to be little prospect of any outstanding recruits being found. A suggestion that the club should go open is being resisted by members, but in any case who will wish to join a club that is in decline? It is a major dilemma and one of the few consolations has been the defeat of some bizarre motions at the club's annual general meeting, motions which would have added to the problems rather than relieve them. For the record London Welsh played 12 league matches, winning one, drawing one and losing 10, whilst in the Pilkington Cup there was a second successive defeat by Berry Hill (this time in the second round). One would like to be optimistic for the future, but there is little to encourage hope.

LONDON WELSH R.U.F.C.

Founded: 1885
President: Victor T. Watkins
Chairman: Brig. Rolph James
Secretary: Roland Hobbs, 73 Downs Road, Epsom, Surrey KT18 5JT. Tel: 0372 722252 (H) 01 661 1328 (W)
Fixtures Secretary: John Manfield, 13 Prices Lane, Reigate, Surrey RH2 8BB. Tel: 97372 40390
Press officer: John Reed, c/o The Clubhouse. Tel: 01 549 7073 (H)
Club captain (1988–89): Mark Douglas
Club captain (1989–90): Julian Davies
No. of teams: Senior 7, Youth 6, Minis 5
Directions to ground: Next to Kew Gardens in Kew Road leading from Richmond to Key Bridge
Ground capacity: Seating 1,300, Standing 8,000
Clubhouse facilities: Large multi-use unit incorporating Richmond cricket and squash clubs
Floodlights: No
Nickname: The Exiles
Membership fees: Full £23, Playing £10, Social £23, Youth £2, Student £2, OAP £8

Ground admission: £2
Programme: No. of editorial pages 8; No. of advertising pages 26; Price 50p
Programme editor: Paul Beken, 4B Stanley Road, Sutton, Surrey. Tel: 01 643 2456
Local newspapers: Richmond and Twickenham Times, Surrey Comet
League: National Division League 3
League position (1988–89): 12th
League playing record (1988–89): P 35, W 8, D 2, L 25, F 502, A 898
Most capped players: J.P.R. Williams 55, Gerald Davies 46, Mervyn Davies 38, B.V. Meredith 34, Wick Powell 27, John Taylor 26, Arthur Harding 20 (for Wales)
Players' appearances (1988–89): Julian Davies Prop 30, Guy Leleu Centre 26, Malcolm Hall Lock 26, Jim Williams Centre 26, Mark Humphreys-Evans Hooker 25
Leading scorers (1988–89): Chris Cormack 113 (1 T, 17 C, 25 P), Nathan Humphreys 56 (1 T, 2 C, 16 P), Guy Leleu 36 (9 T), John Walters 36 (9 T)

The "wills and won'ts" of the new season! London Welsh will meet Exeter, whose fly-half is in control here against Plymouth Albion's Dominic Cundy (left) and Bruce Fairgrieve. Welsh will not be meeting Plymouth in the League as they have crossed each other's paths in the annual promotion and relegation turnovers. Photo: Nigel Chanter, Broadclyst, Devon.

LYDNEY

Regentsholm, Regent Street, Lydney, Glos.
Tel: 0594 842479

COLOURS Black and white hoops.
(*Change colours*: Red)

Lydney win the 1988 Flowers – Gloucestershire Cup Final against Berry Hill, who make amends in 1989 by winning and qualifying for the Pilkington Cup again. Lydney – in Courage Division Three – do so automatically.

REVIEW OF SEASON

For Lydney this was an excellent season with the Area League South title won with a record of eight wins from their ten matches plus a draw and only one defeat; the points differential was 240–98. The overall record for the season was also good with a massive 42 matches played, of which 25 were won, three drawn and 14 lost for a points differential of 873 against 547. The club has worked hard for its success and all members will hope that in higher company they manage at least to hold their own. There is no lack of ambition to do well.

LYDNEY R.U.F.C.

Founded: 1887
President: Mrs. John H. Watts
Chairman: Anthony Sidney Peter Wolfe
Secretary: Albert John Jones, 5 Kimberley Close, Lydney, Glos. GL15 5AE. Tel: 0594 842709 (H), 842777 (W)
Fixtures Secretary: David Nelmes, Pine View, Forest Road, Bream, Lydney, Glos. Tel: 0594 562038
Press Officer: As Fixtures Secretary
Coach: Peter Eastwood
Club captain (1988–89): Rhodri Lewis
Club captain (1989–90): Keith Davis
No. of teams: Senior 3 + Colts, Youth 3, Minis 2
Directions to ground: Through Swan Lane off main A48 trunk road in centre of town
Ground capacity: Seating 260, Standing 2500
Clubhouse facilities: 30 ft. serving bar plus players bar and sponsors bar
Nickname: Severnsiders
Floodlights: Yes
Membership fees: Full £15, Playing £20, Social £7.50,
Student £10, OAP £7.50 (88–89) 89–90 T.B.D.
Ground admission: £1
Programme: No. of editorial pages 2; No. of advertising pages 10; Price 20p
Programme editor: As Fixtures Secretary
Local newspapers: Gloucester Citizen, Lydney Observer, Western Daily Press
League: National League Division 3
League position (1988–89): 1st
League playing record (1988–89): P 10, W 8, D 1, L 1, F 240, A 98
Most capped players: R.J. Lewis 7 (Wal), Bev Dovey 4 (Eng), P. Kingston 3 (Eng), T.C. Wintle (Eng) 2, C. Williams (Eng) 1, G.A.F. Sargent (Eng) 1. None directly from Lydney
Players' appearances: (1988–89): A. Brooks 37, R. Morgan 36, S. Morris 33, M. Rogers 33, S. Baker 31
Leading scorers (1988–89): G. Prices 158 (3 t, 35 cons, 20 pens, 4 d.g.), P. Morris 104 (22 cons, 20 pens), S. Morris 68 (17 t), M. Howells 68 (17 t)

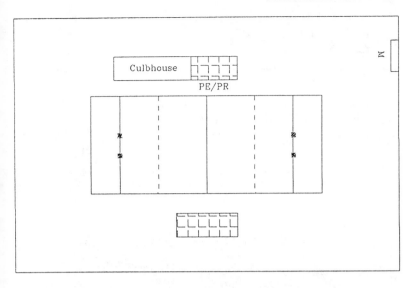

Culbhouse

PE/PR

M

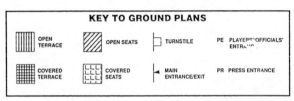

KEY TO GROUND PLANS

OPEN TERRACE   OPEN SEATS   TURNSTILE   PE PLAYERS'/OFFICIALS' ENTRANCE

COVERED TERRACE   COVERED SEATS   MAIN ENTRANCE/EXIT   PR PRESS ENTRANCE

Lydney – Area League South champions 1988–89.

NUNEATON

The Harry Cleaver Ground, Attleborough Road, Nuneaton. Tel: 0203 383206/383925

COLOURS Black red and white hoops

REVIEW OF SEASON

Nuneaton made such a good start to the season that they won the first Rugby World & Post Club of the Month award and, whilst they were unable to keep up that excellent form, they could feel pleased with a final record which showed them breaking even in all matches, whilst their Division Three final position was a reasonable fifth. The team only managed to survive to the Second Round of the Pilkington Cup after a win at Stoneygate (30–9); a visit to Bedford was their undoing (16–0). Five senior players represented Warwickshire with Bob Massey as captain and Gareth Mitchell at colts level represented Warwickshire, the Midlands and England. If the club can avoid another end of season slump they should have another good season overall.

NUNEATON R.U.F.C.

Founded: 1879
President: Dr. C.J. McKeown
Chairman: M.J. Burns
Secretary: D.D. Swarbrigg, 70 Chetwynd Drive, Nuneaton, Warwickshire CV11 4TJ. Tel: 0203 327426 (H), 694400 ext. 3147 (W)
Fixtures Secretary: G.J. Davies, 3 Saints Way, Nuneaton. Tel: 0203 370011 (H), 344800 (W)
Press Officer: Nuneaton Evening Tribune, Watling Houswe, Whitacre Road, Nuneaton, Warwicks, CV11 6BT Tel: 0203 382251 (W)
Coach: Terry McCarthy
Club captain (1988–89): Roger Burton
Club captain (1989–90): Roger Burton
No. of teams: Senior 3, Youth 6, Minis 5
Directions to ground: 1: M6 Junction 3 A444 to Nuneaton town centre then Attleborough Road. 2: M69 Junction 1 (as to Nuneaton), A47 to Nuneaton town centre then Attleborough Road
Ground capacity: Seating 490, Standing 5000
Nickname: Nuns

Floodlights: Yes
Membership fees: Full £20, Playing £18, Youth £6, Student £6, OAP £6
Ground admission: £2
Programme: No. of editorial pages 4; No. of advertising pages 12; Price 30p
Programme editor: c/o Nuneaton R.F.C., The Harry Cleaver Ground, Attleborough Road, Nuneaton. Tel: 0203 383206/383925
Local newspaper: Evening Tribune
League: National League Division 3
League position (1988–89): 5th
League playing record (1988–89): P 31, W 20, D 1, L 20, F 740, A 716
Most capped players (including British Lions appearances): W.A. Holmes 16 (Eng)
Players' appearances: (1988–89): D. Garforth 40, P. Clayton 35, N. Topping 35, R. Burton 32, C. Leake 32
Leading scorers (1988–89): M. Drane 136 (1 t, 27 cons, 24 pens, 2 d.g.), W. Masser 65 (10 cons, 14 pens, 1 d.g.), C. Leake 64 (16 t), M. Calverley 60 (15 t), D. Garforth 52 (13 t)

RESULTS

Date	Opponents	Venue	Points		Opponents	Venue	Points	
					Pontypool	H	10	10
					Sheffield*	A	25	16
	Burton	A	0	18	Cheltenham	A	10	19
	Halifax	H	14	6	Oxford Univ.	A	25	16
	Maidstone*	A	11	28	Cambridge Univ.	H	21	16
	Stoneygate (P.C.)	A	9	30	Abertillery	A	28	0
	Fylde*	H	24	10	Nottingham	A	29	17
	Coventry	A	15	9	Loughborough	A	7	22
	Roundhay	H	21	9	Blackheath	H	17	18
	Exeter*	A	12	25	Stroud	H	57	11
	Broughton Park	H	12	10	Askeans*	H	12	19
	Rugby*	H	15	18	Birkenhead Park	H	21	4
	Saracens	H	8	40	Coventry	H	10	12
	Bedford (P.C.)	A	16	0	Pontypool	A	50	8
	West Hartlepool*	H	22	18	Oxford	A	22	36
	Wakefield*	A	42	4	Plymouth*	H	3	21
	Vale of Lune*	H	16	6	Burton	H	48	3
	Bradford	H	6	18	Sudbury	H	52	6
	Morley	A	35	8	Met. Police*	A	32	13
	Moseley	A	19	10	Bridgwater	A	4	33
	New Brighton	A	24	17				
	Leicester	H	13	39				

* = Courage Clubs Championship Division 3   (P.C.) = Pilkington Cup

ROUNDHAY

Chandos Park, Lidgett Lane, Leeds 8. Tel:
0532 661815

COLOURS Emerald green, red, white hoops.
(*Change colours*: Red)

REVIEW OF SEASON

When the Third Division was first formed Roundhay were founder members, but their first season there (1986–87) was a disaster and for 1987–88 they were replaced by Maidstone and found themselves in Area League North, where they spent a satisfactory first season (1987–88) re-grouping. With promotion and relegation established between Division Three and the Area Leagues they made a special effort and by drawing with Lichfield in their last league game at the same time that main rivals Broughton Park lost, they regained their senior spot in Division Three and are determined not to go down again.

RESULTS

Date	Opponents	Venue	Points		Date	Opponents	Venue	Points	
Sept 3	Gosforth	H	13	12	**Jan** 1	Roundhegians	H	16	16
10	Northern	A	10	6	7	Vale of Lune	H	34	16
17	Hull & E.R.	A	10	12	14	Broughton Park	A	0	10
24	Preston G'hoppers	H	22	9	21	Sandal	H	17	7
Oct 1	Nuneaton	A	9	21	28	Fylde	A	17	35
8	Middlesbrough	A	10	15	**Feb** 4	Hawick	H	7	25
15	Kendal	H	33	6	11	Walsall	H	9	8
22	Stoke	A	19	9	18	Gala	A	3	30
26	Headingley	0	30		25	Sheffield	H	13	17
29	L'pool St. Helens	A	16	22	**Mar** 1	RAF	H	19	21
Nov 5	Halifax	H	35	7	4	Met. Police	H	20	7
12	Winnington Park	H	48	12	11	Morley	H	13	9
19	Stourbridge	A	10	0	18	Sale	H	10	24
26	Birmingham	H	79	0	25	Wrexham	H	16	9
Dec 3	West Hartlepool	H	6	24	30	Huddersfield (YC)	A	30	14
10	Huddersfield	A	30	0	**Apr** 1	Bradford & Bingley	H	16	13
17	Wakefield	A	10	15	4	Wakefield (YC)	H	3	16
24	Harrogate	H	9	16	8	Durham City	A	24	16
31	Otley	A	9	15	22	Lichfield	H	10	10
					29	Orrell	A	8	30

ROUNDHAY R.U.F.C.

Founded: 1924
President: Ronald A. Bidgood J.P.
Chairman: John Hopkins
Secretary: Michael Bidgood, 41 West Hill Avenue, LS7 3QH. Correspondence to: 433 Meanwood Road, Leeds LS7 2LL
Fixtures Secretary: David A. Fawcett, 433 Meanwood Road, Leeds LS7 2LL. Tel: 0532 453606
Press officer: A. Riddel, Roundhay Rugby Club, Chandos Park, Lidgett Lane, Leeds LS8 1QX
Club captain (1988–89): R. Burman
Club captain (1989–90): Sean Bainbridge
No. of teams: Senior 4
Directions to ground: Harrogate road, north from Leeds Centre (all Harrogate signs off M1/M621), Lidgett Lane right hand turn opposite St Gemmas Hospice, Chandos Park right hand turn off Lidgett Lane
Ground capacity: Seating 400. Standing 2,000

Clubhouse facilities: 3 bars, 8 changing rooms, committee room
Floodlights: Yes
Membership fees: Full £12, Playing £12, Social £12, Student £6, OAP £6
Ground admission: £1.50
Programme: Price 50p
Programme editor: R. Pyke
Local newspapers: Yorkshire Press, Morning/Evening
League: National Division League 3
League position (1988–89): Champions Area North
League playing record (1988–89): P 10, W 8, D 1, L 1
Players' appearances (1988–89): J. Malinder Full Back, N. Lineham Hooker, B. Willis Loose Forward, T. McMan Scrum Half, P. Gray Fly Half
Leading scorers (1988–89): J. Malinder 22 Tries, G. Walker 22 Tries

Peter Robinson, a gallant West Hartlepool veteran, scored his 200th try for his club last season – against Rugby – and is here seen on a typical rampaging charge. Photo: The Mail, Hartlepool

SHEFFIELD

Abbeydale Park, Dore, Sheffield S17 3LJ.
Tel: 0742 362040

COLOURS Blue/white hoops. (*Change colours*: Red shirts]

REVIEW OF SEASON

The overall results of a strengthened fixture list were good by any standards so it was a surprise to find Sheffield struggling in the Third Division, where they needed a win in their final match against Fylde to survive; this was achieved comfortably and they will hope to challenge for promotion next season with much the same team. During the recent campaign Bill Reichwald led the team for the 300th time.

Sheffield veteran Andy Reichwald tries to halt the progress of Exeter flanker Graham Bess as the West Country team send back their visitors pointless (19–12). Photo: Nigel Chanter, Broadclyst, Devon.

SHEFFIELD R.U.F.C.

Founded: 1902
President: Edward E. Williams
Secretary: James Goulding, Buck Trap, Andwell Lane, Sheffield S10 4QF. Tel: 0742 308838 (H), 725573 (W)
Fixtures Secretary: Q. Robert Dean, 92 Riverdale Road, Sheffield S10 3FD. Tel: 0742 301021 (H), 0709 371234 (W)
Press Officer: Andrew Reichwald, 93 Whirlowdale Road, Sheffield S7 2NF. Tel: 0742 363651 (H), 720966 (W)
Coach: Mike Richmond
Club captain (1988–89): Bill Reichwald
Club captain (1989–90): Bill Reichwald
No. of teams: Senior 5, Youth 1, Minis 2
Directions to ground: 1: See attached map
Ground capacity: Seating 100, Standing 1000
Clubhouse facilities: Sports club with separate restaurant/dance room, lounge for wives and children
Floodlights: Yes (training only)

Membership fees: Playing £15, Social £30, Youth £2, Student £10
Ground admission: £1
Programme: No. of editorial pages 8; No. of advertising pages 28; Price £1
Programme editor: As Press Officer
Local newspapers: Sheffield Star, Yorkshire Post
League: National League Division 3
League position (1988–89): 6th
League playing record (1988–89): P 11, W 4, D 1, L 6, F 170, A 182
Most capped players (including British Lions appearances): A.G.B. Old 16 (Eng) (4)
Players' appearances: (1988–89) Steve Hodgson 36, Robin Goodliffe 35, David Fairclough 33, Bill Reichwald 33, Rob Parr 31
Leading scorers (1988–89): Robin Goodliffe 278 (4 t, 53 cons, 52 pens), David Fairclough 92 (23 t), Kerry Morley 56 (14 t)

RESULTS

Date	Opponents	Result	Points		Date	Opponents	Result	Points	
	Exeter*	L	12	19		Moseley†	L	10	49
	Rugby*	L	6	22						
	Plymouth Albion*	L	13	34		Otley†	W	19	9
	Met. Police*	W	10	6		Sheffield Univ.†	W	34	3
	Vale of Lune*	D	9	9		Preston Grass.†	W	16	3
	West Hartlepool*	L	4	12		Morley†	W	12	9
	Askeans*	L	17	27		Waterloo	L	13	16
	Nuneaton*	W	25	16		Hull & E.R.†	W	35	3
	Wakefield*	L	22	25		Hartlepool Rovers†	W	23	12
	Maidstone*	W	28	3		Winnington Park†	W	20	3
	Fylde*	W	24	9		Kendal†	D	13	13
	Wakefield (P.C.)	L	3	16		Harrogate†	L	16	33
	Hemsworth (Y.C.)	W	17	6		Broughton Park†	W	15	3
	Rotherham	L	3	4		Burton†	W	32	4
	Wharfedale†	W	19	0		Halifax†	W	12	4
	Middlesbrough†	W	29	0		Roundhay†	W	17	13
	Birkenhead Park†	W	26	3		Stockton†	W	24	4
	Nottingham†	D	13	13		Durham City†	L	15	23
	Sale†	L	12	16		Huddersfield†	W	43	17

* = Courage Clubs Championship Division 3   (P.C.) = Pilkington Cup   (Y.C.) = Yorkshire Cup   † = Other

Sheffield 1988–89 (standing l to r): P.J.Tear (President), D. Fairclough, D. Bosworth, A. Hayes, A. Gough, D. Watson, W. Reichwald (capt.), S. Hodgson, K. Morley, M. Pierce, T. Swainson. (Kneeling): A. Sandilands, R. Parr, B. O—Sullivan, A. Challoner, C. Saul, S. Grieve, R. Goodliffe.

It's not Mike Tyson against his latest victim. No! Exeter's Graham Bess denies the ball to Sheffield Centre Andy Reichwald and the Yorkshiremen go home empty-handed (19–12). Photo: Nigel Chanter, Broadclyst, Devon

Exeter's skipper Dave Hartland emerges from a maul but Nuneaton win at Exeter (25–12). Photo: Nigel Chanter, Broadclyst, Devon

VALE OF LUNE

Powderhouse Lane, Lancaster. Tel: 0524 64029

COLOURS Cherry and white hoops, blue shorts.

Change colours: Blue white hoops

REVIEW OF SEASON

Overall a most difficult season for the Vale in which they used 59 players in a rebuilding programme. However, a young side began to gel and they ensured another season in Division 3 following a home victory against Fylde, and an emotional win at Exeter in the final game of the season.

Skipper Sam Hodgson added to his list of honours when he was selected for England 'B' to play against the Australians at Sale. Former skipper Jim Ashworth gained his 'Blue' for Cambridge University. Stuart Reid, who had toured Australia and New Zealand with England Schools in the summer of 1988, was selected for Scotland's Under 21's.

Long serving player Mark Nelson retired at the end of the season after playing 311 first team games. He made his debut in March 1977, and has scored a total of 190 tries, including the club record of 36 set in the 83/84 season.

For the second year the club hosted a National Under 17's 15 C side tournament. Saracens were the winners of the main competition, defeating Boroughmuir. In the Plate competition Huddersfield were winners against Otley in an event that is growing in popularity.

VALE OF LUNE R.U.F.C.

Founded: 1900
President: T.B.A.
Chairman: T.B.A.
Secretary: James Edward Cowper, 53 Torris-holme Road, Lancaster LA1 2UA. Tel: 0524 658008 (H), 0524 65800 (W)
Fixtures Secretary: F.W. Swarbrick, Oxendale Farm, Wyresdale Road, Lancaster. Tel: 0524 37601 (H), 64055 (W)
Press Officer: Stuart Vernon, 16 Slyne Road, Bolton-le-Sands, Carnforth, Lancs LA5 8BQ. Tel: 0524 822092 (H), 416830 (W)
Coach: Tim Becker
Club captain (1988–89): Sam Hodgson
Club captain (1989–90): T.B.A.
No. of teams: Senior 5, Youth 2, Minis 8
Directions to ground: Leave M6 at Junc. 34, follow signs for Morecambe. 1 mile after crossing river turn right down Penrhyn Road which becomes Powderhouse Lane (rt turn is 250 yds past Lancastrian Hotel)
Ground capacity: Seating 300, Standing 9500
Clubhouse facilities: Club bar, lounge bar. Open all year every evening and Sun. lunch
Nickname: 'The Vale'
Floodlights: No

Membership fees: Full £12, Playing £20, Social £2, Squash £30
Ground admission: Varies
Programme: No. of editorial pages 2; No. of advertising pages 10; Price 20p
Programme editor: Peter Lovett-Horn, 41 Watery Lane, Lancaster. Tel: 0524 61170
Local newspapers: The Visitor, Lancaster Guardian Series
League: National League Division 3
League position (1988–89): 7th
League playing record (1988–89): P 11, W 4, D 1, L 6, F 120, A 145
Most capped players (including British Lions appearances): Sam Hodgson (Eng B, Barb, N. of Eng Cumb), Les Dent/Richard Taylor (Cumb), Andy Higgin (Lanc), Steve Gill (Chesh), Stuart Reid (Scot U21)
Players' appearances: (1988–89): Richard Taylor 34, Andy Higgin 33, Mike Kirby 29, Mark Nelson 29, Andy Rice 28
Leading scorers (1988–89): Andy Higgins 258 (3 t, 38 cons, 38 pens, 6 d.g.), Mike Kirby 30 (6 t, 2 d.g.), Mark Nelson (9 t), Ian Ralston (8 t)

RESULTS

Opponents	Venue	Result	Points		Opponents	Venue	Result	Points	
West of Scotland	H	W	17	9	Roundhay	A	L	16	34
Rugby[3]	A	L	9	28	Wakefield[3]	H	L	4	19
Rugby (P.C.)	H	L	6	27	Morley	H	D	22	22
Plymouth Albion[3]	H	L	6	20	Coventry	A	L	12	13
Otley	H	L	0	40	Headingley	A	L	3	25
Met. Police[3]	A	L	7	13	Keighley	H	W	23	13
Durham City	H	L	13	15	Cambridge Univ.	H	D	6	6
Maidstone[3]	H	W	12	7	Gosforth	A	L	10	21
Waterloo	A	L	7	40	Birkenhead Park	H	W	37	3
Liverpool St. Helens	H	L	13	22	West Hartlepool[3]	A	L	6	9
Sheffield[3]	A	D	9	9	Lancaster Univ.	H	W	32	0
Askeans[3]	H	W	29	12	Northern	A	W	13	3
Nuneaton[3]	A	L	6	16	Saracens	A	L	7	49
Harrogate	A	L	16	18	Sale	H	L	6	28
Lichfield	H	W	38	19	Northampton	A	L	0	48
Wigan	A	W	10	9	Sedgley Park (L.S.C.)	H	W	26	0
London Irish	A	L	12	24	Fylde[3]	H	W	6	0
Broughton Park	H	W	9	7	Waterloo (L.S.C.)	A	L	0	74
Kendal	A	L	0	13	Orrell	H	L	23	40
Preston Grass.	H	W	38	10	Exeter[3]	A	W	26	12
					Wilmslow	H	W	29	6

[3] = Courage Division 3   L.S.C. = Lancashire Senior Cup

Exeter scrum-half Andy Maunder is fed by no. 8 Mike Cathery, but their efforts are in vain. Nuneaton win away (25–12). Photo: Nigel Chanter, Broadclyst, Devon.

The Vale of Lune defence crowds out Exeter prop Richard Gibbins and win in the West Country (26–12). Photo: Nigel Chanter, Broadclyst, Devon.

WAKEFIELD

Pinderfields Road, College Grove, Wakefield.
Tel: 0924 372038

COLOURS Black and gold hoops.
Change colours: Black and gold

REVIEW OF SEASON

After being denied promotion in 1988 through the existing rules
Wakefield had an even sadder fate in 1989 when they lost out again
on promotion as a result of a single point defeat at Rugby in the final
league game of the campaign. It was pure irony that the losing points
came well into injury time after the depleted Wakefield (a player
having been dismissed in the first half) had led until that point. It was
a gallant failure in a good season, in which the club also reached the
Fourth Round of the Pilkington Cup before falling at home to
Gloucester (13–28). They must now hope that the fates will be kinder
this coming season.

*Wakefield's former
England wing and
captain, Mike Harrison,
looks for an opening.
Photo: Yorkshire
Weekly Newspaper
Group*

WAKEFIELD R.U.F.C.

Founded: 1901
President: John Waind
Chairman: Alan Calvert
Secretary: Robin Foster, 27 Carr Lane, Sandal, Wakefield WF2 6HJ. Tel: 0924 250116 (H), 371501 (W)
Fixtures Secretary: Bill Halstead, Whitcliffe Road, Cleckheaton BD19 3DR. Tel: 0274 872710
Press Officer: As Secretary
Coach: Mich DearMan
Club captain (1988–89): Mark Rawnsley
Club captain (1989–90): Bryan Barley
No. of teams: Senior 4, Youth 1
Directions to ground: Into the centre of Wakefield and ask for College Grove, 500 yds from centre towards Pinderfields Hospital
Ground capacity: Seating 500, Standing 3500/4000
Clubhouse facilities: Lounge and sports rooms, both with bars
Floodlights: Yes
Membership fees: Full £30, Playing £30, Youth £8, Student £10, OAP £15

Ground admission: £2, Senior Citizens/Children £1
Programme: No. of editorial pages 6; No. of advertising pages 12; Price 20p
Programme editor: Nigel Foster, Highfield, Church Lane, Goldsborough, Nr. Knaresborough, North Yorks. Tel: 0423 866093 (H), 0924 893159
Local newspaper: Wakefield Express
League: National League Division 3
League position (1988–89): 3rd
League playing record (1988–89): P 11, W 9, D 0, L 2, F 282, A 114
Most capped players (including British Lions appearances): Mike Harrison 15 (Eng), Bryan Barley 7 (Eng)
Players' appearances: (1988–89): Andy Atkinson, Bryan Barley, Steve Townend, Dave Scully, Paul Wood, Mark Rawnsley
Leading scorers (1988–89): Andy Atkinson 207 (10 t, 34 cons, 33 pens)

RESULTS

Date	Opponents	Venue	Points	
Sept. 1988				
1	Moseley	A	17	24
3	Durham City	H	9	9
10	Plymouth Albion*	A	12	21
17	Sheffield (P.C.)	A	16	3
24	Metropolitan Police*	H	70	0
Oct 1	Harrogate	A	10	34
8	Maidstone*	A	23	6
15	Otley	A	7	18
22	Fylde*	H	10	6
29	Hartlepool Rovers	A	10	9
Nov. 5	Headingley (P.C.)	A	10	7
12	Askeans*	A	23	10
19	Nuneaton*	H	42	4
26	West Hartlepool*	A	16	9
Dec. 3	Saracens	A	3	26
10	Gosforth	H	7	7
17	Roundhay	H	15	10
24	Orrell	A	8	31
31	Headingley	A	18	31

Date	Opponents	Venue	Points	
Jan. 1989				
7	Bedford	A	13	17
14	Vale of Lune*	A	19	4
21	Liverpool St. Helens	H	13	17
28	Gosforth (P.C.)	A	29	9
Feb. 4	Broughton Park	H	37	7
11	Havant	H	18	10
18	Blackheath	H	27	9
25	Gloucester (P.C.)	H	13	25
28	Halifax	H	24	16
Mar. 4	Preston Grass.	H	Cancelled	
11	Sheffield*	H	25	22
14	Nottingham	H	Cancelled	
18	Headingley	H	10	3
25	Waterloo	A	15	25
30	Bradford and Bingley (Y.C.)	H	18	6
Apr. 1	Sale	A	Cancelled	
8	Exeter*	H	29	18
15	Northern	H	19	33
22	Rugby*	A	13	14
May 4	Roundhay (Y.C.)	A	16	3
12	Keighley (Y.C.)	H	51	9
19	Headingley (Y.C.)†	A	0	74

* = Courage League Division 3   P.C. = Pilkington Cup   Y.C. = Yorkshire Cup   † = Fielded entire second team due to League commitments

WEST HARTLEPOOL

Brierton Lane, Hartlepool. Tel: 0429 272640
COLOURS Green, red and white hoops.
Change colours: Blue and white hoops

Peter Robinson (West Hartlepool) scored his 200th first team try against Rugby.
Photo: The Mail, Hartlepool.

Founded: 1881
President: Neville Brown
Chairman: Bob Bateman
Secretary: Tony Savage, 12 Barford Close, Hartlepool. Tel: 0429 870563 (H), 266522 (W)
Fixtures Secretary: Les Smith, 2 Elm Grove, Hartlepool. Tel: 0429 231000
Press Officer: Steve Murray, 35 Grantham Avenue, Hartlepool. Tel: 0429 221172 (H), 267828 (W)
Coach: Dave Stubbs
Club captain (1988–89): Paul Stacey
Club captain (1989–90): John Stabler
No. of teams: Senior 5, Youth 6, Minis 4
Directions to ground: From A1 or A19 take the A689 to Hartlepool. Within a mile of the first houses turn left into Brierton Lane (signpost: Boys Scout H.Q.). Ground is ½ mile up on the left
Ground capacity: Seating 600, Standing 5500
Clubhouse facilities: 2 public bars, 1 committee and 1 sponsors bar, 4 squash courts
Floodlights: Yes
Membership fees: Full £13, Playing £13, Social £5, Youth £5
Ground admission: £1.50
Programme: No. of editorial pages 4; No. of advertising pages 12; Price Free with admission

Programme editor: Steve Smith, c/o W.H. R.F.C., Brierton Lane, Hartlepool. Tel: 0429 272160
Local newspapers: Hartlepool Mail, Northern Echo (Darlington), Journal (Newcastle), Evening Gazette (Middlesbrough)
League: National League Division 3
League position (1988–89): 4th
League playing record (1988–89): P 44, W 27, D 1, L 16, F 812, A 628
Competitions won: Durham County Cups at 1st XV and 2nd XV + U16. Great North 7's
Most capped players (including British Lions appearances): C.D. Aarvold 21 (5), J.T. Taylor 11 (both Eng)
Players' appearances: (1988–89): Paul Stacey 41, Dave Cooke 34, Dave Mitchell 34, Mark Baggs 33, Owen Evans 32
Leading scorers (1988–89): John Stabler 168 (4 t, 34 cons, 22 pens, 6 d.g.), Dave Cooke 94 (23 t, 1 con)
Season's review: A season dogged by unavailability due to work commitments of a number of key players. Although finishing fourth in Division Three didn't really challenge for promotion the opportunity was taken to blood a number of promising young players and newcomers with an eye to promotion to 2nd Division in 1989/90

RESULTS

Date	Opponents	Venue	Points		Date	Opponents	Venue	Points	
Sept. 1988					**Jan. 1989**				
1	Gateshead Fell	A	21	7	2	Durham City	A	13	10
3	Saracens	H	10	25	7	Moseley	A	16	31
10	Met. Police*	A	25	10	14	Askeans*	A	10	10
17	Harrogate (P.C.)	A	22	10	21	Halifax	H	19	13
24	Maidstone*	H	37	9	28	New Brighton	A	17	15
25	Darlington	A	31	0	**Feb.** 4	Otley	H	30	10
Oct 1	Kendal	A	9	15	11	Harrogate	H	11	24
2	John Groves XV	H	50	32	12	Horden (D.S.C.)	H	28	0
8	Fylde*	A	13	18	18	Blaydon	A	23	4
15	Headingley	A	13	44	25	Orrell	A	6	38
22	Exeter*	H	16	3	**Mar.** 4	Liverpool/St. Helens	H	19	7
29	Middlesbrough	A	19	9	11	Vale of Lune*	H	9	6
Nov. 5	Rugby (P.C.)	H	9	30	18	Morley	H	22	18
12	Nuneaton*	A	18	22	25	Gosforth	A	0	21
19	Sheffield*	H	12	4	27	Acklam	A	27	4
26	Wakefield*	H	9	16	**Apr.** 1	Northern	H	4	23
Dec. 3	Roundhay	A	24	6	8	Rugby*	H	3	15
10	Sale	A	3	37	12	Darlington (D.S.C.)	A	34	9
17	Hull & E.R.	H	42	7	18	Gateshead			
24	Stockton	A	3	4		Fell (D.S.C.)	H	44	10
26	Hartlepool Rovers	A	12	9	22	Plymouth Albion*	A	12	20
					26	Hartlepool			
						Rovers (D.S.C.)	A	19	6
					29	Abertillery	H	18	14

* = Courage League Division 3 P.C. = Pilkington Cup
D.S.C. = Durham Senior Cup

AREA
LEAGUES

COURAGE AREA LEAGUE NORTH
Results Season 1987–88

	1	2	3	4	5	6	7	8	9	10	11	12
1 Birkenhead P		7-6		9-26		10-21		16-28		28-3		
2 Broughton P			19-6		23-9		24-12		16-20		20-6	
3 Derby	11-16			33-13		9-14		6-12		34-8		
4 Durham		4-0			23-15		12-10		9-12		30-12	
5 Lichfield	27-0		11-7			27-9		10-27		18-13		
6 Northern		15-13		3-12			6-22		17-27		16-10	
7 Preston G	24-17		22-10		19-15			6-6			31-9	
8 Roundhay		20-6		6-12		0-0			4-8		16-13	
9 Rugby	20-0		28-16		24-12		24-12			21-3		
10 Solihull		7-14		0-24		7-16		0-12			9-21	
11 Stourbridge	13-14		21-4		9-6		26-15		11-0			

AREA LEAGUE NORTH
Results Season 1988–89

	1	2	3	4	5	6	7	8	9	10	11	12
1 Birmingham				12-33	0-29		7-20		0-10	0-31		
2 Broughton P	V*		45-9			14-9		10-0			23-9	
3 Durham	54-0			9-16	20-13		16-24				22-10	
4 Lichfield		12-3	15-9				6-15		17-6	6-10		
5 Morley		10-34		13-3			12-10		15-13	6-15		
6 Northern	52-7			19-10	21-9			6-10			16-9	
7 Preston G		13-30	31-12			15-25			25-7	11-4		
8 Roundhay	79-0			10-10	13-9		22-9				48-12	
9 Stoke		12-17	3-9			9-6		9-19		13-3		
10 Stourbridge		18-3	0-12			28-15		0-10			9-3	
11 Winnington P	63-3			16-0	23-16		16-12		27-6			

*Void. Not played. Match points to Broughton Park.

AREA LEAGUE NORTH

A weak Birmingham side, who, incidentally, merge with Solihull this season, almost caused problems in Area League North, having lost 79-0 to Roundhay and conceding points to Broughton Park without playing the fixture. This caused problems with points differences which were not resolved until the end of the season.

As it was Park were heavily defeated by the highly competent Stourbridge side and Roundhay just managed to draw their home game with Lichfield, another tough proposition for any worried side, which all left Roundhay promoted by a point.

As two Southern teams were relegated from Division 3 the rules allowed for only one side to drop out of this league and there was effectively no pressure on those who were inevitably above Birmingham in the table. For the record Stoke would have gone down had two teams been forced to descend and the other teams in the league had their good days.

Stoke had come up from Midlands 1 the previous season and struggled, but the North 1 promoted team Winnington Park, even without Dewi Morris who had moved on to Liverpool St. Helens, had every reason to be satisfied with their form in higher company.

The others – Northern, Preston Grasshoppers (with Wade Dooley), Durham City and Morley – will have also been happy to survive and hope to make reaslistic challenges in the new season.

AREA LEAGUES CO-ORDINATOR

John A Jeavons-Fellows
Wychbury Court
Pedmore
Stourbridge   (H) 0562 885663
West Midlands DY9 0SX   (B) 0543 466664

TABLES 1987–88

AREA LEAGUE NORTH

	P	W	D	L	F	A	PTS
Rugby	10	9	0	1	184	100	18
Durham	10	8	0	2	165	100	16
Roundhay	10	6	2	2	131	67	14
Preston G'hoppers	10	5	1	4	178	149	11
Northern	10	5	1	4	121	137	11
Broughton Park	10	5	0	5	152	106	10
Stourbridge	10	5	9	5	132	134	10
Lichfield	10	4	0	6	150	165	8
Birkenhead Park	10	4	0	6	117	179	8
Derby	20	2	0	8	136	197	4
Solihull	10	0	0	10	59	219	0

TABLES 1988–89

AREA LEAGUE NORTH

	P	W	D	L	F	A	PTS
Roundhay	10	8	1	1	235	81	17
Broughton Park	10	8	0	2	179	92	16
Stourbridge	10	6	0	4	118	79	12
Northern	10	5	0	5	182	131	10
Winnington Park	10	5	0	5	188	155	10
Preston G'hoppers	10	5	0	5	161	141	10
Durham City	10	5	0	5	172	157	10
Morley	10	5	0	5	135	141	10
Lichfield	10	4	1	5	112	113	9
Stoke on Trent	10	3	0	7	88	138	6
Birmingham	10	0	0	10	29	171	0

AREA LEAGUE NORTH FIXTURES 1988/89

Sat. 9th September (Week 2)
Kendal v Broughton
Walsall v Northern
Stoke v Lichfield
Winnington v Durham C
Stourbridge v Morley

Sat. 23rd September (Week 4)
Morley v Kendal
Durham C v Stourbridge
Lichfield v Winnington
Northern v Stoke
Preston v Walsall

Sat. 14th October (Week 6)
Kendal v Durham C
Broughton v Morley
Stoke v Preston
Winnington v Northern
Stourbridge v Lichfield

Sat. 28th October (Week 8)
Durham C v Broughton
Lichfield v Kendal
Northern v Stourbridge
Preston v Winnington
Walsall v Stoke

Sat. 11th November (Week 10)
Kendal v Northern
Broughton v Lichfield
Morley v Durham C
Winnington v Walsall
Stourbridge v Preston

18th November (Week 11)
Lichfield v Morley
Northern v Broughton
Preston v Kendal
Walsall v Stourbridge
Stoke v Winnington

Sat. 25th November (Week 12)
Kendal v Walsall
Broughton v Preston
Morley v Northern
Durham –C v Lichfield
Stourbridge v Stoke

Sat. 13th January (Week 18)
Northern v Durham C
Preston v Morley
Walsall v Broughton
Stoke v Kendal
Winnington v Stourbridge

Sat. 10th March (Week 26)
Kendal v Winnington
Broughton v Stoke
Morley v Walsall
Durham C v Preston
Lichfield v Northern

Sat. 31st March (Week X7)
Preston Grasshoppers v Lichfield
Walsall v Durham City
Stoke v Morley
Winnington Park v Broughton Park
Stourbridge v Kendal

Sat. 28th April (Week 32)
Broughton Park v Stourbridge
Morley v Winnington Park
Durham City v Stoke
Lichfield v Walsall
Northern v Preston Grasshoppers

BROUGHTON PARK

Chelsfield Gove, Mauldeth Road, West Chorlton, Manchester M21 2SU. Tel: 061 8812481
Founded: 1882
President: Jess Waring
Chairman: Glyn Pary
Secretary: Ronald Greenwall, 260 Barlow Moor Road, Chorlton, Manchester M21 2HA. Tel: 061 8610457 (H), 061 7666098 (W)
Fixtures Secretary: K.R. Hanham, 1 Broad Meadow, Bromley Cross, Bolton, Lancs. Tel: 0204 56524
Press Officer: Archie MacCallum, 103 Rectory Lane, Prestwich, Manchester. Tel: 061 7736381
Coach: P. Stenhouse
Club captain (1988–89): Andy Rimmer
Club captain (1989–90): Graham Higginbotham
No. of teams: Senior 4, Youth 2, Minis 6
Directions to ground: From South: M6 leave at Junc.19 → M56 continue to A5103 slip road, left onto Barlow Moor Road, right at traffic lights, ground on left. From North: M62–63 leave at Junc 7 → A56 right at Edge Lane, at 3rd traffic lights turn right → left at Park Groun on left
Ground capacity: Seating 600, standing 3000
Club colours: Black/white hoops. *Change colours:* Red or pale blue)

Nickname: Park
Floodlights: No
Membership fees: Full £28, Playing £28, Social £6, Youth £6, Student £6, OAP £6
Ground admission: £1.50
Programme: No. of editorial pages 2; No. of advertising pages 8; Price 30p
Programme editor: As Press Officer
Local newspaper: M/C Evening News
League: Area League North
League position (1988–89): 2nd
League playing record (1988–89): P 10, W 8, D 1, L 1, F 179, A 92
Most capped players (including British Lions appearances): A. Neary 49 (3)
Players' appearances 1988–89: K. O'Brien, K. Knowles, A. Rimmer
Season's review: Failure to win their final Area League North match at Stourbridge (18–3), when promoted Roundhay could only draw theirs, brought disappointment to Broughton Park and relief to the league's organisers since with the cancellation of the match against Birmingham the club were rightly awarded the match points but no actual game points in lieu. Apart from that near success in the league the highlight of the season was an appearance in the final of the Lancashire Cup as a result of wins over Rossendale (19–6), Fylde (17–6) and Waterloo (22–19 in the semi-final), but Orrell were too good in the final (48–6)

DURHAM CITY

Hollow Drift, Green Lane, Durham City.
Tel: 091 3861172
Founded: 1872
President: James Thompson
Secretary: John Jude, 33 Gladstone
Terrace, Beamish, Co. Durham DM9
1QL. Tel: 091 3700371 (H), 091 3843576
(W)
Fixtures Secretary: J.H. Thompson,
Market Place, Crook, Co. Durham, West
View. Tel: 0388 528071 (H), 0388 762522
(W)
Press Officer: Harry Kirkup, 8 Meldon
Way, High Shincliffe, Durham. Tel: 091
3861423
Coach: Tony Butlin
Club captain (1988–89): Howard Nicholson
Club captain (1989–90): Stephen Kirkup
No. of teams: Senior 5, Youth 3, Minis 4
Directions to ground: Centre of Durham,
turn into Old Elvet at Royal County Hotel,
left fork at Magistrates' Court. Ground
150 yds on right
Ground capacity: Seating 400, standing
3000
Clubhouse facilities: Yes
Club colours: Navy blue and gold. (*Change
colours:* White or navy blue)
Floodlights: Yes
Membership fees: Full £22, Playing £22,
Social £10, Youth £10, Student £10, OAP
£2
Ground admission: £1.50
Programme: No. of editorial pages 4; No.
of advertising pages 20; Price included in
admission
Programme editor: G. Moore, 6 Ferndale,

Belmont, Durham. Tel: 091 3863586
Local newspaper: Newcastle Journal,
Northern Echo
League: Area League North
League position (1988–89): 7th
League playing record (1988–89): P 10,
W 5, D 0, L 5, F 172, A 157
Competitions won: Durham County Colts
Sevens
Most capped players (including British
Lions appearances – all England unless otherwise stated): M. Weston 28, S. Holgson
11, J. Ranson 8, R. Smeddle 4, G. Kerr 3
(Scot), A. Maynard 3, J. Askew 3
Players' appearances 1988–89: H. Nicholson
33, N. Robson 32, J. Bland 31, W. Dryden
30, P. Joyce 30
Leading scorers 1988–89: J. Bland 236 (3 t,
56 cons, 150 pens, 6 d.g.), D. Furn 56
(14 t), S. Kirkup 31 (4 t, 3 cons, 3 pens), N.
Robson 28 (7t)
Season's review: Although they broke even
in league results the team finished in an
unflattering seventh position in Area League North, but the team has the capacity to
do better and mount a genuine challenge for
a place at least in Division Three. Bland
played for the winning Durham side in the
Toshiba County Championship, leading
them from fullback, whilst prop Fenwick
was another member of that successful
county side. In the Pilkington Cup the team
won narrowly at Sandal in the first round
and then shcoked the visiting Sale team in
the second round (19–10). A visit to Wasps
put an end to a brave run (33–3)

*Kendal's "points man" – David Bell. 399 was his tally in 1987–88 and 364 in 1988–89.
That is one way clubs can be assured of good results*

KENDAL

Mintbridge, Kendal, Cumbria. Tel: 0539 24239
Founded: 1905
President: Derek Healey
Chairman: Colin Baker
Secretary: Peter Briggs, 22 Long Wealdon Lane, Natland, Kendall, Cumbria. Tel: Sedgwck 61103
Fixtures Secretary: Rod Short, Cocken Farm, Whinfell, Kendall, Cumbria. Tel: 0539 84251 (H), 22635 (W)
Press Officer: John Kremer, Arclid, Ackenthwaite, Wilnthorpe, Cumbria. Tel: Milnthorpe 3053
Coach: Raymond Lee
Club captain (1988–89): Darren Sharpe
Club captain (1989–90): Darren Sharpe
No. of teams: Senior 4, Youth 4
Directions to ground: Take A6 north from town centre, ground on l.h. side of road
Ground capacity: Seating 500, Standing 5000
Clubhouse facilities: Large function room, dining room, members bar
Club colours: Black and amber. (*Change colours:* Black)
Nickname: Hornets
Floodlights: No

Membership fees: Full £15, Playing £5, Social £1, Youth £1, Student £1
Ground admission: £1.50
Programme: No. of editorial pages 4; No. of advertising pages 10; Price inclusive with groud admission
Programme editor: Colin Baker/John Kremer, As Press Secretary
Local newspapers: Westmorland Gazette, Barrow Evening Mail, Lakes Leader, Lancashire Evening Post
League: Area League North
League position (1988–89): 1st (promoted)
League playing record (1988–89): P 39, W26, D 1, L 12, F 706, A 402
Competitions won: Courage North 1 Winners
Season's review: Kendal after a nail-biting finish took top place in North One and will operate next season in Area League North. With the players at their disposal and the reliable boot of David Bell they should do well in higher company and at least stay up. North One may well be the strongest of the divisional league and to end the season ahead of such strong sides as Aspatria was a most praiseworthy achievement.

Kendal – North Division One champions 1988–89. Photo: Westmorland Gazette.

LICHFIELD

Cooke Fields, Tamworth Road, Lichfield, Staffordshire. Tel: 0543 263020
Founded: 1874
President: Paddy N. Martin
Chairman: David H. Lewis
Secretary: Chris R. Smith, The Old School House, Edingale, Tamworth, Staffordshire. Tel: 082 785673
Fixtures Secretary: Tony G. Young, 5 Covey Close, Lichfield, Staffordshire. Tel: 0543 262832
Press Officer: Andy Wilson, 6 Burns Close, Lichfield, Staffordshire. Tel: 0543 254041
Coach: Adrian G. Gouldstone
Club captain (1988–89): Paul Massey
Club captain (1989–90): Mark Davis
No. of teams: Senior 6, Youth 1, Minis 9
Directions to ground: On A51 Tamworth Road, out of Lichfield, at rear of Horse & Jockey pub
Ground capacity: Seating 400, standing 5000
Clubhouse facilities: New facilities including large bar area, cafeteria and sponsors lounge
Club colours: Myrtle green shirts, navy blue shorts, red socks. (*Change colours:* Navy and red hooped shirts)
Nickname: 'Lich'
Floodlights: No
Membership fees: Full £24, Playing £24, Social £7.50, Youth £5, Student £5
Ground admission: £1 (including programme)

Programme: No. of editorial pages 7; No. of advertising pages 9; Price 30p
Programme editor: As Press Officer
Local newspapers: Lichfield Mercury, Express & Star, Birmingham Evening Mail
League: Area League North
League position (1988–89): 9th
League playing record (1988–89): P 36, W 22, D 1, L 13, F 647, A 491
Competitions won: Staffordshire Sevens, April '88
Players' appearances 1988–89: Ian Callinswood 35, Paul Massey 33, Paul Tinsley 32, Paul Butler 31, Ian Wicklin 31, Ian Broadhead 30, Stuart Potter 28, Dave Richards 24
Leading scorers 1988–89: Dave Richards 192 (2 t, 35 cons, 38 pens), Barry Broad 90 (6 t, 15 cons, 12 pens), Stuart Potter 68 (17 t), Paul Butler 52 (13 t), Ian Broadhead 40 (10 t), Ian Potter 37 (4 t, 9 cons, 1 d.g.)
Player of the Year 1988–89: Stuart Potter
Season's review: Considering the wholesale changes made to the 1st XV due to injuries and retirements, 48 played for the 1st XV this season, the youngsters showed what a tremendous future we have in the offering. When times were hardest the team showed their true metal by beating Broughton Park and Durham, together with the unforgettable draw at Roundhay in the League. With a little bit of luck on two occasions we could have finished 3rd in the League instead of 9th plus a stronger belief in themselves the Staffs Cup could have returned to Cooke Fields

Lichfield – 1988–89: (Back-row – l to r): R. Buckle, I. Cobden, I. Callinswood, A. Bartlett, I. Broadhead, M. Davis, P. Tinsley, T. Bishop, S. Joesbury, S. Potter, C. Atkin, A. Gouldstone. (Kneeling): M. Fisher, A. Davis, P. Butler, P. Massey, D. Richards, I. Wicklen. Photo: J. Wall.

MORLEY

Morley, Leeds LS27 1XX. Tel: 0532 533487
Founded: 1878
President: Peter C. Aveyard
Chairman: Tom Long
Secretary: Bob Lloyd, 5 Shepley Bridge, Mirfield, West Yorkshire WF14 9HR. Tel: 0924 494612
Fixtures Secretary: Trevor Richmond, 101 Carlinghow Hill, Batley, West Yorkshire WF17 0AG. Tel: 0924 472705 (H), 0274 480741 (W)
Press Officer: G. Fred Pickstone, Westbourne, St. Andrews Avenue, Morley, Leeds LS27 0JT. Tel: 0532 533508
Coach: John Shepherd
Club captain (1988–89): Owen Murphy
Club captain (1989–90): John Orwin
No. of teams: Senior 5, Youth 5, Minis 5
Directions to ground: From west: leave M62 Junc 27, A650 to Wakefield 1.2 miles turn left into St. Andrews Avenue, 0.3 miles to club. From east: leave M62 Junc 28, A650 to Bradford 1.7 miles turn right into St. Andrews Avenue, 0.3 miles to club
Ground capacity: Seating 1000, standing 5000
Clubhouse facilities: 3 bars, function suite, presidents lounge, physio room, etc.
Club colours: Maroon. (*Change colours:* Cambridge blue)
Floodlights: Yes

Membership fees: Full £20, Playing £20, Youth £3, OAP £3
Ground admission: £1.50
Programme: No. of editorial pages 4; No. of advertising pages 20; Price 30p
Programme editor: As Press Officer
Local newspapers: Morley Advertiser, Morley Observer, Yorkshire Post, Evening Post
League: Area League North
League position (1988–89): 8th
League playing record (1988–89): P 10, W 5, D 0, L 5, F 135, A 141
Competitions won: Halifax Guinness 7's, April '89
Most capped players (including British Lions appearances): G.M. Marsden 3 (Eng), J.P. Shooter 4 (Eng)
Players' appearances 1988–89: Tony Clark 33, Jamie Grayshon 33, Gary Breheny 30, Derek Falkingham 28, Sean Lill 28
Leading scorers 1988–89: Jamie Grayshon 273 (4 t. 28 cons, 64 pens, 3 d.g.), Tony Clark 40 (10 t), Graham Wilson 20 (5 t), Derek Falkingham 16 (4 t)
Season's review: We stayed in Area League North by winning 5 and losing 5 matches. Three of the matches we lost wer close and we were beaten by the boot, giving away too many penalties. Honours this season go to Jamie Grayshon, Yorkshire U21; Andrew Sales, Yorkshire Colts

RESULTS

Date	Opponents	Venue	Points		Date	Opponents	Venue	Points	
Sept. 1988					**Jan. 1989**				
3	Sale	A	6	64	7	Orrell	H	15	28
10	Stourbridge*	H	6	15	14	Preston Grass.*	H	12	10
17	Kendal	A	16	18	21	Vale of Lune	A	22	22
24	Birmingham*	A	29	0	28				
Oct 1	Headingley	A	3	58	**Feb. 4**	Halifax	A	6	7
8	Broughton Park*	H	10	34	11	Coventry	A	3	44
15	Harrogate	A	7	4	18	Birkenhead Park	A	15	3
22	Wrexhan	H	6	6	25	Hull & East Riding	H	9	15
29	Fylde	A	6	25	**Mar. 4**	Bramley	H	12	18
Nov. 5	Loughboro Colleges	H	19	4	11	Roundhay*	A	9	13
12	Durham City*	A	16	9	18	West Hartlepool	H	18	22
19	Lichfield*	H	13	3	25	Bedford	H	22	48
26	Northern*	A	9	21	30	West Park, Bramhope (C)	A	7	9
Dec. 3	Hartlepool Rovers	H	35	8	**Apr. 1**	Waterloo	H	21	48
10	Nuneaton	H	35	8	8	Stoke*	H	15	13
17	Sheffield	A	9	12	15	Middlesbrough	A	15	32
24	Bradford & Bingley	A	15	7	22	Winnington Park*	A	16	23
26	Otley	H	12	12					
31	Huddersfield	H	0	18					

* = Area League North match
C = Cup

NORTHERN

McCracken Park, Great North Road, Newcastle-upon-Tyne. Tel: 091 2363369
Founded: 1876
President: Ian Percy
Chairman: Richard Appleby
Secretary: Eric Wilkins, 27 Kingsley Avenue, Melton Park, Gosforth, Newcatle-upon-Tyne. Tel: 091 2365557 (H), 2614707 (W)
Fixtures Secretary: Eric Armstrong, The Fawdon, Red House, Gosforth, Newcastle-upon-Tyne. Tel: 091 2857449 (H), 2321497 (W)
Press Officer: Walter Ritchie, McCracken Park, Great North Road, Newcastle-u-Tyne. Tel: 091 2363369
Coach: Peter Schofield
Club captain (1988–89): J. Baldwin
Club captain (1989–90): P. Watson
No. of teams: Senior 6, Youth 3, Minis 4
Directions to ground: On Great North Road (old A1) north of Gosforth
Ground capacity: Seating 200, standing 1000
Clubhouse facilities: 2 bars, function rooms, changing facilities
Club colours: White shirts, blue shorts, red socks. (*Change colours:* White, red and blue hoops on shirts)

Floodlights: No
Membership fees: Full £40, Playing £40, Social £24.50, Youth £9, Student £14.50, OAP £12
Ground admission: £1.50
Programme: No. of editorial pages 2; No. of advertising pages 8; Price included in
Programme editor: R.S. Appleby, 38 Elmfield Road, Gosforth, Newcastle
Local newspapers: Journal, Evening Chronicle
League: Area League North
League position (1988–89): 4th
League playing record (1988–89): P 10, W 5, D 0, L 5, F 182, A 131
Competitions won: Northumberland Senior County Cup, April '89
Season's review: Although Northern only broke even in Area League North they scored more points than their immediate rivals below them and finished a very credi-table fourth in the table. By also winning the Northumberland Senior Cup they qualify for the Pilkington Cup next season, which they will be anticipating with some optimism

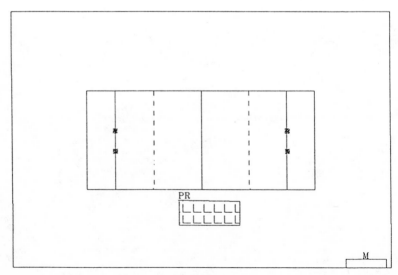

Great North Road

PRESTON GRASSHOPPERS

Lightfoot Green, Fulwood, Preston PR4 0AP. Tel: 0772 863546/863027/862605 (Press box)
Founded: 1869
President: A.H. Pym Simons
Chairman: George E. Thompson
Secretary: Leslie Anson, Oak Tree, 110 Whittingham Lane, Broughton, Preston PR3 5DD. Tel: 0772 862050
Fixtures Secretary: John M. Powell, 121 Bare Lane, Bare, Morecambe LA4 4RD. Tel: 0524 424514
Press Officer: As Secretary
Coach: Keith Aitchison/Dave Worth
Club captain (1988–89): Roy Dransfield
Club captain (1989–90): Dave Percy
No. of teams: Senior 6, Youth 1, Minis 11
Directions to ground: M6, Junc. 32, turn left towards Preston, left again in 50 yds, follow signs to Ingrol. Ground less than 1 mile from motorway
Ground capacity: Seating 250, Standing 2500
Clubhouse facilities: Large main bar, lounge, committee room, admin office, 6 dressing rooms, 4 squash courts, rifle/pistol range
Club colours: Navy blue/white. (*Change colours:* Emerald green)
Nickname: 'Hoppers
Floodlights: No
Membership fees: Ordinary £12, Playing £25, Social £6, VPs £28, Youth £5, Student £12, Rugby/squash £45
Ground admission: £1.50 inc. programme
Programme: No. of editorial pages 2; No. of advertising pages 0; Price inc. in admission
Programme editor: As Secretary
Local newspaper: Lancashire Evening Post
League: Area League North
League position (1988–89): 6th
League playing record (1988–89): P 10, W 5, D 0, L 5, F 161, A 141
Most capped players (including British Lions appearances): Wade A. Dooley 29 (1 – Centenary match)
Players' appearances 1988–89: Ian Jackson 34, Dave Percy 32, Les Ross 32, Ian Ashton 31, Gordon Humphreys 29, Shaun Griffin 29
Leading scorers 1988–89: Steve Kerry (now Salford R.L.) 152 (8 t, 21 cons, 26 pens), Ian Jackson 134 (19 cons, 30 pens, 2 d.g.), Ian Ashton 48 (12 t), Dave Percy 32 (8 t)
Season's review: 'Hoppers did well to break even in their Area League North results and finish in sixth place on the basis of points difference. They also had the great honour of having Wade Dooley confirmed as an England lock yet again and gain an even bigger reward as a member of the British Lions team to Australia. Unfortunately – and inevitably – his representative appearance tended to restrict his club game. The most consistent players were Steve Kerry, fly-half Ian Jackson, scrum-half Dave Percy, flanker Ian Aston, hooker Les Ross, prop Gordon Humphreys and centre Shaun Griffin. If they continue to play to form there should be no worries for the club next season

RESULTS

Date	Opponents	Venue	Points		Date	Opponents	Venue	Points	
Sept. 1988					**Jan.**				
3	Blackburn	H	45	0	**1989** 7	Kendal	A	7	30
3	Wrexham	H	12	6	14	Morley*	A	10	12
10	Birkenhead Park	A	41	4	21	Widnes	H	9	14
17	New Brighton	A	17	0	28	Wolverhampton	H	45	0
24	Roundhay*	A	9	22	**Feb.** 4	Wilmslow	A	21	10
Oct 1	Hull & East Riding	A	12	26	11	Loughborough Stud.	A	15	12
8	Stoke*	H	25	7	18	Otley	H	12	1
15	Manchester	A	22	1	25	West Park	H	28	3
22	Winnington Park*	A	12	16	**Mar.**11	Durham City*	H	31	12
29	Aspatria	H	27	7	18	Rugby	A	11	38
Nov. 5	Waterloo	A	16	39	27	Middlesbrough	H	10	9
12	Stourbridge*	A	11	4	**Apr.** 1	Tynedale	H	7	19
19	Birmingham*	A	20	7	5	Southport (WP)	H	19	6
26	Broughton Park*	H	13	30	8	Lichfield*	A	15	6
Dec. 3	Gala	H	21	17	12	Orrell (C)	H	3	17
10	Sheffield	H	3	16	15	Davenport	A	30	15
17	Huddersfield	A	0	6	22	Northern*	H	15	25
26	Fylde	A	3	13	26	Wigan	A	9	29
31	Vale of Lune	A	10	38	29	Liverpool St. Helens	H	0	22

* = Area League North match C = Cup

STOKE-ON-TRENT

Hartwell Lane, Barlaston, Stoke-on-Trent.
Tel: Barlaston 2807
Founded: 1884
President: Anthony Walker
Chairman: Maurice Mosley
Secretary: Ian P. Godfrey, 78 Caveswall
Road, Blythe Bridge, Stoke-on-Trent. Tel:
0782 393307 (H), 0283 216161 (W)
Fixtures Secretary: Paul Danies, 28
Golborn Avenue, Meir Heath, Stoke-on-
Trent. Tel: 0782 396738 (H), 289711 (W)
Press Officer: Tom Marbrey, 225 Weston
Road, Meir, Stoke-on-Trent. Tel: 0782
313346 (H), 838857 (W)
Coach: Neil McPherson
Club captain (1988–89): Steve Teasdale
Club captain (1989–90): Jim Cheadle
No. of teams: Senior 4, Youth 1, Minis 3
Directions to ground: From North: – leave
M6 at Junc 5, follow A34 south and then
follow sign to Barlaston. Go through
village and ground is 1 mile on the right.
From South: leave M6 at Junc 14, follow
A34 north, directions then as above
Ground capacity: Standing 5000
Clubhouse facilities: Changing facilities for
6 teams, bar, seating capacity 120, separate
private function room for 50
Club colours: Cambridge/navy blue shirts,
black shorts, navy blue socks.

(*Change colours:* Black)
Floodlights: Yes
Membership fees: Full £25, Playing £25,
Social £15, Youth £2, Student £2
Ground admission: £1
Programme: No. of editorial pages 1; No.
of advertising pages 10; Price included in
admission
Programme editor: Stephen Beck, 10
Hillside Close, Fulford, Stoke-on-Trent.
Tel: 0782 398090 (H), 0902 311111 (W)
Local newspaper: The Sentinel
League: Area League North
League position (1988–89): 10th
League playing record (1988–89): P 33,
W 17, D 0, L 16, F 413, A 352
Players' appearances 1988–89: Jim Cheadle
33, Dave Potts 33, Clive Cooper 32, Danny
Hunt 31
Season's review: Although they enjoyed an
adequate season overall Stoke did not have
a very happy time in Area League North
and only escaped relegation after finishing
in 10th place because the regulations
decreed that three clubs should be
relegated from Area League South. Only
Birmingham had a worse season and the
club will need to work hard to avoid
another spell of trauma

STOURBRIDGE

Bridgnorth Road, Storton, Stourbridge.
Tel: 0384 393889
Founded: 1876
Chairman: Melvin Williams
Secretary: Richard Mark Baker, 26
Thicknall Drive, Pedmore, Stourbridge,
West Midlands DY9 0YH. Tel: 0384
374991 (H), 66523 (W)
Fixtures Secretary: Alan McCreadie, 24
Leavale Road, Norton, Stourbridge. Tel:
0384 373904
Press Officer: Jack Standish, The
Paddocks, Greensforge, Wall Heath, Nr.
Stourbridge. Tel: 0384 292483
Coach: David Fourness
Club captain (1988–89): Kevin Astley
Club captain (1989–90): Kevin Astley
No. of teams: Senior 6, Youth 6, Minis 5
Directions to ground: On A458 Bridgnorth
Road out of Stourbridge approx 3 miles on
left-hand side
Ground capacity: standing Unlimited
Clubhouse facilities: Two-storey clubhouse,
eight changing rooms, weights room
Club colours: Navy blue/white hoop shirts,
navy blue shorts. (*Change colours:* Red/
yellow hoop shirts, navy blue shorts)
Floodlights: Yes
Ground admission: £1

Programme: Price £1
Programme editor: Ceri Davies, 3
Eggington Road, Wolleston, Stourbridge.
Tel: 0384 376201
Local newspaper: Stourbridge News,
Express & Star, Birmingham Post
League: Area League North
League position (1988–89): 3rd
League playing record (1988–89): P 10,
W 6, D 0, L 4, F 118, A 79
Competitions won: Kidderminster 2nd XV
Cup
Most capped players (including British
Lions appearances): Huw Davies
Season's review: By finishing fourth in Area
League North Stourbridge could be said to
have enjoyed a satisfactory season, their
main achievement being their win over promotion hunting Broughton Park in the
campaign's final match, which – if justice
were to be done – should have brought them
a case of champagne from the competitions
committee, who might have been left with
some nasty problems had the result being
something different. In an area which is not
teeming with top-level rugby clubs Stourbridge have the scope to make an even
better showing nationally and draw plenty
of support in the process

WALSALL

Delves Road, Broadway, Walsall. Tel:
0922 26818
Founded: 1923
President: W.F. Perkins
Chairman: M. McCluney
Secretary: D.E. Horton, 53 Stonnall Road,
Aldridge, Walsall, Wet Midlands. Tel:
0922 55320 (H), 27531 (W)
Fixtures Secretary: T.F. Day, 20 Daffodil
Place, Walsall, West Midlands. Tel: 0922
611729
Press Officer: H. Clews, 20 Fallowfield
Road, Walsall, West Midlands. Tel: 0922
37528
Coach: Russell Field/Colin Jarvis/Steve
King
Club captain (1988–89): R. Harding
Club captain (1989–90): R. Harding
No. of teams: Senior 5, Youth 4, Minis 7
Directions to ground: Broadway (Walsall)
Ground capacity: Seating 500, standing
2000
Clubhouse facilities: Excellent beer and
food

Club colours: Scarlet jerseys/stockings,
black shorts
Floodlights: No
Membership fees: Full £25, Playing £25,
Social £25, Youth £10, Student £10, OAP
£7.50
Programme: No. of editorial pages 2; No.
of advertising pages 4; Price 50p
Programme editor: As Press Officer
Local newspapers: Walsall Advertiser,
Walsall Observer
League: Area League North
League position (1988–89): 1st
League playing record (1988–89): P 10,
W 10, D 0, L 0, F 210, A 71
Competitions won: Midland League
Division 1, Sutton Coldfield 7's
Players' appearances 1988–89: John Dow-
deswell, Richard Morgan, Richard Mills,
Robert Harding, Dave Knowles
Season's review: Winners of Midland Div-
ision 1

WINNINGTON PARK

Burrows Hill, Northwick, Cheshire. Tel:
0606 74242
Founded: 1907
President: Sidney Bowden
Chairman: Donald Arthur Gray
Secretary: Thomas Roy Palin, Woodville,
Dalefords Lane, Whitegate, Northwich,
Cheshire CW8 2BW. Tel: 0606 882052 (H),
0928 87226/87012 (W)
Fixtures Secretary: Christopher F. Gleave,
Westerley West Road, Weaverham,
Northwich, Cheshire. Tel: 0606 853999
(H), Lymm 2016 (W)
Press Officer: Christopher A. hardy, 36
Park Street, Castle, Northwich, Cheshire
CW8 1HQ. Tel: 0606 79115 (H), 42441
(W)
Coach: Douglas K. Hill
Club captain (1988–89): Roy Allcock
Club captain (1989–90): Roy Allcock
No. of teams: Senior 6, Youth 2, Minis 8
Directions to ground: One mile from
Hartford turn on A556, turn left by traffic
lights at Hartford Church, then right into
Beech Road – B5152. First left is Burrows
Hill, ground on right
Ground capacity: Standing Ample
Clubhouse facilities: Excellent two-storey
clubhouse built 1974
Club colours: White with sky and royal
blue circlet. (*Change colours:* Blue)
Nickname: Park
Floodlights: Yes
Membership fees: Full £20, Playing £20,
Social £8, Youth £5, Student £10, OAP £10
Ground admission: £1
Programme: No. of editorial pages 1; No.
of advertising pages 10; Price 50p
Programme editor: D.A. Gray, Willow
Moss, Alprabham Tavporley, Cheshire. Tel:
08923 2896

Local newspapers: Northwich Guardian,
Northwich Chronicle, Manchester Evening
News
League: Area League North
League position (1988–89): 5th
League playing record (1988–89): P 10,
W 5, D 0, L 5, F 188, A 155
Most capped players (including British
Lions appearances): Dewi Morris (now with
Liverpool St. Helens) 5 (Eng), David
Wrench (later with Harlequins) 3 (Eng)
Players' appearances 1988–89: Steve
Parsonage 38, Dave Allcock 35, Chris Sutton 35, Chris Gleave 32, Roy Allcock 31
Leading scorers 1988–89: Mike Hall 180
(3 t, 45 cons, 26 pens), Andy McGarrigle 88
(22 t)
Season's review: Park did well to finish fifth
in the Area North Courage Leaue, thus confirming their position in the top sixty clubs
of the country. The full playing record was:
P 40, W 24, L 16, F 745, A 506

RESULTS

(Area League North)

Opponents	Venue	Result	Points	
Durham City	A	L	10	22
Lichfield	H	W	16	0
Northern	A	L	9	16
Preston				
Grasshoppers	H	W	16	12
Roundhay	A	L	12	48
Stoke	H	W	27	6
Stourbridge	A	L	3	9
Birmingham	H	W	6	33
Broughton				
Park	A	L	9	23
Morley	H	W	23	16

COURAGE AREA LEAGUE SOUTH

AN EXCITING campaign in theory depended on the final matches with Lydney two points out in front of Havant needing to avoid heavy defeat at Southend and the Hampshire Cup winners requiring a big win at Redruth to take top spot.

In the event Lydney did lose, but only by a single point to the improved Essex team, whilst Havant could only manage victory themselves by one point in Cornwall, so the Gloucestershire team's only defeat made no difference to their title chance. Havant will have to try again, but they have the talent and organisation to achieve the higher status they deserve. Had the actual match at Lydney between the two teams not ended in a draw (16–16) we might be telling a different tale!

At various times Redruth, Camborne and Sudbury all looked as if a challenge from them was possible and all will look forward to doing better next season, whilst Cheltenham seem to be on the way up after being in the doldrums for many seasons – they have a successful youth policy – and Salisbury are another club in a none too strong rugby area (Wiltshire), who might yet come to the fore.

Sidcup lost all their games having failed the previous season to gain promotion by losing on the last day at home to Lydney, so they go down. Stroud were one away from bottom place on points difference from Ealing and if there was any justice in this world they would be the only other team to descend to regional rugby, but a quaint and unimaginative ruling left both sides being relegated and Ealing, only promoted from London 1 the previous season, deserve a great deal of sympathy even if they did struggle in higher company. It now remains to be seen whether Lydney can stay the course in Division 3, although there will be a large number of fans who hope that they will and thus give the new leagues another boost in revising the pecking order.

AREA LEAGUE SOUTH:
CO-ORDINATOR

John A Jeavons-Fellows
Wychbury Court
Pedmore
Stourbridge   (H) 0562 885663
West Midlands DY9 0SX   (B) 0543 466664

TABLES 1987–88

AREA LEAGUE SOUTH

	P	W	D	L	F	A	PTS
Askeans	10	8	1	1	141	83	17
Sidcup	10	7	2	1	130	72	16
Lydney	10	7	0	3	173	99	14
Camborne	10	5	2	3	113	119	12
Havant	10	5	0	5	116	102	10
Stroud	10	5	0	5	112	114	10
Southend	10	5	0	5	63	108	10
Sudbury	10	3	2	5	125	106	8
Salisbury	10	3	1	6	84	94	7
Cheltenham	10	3	0	7	95	152	6
Streatham/Croydon	10	0	0	10	70	173	0

TABLES 1988–89

AREA LEAGUE SOUTH

	P	W	D	L	F	A	PTS
Lydney	10	8	1	1	240	98	17
Havant	10	8	1	1	177	92	17
Camborne	10	6	1	3	198	126	(3
Redruth	10	6	1	3	136	81	13
Sudbury	10	5	1	4	141	89	11
Cheltenham	10	4	2	4	122	151	10
Salisbury	10	4	1	5	113	139	9
Southend	10	4	0	6	116	168	8
Ealing	10	3	0	7	144	188	6
Stroud	10	3	0	7	119	180	6
Sidcup	10	0	0	10	74	168	0

COURAGE AREA LEAGUE SOUTH

Results Season 1987–88

	1	2	3	4	5	6	7	8	9	10	11
1 Askeans		14-0		14-3		17-12		13-4		23-9	
2 Camborne			17-6		23-13		19-19		10-8		10-10
3 Cheltenham	3-20			11-15		16-12		15-0		4-16	
4 Havant		6-7			19-11		6-10		25-15		14-10
5 Lydney	25-3		26-12			10-0		21-0		24-3	
6 Salisbury		6-6		3-17		9-15			28-4		10-0
7 Sidcup	3-3		17-3		6-9			20-3		12-8	
8 Southend		6-18		12-4		9-4			3-0		10-3
9 Stre/Croydon	9-18		6-19		10-20		6-16			9-15	
10 Stroud		31-9		9-7		19-10		10-16			11-10
11 Sudbury	15-16		23-6		23-14		12-12		19-3		

Results Season 1988–89

	1	2	3	4	5	6	7	8	9	10	11
1 Camborne			45-12	21-18		18-0		6-19	33-13		
2 Cheltenham	10-34				3-35	16-6		20-4			15-15
3 Ealing		12-6			17-21	3-15		53-12			13-10
4 Havant		23-4	29-4				6-3		15-6	29-7	
5 Lydney	27-12			16-16		14-9		47-0			17-7
6 Redruth	9-9			15-16			11-0		14-4		15-0
7 Salisbury		9-9	13-10		9-32			22-15	13-6		
8 Sidcup	9-20			16-19		4-26	9-37				4-11
9 Southend		13-19	19-17		16-15			15-10		3-25	
10 Stroud		0-20	18-3		9-16	15-16		20-6			
11 Sudbury	9-0			0-6			23-7		25-6	41-6	

AREA LEAGUE SOUTH FIXTURES 1989/90

Sat. 9th September (Week 2)
Basingstoke v Camborne
Southend v Salisbury
Redruth v Clifton
Met Police v Havant
Sudbury v Cheltenham

Sat. 23rd September (Week 4)
Cheltenham v Basingstoke
Havant v Sudbury
Clifton v Met Police
Salisbury v Redruth
Maidstone v Southend

Sat. 14th October (Week 6)
Basingstoke v Havant
Camborne v Cheltenham
Redruth v Maidstone
Met Police v Salisbury
Sudbury v Clifton

Sat. 28th October (Week 8)
Havant v Camborne
Clifton v Basingstoke
Salisbury v Sudbury
Maidstone v Met Police
Southend v Redruth

Sat. 11th November (Week 10)
Cheltenham v Havant
Camborne v Clifton
Basingstoke v Salisbury
Sudbury v Maidstone
Met Police v Southend

18th November (Week 11)
Maidstone v Basingstoke
Salisbury v Camborne
Clifton v Cheltenham
Redruth v Met Police
Southend v Sudbury

Sat. 25th November (Week 12)
Havant v Clifton
Cheltenham v Salisbury
Camborne v Maidstone
Basingstoke v Southend
Sudbury v Redruth

Sat. 13th January (Week 18)
Redruth v Basingstoke
Southend v Camborne
Maidstone v Cheltenham
Salisbury v Havant
Met Police v Sudbury

Sat. 10th March (Week 26)
Clifton v Salisbury
Havant v Maidstone
Cheltenham v Southend
Camborne v Redruth
Basingstoke v Met Police

Sat. 31st March (Week X7)
Sudbury v Basingstoke
Met Police v Camborne
Redruth v Cheltenham
Southend v Havant
Maidstone v Clifton

Sat. 28th April (Week 32)
Salisbury v Maidstone
Clifton v Southend
Havant v Redruth
Cheltenham v Met Police
Camborne v Sudbury

BASINGSTOKE

Down Grange, Pack Lane, Basingstoke, Hants. Tel: 0256 23308.
Founded: 1948
Secretary: D.A. Williams, 150A Pack Lane, Kempshott, Basingstoke, Hants RG22 5HR. Tel: 0256 58667 (H), 0256 51821 (W).
League contact: R.F. Taylor, 17 Landseer Close, Black Dam, Basingstoke, Hants

RG21 3EN. Tel: 0256 53056
Press Officer: Secretary
Colours: Amber/Blue
League: London 2S
Final position (1987–88): 1st (Promoted)
Playing record (1987–88): P 34, W 24, L 10. F 786, A 365.
Competitions won: London 3S

CAMBORNE

The Recreation Ground. Tel: 0209 713227
Founded: 1878
President: J.M. Trott
Chairman: L. Ptifrsuc
Coach: R.G. Tonkin
Secretary: S.C. West, "Shalimar", Shorts Hill, Treslothan, Camborne. Tel: 0209 716665 (H). 0209 713170 (W).
Fixtures Secretary: E.T. Pascoe, 51 St. Meriadoc Road, Camborne. Tel: 0209 718158.
Press Officer: Secretary
Club captain (1987–88): P. Trudgeon
Club captain (1988–89): C. Alcock
No. of teams: Senior 3. Youth & Minis 5.
Directions to Ground: Leave A30 Camborne/Redruth by-pass at junction 'Camborne West'. enter town from west follow signs marked 'Recreation Ground'.

Ground capacity: 2000. Stand, 600.
Clubhouse: mile approx from ground at 5 South Terrace, Camborne. Tel: 0209 712684.
Colours: Cherry and white. (*Change colours:* Blue).
Floodlights: No
Admission: 80p and 40p OAPs. (Different prices for some games).
Membership:
Programme: Produced per match 20p. (Editor: S.C. West)
Local newspaper: Camborne/Redruth Packet and West Briton.
League: Area League South
Final position (1988–89): 3rd
Competitions won: Cornwall Merit Table Champions 77/78, 78/79, 79/80, 80/81, 81/82, 84/85 and 85/86. County Cup Winners 77/78, 84/85 and 86/87.

CHELTENHAM

Prince of Wales Stadium, Tommy Taylors Lane, Cheltenham, Glos. Tel: 0242 525393
Founded: 1889
President: Ted Nicholas
Chairman: Roger Bacon
Secretary: Tom Parker, 39 Long Mynd Avenue, Cheltenham, Glos GL51 5QT. Tel: 0242 521076
Fixtures Secretary: Mike Edwards, 2 Greenbank Cottages, Guiting Power, Glos. Tel: 04515 232 (H), 0242 41821 (W)
Press Officer: As Secretary
Coach: Richard Akenhead
Club captain (1988–89): Cyril Kelly
Club captain (1989–90): David Kearsey
No. of teams: Senior 3, Youth 4, Minis 8
Ground capacity: Seating 500, standing 2000
Clubhouse facilities: Large clubhouse with changing facilities
Club colours: Red/black. (*Change colours:* White)
Floodlights: Yes

Membership fees: Full £20, Playing £20, Social £7, Youth £6, Student £20, OAP £10
Ground admission: £1.50
Programme: No. of editorial pages 2; No. of advertising pages 8; Price 20p
Programme editor: As Secretary
Local newspaper: Gloucestershire Echo (Evening)
League: Area League South
League position (1988–89): 6th
League playing record (1988–89): P 10, W 4, D 2, L 4, F 122, A 151
Season's review: Just ended our centenary season and our second in Area League South. We have had a number of special events including a dinner attended by 300 (including the President of the R.U.), matches against Gloucestershire (which we won), sevens competition, juniors and minis comps. Dinners for youth sides, etc. Fortnigh's overseas tour to Vancouver.
Full record: P 44, W 23, D 2, L 19, F 805, A 706

CLIFTON

Station Road, Cribbs Causeway, Henbury, Bristol BS10 7TT. Tel: 0272 500445
Founded: 1872
President: Grant S. Watson
Chairman: Norman Golding
Secretary: Ian Carpenter, 62 Oakfield Road, Clifton, Bristol BS8 2BG. Tel: 0272 741021 (H), 732779 (W)
Fixtures Secretary: Brian Jordan, 17 Royal Close, Henbury, Bristol. Tel: 0272 504723
Press Officer: As Fixtures Secretary
Coach: Roger Jordan
Club captain (1988–89): Neil Morgan
Club captain (1989–90): Mark Williams
No. of teams: Senior 7, Youth and Minis 10
Directions to ground: Clifton junction of M5, travel down Cribbs Causeway (dual carriageway). Club on right at bottom of Cribbs Causeway, signposted from there
Clubhouse facilities: Open every lunchtime and evening
Club colours: Lavender and black. (*Change colours:* Yellow)
Floodlights: Yes

Membership fees: Full £7.50, Playing £30, Social £3, Student £20
Programme editor: B. Jordan/I. Carpenter, address as above
Local newspaper: Evening Post
League: Area League South
League position (1988–89): 1st (promoted)
League playing record (1988–89): P 40, W 28, D 0, L 12, F 840, A 587
Competitions won: Courage League South West Division 1
Season's review: Clifton were the surprise team of South-West One and by taking top spot they gained promotion to Area League South, from which they aspire to even higher things. To do so they had to fight off the challenge of such strong teams as Berry Hill, High Wycombe and Reading, which puts their achievement into perspective. Although they have to live in the shadow of mighty neighbours Bristol they are a popular team and their improved status can do nothing but good. Many will be confident that they can at least survive.

HAVANT RFC

Hooks Lane, Fraser Road, Bedhampton, Havant, Hants PO9 3DT. Tel: (0705) 477843
Founded: 1951
President: Bob Iverson
Chairman: Dave Platt
Coach: Brian Powell
Secretary: Jim Doyle, 62 Corbett Road, Waterlooville, Portsmouth, Hants PO7 5TA. Tel: (0705) 259787
Fixtures Secretary: Mick Chalk, 16 Highclere Avenue, Leigh Park, Havant. Tel: (0705) 472239.
Club captain (1987–88): Andy Perry
Press Officer: Ray Quinn, Tel: 0705 593368.**Club captain** (1988–89): Andy Perry

No. of teams: Senior 7. Youth & Minis 6.
Directions to Ground: Off A3M on M27 for Havant, near Bedhampton Station.
Colours: Shirts – Navy and white hoops, Shorts & socks – Navy. *Change colours:* Shirts – Red.
Floodlights: No.
Membership: £25.
Programme: Teams and adverts. 50p.
Editor: Dave Platt, 9 Brookside Road, Bedhampton, Havant.
Local newspaper: The News (Portsmouth)
League: Area South
Final position (1988–89): 2nd
Competitions won: Hampshire Cup 1989 (and previous 5 years).

Lydney gave a foretaste of events to come by winning the Flowers Gloucestershire Cup in 1988 by beating Berry Hill – this year's winners – in the final.

MAIDSTONE

William Day Memorial Ground, The Mote, Willow Way, Maidstone. Tel: Maidstone 54159
Founded: 1880
President: Brian Bills
Chairman: Harry Green
Secretary: Geoffrey Burr, Hush Heath Oast, Hust Heath Hill, Cranbrook, Kent. Tel: 0580 211661 (H), 0622 690691 (W)
Fixtures Secretary: Tony Morris, 7 Camden Street, Maidstone, Kent. Tel: 0622 673120
Press Officer: Ray Vale, 18 Upper Mill, Wateringbury, Maidstone, Kent ME18 5PD. Tel: 0622 812700
Coach: Steve Farr
Club captain (1988–89): Martyn Michael
Club captain (1989–90): Martyn Michael
No. of teams: Senior 6, Youth and Minis 8
Directions to ground: From the centre of town go out on the Ashford Road. After mile turn right at traffic lights (opposite Haynes Bros. Ford dealers) into Square Hill Road. Down the hill and up again, second left into Mote Avenue, turn right into Willow Way before the Mote Park entrance. Ground 400 metres on left
Clubhouse facilities: Large bar and clubhouse with four large changing rooms, separate referees changing room
Club colours: Red, black and white, hoops, black shorts, red stockings. (*Change colours:* Bottle green shirts)
Floodlights: Yes (training only)
Membership fees: Full £25, Non-Playing £15
Ground admission: £2 League matches (£1 members), Non-League £1 (50p members with programme)

Programme: No. of editorial pages 4; No. of advertising pages 13; Price £2 League matches (Members £1), Non-League £1 (Members 50p)
Programme editor: As Press Officer
Local newspapers: Kent Messenger, Kent Evening Post
League: Area League South
League position (1988–89): 11th (relegated)
League playing record (1988–89): P 11, W 0, D 0, L 11, F 74, A 289
Competitions won: Kent Sevens Tournament Winners
Players' appearances 1988–89: Ian Baker 29, Martyn Michael 28, Peter Mattinson 26, harold Osenton 26, Rob Kift 27
Leading scorers 1988–89: Rob Kift 100 points (3 t, 11 cons, 21 pens)
Season's review: This was a most disappointing season with the club being relegated from Division III due mainly to a long injury list for much of the season and the loss of several key players. However the emergence of a number of the young players and the introduction of an Under-21 side together with the liaison drive with local schools, augurs well for next season. Maidstone have elected Des Diamond, former Blackheath and Kent coach as their new Chairman of Selectors, responsible for the playing side of the club. Martyn Michael who played for Kent was re-elected captain. Mike Dyrda and Andy Cushing played for Sussex
Full record: P 34, W 10, D 1, L 23, F 398, A 729

Sean Charlton, Maidstone's scrum-half, dive passes against Sale. Photo: Peter Barton.

METROPOLITAN POLICE

Imber Court, Police Sports Club, Ember Lane, East Moseley, Surrey. Tel: 01–398 1267
President: Sir Peter Imbert, Q.P.M.
Chairman: Kenneth J. Will
Secretary: David Barham
Fixtures Secretary: MPAA Office, Room G11, Wellington House, 67–73 Buckingham Gate, London SW1E 6BE. Tel: 01–422 4966 (H), 01–230 7108 (W)
Press Officer: William Hamilton, 395 St. Margaret's Road, Twickenham, Middlesex TW7 7BZ. Tel: 01–891 1809
Coach: Anthony V. Boddy
Club captain (1988–89): David Kyffin
Club captain (1989–90): Stephen Innes
No. of teams: Senior 3
Directions to ground: Train: Waterloo to Thames Ditton or Esher Road. From North: M25 to Junc. 12, turn onto M3 (London) to Junc. 1, follow A308 Hampton Court, turn right onto A309 and at 1st roundabout take right into Ember Court Road. Clubhouse opposite end of road
Ground capacity: Seating 750, standing 3000
Clubhouse facilities: General sports club
Club colours: Blue and white hoops, blue shorts and socks. (*Change colours:* Blue and yellow quarters)
Floodlights: Yes
Membership fees: Full £10, Playing £5, Social £10
Ground admission: £2
Programme: No. of editorial pages 2–6; No. of advertising pages 10
Programme editor: As Press Officer
Local newspapers: Kingston Informer, Surrey Comet
League: Area League South
League position (1988–89): 10th (relegated)
League playing record (1988–89): P 11, W 4, D 0, L 7, F 130, A 275
Most capped players (including British Lions appearances): D.S. Wilson 8 (Eng), A.M. Rees 13 (Wal)
Players' appearances 1988–89: Derek Barham 37, Steve Robb 33, Paul Galvin 32, Dean Jeffrey 31, Ian Burrell 29
Leading scorers 1988–89: John Kerr 93 (9 t, 9 cons, 13 pens), Steve Robb 48 (12 t), Andy Macrell 44 (2 t, 9 cons, 6 pens), Stuart O'Reilly 42 (9 t, 2 pens)
Season's review: Although relegated the club played better rugby than for the previous four seasons and must now concentrate on regaining National League status

REDRUTH

The Recreation Ground, Redruth. Tel: 0209 215520
Founded: 1875
President: J. Penberthy
Chairman: W.R. Peters
Secretary: Ivor Horscroft, 6 Penryn Street, Redruth TR15 2SP. Tel: 0209 719920 (H), 215941 (W), 214019 (Fax)
Fixtures Secretary: Simon Blake, 67 Albany Road, Redruth. Tel: 0209 215025
Press Officer: Jerry Clarke, Cindy Wheal Rose, Scorrier, Redruth. Tel: 0872 75421
Coach: Terry Pryor
Club captain (1988–89): Ralph Tregonning
Club captain (1989–90): Adrian Curtis
No. of teams: Senior 3, Youth 1, Minis 3
Ground capacity: Seating 675, standing 25,000
Clubhouse facilities: Main and lounge bars
Club colours: Red shirts, white shorts. (*Change colours:* Black shirts)
Nickname: Reds
Floodlights: No
Membership fees: Full £14, Social £3
Ground admission: £1.50
Programme: No. of editorial pages 2; No. of advertising pages 6; Price 25p
Programme editor: As Secretary
Local newspaper: West Briton
League: Area League South
League position (1988–89): 4th
Full playing record (1988–89): P 40, W 35, D 1, L 4, F 840, A 298
Competitions won: Cornwall K.O. Cup
Season's review: The Reds had a tremendous season overall with 35 wins in 40 matches, one draw and only four defeats. They conceded only 298 points against 840 scored and the only piece of sadness came from the fact that they managed to include that draw and three of the defeats in their league results and this left them four points short of the top teams, of whom Lydney went up. There was consolation in yet another Cornwall Knock-Out Cup victory, which puts them back in the Pilkington Cup; in that competition last season they beat Worthing (21–6) in the first round, but then lost away to resurgent Exeter (18–3)

SALISBURY

Castle Road, Salisbury. Tel: 0722 25317
Secretary: R.J. Larcombe, Spindleberry,
Stratford-sub-Castle, Salisbury, Wilts SP1
3LG. Tel: 0722 336712 (H)
Press Officer: R.H. Howland. Tel: 0752
22064.
Club Colours: Green/White.
Coach: S. Ralph-Bowman
Club captain (1988–89): David Murley

Club captain (1989–90): David Murley
No. of teams: Senior 4, Youth 6, Minis 6
Membership fees: Full £15, Playing £20,
Social £1, Youth £10, Student £10
League: Area League South
League position (1988–89): 7th
League playing record (1988–89): P 10,
W 4, D 1, L 5

The Lydney pack in determined action as they win the Area League South title in
1988–89

SOUTHEND

Warners Park, Sutton Road, Southend-on-Sea, Essex SS2 5RR. Tel: 0702 546682
Founded: 1870
President: F. Dyton
Chairman: T. Webb
Secretary: J.D. Barty, 12 Broad Close, Hockley, Essex SS5 5DE. Tel: 0702 204793 (H), 364394 (W)
Fixtures Secretary: As Secretary
Coach: P. Lane
Club captain (1988–89): N. Branch
Club captain (1989–90): N. Branch
No. of teams: Senior 6, Youth 1
Directions to ground: A127 to Southend at roundabout after Bell pub. Go straight on past Access Head Office to next traffic lights. Turn left, go to next roundabout, turn left, follow road to clubhouse
Ground capacity: Standing 5000
Clubhouse facilities: Brick-built 11 yrs old, baths, showers, bars, sponsors room, balcony. Food available

Club colours: Chocolate and white. (*Change colours:* Chocolate and white hoops)
Floodlights: Yes
Membership fees: Full £20, Playing £20, Social £15, Youth £7.50, Student £7.50
League: Area League South
League position (1988–89): 8th
League playing record (1988–89): P 10, W 4, D 0, L 6, F 116, A 168
Season's review: In undistinguished season Southend's main achievement was to survive in Area League South, but their four wins from 10 matches left them only two points clear of the relegation trio, which was far too close for comfort. Cup performances were also modest and they will again miss out on the Pilkington Cup next season

SUDBURY

Moorsfield, Rugby Road, Great Cornard, Sudbury, Suffolk. Tel: 0787 77547
Founded: 1925
President: T. McConnell
Chairman: T.F. McNeil
Secretary: C.R. Donnelly, 1 Prince Charles Close, Acton Lane, Sudbury, Suffolk CO10 6YT. Tel: 0787 75808 (H), 0473 256731 (W)
Fixtures Secretary: G. Underwood, Mill Cottages, 11 Bures Road, Sudbury, Norfolk. Tel: 0787 73045
Press Officer: F. Day. Tel: 0787 70025
Coach: R.P. Day
Club captain (1988–89): R. Sumner
Club captain (1989–90): C. Newman
No. of teams: Senior 5, Youth 4, Minis 3
Directions to ground: A12 to Colchester, A134 to Sudbury, at roundabout take 1st left (Northern Road), after mile turn right, follow signposts

Ground capacity: Standing 1000+
Clubhouse facilities: Bar, kitchen, toilets, 8 changing rooms, 2 baths, showwers, squash court, weights gym
Club colours: Navy blue/white. (*Change colours:* Claret/navy blue)
Floodlights: Yes
Membership fees: VPs £30, Playing £30, Non-Playing £20, Youth £10, Student £10, Minis £5
Ground admission: 50p/£1
Programme: Price 50p/£1
Local newspapers: Suffolk Free Press, East Anglian Daily Times
League: Area League South
League position (1988–89): 5th
Competitions won: Suffolk Knockout Cup

NORTHERN DIVISION

A total of 25 leagues take part in the Northern Division with the two top competitions being North 1 and North 2. Yorkshire have six divisions and Durham and Northumberland four both feeding two top North-East leagues with the rest being covered by the North-West complex which once again provided some stiff competition for everyone involved. Whilst the North 1 campaign provided a finish where only one point divided the first four teams the North 2 programme was always going to be a private benefit for the all-conquering Bradford & Bingley club.

Both Kendal, who went up to Area League North, and the Bradford club should be watched as prospects for the future and it can't be long before the tremendous talents of Aspatria will be rewarded by promotion. The competition there is not overwhelming as Winnington Park have proved after a move to better company.

With clubs like Tynedale, Harrogate, Halifax,Otley, Hull & East Riding, Hartlepool Rovers and Birkenhead Park (in addition to Aspatria) among its ranks the standard of competition is high.

NORTHERN DIVISION STRUCTURE

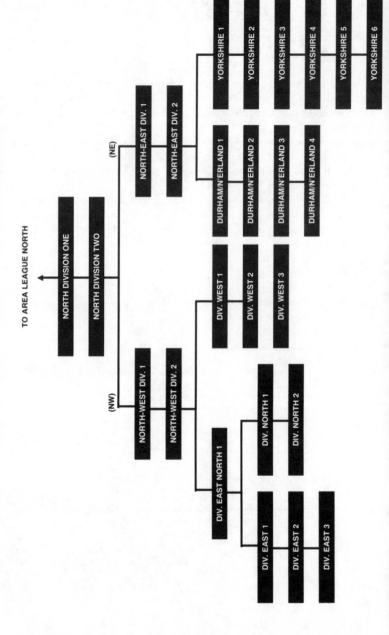

TO AREA LEAGUE NORTH

NORTH DIVISION ONE

NORTH DIVISION TWO

(NW)

(NE)

NORTH-WEST DIV. 1

NORTH-WEST DIV. 2

NORTH-EAST DIV. 1

NORTH-EAST DIV. 2

DIV. EAST NORTH 1

DIV. NORTH 1

DIV. NORTH 2

DIV. EAST 1

DIV. EAST 2

DIV. EAST 3

DIV. WEST 1

DIV. WEST 2

DIV. WEST 3

DURHAM/N'ERLAND 1

DURHAM/N'ERLAND 2

DURHAM/N'ERLAND 3

DURHAM/N'ERLAND 4

YORKSHIRE 1

YORKSHIRE 2

YORKSHIRE 3

YORKSHIRE 4

YORKSHIRE 5

YORKSHIRE 6

NORTHERN DIVISION: COURAGE CLUBS CHAMPIONSHIP RULES

1.   These Rules are in addition to and not in substitution for the Regulations as laid down by the R.F.U.

2.   The Divisional Committee shall comprise the Chairman who shall also be the Secretary of the Committee and Vice-Chairman appointed by the Divisional Committee and one member from each Constituent Body to be appointed by the Constituent Body.

3.   For administrative purposes the League Committee will be split North-East/North-West and a Co-ordinator will be appointed for each side of the Pennines.

4.   Each League will appoint from its participating Clubs a Co-ordinating Club, who in turn will appoint a League Secretary by the 1st July in each year.

5.   The Coordinating Clubs in Northern Division Leagues 1 and 2 will supply to the Chairman of the League Committee the name, address and telephone number of their League Secretaries by the 1st July in each year. In other Leagues within the Division, the Co-ordinating Clubs will supply the name of the Secretaries with addresses and telephone numbers to the North-East/North-West Co-ordinator as the case may be by the 1st July in each year.

6.   On League Saturdays, both Clubs will telephone the result through to their League Secretary *and* the home Club within 48 hours confirm the result and score in writing to the League Secretary on a card signed by the match Referee.

(a) In the case of Northern Division Leagues 1 and 2 such telephone calls shall be made not later than 6.00 pm on each evening of the game and the League Secretary shall report the results to Graham Snowdon News Service at 6 Hallam Grange Croft, Sheffield, South Yorkshire S10 4BP. Tel: Sheffield (0742) 302128 (24 hour answering copy line).

(b) The remaining League Secretaries will telephone the result and scores not later than 3.00 pm the Sunday following the League Match to Graham Snowdon News Service. Tel: Sheffield (0742) 303093/4 (24 hour answering copy line).

(c) In Northern Division Leagues 1 and 2 the League Secretaries will remit to the Vice-Chairman the scores and results in writing within 48 hours. The remaining League Secretaries will remit the results and the scores in writing to their North-East or North-West Co-ordinator within 48 hours.

(d) In the case of an abandoned match the Secretary of the League must be supplied by the home Club with a Certificate signed by the Referee indicating the point at which the match was abandoned, and the score.

(e) These arrangements do not prohibit local publicity and Clubs are advised to maintain and improve local publicity by informing their local press as usual.

(f) Any Club failing to notify the result in accordance with this Rule shall on the first occasion during any season be fined £10, on the second occasion be fined £25 and on the third occasion there will be a recommendation to the R.F.U. that the Club be suspended or expelled from the league. Should payment of fines not be honoured within 28 days of the date of Invoice, the offending club will lose 2 league points.

7.   The complaints procedure whatever the nature of the complaint will be as follows:-

(a) The complaining Club shall make the complaint by telephone to the Secretary within 24 hours of the occurrence giving rise to the complaints.

(b) The complaint will then be submitted by the complaining Club to the Secretary in writing within a further 48 hours, and no action will be taken until such time as the complaint has been reduced to writing. The written complaint must be accompanied by £10 administration fee which will be repaid to the complaining Club if the complaint is found to be justified.

(c) In respect of complaints arising from Northern Division 1 and Northern Division 2 the Secretary will report the complaint to the League Vice-Chairman. In all other cases the Secretary will report the complaint to the East or West Co-ordinator, whichever is appropriate.

(d) Complaints concerning Northern Division 1 and 2 will be dealt with by the Vice-Chairman and the Co-ordinators of both East and West.

(e) Other complaints will be dealt with by the Co-ordinators of the East or West as appropriate, together with the two other Members of the Committee from the relevant region i.e. the Complaints Committee on each occasion will comprise 3 people.

(f) The decision of the Complaints Committee will be made known to the complaining Club and the Club against whom the complaint is made in writing within 14 days of the receipt of the written complaint from the complaining Club, unless either Club requires an oral hearing of the complaint, when the decision shall be within 14 days of the oral hearing.

(g) The above procedure is without prejudice to the overriding authority of the R.F.U. Competition Sub-Committee.

8.   Each League Secretary will keep an up-to-date League Table showing the number of games played, the points scored for and against, and will submit to the North-West/North-East Co-ordinators and to the Chairman of the Committee, as is appropriate, a copy of such Table within 7 days of the completion of each League match.

9.   Each Club participating in the Leagues shall have a team sheet signed by an official of the Club sufficiently identifying the names of the players and the positions in which they played, such team sheets are to be retained by each Club until the 1st September the following season, and shall on request by the Committee send copies of any team sheet required by the Committee within 48 hours of a written request being received from the Committee. Failure to keep such team sheets will be a disciplinary offence.

10.   The Referee will be arranged by the home Club subject to any appointment by the R.F.U. and the normal appointment system as for non-league matches will be followed.

11.   The League Committee shall have power to discipline by way of loss of points, transference of points, review of result, or fine any Club participating in the Leagues for any breach of these Rules or of the Regulations of the Competition.

12.   Any representations as opposed to complaints shall be made in writing to the Constituent Body Committee Member of the Club wishing to make representations and, save in emergency, telephone representations cannot be entertained.

13.   In the event of adverse weather affecting a considerable number of League Matches on any given day, the Committee will appoint a further Saturday to be a League Saturday when such abandoned and/or cancelled fixtures will be played, and an announcement will be made to that effect, otherwise the Courage Clubs Championship Rules will apply.

14.   The Fixture Secretary of the home Club will confirm the match to the visiting Club not less than 3 days prior to the match, giving the kick-off time and the name of the Referee and the venue.

15.   The kick-off time of each League Match shall be in September, October, March and April 3.00 pm, and in November, December, January and February 2.15 pm.

16.   Each Club in membership shall appoint a member to be League Liaison Officer and shall give the name, address and telephone number of the Appointee to their League Secretary and Co-ordinator by the 25th August in each year.

RULES AND REGULATIONS FOR PLAYER REGISTRATION

1.   Each Club shall be responsible for the completion of the official Northern Division form for each of its players who are eligible to compete in the League matches.

2.   The registration document must be completed in full otherwise the document will be null and void and render the player ineligible for a League team with the exception of the payment of subscription which will be subject to the Club's normal rules in relation to subscriptions.

3.   The registration document is to be signed by the player and the Club Secretary or other authorised person on behalf of the Club.

4.   The Club shall keep the registration document for its players on file at its Club premises, save and except when it is required when visiting another Club.

5.   Each Club must make its registration file available to its opponent Club for at least ten minutes before the commencement of each League game and for one hour subsequent to the game.

6.   Failure to take the official Club registration file to an away game may well render the visiting Club liable to a penalty by way of loss of points or other penalty that the League Committee shall decide.

7.   In the event of dispute, any Club may ask for the League Secretary to check the registration of any Club with whom it has played a game. The Club requiring such step shall pay to the Northern Divisional Treasurer the sum of £10 to cover expenses which shall be recoverable by that Club if its enquiry proves justifiable and reveals error on the part of any Club.

8.   A player leaving a Club will inform the Club Secretary and request for his registration document to be passed on to his new Club. The new Club will complete a new registration form lodging one copy with the County League representative, one will be handed to the player and one retained by the new Club.

9.   Any Club withholding unreasonably a player's registration document will be liable to a penalty as decided by the Divisional Committee.

10.   All Clubs shall have available to the Divisional Committee on demand its registration file and at the Division's expense provide copies of such file within seven days of a request being made to that Club by the authorised Divisional Officer.

11.   A player may only be registered with one Club at any time for League Rugby. This requirement shall only apply to League Rugby and shall not in any way interfere with the right of a player to be a member of one or more Clubs.

12.   Any Club in doubt as to the requirements is required to contact its County League Representative, save and except those Clubs in North Division 1 and North Division 2 shall refer to the Deputy Chairman.

NORTHERN DIVISION: List of Officials

CHAIRMAN, LEAGUE SUB-COMMITTEE:

R. Archer,
"Brookfield House",
Scotland Head,
Winlaton, Tyne & Wear
NF21 6PL   (H) 091 4143532

N.E. CO-ORDINATOR & YORKSHIRE LEAGUES:

L. W. Bentley,
32 Moorhead Terrace,
Shipley,
W. Yorkshire
BD18 4LB   (O) 0274 585460

DURHAM:

R.T. Thoburn
70 Theresa Street,
Blaydon,
Tyne & Wear   (H) 091 414 2669

NORTHUMBERLAND:

G. Baty
5 Brooklands,
Ponteland,
Northumberland
NF20 9LZ   (H) 0661 23527

DEPUTY CHAIRMAN, LEAGUE SUB-COMMITTEE:

D. O. Diamond,
26 Nicholas Street,
Chester, Cheshire
CH1 2PQ   (O) 0244 40111

N.W. CO-ORDINATOR & LANCASHIRE LEAGUES:

W.D. Chappell,
Seawood House,
Carter Road, Kents Bank,
Grange-Over-Sands,
CumbriaLA11 7AS   (H) 0532 33456

CHESHIRE:

G.S. Andrews,
2 Ravenswood Road,
Heswall, Wirral,
Merseyside   (H) 051-342 2170
L61 6UA   (O) 0244 377111 Ext 273

CUMBRIA:

W. Anderson,
18 Hensingham Road,   (H) 0946 2844
Whitehaven,   (O) 0946 3881
Cumbria   Ext. 21900

NORTHERN MEDIA CONTACTS

BBC RADIO CLEVELAND:

PO Box 1548,
Broadcasting House,
Newport Road,
Middlesbrough TS1 5DQ   0642 225211

TFM:

74 Dovecote Street,
Stockton-on-Tees,
Cleveland TS18 1HB   0642 615111

BBC RADIO CUMBRIA:

Hilltop Heights,
London Road,
Carlisle CA1 2NA   0228 31661

BORDER TV:

TV Centre,
Carlisle
Cumbria   0228 25101

BBC RADIO FURNESS:

Hartington Street,
Barrow-in-Furness, Cumbria   0229 36767

BBC TV NORTH WEST:

New Broadcasting House,
Oxford Road, Manchester M60 1SJ
061 236 8444

GREATER MANCHESTER RADIO:

New Broadcasting House,
PO Box 90, Oxford Road,
Manchester M60 1SJ   061 228 3434

PICCADILLY RADIO:

127/131 The Piazza,
Piccadilly Plaza,
Manchester M1 4AW   061 236 9913

GRANADA TV:

Granada TV Centre,
Quay Street
Manchester M60 9EA   061 832 7211

BBC RADIO HUMBERSIDE:

63 Jameson Street, Hull,
N. Humberside HU1 3NU   0482 23232

VIKING RADIO:

Commercial Road, Hull,
N. Humberside HU1 2SG   0482 25141

BBC RADIO LANCASHIRE:

Darwen Street,
Blackburn BB2 2EA   0254 62411

RED ROSE RADIO:

PO Box 301, St. Paul's Square,
Preston, Lancs. PR1 1YE   0772 556301

BBC RADIO MERSEYSIDE:

53 Paradise Street,
Liverpool L1 3BP   051 708 5500

RADIO CITY:

P.O. Box 194,
8–10 Stanley Street,
Liverpool, Merseyside L69 1LD   051 227 5100

TYNE TEES TV:

Television Centre, City Road,
Newcastle-Upon-Tyne
NE1 2AL   091 261 0181

BBC RADIO NEWCASTLE:

Broadcasting Centre, Fenham,
Newcastle-Upon-Tyne
NE99 1RN   091 232 4141

METRO RADIO:

Newcastle-Upon-Tyne
NE9 1BB   091 488 3131

BBC TV NORTH EAST:

Broadcasting Centre,
Barrack Road,
Newcastle-Upon-Tyne
NE99 2NE   091 232 1313

PENNINE RADIO:

PO Box 235, Pennine House,
Forster Square,
BradfordBD1 5NP   0274 731521

BBC RADIO YORK:

20 Bootham Row,
York YO3 7BR   0904 641351

YORKSHIRE TV:
Television Centre,
Leeds LS3 1JS   0532 438283

BBC TV & RADIO NORTH

Broadcasting Centre,
Woodhouse Lane,
Leeds LS2 9BX   0532 441188

BBC RADIO SHEFFIELD:

Ashdell Grove,
60 Westbourne Road,
Sheffield S10 2QU   0742 686185

BBC RADIO LEEDS:

Broadcasting House,
Woodhouse Lane,
Leeds LS2 9PN   0532 442131

WEST LANCS EVENING GAZETTE:

PO Box 55, Victoria Street,
Blackpool   0253 25231

LANCS EVENING TELEGRAPH:

New Telegraph House,
High Street,
Blackburn BB1 1HT   0254 63588

EVENING NEWS:

Churchgate,
Bolton BL1 1DE   0204 22345

BRADFORD TELEGRAPH AND ARGUS:

Hall Ings,
Bradford BD1 1JR   0274 729511

CUMBERLAND EVENING NEWS AND STAR:

Newspaper House,
Dalston Road,
Carlisle CA2 5UA   0228 23488

NORTHERN ECHO:

88 Priestgate,
Darlington DL1 1NF   0325 381313

GRIMSBY EVENING TELEGRAPH:

80 Cleethorpes Road,
Grimsby DN31 3EH   0472 359232

HALIFAX EVENING COURIER:

PO Box 19, King Cross Street,
Halifax HX1 2SF   0422 365711

HARTLEPOOL MAIL:

West House, Clarence Road,
Hartlepool TS24 8BX   0429 274441

HULL DAILY MAIL:

PO Box 34
84/86 Jameson Street,
Hull HU1 3LF   0482 27111

HUDDERSFIELD DAILY EXAMINER:

Ramsden Street,
Huddersfield, West Yorks   0484 537444

Old Salians 1st XV – Griffin Plaque winners 1989. Photo: Peter Barton

Halifax go down at home to Otley (10–16) in North One. Here beneath the mass of bodies is a ball, which is over the line as the referee signals the visitors' first try at Ovenden Park.

NORTH DIVISIONS ONE and TWO

Only one point separated the first four clubs in North One and at the end of the day Kendal finished that single point ahead of the other three – the talented sides from Tynedale, Aspatria and Harrogate – so the Lakes District club will play in Area League North this coming season. All the others will feel that they could well have owned that promotion spot, but they are good enough to make a strong challenge immediately. Halifax, Otley and Wigton also made useful contributions to a strong league, but Hull & East Riding, Hartlepool Rovers and the famous Birkenhead Park struggled for survival.

At the foot of the top league it was sad to see West Park, who had tried so hard for promotion the previous season, end up with only four points and an inferior points difference to Birkenhead Park.

So down go West Park and their place goes to Bradford & Bingley, who had an outstanding season overall and deserved promotion after missing out the previous season on points difference. Back also in the top league will be Middlesbrough, whose season in North 2 undoubtedly helped them to re-group and they will hope to stay up – at the very least – this coming season. Another Yorkshire club – Wharfedale – made a gallant attempt to be promoted for a second successive season, but they ended up two points adrift even thought they thrashed the champions in the final match (32–3).

Davenport, who struggled the previous term, could not improve this time round and went down with New Brighton escaping on points difference. In an area so strong overall in club rugby getting back will not be easy.

NORTH DIVISION ONE: OFFICIAL

W.K. Davies,
103 Crimple Meadows,
Pannal,
Harrogate   0423 871225

NORTH DIVISION TWO: OFFICIAL

David Cook,
4 Moorview Crescent,Lee Lane,
Cottingley   (H) 0274 487908
Bingley BD16 1UE   (O) 0532 564338

TABLES 1987–88

NORTH ONE

	P	W	D	L	F	A	PTS
Winnington Pk	10	8	0	2	211	74	16
Kendal	10	7	0	3	135	104	14
West Park	10	7	0	3	135	107	14
Otley	10	5	1	4	147	113	10
Harrogate	10	5	0	5	147	113	10
Tynedale	10	5	0	5	96	116	10
Wigton	10	4	2	4	80	135	10
Hartlepool R	10	4	1	5	104	162	9
Hull & ER	10	3	1	6	96	128	7
Widnes	10	3	0	7	80	143	6
Middlesbrough	10	1	1	8	81	155	3

NORTH TWO

	P	W	D	L	F	A	PTS
Aspatria	10	8	0	2	263	60	16
Halifax	10	8	0	2	225	83	16
Bradford & Bingley	10	8	0	2	144	80	16
Sandal	10	6	0	4	142	92	12
Alnwick	10	6	0	4	121	75	12
Lymm	10	6	0	4	111	119	12
New Brighton	10	4	0	6	108	157	8
Huddersfield	9	4	0	5	79	171	8
Davenport	9	3	0	6	78	142	6
Manchester	10	1	0	9	55	140	2
Wilmslow	10	0	0	10	42	249	0

TABLES 1988–89

NORTH ONE

	P	W	D	L	F	A	PTS
Kendal	10	8	0	2	188	88	16
Tynedale	10	7	1	2	215	123	15
Aspatria	10	7	1	2	190	100	15
Harrogate	10	7	1	2	204	120	15
Halifax	10	5	1	4	146	147	11
Otley	10	5	0	5	199	112	10
Wigton	10	4	1	5	105	120	9
Hull & East Riding	10	3	0	7	97	224	6
Hartlepool Rovers	10	2	1	7	112	197	5
Birkenhead Park	10	2	0	8	106	188	4
West Park	10	2	0	8	119	262	4

NORTH TWO

	P	W	D	L	F	A	PTS
Bradford & Bingley	10	9	0	1	204	95	18
Middlesbrough	10	8	0	2	133	71	16
Wharfdale	10	7	0	3	220	96	14
Sandal	10	6	0	4	128	113	12
Alnwick	10	6	0	4	104	109	12
Widnes	10	5	0	5	121	103	10
Lymm	10	5	0	5	137	132	10
Carlisle	10	3	1	6	68	115	7
Huddersfield	10	2	1	7	105	186	5
New Brighton	10	1	1	8	80	156	3
Davenport	10	1	1	8	35	159	3

NORTH DIVISION FIXTURES 1989/90

NORTH DIVISION ONE

Sat. 9th September (Week 2)
Hull & E R v Wigton
Harrogate v Aspatria
Bradford & Bingley v Hartlepool Rovers
Otley v Tynedale
Halifax v Middlesborough

Sat. 23rd September (Week 4)
Middlesbrough v Hull E R
Tynedale v Halifax
Hartlepool Rovers v Otley
Aspatria v Bradford & Bingley
Birkenhead Park v Harrogate

Sat. 14th October (Week 6)
Hull & E R v Tynedale
Wigton v Middlesborough
Bradford & Bingley v Birkenhead Park
Otley v Aspatria
Halifax v Hartlepool Rovers

Sat. 28th October (Week 8)
Tynedale v Wigton
Hartlepool Rovers v Hull & E R
Aspatria v Halifax
Birkenhead Park v Otley
Harrogate v Bradford & Bingley

Sat. 11th November (Week 10)
Hull & E R v Aspatria
Wigton v Hartlepool Rovers
Middlesbrough v Tynedale
Otley v Harrogate
Halifax v Birkenhead Park

18th November (Week 11)
Hartlepool Rovers v Middlesborough
Aspatria v Wigton
Birkenhead Park v Hull E R
Harrogate v Halifax
Bradford & Bingley v Otley

Sat. 25th November (Week 12)
Hull & E R v Harrogate
Wigton v Birkenhead Park
Middlesborough v Aspatria
Tynedale v Hartlepool Rovers
Halifax v Bradford & Bingley

Sat. 13th January (Week 18)
Aspatria v Tynedale
Birkenhead Park v Middlesborough
Harrogate v Wigton
Bradford & Bingley v Hull E R
Otley v Halifax

Sat. 10th March (Week 26)
Hull & E R v Otley
Wigton v Bradford & Bingley
Middlesborough v Harrogate
Tynedale v Birkenhead Park
Hartlepool Rovers v Aspatria

Sat. 31st March (Week X7)
Birkenhead Park v Hartlepool Rovers
Harrogate v Tynedale
Bradford & Bingley v Middlesborough
Otley v Wigton
Halifax v Hull & East Riding

Sat. 28th April (Week 32)
Wigton v Halifax
Middlesborough v Otley
Tynedale v Bradford & Bingley
Hartlepool Rovers v Harrogate
Aspatria v Birkenhead Park

NORTHERN DIVISION FIXTURES 1989/90

NORTH DIVISION TWO

Sat. 9th September (Week 2)
Alnwick v Rotherham
Wigan v West Park
New Brighton v Widnes
Carlisle v Sandal
Huddersfield v Lymm

Sat. 23rd September (Week 4)
Lymm v Alnwick
Sandal v Huddersfield
Widnes v Carlisle
West Park v New Brighton
Wharfedale v Wigan

Sat. 14th October (Week 6)
Alnwick v Sandal
Rotherham v Lymm
New Brighton v Wharfedale
Carlisle v West Park
Huddersfield v Widnes

Sat. 28th October (Week 8)
Sandal v Rotherham
Widnes v Alnwick
West Park v Huddersfield
Wharfedale v Carlisle
Wigan v New Brighton

Sat. 11th November (Week 10)
Alnwick v West Park
Rotherham v Widnes
Lymm v Sandal
Carlisle v Wigan
Huddersfield v Wharfedale

Sat. 18th November (Week 11)
Widnes v Lymm
West Park v Rotherham
Wharfedale v Alnwick
Wigan v Huddersfield
New Brighton v Carlisle

Sat. 25th November (Week 12)
Alnwick v Wigan
Rotherham v Wharfedale
Lymm v West Park
Sandal v Widnes
Huddersfield v New Brighton

Sat. 13th January (Week 18)
West Park v Sandal
Wharfedale v Lymm
Wigan v Rotherham
New Brighton v Alnwick
Carlisle v Huddersfield

Sat. 10th March (Week 26)
Alnwick v Carlisle
Rotherham v New Brighton
Lymm v Wigan
Sandal v Wharfedale
Widnes v West Park

Sat. 31st March (Week X7)
Wharfedale v Widnes
Rotherham v Sandal
New Brighton v Lymm
Carlisle v Rotherham
Huddersfield v Alnwick

Sat. 28th April (Week 32)
Rotherham v Huddersfield
Lymm v Carlisle
Sandal v New Brighton
Widnes v Wigan
West Park v Wharfedale

ASPATRIA

Bower Park, Station Road, Aspatria, Cumbria. Tel:
0965 20420
Founded: 1875
President: R.J. Hanvey
Chairman: D.G. Miller
Secretary: J.M. Hanley, 7 King Street, Aspatria,
Cumbria CA5 3AD. Tel: 0965 20420 (H). 0946 66341
(W)
Fixtures Secretary: P. Gray, 4 Queen Street,
Aspatria, Cumbria. Tel: 0965 21760
Press Officer: J.M. Hanley, 7 King Street, Aspatria,
Cumbria CA5 3AD. Tel: 0965 20420 (H). 00946 66341
(W)
Coach: D. Robley
Club captain (1988–89):
Club captain (1989–90):
No. of teams: Senior 3, Youth 1
Directions to ground: Situated 20 miles south of
Carlisle, accessible from M6 at Penrith
Ground capacity: Unlimited, stand 300
Clubhouse facilities: 250 limit, consists of lounge,
entertainment, and committee rooms
Club colours: Black/red hoops. (*Change colours:* Red
shirts)
Floodlights: Yes
Membership fees: Social £3, Playing £10
Ground admission: £1
Programme: Weekly–24 pages, 25p
Programme editor: M. Hanley
Local newspaper: Cumberland News
League position: (1988–89): Joint 2nd
League playing record (1988–89): P 11, W 8, D 1, L 2
Competitions won: Cumbria County Cup

BIRKENHEAD PARK

The Upper Park, Park Road North, Birkenhead,
Merseyside. Tel: 051 6521536
Founded: 1871
President: G.B. Porter MA, MP
Chairman: A.R. Abraham
Secretary: Hon. Secretary, Birkenhead Park Football
Club, Park Road North, Birkenhead L41 8AA. Tel:
051 6524646
Fixtures Secretary: Graeme Marrs, 501 Tower
Building, Water Street, Liverpool, Merseyside L3
1BL. Tel: 051 6521536 (H). 2363191 (W)
Press Officer: T.B.A.
Coach: R. Tinsley
Club captain (1988–89): Eric Thomas
Club captain (1989–90): Christopher Wainwright
No. of teams: Senior 5, Youth 2, Minis 2
Directions to ground: Road from M56, Exit 1; head
for Birkenhead, round St James Church, along Laird
Street, right into Mallaby Street, left into Park Road
North. From M62 and M58, to Birkenhead Tunnel (4
lane), through Tunnel, up onto flyover, along Conway
Street, fork left into Park Road North. Rail:
Merseyrail to Birkenhead Park – 5 minutes walk
Ground capacity: Seating up to 450, standing 8000
Clubhouse facilities: 4 dressing rooms, referees room,
medical room, function/dining room, kitchen, cocktail
bar, main bar, lavatories
Club colours: Red, white, blue hoops, white shorts,
red stockings. (*Change colours:* Black shirts, red
collar and cuffs, white shorts, red stockings)
Nickname: Park
Floodlights: Yes
Membership fees: Full £30, Playing £30, Social £5,
Youth £3, Student £6, OAP £3
Ground admission: £1.50, 50p children
Programme: No. of editorial pages 1, 2 pages fixtures
and results, 1 page League status, 1 page player
record; No. of advertising pages 16; Price: included
free with the £1.50 gate admission
Programme editor: T.B.A.
Local newspapers: Liverpool Daily Post (a.m.),

Liverpool Echo (p.m.), Birkenhead News, Wirral
News (mid-week)
League position (1988–89): 10th
League playing record (1988–89): P 10, W 2, D 0,
L 8, F 106, A 188

BRADFORD AND BINGLEY

Wagon Lane & Aire View, Cottingley, Bingley,
W. Yorks. Tel: 0274 563480
Founded: BFD 1866, Bing'y 1876
President: D.J. Dattine
Chairman: J.D.V. Cook
Secretary: W.P. Dennis, 2 Hesp Hills, Beckfoot Lane,
Bingley BD16 1AR. Tel: 0274 567500 (H). 0274
722118 (W)
Fixtures Secretary: W.K. Wilkinson, Green Acres,
Station Lane, Birkenshaw, Bradford, W. Yorks. Tel:
0274 681231
Press Officer: M. Dixon, 32 Ridgeway, Tranmere
Park, Guiseley, Leeds. Tel: 0943 77535 (H). 726965
(W)
Coach: M. Elford
Club captain (1988–89): J.W. Fletcher
Club captain (1989–90): J.W. Fletcher
No. of teams: Senior 6, Youth 4, Minis 4/6
Directions to ground: A650 Bradford to Bingley turn
right immediately having crossed River Aire onto
Wagon Lane. 200 yards LH bend – straight ahead
Ground capacity: Seating 150, standing 3000
Groundsman:
Clubhouse facilities: 4 Ale bars (2) – spacious club
room (new)
Club colours: Red amber and black hoops. (*Change
colours:* Red or blue)
Nickname: Bees
Floodlights: $\frac{1}{2}$ set
Membership fees: Full £25, Playing £25, Social £5,
Youth £5, Student £5, OAP £5
Ground admission: £1.50
Programme: No. of editorial pages 2; No. of
advertising pages 20; Price 50p
Programme editor: E. Cummins & Co.
Clubhouse: Wagon Lane, Bingley
Local newspapers: Yorks Post, Yorks Evening Post,
Bradford Telegraph and Argus
League position: (1988–89): 1st
League playing record (1988–89): P 10, W 9, D 0,
L 1, F 204, A 95
Competitions won: Div II – North Champions

HALIFAX

Standeven Memorial Ground, Ovenden Park,
Keighley Road, Halifax. Tel: 0422 65926
Founded: 1873 Reformed 1923 (following Northern
Union R.L. split)
President: D.M. Hoyle
Chairman: D. Dalton
Secretary: Derrick T. Barker, 2 High Street Court,
Luddenden, Halifax, W. Yorks. Tel: 0422 885978
(H), 0422 365761 (W)
Coach: Peter Walker
Fixtures Secretary: R.A. Childs, 7 Horton Place,
Bradshaw, Halifax, W. Yorks. Tel: 0422 244608
Press and PR Officer: Dai Davies, Stansfield Cottage
West, Todmorden, Lancs. OL14 8DD. Tel: 0706
812891
Commercial Manager: John –T–obin, 114 King Corss
Road, Halifax, W. Yorks. Tel: 0422 57324
Club captain: (1988–89) Phil Horton
Club captain: (1989–90) Jason Georgiou
No of teams: Senior 4, Youth 4 (U13, 15, 17, 19)
Directions to ground: Take A629 Keighley road out of
Halifax, for 1½ miles. 330 yards past Railway Inn
traffic lights, the ground is signposted to the right,
immediately past a school.
Clubhouse facilities: Excellent facilities, available for
social functions by request.

Club colours: Light blue, dark blue, white hoops, white shorts.
Floodlights: Yes
Membership fees: V.P.s £22, Players £16, Youth 50p up to £5 according to age. Archery, squash, aerobic sections.
Ground admission: £1.50 including programme 50p.
Editor I.P. Booth
Local newspapers: Halifax Courier
League position: (1988–89): 5th (promoted in 1987–88)
League playing record (1988–89): P 39, W 14, D 2, L <23, F 533, A 610
Competitions won: Yorkshire cup in first year 1876, and 15 more times since – last in 1971. Record for most wint (16 times). Sale Sevens in 196s, premier Northern event. CCC North Div Two Runners-up 1987/88 promoted to North 1. Halifax host the premier Northern Severns currently the Halifax Guinness Sevens. First three champsions Wakefield, Jedforrest, Swansea.

HARROGATE

The County Ground, Claro Road, Harrogate, North Yorkshire HG1 4AG. Tel: 0423 566966
Founded: 1871
President: John A. Englefield
Chairman: Michael Newport
Secretary: Allen M. Tattersfield, 23 St Helens Road, Harrogate, North Yorkshire HG2 8LB. Tel: 0423 885710 (H). 0532 832000 (W)
Fixtures Secretary: John M. Ashman, 38 Hollins Lane, Hampsthwaite, Harrogate, North Yorkshire. Tel: 0423 770354 (H). 505023 (W)
Press Officer: B. Rodney Spragg, 'Pear Tree Cottage', Town Street, Nidd, Harrogate, North Yorkshire. Tel: 0423 770126 (H). 771870 (W)
Coach: Peter J. Clegg
Club captain (1988–89): Garry J.M. Irvine
Club captain (1989–90): Garry J.M. Irvine
No. of teams: Senior 5. Youth & Minis 10
Directions to ground: Claro Road goes directly from the A59 Skipton/Harrogate/York Rd and is between the County and Granby Hotels, both of which face onto the A59. The ground is directly behind the Granby Hotel and Granby Park flats
Ground capacity: Seating 500, standing 4000
Clubhouse facilities: Full catering facilities. Main bar and cocktail bar. Two hospitality rooms, one with viewing area of first team playing enclosure
Club colours: Red, amber and black. (*Change colours:* White)
Floodlights: No
Membership fees: Full £28, Playing £28, Social £8, Youth £12, Student £12, OAP £8
Ground admission: £2 (including programme and car parking)
Programme: No. of editorial pages 4; No. of advertising pages 12; Price 30p
Programme editor: B. Rodney Spragg, 'Pear Tree Cottage', Town Street, Nidd, Harrogate, North Yorkshire
Local newspapers: Harrogate Advertiser, Harrogate Herald
League position: (1988–89): 4th
League playing record (1988–89): P 10, W 7, D 1, L 2, F 204, A 120

HARTLEPOOL ROVERS

The Friarage, Westview Road, Hartlepool, Cleveland. Tel: 0429 267741
Founded: 1879
President: J.H. Peart
Chairman: A.J. Hill
Secretary: Phillip G. Mitchell, 155 York Road, Hartlepool, Cleveland. Tel: 0429 261742 (H). 274732 (W)
Fixtures Secretary: C. Winspear, Welldeck Road, Hartlepool, Cleveland
Club captain (1988–89): Kevin Robinson/Jonathon

Wrigley
Club captain (1989–90): Jonothan Wrigley
No. of teams: Senior 4, Minis 6
Directions to ground: Enter Hartlepool from either A689 or A19. Head for the Headland; Rovers on Westview Road
Ground capacity: Seating 500, standing 5000
Clubhouse facilities: Bar/lounge
Club colours: White shirts, red socks, black shorts. (*Change colours:* Red, black and white hooped shirts)
Nickname: Rovers **Floodlights:** Yes
Ground admission: £1
Programme: £1
Programme editor: Ernest Dring, c/o Clubhouse
Local newspapers: Hartlepool Mail

HULL & EAST RIDING

Sports Club, The Club, The Circle, Anlaby Road, Hull. Tel: 0482 507098/918
Founded: 1901
Secretary: C. Brown, 49 Westlands Road, Sproatley, N. Humberside, HU11 4XG. tyel: 0482 813436 (H) 0482 222166 (W)
Fixtures Secretary: S. Elliot, 73 Kingtree Avenue, Cottingham, North Humberside HU16 4DR. Tel: 0482 847485
League: North 1
Colours: Cherry/White

MIDDLESBROUGH

Acklam Park, Green Lane, Middlesbrough. Tel: 0642 818567.
Founded: 1872
President: N.P. Clarkson
Chairman: S. Foster
Coach: B. Coyne
Secretary: D. Brydon, 20 Westwood Avenue, Linthorpe, Middlesbrough. Tel: 0642 819954.
Fixtures Secretary: M. Wright, 30 Margill Close, Marton, Middlesbrough. Tel: 0642 310711.
Club captain (1987–88): A.D. Duff
Club captain (1988–89): A.D. Duff
No. of teams: Senior 5. Youth & Minis 9.
Directions to Ground: A19 (to Acklam turnoff). Follow signs to Middlesbrough (left fork, across main road, 500m on right).
Stand capacity: 400
Ground capacity: 2500 normally
Clubhouse: 2 bars, 1 lounge.
Colours: Maroon shirts, white shorts. (*Change colours:* White shirts)
Nickname: Boro
Floodlights: No
Admission: £1
Membership: £12.50
Programme: 20p (Editor: D. Brydon)
Local newspaper: Evening Gazette

OTLEY

Cross Green, Otley. Tel: Otley 461180
Founded: 1865
President: G. Matthewman
Chairman: M. Anderton
Secretary: G. Hinchliffe, 22 Cyprus Drive, Thackley, Bradford BD10 0AJ. Tel: 0274 615543 (H). 724282 (W)
Fixtures Secretary: C. Wright, 'Wrenberry', 2 St Clair Road, Otley. Tel: Otley 465589
Press Officer: J. Finch, 9 Glen Mount, Menston, Ilkley. Tel: Menston 72491
Club captain (1988–89): W. Holdsworth
Club captain (1989–90): R. Booth
No. of teams: Senior 6, Youth 5, Minis 6
Directions to ground: Take Pool Road out of Otley. Ground about 800 yards on left
Ground capacity: Seating 850, standing 6150
Clubhouse facilities: Open match days and Training evenings

Club colours: Black and white. (*Change colours:* Red)
Floodlights: No
Local newspaperS: Airedale & Wharfedale Observer,
Telegraph & Argus, **League position:** (1988–89): 5th
League playing record (1988–89): P 10, W 5, D 0,
L 5, F 197, A 112

TYNEDALE

Tynedale Park, Corbridge, Northld. NE45 5AY. Tel:
0434 71 2996/7
Founded: 1876
President: John Clark
Chairman: Edward Robson
Secretary: James Chapman, Temperley Grange,
Corbridge, Northld. NE45 5RX. Tel: 0434 71 2943
(H). 091 261 1841 (W)
Fixtures Secretary: J.A. Suddes, Glendalough, 2 West
Hextol Close, Hexham NE46 2BS. Tel: 0434 603989
(H). 0660 20200 (W)
Press Officer: J.B. Shotton, 5 Millfield Court,
Hexham, Northld. Tel: 0434 607 546 (H). 0498 20598
(W)
Coach: George Haldane
Club captain (1988–89): A.T. Gledson
Club captain (1989–90): A.T. Gledson
No. of teams: Senior 5, Youth 3, Minis 4
Directions to ground: Immediately adjoining BR
Corbridge
Ground capacity: 5000. Stand 2000
Clubhouse facilities: Open match days, Sunday Lunch,
Tuesday and Thursday evenings
Club colours: Blue and white horiz. stripes, white
shorts. (*Change colours:* White)
Floodlights: Training only
Membership fees: Full £28
Ground admission: £1.50
Programme: No. of editorial pages 3; No. of
advertising pages 32; Price 50p
Local newspapers: Hexham Courant, Newcastle
Journal, Newcastle Evening Chronicle
League position: (1988–89): 2nd
League playing record (1988–89): P 38, W 29, D 3,
L 6, F 800, A 384
Competitions won: Northumberland R.U. 2nd Team
Cup, J&B Journal 1st Division League, J&B Journal
2nd Division League, 2nd XV J&B Journal Team of
Season

WIGTON

Lowmoor Road, Wigton, Cumbria. Tel: 0965 42206
Founded: 1882
President: David Everett
Chairman: Alan Robson
Secretary: Michael Penrice, 6 Wheatsheaf Lane,
Wigton. Tel: 0965 42206
Fixtures Secretary: Alan Robson, 2 Station Hill,
Wigton. Tel: 0965 42310
Press Officer: See Fixtures Secretary
Coach: The club currently operates with an
experienced coaching panel
Club captain (1988–89): Neil Carruthers/Mark Daley
Club captain (1989–90): Mark Daley
No. of teams: Senior 3, Youth 3, Minis 1
Directions to ground: Leave M6 Penrith and drive up
the B530 to Wigton (signposted). Cross staggered X
roads over A596 and bear right to Rugby Club
Ground capacity: 2000. Stand 120
Groundsman:
Clubhouse facilities: Clubhouse completely
refurbished for 1989-90 season, including sponsors'
lounge. Multi-gym and squash courts in club. Club
open every evening, available for weddings, 21sts etc
Club colours: Green tops, white shorts. (*Change
colours:* White)
Floodlights: Training only
Membership fees: Full £20, 16–19 £5, U.16 £2, Social
£2
Ground admission: £1
Programme: Programme given with admission charge

Programme editor: Michael Penrice
Local newspapers: Cumberland News/Evening News
& Star
League position: (1988–89): 7th
League playing record (1988–89): P 10, W 4, D 1,
L 5, F 105, A 120
Competitions won: Winners Cumbria Under 21s Cup,
Runners-up Cumbria Colts Cup

NORTH 2

ALNWICK

Greensfield, Alnwick, Northumberland. 0665 602342
Founded: 1962
President: Bill Robinson
Chairman: David Bell
Secretary: Simon Brierley, East Cawledge Farm,
Alnwick, Northld. NE66 2HB. Tel: 0665 602426 (H).
710172 (W)
Fixtures Secretary: Andrew Bell, Greensfield Moor
Farm, Alnwick, Northld. Tel: 0665 603891 (H). 0665
603443 (W)
Press Officer: Bob Bingham, 4 St Georges Crescent,
Alnwick, Northld. Tel: 602041
Coach: Peter Scurfield
Club captain (1988–89): James Black
Club captain (1989–90): Dawson Lillee
No. of teams: Senior 5, Youth 2, Minis 4
Ground capacity: Seating 200, standing 3000
Clubhouse facilities: Bars, changing rooms, baths,
showers, hospitality room
Club colours: Blue shirts, white shorts, blue and gold
socks.(*Change colours:* No)
Floodlights: Yes
Membership fees: Playing £15, Social £1, Youth £2,
Student £2
Programme: No. of editorial pages 1; No. of
advertising pages 6
Programme editor: See Fixtures Secretary
Local newspaper: Northumberland Gazette
League position: (1988–89): 5th
League playing record (1988–89): P 10, W 6, D 0,
L 4, F 104, A 109

CARLISLE

Warwick Road, Carlisle. Tel: 0228 21300
Founded: 1873
Secretary: W.A. Swarbrick, 5 St. Aidans Road,
Carlisle. Tel: 0228 29287 (H) or 23456 (W)
League: North West 1
Colours: Red/White/Navy

HUDDERSFIELD

Tandem, Waterloo, Huddersfield, West Yorkshire
HD5 0AN. Tel: 0484 423864
Founded: 1870 (re-formed 1909)
President: Jack Wade
Chairman: Mick Brown
Secretary: Martin Noble, Wheatfield House,
Brockholes, Huddersfield, West Yorks. HD7 7AG.
Tel: 0484 6662006
Fixtures Secretary: Barrie Starbuck, 2 The Cottages,
Upper Thong, Holmfirth, Huddersfield, West Yorks.
HD7 2UX. Tel: 0484 686059
Coach: P. Nicholas and E. Whitwam
Club captain (1988–89): J. Sharpe and R. Auckland
Club captain (1989–90): J. Taylor
No. of teams: Senior 5, Youth 2, Minis 5
Ground capacity: Seating 300, standing 2000
Club colours: Maroon, claret and gold stripes.
(*Change colours:* Maroon and gold quarters)
Floodlights: No
Ground admission: 1.50p
League position (1988–89): 8th
League playing record (1988–89): P 35, W 13, D 2,
L 20

LYMM

'Beechwood', Crouchley Lane, Lymm, Cheshire. Tel: 0925 75 3212
Founded: 1960
President: Paul Johnston
Chairman: Jim Knowles
Secretary: Keith Etherington, 73 Booths Lane, Lymm, Cheshire WA13 0PF. Tel: 0925 75 5008 (H). 061 872 5959 (W)
Fixtures Secretary: See Secretary
Press Officer: Malcolm Pritchard, 3A West Hyde, Lymm, Cheshire. Tel: 0925 75 7364 (H). 061 236 7687 (W)
Coach: Steve Fox/Andy Phillips
Club captain (1988–89): Colin Rowe
Club captain (1989–90): Huw Thomas
No. of teams: Senior 4, Youth 4, Minis 5
Directions to ground: Junction 20 on M6 to Lymm, 1st left signed Lymm. 1½ miles to T-junction, turn right. ½ mile (past lake and church on right hand side) turn right into Crouchley Lane. Club 150 yards on right
Club colours: Green/black/white (*Change colours:* Light blue/dark blue)
Floodlights: No
Membership fees: Full £35, Playing £30, Social £10, Youth £10, Student £10
Ground admission: £1.50
Programme: No. of editorial pages 2; No. of advertising pages 14; Price with admission
Local newspapers: Warrington Guardian, Manchester Evening News and Sporting Pink
League position: (1988–89): 7th
League playing record (1988–89): P 38, W 30, D 0, L 8, F 771, A 361
Competitions won: Cheshire County Cup winners 1988/89

NEW BRIGHTON

Reeds Lane, Leasowe, Wirral, Merseyside L46 3RH. Tel: 051 677 1873
Founded: 1875
President: Doug Thorpe
Chairman: Denis Morgan
Secretary: Joe Pinnington, The Dalbery, 91 Telegraph Road, Heswall, Merseyside L60 0AE. Tel: 051 342 7773 (H). 0244 390440 (W)
Fixtures Secretary: David Pennington, 62 Broadway Avenue, Wallasey, Merseyside. Tel: 051 638 8379 (H). 051 334 4090 (W)
Press Officer: David Norton, 167 Brookdale Avenue, Creasby, Wirral L49 1SR. Tel: 051 677 0206
Coach: William Vance and John Lander
Club captain (1988–89): John Houghton
Club captain (1989–90): Simon Wright
No. of teams: Senior 5, Youth 4, Minis 3
Directions to ground: Junction 1 on the M53 to New Brighton. After ¼ mile left to Moreton/Hoylake. One more mile turn left at Shell garage. Ground 200 yards on left
Ground capacity: Seating 600, standing 5400
Groundsman:
Clubhouse facilities: 2 Bars open every night. Plus 8 Squash courts and Multi Gym
Club colours: Navy blue shirts and white shorts (*Change colours:*White shirts)
Nickname: Seasiders or Brighton or Gentlemen in Blue
Floodlights: Yes
Membership fees: Full £45, Playing £45, Social £15, Youth £3, Student £10, OAP £15
Ground admission: £1 or OAP and children 50p
Programme: No. of editorial pages 2; No. of advertising pages 13; Price with admission
Programme editor: Hon. Secretary, see above
Local newspapers: Wallasey News/Liverpool Daily Post/Echo
League position: (1988–89): 10th
League playing record (1988–89): P 10, W 1, D 1, L 8, F 80, A 158

ROTHERHAM

Clifton Lane, Rotherham. Tel: 0709 370763
Founded: 1923
Chairman: Peter Hind
Secretary: John W. Clay, 66 Warren Road, Wickersley, Rotherham S66 0HQ. Tel: 0709 549111 (H). 542147 (W)
Fixtures Secretary: Andy Fraser, 10 Birch Close, Killamarsh, Sheffield. Tel: 0742 482051
Coach: Barry Foster
Club captain (1988–89): Richard Selkirk
Club captain (1989–90): Richard Selkirk
No. of teams: Senior 4, Youth 4, Minis 4
Directions to ground: From M1 Junction 33 left. Right at roundabout, through lights. 1st left at roundabout, next roundabout right, Club on right. From M18 Junction 1 right. Follow Rotherham sign until large advertising hoardings on right. Roundabout right, Club on right
Ground capacity: Standing 1000
Clubhouse facilities: Very good, open 7 evenings, Sat/Sun lunch
Club colours: Maroon and light blue.
Floodlights: Yes
Membership fees: Playing £15, Social £8, Youth £5, Student £5
Ground admission: £1
Programme: No. of editorial pages 4; No. of advertising pages 16; Price 30p
Programme editor: Malcolm Salter, 46 Broom Grove, Rotherham
Local newspapers: Rotherham Advertiser, The Star (Sheffield)
League position (1988–89): 1st
Competitions won: Yorkshire Nomination for Pilkington Cup, won South Yorkshire Trophy

SANDAL

Milnthorpe Green, Standbridge Lane, Sandal, Wakefield WF4 3BQ. Tel: 0924 250661
Founded: 1927
President: Jack Adams
Chairman: Russell Holmes
Secretary: Stuart J. Powers, 39 Durkar Low Lane, Durkar, Wakefield. Tel; 0924 252148 (H). 0532 463362 (W)
Fixtures Secretary: Colin Critchett, 48 Sinclair Garth, Sandal, Wakefield. Tel: 0924 254329
Press Officer: As Secretary
Coach: Martin Shuttleworth
Club captain (1988–89): Nick Powell
No. of teams: Senior 5, Youth 4, Minis 6
Directions to ground: Junction 39 M1, A636 towards Wakefield, turn right at Asdale Road, Ground is approx. mile on left
Ground capacity: Standing 1000
Clubhouse facilities: 2 Bars, 2 lounges
Club colours: Maroon with gold and white hoops. (*Change colours:* Gold with maroon and white hoops)
Floodlights: Yes
Ground admission: £1.50
Programme: No. of editorial pages 4; No. of advertising pages 18; Price 20p
Programme editor: Russell Holmes, 7 Ashdene Crescent, Crofton, Wakefield
Local newspapers: Wakefield Express, Yorkshire Evening Post
League position (1988–89): 4th
Competitions won: Yorkshire Colts Cup

WEST PARK

Eccleston Hill, Prescot Road, St Helens, Lancs. WA10 3AG. Tel: 0744 26138
Founded: 1947
President: Henry Gordon Huyton
Chairman: Malcolm Worsley
Secretary: William Bold, West Park R.F.C. as above
Fixtures Secretary: Eric Briers, 5 Daresbury Road, Eccleston, St Helens, Lancs. WA10 5DR. Tel: 34665

Press Officer: see Fixtures Secretary
Coach: Michael Gilman
Club captain (1988–89): Anthony Mousdale
Club captain (1989–90): Graham Houghton
No. of teams: Senior 5, Youth 1, Minis 6
Directions to ground: A58 from St Helens to
Liverpool. Next to Carmel College, opposite Hatton's
Garage
Ground capacity: Seating 270, standing 1200
Clubhouse facilities: Large concert room. Separate
members' lounge
Club colours: Green and gold (*Change colours:* Red)
Floodlights: No
Membership fees: Full £13.80, Playing £13.80, Social
£13.80, Youth £3.45, Student £3.45, OAP £13.80
Ground admission: 50p to £1
Programme: No. of editorial pages 3; No. of
advertising pages 10; Price included in Entrance Fee
to ground
Programme editor: Eric Briers, 5 Daresbury Road,
Eccleston, St Helens, Lancs. WA10 5DR
Local newspapers: St Helens Reporter, St Helens
Star, St Helens LeaLeague: North 2
League position (1988–89): North Division 1 bottom
of league

WHARFEDALE

Wharfeside Avenue, Threshfield, Skipton, N. Yorks.
Tel: 752547
Founded: 1923
President: John S. Spencer
Chairman: Frank W. House
Secretary: Peter W. Hartley, 46 Shortbank Road,
Skipton, North Yorks. Tel: 0756 4929 (H). 0756
749561 (W)
Fixtures Secretary: J.M. Harrison, Old Hall Farm,
Threshfield, Skipton, North Yorks. Tel: 0756 752777
Coach: J.M. Harrison, M. Wright
Club captain (1988–89): L. Ingham
Club captain (1989–90): L. Ingham
No. of teams: Senior 5, Youth 3, Minis 4
Directions to ground: 9 miles north of Skipton on
B6265
Ground capacity: Seating 100, standing 1000
Club colours: Emerald Green (*Change colours:*
Maroon)
Floodlights: Yes
Membership fees: Full £5, Playing £1, Social £1,
Youth £3, Student £1, OAP £5
Ground admission: £1
Programme: No. of editorial pages 4; No. of
advertising pages 12; Free with admission
Programme editor: P.W. Hartley, 46 Shortbank Road,
Skipton, North Yorks.
Local newspapers: Yorkshire Post, Craven Herald
League position: (1988–89): 3rd
League playing record (1988–89): P 10 W 7 L 3 F 220
A 96

WIDNES

Heath Road, Widnes, Cheshire WA8 7NU. Tel: 051
424 2575
Founded: 1924
President: David Caldwell
Chairman: John McCann
Secretary: Alan Roberts, 21 Belmont Road, Widnes,
Cheshire WA8 0JB. Tel: 051 424 0654
Fixtures Secretary: Ray Heapey, 108 Coroners Lane,
Widnes, Cheshire WA8 9HZ. Tel: 051 424 6565
Press Officer: Robert Wasson, 27 Pythian Crescent,
Penketh. Tel: Penketh 3483 (H). 051 486 3900 Ext
6929 (W)
Coach: Mike Ryan
Club captain (1988–89): Graham Forshaw
Club captain (1989–90): Paul Newall

No. of teams: Senior 4, Youth 1
Directions to ground: Exit Junction 7 M62. Take 2nd
exit signposted for Widnes. After ¾ mile turn right at
a small island. After 1 mile turn left at a set of traffic
lights. After ¾ mile over a bridge ground is on the left
Ground capacity: Standing 2000
Clubhouse facilities: Large clubroom, luxurious lounge
bar open each evening and match days
Club colours: Red and black hoops. (*Change colours:*
White)
Nickname: The Wids
Floodlights: No
Membership fees: Playing £15, Social £6, Student
£1.50
Ground admission: £1 and £1.50 League and Cup
Programme: No. of editorial pages 2; No. of
advertising pages 10; Free with admission charge
Programme editor: Robert Wasson (Press Officer),
Heath Road, Widnes, Cheshire WA8 7NU
Local newspapers: Widnes Weekly News, Widnes
World, Liverpool Daily Post
League position: (1988–89): 6th

WIGAN

Douglas Valley, Wingates Road, off Leyland Mill
Lane, Wigan, Lancs. Tel: 0942 42556
Founded: 1913
President: Brian Leigh
Chairman: Cliff Brookwell
Secretary: John Gee, 27 Brookside Road, Standish,
Wigan, Lancs. WN1 2TZ. Tel: 0257 422397 (H). 0942
494911 Ext 2753 (W)
Fixtures Secretary: David Clarke, 224 Billinge Road,
Wigan, Lancs. Tel: 0942 217853
Press Officer: Alan Hodkinson, 69 Lessingham
Avenue, Wigan. Tel: 0942 36395
Coach: John Coombs
Club captain (1988–89): Andrew Knowles
Club captain (1989–90): Paul Keegan
No. of teams: Senior 5, Youth 1, Minis 2
Directions to ground: From N or S, leave the M6 at
Exit 27 (for Standish), follow signs for and drive into
Standish, turn right at the traffic lights onto the A49
towards Wigan, drive for about 1 mile towards Wigan
to a pub called the Cherry Gardens on the left, turn
1st left past it, then 1st very sharp left, drive 300 yards
on a country road and turn first right, then proceed up
another country lane for 50 yards to Wigan RUFC
ground
Ground capacity: Seating 100, standing 2500
Groundsman:
Clubhouse facilities: Clubroom, lounge (and 2 squash
courts), open Match days and training nights
Club colours: irregular black and white hoops, black
shorts, black socks. (*Change colours:* Red Jerseys,
black shorts, black socks)
Nickname: Known by older people as 'The Old Boys'
(we were once an Old Boys Club – until 1962)
Floodlights: Training floodlights only
Membership fees: Playing £2, Social £10, Youth £2,
Student £10
Ground admission: £1 for League and Cup matches,
50p for friendlies
Programme: No. of editorial pages 4; No. of
advertising pages 8; Price: free with admission fee
Programme editor: Brian Leigh, 36 Knowsley Road,
Wigan, Lancs.
Local newspapers: Wigan Observer, Wigan Reporter,
Evening Post
League position: (1988–89): 1st
Competitions won: Champions of Courage Division,
North West 1 and promoted to North 2 (in our 75th
Anniversary season)

NORTH WEST LEAGUES

A system which accounts for 10 leagues continued to flourish under the "North West" heading and as expected and forecast last season Wigan went up to North 2 with a comfortable margin over all their pursuers. There were no obvious outstanding challengers to them, so it might be a good idea to watch out for Cockermouth, who are strong challengers to Aspatria nowadays in the Cumbria Cup, to gain promotion once again, having risen convincingly from North-West 2.

It is sad to see Manchester and Wilmslow descend yet again and their supporters must be hoping that they can steady their boats soon as they have enjoyed better days. Old Aldwinians, having been promoted from North East/North 1 last season challenged Macclesfield strongly for the second North-West 1 promotion spot, so watch out for them also. Moresby fought off the threat of Windermere in North-West North 1 and Ashton-on-Mersey in the East of the Area won all their matches (10 in total), but the only other side to win all their games was Upper Eden in North-West North 2 and they were restricted to five games.

The fact that the local committee had judged the merits of their teams well – certainly in terms of promotion – was shown by the fact that no team in the area gained promotion in successive seasons, but both Bolton and Halton – promoted from their leagues last season – found themselves being relegated again and now hope that they can recover and not suffer similar further indignities.

NORTH WEST DIVISION ONE:
OFFICIAL:

David Howard,
14 Brookfield Drive,
Holmes Chapel,
Cheshire CW4 7DT   (H) 0477 32948

NORTH WEST DIVISION TWO:
OFFICIAL

Ivon Hodgson,
Kimberley End, 22 Capesthorne Close,
Holmes Chapel, Nr. Crewe,
Cheshire CW4 2EW   0477 33406

TABLES 1987–88

NORTH WEST 1

	P	W	D	L	F	A	PTS
Carlisle	10	9	0	1	195	58	18
Wirral	10	8	0	2	133	99	18
Wigan	10	6	2	2	140	103	14
Caldy	10	6	0	4	119	111	12
Chester	10	5	1	4	118	99	11
Mid-Cheshire	5	0	5	129	123	10	
Rochdale	10	4	1	5	110	112	9
Egremond	10	3	1	6	138	128	7
Southport	10	3	0	7	72	168	6
Netherall	10	2	1	7	64	146	5
Blackburn	10	1	0	9	69	140	2

NORTH WEST 2

	P	W	D	L	F	A	PTS
Sedgley Park	10	8	1	1	263	60	16
Sandbach	10	8	0	2	195	64	16
Macclesfield	10	7	0	3	122	62	14
Leigh	10	6	0	4	110	135	12
Burnage	10	5	1	4	97	110	11
Workington	10	5	1	4	94	131	11
Cockermouth	10	4	1	5	167	124	9
Penrith	10	3	1	6	108	106	7
Newton le Willows	10	3	1	6	108	148	7
Heaton Moor	10	1	1	8	46	144	3
Warrington	10	1	1	8	35	167	3

TABLES 1988–89

NORTH WEST 1

	P	W	D	L	F	A	PTS
Wigan	10	9	0	1	233	75	18
Egremont	10	5	2	3	142	121	12
Sedgley Park	10	6	0	4	108	132	1(2
Mid-Cheshire	10	5	1	4	141	104	11
Sandbach	10	5	0	5	128	126	10
Wirral	10	5	0	5	92	150	10
Rochdale	10	4	1	5	80	87	9
Chester	10	4	1	5	93	121	9
Caldy	10	3	1	6	102	148	7
Manchester	10)	3	0	7	115	128	6
Wilmslow	10	3	0	7	78	110	6

NORTH WEST 2

	P	W	D	L	F	A	PTS
Cockermouth	10	8	1	1	146	69	17
Macclesfield	10	7	1	2	200	96	15
Old Aldwinians	10	7	0	3	182	87	14
Merseyside Police	10	6	1	3	179	146	13
Penrith	10	5	1	4	108	108	11
Blackburn	10	5	1	4	131	138	11
Workington	10	3	2	5	117	165	8
Netherall	10	3	2	5	78	137	8
Southport	10	3	1	6	118	140	7
Leigh	10	1	2	7	86	146	4
Burnage	10	1	0	9	65	178	2

NORTHERN DIVISION FIXTURES 1989/90

NORTH DIVISION WEST ONE

Sat. 9th September (Week 2)
Egremont v Sandbach
Sedgley v Wirral
Cockermouth v Chester
Rochdale v Davenport
Caldy v Macclesfield

Sat. 23rd September (Week 4)
Macclesfield v Egremont
Davenport v Caldy
Chester v Rochdale
Wirral v Cockermouth
M. Cheshire v Sedgley

Sat. 14th October (Week 6)
Egremont v Davenport
Sandbach v Macclesfield
Cockermouth v M. Chester
Rochdale v Wirral
Caldy v Chester

Sat. 28th October (Week 8)
Davenport v Sandbach
Chester v Egremont
Wirral v Caldy
M. Chester v Rochdale
Sedgeley v Cockermouth

Sat. 11th November (Week 10)
Egremont v Wirral
Sandbach v Chester
Macclesfield v Davenport
Rochdale v Sedgley
Caldy v M. Cheshire

18th November (Week 11)
Chester v Macclesfield
Wirral v Sandbach
M. Cheshire v Egremont
Sedgley v Caldy
Cockermouth v Rochdale

Sat. 25th November (Week 12)
Egremont v Sedgley
Sandbach v M. Cheshire
Macclesfield v Wirral
Davenport v Chester
Caldy v Cockermouth

Sat. 13th January (Week 18)
Wirral v Davenport
M. Chester v Macclesfield
Sedgley v Sandbach
Cockermouth v Egremont
Rochdale v Caldy

Sat. 10th March (Week 26)
Egremont v Rochdale
Sandbach v Cockermouth
Macclesfield v Sedgley
Davenport v M. Cheshire
Chester v Wirral

Sat. 31st March (Week X7)
Mid Cheshire v Chester
Sedgley Park v Davenport
Cockermouth v Macclesfield
Rochdale v Sandbach
Caldy v Egremont

Sat. 28th April (Week 32)
Sandbach v Caldy
Macclesfield v Rochdale
Davenport v Cockermouth
Chester v Sedgley Park
Wirral v Mid Cheshire

NORTH DIVISION WEST TWO

Sat. 9th September (Week 2)
Manchester v Moresby
Blackburn v Wilmslow
O. Aldwinians v Penrith
Warrington v Workington
Southport v Netherhall

Sat. 23rd September (Week 4)
Netherhall v Manchester
Workington v Southport
Penrith v Warrington
Wilmslow v O. Aldwinians
M. Police v Blackburn

Sat. 14th October (Week 6)
Manchester v Workington
Moresby v Netherhall
O. Aldwinians v M. Police
Warrington v Wilmslow
Southport v Penrith

Sat. 28th October (Week 8)
Workington v Moresby
Penrith v Manchester
Wilmslow v Southport
M. Police v Warrington
Blackburn v O. Aldwinians

NORTHERN DIVISION FIXTURES 1989/90

Sat. 11th November (Week 10)
Manchester v Wilmslow
Moresby v Penrith
Netherall v Workington
Warrington v Blackburn
Southport v M. Police

18th November (Week 11)
Penrith v Netherhall
Wilmslow v Moresby
M. Police v Manchester
Blackburn v Southport
Aldwinians v Warrington

Sat. 25th November (Week 12)
Manchester v Blackburn
Moresby v M. Police
Netherhall v Wilmslow
Workington v Penrith
Southport v Aldwinians

Sat. 13th January (Week 18)
Wilmslow v Workington
M. Police v Netherhall
Blackburn v Moresby
Aldwinians v Manchester
Warrington v Southport

Sat. 10th March (Week 26)
Manchester v Warrington
Moresby v Adlwinians
Netherhall v Blackburn
Workington v M. Police
Penrith v Wilmslow

Sat. 31st March (Week X7)
Merseyside Police v Penrith
Blackburn v Workington
Old Aldwinians v Netherhall
Warrington v Moresby
Southport v Manchester

Sat. 28th April (Week 32)
Moresby v Southport
Netherhall v Warrington
Workington v Old Aldwinians
Penrith v Blackburn
Wilmslow v Merseyside Police

Workington of North-West Two – 1988–89

CALDY (formerly Old Caldeians R.F.C.)

Paton Field, Lower Caldy Crossroads, West Kirby, Wirral, Merseyside. Tel: 051 625 8043
Founded: 1924
President: John Butler
Chairman: Alan Jeffcoat
Secretary: T.I. Frank Price, 6 Graham Road, West Kirby, Wirral L48 5DW. Tel: 051 632 5232 (H). 3201 (W)
Fixtures Secretary: Not yet appointed. Forward all correspondence to Hon. Sec. at above address
Press Officer: Andy Blackstock, The Willows, Manorial Road, Parkgate, South Wirral L64 6SA. Tel: 051 336 2402
Coach: Tony Atherton
Club captain (1988–89): Gary Devaney
Club captain (1989–90): Colin Lamphrey
No. of teams: Senior 7, Youth 1, Minis 7
Directions to ground: On the A540 West Kirby to Chester Road – just outside West Kirby
Ground capacity: Standing 3000 + suitable car parking
Clubhouse facilities: 2 Bars, changing facilities for 5 matches
Club colours: Sable, claret, gold and silver hoops. (*Change colours:* Claret)
Floodlights: Yes, on 2nd XV pitch
Membership fees: Playing £20, Social £15, Youth £5, Student £10
Ground admission: By donation for programme
Programme: No. of editorial pages 2; No. of advertising pages 4; Price: donation
Programme editor: B. Quatermass, Paton Field, Lower Caldy Crossroads, West Kirby, Wirral, Merseyside
Local newspapers: Liverpool Echo, Liverpool Daily Post, Wirral News, Wirral Globe
League: North West 1
League position (1988–89): 8th
League playing record (1988–89): P 39, W 21, D 2, L 16, F 651, A 566
Competitions won: 1988/89 Wirral Merit Winners

CHESTER

Hare Lane, Vicars Cross, Chester. Tel: 336017
Founded: 1925
President: David Roberts
Chairman: M.J. Lord
Secretary: Stephen Maddox, 8 Fairfield Road, Hoole, Chester. Tel: Chester 45438 (H), 051 6387070 (W)
Fixtures Secretary: Craig Cawthorn, 21 Oaklands Drive, Tattenhall. Tel: 70498
Coach: Mark Allen
Club captain (1988–89): David Williams
Club captain (1989–90): David Williams
No. of teams: Senior 6, Youth 11+
Directions to ground: Approaching Chester on A56 ground is located on R before arriving at A41 ring road
Ground capacity: Seating 3000, Standing 900
Club colours: Red. (*Change colours:* Blue)
Floodlights: No
Membership fees: Playing £31.50
Local newspapers:
League: NW 1
League position (1988–89): 8th
League playing record (1988–89): P 10, W 4, D 1, L 5, F 93, A 121

COCKERMOUTH

Laithwaite, Workington Road, Cockermouth
Founded: 1878
President: Mrs Audrey Lane
Chairman: David Coulthard
Secretary: Bill McDowell, 10 The Green, Cockermouth, Cumbria CA13 9AS. Tel: 0900 824274 (H). 0900 823031 (W)
Fixtures Secretary: Andrew Quarey, 15 Beech Lane, Cockermouth. Tel: 0900 824282
Press Officer: See Secretary
Coach: John Cusack
Club captain (1988–89): Mark McDowell
No. of teams: Senior 3, Youth 1, Minis 4
Directions to ground: Workington Road, Cockermouth, behind Lloyds garage and showrooms (Volvo-BMW)
Ground capacity: Seating 100, standing 500
Clubhouse facilities: Changing only
Club colours: Black and amber. (*Change colours:* Red)
Floodlights: No
League: North West 2
League position (1988–89): 1st
League playing record (1988–89): P 10, W 8, D 1, L 1

DAVENPORT

Bridge Lane Memorial Ground, Headlands Road, Bridge Lane, Bramhall SK7 3AN. Tel: 061 439 2150
Founded: 1923
President: Ken Bentley
Chairman: Roger Handley
Secretary: Martin Wroe, 138 Moor Lane, Woodford, Stockport SK7 1PJ. Tel: 061 440 8536 (H). 061 456 3122 (W)
Fixtures Secretary: See Secretary
Coach: Dereck Wilkinson
Club captain (1988–89): Mark Smith
Club captain (1989–90): Alistair Russell
No. of teams: Senior 5, Youth 3, Minis 5
Clubhouse facilities: Squash courts
Club colours: Red white green hoops. (*Change colours:* No)
Floodlights: Yes
League: North West 1
League position (1988–89): Bottom

EGREMONT

Bleach Green, Egremont, Cumbria. Tel: 0946 820645
Founded: 1878
President: Dr J.W. Strain
Chairman: Dr John W. Veitch
Secretary: William Hugh Francis Moran, 58 Dent View, Egremont, Cumbria CA22 2ET. Tel: 0946 82219 (H). 09467 71396 (W)
Fixtures Secretary: John W.A. Crichton, 25 Springfield Gardens, Bigrigg, Egremont, Cumbria. Tel: 0946 811933
Press Officer: P. Branthwaite, 1 Chatsworth Drive, Whitehaven, Cumbria. Tel: 0946 62078
Coach: Jeffrey Edgar
Club captain (1988–89): John Routledge
Club captain (1989–90): John Routledge
No. of teams: Senior 3, Youth 3
Directions to ground: From South turn off M6 at Junction 36, follow A590 then A595 Barrow–Carlisle Road. From North turn off Junction 44 (M6), follow A595 South
Ground capacity: Standing 500
Club colours: Black/yellow (quarters). (*Change colours:* All black with thin yellow stripes)
Floodlights: Training lights only
Membership fees: Full £10, Playing £10, Social £2, Youth £1, Student £5, OAP no charge
Ground admission: £1 league and cup matches only
Programme: No. of editorial pages 4; No. of advertising pages 20; Price 30p
Programme editor: Edward (Pop) Long, 12 Southey Avenue, Orgill, Egremont, Cumbria
Local newspapers: Whitehaven News, Evening News & Star
League: North West 1
League position (1988–89): 2nd

League playing record (1988–89): P 32, W 21, D 3,
L 8, F 449, A 305
Competitions won: Colin Lee Memorial Trophy (U17)

MACCLESFIELD

Priory Park, Priory Lane, Macclesfield, Cheshire. Tel:
0625 827899
President: Tony Close
Chairman: Alun Evans
Secretary: Richard Farrimond, 8 Pool End Close,
Macclesfield, Cheshire SK10 2LD. Tel: 0625 28308
(H), 0260 275333 (W)
Fixtures Secretary: Alan Johnson, 6 Rugby Drive,
Macclesfield, Cheshire. Tel: 0625 614697
Press Officer: Geoff Allen, 69 Tytherington Drive,
Macclesfield, Cheshire. Tel: 0625 32345 (H), 610000
(W)
Coach: Peter Matthews
Club captain (1988–89): Anthony Walker
No. of teams: Senior 7, Youth 6, Minis 4
Clubhouse facilities: Modern and spacious
Club colours: Blue and white 3″ hoops. (*Change
colours:* Red)
Floodlights: Yes (training)
Membership fees: Full £35, Playing £35, Social £15
Ground admission: Nil
Programme: No. of editorial pages 6; No. of
advertising pages 20; Price Free
Programme editor: Clive Kirkham, 11 Clare Drive,
Macclesfield, Cheshire
Local newspapers: Macclesfield Express, Macclesfield
Messenger, Community News, Manchester Evening
News
League: NW1
League position (1988–89): 2nd
League playing record (1988–89): P 10, W 7, D 1, L 2

MID CHESHIRE COLLEGE

Moss Farm Leisure Complex, Moss Road, Northwich,
Cheshire. Tel: 0606 79987
Founded: 1965
President: Derek Campbell
Chairman: Brian Saunt
Secretary: Ron McLaverty, 7 Pear Tree Drive,
Wincham, Northwich, Cheshire CW9 6EZ. Tel: 056
589 3997 (H). 061 832 3082 (W)
Fixtures Secretary: Keith Naylor, 272 London Road,
Leftwich, Northwich, Cheshire. Tel: 0606 43482 (H).
0270 255155 Ext 3464 (W)
Press Officer: Colin Naylor, 23 Booth Road,
Hartford, Northwich, Cheshire. Tel: 0606 871547 (H).
0244 350000 Ext 2051 (W)
Coach: Colin Naylor
Club captain (1988–89): Rick Dodd
Club captain (1989–90): Tim Wilding
No. of teams: Senior 5, Youth 3
Directions to ground: Top of Castle Hill in Northwich,
turn right into Moss Road, Ground on left
Clubhouse facilities: Changing rooms, Bar, Function
room
Club colours: Black shirts/black shorts. (*Change
colours:* Maroon and white stripe shorts)
Floodlights: Only training lights
Membership fees: Full £22, Social £10, Youth £5,
Student £11
Programme: No. of editorial pages 2; No. of
advertising pages 6; Price 90p
Programme editor: see Fixtures Secretary
Local newspapers: Northwich Guardian, Northwich
Chronicle
League: North West 1
League position (1988–89): 4th
League playing record (1988–89): P 10, W 5, D 1,
L 4, F 141, A 104
Competitions won: Cheshire Cup Finalist – April
1989, Berlin Plate Sevens – March 1989

ROCHDALE

Moorgate Avenue, Bamford, Rochdale. Tel: 0706
46863
Founded: 1921
President: H. Deasey
Chairman: J. Cooper
Secretary: I.R. Coates, 16 Woodcock Close,
Bamford, Rochdale OL11 5QA. Tel: 0706 58413 (H).
32661 (W)
Fixtures Secretary: I. Coates, 32 Links View,
Rochdale OL11 4DD. Tel: 0706 59980
Club captain (1988–89): John Deasey
Club captain (1989–90): Paul Kelly
No. of teams: Senior 5, Youth 1, Minis 5
Directions to ground: Junction 20 M62, at second
roundabout follow Blackburn. At traffic lights turn
left (to Bury). Moorgate Avenue third on right
Ground capacity: Standing 1000
Clubhouse facilities: 3 Lounges
Club colours: Maroon and white. (*Change colours:*
No)
Floodlights: Yes
League: North West 1
League position (1988–89): 7th
League playing record (1988–89): P 39, W 17, D 4,
L 18, F 535, A 473

SANDBACH

Bradwell Road, Sandbach, Cheshire CW11 9AP. Tel:
0270 762475
Founded: 1986
President: Mike Hopkins
Chairman: John Cooper
Secretary: John Frayling, 6 Blackacres Close,
Sandbach, Cheshire CW11 9DR. Tel: 0270 764007
(H), 0782 811041 (W)
Fixtures Secretary: Steve Clayton-Barker, 68 Abbey
Road, Sandbach, Cheshire CW11 9HB. Tel: 0270
762679 (H), 762679 (W)
Press Officer: Chris Allen, 8 St. Peters Road,
Congleton, Cheshire CW12 3AN. Tel: 0260 281179
(H), 273547 (W)
Coach: Phil Bell
Club captain (1988–89): Paul Brough
Club captain (1989–90): Paddy Davenport
No. of teams: Senior 5, Colts 1, Minis 7
Directions to ground: From the M6 Exit 17 take road
toward Sandbach, turn right into Congleton Road,
turn right at 'keep left' signs into Offley Road, then
right again into Bradwall Road
Ground capacity: Standing 500
Clubhouse facilities: 2 bars, 6 changing rooms,
multigym, sauna, 2 baths, showers, injury treatment
room
Club colours: Emerald with 6″ scarlet chestband
Floodlights: Yes (training only)
Membership fees: Full £17.50, Playing £17.50, Social
£12, Mini/Junior £4, Student £6, OAP Disc.
Ground admission: 50p
Programme: No. of editorial/match notes pages 2; No.
of advertising pages 22; Price 50p
Programme editor: Chris Allen, 8 St. Peters Road,
Congleton, Cheshire CW12 3AN
Local newspaper: Sandbach Chronicle
League: NW 1
League position (1988–89): 5th
League playing record (1988–89): P 10, W 5, D 0,
L 5, F 128, A 126

SEDGLEY PARK

Park Lane, Whitefield, Manchester. Tel: 061 766 5050
Founded: 1932
President: A.G. Smith
Chairman: D.H. Smith
Secretary: Mark Mold, 32 Vicarage Avenue, Cheadle
Hulme, Cheadle, Stockport SK8 7JW. Tel: 061 486
0496 (H). 061 794 4755 (W)
Fixtures Secretary: D.W. Morton, 34 Delaunays

Road, Manchester M8 6QS. Tel: 061 795 1644
Press Officer: See Fixtures Secretary
Coach: To be appointed
Club captain (1988–89): R. Hall
Club captain (1989–90): P. Egan
No. of teams: Senior 4, Colts 1, Juniors 3, Minis 2
Directions to ground: M62 Junction 17, A56 Bury,
bear left at lights, left again at next lights (Park Lane)
Clubhouse facilities: Large 2-storey clubhouse
completed 1980 – open every evening during season
Club colours: Claret and gold. (*Change colours:*
Maroon)
Nickname: Tigers
Floodlights: Training lights installed 1989
Membership fees: Playing £23, Social £3, Youth £7
Ground admission: Free
Programme: No. of editorial pages 4; No. of
advertising pages approx. 30; Price: Free on 1st XV
home days
Programme editor: See Fixtures Secretary
Local newspapers: Bury Times, Prestwich &
Whitefield Guide
League: North West 1
League position (1988–89): 3rd
League playing record (1988–89): P 10, W 6, D 0,
L 4, F 108, A 132
Competitions won: Runners up: Girobank Lancashire
Trophy – 1st XV; Winners: New Brighton Sevens –
under 15

WIRRAL

The Memorial Ground, Thornton Common Road,
Thornton Hough, Wirral. Tel: 051 334 1309
Founded: 1937
President: Dudley Lewis
Chairman: Geoff Dean
Secretary: Rod Backhouse, 35 Raby Drive, Raby
Mere, Wirral, Merseyside L63 0NQ. Tel: 051 334
6591 (H). 691 1747 (W)
Fixtures Secretary: Peter White, 36 Withert Avenue,
Bebington, Wirral, Merseyside. Tel: 051 645 7208
Coach: Mike Briers and Danny Hughes
Club captain (1988–89): Chris Whorton
Club captain (1989–90): Chris Whorton
No. of teams: Senior 5, Youth 4, Minis 6
Directions to ground: M53
Club colours: Maroon and white hoops. (*Change
colours:* Blue)
Floodlights: No
League: North West 1
League position (1988–89): 6th
League playing record (1988–89): P 10, W 5, D 0, L 5
Competitions won: Birkenhead Park Floodlit Cup
Winners

NORTH WEST 2

BLACKBURN

Ramsgreave Drive, Blackburn BB1 8NB. Tel: 0254
47669
Founded: 1877
Secretary: J.T. Shaw, 26 Openshaw Drive, Blackburn
BB1 8RH. Tel: 0254 663338 (H)

Fixtures Secretary: P. Dixon, 113 Brownhill Road,
Blackburn. Tel: 0254 47669
League: North West 1

MANCHESTER

Grove Park, Grove Lane, Cheadle Hulme, Cheadle,
Cheshire. Tel: 061 485 1115
Founded: 1860
President: G.R.C. (Roy) McDowell
Chairman: W.R.M. (Russ) Jenkins
Secretary: P.C. (Peter) Beeley, 4 St Andrews Road,
Heald Green, Cheadle, Cheshire SK8 3ES. Tel: 061

428 9895 (H). 061 873 7300 (W)
Fixtures Secretary: Derek Partington, 28 Crossfield
Drive, Worsley, Lancs. Tel: 061 790 6742
Press Officer: A.S. (Alan) Hanson, 1 Hazelbadge
Road, Poynton, Cheshire SK12 1HZ. Tel: 0625
875636 (H). 061 236 4071 (W)
Coach: A.S. (Alan) Hanson
Club captain (1988–89): Denis Kelly
Club captain (1989–90): Denis Kelly
No. of teams: Senior 5, Youth & Minis 6
Directions to ground: Along A34 turn into Stanley
Road at traffic lights at Belfrey Hotel, Cheadle
Hulme. Ground mile on right
Ground capacity: Seating 300, standing 4-5000
Clubhouse facilities: Players bar, lounge bar,
badminton and functions hall, 6 squash courts,
kitchen
Club colours: Red and white hoops. (*Change colours:*
Red)
Floodlights: For training
Membership fees: Full £39, Playing £39, Social £12,
Student £18
Ground admission: £1
Programme: Notes teams and adverts. Included in
admission
Programme editor: See Secretary
Local newspapers: Manchester Metro News,
Manchester Evening News, Stockport Messenger
League: North West 2
League position (1988–89): 10th (NW Div 1)
League playing record (1988–89): P 10, W 2, D 0,
L 8, F 102, A 119

MERSEYSIDE POLICE

Merseyside Police Sports Club, Riversdale Road,
Aigburth, Liverpool 19. Tel: 051 427 2208
Founded: 1960
President: Mr James Sharples, QPM, Chief Constable
Chairman: Mr David Howe, BA, Deputy Chief
Constable
Secretary: Det. Sgt. George H. Dafnis, St Andrews,
72 Bertram Drive, Meols, Wirral, Merseyside L47
0LJ. Tel: 051 632 5927 (H). 051 777 3632 (W)
Fixtures Secretary: Constable Ceredig Evans, 43
Queens Avenue, Meols, Wirral, Merseyside L47 0LJ.
Tel: 051 632 4618 (H). 051 709 6010 Ext 4280 (W)
Press Officer: Sgt. James Turner, 58 Waylands Drive,
Liverpool L25 0LX. Tel: 051 486 1666 (H). 051 709
6010 Ext 2627 (W)
Coach: D/Con. Philip Atherton
Club captain (1988–89): Alex Donkor
Club captain (1989–90): Gareth Howells
No. of teams: Senior 4
Directions to ground: M62, Queens Drive South,
Allerton Road, Mather Avenue, right along Booker
Avenue, Holmefield Road, cross Aigburth Road into
Riversdale Road
Ground capacity: Open ground round pitch
Clubhouse facilities: Bar, 4 changing rooms. Capacity
200/300
Club colours: Blue. (*Change colours:* Blue and gold
hoops)
Floodlights: No
Local newspaper: Liverpool Daily Post and Echo
League: North West 2
League position (1988–89): 4th
League playing record (1988–89): P 10, W 6, D 1,
L 3, F 179, A 146
Competitions won: Wallasey RUFC Sevens, 25.9.88

MORESBY PARKS

Walkmill Park, Moresby Parks, Whitehaven,
Cumbria. Tel: Whitehaven 695984
Founded: 1915
President: John Casson
Chairman: Colin Denwood
Secretary: Martin Simpson, 54 Thornton Road, High
Meadows, Whitehaven, Cumbria. Tel: 67514
Fixtures Secretary: Sid Bray, address as Secretary

Press Officer: Jeff Peet, address as Secretary
Coach: Frank Fee
Club captain (1988–89): Jeff Peet
Club captain (1989–90): Jeff Peet
No. of teams: Senior 3
Directions to ground: Follow A595 to Distington, turn left at Castle Inn – 2 miles to Moresby
Clubhouse facilities: 2 main rooms and changing facilities
Club colours: Red shirts, white shorts. (*Change colours:* Red/white hooped shirts)
Nickname: Red Devils
Floodlights: No
Membership fees: Full £1.50, Playing £10, Social £1.50, Student free, OAP free
Local newspapers: Whitehaven News – Times and Star
League: NW E/North 1
League position (1988–89): 1st
League playing record (1988–89): P 29, W 20, D 2, L 7
Competitions won: League promotion

NETHERHALL

Netherhall Park, Netherhall Road, Maryport, Cumbria. Tel: 0900 815833. Office: Crosby Street, Maryport, Cumbria. Tel: 0900 813845
Founded: 1960
President: Dr Basil Havard
Chairman: Joseph Jackson Eve
Secretary: Archibald Scholey, Hillmore House, High Street, Maryport, Cumbria 6A15 6BE. Tel: 0900 813935
Fixtures Secretary: Brian Edmondson, 76 Thirlmere Avenue, Workington, Cumbria. Tel: 0900 603398 (H). 0900 602026 (W – urgent only)
Press Officer: William Merrin, 15 Suncroft, Crosby, Maryport. Tel: 0900 812047
Coach: Neil Birkett
Club captain (1988–89): Lawrence Rumney
Club captain (1989–90): Mark Welch
No. of teams: Senior 3, Youth 2, Minis 2
Directions to ground: From South leave M6 at Junction 40, continue on A66 to Cockermouth. Go through Cockermouth, follow sign for Maryport. At Netherhall Corner (Maryport) turn right, Ground mile along Netherhall Road on right
Ground capacity: Standing 500–1000
Clubhouse facilities: 6 changing rooms, 4 large baths, shower room, function room, etc.
Club colours: Claret and gold. (*Change colours:* Red)
Floodlights: No
Membership fees: Full £6, Playing £6, Social 50p, Youth 50p, Student 50p, OAP 50p
Programme: No. of editorial pages 10; No. of advertising pages 6
Programme editor: See Secretary
Local newspapers: West Cumbria Evening News & Star, Times & Star
League: North West 2
League position (1988–89): 7th
League playing record (1988–89): P 10, W 3, D 2, L 5, F 78, A 135
Competitions won: Cumbria Colts 1988-89, Alf Cartwright Memorial Cup (under 17s) 1988-89, Robinson Sevens (under 17s) 1988-89

OLD ALDWINIANS

Audenshaw Park, Droylsden Road, Audenshaw, Manchester. Tel: 061 301 1001
Founded: 1936
President: Dennis Harvey
Chairman: William Stuart Thorpe
Secretary: Graham Hatton J.P., Oakdale Post Office, Manchester Road, Denton, Manchester M34 2NA. Tel: 336 2528
Fixtures Secretary: Alan Whalley (present), Greenside Lane, Droylsden, Manchester. Tel: 061 370 0921. Barry Ross (future). Tel: 061 301 3814

Press Officer: Len Deacon, 66 Clarendon Road, Audenshaw, Manchester. Tel: 061 370 3027 (H). 061 339 3711 (W)
Coach: Philip Lord, Leonard Deacon, Gordon Longley, Trevor Hulme and John Lane
Club captain (1988–89): Gordon Longley
Club captain (1989–90): Graham Murray
No. of teams: Senior 7, Youth 6, Minis 5
Directions to ground: Main entrance off A662 Manchester to Ashton-under-Lyne Road. Pitches to be seen from A635 Manchester to Ashton-under-Lyne Road
Ground capacity: Seating 200, standing 3500
Clubhouse facilities: 2 luxurious lounges, viewing lounge, club room, 8 changing rooms, 2 baths, shower area and referee room
Club colours: Red and white hooped shirts, navy shorts, red socks. (*Change colours:* Blue (navy), black and white hoops, yellow)
Nickname: Shaw
Floodlights: For training
Membership fees: Full £25, Playing £25, Social £5, Youth £1, Student £1, OAP £1
Ground admission: £1 on league and cup matches
Programme editor: See Press Officer
Local newspaper: Reporter and Advertiser (Tameside)
League: North West 2
League position (1988–89): 3rd
League playing record (1988–89): P 10, W 7, D 0, L 3, F 178, A 87
Competitions won: Lancashire Colts Cup Winners, Lancashire U14s Cup Joint Winners, Toc H Sevens Finalists

PENRITH

Winters Park, Penrith, Cumbria. Tel: 0768 63151
Founded: 1881
President: Harvey Askins
Secretary: Malcolm Hendrie, 25 Frenchfield Way, Penrith, Cumbria CA11 8TW. Tel: 0768 65791 (H). 62733 (W)
Fixtures Secretary: Willie Mounsey, The Luham, Edenhall, Penrith, Cumbria. Tel: 0768 881 202
Press Officer: Taff Bevan. Tel: 0524 35339
Club captain (1988–89): Graham Robertson
Club captain (1989–90): Nigel Beaty
No. of teams: Senior 3, Youth 3, Minis 3
Directions to ground: M6 leave at Junction 40 – take A66 towards Scotch Corner – next roundabout travel towards Alston – Club on left mile from roundabout
Ground capacity: Seating 350/400, standing 5000
Clubhouse facilities: Club, bar dance hall, 4 squash and tennis courts
Club colours: Myrtle green/white hoops. (*Change colours:* No)
Floodlights: No
Membership fees: Full £17, Playing £17, Social £6, Youth £3, Student £6, Patron £10
Ground admission: Nil
Programme: No. of editorial pages 8; No. of advertising pages 6; Price 50p
Programme editor: See Secretary
Local newspaper: Cumberland and Westmorland Herald
League: North West 2
League playing record (1988–89): P 39, W 20, D 2, L 17, F 522, A 488
Competitions won: 17th April: Under 17 won County Under 17 Cup

SOUTHPORT

Waterloo Road, Hillside, Southport. Tel: 69906
Founded: 1872
President: S.M. Wilson
Chairman: John Winn
Secretary: Roger Fischer, 66 Southbank Road, Southport, Merseyside PR8 6QN. Tel: 43654
Fixtures Secretary: Keith J. Shorrock, 28A Alexandra

Road, Southport, Merseyside. Tel: 37420
Press Officer: As Secretary
Coach: S. Fletcher
Club captain (1988–89): Peter Jones
Club captain (1989–90): Ian Singleton
No. of teams: Senior 4, Youth 2, Minis 5
Directions to ground: 1 miles due South of Southport
on main road through Southport to Liverpool, mile
past Hillside Railway Station on A565
Ground capacity: Seating 200, standing 2000+
Clubhouse facilities: 2 Bars, kitchen, 5 changing
rooms, 3 baths & showers
Club colours: Red black amber. (*Change colours:*
Dark blue)
Floodlights: Training
Local newspaper: Southport Visitor
League: North West 2
League playing record (1988–89); p 10, W 3, D 1, L 6

WARRINGTON

Bridge Lane, Appleton, Warrington, Cheshire WA4
3NN. Tel: 0925 64159
Founded: 1923
President: Peter B. White
Chairman: Michael Cornelia
Secretary: J. Keith Fletcher, 472 Manchester Road,
Paddington, Warrington, Cheshire WA1 3HT. Tel:
0925 814182 (H). 31244 (W)
Fixtures Secretary: W. Kenneth Wilkinson, 5 Osborne
Road, Lower Walton, Warrington, Cheshire. Tel:
0925 67964
Press Officer: Roy T. Potts, 37 Whitefield Road,
Stockton Heath, Warrington, Cheshire. Tel: 0925
63799
Coach: Peter J. Riley
Club captain (1988–89): R. William Stokes
Club captain (1989–90): R. William Stokes
No. of teams: Senior 4, Youth 1
Directions to ground: Leave M6 at Junction 20, follow
A50 toward Warrington to 1st set of traffic lights (2
miles), turn left. Follow road 2 miles to Bethesda
Church, turn left under bridge then 1st right
Clubhouse facilities: Dressing rooms, baths, club
room, lounge, kitchen
Club colours: Red white and green hoops. (*Change
colours:* Green)
Floodlights: No
Membership fees: Full £20, Playing £20, Social £6.50,
Youth £2.50, Student £2.50
Programme: No. of editorial pages 1; No. of
advertising pages 4; Price 20p
Local newspaper: Warrington Guardian
League: North West 2
League position (1988–89): 1st
League playing record (1988–89): P 42, W 24, D 3,
L 15, F 542, A 572

WILMSLOW

Kings Road, Wilmslow. Tel: 0625 522274
Founded: 1884
President: Richard Green
Chairman: Ray Morris
Secretary: Graham Coles, 21 Woodlands Road,
Handforth, Wilmslow. Tel: 0625 523860
Fixtures Secretary: G. Mitchell, Green Bank Farm,
Smallwood. Tel: Smallwod 329
Press Officer: Adam Egar, 43 Mainwaring Drive,

Wilmslow. Tel: 0625 524676 (H). 061 927 7040 (W)
Coach: Not yet finalised
Club captain (1988–89): Nigel Burrows
Club captain (1989–90): Mark Hooper
No. of teams: Senior 5, Youth 7, Minis 4
Directions to ground: From Junction 6 on M56 take
A538 towards Wilmslow. Kings Road is 4 miles on
right immediately after Texaco Petrol Station
Ground capacity: Seating 500, standing 3/4000
Clubhouse facilities: Large players bar and cocktail
bar
Club colours: Sky blue, maroon & white hoop.
(*Change colours:* Navy)
Floodlights: Yes
Membership fees: Full £10, Playing £20, Social £5,
Youth £6, Student £6, OAP £2.20
Ground admission: £1
Programme: No. of editorial pages 3; No. of
advertising pages 9; Free
Programme editor: Vaudrey Middleton, Club address
Local newspapers: Wilmslow World,
Express/Advertiser
League: North West 2
League position (1988–89): Bottom (Relegated)
League playing record (1988–89): P 10, W 3, D 0, L 7
Competitions won: U17s Cheshire Cup

WORKINGTON

Ellis Sports Ground, Mossbay Road, Workington.
Tel: 0900 602625
Founded: 1877
President: George Nicholson
Chairman: Ken Dixon
Secretary: Michael Heaslip, as Ground or 32
Elizabeth Street, Workington CA14 4DB. Tel: 0900
66339 (H). 65656 (W)
Fixtures Secretary: Joe Heaslip, 3 St Michael's Road,
Workington, Cumbria. Tel: 0900 602449
Press Officer: John Murray, 35 Clifton Court,
Workington. Tel: 0900 62496
Coach: Glen McCrickerd
Club captain (1988–89): Steve Thompson; David
Exley (mid-season change)
Club captain (1989–90): T.B.A.
No. of teams: Senior 3, Youth 4
Directions to ground: mile South of town centre,
between A597 and B5296
Ground capacity: Seating 2000, standing 17000
Clubhouse facilities: Bar, lounge, functions, catering,
open Match days and evenings
Club colours: Black and white hoops, black shorts.
(*Change colours:* All black)
Nickname: Zebras
Floodlights: Yes
Membership fees: Full £5.75, Playing £12.65, Social
£2.30, Student £12.65
Ground admission: varies
Programme: No. of editorial pages 4; No. of
advertising pages 4; Price 50p
Programme editor: See Press Officer
Local newspapers: West Cumberland Times & Star
League: North West 2
League position (1988–89): 8th
League playing record (1988–89): P 10, W 3, D 2,
L 5, F 107, A 164

NORTH WEST, EAST NORTH LEAGUE

**NORTH WEST DIVISION
EAST NORTH ONE: OFFICIAL**

Rudy Speed
9 Moorfield Road,
West Didsbury,   (H) 061 434 2956
Manchester M20 8UZ   (O) 061 873 7949

TABLES 1987–88

NORTH WEST EAST/NORTH 1

	P	W	D	L	F	A	PTS
Old Aldwinians	10	8	1	1	209	47	17
Vickers	10	8	0	2	214	47	16
Furness	10	7	1	2	134	97	15
Moresby	8	7	0	1	120	63	14
Fleetwood	10	5	2	3	133	77	12
Oldham	10	5	0	5	69	93	7
Eccles	9	3	1	5	69	93	7
Littleborough	9	3	1	5	81	129	7
Toc H	9	2	0	7	62	94	4
Calder Vale	10	1	0	9	82	174	2
Colne & Nelson	10	1	0	9	47	359	2

TABLES 1988–89

NORTH WEST EAST/NORTH 1

	P	W	D	L	F	A	PTS
Moresby	10	9	0	1	219	74	18
Windermere	10	7	0	3	166	80	14
Furness	10	6	0	4	160	132	12
De La Salle (Salford)	10	6	0	4	135	118	12
Oldham	10	6	0	4	107	115	12
Heaton Moor	10	4	0	6	115	139	8
Eccles	10	4	0	6	93	130	8
Fleetwood	10	4	0	6	66	117	8
Vickers	10	3	1	6	91	111	7
Toc H	10	3	0	7	103	163	6
Littleborough	10	2	1	7	58	134	5

Mid-Cheshire College action in North-West One – 1988–89. Photo: Cheshire County Newspapers

NORTH WEST DIVISION FIXTURES 1989/90

EAST NORTH ONE

Sat. 9th September (Week 2)
Vickers v Kirby
Ashton v Fleetwood
Kirby v Eccles
Heaton Moor v Windermere
Oldham v De La Salle

Sat. 23rd September (Week 4)
De La Salle v Vickers
Windermere v Oldham
Eccles v Heaton Moor
Fleetwood v Burnage
Furness v Ashton

Sat. 14th October (Week 6)
Vickers v Windermere
Kirby v De La Salle
Burnage v Furness
Heaton M. v Fleetwood
Oldham v Eccles

Sat. 28th October (Week 8)
Windermere v Kirby
Eccles v Vickers
Fleetwood v Oldham
Furness v Heaton Moor
Ashton v Burnage

Sat. 11th November (Week 10)
Vickers v Fleetwood
Kirby v Eccles
De La Salle v Windermere
Heaton Moor v Ashton
Oldham v Furness

18th November (Week 11)
Eccles v De La Salle
Fleetwood v Kirby
Furness v Vickers
Ashton v Oldham
Burtnage v Heaton Moor

Sat. 25th November (Week 12)
Vickers v Ashton
Kirby v Furness
De La Salle v Fleetwood
Windermere v Eccles
Oldham v Burnage

Sat. 13th January (Week 18)
Fleetwood v Windermere
Furness v De La Salle
Ashton v Kirby
Burnage v Vickers
Heaton Moor v Oldham

Sat. 10th March (Week 26)
Vickers v Heaton Moor
Kirby v Burnage
De La Salle v Ashton
Windermere v Furness
Eccles v Fleetwood

Sat. 31st March (Week X7)
Furness v Eccles
Ashton on Mersey v Windermere
Burnage v De La Salle
Heaton Moor v Kirby Lonsdale
Oldham v Vickers

Sat. 28th April (Week 32)
Kirby Lonsdale v Oldham
De La Salle v Heaton Moor
Windermere v Burnage
Eccles v Ashton on Mersey
Fleetwood v Furness

NORTH WEST EAST NORTH 1

ASHTON ON MERSEY

Barrack Lane off Carrington Lane, Ashton-on-
Mersey, Sale, Cheshire. Tel: 061 973 6637
Founded: 1930
President: Peter Citrine
Chairman: Joseph Peden
Secretary: Frank Martin Scott Ashton, 188A Ashley
Road, Hale, Altrincham, Cheshire WA15 9SF. Tel:
061 941 3796 (H). 061 928 4647 (W)
Fixtures Secretary: Nigel Carter, 48 Hollinwood
Road, Disley, Stockport, Cheshire SK12 2EB. Tel:
0663 64620 (H). 061 427 0456 (W)
Press Officer: Raymond Denham, 38 Braemar Drive,
Ashton-on-Mersey, Sale, Cheshire. Tel: 061 962 1771
Coach: Michael Murray
Club captain (1988–89): Kevin Crowther
Club captain (1989–90): Geraint Williams
No. of teams: Senior 6, Youth 5, Minis 3
Directions to ground: M63 new Junction 5 approach
from either East or West bound, turn on to
Carrington Spur and drive to the end of the Spur
Road to the traffic lights. Turn right at lights and
follow the road round past a Sports Club to the
Rugby Club at the end of Barrack Lane
Ground capacity: Standing 1000
Clubhouse facilities: Open Match days and Training
nights (Mondays and Thursdays)
Club colours: Maroon shirts, navy shorts. (*Change
colours:*Green shirts, navy shorts)
Floodlights: Yes
Membership fees: Full £30, Playing £30, Social £15,
Youth £15, Student £15, OAP £30
Ground admission: Nil
Local newspapers: Sale & Altrincham Guardian, Sale
& Altrincham Messenger
League: NW East 1
League position (1988–89): 1st
League playing record (1988–89): P 10, W 10, D 0,
L 0, F 197, A 30
Competitions won: League North West East 1, and
also Cheshire County Plate Competition

BURNAGE

Varley Park, Battersea Road, Heaton, Mersey,
Stockport SK4 3EA. Tel: 061 432 2150
Founded: 1936
President: D. James Esq.
Chairman: Adrian Knight
Fixtures Secretary: R. Howarth, 159 Arnesby Road,
Sale, Cheshire. Tel: 061 969 8866
Press Officer: I. Hodgson, Kimberley End, 22
Capesthorne Close, Holmes Chapel, Crewe,
Cheshire, CW4 7EN. Tel: 0477 33406 (H). 061 881
0012 (W)
Club captain (1989–90): L. Georgiou
No. of teams: Senior 5, Youth & Minis 6
Directions to ground: Junction 12–M63. Turn left on
A5145 to Station Road and then Heaton Mersey
Industrial Estate
Clubhouse facilities: Two bars and 6 changing rooms
Club colours: Black. (*Change colours:* Amber)
Floodlights: Training
Membership fees: £30
Local newspaper: Manchester Evening News
League: North West 2
League position (1988–89): 11th
League playing record (1988–89): P 40, W 12, D 2,
L 26, F 381, A 613

DE LA SALLE

Lancaster Road, Salford. Tel: 061 789 2261.
Founded: 1946
President: Rev Bro. Phillip
Chairman: J. Collins
Secretary: K. Hazeldine, 37 Granary Lane, Worsley,
Manchester. Tel: 061 794 4409.

Fixtures Secretary: J.L. Hibbert, 2 Duchy Avenue,
Worsley, Manchester. Tel: 061 799 0143.
Club captain (1988–89): Paul Andrews
No. of teams: Senior 4. Youth & Minis 4.
Directions to Ground: First exit off M602, turn left.
Third set of traffic lights, turn left into Lancaster
Road, 200 yards on left.
Colours: Scarlet and old gold hoops, black shorts.
(*Change colours:* Blue)
Floodlights: No
Admission: Free
Membership: £17
Programme: 50p. (Editor: K. Hazeldine)
Local newspaper: Salford Advertiser
League: NW East North 1

ECCLES

Guildford Road, Peel Green, Eccles, Manchester.
Tel: 061 789 2613
Founded: 1897
Secretary: M. Dutton, 10 Ashley Drive, Swinton
M27 3AX. Tel: 061 794 2904 (H) or 061 480 0634 (W)
League: NW E/North 1

FLEETWOOD

Molbourne Avenue, Fleetwood. Tel: 03917 4774
Founded: 1932
Secretary: T.M. Jones, The Cottage, Derby Road,
Poulton le Fylde, Nr. Blackpool, Lancs. Tel: 0253
899352 (H) or 03917 3030 (W)
League: NW E/North 1

FURNESS

Strawberry Grounds, Abbey Road, Barrow-in-
Furness, Cumbria. Tel: 0229 25226
Founded: 1902
Secretary: John Kennedy, Wheeler, Dane Avenue,
Barrow-in-Furness, Cumbria LA14 4JS. Tel: 0229
22397 (H) 0657 2225 (W)

HEATON MOOR

Green Lane, Heaton Moor, Stockport, Cheshire. Tel:
061 432 3407
Founded: 1899
President: K. Howard
Chairman: G. Costello
Secretary: Ian Sinclair, 13 Norman Road, Heaton
Moor, Stockport, Cheshire. Tel: 061 4323071
Fixtures Secretary: J. James, 22 Hillcrest Road,
Bramhall, Stockport, Cheshire
Coach: J. Ashley
Club captain (1988–89): D. Beckley
No. of teams: Senior 4, Youth 3+
Directions to ground: M63 Junc. 12, hard left A5145,
1 might right at sign to Heaton Moor, right into
Green Lane at crossroads
Clubhouse facilities: 1st class
Club colours: Red/black/amber. (*Change colours:*
Red/gold/black)
Floodlights: No
Membership fees: Playing £25, Social £10
Ground admission: Nil
Programme: Price 50p
Programme editor: D.H. Huxstep
League: NW EN1
League position (1988–89): 6th
League playing record (1988–89): P 10, W 4, D 0,
L 6, F 115, A 139

KIRKBY LONSDALE

Underley Park, Kirkby Lonsdale, Carnforth, Lancs.
Tel: 0468 71780
Founded: 1877
President: James Thompson

Chairman: M.J. Neal
Secretary: W.M. Martindale, 89 Fairgarth Drive,
Kirkby Lonsdale, Carnforth, Lancs. LA6 2DT. Tel:
0468 71168 (H). 71254 (W)
Fixtures Secretary: N.R. Winn, Ferry Cottage,
Arkholme, Carnforth, Lancs. Tel: 05242 21489
Coach: M.E. Nelson
Club captain (1988–89): I.S.H. Wade
Club captain (1989–90): I.S.H. Wade
No. of teams: Senior 3, Youth 1, Minis 1
Directions to ground: M6 Junction 36. A65 Skipton,
left at Kirkby Lonsdale sign then mile take left fork
down into town, then left on B6254 past church for
mile. Turn right through road 'Raygarth'
Ground capacity: Seating 50, standing 1500
Clubhouse facilities: New 1987, 4 teams changing
Club colours: Red, amber, black. (*Change colours:*
Royal blue)
Nickname: The Rams
Floodlights: No
Membership fees: Playing £10, Social £2.50
Local newspapers: Westmorland Gazette, Lancaster
Guardian
League: NW North 1
League position (1988–89): 1st
League playing record (1988–89): P 36, W 22, D 1,
L 13, F 622, A 334
Competitions won: Winners NW North 1 league

OLDHAM

Manor Park, Byrth Road, Bardsley, Oldham. Tel: 061
624 6383
Founded: 1904
President: Terence Hurst
Chairman: Stephen Fox
Secretary: Timothy J. Brown, 12 Tilton Street,
Oldham, Lancs. Tel: 061 620 1878 (H). 061 248 6161
(W)
Fixtures Secretary: Stephen J. Kenney, 32 Sholver
Hill Close, Moorside, Oldham, Lancs. Tel: 061 633
7900
No. of teams: Senior 4
Clubhouse facilities: Open Match days, evenings and
Sunday Lunch
Club colours: Red and white hoops, navy shorts, red
socks. (*Change colours:* All royal blue)
Floodlights: No
Ground admission: Nil
Local newspapers: Oldham Evening Chronicle,
Oldham Advertiser
League: NW E/North 1
League position (1988–89): 5th
League playing record (1988–89): P 10, W 6, D 0,
L 4, F 105, A 115

VICKERS

Hawcoat Park, Hawcoat Lane, Barrow-in-Furness,
Cumbria. Tel: 0229 25296
Founded: 1930
President: A.C. Peak
Chairman: K. Mills

Secretary: E. France, 20 Rydal Avenue, Barrow-in-
Furness, Cumbria LA14 4NW. Tel: 0229 24536 (H).
874298 (W)
Fixtures Secretary: C.J. High, 19 Cowlarns Road,
Barrow-in-Furness, Cumbria. Tel: 0229 26886 (H).
874231 (W)
Press Officer: As Fixtures Secretary
Coach: J. Richardson
Club captain (1988–89): J. Steel
Club captain (1989–90): M. Grainger
No. of teams: Senior 4, Youth 1
Directions to ground: Leave M6 at Junction 36, take
A590 to Barrow, turn right first set of traffic lights,
Ground mile on the left
Ground capacity: Seating 500
Clubhouse facilities: Multi-sports, 12 changing rooms
Club colours: Maroon and white. (*Change colours:*
Maroon or blue)
Floodlights: No
Membership fees: Full £6.20, Playing £6.20, Youth
£6.20
Local newspapers: Evening Mail
League: NE North 1
League position (1988–89): 9th
League playing record (1988–89): P 10, W 3, D 1,
L 1, F 91, A 111

WINDERMERE

Longlands, Bowness-on-Windermere, Cumbria LA23
3AS. Tel: 09662 3066
Founded: 1921 (official). Originally 1886 – not
continuous from this date
President: Alex L. McGlasson
Chairman: Alan L. Jones
Secretary: R. Nigel Rimmer, Langrigge Close,
Langrigge Drive, Bowness-on-Windermere, Cumbria
LA23 3AF. Tel: W'mere 5540 (H). 0539 20028 (W)
Fixtures Secretary: Guy W. Aspinwall, 40 Oakthwaite
Road, Windermere, Cumbria LA23 2BD. Tel:
W'mere 2708 (H). W'mere 3358 (W)
Press Officer: See Secretary
Coach: Graham Smith/Ian Rukin
Club captain (1988–89): David J. Fletcher
Club captain (1989–90): David J. Fletcher
No. of teams: Senior 2
Directions to ground: Follow directions to
Windermere (A591) then follow signs to Bowness,
first turn right (at Cinema) onto Longlands
Ground capacity: Seating 50, standing not sure
Club colours: Amber shirts/black shorts (*Change
colours:*Black shirts)
Floodlights: For training
Membership fees: Patrons £5 (min), Playing £8 plus
match fees
Local newspaper: Westmorland Gazette
League: NW North 1
League position (1988–89): 2nd
League playing record (1988–89): P 10, W 7, D 0,
L 3, F 166, A 80

NORTH WEST EAST LEAGUES

**NORTH WEST DIVISION
EAST ONE: OFFICIAL**

Peter Citrine,
27 Barwell Road,
Sale,   (H) 061 973 1937
Cheshire M33 5FE   (O) 061 973 6637

**NORTH WEST DIVISION
EAST TWO: OFFICIAL**

Ken Punshon,
24 Newcombe Road,
Holcombe, Brook, nr Bury,
Lancashire   0204 88 4886

**NORTH WEST DIVISION
EAST THREE: OFFICIAL**

Ian O'Donnell,
53 Leigh Road,
Atherton,
Manchester M29 0LX   (H) 0942 874041

TABLES 1987–88

NORTH WEST EAST ONE

	P	W	D	L	F	A	PTS
De La Salle	10	10	0	0	252	42	20
Metrovick	10	8	0	2	153	70	16
Ashton on Mersey	10	6	0	4	159	70	12
Tyldesley	10	5	1	4	116	67	11
O Salians	10	5	1	4	108	96	11
O Bedians	10	5	0	5	124	75	10
Kersal	10	5	0	5	124	75	10
Congleton	9	3	0	6	58	129	6
Ashton-under-Lyne	10	3	0	7	50	146	6
N Manchester	10	2	1	7	52	262	5
Bowden	9	0	0	9	76	198	0

NORTH WEST EAST TWO

	P	W	D	L	F	A	PTS
Bolton	9	9	0	0	216	53	18
Crewe & Nantwich	9	7	0	2	142	59	14
Gtr Man Fire Service	9	6	2	1	173	80	12
Broughton	9	5	2	2	173	80	12
Bury	9	4	0	5	126	134	8
Manchester YMCA	9	3	0	6	83	143	6
Oldham Coll	8	2	1	5	67	109	5
Chorley	8	2	1	5	56	100	5
Dukinfield	9	2	0	7	94	135	4
Marple	9	0	0	9	40	238	0

TABLES 1988–89

NORTH WEST EAST ONE

	P	W	D	L	F	A	PTS
Ashton on Mersey	10	10	0	0	195	32	20
Old Salians	10	8	0	2	201	77	16
Kersal	10	8	0	2	174	75	16
Crewe & Nantwich	10	6	0	4	100	67	12
Tyldesley	10	4	1	5	87	115	9
Metrovick	10	4	0	6	91	89	8
Old Bedians	10	4	0	6	82	160	8
Colne & Nelson	10	3	1	6	84	154	7
Bolton	10	3	0	7	73	142	6
Calder Vale	10	3	0	7	47	136	6
Congleton	10	1	0	9	66	153	2

NORTH WEST EAST TWO

	P	W	D	L	F	A	PTS
Broughton	11	9	0	2	194	80	18
Gtr Man Fire Serv	11	8	0	3	174	69	16
Ashton Under Lyne	11	8	0	3	147	90	16
Bury	11	6	3	2	124	81	15
Dukinfield	11	6	1	4	132	79	13
Chorley	11	5	1	4	86	146	11
N. Manchester	11	5	1	4	86	146	11
Marple	11	4	1	6	77	165	9
Man YMCA	11	3	2	6	106	102	8
Agecroft	11	3	0	8	79	206	3
Bowden	11	1	2	8	100	146	4
Oldham College	11	1	1	9	38	121	3

NORTH WEST EAST THREE
Constituted: 1988–89

NORTHERN DIVISION FIXTURES 1989/90

NORTH WEST EAST ONE

Sat. 9th September (Week 2)
L/borough v Man. F.S.
Metrovick v O. Bedians
Crewe v Kersal
Broughton v Colne
Tyldesley v Toc H

Sat. 23rd September (Week 4)
Toc H v Littlebrough
Colne v Tyldesley
Kersal v Broughton
Old Bedians v Crewe
Old Salians v Metrovick

Sat. 14th October (Week 6)
Littleborough v Colne
Man. F.S. v Toc H
Crewe v Old Salians
Broughton v Old Bedians
Tyldesley v Kersal

Sat. 28th October (Week 8)
Coln v Man. F.S.
Kersall v Littlebrough
Old Bedians v Tyldesley
Old Salians v Broughton
Metrovick v Crewe

Sat. 11th November (Week 10)
Littlebrough v O. Bedians
Man. F.S. v Kersal
Toc H v Colne
broughton v Metrovick
Tyldesley v Old Salians

18th November (Week 11)
Kersal v Toc H
Old Bedians v Man. F.S.
Old Salians v Littlebrough
Metrovick v Tyldesley
Crewe v Broughton

Sat. 25th November (Week 12)
Littlebrough v Metrovick
Man. F.S. v Old Salians
Toc H v Old Bedians
Colne v Kersal
Tyldesley v Crewe

Sat. 13th January (Week 18)
Old Bedians v Colne
Old Salians v Toc H
Metrovick v Man. F.S.
Crewe v Littlebrough
Broughton v Tyldesley

Sat. 10th March (Week 26)
Littlebrough v Broughton
Man. F.S. v Crewe
Toc H v Metrovick
Colne v Old Salians
Kersal v Old Bedians

Sat. 31st March (Week X7)
Old Salians v Kersal
Metrovick v Colne & Nelson
Crewe & Nantwich v Toc H
Broughton v Gtr. Man. Fire Service
Tyldesley v Littlebrough

Sat. 28th April (Week 32)
Grt. Man. F.S. v Tyldesley
Toc H v Broughton
Colne & Nelson v Crewe & Nantwich
Kersal v Metrovick
Old Bedians v Old Salians

NORTH WEST EAST TWO

Sat. 9th September (Week 2)
Bolton v Congleton
Caldervale v N. Manchester
Marple v Ashton
Agecroft v Chorley
Man. YMCA v Bury

Sat. 23rd September (Week 4)
Bury v Bolton
Chorley v Man. YMCA
Ashton v Agecroft
N. Manchester v Marple
Dunkinfield v Caldervale

Sat. 14th October (Week 6)
Bolton v Chorley
Congleton v Bury
Marple v Dukinfield
Agecroft v N. Man.
Man. YMCA v Ashton

Sat. 28th October (Week 8)
Chorley v Congleton
Ashton v Bolton
N. Manchester v Man. YMCA
Dukinfield v Agecroft
Caldervale v Marple

NORTHERN DIVISION FIXTURES 1989/90

Sat. 11th November (Week 10)
Bolton v N. Manchester
Congleton v Ashton
Bury v Chorley
Agecroft v Caldervale
Man. YMCA v Dunkinfield

18th November (Week 11)
Ashton v Bury
N. Man. v Congleton
Dukinfield v Bolton
Caldervale v Man. YMCA
Marple v Agecroft

Sat. 25th November (Week 12)
Bolton v Caldervale
Congleton v Dunkinfield
Bury v N. Manchester
Chorley v Ashton
Man. YMCA v Marple

Sat. 13th January (Week 18)
N. Manchester v Chorley
Dunkinfield v Bury
Caldervale v Congleton
Marple v Bolton
Agecroft v Man. YMCA

Sat. 10th March (Week 26)
Bolton v Agecroft
Congleton v Marple
Bury v Caldervale
Chorley v Dunkinfield
Ashton v N. Manchester

Sat. 31st March (Week X7)
Dunkinfield v Ashton-under-Lyne
Caldervale v Chorley
Marple v Bury
Agecroft v Congleton
Manchester YMCA v Bolton

Sat. 28th April (Week 32)
Congleton v Manchester YMCA
Bury v Agecroft
Chorley v Marple
Ashton-under-Lyne v Caldervale
North Manchester v Dunkinfield

NORTH WEST EAST THREE

Sat. 9th September (Week 2)
Atherton v Bowden

Sat. 23rd September (Week 4)
Holmes Chaple v Atherton

Sat. 14th October (Week 6)
Atherton v Lostock
Bowden v Holmes Chapel

Sat. 28th October (Week 8)
Lostock v Bowden
Oldham Coll v Atherton

Sat. 11th November (Week 10)
Atherton v Shell
Bowden v Oldham Coll
Holmes Chapel v Lostock

18th November (Week 11)
Oldham College v Holmes
Shell v Bowden
Wigan Tech v Atherton

Sat. 25th November (Week 12)
Bowden v Wigan Tech
Holmes Chapel v Shell
Lostock v Oldham Coll

Sat. 13th January (Week 18)
Shell v Lostock
Wigan Tech v Holmes

Sat. 10th March (Week 26)
Lostock v Wigan Tech
Oldham Coll v Shell

Sat. 31st March (Week X7)
Wigan Tech v Oldham College

Sat. 28th April (Week 32)
Shell Carrington v Wigan Tech

NORTH WEST EAST 1

BROUGHTON

Yew Street, Broughton, Salford M7 9HL. Tel: 061 792 2920
Founded: 1913
President: William McLoughlin
Chairman: Patrick Tyson
Secretary: William Lorains, 191 Longhurst Lane, Mellor, Stockport, Cheshire SK6 5PN. Tel: 061 427 2250 (H). 061 449 0771 (W)
Fixtures Secretary: Alan Murphy, 3 Blundell Close, Bury, BL9 8LH. Tel: 061 766 6825 (H). 061 300 6170 (W)
Press Officer: Anthony Plant, Yew Street, Broughton, Salford M7 9HL. Tel: 061 792 2920
Coach: David Coventry
Club captain (1988–89): Daniel Smyth
Club captain (1989–90): Daniel Smyth
No. of teams: Senior 4, Youth 1
Directions to ground: M63 motorway, M602 to Salford – signs Salford University, Yew Street off Lower Broughton Road
Ground capacity: Standing 1000
Clubhouse facilities: 4 changing rooms, 2 Bars, Committee room, etc
Club colours: Navy blue, maroon, gold hoops (*Change colours:* Gold)
Nickname: Old Salfordians
Floodlights: No
Membership fees: Full £15, Playing £15, Social £3, Youth £8, Student £3, OAP £3
Local newspapers: Salford City Reporter, Manchester Evening News
League position (1988–89): 1st
League playing record (1988–89): P 11, W 9, D –, L 2, F 192, A 80
Competitions won: Champions East Division Two League

COLNE AND NELSON

Holt House, Harrison Drive, Colne, Lancs. Tel: 0282 863339
Founded: 1926/27
President: Dick Robertson
Chairman: Jack Neal
Secretary: Keith Ian Thornton, 12 Camden Street, Nelson, Lancs. BB9 0BL. Tel: 0282 63612 (H). 0282 869659 Ext 25 (W)
Fixtures Secretary: John Tindall, 108 Skipton Road, Colne, Lancs. Tel: 0282 863762
Press Officer: Ron Tindall, 80 Ruskin Avenue, Colne, Lancs. Tel: 0282 869685
Coach: Graham Radcliffe
Club captain (1988–89): Graham Tindall
Club captain (1989–90): Graham Tindall
No. of teams: Senior 2, Youth 1
Directions to ground: From the East: Follow the A6068 (Keighley to Colne road) through Laneshawbridge and into the outskirts of Colne. At the first roundabout follow the sign for the M65/Ring-Road (3rd exit off the roundabout). Continue on this road and you will come to another roundabout (after approx 1 miles) with a public house in the middle of it (North Valley Hotel). Take the last exit off the roundabout and continue up the hill which terminates in the Club car-park. From the West: Follow the M65 to its last roundabout and take the first exit – signed Ring-Road/Skipton. After approx mile another roundabout is reached. Take the first exit on the left and follow the road uphill which terminates in the Club car-park
Clubhouse facilities: Open Match days plus Monday and Thursday evenings
Club colours: Black and white hooped shirts (*Change colours:* Maroon shirts)
Floodlights: Training area only
Membership fees: Full £20, Playing £20, Social £5, Youth £10, Student £10

Ground admission: Nil
Programme: No. of editorial pages 4; No. of advertising pages 4; *Price 20p; *Only produced for special matches, eg Cup Games
Programme editor: Jack Neal, 29 Leach Street, Colne, Lancs. Tel: 0282 865930
Local newspapers: Nelson Leader/Colne Times, Lancashire Evening Telegraph, Pendle Mail, Pendle Citizen (freesheet)
League position (1988–89): 8th
League playing record (1988–89): P 10, W 3, D 1, L 6, F 84, A 154

CREWE AND NANTWICH

Barony Park, Nantwich, Cheshire. Clubhouse: Whitehouse Lane, Nantwich, Cheshire CW5 6HH. Tel: 0270 626155
Founded: 1922
President: David Potts
Chairman: Stuart Flood
Secretary: Alan Jones, 9 Gingerbread Lane, Nantwich, Cheshire CW5 6NH. Tel: 0270 625737 (H). 213261 (W)
Fixtures Secretary: Current Season – Rob Holland, 88 Rope Lane, Wistaton, Crewe. Tel: 0270 666773 (H). 0782 263711 (W). Future Seasons – Alan Sproston, Meadowcroft, Poole, Nantwich. Tel: 0270 626574
Press Officer: See Secretary
Coach: Robert Christie
Club captain (1988–89): Rob Foden
Club captain (1989–90): Andy Brown
No. of teams: Senior 4, Youth 2
Clubhouse facilities: Open Match days plus selected evenings
Club colours: White with single black circlet. (*Change colours:* Red)
Floodlights: No
Membership fees: Full £30, Playing £30, Social £6, Youth £7, Student £5
Local newspapers: The Nantwich Chronicle, Crewe Chronicle, The Guardian, The Evening Sentinel
League position (1988–89): 4th
League playing record (1988–89): P 10, W 6, D 0, L 4, F 100, A 67
Competitions won: Colts won Cheshire Colts Shield

DIDSBURY TOC H

Simon Field, Ford Lane, Didsbury, Manchester 20. Tel: 061 446 2146
President: Michael B. Dutch
Chairman: Philip Bayliss
Secretary: Rudy F. Speed, 9 Moorfield Road, West Didsbury, Manchester M20 84Z. Tel: 061 434 2956 (H), 061 873 7949 (W)
Fixtures Secretary: As Secretary
Press Officer: Tony Woods, 5 Rectory Green, Prestwich, Manchester. Tel: 061 773 2039
Coach: Alan Cupello
Club captain (1988–89): Stephen Popoola
Club captain (1989–90): Timothy Baklow
No. of teams: Senior 4
Directions to ground: Via Wilmslow Road to Didsbury in Manchester. Through Didsbury village to traffic lights and then turn right and immediately left into Ford Lane. Clearly marked in Manchester A-Z
Ground capacity: Standing Ample
Clubhouse facilities: Excellent
Club colours: Black jersey with one amber band, black shorts and stockings. (*Change colours:* Maroon)
Nickname: Toc
Floodlights: No
Membership fees: Full £25, Playing £25, Social £5, Youth £5, Student £5, OAP £5
Ground admission: Nil
Local newspapers: South Manchester Reporter, Manchester Evening News
League: NWest E1

League position (1988–89): 10th
League playing record (1988–89): P 34, W 16, D 2,
L 16, F 482, A 407

GREATER MANCHESTER FIRE SERVICE

Old Street FC, Highfield Grove, Stretford,
Manchester. Tel: 061 8650146
Founded: 1965
Chairman: P.C. Rooney
Secretary: G. SMith, 22 Fistral Crescent, Stalybridge,
Cheshire
Fixtures Secretary: C. Clinkard, 36 Torkington Road,
Gatley, Manchester. Tel: 061 4283597
Club captain (1988–89): R. Saunders
Club captain (1989–90): R. Saunders
No. of teams: Senior 2
Directions to ground: Off M63 Junc. 7 head towards
Manchester. Ground 200 yds on right
Clubhouse facilities: Guests at football club
Club colours: Red. (Change colours: Amber/black)
Floodlights: No
League position (1988–89): 2nd
League playing record (1988–89): P 11, W 8, D 0,
L 3, F 174, A 69

KERSAL

Stelfox Avenue, Timperley, Altrincham, Cheshire.
Tel: 061 973 9157
Founded: 1879
President: Donald Williams
Chairman: Paul Nice
Secretary: Alec Forbes, 6 Crampton Drive, Hale
Barns, Altrincham, Cheshire WA15 0HH. Tel: 061
980 3661 (H). 875 7529 (W)
Fixtures Secretary: Alan Long, 59 Dennison Road,
Hazel Grove, Stockport. Tel: 0625 873360
Club captain (1988–89): Ian Wright
Club captain (1989–90): Sean Grady
No. of teams: Senior 5
Directions to ground: A56 to Marslands Road, turn
right into Brooklands Road to roundabout, take 4th
exit, Stockport Road, Timperley. Stelfox Avenue is
1st road on right
Clubhouse facilities: 2 bars, large clubroom, 6 dressing
rooms, 3 baths, showers
Club colours: Red, black, white hoops. (Change
colours: Plain black and red jerseys)
Floodlights: No
League: NW East 1
League position (1988–89): 3rd
League playing record (1988–89): P 38, W 24, D 3,
L 11, F 647, A 278
Competitions won: Winners of Lancashire Trophy
1988-89 season

LITTLEBOROUGH

Rakewood, Hollingworth Lane, Littleborough, Lancs.
Tel: 0706 70220
Founded: 1930
Secretary: John Dawson, 11 Coleridge Drive, Smith
Bridge, Littleborough. Tel: 0706 73707 (H) 0282
27321 (W)
Club colours: Green/Black/Amber
League: NWE 1

METROVICK

McPherson Park, Finney Bank Road, Sale, Cheshire.
Tel: 061 973 7061
Founded: 1923
President: D. Edwards
Chairman: J. Ward
Secretary: Dr. Fewster, 61 Grappenhall Road,

Warrington. Tel: 0925 66219
Fixtures Secretary: C. Barton, 4 Oulderhill Drive,
Rochdale, Lancs. Tel: 0706 350312 (H), 623627 (W)
Coach: G. Hawkins
Club captain (1988–89): S. Diamond
No. of teams: Senior 5
Directions to ground: M63 Junc. 6 A56 towards Sale,
right at 1st lights into Glebelands Road → 2nd right
Finney Bank Road
Clubhouse facilities: Large
Club colours: Black/white. (Change colours: Blue)
Floodlights: Yes
Membership fees: Playing £18
League: NW E1
League position (1988–89): 6th
League playing record (1988–89): P 10, W 4, D 0,
L 6, F 91, A 89

OLD BEDIANS

Millgate Lane, Didsbury. Tel: 061 445 8862
Founded: 1954
Secretary: J. Dunn, 1 Lynmouth Avenue, Withington,
Manchester. Tel: 061 228 1100
Club colours: Royal blue/white
League: NW East 1
Final position (1987–88): 6th

OLD SALIANS

Rookwood, Clarendon Crescent, Sale, Cheshire M33.
Tel: 061 973 7250
Founded: 1944
President: H.W. Thomas
Chairman: Tony Roberts
Secretary: Andy Frost, Limehurst, 35 Priory Road,
Sale, Cheshire M33 2BU. Tel: 061 976 2607 (H). 061
428 0880 (W)
Fixtures Secretary: Frank Sheldon, 4 Oban Drive,
Sale, Cheshire. Tel: 061 962 2878 (H). 061 236 8585
(W)
Press Officer: Colin S. Taylor, 99 Woodhouse Lane,
Sale, Cheshire. Tel: 061 973 4236 (H). 061 953 1000
(W)
Coach: Rodger Alderson
Club captain (1988–89): Guy Middlebrook
Club captain (1989–90): Guy Middlebrook
No. of teams: Senior 5, Youth 2
Directions to ground: Exit M63 Junction 8. Turn 1st
right into Dane Road. Club mile on left
Ground capacity: Standing 400
Clubhouse facilities: 3 Bars, cricket, hockey, tennis
and ballroom
Club colours: Navy with white band, blue shorts and
socks (Change colours: Green, red, white hoops)
Nickname: Sealions
Floodlights: No
Membership fees: Full £22, Playing £22, Social £7,
Youth £11, Student £11, OAP £7
Local newspaper: S.A.M. Guardian
League: NW East 1
League position (1988–89): 2nd
League playing record (1988–89): P 40, W 30, D 4,
L 6, F 738, A 300
Competitions won: Final Griffon Plaque winners,
Semi-Final Cheshire Cup

TYLDESLEY

Well Street, Tyldesley. Tel: 0942 882967
Founded: 1881
Secretary: M.P. Taylor, "Garthmere", Garthmere
Road, Atherton, Lancs. Tel: 0942 883237 (H) 0942
870893 (W)
League: NWE1

AGECROFT

Ordsal Park Rugby Field, Salford, off Trafford Road
Chairman: A. Bebbington
Secretary: S.E. Brayshaw, 15 Welbeck Grove, Salford 7 M7 0DF. Tel: 061 792 2006 (H), 061 875 4193 (W)
Fixtures Secretary: H. Getz, 11 Rockley Gardens, Salford 6
Club captain (1988–89): M. Wheeler
Club captain (1989–90): M. Wheeler
No. of teams: Senior 2
Directions to ground: Onto Trafford Road travelling into Trafford Park, turn left at dock gates
Club colours: Red and black hoops, black shorts
Floodlights: No
Local newspaper: Salford Advertiser
League: NW 2E

ASHTON-UNDER-LYNE

Gambrel Bank, St Albans Avenue, Ashton-Under Lyne. Tel: 061 330 1361
Founded: 1884
President: B.S. Fisher
Chairman: I. Crickett
Secretary: M.W. Crebbin, 'Grasmere', High Grove Road, Grasscroft, Oldham OL4 4HG. Tel: 045 787 3605
Coach: A. Roylance and J. Hutchinson
Club captain (1988–89): Steve Hett
Club captain (1989–90): Scott Pearson
No. of teams: Senior 3, Youth (U.16) 1, Minis started this season
Directions to ground: From Ashton-under-Lyne market, go up Henrietta Street to Broadoak Hotel, then third right at roundabout. This is St Albans Avenue, club 300 yards on the right
Clubhouse facilities: Two storeys – changing downstairs, bar-lounge up
Club colours: Black, amber and gold hoops. (*Change colours:* Red shirts)
Floodlights: For training
Membership fees: Full £20, Playing £20, Social £1, Youth £4, Student £4
Local newspaper: Advertiser and Ashton Reporter
League: NW East 2
League position (1988–89): 2nd
League playing record (1988–89): P 37, W 14, D 1, L 22, F 340, A 479

BOLTON

Mortfield Pavillion, Avenue Street, Bolton BL1 3AW. Tel: 0204 363710
Founded: 1974
President: Tom Holden
Chairman: Alex Brodie
Secretary: Roy Pemberton, Mortfield Pavillion as above
Fixtures Secretary: David Patchett, 2 Richmal Terrace, Ramsbottom. Tel: 0706 82 6298
Coach: Alan and Bert Catterall
Club captain (1988–89): L. Towler
No. of teams: Senior 5, Minis 1
Directions to ground: mile up Chorley Old Road from town centre of Bolton. Right turn (marked) onto Avenue Street
Clubhouse facilities: New Clubhouse, excellent facilities
Club colours: Red and white hoops. (*Change colours:* Blue)
Floodlights: No
Membership fees: Full £16.40
Local newspapers: Bolton Evening News, Bolton Chronicle
League: NW East 1
League position (1988–89): 9th
League playing record (1988–89): P 10, W 3, D 0, L 7, F 73, A 142

BURY

Radcliffe Road, Bury. Tel: 061 764 1528
Founded: 1875
Secretary: G. Hilton, 66 Twiss Green Lane, Culceth. Tel: 092576 2119.

Fixtures Secretary: K. Punshon, 24 Newcombe Road, Holcombe Brook, Bury. Tel: Tottington 4886
Club colours: Red/Yellow/Blue
League: NW East 2
Final position (1987–88): 5th
Playing record (1987–88): P 34, W 13, D 0, L 21, F 365, A 577

CALDER VALE

Holden Road, Burnley, Lancs. Tel: 0282 24337
Founded: 1926
President: Bill West
Chairman: Graham Downey
Secretary: Mick Skelton, 4 Van Dyke Avenue, Burnley. Tel: 0282 411836 (H). 699931 (W)
Fixtures Secretary: T.F. Boyle, 352 Coal Clough Lane, Burnley. Tel: 0282 24218 (H). 36317 (W)
Press Officer: David Capstick, c/o Calder Vale, Holden Road, Burnley. Tel: 0282 24337
Coach: Tony Finnan
Club captain (1988–89): John McNabb
Club captain (1989–90): Ian Austen
No. of teams: Senior 4, Youth 1, Minis 6
Directions to ground: M65 exit No. 12. Up the slip road to roundabout, turn right. Club is behind Oaks Hotel 2 miles from M65 exit
Clubhouse facilities: Open 7 evenings plus Saturday and Sunday lunch
Club colours: Royal blue and old gold hoops, blue shorts.
Floodlights: No
Membership fees: Full £12, Playing £12, Social £5, Youth £3, Student £1, OAP £5
Local newspapers: Burnley Express, Lancashire Evening Telegraph
League: NW East 2
League position (1988–89): 10th
League playing record (1988–89): P 32, W 12, D 3, L 17, F 336, A 546
Competitions won: Lancashire County Colts Competition Plate winners

CHORLEY

Brookfields, Chancery Road, Astley Village, Chorley, Lancs. PR7 1XP. Tel: 02572 68806
Founded: 1972
President: John Lucas
Chairman: Tony Callander
Secretary: Malcolm Walkden, 18B The Farthings, Astley Village, Chorley, Lancs. PR7 1TP. Tel: 02572 72825 (H). 0772 34851 (W)
Fixtures Secretary: Dave Edwards, 34 Higher Meadow, Clayton Le Woods, Leyland, Lancs. Tel: 0772 424403
Press Officer: Phil Godwin, 20 Gaythorne Avenue, Farrington Park, Preston, Lancs. Tel: 0772 791544
Coach: Dave Edwards
Club captain (1988–89): Dave Muir
Club captain (1989–90): Dave Muir
No. of teams: Senior 3, Youth 1
Directions to ground: M61 to Junction 8 towards Chorley. Left on A6, right on B5252. Left at first roundabout, 200 yards on right. From M6 southbound Junction 28, follow A49 to Euxton, left at Bay Horse to roundabout, straight on into Chancery Road, ground on right
Ground capacity: Standing 2000
Clubhouse facilities: Open Match days plus evenings and Sunday lunch
Club colours: Black and white hoops. (*Change colours:* Blue and green hoops)
Nickname: The Black & Whites

Floodlights: yes
Membership fees: Full £25, Playing £25, Social £3.50, Youth £5, Student £5
Local newspapers: Chorley Guardian/Chorley Citizen
League: NW East 2
League position (1988–89): 5th
League playing record (1988–89): P 11, W 6, D 1, L 4, F 120, A 95
Competitions won: Quarter Finalists – Lancashire Trophy

CONGLETON

The Woodman, Park Street, Congleton, Cheshire. Tel: 0260 273338
Founded: 1860
President: Mr Martin Wright
Chairman: Mr David Ingham
Secretary: Mr Martyn Dale, 34 Howey Hill, Congleton, Cheshire CW12 4AF. Tel: 0260 277718 (H). 272208 (W)
Fixtures Secretary: Mr Ken Williams, 2 Sprink Lane, Timbersbrook, Congleton, Cheshire. Tel: 0260 279202 (H). 274492 (W)
Press Officer: Mr Dennis Thorley, 46 Bladon Crescent, Alsager, Stoke-on-Trent. Tel: 0270 878293
Club captain (1988–89): Mr Steven Hough
Club captain (1989–90): Mr Ross Tye
No. of teams: Senior 4
Ground capacity: Open park land
Clubhouse facilities: Ex-Public House
Club colours: Red/white/black hoops. (*Change colours:* Red or blue/white hoops)
Floodlights: No
Membership fees: Full £20, Playing £20, Social £1, Youth £2.50, Student £2.50, OAP £1
Programme: Free monthly newsletter
Programme editor: see Press Officer
Local newspaper: Congleton Chronicle
League: NW East 2
League position (1988–89): 10th (relegated)
League playing record (1988–89): P 36, W 14, D 1, L 21

DUKINFIELD

Blocksages, Birch Lane, Dukinfield, Cheshire. Tel: 061 343 2592
Founded: 1880
President: Maurice Barry Cuttle
Chairman: Albert Ernest Taylor
Secretary: Allan Edward Hilton, Old St Georges Vicarage, 11 Penning View, Heyrod, Stalybridge, Cheshire SK15 3BT. Tel: 061 338 3410
Fixtures Secretary: see Secretary
Press Officer: Tim Spiers, 286 Huddersfield Road, Stalybridge, Cheshire. Tel: 061 303 2168
Club captain (1988–89): Michael McQuillan LLB
Club captain (1989–90): Craig Samuels
No. of teams: Senior 4, Youth 2
Directions to ground: Recreation grounds next to Dukinfield Baths, on the B6170 that runs between A635 at Ashton-under-Lyne and the A57 at Hyde
Clubhouse facilities: Open Match days and evenings, plus Gymnasium
Club colours: Royal blue and gold hoops, black shorts and socks. (*Change colours:* Red and black hoops)
Nickname: Dukinfield Tigers
Floodlights: Training only
Membership fees: Full £23, Playing £23, Social £5.75, Youth £2.50, Student £2.50, OAP £5.75
Programme editor: Tim Spiers, see Press Officer
Local newspapers: Dukinfield and Ashton Reporters, Dukinfield and Ashton Advertiser
League: NW East 2
League position (1988–89): 5th
League playing record (1988–89): P 11, W 6, D 1, L 4, F 124, A 79
Competitions won: Bowdon Plate (sevens), Les Thomas Shield

MANCHESTER Y.M.C.A.

Princess Road, Alexandra Park, Manchester. Tel: 061 226 6814
Founded: 1905
President: Lawrence Dodd
Chairman: Brian Nithsdale
Secretary: Christopher Peters, 9 Boardman Road, Crumpsall, Manchester M8 6NT. Tel: 061 740 1021 (H). 061 795 4567 Ext 2409 (W)
Fixtures Secretary: Neil Murphy, 2 Mountford Avenue, Crumpsall, Manchester. Tel: 061 720 7478 (H). 061 928 9626 (W)
Press Officer: See Secretary
Club captain (1988–89): Frank Boggiano
Club captain (1989–90): Paul Barratt
No. of teams: Senior 3
Directions to ground: On Princess Road between Manchester city centre and the start of the M56 motorway
Clubhouse facilities: Yes, open Match days and evenings
Club colours: Red/black/white hoops. (*Change colours:* Black/white hoops)
Floodlights: No
League: NW East 2
League playing record (1988–89): P 35, W 12, D 2, L 21, F 353, A 492
Note: Although changing at present facility, the 1989-90 season will see us playing at our new ground – The 'Hollies' Playing Fields, Mersey Road, Didsbury, Manchester. We will move to our new clubhouse at the above address in Jan./Feb. 1990. Our new facilities include a floodlit all-weather training area.

MARPLE

Brabyns Park, Brabyns Brow, Marple Bridge, Nr. Stockport, Cheshire. Tel: 061 449 8636
Founded: 1971
President: Nick Boyle
Chairman: John Harrison
Secretary: Kenneth Abbott, Marple RUFC, 136 Station Road, Hadfield, via Hyde, Cheshire SK14 7AA. Tel: 04574 61516 (H). 061 8325705 (W). (Fax: 061 832 1676)
Fixtures Secretary: Neil Hawkley, Bottomlock Cottage, Marple Bridge, Stockport, Cheshire SK6 5LB. Tel: 061 449 9985 (H). 061 273 3322 (W)
Press Officer: See Secretary
Club captain (1988–89): Paul Hope
Club captain (1989–90): Graham Bennett
No. of teams: Senior 3
Directions to ground: A626 (Stockport Road) to Marple, past Rose Hill Marple Railway Station on right hand side to next set of lights. Turn left along A626 (Station Road) down hill past Marple Railway Station on left hand side. Brabyns Park entrance is 100/200 yards further on left hand side. From car park take track 400 yards to changing rooms.
Ground capacity: Standing unlimited
Clubhouse facilities: Bar
Club colours: Red/black. (*Change colours:* No)
Floodlights: No
Membership fees: Full £20, Playing £20, Social £10, Student £10
Ground admission: Free
Local newspaper: Stockport Messenger
League: NW East 2
League position (1988–89): Mid-table, leagues not finalised
League playing record (1988–89): P 11, W 4, D 1, L 6

NORTH MANCHESTER

Victoria Avenue East, New Moston, Manchester. Tel: 0761-682 9234.
Founded: 1983—84
Secretary: B.H. Stott, 8 Ballea –Avenue, New Moston, Manchester M10 0WL. Tel: 061 682 0541.
Club Colours: Sky bluer/gold/scarlet hoops

ATHERTON

No further information available.

BOWDON

Clay Lane, Timperley, Altrincham, Cheshire. Tel: 061 980 8321
Founded: 1877
President: Ian Pullan
Secretary: Jurek Piatkiewicz, 14 Queens Road, Hale, Altrincham, Cheshire WA15 9HF. Tel: 061 941 5503 (H). 0925 51277 (W)
Fixtures Secretary: Jon Daldrey, 77 Navigation Road, Altrincham, Cheshire. Tel: 061 928 1757 (H). 061 928 8143 (W)
Press Officer: Simon Schouten, 2 Burlington Drive, Altrincham, Cheshire. Tel: 061 928 9449
Club captain (1988–89): Andrew Hines
Club captain (1989–90): Andrew Hines
No. of teams: Senior 4
Directions to ground: Clay Lane is off Thorley Lane, Timperley, which links with the A560 and the A538
Clubhouse facilities: Open every evening and Match days, include 2 Squash courts and indoor archery range
Club colours: Claret white black (*Change colours:* No)
Floodlights: Yes
Membership fees: Full £42.50, Social £13, Student £13
Programme: Programmes for special matches and sevens tournament
Programme editor: Contact Hon. Sec./Press Officer address above
Local newspapers: Sale & Altrincham Messenger, Altrincham Guardian, Manchester Evening News
League: NW East 2
League playing record (1988–89): P 11, W 1, D 2, L 8, F 100, A 140

HOLMES CHAPEL

No further information available.

LOSTOCK

No further information available.

OLDHAM COLLEGE

Chapel Road, Oldham, Lancashire. Tel: 061 624 2794
Founded: 1967
Secretary: Kevin McGuire, 5 Gleneagles Avenue, Hopwood, Heywood, Lancs. OL10 2BZ. Tel: 0706 622203 (H). 01 659 2323 (W)
Fixtures Secretary: Steve Baker, c/o 5 Gleneagles Avenue, Hopwood, Heywood, Lancs. OL10 2BZ. Tel: 0706 622203 (H). 01 659 2323 (W)
Press Officer: As Secretary
Coach: Alec Southern

Club captain (1988–89): Keith Broadbent
Club captain (1989–90): Tony Ireson
No. of teams: Senior 2
Directions to ground: Manchester A-Z page 43 1D
Ground capacity: Standing 2000
Clubhouse facilities: Church Inn, Chapel Road, Oldham
Club colours: Green and black hoops. (*Change colours:* Red and white)
Floodlights: No
Membership fees: Full £2.50, Playing £2.50, Social £2.50, Youth £1.25, Student £1.25, OAP £1.25
Ground admission: Free
Local newspapers: Oldham Chronicle, Manchester Evening News
League: NW East 2

SHELL CHARRINGTON

Carrington Lane, Urmston, Manchester. Tel: 061 775 3987.
Secretary: J.B. Bush, 249 Woodsend Road, Urmston, Manchester M31 2QB. Tel: 061 748 9066 (H) 061 776 3103 (W).
Club colours: Red/Yellow
League: NWW3
League position 1988–89: 11th

WIGAN COLLEGE OF TECHNOLOGY

Christopher Park, Wigan Lower Road, Standish Lower Ground, Wigan. Tel: 0942 41140
Founded: 1925
President: Terry Sweeney
Chairman: John Grimes
Secretary: Ian Parker, 32 Moore Street, Whelley, Wigan. Tel: 0942 48440 (H). 061 855 7390 (W)
Fixtures Secretary: See Secretary
Press Officer: See Secretary
Coach: Terry Sweeney
Club captain (1988–89):Neil Smith
Club captain (1989–90): Ian Parker
No. of teams: Senior 2
Directions to ground: Follow B5375, Woodhouse Lane, out of Wigan, through Junction with Scot Road onto Wigan Lower Road, Christopher Park is approx. mile along on right, next to new houses
Club colours: Scarlet (*Change colours:* Black, white, red hoops)
Nickname: Old Collegians
Floodlights: No
Membership fees: Full £7.50, Playing £7.50, Student £3.75
Local newspaper: Lancashire Evening Post
League: NW West 3
League position (1988–89): 8th
League playing record (1988–89): P 31, W 12, D 1, L 18, F 468, A 456

NORTH WEST: NORTH LEAGUES

NORTH WEST DIVISION NORTH ONE: OFFICIAL

Bill Hopkinson,
Far Hey Head Farm,   (H) 0706 79879
Little Borough,Rochdale,   (O) 0706 47474
Lancashire OL15 9NS   Ext. 4531

NORTH WEST DIVISION NORTH TWO: OFFICIAL

E. McConnell
38 Loop Road South,
Whitehaven,
Cumbria CA28 7SE   0946 692225

TABLES 1987–88

NORTH WEST DIVISION NORTH ONE

	P	W	D	L	F	A	PTS
Windermere	9	9	0	0	214	41	18
Keswick	9	8	0	1	129	46	16
Kirkby Lonsdale	9	6	0	3	185	92	12
Rossendale	9	6	0	3	153	97	12
Creighton	9	4	0	5	98	197	8
St Benedicts	9	3	1	5	87	107	7
Blackpool	9	3	0	6	65	129	6
Carnforth	9	2	2	5	733	138	6
Millom	9	1	1	7	41	135	3
Whitehaven	9	1	0	8	105	162	2

NORTH WEST DIVISION NORTH TWO

	P	W	D	L	F	A	PTS
Thornton Cleveleys	7	6	0	1	145	41	12
British Steel	7	6	0	1	88	565	12
U Eden	7	5	0	2	115	62	10
Ambleside	7	4	0	3	98	79	8
Silloth	7	3	0	4	64	67	6
Smith Bros	6	2	0	4	81	100	4
Lanc Moor Hosp	6	0	0	6	35	122	0

TABLES 1988–89

NORTH WEST DIVISION NORTH ONE

	P	W	D	L	F	A	PTS
Kirkby Lonsdale	9	8	1	0	220	41	17
Rossendale	9	7	1	1	157	65	15
Keswick	9	6	0	3	164	73	12
Thornton Cleveleys	9	6	0	3	112	92	12
St Benedicts	8	5	0	3	122	95	10
British Steel	9	3	0	6	108	129	6
Carnforth	9	3	0	6	99	140	6
Blackpool	8	2	1	5	37	128	5
Millom	9	1	1	7	42	143	3
Creighton	9	1	0	8	70	225	2

NORTH WEST DIVISION NORTH TWO

	P	W	D	L	F	A	PTS
Upper Eden	5	5	0	0	96	22	10
Whitehaven	5	4	0	1	74	32	8
Silloth	5	3	0	2	136	33	4
Ambleside	5	0	1	4	22	125	1
Clitheroe	5	0	1	4	12	144	1

South Liverpool of North-West West One 1988–89

NORTHERN DIVISION FIXTURES 1989/90

NORTH WEST NORTH ONE

Sat. 9th September (Week 2)
Rossendale v Whitehaven
St Benedicts v Keswick
Thornton v Upper Eden
British Steel v Carnforth

Sat. 23rd September (Week 4)
Upper Eden v British Steel
Keswick v Thornton
Whitehaven v St Benedicts
Millom v RosSendale

Sat. 14th October (Week 6)
Blackpool v Carnforth
St Benedicts v Millom
Thornton v Whitehaven
British Steel v Keswick

Sat. 28th October (Week 8)
Upper Eden v Blackpool
Whitehaven v British Steel
Millom v Thornton
Rossendale v St Benedicts

Sat. 11th November (Week 10)
Blackpool v Keswick
Carnforth v Upper Eden
Thornton v Rossendale
British Steel v Millom

18th November (Week 11)
Keswick v Carnforth
Whitehaven v Blackpool
Rossendale v British Steel
St Benedicts v Thornton

Sat. 25th November (Week 12)
Blackpool v Millom
Carnforth v Whitehaven
Upper Eden v Keswick
British Steel v St Benedicts

Sat. 13th January (Week 18)
Whitehaven v Upper Eden
Millom v Carnforth
Rossendale v Blackpool
Thornton v British Steel

Sat. 10th March (Week 26)
Blackpool v St Benedicts
Carnforth v Rochdale
Upper Eden v Millom
Keswick v Whitehaven

Sat. 31st March (Week X7)
Millom v Keswick
Rossendale v Upper Eden
St Benedicts v Carnforth
Thornton Cleveleys v Blackpool

Sat. 28th April (Week 32)
Blackpool v British Steel
Carnforth v Thornton Cleveleys
Upper Eden v St Benedicts
Keswick v Rossendale
Whitehaven v Millom

NORTH WEST NORTH TWO

Sat. 9th September (Week 2)
Clitheroe v Ambleside

Sat. 23rd September (Week 4)
Ambleside v Silloth

Sat. 14th October (Week 6)
Smith Bros v Ambleside
Silloth v Clitheroe

Sat. 28th October (Week 8)
Clitheroe v Smith Bros
Ambleside v Creighton

Sat. 11th November (Week 10)
Creighton v Clitheroe
Smith Bros v Silloth

18th November (Week 11)
Silloth v Creighton

Sat. 25th November (Week 12)
Creighton v Smith Bros

NORTHERN DIVISION FIXTURES 1989/90

Sat. 11th November (Week 10)
Shell v Port Sunlight
Aspull v Old Anselmians
Hightown v O Rockferrians
Vulcan v Sefton
Hoylake v Birchfield

18th November (Week 11)
O Anselmians v Hightown
Port Sunlight v Aspull
Birchfield v Shell
Sefton v Hoylake
Eagle v Vulcan

Sat. 25th November (Week 12)
Shell v Sefton
Aspull v Birchfield
Hightown v Port Sunlight
O Rockferrians v O Anselmians
Hoylake v Eagle

Sat. 13th January (Week 18)
Port Sunlight v O Rockferrians
Birchfield v Hightown
Sefton v Aspull
Eagle v Shell
Vulcan v Hoylake

Sat. 10th March (Week 26)
Shell v Vulcan
Aspull v Eagle
Hightown v Sefton
O Rockferrians v Birchfield
O Alsemians v Port Sunlight

Sat. 31st March (Week X7)
Birchfield v O Anselmians
Sefton v Old Rockferrians
Eagle v Hightown
Vulcan v Aspull
Hoylake v Shell Stanlow

Sat. 28th April (Week 32)
Aspull v Hoylake
Hightown v Vulcan
Old Rockferrians v Eagle
O Anslemians v Sefton
Port Sunlight v Birchfield

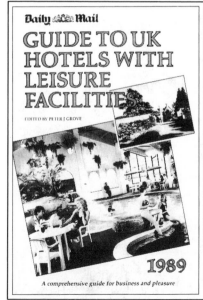

NORTH WEST NORTH 1

BLACKPOOL

Fleetwood Road, Norbreck. Tel: 0253 3308
Founded: 1959
President: Ted Schools
Chairman: Howell Williams
Secretary: Cliff Wainscott, 15 Stafford Avenue, Poulton-Le-Fylde FY6 8BJ. Tel: 0253 885151
Fixtures Secretary: Ted Schools, 347a Whitegate Drive, Blackpool FY3 9PH. Tel: 0253 65329
Press Officer: Andrew Parr, 35 Rathlyn Avenue, Blackpool. Tel: 0253 65329
Coach: Howell Williams
Club captain (1988–89): A.J.R. Hopton
Club captain (1989–90): Frazer Bagnall
No. of teams: Senior 3, Youth & Minis 3
Directions to ground: M55 (leave Junction 4). A583 (to Blackpool), right at Oxford Square, B5124, joins A587 (signs to Fleetwood) ground on right mile past Red Lion
Clubhouse facilities: Bar, lounge, showers, 4 changing rooms
Club colours: Red & blue hoops. (*Change colours:* Dark blue)
Floodlights: Yes (for training only)
Membership fees: £18
Local newspaper: Evening Gazette
League: NW North 1
League position (1988–89): 8th
League playing record (1988–89): P 37, W 17, D 5, L 15, F 378, A 443

BRITISH STEEL

Moss Bay, Workington, Cumbria. Tel: 0900 3570
Founded: 1953
President: A. Williams
Chairman: T. Moore
Secretary: B. Rumney, 14 Walls Road, Salterbeck, Workington, Cumbria
Fixtures Secretary: G. Stoddart
Press Officer: As Secretary
Coach: M. Rafferty
Club captain (1988–89): P. Phillips
Club captain (1989–90): P. Phillips
No. of teams: Senior 2, Youth 1
Clubhouse facilities: Bar, committee room, large concert room
Club colours: Red, white, blue hooped shirts and socks, black shorts. (*Change colours:* Blue, white hooped shirts)
Nickname: Steels
Floodlights: No
Membership fees: Full £5, Playing £2.50, Social £2.50, Youth £2
Ground admission: £1 (50p OAP)
Programme: Price 50p
Programme editor: As Secretary
Local newspapers: Cumbria Evening News and Star
League: NW North 1
League position (1988–89): 6th
League playing record (1988–89): P 9, W 3, D 0, L 6, F 108, A 129
1st XV: P 29, W 14, D 3, L 12, F 394, A 292
Competitions won: Alf Crone Memorial Trophy 15 A Side Winners, Moresby Sevens, Runners Up Cumbria Shielf Div I

CARNFORTH

Carnforth High School, Kellet Road, Carnforth
Founded: 1980
President: Ronald Gunn
Chairman: John Gordon Wilson
Secretary: John Samuel Marsden, 'Whinfell', Eden Mount Way, Carnforth, Lancashire LA5 9XN. Tel: 0524 734832
Fixtures Secretary: Robert H. Wilkinson, 3 Main Street, Warton, Carnforth, Lancs. Tel: 0524 734461

Press Officer: Allan Hardy, 4 Preston Street, Carnforth, Lancs. Tel: 0524 733799
Club captain (1988–89): Stephen Vose
Club captain (1989–90): Stephen Vose
No. of teams: Senior 3, Minis 1
Directions to ground: Junction 35 on M6, turn right at roundabout above motorway, right at T-junction, school on right 100 yards
Clubhouse facilities: Snooker, darts, dancing, bar
Club colours: Green and black hoops (2"). (*Change colours:* Red)
Floodlights: No
Membership fees: Full £30 (£20 if paid before 31.10.89 or within 1 month of being a new member), Social £2, Youth & Student £10
Ground admission: Nil
Local newspapers: Lancaster Guardian, Citizen (free), Morecambe Visitor
League: NW North 1
League position (1988–89): 7th

KESWICK

Davidson Park, Keswick. Tel: 72823
Founded: 1879
President: Ronald F. Green
Chairman: Anthony J. Bragg
Secretary: Malcolm E. Bowman, 3 Briar Rigg, Keswick CA12 4NW. Tel: 72461
Fixtures Secretary: A.J. Bragg, 7 Greta Court, Keswick. Tel: 74734
Press Officer: As Fixtures Secretary
Club captain (1988–89): G. Timothy Bunting
Club captain (1989–90): T.B.A.
No. of teams: Senior 3, Youth 1
Directions to ground: Within 300 yards of town centre
Ground capacity: Seating 200
Groundsman:
Clubhouse facilities: Bar, clubroom, 3 changing rooms
Club colours: Navy, green and yellow hoops. (*Change colours:* No)
Floodlights: No
League: NW North 1
League position (1988–89): 3rd
League playing record (1988–89): P 9, W 6, D 0, L 3, F 162, A 73

MILLOM

The Dunes, Seaview, Haverigg, Millom, Cumbria. Tel: c/o Harbour Hotel Haverigg 0657 2764, Castle Hotel Millom 0657 2721
Founded: 1873
President: James Wilson
Chairman: Neal Hartley
Secretary: Pauline Hartley, 50 Palmers Lane, Millom, Cumbria. Tel: 0657 4407 (H). 2300 (W)
Fixtures Secretary: Terry Sumner, Sonnenberg, Butler Street, Millom. Tel: 0657 3254 (H). 0657 2300 (W)
Press Officer: J.A. Parsons, The Orchards, The Hill, Millom. Tel: 0657 2515 (H). 0657 2319 (W)
No. of teams: Senior 2, Youth 2
Clubhouse facilities: Not at present
Club colours: White with blue hoop. (*Change colours:* No)
Floodlights: No
League: NW North 1
League position (1988–89): 9th
League playing record (1988–89): P 8, W 1, D 1, L 6, F 36, A 107

ROSSENDALE

Rossendale Sports Club, Newchurch Road, Rawtenstall, Rossendale, Lancs. Tel: 0706 229152
Founded: 1970
President: James Howarth
Chairman: Terrence Kelly
Secretary: Peter Brotherton, 47 Poulton Avenue, Accrington, Lancs. BB5 5EP. Tel: 0254 34310 (H). 0282 72511 Ext 2556 (W)

Fixtures Secretary: Terrence kelly, 111 Pilkington Terrace, Broadway, Haslingden, Rossendale, Lancs. Tel: 0706 217361
Press Officer: Robert Holmes, 10 Whitehead Street, Rawtenstall, Rossendale, Lancs.
Club captain (1988–89): Pat Killelea
Club captain (1989–90): T.B.A.
No. of teams: Senior 4, Youth 1
Directions to ground: From M62 take M66 north through to centre of Rawtenstall. Then follow A682 to Burnley, turn right at traffic lights on dual carriageway following signs to Marl Pits Sports Centre
Ground capacity: Standing 200
Clubhouse facilities: Open Match days, Sunday and each weekday evening
Club colours: Maroon and white. (*Change colours:* Amber and white, blue and white)
Floodlights: No
Membership fees: Full £20, Playing £20, Social £10, Youth £3, Student £8
Local newspapers: Rossendale Free Press
League: NW North 1
League position (1988–89): 2nd
League playing record (1988–89): P 9, W 7, D 1, L 1, F 157, A 65

ST BENEDICTS

Ground situated at Newlands Avenue, Mirehouse. Club address: St Benedicts Social Centre, Whinlatter Road, Mirehouse, Whitehaven. Tel: 0946 61753, licensing hours only
Founded: 1974
President: Rev. Brian Noble
Chairman: Mr J. Relph
Secretary: Mr W. Dougan, 9 Crow Park, Loop Road South, Whitehaven, Cumbria CA28 7SF. Tel: 0946 66679
Fixtures Secretary: Mr J. Davies, 18 Borrowdale Road, Mirehouse, Whitehaven, Cumbria. Tel: 61940
Coach: Michael Morgan
No. of teams: Senior 2
Directions to ground: Leave M6 Junction 40, take A66 to Workington, join A595 at Bridgefoot. Turn off 595 1st right after passing West Cumberland Hospital on your left, Club at bottom of hill
Ground capacity: Standing 400
Clubhouse facilities: Match days and training nights
Club colours: Black and gold variations. (*Change colours:* Black and green variations)
Nickname: Benny's or Saint's
Floodlights: No
Membership fees: Full £5, Playing £5, Youth optional, Student optional, OAP free
Ground admission: free
Local newspaper: Whitehaven News
League: NW North 1
League position (1988–89): 3rd
League playing record (1988–89): P 10, W 7, D 0, L 3
Competitions won: Premier Comp. Isle of Man Rugby Festival

THORNTON CLEVELEYS

Fleetwood Road North, Thornton Cleveleys, Lancashire. Tel: 0253 854104
Founded: 1927
President: Elwyn Nicol
Chairman: Michael Brennand
Secretary: Michael Boardman, 41 Roylen Avenue, Carleton, Poulton-Le-Fylde, Lancs. Tel: 0253 890099 (H). 856123 Ext 5325 (W)
Fixtures Secretary: Barry Hirst, 46 Farnham Way, Carleton, Poulton-Le-Fylde, Lancs. Tel: 0253 892856
Press Officer: As Secretary
Coach: T.B.A.
Club captain (1988–89): John Turnbull
Club captain (1989–90): John Turnbull
No. of teams: Senior 5, Youth 1, Minis 1

Directions to ground: Off M55 at Junction 3, A585 towards Fleetwood, approx. 7 miles. Right at roundabout on B5268. through traffic lights, windmill on left. Club is mile further on, on left
Ground capacity: Standing 300
Clubhouse facilities: Wooden pavilion, changing, bar, social and kitchen areas
Club colours: Red, black and amber. (*Change colours:* Yellow or blue)
Floodlights: No
Membership fees: Full £5, Playing £5, Social £7, Youth £2.50, Student £2.50
Programme: One A4 sheet; Free
Programme editor: T.B.A.
Local newspapers: West Lancashire Evening Gazette
League: NW North 1
League position (1988–89): 4th
League playing record (1988–89): P 9, W 6, D 0, L 3, F 103, A 91
Competitions won: Fylde Coast Cup (known as 'Standard Life Trophy')

UPPER EDEN

Pennine Park, Westgarth, Kirkby Stephen, Cumbria CA17. Tel: 07683 71585
Founded: 1975
President: D. Lawrence
Chairman: T. Braithwaite
Secretary: S. Moffat, 1 The Arcade, Market Street, Kirkby Stephen, Cumbria CA17 4QN. Tel: 07683 71794
Fixtures Secretary: Graham Todd, Mellbecks House, Kirkby Stephen, Cumbria CA17 4AB. Tel: 07683 71562
Press Officer: R. Thompson
Coach: C. Sowerby
Club captain (1988–89): I. Collinson
Club captain (1989–90): J. Whittle
No. of teams: Senior 2, Youth 1
Directions to ground: From town centre, turn right off High Street through Broughm Lane and cross to Westgarth Road. Ground at end of road
Clubhouse facilities: Open Match days and training nights
Club colours: Black/white hooped shirts. (*Change colours:* Black/white shirts)
Floodlights: No
Membership fees: Full £10, Playing £10, Social £7, Youth £2, OAP £2
Local newspaper: Cumberland and Westmorland Herald
League: NW North 1
League position (1988–89): 1st
League playing record (1988–89): P 33, W 19, D 1, L 13
Competitions won: Courage League Champions, Westmorland and Furness Cup

WHITEHAVEN

The Playground, Richmond Terrace, Whitehaven. Tel: 0946 69 5253
Founded: 1876-7
President: William G. Anderson
Chairman: Howard Connor
Secretary: Ernest McConnell, 38 Loop Road South, Whitehaven, Cumbria CA28 7SE. Tel: 0946 831200
Fixtures Secretary: H. Diamond, 20 Lakeland Avenue, Kells, Whitehaven. Tel: 0946 69 2225
Press Officer: As Secretary
Coach: Reg Harrison/Colin Murdock
Club captain (1988–89): Garry McGinness
Club captain (1989–90): Garry McGinness
No. of teams: Senior 3, Youth 1
Ground capacity: Seating 400, standing 1500
Clubhouse facilities: Yes
Club colours: Maroon/white hoops, white shorts. (*Change colours:* Maroon/white shorts)
Floodlights: No
Membership fees: Full £10, Playing £10, Social £2.50,

OAP £2
Local newspaper: Whitehaven News
League: North West North 2
League position (1988–89): Runners up
League playing record (1988–89): P 31, W 15, D 1, L 15, F 340, A 297

NORTH WEST NORTH 2

AMBLESIDE

Galava Park, Borrans Road, Ambleside, Cumbria. Tel: 0966 32536
Founded: 1874
Secretary: J.P. Stead, Gale Crescent Hotel, Low Gale, Ambleside. Tel: Ambleside 32284 (H) or 0966 32066 (W)
League: NW North 2
Club Cololurs: Amber/Black

CLITHEROE

Littlemoor Park, Littlemoor Road, Clitheroe. Tel:

Clitheroe 22261
Founded: 1978
President: Colin Silcock
Chairman: Dougie Woodburn
Secretary: John Hyde, Moorhey Cottge, Knowle Green, Longridge, Preston PR3 2XE. Tel: 0254 878402 (H), 0282 24201/41554 (W)
Fixtures Secretary: Chris Thomas, 2 Hereford Drive, Clitheroe. Tel: 0200 28184
Coach: George Giles
Club captain (1988–89): Roger Holmes
Club captain (1989–90): Roger Holmes
No. of teams: Senior 2
Ground capacity: Standing 400
Clubhouse facilities: Bar, changing rooms, kitchen, showers
Club colours: Maroon and gold striped jerseys, black shorts. (*Change colours:* Black, white and black)
Floodlights: No
Membership fees: Full £25, Social £7.50, Youth £4, Student £11
Local newspaper: Clitheroe Advertiser & Times
League: North West 2
League position (1988–89): 11th
League playing record (1988–89): P 6, W 1, D 1, L 4

CREIGHTON

Carrs Field, off Newtown Road, Carlisle. Tel: 0228 21169
Founded: 1927
Chairman: Michael Simpson
Secretary: Dave J. Thomlinson, 146 Moorhouse Road, Carlisle. Tel: 0228 35111 (H). 24379 (W)

Fixtures Secretary: John W. Graham, 4 Carlton Gardens, Carlisle. Tel: 0228 26705
Press Officer: See Secretary
Club captain (1988–89): C. Whalley
Club captain (1989–90): T.B.A.
No. of teams: Senior 3
Directions to ground: Follow directions to Cumberland Infirmary, ground 300 yards further
Clubhouse facilities: Basic bar and changing
Club colours: Navy blue (*Change colours:* Light and dark blue hoops)
Floodlights: No
Membership fees: Full £10, Playing £10, Social £7.50
Local newspaper: Cumberland News
League: NW North 2
League position (1988–89): Bottom
League playing record (1988–89): P 10, W 1, D 0, L 9
Competitions won: Creighton Sevens once again no other sides invited!

SILLOTH

Old Marshalling Yard, Eden Street, Silloth, Cumbria. Tel: 0965 32299
Founded: 1973
President: J.O. Holliday, J.P.
Chairman: P. Long
Secretary: Mr R.G. Edwards, Mayfair, Beckfoot, Silloth, Cumbria. Tel: 0965 31382
Fixtures Secretary: Mr G. Jones, Friars Garth, Abbeytown, Silloth, Cumbria
Press Officer: Mr D. Wood, Esk Street, Silloth, Cumbria. Tel: 0965 31318
Coach: J. Lettice
Club captain (1988–89): B. Wood
Club captain (1989–90): B. Wood
No. of teams: Senior 2, Youth 1
Directions to ground: Silloth playing field area
Clubhouse facilities: Bar, lounge, showers, toilet facilities, changing rooms
Club colours: Green and black hooped shirts, black shorts. (*Change colours:* No)
Floodlights: No
League: NW North 2
League position (1988–89): 3rd
League playing record (1988–89): P 5, W 3, D 0, L 2, F 50, A 34
Competitions won: Courage Cumbria Shield League – Division 3

SMITH BROS

Seven Fields, Bransty
Founded: 1964
Secretary: W. Barwise, 101 Bransty Road, Bransty, Whitehaven, Cumbria CA28 6HF. Tel: 62567
League: NW North 2
Final position (1987–88): 6th

NORTH WEST: WEST LEAGUES

NORTH WEST DIVISION WEST ONE: OFFICIAL

Mike Massey
Fieldside,
Grange Road,
Bowdon, Cheshire   061 928 2997

NORTH WEST DIVISION WEST TWO: OFFICIAL

John Burton,
14 Seaview Lane,
Irby,   (H) 051 648 4341
Merseyside L61 3UL   (C) 051 638 1486

NORTH WEST DIVISION WEST THREE: OFFICIAL

Joseph A. Cooke,
23 Knight Road,
Burtonwood,
Warrington WA5 4QQ   09252 28466

TABLES 1987–88

NORTH WEST DIVISION WEST ONE

	P	W	D	L	F	A	PTS
Mersey Police	10	10	0	0	239	69	20
Liverpool Coll	10	8	0	2	109	72	16
Ormskirk	10	5	0	5	116	82	10
Old Parkonians	10	5	0	5	102	94	10
Douglas (IOM)	10	5	0	5	127	146	10
Aspull	10	4	0	6	122	145	8
St Edwards OB	10	4	0	6	108	143	8
Birchfield	10	3	2	5	85	132	8
Eagle	10	4	0	6	65	136	8
Old Anselmians	10	3	1	6	103	151	7

NORTH WEST DIVISION WEST TWO

	P	W	D	L	F	A	PTS
Old Instonians	10	7	1	2	155	74	15
Ruskin Park	10	7	1	2	168	97	15
Vulcan	10	7	1	2	168	97	15
Sefton	10	6	1	3	142	78	13
Hightown	10	4	3	3	118	120	11
S Liverpool	10	4	2	4	101	113	10
Port Sunlight	10	3	3	4	146	113	9
Chester Coll	9	4	1	4	120	132	9
St Mary's OB	9	2	2	5	51	128	6
Moore	10	1	1	8	79	205	3
Wallasey	10	0	2	8	72	136	2

NORTH WEST DIVISION WEST THREE

	P	W	D	L	F	A	PTS
Halton	9	9	0	0	229	38	18
Old Rockferrians	8	7	0	1	152	38	14
Helsby	9	5	2	2	134	83	12
Mossley Hill	9	6	0	3	99	97	12
Shell (Stanlow)	9	4	2	3	129	67	10
Hoylake	9	4	0	5	110	113	8
Prescot	9	1	4	4	59	84	6
Wigan Tech	9	1	1	7	55	146	3
Agecroft	9	1	1	7	47	199	3
Burtonwood	8	1	0	7	50	199	2

TABLES 1988–89

NORTH WEST DIVISION WEST ONE

	P	W	D	L	F	A	PTS
Warrington	10	7	1	2	108	118	15
Old Parkonians	10	7	0	3	116	57	14
St Edwards OB	10	6	1	3	173	117	13
Newton-Le-Willows	10	6	1	3	128	95	13
Ormskirk	10	6	0	4	135	121	12
Old Instonians	10	5	0	5	91	101	10
Liverpool Coll OB	10	4	0	6	168	125	8
Ruskin Park	10	4	0	6	150	160	8
Douglas (IoM)	10	4	0	6	158	192	8
Aspull	10	3	0	7	165	146	6
Birchfield	10	1	1	8	49	209	3

NORTH WEST DIVISION WEST TWO

	P	W	D	L	F	A	PTS
Oldershaw	9	8	1	0	164	65	17
South Liverpool	9	7	2	0	126	57	16
Old Rockferrians	9	7	0	2	121	73	14
Eagle	9	4	1	4	102	127	9
Port Sunlight	9	4	0	5	106	87	8
Vulcan	9	3	0	6	97	113	6
Old Anselmians	9	3	0	6	84	103	6
Sefton	9	3	0	6	102	137	6
Hightown	9	2	0	7	85	150	4
Halton	9	2	0	7	79	154	4

NORTH WEST DIVISION WEST THREE

	P	W	D	L	F	A	PTS
Hoylake	11	10	0	1	280	32	20
Shell Stanlow	11	9	1	1	198	73	19
St Mary's OB	11	9	0	2	299	82	18
Mossley Hill	11	8	0	3	164	103	16
Helsby	11	6	1	4	148	107	13
Moore	11	6	1	4	97	167	13
Wallasey	11	6	0	5	111	102	12
Wigan Coll of Tech	11	3	0	8	153	174	6
Prescot Rainhill	11	3	0	8	101	241	6
Burtonwood	11	2	0	9	85	214	4
Shell Carrington	11	1	1	9	77	266	3
Lucas	11	1	0	10	93	245	2

NORTHERN DIVISION FIXTURES 1989/90

NORTH WEST WEST ONE

Sat. 9th September (Week 2)
S L'pool v Oldershaw
Ormskirk v Istonians
Parkonians v Leigh
St Edwards v L'pool Coll
Douglas v Newton

Sat. 23rd September (Week 4)
Newton v S. L'pool
L'pool Coll v Douglas
Leigh v St Edwards
Istonains v Parkonians
Ruskin v Ormskirk

Sat. 14th October (Week 6)
S L'pool v L'pool Coll
Oldershaw v Newton
Parkonians v Ruskin
St Edwards v Istonians
Douglas v Leigh

Sat. 28th October (Week 8)
L'pool Coll v Oldershaw
Leigh v S. L'pool
Istonians v Douglas
Ruskin v St Edwards
Ormskirk v Parkonians

Sat. 11th November (Week 10)
S L'pool v Istonians
Oldershaw v Leigh
Newton v L'pool Coll
St Edwards v Ormskirk
Douglas v Ruskin

18th November (Week 11)
Leigh v Newton
Istonians v Oldershaw
Ruskin v S L'pool
Ormskirk v Douglas
Parkonians v St Edwards

Sat. 25th November (Week 12)
S L'pool v Ormskirk
Oldershaw v Ruskin
Newton v Istonians
L'pool Coll v Leigh
Douglas v Parkonians

Sat. 13th January (Week 18)
Istonians v L'Coll
Ruskin v Newton
Ormskirk v Oldershaw
Parkonians v S L'pool
St Edwaqrds v Douglas

Sat. 10th March (Week 26)
S L'pool v St Edwards
Oldershaw v Parkonians
Newton v Ormskirk
L'pool Coll v Ruskin
Leigh v Istonians

Sat. 31st March (Week X7)
Ruskin Park v Leigh
Ormskirk v Liverpool Coll OB
Old Parkonians v Newton le Willows
St Edwards OB v Olcershaw
Douglas (I.o.M.) v – South Liverpool

Sat. 28th April (Week 32)
Oldershaw v Douglas (I.o.M.)
Newton le Willows v St Edwards OB
L'pool Coll OB v Old Parkonians
Leigh v Ormskirk
Old Istonians v Ruskin Park

NORTH WEST WEST TWO

Sat. 9th September (Week 2)
Shell v Aspull
Sefton v Port Sunlight
Eagle v O. Anselmians
Vulcan v O. Rockferrians
Hoylake v Hightown

Sat. 23rd September (Week 4)
Hightown v Shell
O. Rockferrians v Hoylake
O. Anselmians v Vulcan
Port Sunlight v Eagle
Birchfield v Sefton

Sat. 14th October (Week 6)
Shell v O. Rockferrians
Aspull v Hightown
Eagle v Birchfield
Vulcan v Port Sunlight
Hoylake v O Anselmians

Sat. 28th October (Week 8)
O Rockferrians v Aspull
O Anselmians v Shell
Port Sunlight v Hoylake
Birchfield v Vulcan
Sefton v Eagle

NORTHERN DIVISION FIXTURES 1989/90

Sat. 11th November (Week 10)
Shell v Port Sunlight
Aspull v Old Anselmians
Hightown v O Rockferrians
Vulcan v Sefton
Hoylake v Birchfield

18th November (Week 11)
O Anselmians v Hightown
Port Sunlight v Aspull
Birchfield v Shell
Sefton v Hoylake
Eagle v Vulcan

Sat. 25th November (Week 12)
Shell v Sefton
Aspull v Birchfield
Hightown v Port Sunlight
O Rockferrians v O Anselmians
Hoylake v Eagle

Sat. 13th January (Week 18)
Port Sunlight v O Rockferrians
Birchfield v Hightown
Sefton v Aspull
Eagle v Shell
Vulcan v Hoylake

Sat. 10th March (Week 26)
Shell v Vulcan
Aspull v Eagle
Hightown v Sefton
O Rockferrians v Birchfield
O Alsemians v Port Sunlight

Sat. 31st March (Week X7)
Birchfield v O Anselmians
Sefton v Old Rockferrians
Eagle v Hightown
Vulcan v Aspull
Hoylake v Shell Stanlow

Sat. 28th April (Week 32)
Aspull v Hoylake
Hightown v Vulcan
Old Rockferrians v Eagle
O Anslemians v Sefton
Port Sunlight v Birchfield

NORTH WEST WEST THREE

Sat. 9th September (Week 2)
Lucas v St Marys
Vagabonds v Helsby
Mossley Hill v Burtonwood

Sat. 23rd September (Week 4)
Burtonwood v Lucas
Wallasey v Mossley Hill
Halton v Vagabonds

Sat. 14th October (Week 6)
Lucas v Wallasey
St Marys v Burtonwood
Vagabonds v Moore
Mossley Hill v Helsby

Sat. 28th October (Week 8)
Wallasey v St Marys
Helsby v Lucas
Halton v Mossley Hill

Sat. 11th November (Week 10)
Lucas v Halton
St Marys v Helsby
Burtonwood v Wallasey
Mossley Hill v Moore

18th November (Week 11)
Helsby v Burtonwood
Halton v St Marys
Moore v Lucas

Sat. 25th November (Week 12)
St Marys v Moore
Burtonwood v Halton
Wallasey v Helsby
Mossley Hill v Vagabonds

Sat. 13th January (Week 18)
Halton v Wallasey
Moore v Burtonwood
Vagabonds v Lucas

Sat. 10th March (Week 26)
St Marys v Vagabonds
Wallasey v Moore
Helsby v Halton

Sat. 31st March (Week X7)
Moore v Helsby
Vagabonds v Burtonwood
Mossley Hill v Lucas

Sat. 28th April (Week 32)
St Marys OB v Mossley Hill
Wallasey v Vagabonds
Halton v Moore

DOUGLAS (I.O.M.)

Club House, Port-e-Chee, Meadows, Douglas. Tel:
0624 76493
Founded: 1949
Secretary: P.E. Garrett, 15 St. Georges Street,
Douglas, I.O.M. Tel: 0524 29037 (H) or 0624 24535
(W)
League: NW West 1

LEIGH

Round Ash Park, Hand Lane, Leigh, Lancs. Tel:
0942 673526
Founded: 1948
President: Brian Drummond
Chairman: John Twentyman
Secretary: Geoff Burrows, 48 Beech Walk, Leigh,
Lancs. WN7 3LL. Tel: 0942 671625 (H).
061 247 3263 (W)
Fixtures Secretary: Tommy Hughes, 2 Launceston
Road, Hindley Green, Wigan, Lancs. Tel: 0942 57427
(H). 0695 33061
Press Officer: Vacant, refer to secretary
Coach: Joe Downs/Ian McMenemy
Club captain (1988–89): Steve Culshaw
Club captain (1989–90): To be elected
No. of teams: Senior 4/5, Youth 1, Minis 5
Clubhouse facilities: Open Sat/Sun and all evenings
Club colours: Black and amber. (*Change colours:*
Blue or black and white hoops)
Floodlights: No
Local newspapers: The Reporter, The Journal
League: North West 1
League position (1988–89): 10th in North West 2
(Relegated)
League playing record (1988–89): P 10, W 1, D 2, L 7
Competitions won: Winners of Lancashire Plate
Competition, 2nd April 1989

LIVERPOOL COLLEGIATE OLD BOYS

Peter Lloyd Leisure Centre, Bankfield Road, West
Derby, Liverpool 13. Tel: 051 220 1011
Founded: 1925
President: Joe Lucas
Chairman: Steven Peters
Secretary: Paul Walsh, 19 Grosvenor Road, Maghull,
Liverpool L31 5NH. Tel: 051 526 4766 (H). 051 236
1090 (W)
Fixtures Secretary: Geoff Lloyd, 39 Glenbank Close,
Liverpool L9 2BR. Tel: 051 525 1491 (H). 71 33133
(W)
Club captain (1988–89): Jimmy Lloyd
Club captain (1989–90): Andy Walsh
No. of teams: Senior 3, Youth 1
Directions to ground: M62 to end. Turn right onto
Queens Drive, fourth set of lights turn left –
Bankfield Road (Jolly Miller Pub) – ground approx.
300 yards on left
Clubhouse facilities: Open Match days and every
evening
Club colours: Navy/sky blue hoops. (*Change colours:*
Maroon)
Floodlights: No
Membership fees: Full £25, Playing £25, Youth £5,
Student £5
Local newspaper: Liverpool Echo
League: NW West 1
League position (1988–89): 7th
League playing record (1988–89): P 10, W 4, D 0, L 6
Competitions won: Hoylake 15s

NEWTON-LE-WILLOWS

Crow Lane East, Newton-Le-Willows, Merseyside.
Tel: 09252 4591
Founded: 1947
President: Geoffrey Lowe
Chairman: William Roberts
Secretary: Melvyn Garside, 1 Kirkham Avenue,
Lowton, Nr Warrington WA3 1LL. Tel: 0942 675785
(H). 0925 53999 (W)
Fixtures Secretary: John Webster, 175 Park Road
South, Newton-Le-Willows, Merseyside WA12 8HU.
Tel: 09252 7418 (H). 0744 24061 Ext 2413 (W)
Press Officer: Owen O'Neil, 62 Crown Street,
Newton-Le-Willows, Merseyside WA12 9BZ. Tel:
09252 21366
Coach: Colin Bailey and John Gilchrist
Club captain (1988–89): Steve Chesworth
Club captain (1989–90): Steve Chesworth
No. of teams: Senior 4, Youth & Minis 9
Directions to ground: From M6/A580 intersection
(Jnct 23), follow A49 South along Lodge Lane/Ashton
Road. At Oak Tree Public House, turn right into
Crow Lane East, Clubhouse 300 yards on right
Ground capacity: Standing 500
Clubhouse facilities: 2 Bars, dance hall, 5 changing
rooms; also cricket, tennis, bowls and ladies hockey
Club colours: Royal blue and gold stripes. (*Change
colours:* Royal blue)
Nickname: Newts
Floodlights: Only for training
Membership fees: Full £16, Playing £10, Social £4,
Youth £4, Student £4, OAP £4
Programme: No. of editorial pages 4; No. of
advertising pages 4; Price 50p
Programme editor: T.B.A.
Local newspaper: Newton and Golborne News
League: NW West 1
League position (1988–89): 4th
League playing record (1988–89): P 10, W 6, D 1,
L 3, F 128, A 95

OLDERSHAW

Belvidere Fields, Belvidere Road, Wallasey. Tel: 051
638 4379
Founded: 1924
President: Barry Scott
Chairman: Gary Horstman
Secretary: Dough Farnworth, 7 Regents Close,
Thingwall, Wirral L61 1BP. Tel: 051 648 4123 (H).
051 228 4830 Ext 2270 (W)
Fixtures Secretary: Peter Purland, 63 Croxteth Road,
Liverpool 8. Tel: 051 733 4854 (H). 051 724 2235 (W)
Press Officer: Gary Laverick, 86 Broadway Avenue,
Wallasey. Tel: 051 630 5932
Club captain (1988–89): Tony Brunsdon
Club captain (1989–90): Tony Brunsdon
No. of teams: Senior 4, Youth 1, Minis 1
Directions to ground: From Mersey Tunnel
(Kingsway) leave at first exit. 2nd exit from
roundabout, through 3 sets of lights, Club 400 yards
on left after 3rd set
Club colours: Navy blue with gold hoops, white
shorts. (*Change colours:* No)
Floodlights: No
Membership fees: Playing £20, Social £5, Student £5,
OAP £5
Local newspapers: Wirral News, Wirral Globe,
Liverpool Echo
League: NW West 1
League position (1988–89): 1st
League playing record (1988–89): P 9, W 8, D 1, L 0
Competitions won: Won League

OLD INSTONIANS

The Pavilion, The Brian Huntriss Memorial Ground,
The Fender, Woodchurch Road, Prenton,
Birkenhead. Tel: 051 608 3187
Founded: 1935

President: Michael Pollard
Chairman: Roy Chappell
Secretary: Gwilym H. Williams, 12 Victoria Mount, Oxton, Birkenhead, Wirral L43 5TH. Tel: 051 652 1923 (H), 051 653 5555 ext. 6548 (W)
Fixtures Secretary: Ian Mackie, 28 Mount Road, Wallasey, Wirral. Tel: 051 639 1167
Press Officer: David Ball, 123 Holmlands Drive, Prenton, Birkenhead. Tel: 051 608 9798
Coach: Peter Collins
Club captain (1988–89): John Tuohy
Club captain (1989–90): Paul Lee
No. of teams: Senior 4–5, Youth 1
Directions to ground: Adjacent to roundabout at Junction 3 on M53 in direction of Birkenhead, turn left immediately before railway bridge
Ground capacity: Standing 1500
Clubhouse facilities: Baths and changing for 6 sides, bar, main room, members' lounge
Club colours: Black and gold hoops. (*Change colours:* Green with yellow collar)
Floodlights: Yes (training only)
League: NM/W 1

OLD PARKONIANS

H. Martin Curpney Memorial Ground, Holm Lane, Oxton, Birkenhead L43 2HU. Tel: 051 652 3105
Founded: 1928
President: Ron Caton
Chairman: Brian Cusick
Secretary: Paul Mullen, 8 Deerwood Crescent, Little Sutton, South Wirral L66 1SE. Tel: 051 339 1270 (H). 051 357 2777 (W)
Fixtures Secretary: Martin Curpney, 8 Christleton Close, Oxton, Birkenhead, Merseyside. Tel: 051 608 4708 (H). 051 521 3319 (W)
Press Officer: J.K. Maner, Cartref, Foxcover Close, Heswall Hills, Wirral. Tel: 051 342 5543 (H). 051 356 1010/9 (W)
Coach: John Lander
Club captain (1988–89): B. Lloyd
Club captain (1989–90): B. Lloyd
No. of teams: Senior 5, Youth 1
Directions to ground: Heading North on M53, come off at Junction ? and take turn off to Prenton
Ground capacity: Standing 250
Clubhouse facilities: Bar, entertainment lounge
Club colours: Maroon blue and white jerseys and stockings and white shorts. (*Change colours:* Black shirts)
Nickname: Old Parks
Floodlights: Only on training ground
Membership fees: Playing £37, Social £18, Student £12
Programme editor: As Secretary
Local newspapers: Liverpool Echo and Liverpool Post
League: NW West 1
League position (1988–89): 2nd
League playing record (1988–89): P 9, W 7, D 0, L 2, F 119, A 57

ORMSKIRK

Green Lane, Ormskirk, Lancashire. Tel: 0695 72523
Founded: 1926
President: David S. Firth
Chairman: Stan Cunliffe
Secretary: Mark Bailie, 7 Pine Grove, Ormskirk, Lancs. L39 2YS. Tel: 0695 70269 (H). 051 220 5552 (W)
Fixtures Secretary: Alan Worthington, 21 Sefton Gardens, Aughton, Ormskirk, Lancs. Tel: 0695 423762
Press Officer: As Secretary
Coach: John Smith-Warren
Club captain (1988–89): Kevin Sketcher
Club captain (1989–90): Chris Arkwright
No. of teams: Senior 6, Youth 1
Directions to ground: From South, A59 to Preston, at Ormskirk turn right onto Green Lane. From North A59 to Liverpool, at Ormskirk turn left onto Green

Lane. From East A570 to Ormskirk, follow one way to church, turn right onto Green Lane
Clubhouse facilities: Players bar, members/sponsors lounge, 6 changing rooms
Club colours: Light blue, dark blue, green hoops, dark blue shorts. (*Change colours:* Dark green shorts, dark blue shorts)
Nickname: The Gingerbreads
Floodlights: No
Membership fees: Full £25, Playing £25, Social £15, Youth £10, Student £10, OAP £8
Programme: No. of editorial pages 2; No. of advertising pages 6 (cup matches only); Price 50p
Programme editor: Sam Botfield, Ormskirk RUFC, Green Lane, Ormskirk, Lancs.
Local newspapers: Ormskirk Advertiser, Ormskirk & Southport Star, Liverpool Daily Post & Echo
League: NW West 1
League position (1988–89): Joint 3rd
League playing record (1988–89): P 10, W 6, D 0, L 4, F 135, A 121
Competitions won: Ormskirk HC Trophy 1988, Southport HC Trophy 1988

RUSKIN PARK

'Pilkington' Sports Ground, Ruskin Drive, St Helens, Lancashire. Tel: 0744 22893
Founded: 1954
President: John Dootson
Chairman: Michael Clarke
Secretary: John Philip Middlehurst, 10 Upholland Road, Billinge, Wigan, Lancs. WN5 7JA. Tel: 0744 892114 (H). 692533 (W)
Fixtures Secretary: Geoffrey Bath, 14 Orville Street, St Helens. Tel: 0744 815719 (H). 0744 611811 (W)
Press Officer: B. Jones, 17 Brooklands Road, Eccleston, St Helens. Tel: 0744 37542
Coach: A. Collins
Club captain (1988–89): Graham Holmes
Club captain (1989–90): William Parr
No. of teams: Senior 4
Directions to ground: A580 East Lans Road. Take sign post A570 St Helens, after mile enter 1-way system, 800 yards right turn, sign post Pilkington Sports Ground, Ruskin Drive
Clubhouse facilities: Open 7 days per week pm and evenings. All day Saturday
Club colours: Blue black and white hoops. (*Change colours:* Yet to be decided for 89/90)
Nickname: Ruskin
Floodlights: No
Membership fees: Ruskin Park RFC is the Rugby Union Section to 'Pilkington' Recreation Club. The fees are: Outside member £17, Employee £5
Programme: League games only; Price: donation
Local newspapers: St Helens Reporter, St Helens Star
League: NW West 1
League position (1988–89): 8th
League playing record (1988–89): P 10, W 4, D 0, L 6, F 149, A 157

ST. EDWARDS OB's

St. Edwards College, Sandfield Park, West Derby, Liverpool. Tel: 051 2281414
Founded: 1950
Chairman: F. Nelson
Secretary: D. Phoenix, 11 Linden Drive, Huyton, Merseyside L36 5TT. Tel: 051 4891221
Fixtures Secretary: R. Reilly, 130 Quarry Street, Wootton
Coach: N. Melville
Club captain (1988–89): P. Falconer
Club captain (1989–90): P. Falconer
No. of teams: Senior 4
Club colours: Blue/yellow
Floodlights: Yes (training)
Membership fees: Playing £18
League: NW W1
League position (1988–89): 3rd

League playing record (1988–89): P 10, W 6, D 1, L 3, F 173, A 117

SOUTH LIVERPOOL

Halewood Leisure Centre, Barncroft Road, Halewood, Liverpool 26. Tel: 051 486 8502
Founded: 1963
President: Cecil Sherrington
Chairman: Ian Bailey, 10 Nicander Road, Liverpool L18 1HY. Tel: 051 734 1403
Secretary: David Edge, 93 Millwood Road, Speke, Liverpool
Fixtures Secretary: Lawrence Sherrington, 14 Brook Way, Great Sankey, Warrington, Cheshire, WA5 1RZ. Tel: Penketh 6768
Press Officer: As Secretary
Coach: Paul Birmingham/Colin Smith
Club captain (1988–89): Thomas Ross
Club captain (1989–90): Chris Greenslade
No. of teams: Senior 2
Club colours: Black. (*Change colours:* Black and amber)
Floodlights: No
League: NW West 1
League position (1988–89): 2nd
League playing record (1988–89): P 9, W 7, D 2, L 0

NORTH WEST WEST 2

ASPULL

Woodshaw Park, Woods Road, Aspull, Wigan, Lancs. Tel: 0942 831611
Founded: 1947
President: John Leyland
Chairman: Steve Bennett
Secretary: Martin Horrobin. Tel: 0257 424729
Fixtures Secretary: Geoff Gregson, 26 Lyndon Avenue, Shevington, Wigan, Lancs. WN6 8BT. Tel: 0257 421421 (H). 0942 492221 (W)
Press Officer: Gary Owen. Tel: 0204 696146 (W)
Coach: Bill Woodcock
Club captain (1988–89): Stephen E. Peet
Club captain (1989–90): Stephen E. Peet
No. of teams: Senior 4, Youth 3, Minis 3
Directions to ground: 4 miles from Junction 25 M6, 3 miles from Junction 6 M61, Ground off Wigan Road, Aspull (B 5238)
Clubhouse facilities: Three pitches, one mini pitch and large floodlit training pitch. Club open every evening
Club colours: Sky and navy blue hoops. (*Change colours:* 1) Maroon; 2) Red and black hoops)
Floodlights: No
Membership fees: Full £20, Playing £20, Social £3, Youth £5, OAP £3
Ground admission: £1
Programme: No. of editorial pages 6; No. of advertising pages 12; Price 50p
Programme editor: Steve Bennett, 3 Fern Close, Shevington, Wigan, Lancs.
Local newspapers: Wigan Observer, Wigan Reporter, Wigan Evening Post
League: NW West 1
League position (1988–89): 10th NW West 1
League playing record (1988–89): P 10, W 3, D 0, L 7, F 163, A 144

BIRCHFIELD

Moor Lane, Witton, Birmingham. Tel: 356 2142
Founded: 1957
Secretary: D.F. Kilmister, 319 Bordesley Green East, Stechford, Birmingham B33 8QF. Tel: 021 784 0460 (H)
League: NW West 2
Club Colours: Green/Black

CHESTER COLLEGE

Chester College, Cheyney Road, Chester CH1 4BJ. Tel: 0244 375444
Founded: 1889
President: P.E. Grinter
Chairman: P.E. Grinter
Secretary: Mark Harrison, address as above
Fixtures Secretary: Stephen Pugh, address as above
Press Officer: Steven Hughes, address as above
Coach: Steven Lander
Club captain (1988–89): Simon John Robertson
Club captain (1989–90): Simon Charles Worrall
No. of teams: Senior 2
Directions to ground: Signposted from Northgate roundabout
Clubhouse facilities: Social club, showers, etc.
Club colours: Green with black and white hoop. (*Change colours:* Reverse)
Floodlights: No
Local newspapers: Chester Chronicle, Tonight, Cheshire Observer
League: North West, West 2
Competitions won: British Colleges League, Ripon and York Sevens

EAGLE

Thornton Road, Gt. Sankey, Warrington. Tel: 0925 32926
Founded: 1962
President: Mr Barry Morris
Chairman: Mr David Attew
Secretary: Mr Joseph Anthony Lasko, 3 Colville Grove, Sale, Cheshire M33 4FW. Tel: 061 969 7808
Fixtures Secretary: Bernard Lawton, 9 Mullion Grove, Padgate, Warrington. Tel: 0925 811639
Coach: Barry Morris/Nigel Cook
Club captain (1988–89): Vincent Sandwell
Club captain (1989–90): John Hartley
No. of teams: Senior 4
Directions to ground: Follow A562 from Warrington towards Widnes. Turn left into Thornton Road at Lane End's traffic lights
Club colours: Black and white hoops. (*Change colours:* All red)
Floodlights: No
Membership fees: Full £16, Playing £16, Social £10, Youth £3.50, Student £3.50
Local newspaper: Warrington Guardian
League: NW West 2
League position (1988–89): 4th
League playing record (1988–89): P 33, W 19, D 2, L 11, F 483, A 330

HIGHTOWN

Sandy Lane, Hightown, Liverpool. Tel: 051 929 2330
Founded: 1921
Chairman: Terry T. Mottram
Secretary: Lawrence Crawford, Elwood, 2 The Nurseries, Formby, Merseyside L37 4JG. Tel: 07048 79159 (H). 0772 34777 (W)
Fixtures Secretary: Mr Chris Williams, 75 Blundel Road, Hightown, Liverpool L38. Tel: 051 929 3735
Press Officer: Richard Norriss, c/o Hightown R.U.F.C., Sandy Lane, Hightown, Liverpool L38. Tel: 051 924 2011 (Eve). 051 920 4163 (W)
Coach: Ray Baker/Niel Shaw
Club captain (1988–89): Russell Aikenhead
Club captain (1989–90): Russell Aikenhead
No. of teams: Senior 3, Minis 1
Directions to ground: Junction 7 M57. Turn left A59, 150 yards traffic lights turn right (A565 towards Southport). Next lights (Blundel Pub on right) turn left. T-junction turn right, follow road all the way round, just before bridge left at bollards. 1st left again follow the road round down directly in to Club car park
Clubhouse facilities: Open every day/evenings
Club colours: Brown white blue hoops, blue shorts

and socks. (*Change colours:* Maroon and yellow hoops, blue shorts and socks)
Nickname: Town
Floodlights: Yes
Membership fees: Full £34, Social £12, Youth £4, Student £6
Local newspapers: Cresby Herald, Formby Times
League: North West 2
League position (1988–89): 3rd from bottom
League playing record (1988–89): P 9, W 2, D 1, L 6
Competitions won: Hightown Invitation Sevens, Algarve Open Sevens

HOYLAKE

Melrose Avenue
Founded: 1922
Secretary: A. Warren, 8 Redhouse Bank, West Kirkby, Wirral, L48 5EH. Tel: 051 625 2178 (H). 051 236 2616 (W)
Fixtures Secretary: G. Guest, 8 School Lane, Meols, Wirral. Tel: 051 632 2794
League: NW West 2
Club Colours: Red/Green/White

OLD ANSELMIANS

'Malone Field', Eastham Village Road, Eastham, Wirral, Merseyside. Tel: 051 327 1613
Founded: 1947
President: The Headmaster, St Anselms College
Chairman: Terry Cooke
Secretary: John Moscrop, 8 Whetstone Lane, Birkenhead, Wirral, Merseyside L41 2QR. Tel: 051 632 2899 (H). 2214 (W)
Fixtures Secretary: Tony McArdle, 11 Marksway, Pensby, Wirral, Merseyside L61 9PB. Tel: 051 648 3793 (H). 0244 502446 (W)
Coach: Dave Buttery
Club captain (1988–89): Sean Campbell
No. of teams: Senior 5
Directions to ground: A41 from Birkenhead (New Chester Road) 1st left into Eastham Village Road. Or from M53 Junction 5, A41 towards Eastham, 1st right into Eastham Village Road and through the village
Club colours: Blue, yellow and white hoops and navy blue shorts.
Nickname: The Saints
Floodlights: No
Membership fees: Full £30, Playing £30, Social £15, Student £15
Local newspapers: Liverpool Echo, Daily Post, Wirral News
League: NW West 2
League playing record (1988–89): P 37, W 14, D 2, L 21, F 413, A 433

OLD ROCKFERRIANS

The Pavilion, Prenton Dell Road, Prenton, Birkenhead. Tel: 051 608 1501
Founded: 1928
Secretary: B.P. Meehan, 11 Kings Drive, Irby, Wirral, Merseyside. Tel: 051 648 5695 (H). 051 645 6917 (W)
League: NW West 2
Club Colours: Maroon/Blue/White

PORT SUNLIGHT

Leverhulme Playing Fields, Green Lane, Bromborough. Tel: 051334 3677
Founded: 1908
Secretary: T. Bennion, 12 Grasville Road, Higher Tranmere, Wirra LH2 5PU. Tel: 051 645 9548 (H)
League: NW West 2
Club Colours: Black/White

SEFTON

Thornmead Lane, Layfield Road, West Derby, Liverpool 12. Tel: 051 228 9092
Founded: 1907
Secretary: T.J. Beggs, 38 Plattsville Road, Mossley Hill, Liverpool LT8 0HZ. Tel: 051 722 6986 (H) or 051 546 2961 (W)
League: NW West 2

SHELL STANLOW

Chester Road, Ellesmere Port, Cheshire. Tel: 051 355 2704
Founded: 1948
Chairman: Edward T. Kilshaw
Secretary: Geoffrey M. Pugh, 23 Vale Road, Whitby, Ellesmere Port, Cheshire. Tel: 051 355 5795 (H). 051 373 5219 (W)
Fixtures Secretary: See Secretary
Press Officer: Alec Dale, 12 Archers Way, Great Sutton, Ellesmere Port, Cheshire. Tel: 051 339 7823 (H). 051 355 2125 (W)
Coach: Robert Edwards
Club captain (1988–89): Steven Lundstram
Club captain (1989–90): David Layder
No. of teams: Senior 4
Directions to ground: M531 Junction 6. Head for Ellesmere Port. Turn to Ellesmere Port at the Strawberry roundabout. Clubhouse 400 yards on right
Clubhouse facilities: Full social club
Club colours: Amber. (*Change colours:* Royal blue)
Floodlights: No
Membership fees: Full £5, Playing £5, Social £5
Local newspaper: Ellesmere Port Pioneer
League: NW West 3
League position (1988–89): 2nd
League playing record (1988–89): P 11, W 9, D 1, L 1, F 200, A 73

VULCAN

The Sports Ground, Off Wargrave Road, Newton-le-Willows, Merseyside. Tel: 0925 24180
Founded: 1956
Chairman: Dave Ashton
Secretary: A. Stockton, 58 Westover Road, Padgate, Cheshire. Tel: 0925 827799 (H), 0942 227979 (W)
Fixtures Secretary: J. Bajer, 5 Heylock Close, Newton-le-Willows, Merseyside. Tel: 0925 26533
Club captain (1988–89): M. Hayes
No. of teams: Senior 4
Directions to ground: Junc. 23 M6 to Newton-le-Willows, 1 mile to small r'about at Oak Tree public house after mile left → under railway bridge → Wargrave public house → left into sports ground
Ground capacity: Seating Unrestricted
Club colours: Black/amber. (*Change colours:* Red)
Floodlights: No
Membership fees: Playing £8.50
League: NW W2
League position (1988–89): 6th
League playing record (1988–89): P 9, W 3, D 0, L 6, F 97, A 113

NORTH WEST WEST 3

BURTONWOOD

Fir Tree Lane, Burtonwood, Warrington. Tel: 09252 4480
Founded: 1964
President: Geoffrey Davis
Chairman: Antony Hampson
Secretary: Ray Rigby, Burtonwood Community Centre, Chapel Lane, Burtonwood, Warrington, Cheshire. Tel: 09252 7140 (H). 0925 58766
Fixtures Secretary: Jim Whalin, 88 Fir Tree Lane, Burtonwood, Warrington, Cheshire. Tel: 09252 7079

Press Officer: As Secretary
Coach: Jim Whalin
Club captain (1988–89): Wayne Tapper
Club captain (1989–90): Wayne Tapper
No. of teams: Senior 2
Directions to ground: M6 Junction 21, A49 head for Newton-Le-Willows, at 1st set of traffic lights turn left for 3 miles. At T-junction turn left, Clubhouse 200 yards on left
Clubhouse facilities: Yes
Club colours: Red, black, white hoops. (*Change colours:* All black with red/white hoop)
Floodlights: No
Membership fees: Full £12, Playing £12, Social £3, Youth £2, Student £2
Local Newspapers: Newton and Golbourne Guardian
League: NW West 3
League position (1988–89): 7th
League playing record (1988–89): P 7, W 2, D 0, L 5, F 91, A 157

HALTON

ICI Recreation Ground, Liverpool Road, Widnes. Tel: 051 424 2350.
Secretary: J.F. Brady, 22 Highfield Crescent, Widnes, Cheshire WA8 7DN. Tel: 051 423 1566 (H), 092851 2076 (W)
Press Officer: D.W. Kitty. Tel: 09282 5083
Club Colours: Blue/White
League: NW West 3
Final position (1987–88): 1st
Competitions won: NW West 3

HELSBY

Bicc Athletic and Social Club, Chester Road, Helsby. Tel: Helsby 2267
Founded: 1962-3
President: R. Highcock
Chairman: J. Gregory
Secretary: E. Lamb, 3 Fairbank, Elton, Nr Chester. After July as it is a new house. Otherwise contact me on Helsby 4039
Fixtures Secretary: A. Ryder, 64 Chester Road, Helsby
Press Officer: T. O'Neil, 9 Mill Close, Cinnamon Brow, Warrington. Tel: 9 812066
Coach: M. Buck
Club captain (1988–89): P. Ashton
Club captain (1989–90): A. Bolland
No. of teams: Senior 3
Club colours: Black/amber hoops. (*Change colours:* All black strip)
Floodlights: No
Membership fees: Playing £15, Social £5
Local newspapers: Chester Chronicle, Runcorn Weekly News
League: NW West 3
League playing record (1988–89): P 11, W 6, D 1, L 4, F 13

LUCAS

Walton Park, Walton Hall Avenue, Liverpool 14. Tel: 051 523 3472
Secretary: Peter Gray, 102 Turnberry, Skelmersdale. Tel: 0695 331195
Press Officer: Peter Hamilton. Tel: 051 226 3592
Club colours: Blue
League: NW West 3
League position (1988–89): 12th

GENTLEMEN OF MOORE

Moss Lane, Moore, Nr Warrington. Tel: 0925 74 473
Founded: 1968
Chairman: M.W. Butler

Secretary: J.E. Horton, 4 Selworthy Drive, Thelwall, Nr Warrington, Cheshire WA4 2HT. Tel: 0925 65625
Fixtures Secretary: R. Johnson, 53 Shepperton Close, Appleton, Nr Warrington. Tel: 0925 604191
Club captain (1988–89): S. Woollacott
Club captain (1989–90): D. Ellis
No. of teams: Senior 3
Directions to ground: M56 Junction 11, A56 towards Warrington, follow signs for Moore. Turn off main road in Village into Moss Lane
Clubhouse facilities: Open Match days and evenings, bowling green
Club colours: Black and gold. (*Change colours:* Red)
Floodlights: No
Membership fees: Playing £7, Social £4
Local newspaper: Warrington Guardian
League: NW West 3
League position (1988–89): 6th
League playing record (1988–89): P 11, W 6, D 1, L 4, F 97, A 155

PRESCOT RAINHILL

Victoria Terrace, Rainhill, Nr. Prescot. Tel: 051 426 2805
Founded: 1949
Secretary: M.S. Hughes,, 12 Grebe Avenue, Eccleston Park, St. Helens, Merseyside. Tel: 0744 56452 (H). 061 998 7919 (W)
League: NW West 3
Club Colours: Maroon/White

MOSSLEY HILL

PO Box 9, Mossley Hill Road, Liverpool L18 8DX. Tel: 051 724 4377
Founded: 1986
President: Fred Hewitson
Chairman: John Parr
Secretary: Andrew Pealing, 41 Shirley Road, Liverpool L19 7NU. Tel: 051 427 4954 (H). 051 236 5428 Ext 3119 (W)
Fixtures Secretary: Keith Spencer, 82 Stevenson Street, Wavertree, Liverpool L15 4HB. Tel: 051 733 6887 (H). 051 922 2723 (W)
Press Officer: As Fixtures Secretary
Club captain (1988–89): Simon Edge
Club captain (1989–90): John Clark
No. of teams: Senior 3
Directions to ground: 2 miles South from end of M62 motorway, signposted for Mossley Hill Station close by. Clubhouse is on Mossley Hill Road behind large church at top of hill
Clubhouse facilities: Open every evening, all day Sat/Sun, multi sports facility
Club colours: Maroon and gold hoops or quarters, white shorts. (*Change colours:* Plain maroon, white shorts)
Floodlights: No
Membership fees: Playing £24, Social £7
Local newspaper: Liverpool Daily Post and Echo
League: NW West 3
League position (1988–89): 4th
League playing record (1988–89): P 11, W 8, D 0, L 3, F 165, A 103

ST MARY'S OLD BOYS

17 Moor Lane, Crosby, Liverpool L23. Tel: 051 924 1774
Chairman: James McInerney
Secretary: Mark John Cunningham, 48 Cambridge Avenue, Crosby, Liverpool L23 7XW. Tel: 051 924 5201
Fixtures Secretary: Peter Moore, 77 Freshfield Road, Formby, Merseyside. Tel: Formby 78537 (H). 051 924 4210 (W)
Press Officer: John Baker, 44 Armaury Road, Thornton, Liverpool 23. Tel: 051 931 1352 (H). 051 709 0692 (W)
Coach: Bernard Gavan

Club captain (1988–89): Bernard Gavan
Club captain (1989–90): Bernard Gavan
No. of teams: Senior 3
Directions to ground: A565 Liverpool to Southport Road, signs Crosby and Hightown
Clubhouse facilities: Bar
Club colours: Maroon, blue, yellow hoops (*Change colours:* White)
Floodlights: Yes
Membership fees: Full £12
Local newspapers: Crosby Herald, Liverpool Echo
League: NW West 3
League position (1988–89): 3rd
League playing record (1988–89): P 11, W 9, D 0, L 2, F 301, A 82

VAGABONDS

Glencrutchery Road, Douglas, Isle of Man
Founded: 1964
Nickname: Vaggas
President: George Shinnie Rae
Chairman: Peter John Barlow
Secretary: Nicholas Williams, 21 Woodbourne Square, Douglas, Isle of Man. Tel: 0624 23221
Fixtures Secretary: Gerald Dawson, Queenscliffe Hoteel, Palace View Terrace, Douglas, Isle of Man Tel: 0624 75831
Press Officer: Ian Forrest, Arkadia, Westminster Drive, Douglas, Isle of Man. Tel: 0624 76106
Coach: Brian Mellor
Club captain (1988–89): Chris Watterson
Club capatai 1989–90): Nigel Callow
No. of teams: Senior 2
Directions to ground: Rear of TT Races Grandstand.
Ground capacity: approx 1000
Clubhouse facilities: Home and visitors changing roomns, showers, bar room and kitchen
Club colours: White, black and yellow shirts, black shorts, black and yellow socks.. (*Change colours:*

black and yellow alternate hoops)
Floodlights: Yes, suitable for training only
Membership fees: Full £15, Playing £15, Social £10, Youth £5.00, Student £5.00.
Ground admission: Free
Local newspapers: IOM Examiner and Manx Independent
League: NW W3
League position (1988–89): 8th

WALLASEY

Cross Lane, Leasowe Road, Wallasey, Merseyside.
Tel: 051 638 1486
Founded: 1926
President: Andrew Rae
Secretary: John Burton, 14 Seaview Lane, Irby, Wirral, Merseyside L61 3UL. Tel: 051 648 4341 (H). 061 236 3707 (W)
Fixtures Secretary: A. Rae, 8 Inchcape Road, Wallasey, Merseyside. Tel: 051 638 6903
Press Officer: Mr J. Banister, 56 Barnston Road, Thingwall, Wirral, Merseyside
Coach: Mike Chatham
Club captain (1988–89): Neil McEwan
Club captain (1989–90): Neil McEwan
No. of teams: Senior 5, Youth 1, Minis 1
Directions to ground: From M53 Junction 1 (Bidston flyover) take spur road to New Brighton/Wallasey. Take 2nd exit road and turn right at traffic lights into Cross lane
Club colours: Red/black/white hoops.
Floodlights: Training lights
Membership fees: Full £25, Playing £25, Social £10
Ground admission: Nil
Local newspaper: Wallasey News
League: NW West 3
League playing record (1988–89): P 10, W 5, D 0, L 5

Wasps and Richmond are the top lassies at the moment, but Sale aim to prove that the North is best at everything. In the photo above Olive Tocher (with ball) bravely holds on supported by skipper Laura Murrell. Photo: Peter Barton

NORTH EAST LEAGUES

ROTHERHAM were the oustanding team in the North-East leagues with their brilliant form running beyond the set programme to the extent that they won a Rugby World & Post Junior Club of the Month award. However, in the competition itself they were invincible, winning all 10 matches for a points differential of 273–54. This left all the others trailing from an early stage, and at the other end the fate of Westoe was sealed also very early. They were replaced by York from North-East 2, who had to fight off a determined challenge from promoted Selby and Roundhegians for the top place.

Other unbeaten teams in North-East competitions were Whitby, a Yorkshire club who won Durham/Northumberland 2, and Barnard Castle who took top place in Durham/Northumberland 4 with an unblemished record. Bramley (Yorkshire 1) drew one and won the rest of their 10 matches, Yarnbury (Yorkshire 3) drew two but won the rest of their 10 matches and Sheffield Oaks (promoted the previous season) extended their winning run to 19 consecutive league matches (10 in 1988–89), a figure also achieved by Whitby – another to be promoted in consecutive seasons.

Bridlington, who lost only one match and drew another over two seasons, were the only other team to be promoted twice, although Mowden Park, the Darlington club, came close to upsetting Rockcliff in Durham/Northumberland 1.

Houghton (Durham/Northumberland 3) were one team to descend for a second consecutive season, but they were the only ones to suffer such humiliation and again the league committee assessors seem to have done their homework well.

Last season's "worst team" Armthorpe merged with Markham in Yorkshire 6 and the new club won three matches – the same number as Markham managed on their own last time round!

NORTH EAST DIVISION ONE:

Dr. W.L. Hetherington,
97 Kells Lane, Low Fell,
Gateshead, Tyne & Wear   (H) 091 4879128
NE9 5XX   (O) 091 2674393

NORTH EAST DIVISION TWO:

John Scott,
8 Main Street, Cherry Burton,
Beverley   (H) 0964 551340
E. Yorks   (B) 0532 495666

TABLES 1987–88

NORTH EAST 1

	P	W	D	L	F	A	PTS
Wharfedale	10	9	0	1	140	55	18
Rotherham	10	8	0	2	173	52	16
Gateshead Fell	10	7	0	3	122	79	14
O Crossleyans	10	6	1	3	143	105	13
Morpeth	10	6	0	4	90	84	12
Thornesians	10	6	0	4	115	117	12
O Broadleians	10	3	1	6	88	126	7
Westoe	10	3	0	7	98	139	6
Keighley	10	3	0	7	65	118	6
Blaydon	10	3	0	7	107	177	6
Ripon	10	0	0	10	74	163	0

NORTH EAST 2

	P	W	D	L	F	A	PTS
Novocastrians	10	9	1	0	137	72	19
Stockton	10	9	0	1	190	76	18
Pontefract	10	6	1	3	146	144	13
O Hymerians	10	6	0	4	104	95	12
Beverley	10	5	0	5	144	85	10
Selby	10	4	0	6	86	78	8
York	10	4	0	6	105	112	8
Ryton	10	3	0	7	91	134	6
Pocklington	10	3	0	7	94	157	6
Newcastle Univ	10	3	0	7	123	191	6
Barnsley	10	2	0	8	82	158	4

TABLES 1988–89

NORTH EAST 1

	P	W	D	L	F	A	PTS
Rotherham	10	10	0	0	273	54	20
Stockton	10	7	0	3	190	123	14
O Crossleyans	10	7	0	3	119	83	14
Gateshead Fell	10	7	0	3	138	105	14
Novocastrians	10	6	0	4	104	141	12
O Brodleians	10	5	0	5	131	141	10
Keighley	10	4	0	6	113	132	8
Morpeth	10	3	0	7	98	129	6
Thornensians	10	3	0	7	70	104	6
Blaydon	10	2	0	8	85	137	4
Westoe	10	1	0	9	72	244	2

NORTH EAST 2

	P	W	D	L	F	A	PTS
York	10	8	1	1	161	94	17
Selby	10	7	1	2	134	90	15
Roundhegians	10	6	2	2	150	72	14
Pontefract	10	5	1	4	142	112	11
Beverley	10	5	0	5	90	97	10
Newcastle Univ	10	5	0	5	129	154	10
Ripon	10	4	0	6	123	122	8
Blyth	10	3	1	6	113	144	7
O Hymerians	10	3	0	7	107	143	6
Ryton	10	3	0	7	95	152	10
Pocklington	10	3	0	7	75	139	6

NORTHERN DIVISION FIXTURES 1989/90

NORTH EAST ONE

Sat. 9th September (Week 2)
Blaydon v Gateshead Fell
Novocastrians v Old Brodleians
Selby v Morpeth
Keighley v Stockton
Thornensians v York

Sat. 23rd September (Week 4)
York v Blaydon
Stockton v Thornensians
Morpeth v Keighley
Old Brodleians v Selby
Old Crossleyians v Novocastrians

Sat. 14th October (Week 6)
Blaydon v Stockton
Gateshead Fell v York
Selby v Old Crossleyians
Keighley v Old Brodleians
Thornensians v Morpeth

Sat. 28th October (Week 8)
Stockton v Gateshead Fell
Morpeth v Blaydon
Old Brodleians v Thornensians
Old Crossleyians v Keighley
Novocastrians v Selby

Sat. 11th November (Week 10)
Blaydon v Old Brodleians
Gateshead Fell v Morpeth
York v Stockton
Keighley v Novocastrians
Thornensians v Old Crossleyians

Sat 18th November (Week 11)
Morpeth v York
Old Brodleians v Gateshead Fell
Old Crossleyians v Blaydon
Novocastrians v Thornensians
Selby v Keighley

Sat. 25th November (Week 12)
Blaydon v Novocastrians
Gateshead v Old Crossleyians
York v Old Brodleians
Stockton v Morpeth
Thornensians v Selby

Sat. 13th January (Week 18)
Old Brodleians v Stockton
Old Crossleyians v York
Novocastrians v Gateshead Fell
Selby v Blaydon
Keighley v Thornensians

Sat. 10th March (Week 26)
Blaydon v Keighley
Gateshead Fell v Selby
York v Novocastrians
Stockton v Old Crossleyians
Morpeth v Old Brodleians

Sat. 31st March (Week X7)
Old Crossleyians v Morpeth
Novocastrians v Stockton
Selby v York
Keighley v Gateshead Fell
Thornensians v Blaydon

Sat. 28th April (Week 32)
Gateshead Fell v Thornensians
York v Keighley
Stockton v Selby
Morpeth v Novocastrians
Old Brodleians v Old Crossleyians

NORTHERN DIVISION FIXTURES 1989/90

NORTH EAST TWO

Sat. 9th September (Week 2)
Newcastle Univ v Beverley
Pontefract v Old Hymerians
Ryton v Ripon
Blyth v Rockcliff
Westoe v Roundhegians

Sat. 23rd September (Week 4)
Roundhegians v Newcastle Univ
Rockcliff v Westoe
Ripon v Blyth
Old Hymerians v Ryton
Bramley v Pontefract

Sat. 14th October (Week 6)
Newcastle Univ v Rockcliff
Beverley v Roundhegians
Ryton v Bramley
Blyth v Old Hymerians
Westoe v Ripon

Sat. 28th October (Week 8)
Rockcliff v Beverley
Ripon v Newcastle Univ
Old Hymerians v Westoe
Bramley v Blyth
Pontefract v Ryton

Sat. 11th November (Week 10)
Newcastle Univ v Old Hymerians
Beverley v Ripon
Roundhegians v Rockcliff
Blyth v Pontefract
Westoe v Bramley

Sat 18th November (Week 11)
Ripon v Roundhegians
Old Hymerians v Beverley
Bramley v Newcastle Univ
Pontefract v Westoe
Ryton v Blyth

Sat. 25th November (Week 12)
Newcastle Univ v Pontefract
Gateshead v Bramley
Roundhegians v Old Hymerians
Rockcliff v Ripon
Westoe v Ryton

Sat. 13th January (Week 18)
Old Hymerians v Rockcliff
Bramley v Roundhegians
Pontefract v Beverley
Ryton v Newcastle Univ
Blyth v Westoe

Sat. 10th March (Week 26)
Newcastle Univ v Blyth
Beverley v Ryton
Roundhegians v Pontefract
Rockcliff v Bramley
Ripon v Old Hymerians

Sat. 31st March (Week X7)
Bramley v Ripon
Pontefract v Rockcliff
Ryton v Roundhegians
Blyth v Beverley
Westoe v Newcastle Univ

Sat. 28th April (Week 32)
Beverley v Westoe
Roundhegians v Blyth
Rockcliff v Ryton
Ripon v Pontefract
Old Hymerians v Bramley

NORTH EAST 1

BLAYDON

Crow Trees, Hexham Road, Swalwell, Newcastle-Upon-Tyne NE16 3BN. Tel: 091 414 2528
Founded: 1888
President: Albert Forster
Chairman: Barry Urwin
Secretary: Tom Nixon Brown, 5 The Avenue, Axwell Park, Blaydon-On-Tyne, Tyne & Wear NE21 5ND. Tel: 091 414 3698
Fixtures Secretary: James M. Huxley, The Mount, Sunniside Road, Sunniside, Newcastle-Upon-Tyne NE16. Tel: 091 488 7280 (H). 091 388 2521 (W)
Press Officer: Thomas Sidney Robson, 26 Mary Street, Blaydon-On-Tyne, Tyne & Wear NE21 5PZ. Tel: 091 414 3079
Coach: Michael Mahoney
No. of teams: Senior 4, Youth 5
Directions to ground: From South turn off A1(M) on to A69. Turn off at junction signposted Swalwell and keep right on to Hexham Road
Ground capacity: Seating 400, standing 2500
Clubhouse facilities: Open all evenings and mid-day Match days, Sats and holidays
Club colours: Scarlet jerseys, white shorts, scarlet socks with 2 white bars. (*Change colours:* All white)
Nickname: Bricks
Floodlights: Yes
Membership fees: Full £15, Playing £15, Social £1, Youth £6, Student £4
Ground admission: 50p
Programme: No. of editorial pages 4; No. of advertising pages 6; Price 50p
Programme editor: See Fixtures Secretary
Local newspapers: Newcastle Journal, Evening Chronicle
League: North East 1
League position (1988–89): 10th
League playing record (1988–89): P 10, W 2, D 0, L 8, F 85, A 137

GATESHEAD FELL

Hedley Lawson Park, Eastwood Gardens, Low Fell, Gateshead NE9 5UB. Tel: 091 487 5739
Founded: 1907
President: Ronnie Johnston
Chairman: Ian Willis
Secretary: John McMillan, 95 Kells Lane, Low Fell, Gateshead NE9 5XX. Tel: 091 4870355
Fixtures Secretary: Dr Lee Hetherington, 97 Kells Lane, Low Fell, Gateshead NE9 5XX. Tel: 091 4879128 (H). 091 2674393 (W)
Press Officer: As Secretary
Coach: Alan Thompson
Club captain (1988–89): Ronnie Ward
Club captain (1989–90): Graeme Kell
No. of teams: Senior 4, Youth 1, Minis 3
Directions to ground: Take A6127 (Durham Road) through Low Fell, turn right (from S), left (from N) along Dryden Road or Kells Lane to St Peters School. Ground is parallel
Ground capacity: Seating 350, standing 2000
Clubhouse facilities: Lounge/bar, function hall/bar/kitchen, committee room
Club colours: Dark blue/light blue narrow hoops, red socks. (*Change colours:* Red)
Nickname: The Fell
Floodlights: Training only
Membership fees: Full £14, Playing £14, Social £14, Youth 50p, Student £8.50, OAP £8.50
Ground admission: By programme and discretion
Programme: No. of editorial pages 4; No. of advertising pages 6; Price £1
Programme editor: See Fixtures Secretary
Local newspapers: Newcastle Journal, Evening Chronicle, Gateshead Post
League: North East 1
League position (1988–89): Joint 2nd

League playing record (1988–89): P 10, W 7, D 0, L 3, F 138, A 105

KEIGHLEY

Skipton Road, Utley, Keighley, West Yorkshire BD20 6DT. Tel: 0535 602174
Founded: 1919
President: H. Edwin Scott
Chairman: Malcolm Pickles
Secretary: Michael T. Greaves, 24 Devonshire Street, Keighley, West Yorks. BD21 2BD. Tel: 0535 53192 (H). 0535 605646 (W)
Fixtures Secretary: Joe Midgley, 21 Woodville Road, Keighley BD21 6JA. Tel: 0535 602414 (H). 0535 605311 (W)
Press Officer: W. Alden Phillips, 7 Thornhill Road, Steeton, Keighley, West Yorks. BD20 6SU. Tel: 0535 54125 (H). 0943 601555 (W)
Club captain (1988–89): Jeff Inman
Club captain (1989–90): To be appointed
No. of teams: Senior 5, Youth 2, Minis 6
Directions to ground: It is situated on the North side of the A629 Keighley–Skipton road, immediately upon leaving the built-up area. (Do not take the new A650 Keighley–Skipton road which runs parallel to it as there is no access from it to the club)
Ground capacity: Seating 160, standing 1000 at least
Clubhouse facilities: New, well-appointed, brick-built clubhouse with good modern changing facilities
Club colours: Scarlet/green/white. (*Change colours:* Green)
Floodlights: No
Membership fees: Full £20, Playing £20, Social £5, Patron £25, Youth £5, Student £5, OAP £5
Ground admission: £1 – Non-members at First Team matches
Programme: No. of editorial pages 4; No. of advertising pages variable (several); Price: Free
Programme editor: Tony Simpson, 288 Bradford Road, Riddlesden, Keighley, West Yorks.
Local newspaper: Keighley News
League: North East 1
League position (1988–89): 7th
League playing record (1988–89): P 10, W 4, D 0, L 6, F 113, A 132

MORPETH

Grange House Field, Mitford Road, Morpeth NE61 1RJ. Tel: 0670 512508
Founded: 1947
President: Mr David Pringle
Chairman: Mr Harry Kennedy
Secretary: Mr Ken U. Fraser, Solway House, De Merley Road, Morpeth, Northumberland NE61 1HZ. Tel: 0670 511208 (H). 822625 (W)
Fixtures Secretary: Mr W.G. Hewitt (Bill), The Birches, Lane Head Farm, Felton, Northumberland. Tel: 0670 87757
Press Officer: Stephen Foster, Shadfen Farm, Morpeth. Tel: 514178
Coach: Bill Hewitt
Club captain (1988–89): Ian Pledger
Club captain (1989–90): Ian Pledger
No. of teams: Senior 6, Youth 4, Minis 4
Directions to ground: From Newcastle through town centre travelling North. Left onto Mitford Road after Telephone Exchange. Club on right after school
Clubhouse facilities: Open Match days and in evenings. Clubroom, cocktail bar, 2 squash courts, kitchen
Club colours: Scarlet and white hoops (*Change colours:* Blue)
Nickname: Old Edwardians
Floodlights: For training purposes
Membership fees: Squash/Rugby, Full £32, Playing £25, Social £5, Youth £5, Student £8
Programme: No. of editorial pages 4; No. of advertising pages 4; Price: Free
Programme editor: Michael Barry, Northern Press,

Chapter Row, South Shields
Local newspapers: Newcastle Journal, Morpeth
Herald and Gazette
League: North East 1
League position (1988–89): 7th
League playing record (1988–89): P 39, W 20, D 1,
L 18, F 571, A 494
Competitions won: Blyth Sevens, Northumberland
County Sevens – 29th April

NOVOCASTRIANS

Sutherland Park, The Drive, High Heaton,
Newcastle-Upon-Tyne NE7 7SY. Tel: 091 2661247
Founded: 1899
President: G.R.L. Parkinson
Chairman: C. Magnay
Secretary: C.S. Lawson, 10 Westfield Drive,
Newcastle-Upon-Tyne NE3 4XU. Tel: 091 2852630
(H). 0661 23232 (W)
Fixtures Secretary: R.J. Fay, 10 Lyndhurst Crescent,
Gateshead, Tyne & Wear NE9 6BA. Tel: 091 4873393
(H). 091 3885116 (W)
Club captain (1988–89): Graham Ward
Club captain (1989–90): Graham Ward
No. of teams: Senior 7, Youth & Minis 4
Directions to ground: The ground is in the vicinity of
the DHSS headquarters near the junction of the A191
and A188 (Four Lane Ends), and is approached up
the drive which is off the A188 approx. mile south of
Four Lane Ends
Clubhouse facilities: Clubroom and bar, cocktail bar,
spectators verandah
Club colours: Red, white and black hoops. (*Change
colours:* Plain blue)
Nickname: Novos
Floodlights: Training lights
Membership fees: Playing £32, Social £10, Youth £6,
Student £6
Programme: No. of editorial pages 4; No. of
advertising pages 10;
Programme editor: As President
Local newspapers: The (Newcastle) Journal, The
Evening Chronicle
League: North East 1
League position (1988–89): 5th
League playing record (1988–89): P 10, W 6, D 0,
L 4, F 104, A 141
Competitions won: Retained Northumberland Fifth
Team Cup

OLD BRODLEIANS

Woodhead Park, Denholmegate Road, Hipperholme,
Halifax, W. Yorks. Tel: 0422 202708
Founded: 1930
President: D. Robertshaw
Chairman: B. Young
Secretary: G. Pearson, 203 Wakefield Road,
Lightcliffe, Halifax, W. Yorks HX3 8TP. Tel: 0422
206226 (H), 0274 876593 (W)
Fixtures Secretary: P. Sugden, 112 Woodhouse Lane,
Brighouse, W. Yorks. Tel: 0484 721860
Coach: T.B.A.
Club captain (1988–89): J. Murphy
No. of teams: Senior 6, Youth 11+
Directions to ground: Junc. 26 M62, A58 to Halifax, 4
miles turn R. on Keighley Road at Hipperholme and
lights. Club mile on left
Ground capacity: Seating 300, Standing 100
Clubhouse facilities: Full
Club colours: Black/red/white. (*Change colours:* Red)
Nickname: Brods
Floodlights: No
Membership fees: Playing £15
Ground admission: £1
Programme: Price 50p
Programme editor: B. Deadman
League: NE 1
League position (1988–89): 6th

League playing record (1988–89): P 10, W 5, D 0,
L 5, F 131, A 141

OLD CROSSLEYANS

Standeven House, Broomfield Avenue, Halifax. Tel:
0422 63000
Founded: 1923
President: Kenneth Marshall
Chairman: Derek Ainley
Secretary: John Broadbent, 'Thistledown', Old Lane,
Ripponden, Sowerby Bridge, West Yorks. HX6 4PA.
Tel: 0422 822224 (H). 54186 (W)
Fixtures Secretary: Keith Davies, 23 School Close,
Ripponden, Sowerby Bridge. Tel: 0422 823662
Press Officer: Derek B. Greenwood, Standeven
House, Broomfield Avenue, Halifax.
Coach: Steven Whiteley
Club captain (1988–89): Steven Lumb
Club captain (1989–90): David Davis
No. of teams: Senior 4
Directions to ground: M62 Junction 24. Follow signs
to Halifax, after approx. 3 miles turn left up
Dryclough Lane (just past Hospital). Approx. mile
up, Broomfield Avenue is on left
Ground capacity: Seating 250, standing 1000
Clubhouse facilities: 3 Bars, 3 squash courts, multi-
gym, physio room
Club colours: Blue, white and amber. (*Change
colours:* No)
Nickname: Old Crocks
Floodlights: No
Membership fees: Playing £20, V.P. £7.50, Student £5
Ground admission: £1
Programme: No. of editorial pages 6; No. of
advertising pages 18; Price £1
Programme editor: Mr J. Philburn, c/o Old
Crossleyans
Local newspaper: Halifax Courier
League: North East 1
League position (1988–89): Joint 2nd
League playing record (1988–89): P 10, W 7, D 0, L 3

SELBY

Sandhill Lane, Leeds Road, Selby. Tel: 0757 703608
Founded: 1933
President: P. Bramley
Chairman: T.B.A.
Secretary: M.W.M. Blackwell, Top End House,
Cliffe, Selby, North Yorks. Tel: 0757 638666
Fixtures Secretary: T. Smith, 15 Sandhill Lane, Selby,
North Yorks. Tel: 0757 708231
Press Officer: As Secretary
Club captain (1988–89): A.C. Townend
Club captain (1989–90): To be appointed
No. of teams: Senior 5, Youth 4, Minis 4
Directions to ground: Take A63 from Selby towards
Leeds, turn left 1 mile from town centre down
Sandhill Lane
Ground capacity: Seating 350, standing 3000
Clubhouse facilities: 2 Bars, lounge, dining room and
kitchens. Open weekends, Tuesday, Thursday and
Friday evenings.
Club colours: Red, gold and green hoops. (*Change
colours:* Green and red squares)
Floodlights: Yes
Membership fees: Full £12, Playing £18, Youth £4,
Student £4, OAP £4
Ground admission: Collection
Programme: No. of editorial pages 10; No. of
advertising pages 30; Price 30p
Programme editor: T.B.A.
Local newspapers: Yorkshire Post, Yorkshire Evening
Press
League: North East 1
League position (1988–89): 2nd in North East 2
League playing record (1988–89): P 10, W 7, D 1,
L 2, F 134, A 90

STOCKTON

Station Road, Norton. Tel: 0642 554031
Founded: 1873
President: J.Y. Glover
Chairman: D. Trotter
Secretary: D. Chisman, 16 Dunettar Avenue,
Eaglescliffe. Tel: 0642 781339
Fixtures Secretary: B. Waller, 37 Albert Road,
Eaglescliffe. Tel: 0642 780197
Coach: J. Moore
No. of teams: Senior 4, Youth & Minis 8
Directions to ground: Off Junction Road, Norton,
Cleveland
Ground capacity: Seating 200
Club colours: Red (*Change colours:* Blue)
Floodlights: No
Membership fees: £5
Ground admission: £1
Programme: Price 25p
Local newspaper: Evening Gazette
League: North East 1
League position (1988–89): 2nd

THORNENSIANS

The Clubhouse, Coulman Street, Thorne. Tel: 0405
812746
Founded: 1939
President: Denis Harry Talbot Fox
Chairman: Wm. Carr
Secretary: F.J. Rhodes (Jim), 8 High Street, Crowle,
South Humberside DN17. Tel: 0724 711123 (H).
281111 Ext 268 (W)
Fixtures Secretary: Robert Hutchinson, 'Shangri La',
Bellwood Crescent, Thorne, DN8 4BA. Tel: 0405
813757
Press Officer: Major K.D. Roberts MBE,
Sherringham House, The Moors, Crowle, South
Humberside DN17. Tel: 0724 710575
Coach: Malcolm Greenslade
Club captain (1988–89): Raymond Worrall
Club captain (1989–90): Raymond Worrall
No. of teams: Senior 4, Youth 2, Minis 5
Directions to ground: Thorne – on M18 Junction 6.
On entering town turn left at traffic lights, right at
cross roads (200 yards from lights), left at T-junction,
direct to Ground
Ground capacity: Standing 1500 (200 under cover)
Clubhouse facilities: Ample on Ground
Club colours: Royal blue, white and black hoops.
(*Change colours:* Royal blue, black colours and cuffs)
Floodlights: Yes
Membership fees: Full £5, Playing £10, Social £4,
Youth £2, Student £2, OAP £4
Ground admission: 50p
Programme: No. of editorial pages 4; No. of
advertising pages 12; Price 20p
Programme editor: Gordon Gravil, 6 Grampian Way,
Thorne DN8 5YL
Local newspapers: Doncaster Star, Doncaster Free
Press, Thorne Times
League: North East 1
League position (1988–89): 9th
League playing record (1988–89): P 10, W 3, D 0,
L 7, F 70, A 104

YORK

Clifton Park, Shipton Road, York. Tel: 0904 623602
Founded: 1928
President: Geoff Taylor
Chairman: Jack Sinclair
Secretary: Brian McClure, 6 Alwyne Drive, York
YO3 6RS. Tel: 0904 632744 (H). 0532 435282 Ext
4210 (W)
Fixtures Secretary: Andy Sowden, 5 Longley House,
The Old Coach House, Easingwold, York. Tel: 0347
22119
Press Officer: Peter Johnson, 44 The Paddock, York.

Tel: 0904 792012
Coach: Nick Boyle and Allan Robertshaw
Club captain (1988–89): Richard Stevenson
Club captain (1989–90): Nigel Connell
No. of teams: Senior 4, Youth 3, Minis 2, Ladies 1
Directions to ground: Turn south off York Ring Road
on A19 to York City Centre. Club is 1 mile on the
right
Ground capacity: Seating 150, standing 800
Clubhouse facilities: Club room and lounge bar,
squash courts
Club colours: Green, black and white hoops. (*Change
colours:* Yellow)
Floodlights: No
League: North East 1
League position (1988–89): 1st of North East 2
League playing record (1988–89): P 40, W 29, D 2,
L 9, F 670, A 444
Competitions won: Courage League North East 2
Champions

NORTH EAST 2

BEVERLEY

Beaver Park, Norwood, Beverley. Tel: 0482 870306
President: Malcolm Cunningham
Chairman: Howard Joy
Secretary: Andrew Winter, 4 The Vineyards, Leven,
Nr Beverley. Tel: 0964 543981 (H). 0482 867131 Ext
3353 (W)
Fixtures Secretary: Rob Jenner, 3 Spark Mill Terrace,
Beverley. Tel: 0482 868944
Press Officer: John Grimshaw, 20 St Matthews Court,
Minster Moorgate, Beverley. Tel: 0482 871370
Coach: Peter Hardman
Club captain (1988–89): Ian Marlow
Club captain (1989–90): Ian Marlow
No. of teams: Senior 5, Youth 1, Minis 3
Directions to ground: Follow signs through Beverley
for Hornsea. Ground on left just before the railway
crossing and behind Lady Le Gros Public House
Clubhouse facilities: Bar and changing rooms
Club colours: Brown, green and white. (*Change
colours:* No)
Nickname: The Beavers
Floodlights: No
Membership fees: Full £15, Playing £15, Social £2.50,
Youth £5, Student £5
Local newspapers: Beverley Guardian, Hull Daily
Mail
League: North East 2
League playing record (1988–89): P 10, W 5, D 0,
L 5, F 90, A 97

BLYTH

Plessey Road, Blyth, Northumberland. Tel: 0670
352063
Founded: 1961
President: Alan F. Heinzman
Chairman: Alan F. Heinzman
Secretary: Stuart W. Bainbridge, 5 Eddleston
Avenue, Newcastle-Upon-Tyne NE3 4SJ. Tel: 091
2855317 (H). 0670 352556 (W)
Fixtures Secretary: Dave Grey, 12 Winchester
Avenue, Blyth, Northumberland. Tel: 0670 369591
Press Officer: Bill Brown, 4 Haughton Terrace, Blyth,
Northumberland. Tel: 0670 354945 (H). 712267 (W)
Club captain (1988–89): Gary Sinton
Club captain (1989–90): Bruce Ledger
No. of teams: Senior 4, Youth 2, Minis 4
Directions to ground: Principal route – From A189 via
1061 into Blyth (Newcastle Road) to Plessey Road
Clubhouse facilities: Open evenings, Match days and
Sunday lunchtime
Club colours: Emerald green and black hoops, black
shorts. (*Change colours:* Red)
Floodlights: No
Membership fees: Full £17, Playing £22, Social £1,

Youth nominal
Programme: No. of editorial pages 4; No. of advertising pages 4; Price 30p
Programme editor: As Press Officer
Local newspapers: The Journal, (Newcastle Daily) News, Post, Leader (Weekly local free sheet)
League: North East 2
League position (1988–89): 8th
League playing record (1988–89): P 40, W 20, D 2, L 18, F 572, A 569

BRAMLEY

The Warrels, Grosmont Terrace, Warrels Road, Bramley, Leeds LS13 3NY. Tel: 0532 577787
Founded: 1921
President: Roy Gillman
Chairman: Paul Rider
Secretary: David Nesham, 40 Water Lane, Farnley, Leeds LS12 5LX. Tel: 0532 576208 (H). 463320 (W)
Fixtures Secretary: Russ Croisdale, 47 Tofts Grove, Rastrick, Brighouse HD6 3XG. Tel: 0484 712272
Press Officer: As Secretary
Coach: Michael Hardaker
Club captain (1988–89): Steve Shepherd
Club captain (1989–90): Steve Shepherd
No. of teams: Senior 4, Youth 1
Directions to ground: A647 from Leeds, follow signs for Bramley onto Bramley Town Street. Turn left at lights at Bramley centre up Hough Lane then second right onto Warrels Road. Club entrance 8th right – Grosmont Terrace
Ground capacity: Standing 2000
Clubhouse facilities: Open Match days, Sunday lunch, Tuesday and Thursday evenings
Club colours: Green with black and gold chestband. (*Change colours:* White with green, black and gold chestband)
Floodlights: No
Membership fees: Full £15, Playing £12, Social £10, Youth £7, Student £12, OAP £1
Ground admission: £1
Programme: No. of editorial pages 2; No. of advertising pages 4; Price: Free with admission
Programme editor: As Secretary
Local newspapers: Yorkshire Post, Yorkshire Evening Post, Pudsey Times
League: North East 2
League position (1988–89): 1st – Yorkshire Division 1
League playing record (1988–89): P 38, W 30, D 4, L 4, F 874, A 355
Competitions won: League Champions Yorkshire Division 1

NEWCASTLE UNIVERSITY

Cochrane Park, Redhall Drive, Newcastle-upon-Tyne. Tel: 091 266 1164
Secretary: A.G.W. Lewin, 128 Tamworth Road, Fenham, Newcastle-upon-Tyne. Tel: 091 272 4605 (H)
Club colours: Light blue
League: North East 2
League position (1988–89): 6th
League playing record (1988–89): P 10, W 5, D 0, L 5, F 129, A 154

OLD HYMERIANS

Haworth Court, Beverley High Road, Hull. Tel: 0482 802119
Founded: 1925
Chairman: Richard H. Gore
Secretary: Michael Alan Harness, The Cottage, 48 George Street, Cottingham HU16 5QP. Tel: 0482 842138 (H). 224551 Ext 310 (W)
Fixtures Secretary: Neville McDonald, 10 Chilton Rise, Kirkella HU10 7NA. Tel: 0482 657071

Coach: Richard H. Gore
Club captain (1988–89): Andrew J. Woods
Club captain (1989–90): Andrew J. Woods
No. of teams: Senior 5, Minis 3
Directions to ground: A63 follow signs for Ring Road to Beverley High Road/Sutton Road traffic lights. Turn left, 2nd road on the right – Emmott Road – follow this road to the Ground
Ground capacity: Seating 150, standing 3000
Club colours: Chocolate and gold. (*Change colours:* Navy)
Floodlights: Training only
Membership fees: Full £16, Playing £16, Social £10, Youth £5, Student £10, OAP £10
Programme: Price £1
Programme editor: Richard P. Ashton, 162 Westella Road, Kirkella HU10 7RP
Local newspapers: Hull Daily Mail
League: North East 2
League position (1988–89): 9th
League playing record (1988–89): P 29, W 11, D 0, L 18

PONTEFRACT

Moor Lane, Carleton, Pontefract. Tel: 0977 702650
Founded: 1947
President: J. Richard Harker
Chairman: Neil Bowmer
Secretary: M. Trevor Izon, Went Hill House, Wentbridge, Pontefract WF8 3JJ. Tel: 0977 621284 (H). 702029 (W)
Fixtures Secretary: David L. Howdle, 7 Mill Hill Close, Darrington, Pontefract. Tel: 0977 704615
Press Officer: Peter Davis, 17 Pease Close, Carleton Park, Pontefract
Coach: Tony Martin
Club captain (1988–89): Alan H. Boyd
Club captain (1989–90): Alan Copley
No. of teams: Senior 4, Minis 6
Directions to ground: Turn off A1 at Darrington Hotel and follow the road towards Pontefract. On entering Carleton Village take 2nd turn left
Ground capacity: Seating 200, standing 1500
Clubhouse facilities: Open 5 nights weekly
Club colours: Blue. (*Change colours:* Red/green)
Floodlights: Yes
Membership fees: Full £10, Playing £10, Social £4, Youth £1, Student 50p, OAP £4, V.P. £12
Programme: No. of editorial pages 5; No. of advertising pages 30; Price 20p
Programme editor: As Press Officer
Local newspapers: Pontefract and Castleford Express, Yorkshire Evening Post
League: North East 2
League position (1988–89): 4th

RIPON

Mallorie Park, Ripon, N. Yorks. Tel: 0765 4675
President: F. Metcalfe
Chairman: H. Proud
Secretary: K. Green, Byland House, Copt Hewick, Ripon HG4 5BY. Tel: 0765 3443 (H), 0484 511211 (W)
Fixtures Secretary: H. Pound, Lurebank Terrace, Ripon. Tel: 5474
Coach: J. Horsell
Club captain (1988–89): H. Renshaw
No. of teams: Senior 4, Youth 3+
Club colours: Blue/white. (*Change colours:* Green/white)
Floodlights: No
Membership fees: Playing £16, Social £10
Programme: Price 20p
Programme editor: L. Couldwell
League: NE 2
League position (1988–89): 7th
League playing record (1988–89): P 10, W 4, D 0, L 6, F 123, A 122

ROCKLIFF

Lovaine Avenue, WhitleyBay, Tyne & Wear. Tel: 091 251 3704
Founded: 1887
President: J.D. Reid
Chairman: I.G. Firth
Secretary: K. Turner, 1 Osborne Gardens, Monkseaton, Whitley Bay, Tyne & Wear. Tel: 091 253 3079 (H). 091 252 0360 (W)
Fixtures Secretary: D. Johnstone, 9 Western Way, Whitley Bay. Tel: 091 253 3590
Coach: W. Curley and N. Kerr
Club captain (1988–89): M. Wylie
Club captain (1989–90): B. Glendinning
No. of teams: Senior 4, Youth 2, Minis 2
Directions to ground: Off Hill Heads Road along Lovaine Avenue. (Behind Cricket Club)
Ground capacity: Standing 5000
Clubhouse facilities: Spacious clubhouse, separate changing block
Club colours: Cardinal red and gold. (*Change colours: Various*)
Floodlights: No
Membership fees: Ranging from £25 to £3
Local newspaper: Whitley Bay Guardian (weekly)
League: North East 2
League position (1988–89): 1st – Durham/ Northumberland Div. 1
League playing record (1988–89): P 10, W 8, D 0, L 2, F 140, A 83

ROUNDHEGIANS

The Memorial Ground, Chelwood Drive, Leeds 8. Tel: 0532 667377
Founded: 1928
President: William Oliver Boddy
Chairman: Geoffrey Read
Secretary: Arthur James Rowell, 43 West Park Road, Leeds LS8 2HA. Tel: 0532 665906 (H). 610022 (W)
Fixtures Secretary: Michael J. Fletcher, 15 Tynwald Mount, Leeds 17. Tel: 0532 687346 (H). 435746 (W)
Press Officer: G. Read, 11 Crowtrees Park, Rawdon, Nr. Leeds. Tel: 0532 502816
Coach: Alan Green
Club captain (1988–89): Paul Armstrong
Club captain (1989–90): Ben Burgess
No. of teams: Senior 5, Youth 3
Directions to ground: From junction of Moortown Ring Road and A61 (Harrogate Road), turn towards city centre, at first traffic lights turn left onto Street Lane, travel mile to Chelwood Drive on left
Ground capacity: Standing 2000
Clubhouse facilities: 2 Bars, changing rooms, baths and showers, sports hall, dining room
Club colours: Green, black and white hoops – black shorts. (*Change colours:* Red shirts)
Floodlights: Yes
Local newspapers: Yorkshire Post, Skyrack Express
League: North East 2
League position (1988–89): 3rd

League playing record (1988–89): P 10, W 6, D 2, L 2, F 140, A 62

RYTON

Emma Sports Complex, Barmoor, Ryton, Tyne & Wear. Tel: 091 413 3820
Founded: 1880
President: Raymond Thoburn
Chairman: Robert Holmes
Secretary: Leslie Henderson, 8 Reedside, Ryton, Tyne & Wear NE40 3DB. Tel: 091 4133765 (H). 2853151 Ext 254 (W)
Fixtures Secretary: Shaun Richards, 36 Lambton Close, Crawcrook, Tyne & Wear. Tel: 091 4103478
Press Officer: As Secretary
Club captain (1988–89): Keith Dobson
Club captain (1989–90): Keith Dobson
No. of teams: Senior 4, Youth 1, Minis 3
Directions to ground: Take A695 from A1(M) just after Birtley Service Station, continue on through Blaydon, Clubhouse on left of main road through Ryton
Clubhouse facilities: Bar, lounge, games and TV rooms
Club colours: Royal blue and white. (*Change colours:* Dark green)
Floodlights: No
Membership fees: Full £7.50, Playing £13, Social £2, Youth £2, Student £2, OAP 15p
Programme: No. of editorial pages 4; No. of advertising pages 12; Price 50p
Programme editor: As Secretary
Local newspapers: Newcastle Journal, Evening Chronicle
League: North East 2
League position (1988–89): 10th
League playing record (1988–89): P 10, W 3, D 0, L 7, F 108, A 160

WESTOE

Dean Road, South Shields. Tel: 091 4561506
Founded: 1875
Chairman: William Dodds (Bill)
Secretary: John Wells, 240 Mowbray Road, South Shields NE33 3NW. Tel: 091 455 2260 (H). 456 0403 (W)
Fixtures Secretary: Dave Allen, 7 Wood Terrace, South Shields NE33 4UY. Tel: 091 456 9531 (H). 456 1115 (W)
Press Officer: Ken Reay, Winterbottom Hall, South Tyneside College, South Shields
Club captain (1988–89): Simon Musgrove
No. of teams: Senior 5, Youth 4, Minis 5
Club colours: Red, sky and dark blue. (*Change colours:* Light blue)
League: North East 2
League position (1988–89): Bottom of North East 1

YORKSHIRE LEAGUES

N.E. YORKSHIRE ONE:

Bill Barrack,
Lynholme, Eastgate Close,
Bramhope, Leeds LS16 9AP   0532 842540

N.E. YORKSHIRE FOUR:

Richard Birkett,
9 Shay Crescent,   (H) 0274 43479
Bradford BD9 5PW   (O) 0274 575511

N.E. YORKSHIRE TWO:

Steven Corns,
213 Hague Avenue,
Rawmarsh, Rotherham,
South Yorkshire   0709 5275

N.E. YORKSHIRE FIVE:

G. Robinson,
21 Manor Way,
Rawcliffe,   (H) 0904 623243
York YO3 6UQ   (O) 0904 653071

N.E. YORKSHIRE THREE:

Derek Hartley,
177 St. Enoch's Road,   (H) 0274 677255
Bradford 6   (O) 0274 675231

N.E. YORKSHIRE SIX:

V.J. Williams,
Ardara, Back Lane,   (H) 0302 700559
Natar, Doncaster DN6 9EA   (O) 0302 69661

TABLES 1987–88

YORKSHIRE 1

	P	W	D	L	F	A	PTS
Roundhegians	10	10	0	0	256	72	20
Bramley	10	8	1	1	193	71	17
Hemsworth	10	7	1	2	169	80	15
W Pk Bramhope	10	5	1	4	135	99	11
Driffield	10	4	1	5	143	111	9
Goole	10	4	0	6	76	115	8
Castleford	10	4	0	6	123	193	8
Cleckheaton	10	4	0	65	81	162	8
Moortown	10	4	0	6	57	147	8
York RI	10	2	0	8	95	169	4
Scarborough	10	1	0	9	49	158	2

YORKSHIRE 2

	P	W	D	L	F	A	PTS
N Ribblesdale	10	9	0	1	152	70	18
Hudd YMCA	10	7	0	3	196	81	14
Doncaster	10	7	0	3	171	74	14
Wheatley Hs	10	7	0	3	174	84	14
Wath	10	6	2	2	122	69	14
Malton & Nor	10	4	1	5	97	91	9
Ilkley	10	4	1	5	84	140	9
Sheffield Tigs	10	3	0	7	62	122	6
Ionians	10	3	0	7	114	205	6
O Otliensians	10	2	1	7	80	130	5
Leodiensians	10	0	1	9	31	217	1

YORKSHIRE 3

	P	W	D	L	F	A	PTS
Bridlington	10	9	1	0	245	38	19
Marist	10	7	0	3	151	95	14
Baildon	10	6	0	4	143	109	12
Knottingley	10	5	1	4	72	50	11
Heath	10	5	0	5	82	166	10
Leeds CSSA	10	4	1	5	97	121	9
Airebronians	10	4	1	5	114	142	9
Yarnbury	10	3	1	6	107	100	7
Rodillians	10	3	1	6	65	103	7
Bradford Salem	10	3	0	7	63	135	6
Northallerton	10	3	0	7	74	154	6

TABLES 1988-89

YORKSHIRE 1

	P	W	D	L	F	A	PTS
Bramley	10	9	1	0	236	57	19
W Pk Bramhope	10	7	2	1	153	82	16
Hemsworth	10	6	1	3	125	103	13
Driffield	10	5	1	4	138	85	11
N Ribblesdale	10	5	1	4	102	108	11
Barnsley	10	5	0	5	97	114	10
Cleckheaton	10	4	1	5	106	146	9
Hudders YMCA	10	3	1	6	90	116	7
Castleford	10	3	1	6	91	168	7
Goole	10	2	0	8	119	202	4
Moortown	10	1	1	8	55	131	3

YORKSHIRE 2

	P	W	D	L	F	A	PTS
Bridlington	10	9	0	1	243	60	18
Doncaster	10	8	1	1	230	75	17
York RI	10	7	1	2	224	88	15
Wath-on-Dearne	10	6	0	4	140	106	12
Sheffield Tigs	10	5	0	5	93	168	10
Ilkley	10	4	1	5	113	146	9
Malton & Nor	10	4	0	6	166	185	8
Wheatley Hs	10	3	1	6	134	140	7
Scarborough	10	3	0	7	65	164	6
Marist	10	3	0	7	91	215	6
Ionians	10	1	0	9	87	239	2

YORKSHIRE 3

	P	W	D	L	F	A	PTS
Yarnbury	10	8	2	0	171	53	18
O Otliensians	10	8	1	1	227	81	17
Leodiensians	10	7	0	3	136	94	14
Wibsey	10	5	2	3	152	113	12
Knottingley	10	5	0	5	134	133	10
O Modernians	10	4	1	5	139	109	9
Baildon	10	4	1	5	104	141	9
Airebronians	10	4	0	10	86	110	8
Rodillians	10	3	0	7	66	204	6
Leeds CCSA	10	2	1	7	70	148	5
Heath	10	1	0	9	78	213	2

YORKSHIRE 4

	P	W	D	L	F	A	PTS
Wibsey	10	9	0	1	234	50	18
O Modernians	10	8	0	2	199	92	16
Dinnington	10	6	1	3	164	77	13
Hessle	10	6	1	3	141	81	13
West Leeds	10	6	0	4	139	87	12
Hullensians	10	4	1	5	89	106	9
Wetherby	10	3	1	6	85	168	7
Leeds YMCA	10	3	0	7	76	146	6
Yorkshire CW	10	3	0	7	85	208	6
Burley	10	3	0	7	62	189	6
Skipton	10	2	0	8	92	162	4

YORKSHIRE 4

	P	W	D	L	F	A	PTS
Hessle	10	9	0	1	241	68	18
West Leeds	10	9	0	1	211	66	18
Northallerton	10	7	0	3	164	94	14
Bradford Salem	10	6	0	4	149	99	12
Halifax Vs	10	6	0	4	105	130	12
Hullensians	10	5	0	5	128	133	10
Leeds YMCA	10	4	0	6	111	151	8
O Rishworthians	10	3	0	7	74	117	6
Dinnington	10	3	0	7	148	204	6
Yorkshire CW	10	2	0	8	56	242	4
Wetherby	10	1	0	9	97	180	2

YORKSHIRE 5

	P	W	D	L	F	A	PTS
Halifax Vs	10	10	0	0	196	35	20
O Rishworthians	10	8	0	2	233	52	16
Phoenix Pk	10	8	0	2	156	52	16
Leeds Cors	10	6	0	4	121	96	12
Ossett	10	6	0	4	144	133	12
BP Chemicals	10	4	0	6	89	133	8
Yorkshire M	10	3	0	7	93	98	6
Hornsea	10	3	0	7	80	152	6
Rowntrees	10	3	0	7	83	164	6
Withernsea	10	3	0	7	71	182	6
Knaresborough	10	1	0	9	38	207	2

YORKSHIRE 5

	P	W	D	L	F	A	PTS
Sheffield Oaks	10	10	0	0	236	53	20
Phoenix Pk	10	9	0	1	174	61	18
Skipton	10	6	0	4	140	93	12
Burley	10	6	0	4	143	112	12
Yorkshire M	10	5	0	5	119	125	10
Danum Phoenix	10	4	1	5	106	144	9
Rowntrees	10	4	0	6	87	129	8
BP Chemicals	10	4	0	6	72	150	8
Ossett	10	3	0	7	129	135	6
Leeds Cors	10	2	1	7	57	115	5
Hornsea	10	1	0	9	65	241	2

YORKSHIRE 6

	P	W	D	L	F	A	PTS
Sheffield Os	9	9	0	0	293	7	18
Bridon	10	9	0	1	304	34	18
De la Salle	10	7	1	2	176	83	15
Sheff Steels	10	6	0	4	115	98	12
Stocksbridge	10	5	0	5	83	121	10
Granville Coll	10	5	0	5	99	169	10
Sheff Meds	9	4	0	5	173	85	8
Adwick	10	3	1	6	143	171	7
Markham	10	3	0	7	73	128	6
Maltby OB	10	2	0	8	95	272	4
Armthorpe R	10	0	0	10	52	438	0

YORKSHIRE 6

	P	W	D	L	F	A	PTS
De la Salle (Sheff)	10	8	0	2	143	55	16
Withernsea	10	8	0	2	143	79	16
Granville Coll	10	7	1	2	141	102	15
Adwick-le-St	10	7	0	3	128	124	14
Mosborough	10	6	0	4	93	98	12
Knaresborough	10	5	1	4	75	93	11
Malby OB	10	4	1	5	96	101	9
Stocksbridge	10	3	1	6	129	151	7
Arm Markham	10	3	0	7	99	153	6
Sheffield Meds	10	1	0	9	78	130	2
Sheffield Steels	10	0	0	10	36	75	0

The referee lectures the front rows at Heath RUFC of Yorkshire Four

NORTHERN DIVISION FIXTURES 1989/90

YORKSHIRE ONE

Sat. 9th September (Week 2)
Bridlington v Pocklington
Barnsley v Doncaster
North Ribblesdale v Driffield
West Park v Cleckheaton
Huddersfield YMCA v Castleford

Sat. 23rd September (Week 4)
Castleford v Bridlington
Cleckheaton v Huddersfield YMCA
Driffield v West Park
Doncaster v North Ribblesdale
Hemsworth v Barnsley

Sat. 14th October (Week 6)
Bridlington v Cleckheaton
Pocklington v Castleford
North Ribblesdale v Hemsworth
West Park v Doncaster
Huddersfield YMCA v Driffield

Sat. 28th October (Week 8)
Cleckheaton v Pocklington
Driffield v Bridlington
Doncaster v Huddersfield YMCA
Hemsworth v West Park
Barnsley v North Ribblesdale

Sat. 11th November (Week 10)
Bridlington v Doncaster
Pocklington v Driffield
Castleford v Cleckheaton
West Park v Barnsley
Huddersfield YMCA v Hemsworth

Sat 18th November (Week 11)
Driffield v Castleford
Doncaster v Pocklington
Hemsworth v Bridlington
Barnsley v Huddersfield YMCA
North Ribblesdale v West Park

Sat. 25th November (Week 12)
Bridlington v Barnsley
Pocklington v Hemsworth
Castleford v Doncaster
Cleckheaton v Driffield
Huddersfield YMCA v North Ribblesdale

Sat. 13th January (Week 18)
Doncaster v Cleckheaton
Hemsworth v Castleford
Barnsley v Pocklington
North Ribblesdale v Bridlington
West Park v Huddersfield YMCA

Sat. 10th March (Week 26)
Bridlington v West Park
Pocklington v North Ribblesdale
Castleford v Barnsley
Cleckheaton v Hemsworth
Driffield v Doncaster

Sat. 31st March (Week X7)
Hemsworth v Driffield
Barnsley v Cleckheaton
North Ribblesdale v Castleford
West Park v Pocklington
Huddersfield YMCA v Bridlington

Sat. 28th April (Week 32)
Pocklington v Huddersfield YMCA
Castleford v West Park
Cleckheaton v North Ribblesdale
Driffield v Barnsley
Doncaster v Hemsworth

YORKSHIRE TWO

Sat. 9th September (Week 2)
Goole v York RI
Scarborough v Malton & Norton
Old Otliensians v Moortown
Wath on Dearne v Yarnbury
Wheatley Hills v Ilkley

Sat. 23rd September (Week 4)
Ilkley v Goole
Yarnbury v Wheatley Hills
Moortown v Wath on Dearne
Malton & Norton v Old Otliensians
Sheffield Tigers v Scarborough

NORTHERN DIVISION FIXTURES 1989/90

Sat. 14th October (Week 6)
Goole v Yarnbury
York RI v Ilkley
Old Othensians v Sheffield Tigers
Wath on Dearne v Malton & Norton
Wheatley Hills v Moortown

Sat. 28th October (Week 8)
Yarnbury v York RI
Moortown v Goole
Malton & Norton v Wheatley Hills
Sheffield Tigers v Wath on Dearne
Scarborough v Old Otliensians

Sat. 11th November (Week 10)
Goole v Malton & Norton
York RI v Moortown
Ilkley v Yarnbury
Wath on Dearne v Scarborough
Wheatley Hills v Sheffield Tigers

Sat 18th November (Week 11)
Moortown v Ilkley
Malton & Norton v York RI
Sheffield Tigers v Goole
Scarborough v Wheatley Hills
Old Otliensians v Wath on Dearne

Sat. 25th November (Week 12)
Goole v Scarborough
York RI v Sheffield Tigers
Ilkley v Malton & Norton
Yarnbury v Moortown
Wheatley Hills v Old Otliensians

Sat. 13th January (Week 18)
Malton & Norton v Yarnbury
Sheffield Tigers v Ilkley
Scarborough v York RI
Old Otliensians v Goole
Wath on Dearne v Wheatley Hills

Sat. 10th March (Week 26)
Goole v Wath on Dearne
York RI v Old Otliensians
Ilkley v Scarborough
Yarnbury v Sheffield Tigers
Moortown v Malton & Norton

Sat. 31st March (Week X7)
Sheffield Tigers v Moortown
Scarborough v Yarnbury
Old Otliensians v Ilkley
Wath on Dearne v York RI
Wheatley Hills v Goole

Sat. 28th April (Week 32)
York RI v Wheatley Hills
Ilkley v Wath on Dearne
Yarnbury v Old Otliensians
Moortown v Scarborough
Malton & Norton v Sheffield Tigers

YORKSHIRE THREE

Sat. 9th September (Week 2)
Baildon v Old Modernians
Wibsey v West Leeds
Rodillians v Knottingley
Airebronians v Hessle
Ionians v Leodiensians

Sat. 23rd September (Week 4)
Leodiensians v Baildon
Hessle v Ionians
Knottingley v Airebronians
West Leeds v Rodillians
Marist v Wibsey

Sat. 14th October (Week 6)
Baildon v Hessle
Old Modernians v Leodiensians
Rodillians v Marist
Airebronians v West Leeds
Ionians v Knottingley

Sat. 28th October (Week 8)
Hessle v Old Modernians
Knottingley v Baildon
West Leeds v Ionians
Marist v Airebronians
Wibsey v Rodillians

NORTHERN DIVISION FIXTURES 1989/90

Sat. 11th November (Week 10)
Baildon v West Leeds
Old Modernians v Knottingley
Leodiensians v Hessle
Airebronians v Wibsey
Ionians v Marist

Sat 18th November (Week 11)
Knottingley v Leodiensians
West Leeds v Old Modernians
Marist v Baildon
Wibsey v Ionians
Rodillians v Airebronians

Sat. 25th November (Week 12)
Baildon v Wibsey
Old Modernians v Marist
Leodiensians v West Leeds
Hessle v Knottingley
Ionians v Rodillians

Sat. 13th January (Week 18)
West Leeds v Hessle
Marist v Leodiensians
Wibsey v Old Modernians
Rodillians v Baildon
Airebronians v Ionians

Sat. 10th March (Week 26)
Baildon v Airebronians
Old Modernians v Rodillians
Leodiensians v Wibsey
Hessle v Marist
Knottingley v West Leeds

Sat. 31st March (Week X7)
Marist v Knottingley
Wibsey v Hessle
Rodillians v Leodiensians
Airebronians v Old Modernians
Ionians v Baildon

Sat. 28th April (Week 32)
Old Modernians v Ionians
Leodiensians v Airebronians
Hessle v Rodillians
Knottingley v Wibsey
West Leeds v Marist

YORKSHIRE FOUR

Sat. 9th September (Week 2)
Halifax Vs v Old Rishworthians
Leeds CSSA v Leeds YMCA
Sheffield Oaks v Hullensians
Northallerton v Heath
Phoenix Park v Dinnington

Sat. 23rd September (Week 4)
Dinnington v Halifax Vs
Heath v Phoenix Park
Hullensians v Northallerton
Leeds YMCA v Sheffield Oaks
Bradford Salem v Leeds CSSA

Sat. 14th October (Week 6)
Halifax Vs v Heath
Old Rishworthians v Dinnington
Sheffield Oaks v Bradford Salem
Northallerton v Leeds YMCA
Phoenix Park v Hullensians

Sat. 28th October (Week 8)
Heath v Old Rishworthians
Hullensians v Halifax Vs
Leeds YMCA v Phoenix Park
Bradford Salem v Northallerton
Leeds CSSA v Sheffield Oaks

Sat. 11th November (Week 10)
Halifax Vs v Leeds YMCA
Old Rishworthians v Hullensians
Dinnington v Heath
Northallerton v Leeds CSSA
Phoenix Park v Bradford Salem

Sat 18th November (Week 11)
Hullensians v Dinnington
Leeds YMCA v Old Rishworthians
Bradford Salem v Halifax Vs
Leeds CSSA v Phoenix Park
Sheffield Oaks v Northallerton

NORTHERN DIVISION FIXTURES 1989/90

Sat. 25th November (Week 12)
Halifax Vs v Leeds CSSA
Old Rishworthians v Bradford Salem
Dinnington v Leeds YMCA
Heath v Hullensians
Phoenix Park v Sheffield Oaks

Sat. 13th January (Week 18)
Leeds YMCA v Heath
Bradford Salem v Dinnington
Leeds CSSA v Old Rishworthians
Sheffield Oaks v Halifax Vs
Northallerton v Phoenix Park

Sat. 10th March (Week 26)
Halifax Vs v Northallerton
Old Rishworthians v Sheffield Oaks
Dinnington v Leeds CSSA
Heath v Bradford Salem
Hullensians v Leeds YMCA

Sat. 31st March (Week X7)
Bradford Salem v Hullensians
Leeds CSSA v Heath
Sheffield Oaks v Dinnington
Northallerton v Old Rishworthians
Phoenix Park v Halifax Vs

Sat. 28th April (Week 32)
Old Rishworthians v Phoenix Park
Dinnington v Northallerton
Heath v Sheffield Oaks
Hullensians v Leeds CSSA
Leeds YMCA v Bradford Salem

YORKSHIRE FIVE

Sat. 9th September (Week 2)
B.P. Chemicals v Skipton
Burley v Ossett
Rowntrees v Withernsea
Yorkshire Main v Wetherby
Danum Phoenix v De la Salle (Sheffield)

Sat. 23rd September (Week 4)
De la Salle (Sheffield) v B.P. Chemicals
Wetherby v Danum Phoenix
Withernsea v Yorkshire Main
Ossett v Rowntrees
Yorkshire C.W. v Burley

Sat. 14th October (Week 6)
B.P. Chemicals v Wetherby
Skipton v De la Salle (Sheffield)
Rowntrees v Yorkshire C.W.
Yorkshire Main v Ossett
Danum Phoenix v Withernsea

Sat. 28th October (Week 8)
Wetherby v Skipton
Withernsea v B.P. Chemicals
Ossett v Danum Phoenix
Yorkshire C.W. v Yorkshire Main
Burley v Rowntrees

Sat. 11th November (Week 10)
B.P. Chemicals v Ossett
Skipton v Withernsea
De la Salle (Sheffield) v Wetherby
Yorkshire Main v Burley
Danum Phoenix v Yorkshire C.W.

Sat 18th November (Week 11)
Withernsea v De la Salle (Sheffield)
Ossett v Skipton
Yorkshire C.W. v B.P. Chemicals
Burley v Danum Phoenix
Rowntrees v Yorkshire Main

Sat. 25th November (Week 12)
B.P. Chemicals v Burley
Skipton v Yorkshire C.W.
De la Salle (Sheffield) v Ossett
Wetherby v Withernsea
Danum Phoenix v Rowntrees

Sat. 13th January (Week 18)
Ossett v Wetherby
Yorkshire C.W. v De la Salle (Sheffield)
Burley v Skipton
Rowntrees v B.P. Chemicals
Yorkshire Main v Danum Phoenix

NORTHERN DIVISION FIXTURES 1989/90

Sat. 10th March (Week 26)
B.P. Chemicals v Yorkshire Main
Skipton v Rowntrees
De la Salle (Sheffield) v Burley
Wetherby v Yorkshire C.W.
Withernsea v Ossett

Sat. 31st March (Week X7)
Yorkshire C.W. v Withernsea
Burley v Wetherby
Rowntrees v De la Salle (Sheffield)
Yorkshire Main v Skipton
Danum Phoenix v B.P. Chemicals

Sat. 28th April (Week 32)
Skipton v Danum Phoenix
De la Salle (Sheffield) v Yorkshire Main
Wetherby v Rowntrees
Withernsea v Burley
Ossett v Yorkshire C.W.

YORKSHIRE SIX

Sat. 9th September (Week 2)
Adwick-le-Street v Armthorpe Markham
Knarsborough v Mossborough
Sheffield Steels v Maltby OB
Stocksbridge v Hornsea
Granville Coll. v Leeds Corinthians

Sat. 23rd September (Week 4)
Leeds Corinthians v Adwick-le-Street
Hornsea v Granville Coll.
Maltby OB v Stocksbridge
Mossborough v Sheffield Steels
Sheffield Medicals v Knarsborough

Sat. 14th October (Week 6)
Adwick-le-Street v Hornsea
Armthorpe Markham v Leeds Corinthians
Sheffield Steels v Sheffield Medicals
Stocksbridge v Mossborough
Granville Coll. v Maltby OB

Sat. 28th October (Week 8)
Hornsea v Armthorpe Markham
Maltby OB v Adwick-le-Street
Mossborough v Granville Coll.
Sheffield Medicals v Stocksbridge
Knarsborough v Sheffield Steels

Sat. 11th November (Week 10)
Adwick-le-Street v Mossborough
Armthorpe Markham v Maltby OB
Leeds Corinthians v Hornsea
Stocksbridge v Knarsborough
Granville Coll. v Sheffield Medicals

Sat 18th November (Week 11)
Maltby OB v Leeds Corinthians
Mossborough v Armthorpe Markham
Sheffield Medicals v Adwick-le-Street
Knarsborough v Granville Coll.
Sheffield Steels v Stocksbridge

Sat. 25th November (Week 12)
Adwick-le-Street v Knarsborough
Armthorpe Markham v Sheffield Medicals
Leeds Corinthians v Mossborough
Hornsea v Maltby OB
Granville Coll. v Sheffield Steels

Sat. 13th January (Week 18)
Mossborough v Hornsea
Sheffield Medicals v Leeds Corinthians
Knarsborough v Armthorpe Markham
Sheffield Steels v Adwick-le-Street
Stocksbridge v Granville Coll.

Sat. 10th March (Week 26)
Adwick-le-Street v Stocksbridge
Armthorpe Markham v Sheffield Steels
Leeds Corinthians v Knarsborough
Hornsea v Sheffield Medicals
Maltby OB v Mossborough

Sat. 31st March (Week X7)
Sheffield Medicals v Maltby OB
Knarsborough v Hornsea
Sheffield Steels v Leeds Corinthians
Stocksbridge v Armthorpe Markham
Granville Coll. v Adwick-le-Street

Sat. 28th April (Week 32)
Armthorpe Markham v Granville Coll.
Leeds Corinthians v Stocksbridge
Hornsea v Sheffield Steels
Maltby OB v Knarsborough
Mossborough v Sheffield Medicals

BARNSLEY

Wombwell Lane, Stairfoot, Barnsley. Tel: 0226
284344
Founded: 1902
Secretary: J. Reed, 79 Roehampton Rise, Ardsley,
Barnsley, S. Yorks. Tel: 0226 284688
League: Yorkshire 1
Final position (1987–88): 11th (bottom)

BRIDLINGTON

Dukes Park, Queensgate, Bridlington. Tel: 0262
676405
Founded: 1926
President: Stanley Wright
Chairman: Philip Preston
Secretary: Stuart Johnson, c/o Clubhouse. Tel: 0262
82347 (H)
Fixtures Secretary: Stanley Wright, c/o Clubhouse.
Tel: 0262 675230 (H)
Coach: Mike Hodgson
Club captain (1988–89): Neil Arton
Club captain (1989–90): Neil Arton
No. of teams: Senior 4, Youth 1, Minis 6
Directions to ground: Off Dudy Road
Ground capacity: Standing 200
Clubhouse facilities: Open each evening 7-11pm,
Saturday and Sunday 12-2pm
Club colours: Blue and amber. (*Change colours:*
White)
Floodlights: Yes
Membership fees: Full £10, Playing £10, Social £8,
Youth £2, Student £2
League: Yorkshire 1
League position (1988–89): 1st
League playing record (1988–89): P 10, W 9, D 0,
L 1, F 243, A 60
Competitions won: Yorkshire Challenge Shield 25.2.89
at Scarborough, final: Bridlington 11 Driffield 3.
Yorkshire 2 Champions

CASTLEFORD

Whitwood Common Lane, Castleford, West Yorks.
Tel: 0977 554762
Founded: 1870
President: H. Schumm
Chairman: J.A. Wandless
Fixtures Secretary: Mr J. Barr, 7 Valley Road,
Darrington, West Yorks. WF8 2BT. Tel: 0977 792090
(H). 556511 (W)
Coach: 1st XV Captain
Club captain (1988–89): S. Davies
Club captain (1989–90): S. Davies
No. of teams: Senior 4
Directions to ground: Leave M62 at Junction 31, take
A655 towards Castleford. Clubhouse within mile on
right hand side
Ground capacity: Standing 1000
Club colours: White; red and blue hoop. (*Change
colours:* Red)
Floodlights: No
Local newspaper: Pontefract and Castleford Express
League: Yorkshire 1
League position (1988–89): 9th

CLECKHEATON

Moorend, Cleckheaton, West Yorkshire. Tel: 0274
873410
Founded: 1924
Chairman: Robert Moore
Secretary: Ian Johnson, 20 St Andrews Crescent,
Oakenshaw, Bradford BD12 7EL. Tel: 0274 601043
(H). 0484 646816 (W)
Fixtures Secretary: Jack Wood, 705 Halifax Road,
Cleckheaton. Tel: 0274 873532 (H). 872423 (W)
Press Officer: Alan Bentley, 12 Ghyllroyd Drive,

Birkenshaw. Tel: 0274 682266
Coach: Dick Bonner
Club captain (1988–89): Tudor Evans
Club captain (1989–90): Tudor Evans
No. of teams: Senior 4, Youth 2, Minis 4
Ground capacity: Seating 250+, standing 4-5000
Clubhouse facilities: Lounge bar, club bar, dining
room and kitchen
Club colours: Red/white hoops. (*Change colours:*
Black shirts/white collars)
Floodlights: Training only
Membership fees: Full £15, Playing £15, Social £10,
Youth £6, Student £6, OAP £10
Ground admission: Collection only
Programme: No. of editorial pages 6; No. of
advertising pages 12; Price £1
Programme editor: Arthur Crowther, 381 Whitehall
Road West, Cleckheaton, W. Yorks.
Local newspapers: Yorkshire Post, Yorkshire Evening
Post, Spenborough Guardian, Cleckheaton Reporter
League: Yorkshire 1
League position (1988–89): 7th
League playing record (1988–89): P 34, W 19, D 1,
L 14, F 446, A 399

DONCASTER

Sandal Beat Lane (off Armthorpe Road), Armthorpe,
Doncaster, South Yorks. Tel: 0302 831388
Founded: 1875
President: Norman Micklethwaite
Chairman: Roger Linsley
Secretary: Paul Burton, 64 Bennetthorpe, Doncaster,
South Yorks. DN2 6AD. Tel: 0302 320062 (H).
731710 (W)
Fixtures Secretary: Andrew Bowes, 1 Dunscroft
Grove, Littlesworth Park, Rossington, Doncaster.
Tel: 0302 867277
Press Officer: Roger Linsley, The Barn House, Wilsic,
Doncaster. Tel: 0302 851847 (H). 856382 (W)
Coach: David Stacey
Club captain (1988–89): Drew Noble
Club captain (1989–90): Howard Thompson
No. of teams: Senior 5, Youth 1, Minis 6
Directions to ground: Travelling East out of Doncaster
follow signs to Armthorpe. When passing water tower
to the right, entrance 600m on the right (signposted)
Ground capacity: Seating 250, standing 2000
Clubhouse facilities: Club bar and stage, lounge bar,
kitchen. Also weights room and physio facilities
Club colours: Navy blue, red, white. (*Change colours:*
Red, navy, white)
Floodlights: Yes
Membership fees: Full £20, Playing £20, Social £7,
Youth £10, Student £6, VP: donation
Ground admission: nil, except for specials
Programme: No. of editorial pages 4; No. of
advertising pages 8; Price 50p
Programme editor: Malcolm Greenwood, 5 Saxton
Avenue, Bessecarr, Doncaster
Local newspaper: Doncaster Star
League: Yorkshire 1
League position (1988–89): 2nd
League playing record (1988–89): P 32, W 16, D 3,
L 13
Competitions won: Winners South Yorkshire Sevens –
April 1989

DRIFFIELD

The Clubhouse, Kellythorpe, Driffield, N.
Humberside. Tel: 0377 46598
Founded: 1925
President: John 'Jo' Burdass
Chairman: 'Pip' Megginson
Secretary: R. Weekes, 8 Kings Mill Road, Driffield,
N. Humberside. Tel: 0377 43832
Fixtures Secretary: JOhn Harrison, 9 Parsonage
Close, Nafferton, Driffield, E. Yorks. Tel: 0377 43032
(H), 43631 (W)
Coach: Roger Iveson

Club captain (1988–89): Charlie Burdass
No. of teams: Senior 4, Youth 2+
Directions to ground: A163, clubhouse on 1st r'about
after El Alamein Army Camp
Clubhouse facilities: Large, full
Club colours: Black/white/blue. (*Change colours:*
Yellow or red)
Floodlights: No
Membership fees: Playing £20, Social £12
Ground admission: Nil
Programme: No. of editorial pages Variable; No. of
advertising pages Variable
Programme editor: As Secretary
League: York 1
League position (1988–89): 4th
League playing record (1988–89): P 10, W 5, D 1,
L 4, F 138, A 85

HEMSWORTH

Moxon Fields, Lowfield Road, Hemsworth. Tel: 0977
610078
Founded: 1961
President: Brian May
Chairman: Les Kemp
Secretary: Mike Illingworth, 87 West Lane, Sharlston,
Wakefield WF4 1EP. Tel: 0924 862947 (H). 862412
(W)
Fixtures Secretary: Tony Lewis, 28 Beverly Garth,
Ackworth, Pontefract. Tel: 0977 612683
Club captain (1988–89): Mick Murtagh
Club captain (1989–90): John Beddis
No. of teams: Senior 3, Youth 1
Directions to ground: Turn right off Station Road into
Lowfield Road and to end of housing estate, over
railway bridge onto car park
Ground capacity: 1500
Clubhouse facilities: Changing and bar facilities
Club colours: Navy blue. (*Change colours:* Red or red
and white hoops)
Floodlights: No
Membership fees: £20 (£5 rebate before October)
Ground admission: £2
Local newspaper: Hemsworth and South Elmsal
Express
League: Yorkshire 1
League position (1988–89): 3rd
League playing record (1988–89): P 34, W 21, D 2,
L 11, F 696, A 388

HUDDERSFIELD YMCA

Laund Hill, Salendine Nook, Huddersfield. Tel: 0484
654052
Founded: 1927
Secretary: D.B. Tomkins, 3 Celandine Drive,
Salendine Nook, Huddersfield, W. Yorks HD3 3UT.
Tel: 0484 655523 (H)
Press Officer: As Secretary
Club colours: Red/black
League: Yorkshire 1
League position (1988–89): 8th
League playing record (1988–89): P 10, W 3, D 1,
L 6, F 90, A 116

NORTH RIBBLESDALE

Grove Park, Settle, North Yorks. Tel: 072 92 2755
Founded: 1923
President: Tom Sharp
Chairman: Trevor Graveson
Secretary: Bill Smith, 7 Sandholme Close,
Giggleswick, Settle, North Yorks. BD24 0AF. Tel:
072 92 2403 (H). 0942 714109 (W)
Fixtures Secretary: Andrew Davidson, 13 Halsteads
Cottages, Settle, N. Yorks. Tel: 072 92 2078
Club captain (1988–89): Andrew Haggas
Club captain (1989–90): Andrew Haggas
No. of teams: Senior 3, Youth 1, Minis 3
Directions to ground: Signposted off A65 between
Skipton and Kendal, adjacent to Falcon Manor Hotel

Clubhouse facilities: Friday, Saturday and Sunday
Club colours: Royal blue and white (*Change colours:*
White and maroon)
Nickname: Ribb
Membership fees: Full £5 min., Playing £10, Social £3,
Student 25p, OAP 25p
Local newspaper: Craven Herald, Skipton
League: Yorkshire 1
League position (1988–89): 4th
League playing record (1988–89): P 10, W 5, D 1,
L 4, F 102, A 106

POCKLINGTON

Percy Road, Pocklington. Tel: 07592 3358
Founded: 1928
Secretary: M.B. Herring, 34 Hill Rise Drive, Market
Weighton, York YO4 3JZ. Tel: 0696 72156 (H). 0482
666198 (W)
Press Officer: P.G. Gilbank. Tel: 0759 302243
Club colours: Navy blue/white.
League: Yorkshire 1
League position (1988–89): 11th (NE 2)

WEST PARK
BRAMHOPE

The Sycamores, Bramhope, Leeds 16. Tel: 0532
671437
Founded: 1959
President: Derek Thomas Munn
Chairman: Alun Jeffrey Davies
Secretary: William Wilson Barrack, Lynholme, 15
Eastgate Close, Bramhope, Leeds LS16 9AA. Tel:
0532 842540
Fixtures Secretary: Michael Openshaw, 5 Victoria
Grove, Horsforth, Leeds. Tel: 0532 587338
Press Officer: Paul Hatfield, 25 Pool Road, Otley,
Yorkshire LS21 1HL. Tel: 0943 467950
Coach: Frank Child
Club captain (1988–89): Barry Norcliffe
Club captain (1989–90): Patrick John Knowles
No. of teams: Senior 4, Youth 2, Minis/Juniors 10
Directions to ground: A660 from Leeds towards
Otley. After passing Parkway Hotel on right, look for
a Shell filling station a mile further on the left. Turn
left immediately before the filling station
Ground capacity: Seating 250, standing 1000
Clubhouse facilities: 2 well appointed bars, open
Match days and evenings. Excellent changing facilities
Club colours: Black with gold band. (*Change colours:*
Gold)
Floodlights: No
Local newspaper: Wharfedale and Airedale Observer
League: Yorkshire 1
League position (1988–89): 2nd
League playing record (1988–89): P 38, W 27, D 2,
L 9, F 575, A 284
Competitions won: Pocklington Sevens, Sheffield
Tigers' Sevens

YORKSHIRE 2

GOOLE

Murham Avenue, Goole. Tel: 0405 2018
Founded: 1928
President: H. Walton (Hughie)
Chairman: C.M. England (Mac)
Secretary: Ian R. Higgins, 14 The Meadows,
Howden, N. Humberside DN14 7DX. Tel: 0430
430037 (H). Tel: 0405 768621 (W)
Fixtures Secretary: Phil Shand, Hallgarth, Ledgate
Lane, Burton Salmon, Leeds LS25 5JY. Tel: 0977
87660 (H). 703357 (W)
Club captain (1988–89): Peter Hardman
Club captain (1989–90): Jeremy Longhorn
No. of teams: Senior 4
Directions to ground: M62. Leave at Junction 36

(Goole exit), follow road through 2 sets of traffic lights until Vikings Hotel is reached, turn left here into Western Road, Murham Avenue is mile down Western Road
Ground capacity: Standing 1000
Clubhouse facilities: Clubroom, dining room, 4 changing rooms
Club colours: Navy shirts/gold band, navy shorts. (*Change colours:* Red)
Floodlights: Yes
Membership fees: Full £15, Playing £15, Social £7.50, Youth & Student free
Local newspapers: Goole Times and Chronicle; Courier
League: Yorkshire 2
League position (1988–89): 10th (relegated from Yorkshire 1)
League playing record (1988–89): P 10, W 2, D 0, L 8

ILKLEY

Stacks Field, Denton Road, Ilkley. Tel: 0943 607037
Founded: 1899
President: J.L. Hems
Chairman: M.S. Crannigan
Secretary: J.A.L. Hope, Oak Royd, Oak Avenue, Burley In Wharfedale, Ilkley LS29 7PH. Tel: 0943 863377 (H). 0274 560211 (W)
Fixtures Secretary: J.K. Bernard, 36 Dale View, Ilkley. Tel: 0943 602945 (H). 451000 (W)
Press Officer: Mrs Jan Kennedy, Pl. 17, Deaconness Court, Queens Road, Ilkley. Tel: 600502
Coach: T.B.A.
Club captain (1988–89): Blair Nixon
Club captain (1989–90): Christopher Hems
No. of teams: Senior 5, Youth 3, Minis 2
Directions to ground: From traffic lights at parish church in town centre, turn towards River Wharfe/ Middleton (left from Skipton (Addingham)) right from leeds. Ground easily visible about 200 yards on right
Ground capacity: Seating 200, standing 1800
Clubhouse facilities: At ground, available for private hire
Club colours: White, red, black hoops. (*Change colours:* Black)
Floodlights: Training only
Membership fees: Playing £30, Youth £20, Student £20
Ground admission: Varies
Programme: Sporadic only
Local newspapers: Ilkley Gazette, Wharfe Valley Times
League: Yorkshire 2
League position (1988–89): 6th
League playing record (1988–89): P 10, W 4, D 1, L 5, F 113, A 146
Competitions won: ?

MALTON & NORTON

Peasey Hill Ground, Pasture Lane, Peasey Hill, Malton. Tel: 0653 694657
Founded: 1953
President: John Seekings
Chairman: John Brown
Secretary: John Charman, Beechwood, Middlecave Road, Malton. Tel: 0653 694007
Fixtures Secretary: Ian McDonald, 1 Burdale Close, Malton, N. Yorks. Tel: 0653 694984 (H). 0482 213618 (W)
Press Officer: Chris Wilson, Keldhead hall, Middleton Road, Pickering. Tel: 0751 72754
Club captain (1988–89): Stephen Fothergill
Club captain (1989–90): Russell Stead
No. of teams: Senior 4, Youth 1, Minis 2
Directions to ground: Into Malton on the A64, follow signs to Helmsley and take last right turn before leaving town. Club is approximately 400 yards on the left hand side
Ground capacity: Seating 100
Clubhouse facilities: Modern, 4 changing roms, ref's

room, 2 baths and showers
Club colours: Black, red & white hoops. (*Change colours:* No)
Floodlights: No
Membership fees: Full £25, Social £12.50
Local newspapers: Malton Gazette, Herald/Ryedale Mercury
League: Yorkshire 2
League position (1988–89): 7th
League playing record (1988–89): P 10, W 4, D 0, L 6, F 166, A 185

MOORTOWN

Moss Valley, off The Avenue, Alwoodley, Leeds LS17 7NT. Tel: 0532 678243
Founded: 1932
Chairman: Phil Cook
Secretary: John Hesketh, 3 The View, Alwoodley, Leeds LS17 7NA. Tel: 0532 670151 (H). 462704 (W)
Fixtures Secretary: Paul Guest, 8 Birkdale Grove, Leeds LS17 7SR. Tel: 0532 693641
Press Officer: Neil Bettany, 24 Holmewood Avenue, Leeds LS6 4NJ. Tel: 0532 784946 (H). 528833 (W)
Coach: John Sunderland
Club captain (1988–89): Mark Attrids
Club captain (1989–90): Gary Murray
No. of teams: Senior 4, Youth 1, Minis 7
Directions to ground: Turn away from Leeds at the Sainsbury Complex roundabout o North Leeds Ring Road. Approx. 1 mile on right is The Avenue, and Moss Valley is 4th on right
Club colours: Maroon, green white hoops. (*Change colours:* No)
Floodlights: No
Membership fees: Playing £15, Social £4, (other fees T.B.A.)
Programme: No. of editorial pages 4; No. of advertising pages 8; Price £1
Programme editor: As Fixtures Secretary
Local newspapers: Yorkshire Post and Yorkshire Evening Post
League: Yorkshire 2
League position (1988–89): 10th – Yorkshire 1

OLD OTLIENSIANS

Chaffer's Fields, Pool Road, Otley. Tel: 0943 461476.
Founded: 1927
President: Michael Franklin
Chairman: Noel Fortune
Secretary: J. Kerby, 24 Meadow Lane, Darley, North Yorkshire H63 2PH. Tel: 0423 780968 (H), 885959 ext. 3075 (W)
Fixtures Secretary: Adrian S. Nurmanton, 26 Roseberry Crescent, Great Ayton, Middlesborough, Cleveland TS9 6ER. Tel: 0642 723199 (H), 467144 (W)
Press Officer: Noel Fortune/J. Kerby, 24 Meadow Lane, Darley, North Yorkshire H63 2PH
Club Captain: (1988–89): David Smith
Club Captain: (1989–90): David Smith
No. of Teams: Senior 4, Youth 1
Directions to ground: Behind Smiths Garden Centre on the A659 leaving Otley towards Harrogate
Clubhouse facilities: Bar, colts room, 4 changing rooms, bath and shower area
Club colours: Navy, Royal blue and white hoops, navy shorts. (*Change colours:* Red or white)
Nickname: 'Ensians'
Floodlights: Yes (training only)
Membership fees: Full £14, Playing £14, Social £13, Youth £5, Student £1, Ladies £3
Local Newspapers: Wharfedale & Airdale Observer, Wharfe News
League: Yorkshire 2
League position (1988–89): 2nd
League playing record (1988–89): P 38, W 21, D 3, L 14. F 681, A 436

SCARBOROUGH

The Clubhouse, Scarborough RUFC, Scalby Road, Newby, Scarborough YO12 6EE. Tel: 0723 363039
Founded: 1926
President: Brian Clayton, Esq.
Chairman: Alan R. Elliott
Secretary: Brian M. Clayton, 49 Scalby Avenue, Newby, Scarborough YO12 6HW. Tel: 0723 362290
Fixtures Secretary: A.R. Elliott, 29 Porritt Lane, Irton, Scarborough. Tel: 0723 862263
Press Officer: David Campbell, 58 Scalby Avenue, Newby, Scarborough. Tel: 0723 376339 (H). 367431 (W)
Coach: M.E. Holder
Club captain (1988–89): Clive Burnard
Club captain (1989–90): Shaun Fearn
No. of teams: Senior 4, Youth 1, Minis 4
Directions to ground: A64 from the West, then A171 (Whitby Road) for 2 miles, ground on left opposite Newby Service Station. From North – A171 (Whitby Road), 2 miles short of Scarborough on the right
Ground capacity: Seating 200, standing 1200
Clubhouse facilities: Bar, snooker, pool, darts. Open 7 nights 7.30-11.30. 2 squash courts
Club colours: Maroon, white, blue hoops. (*Change colours:* Navy)
Nickname: Seasiders
Floodlights: Training ground only
Membership fees: Full £16, Playing £16, Country £8, Youth £5, Student £5, Family £19. Rebate of £2 if paid before 1st September
Ground admission: Collection
Programme: No. of editorial pages 4; No. of advertising pages 12; Price: Free
Programme editor: As Press Officer
Local newspapers: Scarboro Evening News, Top Trader (free weekly)
League: Yorkshire 2
League position (1988–89): 9th
League playing record (1988–89): P 10, W 3, D 0, L 7, F 65, A 164

SHEFFIELD TIGERS

Dore Moor, Hathersage Road, Sheffield S11 7EZ. Tel: 0742 360075
Founded: 1933
President: Dr W.F. Anderson
Secretary: Stewart Devitt, 12 Bramwith Road, Sheffield S11 7EZ. Tel: 0742 304186 (H). 444181 (W)
Fixtures Secretary: Fred Senior, 5 Ashurst Road, Sheffield S6 5LP. Tel: 0742 341306
Press Officer: Mark Heaton, 28 Blair Atholl Road, Sheffield. Tel: 0742 668486
Coach: Peter Gadsby
Club captain (1988–89): Mark Heaton
Club captain (1989–90): T.B.A.
No. of teams: Senior 5, Youth 2, Minis 1
Clubhouse facilities: Bar, kitchen
Club colours: Maroon and white hoops, black shorts. (*Change colours:* Maroon hoops, black shorts)
Nickname: Tigers
Floodlights: No
Local newspaper: Sheffield Star
League: Yorkshire 2
League position (1988–89): 6th
League playing record (1988–89): P 10, W 5, D 0, L 5, F 93, A 167

WATH UPON DEARNE

Moor Road, Wath-Upon-Dearne, Nr Rotherham. Tel: 0709 872399
Founded: 1930
President: Philip Ardron
Secretary: Wilf Goddard, 1 Campsall Fields, Wath-Upon-Dearne, Nr Rotherham. Tel: 0709 873420
Fixtures Secretary: Stephen Corns, 213 Hague Avenue, Rawmarsh, Rotherham S62 7QA. Tel: 0709 527522 (H). 894149 (W)
Press Officer: Ed Kird, 66 Wath Wood Road, Wath-Upon-Dearne, Nr Rotherham. Tel: 0709 873479
Coach: Tony Price
Club captain (1988–89): Martin Horton
No. of teams: Senior 3, Youth 2
Clubhouse facilities: Bar
Club colours: Navy with gold and maroon hoop. (*Change colours:* Navy, gold, maroon stripes)
Floodlights: No
Membership fees: Full £16, Playing £16, Social £2, Student £8
Local newspapers: South Yorkshire Times
League: Yorkshire 2
League position (1988–89): 4th
League playing record (1988–89): P 35, W 23, D 0, L 13, F 578, A 346

WHEATLEY HILLS

Wheatley Hills Sports Ground, York Road Ind. Estate, Doncaster. Tel: 0302 784484
Founded: 1962
President: M. Tiplady
Chairman: A. Dunkerley
Secretary: T. Tuck, 91 Crompton Avenue, Sprotbrough, Doncaster, S. Yorks. Tel: 0302 786998
Fixtures Secretary: Chris Wilson, Keldhead Hall, Middleton Road, Pickering. Tel: 0751 72754
Coach: Nick Cooke
Club captain (1988–89): Stephen Fothergill
No. of teams: Senior 4
Directions to ground: Into Malton on A64 follow signs to Helmsley and take last right turn. before leaving town. Club 400 yds on left-hand side
Ground capacity: Standing 100
Clubhouse facilities: Modern
Club colours: Black/red/white. (*Change colours:* Blue)
Floodlights: No
Membership fees: Playing £20
League: York 2
League position (1988–89): 8th
League playing record (1988–89): P 10, W 3, D 1, L 6, F 134, A 140

YARNBURY

Brownberrie Lane, Horsforth LS18 5HB. Tel: 0532 581346
Founded: 1872
President: Raymond Johnson
Chairman: Alf Johnson
Secretary: Allan Rigby, 52 Rufford Avenue, Yeadon, Leeds LS19 7QR. Tel: 0532 509903
Fixtures Secretary: Jack Yeadon, 63 Southway, Horsforth LS18 5RN. Tel: 0532 585387
Press Officer: Rodney Rush, 16 Haw View, Yeadon, Leeds LS19. Tel: 0532 501266
Coach: Alan Giles
Club captain (1988–89): Allan Rigby
Club captain (1989–90): Roger Midwood
No. of teams: Senior 5, Youth 3, Minis 4
Directions to ground: North-west of Leeds city centre, near the Leeds/Bradford airport
Ground capacity: Standing 300
Clubhouse facilities: Open every evening
Club colours: Blue, black and white (uneven hoops). (*Change colours:* Yellow)
Floodlights: No
Membership fees: Playing £15, Social £5, Youth £7.50, Student £7.50
Programme: Only for special matches
Local newspapers: Wharfe Valley Times, Yorkshire Post, Yorkshire Evening Post, Wharfedale & Airedale Observer
League: Yorkshire 3
League position (1988–89): 1st
League playing record (1988–89): P 10, W 8, D 2, L 0, F 171, A 53
Competitions won: Yorkshire 3

YORK RAILWAY INSTITUTE

New Lane, Holgate Road, York. Tel: 0904 78930
Founded: 1932
Chairman: Chris Smith
Secretary: Jim Cooper, 8 Otterwood Bank, Foxwood Hill, Acomb, York, YO2 3JS. Tel: 0904 797858 (H), 628982 (W)
Fixtures Secretary: Bill Cooper, 'Moorcroft', Lucycroft Drive, Baildon, West Yorkshire BD17 5BG. Tel: 0274 584355
Press Officer: Graham Stirk, 28 Dringtorpe Road, Dringhouses, York. Tel: 0904 703639
Coach: T.B.A.
Club captain (1988–89): Neil Exeley
Club captain (1989–90): David Moore
No. of teams: Senior 4, Youth 2
Directions to ground: New Lane off Holgate Road off Tadcaster Road
Ground capacity: Standing Part of communal sports complex
Clubhouse facilities: Bar, changing rooms, baths, showers, etc.
Club colours: Royal blue and white hoops, black shorts, royal blue socks. (*Change colours:* Red shirts)
Floodlights: Yes
Membership fees: Full £16
Ground admission: Free (except for Floodlit Comp.)
Programme: No. of editorial pages 4; No. of advertising pages 14; Price 50p (local Floodlit Comp. League games only)
Programme editor: N. Lowry, c/0 8 Otterwood Bank, Foxwood Hill, Acomb, York YO2 3JS
Local newspapers: Yorkshire Evening Press, Yorkshire Post, Nothern Echo
League: Yorks 2
League position (1988–89): 3rd
League playing record (1988–89): P 38, W 21, D 1, L 16, F 652, A 522
Competitions won: York RI Floodlit Cup, December 1988

YORKSHIRE 3

AIREBRONIANS

Upper Mill Cottages, Esholt Lane, Esholt, Shipley, Bradford. Tel: 0274 587792
Founded: 1960
President: Geof Thompson
Chairman: Ken Hanson
Secretary: John Race, 12 Deighton Road, Wetherby, W. Yorks. Tel: 0937 64750 (H). 0274 881082 (W)
Fixtures Secretary: John Lockwood, 8 Carlton Grange, Yeadon, Leeds LS19 7UY. Tel: 0532 509073
Press Officer: Nigel Crosby, 49A Oxford Road, Guiseley, Leeds. Tel: 0943 72801
Coach: Craig Busby
Club captain (1988–89): John Lockwood
Club captain (1989–90): Greg Marchbank
No. of teams: Senior 4, Youth 1
Directions to ground: From the A6038 Shipley–Guiseley Road, follow the signposts to Esholt
Clubhouse facilities: Open weekends and evenings
Club colours: Maroon/blue/white hoops. (*Change colours:* Black)
Floodlights: Yes
League: Yorkshire 3
League position (1988–89): 7th
League playing record (1988–89): P 34, W 13, D 2, L 19, F 389, A 391

BAILDON

Jenny Lane, Baildon, Bradford. Tel: 582644
Secretary: R.L. Sissons, 2 Southgate, Guiseley, Leeds LS20 8HQ. Tel: 0943 73848 (H)
Club Colours: Red/White/Black

League: Yorkshire 3
Final position (1987–88): 3rd

HESSLE

The Foreshore, Livingstone Road, Hessle, East Yorks. Tel: 0482 643430
Founded: 1926
President: Ossie Sellers
Chairman: Robert Grayson
Secretary: Patrick John Love, 41 Oaklands Drive, Swanland Road, Hessle, East Yorks. HU13 0LT. Tel: 0482 646857 (H). 0757 705621
Fixtures Secretary: Peter Denton, 45 Maplewood Avenue, Anlaby, East Yorks. Tel: 0482 572124
Press Officer: Cec. Nunns, 48 Station Road, Hessle, East Yorks. Tel: 0482 647808
Club captain (1988–89): Colin Spicer
Club captain (1989–90): Paul Hutchinson
No. of teams: Senior 4, Youth 1, Minis 5
Directions to ground: Follow Directions to Humber Bridge Country Park, when on Livingstone Road, Ground and Clubhouse on the right
Ground capacity: Standing unlimited
Club colours: Green, black and white irregular hoops. (*Change colours:* Black)
Floodlights: No
Membership fees: Full £17, Playing £17, Social £2, Youth 25p, Student £1, OAP £2
Ground admission: Nil
Local newspapers: Hull Daily Mail, Haltemprice Herald
League: Yorkshire 3
League position (1988–89): 1st of Yorkshire 4
League playing record (1988–89): P 40, W 28, D 1, L 11, F 715, A 375
Competitions won: Yorkshire Silver Trophy 17.12.88, Yorkshire League Division 4 Winners

IONIANS

Brantingham Road, Elloughton, Brough, N. Humberside. Tel: 0482 667342
Founded: 1926
President: P. Tremere
Chairman: D. Coates
Secretary: Clive Wilkinson, 83 Hall Road, Sproatley, Nr. Hull, N. Humberside. Tel: 0482 811347
Fixtures Secretary: R. Gosling, 11 Ransome Way, Elloughton, Nr. Hull. Tel: 0482 668655
Coach: D. Mil
Club captain (1988–89): J. Cartmell
No. of teams: Senior 12
Directions to ground: 250 yds out of Elloughton village towards Brantingham
Ground capacity: Standing 250
Clubhouse facilities:
Club colours: Blue/green/white. (*Change colours:* Black)
Floodlights: Yes
League: York 3
League position (1988–89): 11th
League playing record (1988–89): P 10, W 1, D 0, L 9, F 87, A 239

KNOTTINGLEY

Howards Field, Marsh Lane, Knottingley. Tel: 0977 82438.
Founded: 1963
Secretary: M. Henderson, 4 Wellington Place, Knottingley, W. Yorks WF11 8LG. Tel: 0977 85754 (H). 0924 829511 (W).
League: Yorkshire 3
Club Colours: Blue/White

LEODIENSIANS

Crag Lane, Off Kings Lane, Alwoodley, Lees. –Tel: 9532 673409

Founded: 1906
Secretary: B. White, 397 Gledhow Lane, leeds 7. Tel: 0532 625484 (H). 450733 (W).
Fixtures Secretary: J.M. Crook, 40 Cookridge Drive, Leeds 16. Tel: 0523 673651.
League: Yorkshire 3

MARIST

Cranbrook Avenue, Cottingham Road, Hull. Tel: 0482 859216.
Founded: 1958
President: Harry Brodie
Chairman: Terry Greenley
Secretary: Nigel Rapson, 21 Swanland Butts Close, Kirkella, Hull HU10 7JG. Tel: 0482 652463 (H) 492241 (W)
Fixtures Secretary: Ralph Ayre, 92 Auckland Avenue, Hull HU6 7SH. Tel: 0482 804166
Press Officer: Gerry Baker, c/o 21 Swanland Butts Close, Kirkella, Hull HU10 7JG. Tel: 0482 652463 (H) 492241 (W)
Coach: John O'Connor
Club Captain: (1988–89): Martin Bird
Club Captain: (1989–90): John O'Connor
No. of Teams: Senior 4
Directions to ground: Follow signs for University
Clubhouse facilities: Open matchdays and training nights (Tues and Thurs)

Club colours: White shirts with blue hoop, blue shorts.. (*Change colours:* All blue)
Nickname: 'Ensians'
Floodlights: No
Membership fees: Full £20, Playing £20, Social £10, Youth £10, Student £10, OAP Nil
Local Newspapers: Hull Daily Mail
League: Yorkshire 3
League position (1988–89): Bottom (relegated)
League playing record (1988–89): P 34, W 14, D 0, L 20. F 394, A 690

OLD MODERNIANS

Cookridge lane, Cookridge, Leeds, West Yorks. LS16 7ND. Tel: 0532 671075
Founded: 1963
President: Graham Castle
Chairman: Ken Shotton
Secretary: Robert J.V. Westmoreland, 92 West End Drive, Horsforth, Leeds 18. Tel: 584278
Fixtures Secretary: David Carter, 81 Green Lane, Cookridge, Leeds 16. Tel: 679718 (H). 432519 (W)
Press Officer: Brian Doyle, c/o Old Modernians RUFC, Cookridge Lane, Cookridge, Leedsd LS16 7ND
Club captain (1988–89): Paul Day
Club captain (1989–90): Paul O'Hanlon
No. of teams: Senior 3
Directions to ground: Take Otley Old Road out of Leeds, Ground is on right hand side on Cookridge Lane going towards Bramhope
Ground capacity: Standing 100
Clubhouse facilities: Lounge, games room, guest room capacity 200 persons
Club colours: Red and black hoops. (*Change colours:* Black shirts)
Nickname: The 'Mods'
Floodlights: No
Membership fees: Full £10
Local newspapers: Wharfe Valley Times, Yorkshire Post
League: Yorkshire 3
Competitions won: Runners Up Aire-Wharfe Cup – April 1989

RODILLIANS

Manley Park, Lee Moor Road, Stanley, Wakefield. Tel: 0924 823619
Founded: 1960

President: Jack Screen
Chairman: Barry Marley
Secretary: Richard Matthews, 27 Newlands Walk, Stanley, Wakefield WF3 4DT. Tel: 0924 828727 (H). 823135 (W)
Fixtures Secretary: Ian Young, 21 Eastfield Drive, Woodlesford, Leeds. Tel: 0532 826743 (H). 448313 (W)
Press Officer: Steve Calline, c/o Ground address
Coach: Richard Moore/Jack Schofield
Club captain (1988–89): Richard Blackburn
Club captain (1989–90): Peter Clacker
No. of teams: Senior 4, Youth 1
Directions to ground: M62 Junction 30 towards Wakefield, 1 mile turn right opposite Gordons tyres, at top of hill turn right, mile turn left through gap in terraced houses just after Working Mens Club
Clubhouse facilities: Open Match days, training nights and Sunday lunch
Club colours: Green, black and white hoops, black shorts, black socks. (*Change colours:* Red shirts)
Floodlights: No
Membership fees: Full £6, Playing £12, Social £5, Student £3, OAP £3
Local newspapers: Wakefield Express, Rothwell Advertiser, Yorkshire Post
League: Yorkshire 3
League position (1988–89): 9th
League playing record (1988–89): P 10, W 3, D 0, L 7, F 66, A 204

WEST LEEDS

Blue Hill Lane, Wortley, Leeds. Tel: 0532 639869
Founded: 1926
Secretary: D. Brealey, 124 New Laithes Road, Hosforth, Leeds LS18 2AY. Tel: Leeds 581314 (H). Leeds 446731 (W)
League: Yorkshire 3.

WIBSEY

143 High Street, Wibsey, Bradford. Tel: 0274 671643
Founded: 1931/32
President: M. Spencer
Secretary: D. Hartley, 143 High Street, Wibsey, Bradford. Tel: 0274 677255 (H). 675231 (W)
Fixtures Secretary: A. Deacon, 18 Overton Drive, Bradford 6. Tel: 0274 574905
Coach: S. Griffin
Club captain (1988–89): Andy Foulds
Club captain (1989–90): T.B.A.
No. of teams: Senior 3
Directions to ground: From end of M606 to Odsal roundabout, turn left on 3rd exit. Carry on about 2 miles over two roundabouts. Turn right 200 yards past Horse and Groom Hotel
Ground capacity: 200
Clubhouse facilities: Tetleys beer, open all week, address as above
Club colours: Green and red hoops. (*Change colours:* Blue)
Floodlights: No
Membership fees: Playing £10, Social £3
Ground admission: Collection
Local newspaper: Telegraph and Argus
League: Yorkshire 3
League position (1988–89): 4th
League playing record (1988–89): P 10, W 5, D 2, L 3

BRADFORD SALEM

Shay Lane, Heaton, Bradford BD9 6SL. Tel: 0274 496430.
Founded: 1924
Secretary: J.C. Dobson, 2 Highfield drive, Heaton, Bradford BD9 5PW. Tel: 0274 487517 (H). 0274

247521 (W).
Fixtures Secretary: R.M. Birkett, 9 Shay Crescent, Heaton, Bradford BD9 5PW. Tel: 0274 43479 (H). 0274 75511 (W).
League: Yorkshire 4
Club Colours: Royal Blue/Black/Yellow

DINNINGTON

Lodge Lane, Dinnington, Sheffield S31 7PB. Tel: 0909 562044
Founded: 1968
President: George Tierney
Chairman: E. (Ted) Taylor
Secretary: Ian W. Goold, 71 New Road, Firbeck, Worksop, Notts S81 8JY. Tel: 0709 817312
Fixtures Secretary: W. (Bill) Gilbody, 16 Devonshire Drive, North Anston, Sheffield S31 7AQ. Tel: 0909 562997
Coach: Alan Donkin
Club captain (1988–89): Cameron Gray
Club captain (1989–90): Eddie Joel
No. of teams: Senior 4, Youth 1, Minis 2
Directions to ground: M1 Junction 31. Take A57 towards Worksop, turn left at lights, turn right at T-junction, turn left to go past school, across X-roads at top, 300 yards on left
Clubhouse facilities: Open every evening and Sunday dinnertime; Saturday dinner during season
Club colours: Gold, white and blue hoops. (*Change colours:* Maroon)
Floodlights: No
Membership fees: Playing £20, Social £5, Youth £10
Local newspapers: Worksop Guardian, Rotherham Advertiser, Rotherham Star
League: Yorkshire 4
League position (1988–89): 9th
League playing record (1988–89): P 10, W 3, D 0, L 7, F 148, A 204

HALIFAX VANDALS

Warley Town Lane, Warley, Halifax. Tel: 0422 831703
President: Robert Ingham
Chairman: Cyril Clegg
Secretary: Steve Beard, c/o Wilson and Royston Ltd, Armytage Road Industrial Estate, Brighouse. Tel: 0484 719642
Fixtures Secretary: David Hellowell, Upper Hoyle Head Farm, Soyland, Halifax. Tel: 0422 823571 (H). 348511 (W)
Press Officer: Bob Walker, c/o Nightfreight (Holdings) Ltd, Unit D19, Dean Clough Industrial Park, Halifax. Tel: 0422 345540 (H). 348511 (W)
Coach: Ken Beaumont
Club captain (1988–89): John Wilkinson
No. of teams: Senior 4
Clubhouse facilities: Open Match days and Tuesdays and Thursdays
Club colours: Blue and white hoops, blue shorts and socks (*Change colours:* Blue and white quartered shirts)
Floodlights: No
Membership fees: Playing £15, Social £2, Youth £5, Student £5, VP: £5 min.
Local newspapers: Halifax Evening Courier, Yorkshire Post
League: Yorkshire 4
League position (1988–89): 4th
League playing record (1988–89): P 10, W 6, D 0, L 4

HEATH

North Dean, Stainland Road, West Vale, Halifax, W. Yorks. Tel: 0422 72920
Founded: 1928
President: J.S. Robertshaw
Chairman: D.W. Bradley
Secretary: Craig Bedford, 58 Hollins Lane, Sowerby Bridge, Halifax. W. Yorks. HX6 2RP. Tel: 0422

834473 (H). 73462 (W)
Fixtures Secretary: Derek Shackleton, 16 Banks End Road, Elland, Halifax, W. Yorks. Tel: 0422 75339 (H). 831751 (W)
Coach: J. Smith
Club captain (1988–89): P. Stewart
Club captain (1989–90): P. Stewart
No. of teams: Senior 3
Directions to ground: Leave M62 Junction 24, follow Halifax signs at roundabout, turn left at Calder & Hebble Pub (approx. 2 mile down hill). mile later turn left at garage
Clubhouse facilities: 2 storey building with changing groundfloor, bar 1st floor
Club colours: Emerald, claret and gold. (*Change colours:* Emerald)
Nickname: Heathens
Floodlights: No
Membership fees: Full £26, Social £5, Student £2
Local newspaper: Halifax Evening Courier
League: Yorkshire 4
League position (1988–89): 11th Yorkshire 3
League playing record (1988–89): P 10, W 1, D 0, L 9, F 78, A 213

HULLENSIANS

Springhead Lane, Anlaby Common, Hull HU4 7RU. Tel: 0482 505656.
Founded: 1924
President: Paul Camm
Chairman: L. Wilcock
Coach: T.B.A.
Secretary: Andrew P. Newton, 32 Goodmanham Way, Cottingham, Hull HU16 5LJ. Tel: (0482) 841101.
Fixtures Secretary: Chris Martin, 20 St Peters Avenue, Anlaby, HU10 7AP. Tel: (0482) 650696.
Club captain (1987–88): K. Osborne
Club captain (1988–89): N. Hare
No. of teams: Senior 3, Youth 1
Directions to Ground: Follow sign posts for Anlaby, look for the "Haltemprice Sports Centre" Rugby club 1 miles down Springfield Way on the left after the church.
Ground capacity: 2000
Clubhouse: Cap. 120 (2 changing rooms, 1 bath, 1 bar lounge)
Colours: Red and black. (*Change colours:* Yellow)
Floodlights: No
Admission: Nil
Membership: £7.50
Local newspaper: Hull Daily Mail
League: Yorks 4
Final position (1987–88): 6th
Playing record (1987–88): P 35, W 16, L 15, D 4.

LEEDS CSSA

Newton Road, Leeds LS7 4HX. Tel: 0532 685755
Founded: 1962
President: Jack Moverley
Chairman: Paul Bettison
Secretary: Steve Sykes, 96 Leasowe Road, Leeds LS10 2EZ. Tel: 0532 779156
Fixtures Secretary: Bob Marshall, 38 Barthorpe Crescent, Leeds LS17 5PE. Tel: 0532 685755
Press Officer: Steve Sykes
Coach: Paul Guthrie
Club captain (1988–89): Hrysko Nemyria
Club captain (1989–90): Paul Guthrie
No. of teams: Senior 3
Directions to ground: From Sherpscar intersection (A61/A58) follow Chapeltown signs onto Chapeltown Road Northbound. Turn left onto Newton Road at RLHQ. From East follow Harehills Lane (B6159) to Hospital, left onto Newton Road
Ground capacity: Standing 200
Clubhouse facilities: Bar, snooker room (3 tables), ballroom, detached changing rooms
Club colours: Red/yellow. (*Change colours:* Navy

blue)
Floodlights: No
Local newspapers: Yorkshire Post/Yorkshire Evening Post
League: Yorkshire 3
League position (1988–89): 10th
League playing record (1988–89): P 11, W 2, D 1, L 7, F 70, A 148
Competitions won: Morely Floodlit Competition – Richmond Trophy

LEEDS Y.M.C.A.

Lawnswood Playing Fields, Otley Road, Leeds. Tel: 0532 678168
Founded: 1926
President: E. Peck
Chairman: S. Goodall
Secretary: T.G. Cook, 39 Langdale Gardens, Headingley, Leeds LS6 3HB. Tel: 0532 780532
Fixtures Secretary: S. Armitage, 276 High Street, Boston Spa, Leeds LS23 6AJ. Tel: 0937 844555 (H). 0532 431557 (W)
Press Officer: As Secretary
Coach: B. Marston
Club captain (1988–89): John Greenwood
Club captain (1989–90): John Greenwood
No. of teams: Senior 3
Directions to ground: Situated near Leeds University Sports Ground on A660 Leeds–Otley Road
Clubhouse facilities: Open Match days
Club colours: Light and dark blue hoops. (*Change colours:* Red)
Floodlights: No
Membership fees: Full £20, Social £6, Youth £12
Local Newspapers: Yorkshire Evening Post, Yorkshire Post
League: Yorkshire 4
League position (1988–89): 7th
League playing record (1988–89): P 10, W 4, D 0, L 6, F 111, A 151
Competitions won: McBride Trophy 1989

NORTHALLERTON

Brompton Lodge, Northallerton Road, Brompton, Northallerton. Tel: 0609 3496
President: Richard Lovelace
Chairman: John S. Turner
Secretary: Stephen Hague, 14 The Stonebow, Thronton-Le-Beans, Northallerton, North Yorkshire DL6 3SR. Tel: 0609 774325 (H). 780780 (W)
Fixtures Secretary: Alan Bradley, 15 Borrowby Avenue, Northallerton, North Yorks. Tel: 0609 2743
Coach: Jock Williamson
Club captain (1988–89): Dave Bowes
Club captain (1989–90): Steve Metcalfe
No. of teams: Senior 4, Youth 3
Directions to ground: Once in Northallerton follow road signs for Teesside/Brompton, then after passing under footbridge turn left at garage
Clubhouse facilities: Changing rooms, Clubhouse on same site as pitches
Club colours: Green/amber/white hoops. (*Change colours:* Amber)
Floodlights: No
League: Yorkshire 4
League position (1988–89): 3rd
League playing record (1988–89): P 10, W 7, D 0, L 3

OLD RISHWORTHIAN

The Clubhouse, Copley, Halifax, West Yorks. Tel: 0422 53919
President: John Fredrick Dawson
Secretary: D.W. Butler, Keepers, Shaw Lane, Holywell Green, Halifax, West Yorks. Tel: 0422 71672
Fixtures Secretary: Malcolm Procter, 138 Wakefield Road, Lightcliffe, Halifax, West Yorks. Tel: 0422 201730 (H). 0274 874222 (W)

Club captain (1988–89): Andrew Finneran
No. of teams: Senior 3
Directions to ground: M62 Junction 24 to Halifax, after 2 miles, left towards Sowerby Bridge, after mile left into Copley Village
Clubhouse facilities: Open Match days and training evenings
Club colours: White/black/maroon hoops. (*Change colours:* Maroon)
Floodlights: No
Membership fees: Full £12, Social £1
Local newspaper: Halifax Courier
League: Yorkshire 4
League position (1988–89): 8th
League playing record (1988–89): P 10, W 3 , D 0, L 7, F 73, A 116

PHOENIX PARK

The Oval Ball, Stony Road, Farsley, Leeds. Tel: 0532 553439
Founded: 1937
President: Donald Campbell Murray
Chairman: Charles Barrie Tinker
Secretary: Michael Ryan, 280 Whitehall Road, Wyke, Bradford BD12 9DX. Tel: 0274 735099 (W)
Fixtures Secretary: Brian Scarth, 5 Hough Side Close, Pudsey, Leeds. Tel: 0532 570741
Press Officer: Steven Ellis, 484 Tong Road, Leeds. Tel: 0274 871429 (W)
Coach: Christopher John Wharton
Club captain (1988–89): Paul Hodgson
Club captain (1989–90): Paul Hodgson
No. of teams: Senior 3, Youth 1
Club colours: Royal blue and gold. (*Change colours:* Yellow)
Floodlights: No
League: Yorkshire 4
League position (1988–89): 2nd
League playing record (1988–89): P 10, W 9, D 0, L 1, F 174, A 61

SHEFFIELD OAKS

Limestone Cottage Lane, Claywheels Lane, Sheffield 6
Founded: 1978
President: Mr William S. Hill
Chairman: Mr Trevor Snell
Secretary: Mr Richard Walton, 1 Little Matlock Way, Stannington, Sheffield S6 6FX. Tel: 0742 349421 (H). 665274 Ext 3475 (W)
Fixtures Secretary: Mr David Hudson, c/o Paltreen Ltd, 9A Sheffield Road, Sheffield 9. Tel: 0742 448695 (W)
Club captain (1988–89): Paul Crookes
Club captain (1989–90): Richard Senior
No. of teams: Senior 3
Clubhouse facilities: Changing rooms, bar/lounge
Club colours: Royal blue and gold hoops/quarters. (*Change colours:* Gold with blue collars)
Floodlights: No
League: Yorkshire 4
League position (1988–89): 1st Division 5
League playing record (1988–89): P 35, W 25, D 4, L 6, F 602, A 220
Competitions won: Simon Allen Trophy, Sherlock Shield, Yorkshire Division 5

YORKSHIRE 5

B.P. CHEMICALS

Saltend, Hull. Tel: 0482 896113
Founded: 1973
President: George Watson
Chairman: Ken Smith
Secretary: Stuart Ladd, 4 Chaucer Street, Westcott Street, Hull HU8 8NA. Tel: 0482 706502 (H). 583251 (W)

Fixtures Secretary: Steve Peat, 10 Albina Garth, Hedon HU12 8LY. Tel: 0482 897428
Press Officer: As Secretary
Coach: Peter Richards
Club captain (1988–89): Graham McKinley
Club captain (1989–90): Graham Riby
No. of teams: Senior 2
Directions to ground: Follow signpost A1033 Hedon, just on outskirts of Hull
Club colours: Maroon and gold. (*Change colours:* Blue and white hoops)
Floodlights: No
Local newspaper: Hull Daily Mail
League: Yorkshire 5
League position (1988–89): 6th
League playing record (1988–89): P 9, W 4, D 0, L 5, F 66, A 131

BURLEY

The Clubhouse, Abbey Road, Leeds LS5 3NG. Tel: 0532 757400
Founded: 1921
President: Raymond P. Leeman
Chairman: George Mather
Secretary: Edward Holdsworth, 15 Carlton Gate, Leeds LS7 1HW. Tel: 0532 442786
Fixtures Secretary: Charles Butcher, 27 Sutton Grange Close, Harrogate, N. Yorks. Tel: 0423 521669
Press Officer: Paul Lupton, 5 Dovedale Gardens, Leeds LS15 8UP. Tel: 0532 402307
Coach: John Addock
Club captain (1988–89): Martin Gosney
Club captain (1989–90): Martin Gosney
No. of teams: Senior 3
Directions to ground: A65 to Kirkstall from city centre. Ground adjacent to Kirkstall Abbey
Clubhouse facilities: Open Match days, every evening, Sunday lunch, throughout the year
Club colours: Maroon and white. (*Change colours:* Green and white)
Floodlights: No
Membership fees: Playing £10, Social £3, Youth (under 18) £2.50, OAP £1
Local newspapers: Yorkshire Post, Yorkshire Evening Post
League: Yorkshire 5
League position (1988–89): 4th
League playing record (1988–89): P 10, W 6, D 0, L 4, F 143, A 112

DANUM PHOENIX

Cantley Park, Cantley, Doncaster
Founded: 1988 (previously Bridon, 1970)
President: Thomas Jones
Secretary: Paul Varley, 29 Bahram Road, Bessacarr, Doncaster DN4 7BG. Tel: 530875
Fixtures Secretary: Vaughn Williams, 'Ardara', Back Lane, Norton, Doncaster. Tel: 700559
Press Officer: As Secretary
Coach: David Townend
Club captain (1988–89): Nigel Sumner
Club captain (1989–90): David Townend
No. of teams: Senior 3
Directions to ground: Cantley Park Playing Fields, Cantley, Doncaster
Clubhouse facilities: Local Public House
Club colours: All black. (*Change colours:* Yellow with red/black hoops)
Floodlights: No
Membership fees: Full £15, Playing £15, Social £5, Youth £7.50, Student £10, OAP £5
Local newspapers: Doncaster Star, Doncaster Free Press
League: Yorkshire 5
League position (1988–89): 6th
League playing record (1988–89): P 35, W 17, D 1, L 17, F 427, A 418

DE LA SALLE

Beauchief Hall, Beauchief Abbey Lane, Sheffield 8. Tel: 367756
Founded: 1956
Secretary: Mrs M. Buckley, 93 Ingram Road, Sheffield S2 2SB. Tel: 0742 720246 (H)
Press Officer: A. Buckley, Tel: 0742 720246
Club Colours: Green/Gold
League: Yorkshire 5

OSSETT

Ossett Cricket & Athletic Club Pavilion, Queens Terrace, Ossett. Tel: 0924 273618
Founded: Re-formed 1979
President: Mr Don Jowett
Chairman: Mr Brian Kattenburg
Secretary: Mr Stephen Deathe, 18 Ledger Lane, Lofthouse, Wakefield WF3 3NG. Tel: 0924 828950 (H). 0532 440171 Ext 306 (W)
Fixtures Secretary: Mr Jeremy Slack, 1 Spa Croft Road, Ossett. Tel: 0924 273952
Press Officer: As Fixtures Secretary
Coach: Mr John Garstang
Club captain (1988–89): Mr Andrew Mills
Club captain (1989–90): Mr Andrew Mills
No. of teams: Senior 2
Directions to ground: M1 Junction 40, follow sign A638 Wakefield, turn right at Ossett Post House Hotel, turn right 800 yards into Spring Mill 9-hole golf course
Clubhouse facilities: Ossett Cricket & Athletic Club Pavilion, bar/kitchen facilities
Club colours: Black and white. (*Change colours:* Red)
Floodlights: No
Membership fees: Full £12.50, Playing £12.50, Social £5, Youth £1.50, Student £1.50, OAP £1.50
Local newspapers: Yorkshire Post, Yorkshire Evening Post, Wakefield Express, Ossett Observer
League: Yorkshire 5
League position (1988–89): 9th
League playing record (1988–89): P 35, W 15, D 0, L 20, F 476, A 464

ROWNTREE

Mille Crux Sportsfield, Rowntree-Mackintosh, Haxby Road, York. Tel: 0904 623933
Founded: 1894, re-founded 1984
President: Ralph A. Kaner
Chairman: Peter M. Cregan
Secretary: George Robinson, 21 Manor Way, Rawcliffe, York YO3 6UQ. Tel: 0904 623243 (H). 653071 Ext 2934 (W)
Fixtures Secretary: Terry Lax, 31 Rosslyn Street, Clifton, York. Tel: 0904 644840
Press Officer: Brian Cottam, 21 Woodlands Place, New Earswick, York. Tel: 0904 766122
Coach: Alan Warriner
Club captain (1988–89): Neil McLeay
Club captain (1989–90): Neil McLeay
No. of teams: Senior 2, Youth 1
Directions to ground: Use the York Ring Road. Leave at sign New Earswick. Ground at mile past village on left. (Near Rowntree factory)
Club colours: Red/black/white 1 inch hoops. (*Change colours:* Black)
Floodlights: No
Local newspaper: York Evening Press
League: Yorkshire 5
League position (1988–89): 7th
League playing record (1988–89): P 10, W 5, D 0, L 5, F 87, A 129

SKIPTON

Sandy Lands, Carleton, New Road, Skipton. Tel: Skipton 3148.
Founded: 1874

Secretary: R. Lumley, 10 Parkwood Drive, Skipton, N. Yorks. Tel: 60766 (H). 0535 36116 (W).
League: Yorkshire 5
Final position (1987–88): 11th (bottom, relegated)
Club Colours: Cardinal

WETHERBY

H.M.Y.C.C., York Road, Wetherby. Tel: 0937 65141.
Founded: 1966
Secretary: J.M. Hopkins, 1 Almsford Close, Harrogate, W. Yorks HG2 8EF.
League: Yorkshire 4

WITHERNSEA

Highfield Ground, Queen Street, Withernsea
Founded: 1938
Chairman: Mr Ian Kemp
Secretary: Mr Anthony Ellis, 11-17 Seaside Road, Withernsea HU19 2DL. Tel: 0964 613278 (H). 613278 (W)
Fixtures Secretary: Mr Peter Vickerman, 216 Queen Street, Withernsea. Tel: 0964 614654
Press Officer: Mr John Littlefair, 55 South Side Road, Patrington, North Humberside. Tel: 0964 630285
Coach: Dr R. Fouracre
Club captain (1988–89): Mr Bob Wardman
Club captain (1989–90): Mr Bob Wardman
No. of teams: Senior 2
Directions to ground: Main Street, Withernsea
Ground capacity: Standing 100
Clubhouse facilities: Bar (Youngers), showers, toilets
Club colours: White, blue hoop. (Change colours: No)
Nickname: Seasiders
Floodlights: No
Membership fees: Playing £15, others by donation
Local newspaper: Holderness Gazette
League: Yorkshire 5
League position (1988–89): 2nd
League playing record (1988–89): P 10, W 8, D 0, L 2, F 143, A 79

YORKSHIRE CW

Pontefract Road, Stanton, Leeds LS10. Tel: 701715 or 701107.
Founded: 1952
Secretary: M. Coates, 4 Baghill Road, Tingley, Near Wakefield. Tel: 0532 518018 (H) 524272 (W)
League: Yorkshire 4

YORKSHIRE MAIN

Yorkshire Main Miners' Welfare, Edlington Lane, Edlington, Doncaster. Tel: 0709 864075
Founded: 1983
Chairman: Gary Makuch
Secretary: Stephen Derrick, 172 Cedar Road, Warmsworth, Doncaster. Tel: 0302 850981 (H), 01-422 3488 (W)
Fixtures Secretary: H. Whiteley, 53 Thompson Avenue, Edlington, Doncaster. Tel: 0709 863446
Club captain (1988–89): Brian Wilson-Storey
Club captain (1989–90): Brian Wilson-Storey
No. of teams: Senior 2
Directions to ground: Along A1 to A630 head towards Roth and Sheffield, turn left at 1st traffic lights to Edlington, 1 mile on left
Ground capacity: Standing 300
Club colours: Green/black. (Change colours: Red/black)
Floodlights: No
Membership fees: Playing £12.50
Ground admission: Nil
League: York 5
League position (1988–89): 5th
League playing record (1988–89): P 10, W 5, D 0, L 5, F 119, A 125

ADWICK-LE-STREET

Tally Ho! Great North Road, Woodlands, Doncaster. Tel: 0302 722372
Founded: 1965
President: W.B. Johnson
Chairman: Kevin Bidmead
Secretary: R.J. Terry, 27 Sherwood Drive, Skellow, Doncaster. Tel: 0302 727580
Fixtures Secretary: Michael Flanagan, 31 Alexandra Road, Bentley, Doncaster. Tel: 0302 834860
Press Officer: Roy Maskrey, 53 Richmond Road, Scawsby, Doncaster, S. Yorks. Tel: 0302 784663
Coach: David Bibby
Club captain (1988–89): Roy Maskrey
Club captain (1989–90): Roy Maskrey
No. of teams: Senior 2
Directions to ground: 4 miles north of Doncaster on A638 Wakefield Road. Near A1(M), M1 M62 motorways.
Clubhouse facilities: Pub, changing rooms
Club colours: Navy/sky hoops. (Change colours: Navy/sky quarters)
Floodlights: No
Membership fees: £7.50
Local newspapers: Doncaster Evening Star, Doncaster Free Press
League: Yorkshire 6
League position (1988–89): 4th

ARMTHORPE MARKHAM

Welfare Cricket Ground, Church Street, Armthorpe, Doncaster, S. Yorks.
Founded: 1989
President: Tony Rear
Chairman: Chris Gryzelka
Secretary: Barry Jones, 98 Laburnham Drive, Armthorpe, Doncaster, S. Yorks. DN3 3HL. Tel: 0302 832804
Fixtures Secretary: Chris Gryzelka, 13 Pinewood Avenue, Armthorpe, Doncaster, S. Yorks. DN3 2HA. Tel: 0302 834567
Press Officer: As Fixtures Secretary
Coach: Chris Gryzelka
Club captain (1988–89): Ray Trewick
No. of teams: Senior 2
Directions to ground: Off M18 at Junction 4 towards Doncaster, left at first roundabout down to another roundabout, 2nd exit through village, on left Markham main colliery, turn in
Clubhouse facilities: Markham Main Officials Club, Armthorpe. Tel: 0302 831609
Club colours: Black, red, white, blue quarters. (Change colours: Red, white, black hoops)
Floodlights: No
Membership fees: Full £12, Playing £12, Social £6
Local newspaper: Doncaster Star
League: Yorkshire 6
League position (1988–89): 8th
League playing record (1988–89): P 10, W 3, D 0, L 7, F 99, A 153

CASTLE COLLEGE

Ash House Lane, Dore, Sheffield 17. Tel: 0742 620332
Founded: 1966 (previously Granville College)
Secretary: Andy Cook, 47 Bishop Hill, Woodhouse, Sheffield S13 7EN. Tel: 0742 696596 (H). 0742 738441 Ext 224 (W)
Fixtures Secretary: As Secretary
Club captain (1988–89): Broderick Howell
Club captain (1989–90): Broderick Howell
No. of teams: Senior 1

Directions to ground: Follow A625 out of Sheffield city centre for 2–3 miles, after passing the Wheatsheaf Pub and the Midland Bank Sports ground, we are next on the left
Club colours: Black and amber quarters. (*Change colours:* Green)
Floodlights: No
Local newspaper: Sheffield Star
League: Yorkshire 6
League position (1988–89): 3rd
League playing record (1988–89): P 11, W 9, D 1, L 2

HORNSEA

Hollis Recreation Ground, Atwick Road, Hornsea. Tel: 0964 534181
Founded: 1924
President: T. Tomlinson
Chairman: R. Scruton
Secretary: G. Steven, 59 Hornsea Road, Leven, Beverley, Humberside HU17 5NJ. Tel: 0964 543868 (H), 562333 (W)
Fixtures Secretary: G. Edmond, Corner Stones, Football Green, Hornsea. Tel: 0964 535714
Club captain (1988–89): M. Seymour
No. of teams: Senior 3
Directions to ground: Off Atwick Road, Hornsea
Ground capacity: Seating 30, Standing 1000
Club colours: Black/green/white. (*Change colours:* Green)
Floodlights: No
Membership fees: Playing £20
Ground admission: Free
League: York 6
League position (1988–89): 11th
League playing record (1988–89): P 10, W 1, D 0, L 9, F 65, A 241

KNARESBOROUGH

Hay-A-Park, Knaresborough, N. Yorks.
Founded: 1982
Secretary: P. Drew, 45 st Catherines road, Harrogate HG2 8LA. Tel: 889034 (H). 867355 (W).
Press Officer: G. Gilmore
League: Yorkshire 6
Club Colours: Amber/Navy

LEEDS CORINTHIANS

Middleton District Centre, Leeds LS10 4RA. Tel: 0532 711574
Founded: 1956
President: Geoff McBride
Secretary: Frank Boon, 39 Neville Grove, Swillington, Leeds LS26 8QN. Tel: 0532 867833 (H). 701107 Ext 3888 (W)
Fixtures Secretary: Geoff McBride, 16 Lodge Lane, Beeston, Leeds LS11 6AZ. Tel: 0532 701619
Press Officer: As Secretary
Coach: Brent Stanley
Club captain (1988–89): Martin Bradford
Club captain (1989–90): David Peace
No. of teams: Senior 2, Youth 2, Minis 5
Directions to ground: Follow signs for A653 on leaving M62, M1. City centre and turn on to ring road at Tommy Wass Pub, approx. 2 miles come to roundabout and proceed to rear of supermarket on to shale track to Clubhouse
Ground capacity: Standing 250
Clubhouse facilities: Open Match days, evenings and Sunday lunch
Club colours: Black, white and gold hoops. (*Change colours:* Red)
Floodlights: No
Membership fees: Full £15, Playing £15, Social £3, Youth £7.50, Student £7.50, OAP £1.50
Ground admission: Free
Local newspapers: Yorkshire Evening Post, Yorkshire Post
League: Yorkshire 5

League position (1988–89): 10th
League playing record (1988–89): P 35, W 10, D 1, L 24, F 282, A 445

MALTBY OLD BOYS

Maltby Comprehensive School, Braithwell Road, Maltby. Tel: 0709 812580
Founded: 1980
Secretary: Kieran McKenna, 25 Bramley Grange Way, Bramley, Rotherham S66 0UW. Tel: 0709 548096
Fixtures Secretary: Ian Vine, 79 Braithwell Road, Maltby. Tel: 0709 816153
Press Officer: Simon Taylor, 73 Norwood Avenue, Maltby
Coach: Stuart Dodds
No. of teams: Senior 2
Clubhouse facilities: Public House
Club colours: Maroon and amber hoops. (*Change colours:* Maroon)
Floodlights: No
League: Yorkshire 6
League position (1988–89): 5th–6th
League playing record (1988–89): P 10, W 4, D 1, L 5, F 96, A 101

MOSBOROUGH

Westfield Sports Centre, Westfield Crescent, Mosborough, Sheffield. Tel: 510376
President: Terence Gaskell
Chairman: Hedley Craney
Secretary: Layton Pope, 49 Churchdale Road, Frecheville, Sheffield S12 4XW. Tel: 0742 393616 (H). 398012 (W)
Fixtures Secretary: Steve Collins, Manor View, Brampton-En-Le-Morthen, Rotherham. Tel: 531732 (H). 0742 395621 (W)
Press Officer: Layton Pope, 49 Churchdale Road, Frecheville, Sheffield S12 4XW. Tel: 0742 393616 (H). 398012 (W)
Coach: Jon Sadler
Club captain (1988–89): Robert Lees
Club captain (1989–90): Kevin Greaves
No. of teams: Senior 2
Directions to ground: M1 leave at Junction 30, A616 to Sheffield. 100 yards after first traffic lights in Mosborough turn right into Westfield Crescent
Clubhouse facilities: Vine Public House, School Street, Mosborough
Club colours: Black and white hooped shirts, black shorts. (*Change colours:* Red shirts, black shorts)
Floodlights: No
Local newspapers: Sheffield Star, Yorkshire Post, The Mosborough Leader
League: Yorkshire 6
League position (1988–89): 5th
League playing record (1988–89): P 10, W 6, D 0, L 4, F 93, A 98

SHEFFIELD MEDICALS

University Sports Ground, Warminster Road, Norton, Sheffield 8. Tel: 0742 554536
Founded: 1953
President: W. Morris-Jones MCh, FRCS
Secretary: Martin Billington, (Sheffield Medicals RUFC), c/o Medical Society, Beech Hill Road, Sheffield S10 2RX. Tel: 0742 766222 Ext 2493 (W)
Fixtures Secretary: Sean Turner, 192 Cobden View Road, Crookes, Sheffield S10 1HT. Tel: 0742 682414
Coach: David 'Obno' Rogers
Club captain (1988–89): David Potter
Club captain (1989–90): Adam Brooks
No. of teams: Senior 2
Directions to ground: University Playing Fields, Norton, via Chesterfield Road
Clubhouse facilities: Numerous changing rooms, showers, bar, food
Club colours: Blue and white hoops. (*Change colours:*

Black with gold hoop)
Nickname: Adam's Babies
Floodlights: No
Membership fees: Full £15, Student £5
Local newspapers: Sheffield Star, Yorkshire Post
League: Yorkshire 6
League position (1988–89): 9th
League playing record (1988–89): P 11, W 4, D 0, L 7

SHEFFIELD STEELS

HQ Prince of Wales Hotel, Ecklington, Derbys
Founded: 1928
Secretary: Darren Shaw, 10 Chesterfield Road,
Ecklington, Sheffield S31 9BD. Tel: 0246 432456
League: Yorkshire 6
Final position (1987–88): 4th

STOCKSBRIDGE

Stone Moor Road, Bolsterstone
Founded: 1963
Secretary: Reg Hirst, 2 Hague Cottages,
Roughbirchworth Lane, Oxspring, Sheffield S30 6YP.

Tel: 0226 765921
Fixtures Secretary: Chris Lambert, 21 Haywood
Avenue, Deepcar, Sheffield S30 5QD. Tel: 0742
885525
Press Officer: David Crossland, Stocksbridge Rugby
Club, 634 Manchester Road, Stocksbridge, Sheffield.
Tel: 0742 885078 (Club)
Club captain (1988–89): Michael Taylor
Club captain (1989–90): Mel Bird
No. of teams: Senior 3
Directions to ground: A57 from Sheffield to Deepcar,
follow Carr Road to Bolsterstone, turn right 500 yards
on left
Clubhouse facilities: Converted Chapel, not on
Ground
Club colours: Royal blue, 2 white hoops. (*Change
colours:* Red, light blue, white hoops)
Floodlights: No
Membership fees: Full £10, Playing £13, Social £2,
Student £2.50, OAP £2
Local newspapers: Sheffield Star
League: Yorkshire 6
League position (1988–89): 6th
League playing record (1988–89): P 32, W 5, D 1,
L 26, F 272, A 649

DURHAM/NORTHUMBERLAND LEAGUES

N.E. DURHAM/NORTHUMBERLAND
ONE: OFFICIAL

Joyce Baty,
5 Broodlands, Ponteland,
Northumberland,   (H) 0661 23527
NE20 9LZ

N.E. DURHAM/NORTHUMBERLAND
TWO: OFFICIAL

Ian Rae,
Kintail, 31 Amble Avenue,
Whitley Bay, Tyne & Wear (H) 0632 2526604

N.E. DURHAM/NORTHUMBERLAND
THREE: OFFICIAL

Mr. C. McLoughlin,
31 Turnstall Avenue, Hartlepool,
Cleveland   (H) 0429 267270
TS26 8NE   (O) 0624 452885

N.E. DURHAM/NORTHUMBERLAND
FOUR: OFFICIAL

A.R. (Tony) Brown,
22 Mill Crescent, Hebburn,
Tyne & Wear NE31 1UQ   091 469 3716

TABLES 1987–88

DURHAM/NORTHUMBERLAND 1

	P	W	D	L	F	A	PTS
Blyth	10	8	0	2	138	99	16
Rockcliff	10	6	1	3	70	74	13
Ponteland	10	6	0	4	95	13	12
Ashington	10	5	1	4	117	96	11
Darlington	10	5	1	4	91	74	11
Seghill	10	5	1	4	100	89	11
Acklam	10	4	2	4	105	62	10
Redcar	10	4	1	5	118	84	9
Horden	10	4	1	5	129	124	9
Winlaton	10	3	0	7	74	132	6
Percy Pk	10	0	2	8	60	150	2

DURHAM/NORTHUMBERLAND 2

	P	W	D	L	F	A	PTS
Mowden Pk	10	9	0	1	259	60	18
Hartlepool	10	9	0	1	196	81	18
Bishop Auck	10	8	0	2	245	87	16
Sunderland	10	5	1	4	160	117	11
Consett	10	5	1	4	109	122	11
Seaham	10	4	2	4	158	109	10
Wallsend	10	3	2	5	128	146	8
Medicals	10	3	0	7	83	139	6
N Durham	10	3	0	7	80	162	6
Hart BBOB	10	3	0	7	105	247	6
Houghton	10	0	0	10	46	299	0

DURHAM/NORTHUMBERLAND 3

	P	W	D	L	F	A	PTS
Whitby	9	9	0	0	256	56	18
Billingham	9	7	0	2	159	78	14
Guisborough	9	6	0	3	100	58	12
Seaton Carew	9	4	0	5	96	99	8
Wearside	9	4	0	5	85	112	8
Chester-le-St	9	4	0	5	71	120	8
Darlington RA	9	3	1	5	94	75	7
N Shields	9	3	1	5	117	143	7
Hart TDS OB	9	3	0	6	59	113	6
Washington	9	1	0	8	51	234	2

DURHAM/NORTHUMBERLAND 4

	P	W	D	L	F	A	PTS
Wensleydale	7	7	0	0	176	21	16
Prudhoe	8	7	0	1	113	84	14
S Tyneside Coll	7	5	0	2	183	65	10
Barnard Castle	7	4	0	3	113	88	10
Richmondshire	8	3	1	4	94	65	7
Jarrovians	8	3	0	5	87	105	6
C Serv Durham	8	2	0	6	54	244	4
Newton Aycliffe*	7	0	1	6	31	109	3

* 2 points awarded.

TABLES 1988-89

DURHAM/NORTHUMBERLAND 1

	P	W	D	L	F	A	PTS
Rockcliff	10	8	0	2	140	83	16
Mowden Pk	10	7	1	2	124	81	15
Seghill	10	6	3	1	106	83	15
Acklam	10	7	0	3	141	84	14
Horden	10	6	0	4	200	98	12
Ashington JW	10	5	0	5	124	129	10
Darlington	10	4	0	6	123	169	8
Ponteland	10	3	1	6	81	143	7
Redcar	10	3	0	7	132	116	6
Hartlepool	10	3	0	7	90	174	6
Winlaton Vs	10	0	1	9	78	179	1

DURHAM/NORTHUMBERLAND 2

	P	W	D	L	F	A	PTS
Whitby	10	10	0	0	255	65	20
Sunderland	10	8	0	2	251	77	16
Seaham	10	6	1	3	143	118	13
Percy Park	10	6	1	3	133	120	13
Bishop Auck	10	5	1	4	204	119	11
Consett	10	5	1	4	141	133	11
Medicals	10	3	3	4	122	114	9
N Durham	10	4	0	6	101	157	8
Wallsend	10	2	1	7	91	198	5
Billingham	10	2	0	8	96	191	4
Hartlepool BBOB	10	0	0	10	76	321	0

DURHAM/NORTHUMBERLAND 3

	P	W	D	L	F	A	PTS
Darlington RA	9	6	2	1	154	63	14
N Shields	9	7	0	2	102	67	14
Wensleydale	9	6	1	2	168	74	13
Wearside	9	6	0	3	128	199	12
Chester-le-St	9	5	1	3	119	78	11
Guisborough	9	4	1	4	87	91	9
Hartlepool TDSOB	9	3	0	6	92	116	6
Prudhoe	9	2	1	6	66	131	5
Seaton Carew	9	2	1	6	78	168	5
Houghton	9	0	1	8	47	144	1

DURHAM/NORTHUMBERLAND 4

	P	W	D	L	F	A	PTS
Barnard Cast	9	9	0	0	181	52	18
S Tyneside Coll	9	7	0	2	228	87	14
Jarrovians	9	7	0	2	114	103	14
Richmondshire	9	5	0	4	182	96	10
Hartlepool Ath	9	5	0	4	94	84	10
Newton Ayc	9	5	0	4	106	111	10
C Serv Durham	9	2	1	6	108	138	5
Sedgefield	9	2	1	6	53	123	5
Shildon Town	9	1	0	8	48	148	2
Benton	9	1	0	8	64	236	2

NORTHERN DIVISION FIXTURES 1989/90

DURHAM/NORTHUMBERLAND ONE

Sat. 9th September (Week 2)
Acklam v Ashington
Ponteland v Sunderland
Redcar v Horden
Seghill v Darlington
Whitby v Hartlepool

Sat. 23rd September (Week 4)
Hartlepool v Acklam
Darlington v Whitby
Horden v Seghill
Sunderland v Redcar
Mowden Park v Ponteland

Sat. 14th October (Week 6)
Acklam v Darlington
Ashington v Hartlepool
Redcar v Mowden Park
Seghill v Sunderland
Whitby v Horden

Sat. 28th October (Week 8)
Darlington v Ashington
Horden v Acklam
Sunderland v Whitby
Mowden Park v Seghill
Ponteland v Redcar

Sat. 11th November (Week 10)
Acklam v Sunderland
Ashington v Horden
Hartlepool v Darlington
Seghill v Ponteland
Whitby v Mowden Park

Sat 18th November (Week 11)
Horden v Hartlepool
Sunderland v Ashington
Mowden Park v Acklam
Ponteland v Whitby
Redcar v Seghill

Sat. 25th November (Week 12)
Acklam v Ponteland
Ashington v Mowden Park
Hartlepool v Sunderland
Darlington v Horden
Whitby v Redcar

Sat. 13th January (Week 18)
Sunderland v Darlington
Mowden Park v Hartlepool
Ponteland v Ashington
Redcar v Acklam
Seghill v Whitby

Sat. 10th March (Week 26)
Acklam v Seghill
Ashington v Redcar
Hartlepool v Ponteland
Darlington v Mowden Park
Horden v Sunderland

Sat. 31st March (Week X7)
Mowden Park v Horden
Ponteland v Darlington
Redcar v Hartlepool
Seghill v Ashington
Whitby v Acklam

Sat. 28th April (Week 32)
Ashington v Whitby
Hartlepool v Seghill
Darlington v Redcar
Horden v Ponteland
Sunderland v Mowden Park

DURHAM/NORTHUMBERLAND TWO

Sat. 9th September (Week 2)
Bishop Auckland v Consett
North Durham v Medicals
Wallsend v Winlaton Vulcans
Seaham v Darlington RA
N Shields v Billingham

Sat. 23rd September (Week 4)
Billingham v Bishop Auckland
Darlington RA v N Shields
Winlaton Vulcans v Seaham
Medicals v Wallsend
Percy Park v North Durham

Sat. 14th October (Week 6)
Bishop Auckland v Darlington RA
Consett v Billingham
Wallsend v Percy Park
Seaham v Medicals
N Shields v Winlaton Vulcans

Sat. 28th October (Week 8)
Darlington RA v Consett
Winlaton Vulcans v Bishop Auckland
Medicals v N Shields
Percy Park v Seaham
North Durham v Wallsend

NORTHERN DIVISION FIXTURES 1989/90

Sat. 11th November (Week 10)
Bishop Auckland v Medicals
Consett v Winlaton Vulcans
Billingham v Darlington RA
Seaham v North Durham
N Shields v Percy Park

Sat 18th November (Week 11)
Winlaton Vulcans v Billingham
Medicals v Consett
Percy Park v Bishop Auckland
North Durham v N Shields
Wallsend v Seaham

Sat. 25th November (Week 12)
Bishop Auckland v North Durham
Consett v Percy Park
Billingham v Medicals
Darlington RA v Winlaton Vulcans
N Shields v Wallsend

Sat. 13th January (Week 18)
Medicals v Darlington RA
Percy Park v Billingham
North Durham v Consett
Wallsend v Bishop Auckland
Seaham v N Shields

Sat. 10th March (Week 26)
Bishop Auckland v Seaham
Consett v Wallsend
Billingham v North Durham
Darlington RA v Percy Park
Winlaton Vulcans v Medicals

Sat. 31st March (Week X7)
Percy Park v Winlaton Vulcans
North Durham v Darlington RA
Wallsend v Billingham
Seaham v Consett
N Shields v Bishop Auckland

Sat. 28th April (Week 32)
Consett v N Shields
Billingham v Seaham
Darlington RA v Wallsend
Winlaton Vulcans v North Durham
Medicals v Percy Park

DURHAM/NORTHUMBERLAND THREE

Sat. 9th September (Week 2)
Wensleydale v Chester-le-Street
Hartlepool BBOB v S Tyneside College
Barnard Castle v Hartlepool TDSOB
Wearside v Prudhoe Hospital
Houghton v Guisborough

Sat. 23rd September (Week 4)
Guisborough v Wensleydale
Prudhoe Hospital v Houghton
Hartlepool TDSOB v Wearside
South Tyneside College v Barnard Castle
Seaton Carew v Hartlepool BBOB

Sat. 14th October (Week 6)
Wensleydale v Prudhoe Hospital
Chester-le-Street v Guisborough
Barnard Castle v Seaton Carew
Wearside v South Tyneside College
Houghton v Hartlepool TDSOB

Sat. 28th October (Week 8)
Prudhoe Hospital v Chester-le-Street
Hartlepool TDSOB v Wensleydale
South Tyneside College v Houghton
Seaton Carew v Wearside
Hartlepool BBOB v Barnard Castle

Sat. 11th November (Week 10)
Wensleydale v South Tyneside College
Chester-le-Street v Hartlepool TDSOB
Guisborough v Prudhoe Hospital
Wearside v Hartlepool BBOB
Houghton v Seaton Carew

Sat 18th November (Week 11)
Hartlepool TDSOB v Guisborough
S Tyneside College v Chester-le-Street
Seaton Carew v Wensleydale
Hartlepool BBOB v Houghton
Barnard Castle v Wearside

Sat. 25th November (Week 12)
Wensleydale v Hartlepool BBOB
Chester-le-Street v Seaton Carew
Guisborough v S Tyneside College
Prudhoe Hospital v Hartlepool TDSOB
Houghton v Barnard Castle

Sat. 13th January (Week 18)
S Tyneside College v Prudhoe Hospital
Seaton Carew v Guisborough
Hartlepool BBOB v Chester-le-Street
Barnard Castle v Wensleydale
Wearside v Houghton

NORTHERN DIVISION FIXTURES 1989/90

Sat. 10th March (Week 26)
Wensleydale v Wearside
Chester-le-Street v Barnard Castle
Guisborough v Hartlepool BBOB
Prudhoe Hospital v Seaton Carew
Hartlepool TDSOB v South Tyneside College

Sat. 31st March (Week X7)
Seaton Carew v Hartlepool TDSOB
Hartlepool BBOB v Prudhoe Hospital
Barnard Castle v Guisborough
Wearside v Chester-le-Street
Houghton v Wensleydale

Sat. 28th April (Week 32)
Chester-le-Street v Houghton
Guisborough v Wearside
Prudhoe Hospital v Barnard Castle
Hartlepool TDSOB v Hartlepool BBOB
S Tyneside College v Seaton Carew

DURHAM/NORTHUMBERLAND FOUR

Sat. 9th September (Week 2)
Richmond v Nomads
Hartlepool Athletic v Benton
Sedgefield v Newton Ayecliffe
Shildon Town v Jarrovians

Sat. 23rd September (Week 4)
Civil Service Durham v Richmond
Newton Ayecliffe v Shildon Town
Benton v Sedgefield
Washington v Hartlepool Athletic

Sat. 14th October (Week 6)
Richmond v Jarrovians
Nomads v Civil Service Durham
Shildon Town v Benton
Sedgefield v Washington

Sat. 28th October (Week 8)
Jarrovians v Nomads
Newton Ayecliffe v Richmond
Hartlepool Athletic v Sedgefield
Washington v Shildon Town

Sat. 11th November (Week 10)
Richmond v Benton
Nomads v Newton Ayecliffe
Civil Service Durham v Jarrovians
Shildon Town v Hartlepool Athletic

Sat 18th November (Week 11)
Newton Ayecliffe v Civil Service Durham
Benton v Nomads
Sedgefield v Shildon Town
Washington v Richmond

Sat. 25th November (Week 12)
Richmond v Hartlepool Athletic
Civil Service Durham v Benton
Jarrovians v Newton Ayecliffe
Nomads v Washington

Sat. 13th January (Week 18)
Benton v Jarrovians
Hartlepool Athletic v Nomads
Sedgefield v Richmond
Washington v Civil Service Durham

Sat. 10th March (Week 26)
Richmond v Shildon Town
Nomads v Sedgefield
Civil Service Durham v Hartlepool Athletic
Newton Ayecliffe v Benton

Sat. 31st March (Week X7)
Hartlepool Athletic v Jarrovians
Sedgefield v Civil Service Durham
Shildon Town v Nomads
Washington v Newton Ayecliffe

Sat. 28th April (Week 32)
Civil Service Durham v Shildon Town
Jarrovians v Sedgefield
Newton Ayecliffe v Hartlepool Athletic
Benton v Washington

ACKLAM

Talbot Park, Saltersgill Avenue, Middlesbrough,
Cleveland TS4 3PR. Tel: 0642 321397
Founded: 1976
President: Colin Sidgwick
Chairman: Phil Taylor
Secretary: Ian McMullan, 16 Linden Grove,
Linthorpe, Middlesbrough, Cleveland TS4 3PR. Tel:
0642 826945 (H). 091 222 1222 (W)
Fixtures Secretary: Dave Lynch, 58 Sandmoor Road,
New Marske, Redcar, Cleveland TS11 8DJ. Tel: 0642
486233
Press Officer: Syd Richardson, 2 Ellerton Road,
Hartburn, Stockton on Tees, Cleveland. Tel: 582818
Coach: Alan Richardson
Club captain (1988–89): Phil MoHan
Club captain (1989–90): Phil Mohan
No. of teams: Senior 4, Youth 5, Minis 2
Directions to ground: From A19 take A174 East, third
exit A172 North towards Middlesbrough, first
downhill turn left at traffic lights (Ladgate Lane), first
right (Broadwell Road), straight on mile down
Cycleway
Ground capacity: Standing 500
Clubhouse facilities: Open Match days and every
evening (excl. Wednesdays)
Club colours: Black, green and white. (*Change
colours:* White, green and black)
Floodlights: No
Membership fees: Full £10, Playing £20, Social £1.50,
Student £2
Programme: No. of editorial pages 1; No. of
advertising pages 4; **Programme editor:** Dave Hall,
627 Marton Road, Middlesbrough, Cleveland
Local newspapers: Evening Gazette, Journal,
Northern Echo
League: Durham/Northumberland 1
League position (1988–89): 4th

ASHINGTON J.W.

Recreation Ground, High Market, Ashington,
Northumberland. Tel: 0670 814123
Founded: 1922
President: A.F. Bewick
Chairman: R.N. Turnbull
Secretary: J.D. Evans, 'Cartref', 20 Blackdene,
Ashington, Northumberland. Tel: 0670 811250 (H).
091 257 5555 (W)
Fixtures Secretary: P. Allison, 34 Newbiggin Road,
Ashington, Northumberland. Tel: 0670 814241
Press Officer: A.F. Bewick, 21 Till Grove, Ellington,
Northumberland. Tel: 0670 860065
Coach: J. Harbottle
Club captain (1988–89): D. Turner
Club captain (1989–90): D. Peary
No. of teams: Senior 4, Youth 1
Directions to ground: Mile north on the A1068 to
Ellington
Ground capacity: Standing 800
Clubhouse facilities: Open Match days, also Tuesday
and Thursday evenings, Sunday lunchtimes
Club colours: Royal blue/amber hooped shirts, white
shorts, royal blue socks. (*Change colours:* Yellow)
Nickname: Ash
Floodlights: Yes
Membership fees: Playing £17.50, Social £6,
Schoolboy/Student nil
Ground admission: Collection only
Programme: No. of editorial pages 8; No. of
advertising pages 8; Price: Free
Programme editor: I. Parsons, 16 Oakland Terrace,
Ashington, Northumberland
Local newspapers: The Journal, Evening Chronicle,
News, Post
League position (1988–89): 6th
League playing record (1988–89): P 10, W 5, D 0,
L 5, F 124, A 129

DARLINGTON

'Lingfield', McHoulen Road, Darlington, Co.
Durham. Tel: 0325 466974
Founded: 1963
President: D.G. Gardner
Chairman: B. Robson
Secretary: A.P.F. Foster, 'Cadogan', 45 Hartford
Road, Darlington DL3 8HF. Tel: 0325 466501 (H).
0325 381818 (W)
Fixtures Secretary: D.G. Gardner, Balder View,
Cotherstone, Barnard Castle
Press Officer: R. Jackson, 36 Southend Avenue,
Darlington. Tel: 0325 51519
Coach: Mr R. Bevan
Club captain (1988–89): G.F. Elgey
Club captain (1989–90): B. Sunderland
No. of teams: Senior 4, Youth & Minis 6
Directions to ground: Turn off A66 bypass along
Yarm Road. Club on outskirts of town
Clubhouse facilities: Bar capacity 100, lounge 100
Club colours: Black and white hoops. (*Change
colours:* Blue)
Floodlights: Yes (training)
Membership fees: Full £20, Playing £20, Social £5,
Youth £2
Programme: No. of editorial pages 2; No. of
advertising pages 8; Price 50p
Programme editor: A. Gunnell
Local newspaper: Northern Echo
League: Durham/Northumberland 1

HARTLEPOOL

Mayfield Park, Easington Road, Hartlepool,
Cleveland. Tel: 0429 266445
Founded: 1893
Secretary: M. Westhorp, 4 Newquay Close, Cliffords
Green, Hartlepool, Cleveland. Tel: 0429 233605 (H).
091 586 2412 (W)
Press Officer: John Bradley. Tel: 0429 271616
Club colours: Black/maroon.
League: Durham/Northumberland 1
League position (1988–89): 10th

HORDEN COLLIERY WELFARE

Welfare Park, Horden, Peterlee. Tel: 091 586 3501
Founded: 1925
President: Peter G. Dunn
Chairman: Joss Fenwick
Secretary: Lol Applegarth, 'Schiehelion', 63 East
Dene Way, Peterlee, Co. Durham. Tel: 091 586 2477
Fixtures Secretary: Nobby Brownless, 20 Manor Way,
Peterlee, Co. Durham. Tel: 091 586 4464
Press Officer: William Featonby, 20 Morpeth Street,
Horden, Co. Durham. Tel: 091 586 2068
Coach: John Fenn
Club captain (1988–89): David Turner
Club captain (1989–90): David Turner
No. of teams: Senior 4, Youth 2, Minis 4
Directions to ground: A19 to Peterlee roundabout,
into Peterlee town centre and follow signs to Horden
Ground capacity: Standing 300
Clubhouse facilities: Open every day and evening
Club colours: Maroon and sky blue. (*Change colours:*
Black and red hoops)
Nickname: Yackers
Floodlights: No
Membership fees: Full £15, Playing £15, Social £10,
Youth £5, Student £5
Ground admission: Collection
Local newspapers: Newcastle Journal, Sunderland
Echo, Hartlepool Mail, Northern Echo
League position (1988–89): 4th
League playing record (1988–89): P 10, W 6, D 0,
L 4, F 200, A 96
Competitions won: J&B Div. 2 (Local Newspaper
League)

MOWDEN PARK

22 Yiewsley Drive, Darlington, Co. Durham DL3
9XS Tel: 0385 465932.
Founded: 1946
President: A.F.W. Hammond
Chairman: P.D. Warne
Coach: M. Lindley
Secretary: M. Cambell, 491 North Road, Darlington,
Co. Durham DL1 3AB.
Fixtures Secretary: D.P. Howland, 33 Enterpen
Close, Yarm, Cleveland. Tel: Eaglescliff 788023.
No. of teams: Senior 4. Youth & Minis 6.
Directions to Ground: B6279 from Darlington. Turn
left into Barnes Road at top turn right. Yiewsley
Drive 2nd on right.
Ground capacity: 5000. Stand, 300.
Colours: Blue and white hoops. (*Change colours:*
Maroon).
Floodlights: No
Membership: £15 playing, £10 other male, £2 ladies.
£3 country member (over 25 miles); £1 juniors, £4
over 65s.
Local newspaper: Northern Echo
League: Durham/Northumberland 1

PONTELAND

Castle Ward Sports Centre, Callerton Lane,
Ponteland Tel: 0661 25441
Founded: 1967
President: Geoffrey G.M. Baty
Chairman: Kenneth Foster
Secretary: Mrs Pamela Williams, 11 South Preston
Terrace, West Albion Road, North Shields, Tyne &
Wear, NE29 0HY. Tel: 091 258 5683 (H). 275 0608
(W)
Fixtures Secretary: Mrs Joyce Baty, 5 Brooklands,
Ponteland, Northumberland. Tel: 0661 23527
Press Officer: Ron Clarke, Longmeadows, Ponteland.
Tel: 0661 23692
Coach: Tom Hannigan
Club captain (1988–89): John Chappell
Club captain (1989–90): Malcolm Jeffries
No. of teams: Senior 4, Youth 1
Club colours: Maroon shirts with black and white
hoops, maroon with white top stockings. (*Change
colours:* White)
Floodlights: No
League: Durham/Northumberland 1
League position (1988–89): 8th
League playing record (1988–89): P 10, W 3, D 1,
L 6, F 81, A 143

REDCAR

MacKinlay Park, Green Lane, Redcar, Cleveland
TS10 3RW. Tel: 0642 482733
Founded: 1920
President: G. Holliday
Chairman: J.S. Fawcett
Secretary: Dennis M. Gidney, 11 Woodlands Drive,
Normanby, Cleveland TS6 0NW. Tel: 0642 456152
(H). 453085 (W)
Fixtures Secretary: Ron Atkinson, 27 Richmond
Road, Redcar. Tel: 0642 471740
Press Officer: Via Secretary (temporary)
Club captain (1988–89): Adrian Evans
Club captain (1989–90): Adrian Evans
No. of teams: Senior 4, Youth 6, Minis 3
Directions to ground: Off coastal road between
Redcar and Marske
Clubhouse facilities: 3 bars, pool room, 23 acres, stand
250
Club colours: White with broad red chest band/white
shorts/red socks. (*Change colours:* No)
Floodlights: No
League: Durham/Northumberland 1

SEGHILL

Welfare Park, Seghill, Cramington, Northumberland
NE23 7ER. Tel: 091 237 0414
Founded: 1921
President: Geoffrey Fenwick
Chairman: Erik Grainger
Secretary: Mark Jenkins, 16 Medburn Road,
Holywell, Whitley Bay, Tyne & Wear NE25 0NE.
Tel: 237 4206
Fixtures Secretary: P. Harvey, 1 Springville, East
Sleekburn, Bedlington, Northumberland NE22 7AZ.
Tel; 0670 825792
Coach: Ken Watson
Club captain (1988–89): David Martin
Club captain (1989–90): David Martin
No. of teams: Senior 3, Youth 1
Directions to ground: Through Tyne tunnel, north on
A1 Spine Road, 2nd left after Coast Road roundabout
signposted Seghill
Ground capacity: 500
Clubhouse facilities: Lounge
Club colours: Scarlet and black hoops. (*Change
colours:* All black shirt)
Floodlights: No
Membership fees: £2 + playing fee £2 per game
Ground admission: Collection
Local newspaper: Newcastle Chronicle and Journal
League: Durham/Northumberland 1
League position (1988–89): 3rd
League playing record (1988–89): P 10, W , D 3, L 1,
F 106, A 83

SUNDERLAND

Ashbrooke, West Lawn, Sunderland, Tyne & Wear.
Tel: 091 528 4536
Chairman: John David Boyd
Secretary: c/o J.D. Boyd, Ground Address
Fixtures Secretary: A. Scott-Gray, 27 Glenesk Road,
Sunderland, Tyne & Wear SR2 9BN. Tel: 091 522
6188
Press Officer: S. Harrison, 9 Gillside Grove, Roker,
Sunderland, Tyne & Wear SR6 9PQ. Tel: 091 548
4272
Coach: David Hodgson
Club captain (1988–89): Jim Smith
Club captain (1989–90): Jim Smith
No. of teams: Senior 3, Youth 3, Minis 5
Directions to ground: Take road into Sunderland from
Road Island on A19 marked 'Sunderland North'. On
reaching Barnes Hotel take route south along Queen
Alexandra Road, go straight over next island, take 1st
left (Willow Bank Road), 1st left again, 400 yds to
club on left
Ground capacity: Seating 250, Standing 1000
Clubhouse facilities: Bar, lounge, kitchen, showers
and baths, squash, tennis, cricket, hockey, bowls
Club colours: Red gold and black hoops and white
shorts
Nickname: Ashbrooke
Floodlights: Yes (training only)
Membership fees: Full £45 (tennis, cricket, hockey
and squash), Playing £30, Social £15, Youth (U16) £5/
(16–20) £15, Student £15
Programme: No. of advertising pages 6; Price 25p
Programme editor: Steve Harrison, 9 Gillside Grove,
Roker, Sunderland, Tyne & Wear SR6 9PQ
Local newspapers: Sunderland Echo, Newcastle
Journal
League: Durham/Northumberland 2
League position (1988–89): 2nd
League playing record (1988–89): P 10, W 8, D 0,
L 2, F 251, A 77

WHITBY

The Showfield, Whiteleys, Whitby, North Yorks. Tel:
0947 603433
Founded: 1951

President: J.A. Stalker
Chairman: P.C. Brown
Secretary: T.M. Marshall, 'Heatherdene', Fairhead, Grosmont, Nr Whitby YO22 5PN. Tel: 0947 85427 (H). 603433 (W)
Fixtures Secretary: T. Coyne, 9 Westbourne Avenue, Whitby, North Yorks. Tel: 0947 602008
Press Officer: As Secretary
Coach: T. Cook
Club captain (1988–89): Darrell Grason
Club captain (1989–90): John Wardell
No. of teams: Senior 3, Youth 1, Minis 3
Directions to ground: Off A171 Stakesby Road, mile town centre
Clubhouse facilities: New Clubhouse with club and lounge bars, open 7 days and six lunchtimes
Club colours: Maroon and black. (*Change colours:* Black and white hoops)
Nickname: Seasiders
Floodlights: No
Membership fees: Playing £11, Social £5,
Local newspapers: Whitby Gazette
League: Durham/Northumberland
League position (1988–89): 1st of D/N 2
League playing record (1988–89): P 33, W 25, D 1, L 7, F 750, A 307
Competitions won: Durham/Northumberland Division 2 Champions

DURHAM/NORTHUMBERLAND 2

BILLINGHAM

Synthonia Sports Club, Belasis Avenue, Billingham, Stockton. Tel: 523788
Founded: 1923
President: J.W.C. Taylor
Chairman: L. Jack
Secretary: N. Taylor, 64 Melrose Avenue, Billingham, Cleveland TS23 2JE. Tel: 0642 554786 (H) 247168 (W)
Fixtures Secretary: J. McCoy, 242 Cotswold Crescent, Billingham, Cleveland. Tel: 0642 533554
Press Officer: P. McPhillips, 103 Upsal Grove, Stockton, Cleveland. Tel: 0642 581759
Coach: B. Woodhouse
Club captain (1988–89): Mike Riby
Club captain (1989–90): Mike Morogan
No. of teams: Senior 3
Directions to ground: Going North A19 take Billingham turn off straight up Central Avenue. Ground on left. Going South A19 etc
Ground capacity: Seating 50-60, standing unlimited
Clubhouse facilities: Shared with other sections in Synthonia Sports Club
Club colours: Green and white hoops. (*Change colours:* No)
Nickname: Synners
Floodlights: No
Membership fees: Full £12, Playing £12, Social £6, Student £6
Local newspapers: Hartlepool Mail
League: Durham/Northumberland 2
League position (1988–89): 10th
League playing record (1988–89): P 10, W 2, D 0, L 8, F 109, A 178

BISHOP AUCKLAND

West Mills, Newton Cap, Bishop Auckland, Co. Durham. Tel: 0388 602922
Founded: 1976
President: A.W. Howells
Chairman: D. Robinson
Secretary: J.W.M. Gill, 38 Kenilworth Avenue, Bishop Auckland, Co. Durham DL14 6NJ. Tel: 0388 602337 (H). 0325 381132 (W)
Fixtures Secretary: E. Farrer, 35 Windermere Drive, West Auckland, Co. Durham. Tel: 0388 832810 (H). 603543 (W)

Coach: M. Graham
Club captain (1988–89): P. Sowerby
Club captain (1989–90): P. Sowerby
No. of teams: Senior 3, Youth 2
Clubhouse facilities: Bar
Club colours: Navy/light blue. (*Change colours:* Scarlet)
Floodlights: No
Local newspapers: Newcastle Journal, Northern Echo
League: Durham/Northumberland 2
League position (1988–89): 4th
Competitions won: Durham City 'Town Gown' Sevens (visitors)

CONSETT AND DISTRICT

Belle Vue Park, Medomsley Road, Consett, Co. Durham. Tel: 0207 504261
Founded: 1923
President: Dereck McVickers
Chairman: Frank G. McDonald
Secretary: Philip H. Carr, 78 Queens Road, Blackhill, Consett, Co. Durham DH8 0BW. Tel: 0207 503841 (H). 504200/500157 (W)
Fixtures Secretary: Hylton Hall, 328 Medomsley Road, Consett, Co. Durham. Tel: 0207 504758
Press Officer: As Secretary
Club captain (1988–89): Michael Breen
Club captain (1989–90): Michael Breen
No. of teams: Senior 3, Minis 4
Directions to ground: Situated behind local council offices approx. half mile out of Consett town centre along Medomsley Road towards Newcastle
Clubhouse facilities: Open Match days and training nights Monday/Thursday (7:00 pm) and Sunday mornings for Minis (10:30 am)
Club colours: Black/amber hoops, black shorts, black socks topped with amber. (*Change colours:* Green shirts)
Floodlights: Training only
Membership fees: Full £10, Playing £10, Social £3, Youth £5, Student £5, OAP £3
Local newspaper: Consett and Stanley Advertiser
League: Durham/Northumberland 2
League position (1988–89): 5th
League playing record (1988–89): (1st XV) P 31, W 21, D 3, L 7, F 456, A 287

DARLINGTON RA

Brinkburn Road, Darlington. Tel: 68125
Founded: 1925
Secretary: S.G. Allison, 2 Rochester Way, Darlington. Tel: 0325 288616 (H)
League: Durham/Northumberland 2
Club colours: Black/Amber

MEDICALS

Cartington Terrace, Heaton, Newcastle on Tyne. Tel: 091 265 6321
Founded: 1898
President: Dr M. McQuillin (Mel)
Chairman: Dr M. McQuillin
Secretary: J.E. Smith (Jason), 75 Osborne Avenue, Jesmond, Newcastle on Tyne, NE2 1JT. Tel: 091 257 2654
Fixtures Secretary: Mr P. Fisher. Tel: 091 490 1515
Press Officer: W. Wight (Bill), Medical School, Framlington Place, Newcastle on Tyne
Coach: E. Kirkham (Eric)
Club captain (1988–89): J. Foster (James)
Club captain (1989–90): S. Turner (Steve)
No. of teams: Senior 4
Directions to ground: Take the coast road (A1068) East and turn right at the Corner House
Ground capacity: Seating 100, standing 400
Clubhouse facilities: Bar and kitchen
Club colours: Maroon shirts, white shorts. (*Change*

colours: Blue shirts, white shorts)
Nickname: Medics
Floodlights: No
Membership fees: Full £11, Student £1
Local newspaper: Journal and Sunday Sun
League: Durham/Northumberland 2
League position (1988–89): 7th
League playing record (1988–89): P 11, W 3, D 3, L 5
Competitions won: Scottish Medical Schools
Tournament (as guests) on 26.4.89 at Edinburgh
University

NORTH DURHAM

Prince Consort Road, Gateshead, Tyne & Wear. Tel:
091 478 3071
Founded: 1875
President: William J. Barnes
Chairman: Charles Stafford
Secretary: Roy Thompson, 3 Ancroft Place,
Newcastle Upon Tyne, NE5 2HN. Tel: 091 274 6041
Fixtures Secretary: Thomas N. Tate, 21 Lynnholme
Gardens, Gateshead. Tel: 091 477 3567
Press Officer: As Secretary
Club captain (1988–89): Neil Wilde
Club captain (1989–90): Willie Gordon
No. of teams: Senior 3, Youth 2
Directions to ground: A1(M) to North. Main road to
Gateshead, turn left at Springfield Hotel. Ground on
left of dual carriageway to Newcastle Upon Tyne
Ground capacity: Standing 2000
Clubhouse facilities: Two storey building, bar and
lounge upstairs. Changing accom downstairs. Open
Match days and evenings
Club colours: Red and white hoops. (*Change colours:*
Green)
Floodlights: No
Membership fees: Full £12.50, Playing £12.50, Social
£2, Youth £7.50, Student £7.50, OAP £2
Local newspapers: Gateshead Post, Newcastle
Journal, Evening Chronicle
League: Durham/Northumberland 2
League position (1988–89): 8th
League playing record (1988–89): P 10, W 4, D 0,
L 6, F 105, A 153

NORTH SHIELDS

Preston Playing Fields, Preston Village, North
Shields, Tyne & Wear. Tel: 091 257 7352
Founded: 1922
President: J.R. Smith
Chairman: R. Hopwood
Secretary: D. Daniels, 1 Highcross Road, North
Shields, Tyne & Wear NE30 3JG. Tel: 091 252 6395
Fixtures Secretary: A.G. Shield, 9 Cresswell Avenue,
North Shields, Tyne & Wear. Tel: 091 259 0402
Press Officer: Steven Cliffe, 67 Eastbourne Gardens,
Whitley Bay, Tyne & Wear. Tel: 091 251 4678
Coach: P. Martin
Club captain (1988–89): Tom Gallon
Club captain (1989–90): Tom Gallon
No. of teams: Senior 4, Youth 1
Directions to ground: From A1 north of Tyne Tunnel
follow directions to Tynemouth. Straight on at end of
dual carriageway, at next roundabout turn right and
right again. ground beside Swimming Baths.
Clubhouse facilities: Club room, lounge, 4 changing
rooms, showers, weights room
Club colours: Royal blue/white hoops; white shorts.
(*Change colours:* Royal blue shirt)
Nickname: Artisans
Floodlights: No
Membership fees: Full £20, Playing £20, Social £2,
Youth £1, Student £1, OAP £2
Ground admission: Nil
Local newspapers: Newcastle Evening Chronicle,
Journal
League: Durham/Northumberland 2
League position (1988–89): 2nd of Durham/North 3
League playing record (1988–89): P 36, W 20, D 0,

L 16, F 444, A 385

PERCY PARK

Preston Avenue, North Shield. Tel: 0632 575710
Founded: 1872
Secretary: A.C. Baker, 30 The Garth, Winlaton,
Tyne & Wear. Tel: 0912 577007 (H). 091 4144869 (W)
Fixtures Secretary: G.R. Moore, 32 Agricola
Gardens, Wallsend NE28 9RX. Tel: 0632 2340657
League: Durham/Northumberland 2
Club colours: Black/White

SEAHAM

New Drive Playing Fields, Seaham
Founded: 1978
President: Dereck Mercer
Chairman: Mathew Bell Burdess
Secretary: Malcolm Smith, 36-37 Cornelia Terrace,
Seaham, Co. Durham. Tel: 5812331
Fixtures Secretary: Alan Mason, 32 Rothbury,
Ryhope, Sunderland, Co. Durham. Tel: 5200282
Coach: Edward Bell
Club captain (1988–89): Henry Brace
Club captain (1989–90): Henry Brace
No. of teams: Senior 3
Directions to ground: Call at Clubhouse first for guide
Clubhouse facilities: Bar, lounge, concert room
Club colours: Red. (*Change colours:* Black)
Floodlights: No
Membership fees: Full £10, Playing £1.50, Social £2,
Youth £1, Student £1
Local newspaper: Sunderland Echo
League: Durham/Northumberland 2
League position (1988–89): 3rd
League playing record (1988–89): P 10, W 6, D 1,
L 3, F 143, A 118

WALLSEND

Wallsend Sports Centre, Bigges Main, Wallsend. Tel:
091 2629431
Founded: 1959
President: D. Douglas
Chairman: A. Rowlands
Secretary: L. Dunne, 23 Laurel Crescent, Walkerville,
Newcastle NE6. Tel: 091 2635398 (H). Blyth 0670
352441 (W)
Fixtures Secretary: F. MacDonald, 88 Appletree
Gardens, Walkerville, Newcastle 6. Tel: 091 2622759
Club captain (1988–89): B. Thirlaway
Club captain (1989–90): B. Thirlaway
No. of teams: Senior 3, Youth 3
Directions to ground: Follow signs to Wallsend then
ask for the sports centre
Clubhouse facilities: Local authority – excellent
Club colours: Green and gold. (*Change colours:*
Yellow on white)
Membership fees: Playing £12
League: Durham/Northumberland 2

WINLATON VULCANS

Axwell View, Winlaton, Tyne & Wear. Tel: 091
4142502
Founded: 1896
President: Robert Archer
Chairman: Alan Archer
Secretary: Michael A. Brown, 20 Clockburnsyde
Close, Fellside Park, Whickham, Tyne & Wear NE16
5UR. Tel: 091 4886081 (H). 091 2355382 (W)
Fixtures Secretary: Ian Billclough, 8 Holly View,
Winlaton Mill, Tyne & Wear. Tel: 091 4148560
Press Officer: Stephen Warwick, 12 Oaklands,
Swalwell, Tyne & Wear. Tel: 091 4885380
Club captain (1988–89): T. Rutherford
Club captain (1989–90): T. Rutherford
No. of teams: Senior 3, Youth 1
Directions to ground: Off A1 follow Newcastle/

Gateshead signs, then Newcastle West sign, turn off at signs for Swalwell, then right at roundabout – straight over at next roundabout, continue one mile. Then left up Bank (turning opposite Blaydon Baths). Club at top of Winlaton Bank
Clubhouse facilities: Lounge, bar, 3 changing rooms and baths
Club colours: Black. (*Change colours:* White)
Nickname: The Vulcans
Floodlights: Yes
Membership fees: Full £10, Playing £10, Social £2, Student 50p, OAP 50p
Local newspaper: Evening Chronicle
League: Durham/Northumberland 2
League position (1988–89): Last in Div. 1
League playing record (1988–89): P 36, W 9, D 1, L 26

DURHAM/NORTHUMBERLAND 3

BARNARD CASTLE

Demesnes, Barnard Castle, Co. Durham. Clubhouse: 7 Birch Road, Barnard Castle, Co. Durham
Founded: 1975
President: Mr F. Lieshman
Chairman: Mr John Stead
Secretary: Mr Tim Worley, 29 Stainton Village, Barnard Castle, Co. Durham DL12 8RB. Tel: 0833 38425 (H). 690305 (W)
Fixtures Secretary: Mr Mark Worley, 23 Coronation Street, Barnard Castle, Co. Durham. Tel: 0833 38284
Coach: Mr John Oates
Club captain (1988–89): Mr Gary Patterson
No. of teams: Senior 2, Minis 2
Club colours: All black. (*Change colours:* No)
Nickname: Castle
Floodlights: No
Membership fees: Playing £10, Social £2, Youth £2, Student £2, OAP £2
Local newspapers: Teesdale Mercury, Horsemarket, Barnard Castle, Co. Durham
League: Durham/Northumberland 4
League position (1988–89): 1st
Competitions won: Durham/Northumberland 4 league

CHESTER-LE-STREET

Riverside Complex, Chester-le-Street, Co. Durham. Tel: 091 3884121
Founded: 1979
President: John Burn
Chairman: Raymond Attle
Secretary: Alan Warren, 10 Carrowmore Road, Parkfields, Chester-le-Street, Co. Durham DH2 3DY. Tel: 091 3887855
Fixtures Secretary: Stan Davison, 9 Lancaster Terraces, Chester-le-Street, Co. Durham. Tel: 091 3880260 (H). 3200344 (W)
Club captain (1988–89): Stephen Peacock
Club captain (1989–90): Neil Stephenson
No. of teams: Senior 2
Club colours: Navy blue shirts. (*Change colours:* Yellow shirts)
Membership fees: Full £10, Social £3,
Local newspaper: Durham Advertiser
League: Durham/Northumberland 3

GUISBOROUGH

Belmangate, Guisborough, Cleveland. Tel: 0287 32966
Founded: 1968
President: W. Henderson
Chairman: A.W. Neville
Secretary: D.F. Childs, 32 Boston Drive, Marton, Middlesbrough, Cleveland TS7 8LZ. Tel: 0642 314081 (H). 468403 (W)
Fixtures Secretary: B. Hanson, 7 Primrose Close, Guisborough, Cleveland. Tel: 0287 33051

Press Officer: C. Stockdale, 89 Whitby Avenue, Guisborough, Cleveland. Tel: 0287 35097
Coach: F. Sweeney
Club captain (1988–89): A. Notman
Club captain (1989–90): R. Atkinson
No. of teams: Senior 3, Youth 1
Directions to ground: A19 to Cleveland; A172 at Tontine; A173 at Stokesley to Guisborough
Clubhouse facilities: Changing including showers, and bar
Club colours: Black and amber. (*Change colours:* Amber)
Nickname: Priorymew
Floodlights: Training area only
Membership fees: £16
Local newspaper: Evening Gazette
League: Durham/Northumberland 3
League position (1988–89): 6th
League playing record (1988–89): P 9, W 4, D 1, L 4, F 81, A 78

HARTLEPOOL BOYS BRIGADE OLD BOYS

Old Friarage, Headland, Hartlepool
President: Jack Waller
Chairman: T. Gordon Rennie
Secretary: G. Keith Faint, 11 Nesbyt Road, Hartlepool, Cleveland TS24 9NB. Tel: 0429 265674 (H). 266688 (W)
Fixtures Secretary: Ian (Paddy) Mulrooney, 65 Percy Street, Hartlepool, Cleveland TS24 9NB. Tel: 0429 278082
Coach: Eric Arnell
Club captain (1988–89): K. Hetherington
No. of teams: Senior 2
Directions to ground: Approach Hartlepool along A19 trunk road taking the A179 Hartlepool turn off, straight over 4 roundabouts following signs for 'A1049' and 'Headland'. Old Friarage is next to tennis courts and bowling green
Club colours: White with broad black band. (*Change colours:* Blue)
Floodlights: No
League: Durham/Northumberland 2
League position (1988–89): 11th
League playing record (1988–89): P 10, W 0, D 0, L 10, F 76, A 321

HOUGHTON

Dairy Lane, Houghton-Le-Spring, Tyne & Wear. Tel: Wearside 584 1460
Founded: 1875
President: Lord Dormand of Easington
Chairman: Petr Charlton
Secretary: David Winthrop, 'Hillcroft', 14 North Road, Hetton-Le-Hole, Tyne & Wear DH5 9JU. Tel: 526 2163 (H). 567 0094 (W)
Fixtures Secretary: John Felton, 37 Larchwood, Haraton Wood, Washington, Tyne & Wear. Tel: 416 1467
Coach: Alex Lee
Club captain (1988–89): Ralph Johnson
Club captain (1989–90): Ralph Johnson
No. of teams: Senior 4, Youth 1, Minis 4, Juniors 2
Directions to ground: Adjacent to A690 in Houghton-Le-Spring
Clubhouse facilities: Bar, lounge, 4 changing rooms, showers
Club colours: Black shirts with white hoop, white shorts, black socks with white tops. (*Change colours:* No)
Floodlights: Yes
League: Durham/Northumberland 3
League position (1988–89): 2nd bottom
League playing record (1988–89): P 9, W 0, D 1, L 8, F 47, A 143

PRUDHOE HOSPITAL

Prudhoe Hospital, Northumberland. Tel: 33068
Founded: 1982
President: Tony Manly
Chairman: Len Franchetti
Secretary: Michael Ruddick, 97 Moorlands, Prudhoe, Northumberland. Tel: 0661 32506 (H). 32501 Ext 2264 (W)
League: Durham/Northumberland 3
League position (1988–89): 7th
League playing record (1988–89): P 10, W 2, D 1, L 7

SEATON CAREW

Hornby Park, Seaton Carew, Hartlepool, Cleveland. Tel: 0429 260945
Founded: 1921
President: Aubrey O. Lancaster
Chairman: Jack Lawn
Secretary: Kenneth Parkes, 7 Ruswarp Grove, Seaton Carew, Hartlepool, Cleveland TS25 2BA. Tel: 0429 223063
Fixtures Secretary: Jack Lawn, 2 Fens Crescent, Fens Estate, Hartlepool, Cleveland. Tel: 0429 268474
Club captain (1988–89): Johnathan Sherry
Club captain (1989–90): Johnathon Sherry
No. of teams: Senior 2
Directions to ground: Seaton Carew Cricket & Sports Club (opposite Seaton Golf Club)
Clubhouse facilities: All full sports facilities
Club colours: Amber/maroon hoops. (*Change colours:* All maroon)
Nickname: Scruf Club
Floodlights: No
Membership fees: Full £6.50, Playing £6.50, Social £4
Local newspaper: The Hartlepool 'Mail'
League: Durham/Northumberland 3
League position (1988–89): 9th
League playing record (1988–89): P 9, W 2, D 1, L 6, F 78, A 168

SOUTH TYNESIDE COLLEGE

Grosvenor Road, South Shields
Founded: 1946
President: College Principal, John Wells
Secretary: Robert Smith, 87 Colman Avenue, South Shields, Tyne & Wear NE34 9AG. Tel: 091 454 2359 (H). 456 0403 Ext 412 (W)
Fixtures Secretary: Colin Moule, 2 Portland Close, Chester-Le-Street, Co. Durham. Tel: 091 388 7548 (H). 456 0403 (W)
Coach: Martin Melling
Club captain (1988–89): Gordon McAlpine
Club captain (1989–90): John Taubbritt
No. of teams: Senior 2
Directions to ground: From South side of Tyne Tunnel travel due east to South Shields to Westoe area (3 miles)
Clubhouse facilities: Open Match days and weekdays
Club colours: Black with 3 narrow hoops – 2 red, 1 gold. (*Change colours:* No)
Floodlights: No
Local newspapers: South Tyneside Gazette
League: Durham/Northumberland 4
League position (1988–89): 2nd
League playing record (1988–89): P 9, W 7, D 0, L 2, F 228, A 87
Competitions won: Promoted to Division 3

WEARSIDE

Thorney Close School Playing Fields, Thorney Close Estate, Sunderland, Tyne & Wear. Tel: Thorney Close Public House 091 5280149
Founded: 1954
President: Gary Johnson

Chairman: Keith Wallace
Secretary: Steve Bruce, 27 Lime Street, Millfield, Sunderland, Tyne & Wear. Tel: 091 5656005
Fixtures Secretary: George Arthurs, 12 Raby Street, Millfield, Sunderland, Tyne & Wear. Tel: 091 5678320
Press Officer: Dean Marshall, 21 Corinthian Square, Hylton Castle Estate, Sunderland, Tyne & Wear. Tel: 091 5490657
Club captain (1988–89): Keith Wallace
Club captain (1989–90): Keith Wallace
No. of teams: Senior 3
Directions to ground: A19 until reach A690 road to Sunderland–Durham. Travelling to Sunderland down A690, signpost Thorney Close Estate on left. Into estate, turn right, left then right, school on left hand side
Club colours: Maroon and blue hoops. (*Change colours:* White)
Floodlights: No
Membership fees: Playing £18, Social £10
Local newspapers: Sunderland Echo, Journal, Northern Echo
League: Durham/Northumberland 3
League position (1988–89): 4th
League playing record (1988–89): P 11, W 8, D 0, L 3

WENSLEYDALE

Cawkill Park, Wensley Road, Leyburn, N. Yorks. Tel: 0969 23067
Founded: 1968
President: E. Hough
Chairman: E. Lowther
Secretary: D. Ward, 3 Kelberdale Terrace, Leyburn, N. Yorks. Tel: 0969 22046 (H), 23394 (W)
Fixtures Secretary: I. Burrow, Lane House Farm, Jervaulx, Ripon. Tel: 0617 60226
Club captain (1988–89): H. Rose
No. of teams: Senior 3
Directions to ground: A684 thro' Leyburn and mile on left
Club colours: Black/amber. (*Change colours:* Blue)
Floodlights: No
Membership fees: Playing £15
League: D/N 3
League position (1988–89): 3rd
League playing record (1988–89): P 9, W 6, D 1, L 2, F 168, A 74

WEST HARTLEPOOL TDS OLD BOYS

Wiltshire Way, Hartlepool, Cleveland. Tel: 0429 233548
Founded: 1953
President: J.S. Howard
Chairman: D. Sweeting
Secretary: D. Bramley, 63 Hutton Avenue, Hartlepool, Cleveland. Tel: 0429 263157 (H). 0642 522459 (W)
Fixtures Secretary: A. Cheshire, 22 Loyalty Road, Hartlepool, Cleveland. Tel: 0429 234659
Club captain (1988–89): J.D. Dove
Club captain (1989–90): C. Turnbull
No. of teams: Senior 4, Minis 3
Clubhouse facilities: Club bar and lounge, changing rooms and showers
Club colours: Royal blue. (*Change colours:* Blue and white hoops)
Floodlights: No
Local newspapers: Hartlepool Mail
League: Durham/Northumberland 3
League position (1988–89): 7th
League playing record (1988–89): P 37

DURHAM/NORTHUMBERLAND 4

BENTON

Civil Service Sports Ground, Darsley Park, Old Whitley Road, Newcastle-Upon-Tyne. Tel: 091 266 2726
President: Mr Dudley F. Gibbs
Chairman: Mr Robert C. Jones
Secretary: Mr C. Reid, 114 Northumberland Street, Wallsend, Newcastle-Upon-Tyne NE12 7PX. Tel: 091 279 3095
Fixtures Secretary: Mr Colin Brown. Tel: 091 268 7121 (H). 279 5342 (W)
Club captain (1988–89): Mr J. Castling
Club captain (1989–90): Mr J. Castling
No. of teams: Senior 1
Directions to ground: As per Novos – follow Benton Park Road to Four Lane Ends, turn right at roundabout, past 2 sets of traffic lights, entrance is on right hand side
Clubhouse facilities: Bar, lounge, changing rooms
Club colours: White shirts with blue hoop, white shorts, red socks. (*Change colours:* Black shirt, white shorts, red socks)
Floodlights: No
Local newspapers: Journal/Evening Chronicle
League: Durham/Northumberland 4
League position (1988–89): Bottom
League playing record (1988–89): W 1

DURHAM CIVIL SERVICE

Civil Service Sports Ground, Belmont, Durham. Tel: 091 386 4615
Chairman: John Joyce
Secretary: Colin Payne, 26 Willowtree Avenue, Giles Gatemoor, Durham
Fixtures Secretary: Mike Taylor, 79 Willowtree Avenue, Giles Gatemoor, Durham DH1 1DZ. Tel: 091 386 1062
Press Officer: As Secretary
Coach: John Joyce
Club captain (1988–89): Mike Roberts
Club captain (1989–90): Neil Charman
No. of teams: Senior 2
Directions to ground: A1(M). Take A690 towards Durham, take first exit and keep turning left
Clubhouse facilities: Changing rooms, bar and hall
Club colours: Light and dark blue squares. (*Change colours:* Light and dark blue hoops)
Floodlights: No
Membership fees: Full £10, Playing £10, Social £8.50
Local newspapers: Durham Advertiser
League: Durham/Northumberland 4
League position (1988–89): Not bottom

HARTLEPOOL ATHLETIC

Oakesway Estate, Hartlepool, Cleveland TS24 0RE. Tel: 0429 274715
President: Robert Mason
Chairman: Malcolm Boagey
Secretary: Jim Ainslie, Archway Cottage, 10 Regent Street, Hartlepool, Cleveland TS24 0QN. Tel: 0429 260003 (H). 0836 258317 (W)
Fixtures Secretary: As Secretary
Press Officer: As Secretary
Coach: Malcolm Boagey
Club captain (1988–89): Brian Robinson
Club captain (1989–90): Brian Robinson
No. of teams: Senior 2
Directions to ground: Leave A19 at A179 Hartlepool turn-off. Follow signs for Headland, at Touchdown Hotel turn right, take first left on to Oakesway Estate, Clubhouse 400 yards on left
Club colours: Sky blue. (*Change colours:* Red)
Floodlights: No

Membership fees: Full £5, Playing £5, Youth £2, Student £2, OAP Nil
Local newspapers: Hartlepool Mail, Newcastle Journal, Northern Echo
League: Durham/Northumberland 4
League position (1988–89): 4th
League playing record (1988–89): P 32, W 18, D 3, L 11, F 417, A 296

JARROVIANS

Recreation Ground, Lukes Lane Estate, Hebburn, Tyne & Wear. Tel: 091 489 3291
Founded: 1961
President: Ian Young OBE
Chairman: David Hill
Secretary: Stephen Softley, 20 Gladstone Street, Hebburn, Tyne & Wear NE31 2XJ. Tel: 091 489 0789 (H). 477 2271 (W)
Fixtures Secretary: Iain R. Hendry, 117 Victoria Road West, Hebburn, Tyne & Wear. Tel: 091 483 6107
Club captain (1988–89): Robert Winn
Club captain (1989–90): Keith Miller
No. of teams: Senior 2
Directions to ground: Adjacent to Monkton Coke Works, north end of A1(M)
Club colours: Black and amber hoops. (*Change colours:* Red)
Floodlights: No
Membership fees: Playing £15
League: Durham/Northumberland 4
League position (1988–89): 3rd
League playing record (1988–89): P 9, W 7, D 0, L 2, F 118, A 103

NEWTON AYCLIFFE

Moor Lane, Newton Aycliffe. Tel: 0325 312768
Founded: 1958
Chairman: R.P. Shepherd Esq.
Secretary: Rev. D. Capron, St. Clares Vicarage, St. Cuthberts Way, Newton Aycliffe, Co. Durham DL5 5NT. Tel: 0325 313613
Fixtures Secretary: Mrs F. Pass, 11 Brough Close, Newton Aycliffe, Co. Durham DL5 6JD. Tel: 0325 310527
Coach: D. Pass Esq.
Club captain (1988–89): D. Pass Esq.
No. of teams: Senior 2
Directions to ground: Turn off A167 into Central Avenue (opposite Childrens Centre), turn left at roundabout, then 4th left into Creighton Road, then 1st right
Clubhouse facilities: Sports and social club
Club colours: Green, maroon and old gold. (*Change colours:* Yellow)
Floodlights: No
Membership fees: Full £2, Playing £2
Local newspapers: Northern Echo
League: Durham/Northumberland 4
League position (1988–89): 4th
League playing record (1988–89): P 8, W 4, D 0, L 4

NOMADS

The Sailing Club, Eastern Road, Portsmouth.
Founded: 1978
Secretary: P. England, 47 Westbourne Road, Copnor, Portsmouth PO2 7LB. Tel: 0705 695889.
League: Hampshire 2

RICHMONDSHIRE

Barrack Hill, Richmond, North Yorkshire
President: J.T. Tomlinson
Secretary: H.M.W. Bingham, 89 Frenchgate, Richomond, North Yorks. DL10 7AE. Tel: 0748 5918 (H). 850111 (W)
Fixtures Secretary: A. Scrivin, 24 Chestnut Crescent,

Catterick Garrison, North Yorks. Tel: 0748 834279
Press Officer: As Secretary
Coach: J.C. Moulding
Club captain (1988–89): J.C. Moulding
Club captain (1989–90): G. Newton
No. of teams: Senior 2
Directions to ground: Entering Richmond from Scotch Corner, cross the first roundabout then turn right at the traffic lights. The Ground is half-way up the hill on the left
Clubhouse facilities: Le Chateau, Frenchgate, Richmond
Club colours: Gold, red and white hoops. (*Change colours:* White)
Floodlights: No
Membership fees: Playing £15
League: Durham/Northumberland 4
League position (1988–89): 4th
League playing record (1988–89): P 9, W 5, D 0, L 4, F 175, A 98

SEDGEFIELD

Secretary: I. Slack, 19 Stobbart Terrace, Fishburn, Stockton-on-Tees, Cleveland. Tel: 0740 21008 (H). 20521 Ext 2035 (W)
League: Durham/Northumberland 4
League position (1988–89): 8th
League playing record (1988–89): P 9, W 2, D 1, L 6, F 53, A 123

SHILDON TOWN

Sunnydale Leisure Centre, Shildon, Co. Durham. Tel: 0388 777340
President: S. Savage (Samuel)
Chairman: J. Walton (John)
Secretary: Peter Plews, 14 Alexandra Street, Shildon, Co. Durham DL4 2EY
Fixtures Secretary: Peter Baronowski, 4 East View Terrace, Shildon, Co. Durham. Tel: 0388 777247 (H). 772367 (W)

Press Officer: Dean Walker, 27 King Edward Street, Shildon, Co. Durham. Tel: 0388 772326
Coach: Gary Mason
Club captain (1988–89): Garry Richardson
Club captain (1989–90): C. Heslop (Charles)/Garry Richardson
No. of teams: Senior 1, Youth 1
Clubhouse facilities: All amenities
Club colours: Red and green quarters. (*Change colours:* No)
Floodlights: No
Membership fees: Playing £10, Youth £2
Local newspapers: Northern Echo, Wear Valley Advertiser
League: Durham/Northumberland 4
League position (1988–89): 8th
League playing record (1988–89): P 9, W 1 D 0, L 8

WASHINGTON

Washington School, Spout Lane, Washington, Co. Durham.
Founded: 1976
President: R. Boyes, MP
Chairman: T.I. Hall
Secretary: N. Cowan, 5 Valebrooks Avenue, Sunderland SR2 7HS.
Club captain (1987–88): J.A. Forsyth
Club captain (1988–89): J.A. Forsyth
No. of teams: Senior 2.
Directions to Ground: Northumbria Centre, Northern Area Playing Fields, Washington.
Colours: Amber & gold hoops. (*Change colours:* Amber)
Floodlights: No
Membership: £6.50
Local newspapers: Sunderland Echo, Newcastle Journal.
League: Northumberland & Durham 3

MIDLANDS DIVISION

THE MIDLANDS organisation is the same as the previous season with a total of 24 leagues spread over the six areas which comprise the local County Championship grouping – Warwickshire, North Midlands, Staffordshire, Leicestershire, East Midlands and Notts., Lincs. & Derbys. – with the Division headed by three elite divisions – Midlands 1, followed by Midlands 2 West and Midlands 2 East. The formula worked well in the initial season and change was not seen to be necessary.

That the Division is so far failing to match the standards required for survival in higher company was suggested by the fact that last season's promoted team from Midlands 1 (Stoke) were only saved from a swift return by the decision only to relegate Birmingham. Walsall will hope for less trouble in their efforts to keep the Midlands flag flying.

They certainly look good.

MIDLANDS DIVISION STRUCTURE

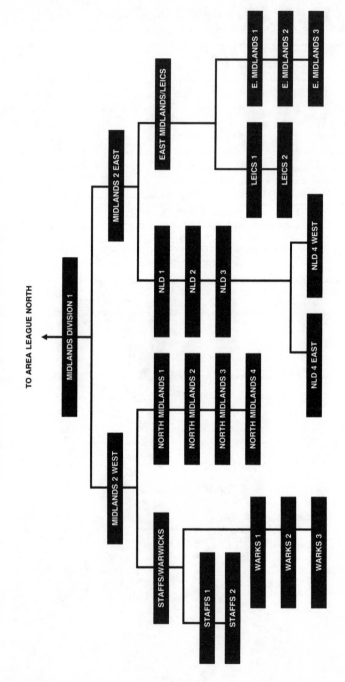

TO AREA LEAGUE NORTH

MIDLANDS DIVISION 1

MIDLANDS 2 WEST

MIDLANDS 2 EAST

STAFFS/WARWICKS

NORTH MIDLANDS 1
NORTH MIDLANDS 2
NORTH MIDLANDS 3
NORTH MIDLANDS 4

NLD 1
NLD 2
NLD 3

EAST MIDLANDS/LEICS

STAFFS 1
STAFFS 2

WARKS 1
WARKS 2
WARKS 3

NLD 4 EAST

NLD 4 WEST

LEICS 1
LEICS 2

E. MIDLANDS 1
E. MIDLANDS 2
E. MIDLANDS 3

MIDLANDS MEDIA CONTACTS

BBC RADIO BEDFORDSHIRE:

PO Box 476, Hastings Street,
Luton LU1 5BA   0582 459111

CHILTERN RADIO:

Chiltern Road, Dunstable,
Beds LU6 1HQ   0582 666001

BBC RADIO CAMBRIDGSHIRE:

PO Box 96, Cambridge CB2 1LD   0223 315970

BORDER TV:

TV Centre, Carlisle
Cumbria   0228 25101

HEREWARD RADIO:

PO BNox 225, Queensgate Centre,
Peterborough,
Cambridgeshire PE1 1XJ   0733 46225

BBC RADIO DERBY:

PO Box 269, Derby DE1 3HL   0332 36111

LEICESTER SOUND:

Granville House, Granville Road,
Leicester LE1 7RW   0533 551616

BBC RADIO LEICESTER:

Epic House, Charles Street,
Leicester LE1 3SH   0533 27113

BBC RADIO LINCOLNSHIRE:

PO Box 219, Newport,
Lincoln LN1 3XY   0522 511411

NORTHANTS 96:

PO Box 1557, Abingdon Street,
Northampton NN1 2HW   0604 29811

RADIO TRENT:

29/31 Castle Gate,
Nottingham NG1 7AP   0602 581731

BBC RADIO NOTTINGHAM:

York House,
Mansfield Road,
Nottingham NG1 3JB   0602 415161

BBC RADIO NORTHAMPTON:

PO Box 1107,
Northampton NN1 2BE   0604 239100

BBC RADIO SHROPSHIRE:

2/4 Boscobel Drive,
Shrewsbury,
Shropshire   0743 248484

BBC RADIO STOKE:

Conway House,
Cheapside,
Hanley,
Stoke-on-Trent ST1 1JJ   0782 208080

SIGNAL RADIO:

Studio 257,
Stoke Road,
Stoke-on-Trent ST4 2SR   0782 747047

BBC TV MIDLANDS:

BBC Broadcasting Centre,
Pebble Mill Road,
Birmingham B5 7QQ   021 414 8888

CENTRAL TV:

Central House,
Broad Street,
Birmingham B1 2JP   021 643 9898

BRMB:

PO Box 555,
Radio House,
Aston Road North,
Birmingham B6 4BX   021 359 4481

BBC RADIO WM:

PO Box 206,
Birmingham B5 7SD   021 414 8484

RADIO TRENT 945 DERBY:

Market Place,
Derby DE1 3AE   0332 292945

PLAYER REGISTRATION

As a result of the success of the experimental South West Division Scheme last season, Player Registration has been extended to other Divisions for a further trial period. The following guidelines will apply in the Midlands Division.

(a) Michael Humphreys & Partners will distribute form sets in the first instance. Additional supplies will be available from League Secretaries.

(b) Club Secretaries (or other delegated officials) should complete the first section of the form for each player eligible to compete in league matches at the start of the Season, and retain all copies.

(c) Should a player seek to leave a Club, the Club Official will complete the second section of the form, and hand the Blue copy to the player.

(d) The player will present the Blue copy to his new Club, and re-register in accordance with (b) above.

(e) The original Club must not withhold a players Registration form, and must retain at least one copy for the whole Season.

(f) The pink copy is spare for club use as required.

MIDLANDS LEAGUES

WALSALL had an outstanding season in Midlands 1 and with their perfect record they now hope to take on Area League North and emerge on top once again. They needed to be good as the rapidly emerging Hereford – promoted last season – showed very convincing form both in the league and in the Pilkington Cup and they should make another stern challenge in the new season.

With Solihull due to merge with the desperate Birmingham only one team – Wolverhampton – went down and the two new teams in the top division next season will be Sutton Coldfield (West) and Leighton Buzzard (East). The latter, although losing one match and drawing another, were comfortably clear of challengers, but Sutton Coldfield had to fight off a strong surge from Bedworth before going up.

Tamworth and Worcester go down from the 2 West section with Hinckley suffering the same fate in the East – a second successive relegation for them and a disaster which Peterborough only averted because they benefit from the Solihull-Birmingham merger. However, Peterborough by winning the East Midlands Cup are in next season's Pilkington Cup, which provides excellent encouragement.

MIDLANDS OFFICIALS

CHAIRMAN:

John A. Jeavons-Fellows,
Wychbury Court, Pedmore,
Stourbridge,   (H) 0562 885663
West Midlands DY9 0SX   (B) 0543 466664

MIDLANDS TWO WEST: OFFICIAL

Rodney Yapp,
55 Long Furlong,
Rugby,   (H) 0788 814879
Warks. CV22 5QT   (B) 0203 433515

MIDLANDS ONE: OFFICIAL

David Robins,
Halus House, Holywell Road,
Malvern,   (H) 06845 64826
Worcs. WR14 4LE   (B) 06845 60247

MIDLANDS TWO EAST: OFFICIAL

Brian Johnston,
284 Uttoxeter Road,
Mickleover,   (H) 0332 511349
Derby DE3 5AE   (B) 0249 443166

TABLES 1987–88

MIDLANDS 1

	P	W	D	L	F	A	PTS
Stoke	10	8	0	2	128	83	16
Barkers' Butts	10	7	0	3	166	87	14
Mansfield	10	7	0	3	106	98	14
Paviors	10	6	0	4	119	92	12
Walsall	10	5	1	4	183	100	11
Westleigh	10	5	1	4	135	114	11
Stockwood Pk	10	5	1	4	118	122	11
Wolverhampton	10	5	0	5	116	149	10
Stafford	10	3	0	7	110	166	6
Hinkley	10	2	1	7	111	157	5
Peterboro	10	0	0	10	71	195	0

TABLES 1988–89

MIDLANDS 1

	P	W	D	L	F	A	PTS
Walsall	10	10	0	0	210	71	20
Hereford	10	8	0	2	163	108	16
Newark	10	7	0	3	197	142	14
Derby	10	6	0	4	156	102	12
Paviors	10	5	0	5	128	119	10
Mansfield	10	5	0	5	130	154	10
Barkers' Butts	10	4	1	5	174	169	9
Stockwood Pk	10	4	1	5	140	67	9
Solihull	10	3	0	7	107	156	6
Westleigh	10	1	0	9	102	205	2
Wolverhampton	10	1	0	9	83	197	2

MIDLANDS 2 WEST

	P	W	D	L	F	A	PTS
Hereford	10	9	0	1	245	54	18
Dixonians	10	7	0	3	117	80	14
S Coldfield	10	7	0	3	125	125	14
Dudley	10	6	0	4	96	76	12
Tamworth	10	6	0	4	97	86	12
Bromsgrove	10	4	1	5	97	91	9
Burton	9	4	0	5	81	85	8
Worcester	10	4	0	6	106	138	8
Newbold	10	3	1	6	56	125	7
Leamington	10	2	0	8	87	155	4
Evesham	9	1	0	8	36	128	2

MIDLANDS 2 EAST

	P	W	D	L	F	A	PTS
Newark	10	9	0	1	243	72	18
Vipers	10	8	0	2	172	77	16
Matlock	10	7	1	2	173	97	15
Syston	10	6	0	4	163	98	12
L Buzzard	10	5	3	3	112	114	12
Kettering	10	5	0	5	145	88	10
Lincoln	10	5	0	5	89	127	10
Stoneygate	10	3	1	6	115	115	7
Stamford	10	3	0	7	103	190	6
Loughboro	10	2	0	8	74	257	4
Wigston	10	0	0	10	49	208	0

MIDLANDS 2 WEST

	P	W	D	L	F	A	PTS
S. Coldfield	10	8	0	2	150	79	16
Bedworth	10	7	1	2	192	95	15
O Yardleians	10	6	1	3	114	116	13
Stafford	10	5	2	3	130	102	12
Dudley	10	5	1	4	120	99	11
Burton-on-T	10	5	0	5	100	128	10
Newbold	10	5	0	5	89	121	10
Bromsgrove	10	3	2	5	90	99	8
Dixonians	10	3	1	6	76	110	7
Tamworth	10	1	3	6	78	108	5
Worcester	10	1	1	8	83	165	3

MIDLANDS 2 EAST

	P	W	D	L	F	A	PTS
Leighton B	10	8	1	1	190	98	17
Syston	10	7	0	3	170	100	14
Moderns	10	6	2	2	131	88	14
Kettering	10	6	0	4	146	115	12
Vipers	10	6	0	4	159	140	12
Stewart & L	10	6	0	4	112	134	12
Lincoln	10	3	2	5	120	138	8
Matlock	10	3	1	6	100	153	7
Stoneygate	10	3	0	7	104	146	6
Peterborough	10	2	0	8	166	160	4
Hinckley	10	2	0	8	96	222	4

MIDLANDS DIVISION FIXTURES 1989/90

MIDLANDS ONE

Sat. 9th September (Week 2)
Birmingham & Solihull v Barker Butts
Sutton Coldfield v Leighton Buzzard
Paviors v Derby
Mansfield v Stockwood Park
Newark v Hereford

Sat. 23rd September (Week 4)
Leighton Buzzard v Birmingham & Solihull
Westleigh v Newark
Hereford v Mansfield
Stockwood Park v Paviors
Derby v Sutton Coldfield

Sat. 14th October (Week 6)
Barker Butts v Leighton Buzzard
Birmingham & Solihull v Derby
Sutton Coldfield v Stockwood Park
Paviors v Hereford
Mansfield v Newark

Sat. 28th October (Week 8)
Stockwood Park v Birmingham & Solihull
Derby v Barker Butts
Newark v Mansfield
Westleigh v Paviors
Hereford v Sutton Coldfield

Sat. 11th November (Week 10)
Sutton Coldfield v Westliehg
Paviors v Newark
Leighton Buzzard v Derby
Barker Butts v Stockwood Park
Birmingham & Solihull v Hereford

Sat 18th November (Week 11)
Westleigh v Birmingham & Solihull
Hereford v Barker Butts
Stockwood Park v Leighton Buzzard
Mansfield v Paviors
Newark v Sutton Coldfield

Sat. 25th November (Week 12)
Derby v Stockwood Park
Leighton Buzzard v Hereford
Barker Butts v Westleigh
Birmingham & Solihull v Newark
Sutton Coldfield v Mansfield

Sat. 13th January (Week 18)
Mansfield v Birmingham & Solihull
Newart v Barker Butts
Westleigh v Leighton Buzzard
Hereford v Derby
Paviors v Sutton Coldfield

Sat. 10th March (Week 26)
Stockwood Park v Hereford
Derby v Westleigh
Leighton Buzzard v Newark
Barker Butts v Mansfield
Birmingham & Solihull v Paviors

Sat. 31st March (Week X7)
Sutton Coldfield v Birmingham & Solihull
Paviors v Barker Butts
Mansfield v Leighton Buzzard
Newark v Derby
Westleigh v Stockwood Park

Sat. 28th April (Week 32)
Hereford v Westleigh
Stockwood Park v Newark
Derby v Mansfield
Leighton Buzzard v Paviors
Barker Butts v Sutton Coldfield

MIDLANDS DIVISION FIXTURES 1989/90

MIDLANDS TWO WEST

Sat. 9th September (Week 2)
Bromsgrove v Bedworth
Dixonians v Keresley
Newbold v Camp Hill
Old Yardleians v Wolverhampton
Stafford v Dudley

Sat. 23rd September (Week 4)
Bedworth v Stafford
Burton v Old Yardleians
Dudley v Newbold
Keresley v Bromsgrove
Wolverhampton v Dixonians

Sat. 14th October (Week 6)
Bromsgrove v Wolverhampton
Camp Hill v Dudley
Dixonians v Burton
Newbold v Bedworth
Stafford v Keresley

Sat. 28th October (Week 8)
Bedworth v Camp Hill
Burton v Bromsgrove
Keresley v Newbold
Old Yardleians v Dixonians
Wolverhampton v Stafford

Sat. 11th November (Week 10)
Bromsgrove v Old Yardleians
Camp Hill v Keresley
Dudley v Bedworth
Newbold v Wolverhampton
Stafford v Burton

Sat 18th November (Week 11)
Burton v Newbold
Dixonians v Bromsgrove
Keresley v Dudley
Old Yardleians v Stafford
Wolverhampton v Camp Hill

Sat. 25th November (Week 12)
Bedworth v Keresley
Camp Hill v Burton
Dudley v Wolverhampton
Newbold v Old Yardleians
Stafford v Dixonians

Sat. 13th January (Week 18)
Bromsgrove v Stafford
Burton v Dudley
Dixonians v Newbold
Old Yardleians v Camp Hill
Wolverhampton v Bedworth

Sat. 10th March (Week 26)
Bedworth v Burton
Camp Hill v Dixonians
Dudley v Old Yardleians
Keresley v Wolverhampton
Newbold v Bromsgrove

Sat. 31st March (Week X7)
Bromsgrove v Camp Hill
Burton v Keresley
Dixonians v Dudley
Old Yardleians v Bedworth
Stafford v Newbold

Sat. 28th April (Week 32)
Bedworth v Dixonians
Camp Hill v Stafford
Dudley v Bromsgrove
Keresley v Old Yardleians
Wolverhampton v Burton

MIDLANDS DIVISION FIXTURES 1989/90

MIDLANDS TWO EAST

Sat. 9th September (Week 2)
Matlock v Lincoln
Peterborough v Towcestrians
Scunthorpe v Stoneygate
Stewart & Lloyds v Moderns
Vipers v Kettering

Sat. 23rd September (Week 4)
Kettering v Matlock
Lincoln v Stewart & Lloyds
Moderns v Scunthorpe
Syston v Peterborough
Towcestrians v Vipers

Sat. 14th October (Week 6)
Matlock v Towcestrians
Scunthorpe v Lincoln
Stewart & Lloyds v Kettering
Stoneygate v Moderns
Vipers v Syston

Sat. 28th October (Week 8)
Kettering v Scunthorpe
Lincoln v Stoneygate
Peterborough v Vipers
Syston v Matlock
Towcestrians v Stewart & Lloyds

Sat. 11th November (Week 10)
Matlock v Peterborough
Moderns v Lincoln
Scunthorpe v Towcestrians
Stewart & Lloyds v Syston
Stoneygate v Kettering

Sat 18th November (Week 11)
Kettering v Moderns
Peterborough v Stewart & Lloyds
Syston v Scunthorpe
Towcestrians v Stoneygate
Vipers v Matlock

Sat. 25th November (Week 12)
Lincoln v Kettering
Moderns v Towcestrians
Scunthorpe v Peterborough
Stewart & Lloyds v Vipers
Stoneygate v Syston

Sat. 13th January (Week 18)
Matlock v Stewart & Lloyds
Peterborough v Stoneygate
Syston v Moderns
Towcestrians v Lincoln
Vipers v Scunthorpe

Sat. 10th March (Week 26)
Kettering v Towcestrians
Lincoln v Syston
Moderns v Peterborough
Scunthorpe v Matlock
Stoneygate v Vipers

Sat. 31st March (Week X7)
Matlock v Stoneygate
Peterborough v Lincoln
Stewart & Lloyds v Scunthorpe
Syston v Kettering
Vipers v Moderns

Sat. 28th April (Week 32)
Kettering v Peterborough
Lincoln v Vipers
Moderns v Matlock
Stoneygate v Stewart & Lloyds
Towcestrians v Syston

BARKERS' BUTTS

Pickford Grange Lane, Allesley, Coventry CV5 9AR.
Tel: 0676 22192
Founded: 1947
President: Robert G. Coward
Chairman: Richard A. Barlow
Secretary: Peter John Jackson, 87 Gretna Road,
Green Lane South, Coventry West Midlands CV3
6DT. Tel: 0203 419595
Fixtures Secretary: Thomas H. Jones, 'Stonehaven',
Tamworth Road, Keresley End, Coventry CV7 8JJ.
Tel: 0203 332015 (H), 340187 (W)
Coach: Panel under Captain
Club captain (1988–89): Nicholas Brown
Club captain (1989–90): Mark Ogleby
No. of teams: Senior 4, Youth 1, Minis 4
Directions to ground: From Coventry: A45 towards
Birmingham, turn off left towards Meriden, first left.
From Birmingham: A45 follow Pickford Green sign
off to right
Ground capacity: Standing 2000
Clubhouse facilities: Brick built, two bars, gymnasium
Club colours: Royal blue and gold. (*Change colours:*
Amber)
Nickname: Butts
Floodlights: (Full training lights only)
Membership fees: Full £17.50, Playing £17.50, Youth
£10.50, Student £10.50, OAP £2.50
Ground admission: Nil
Programme: No. of editorial pages 16; No. of
advertising pages 11; Price 20p
Programme editor: Robert G. Coward, Barkers' Butts
R.F.C., Pickford Grange Lane, Allesley, Coventry
CV5 9AR
Local newspaper: Coventry Evening Telegraph
League: Mid 1
League position (1988–89): 7th
League playing record (1988–89): P 10, W 4, D 1,
L 5, F 174, A 169
Competitions won: Warwickshire Colts Cup, Coventry
& Mid Warwickshire Minor Cup U21's

BIRMINGHAM & SOLIHULL

Sharman's Cross Road, Solihull, West Midlands. Tel:
021–705 7995. (Previously Solihull R.U.F.C.)
President: T.B.A.
Chairman: Christopher Ruff (acting)
Secretary: George Ellis Kirkwood Simpson, 22
Heronfield Way, Solihull, West Midlands B91 2NS.
Tel: 021–704 3899 (H), 0530 417300 (W)
Fixtures Secretary: Alan Morden, 134 Old Station
Road, Hampton-in-Arden, Solihull, West Midlands
B92 0HE. Tel: H-in-A 2462 (H), 021–643 2736 (W)
Press Officer: T.B.A.
Coach: T.B.A.
Club captain (1989–90): T.B.A.
No. of teams: Senior 5, Youth 1, Minis 9
Directions to ground: Sharman's Cross Road off
Streetsbrook Road, Solihull
Ground capacity: Standing 4000
Clubhouse facilities: Open matchdays, Tuesdays and
Thursdays
Club colours: Red, black, gold and white 's, black
shorts, black socks with gold and red hoops. (*Change
colours:* Gold with black collars)
Floodlights: No
Membership fees: T.B.D.
Ground admission: £1
Programme: No. of editorial pages 3; No. of
advertising pages 30; Price 50p
Programme editor: David Radburn, 42 Croft Down
Road, Solihull, West Midlands
Local newspapers: Birmingham Post and Mail,
Solihull News, Solihull Times, Daily News
League: Mid 1

DERBY

Kedleston Road, Derby DE3 2TF. Tel: 0332 44341
President: Dr. Jack Warrack
Chairman: Arwell Davies
Secretary: Gordon John Roulinson, 12 Sandringham
Drive, Spondon, Derby DE2 7QJ. Tel: 0332 671953
(H), 249451 (W)
Fixtures Secretary: Geoffrey Johnson, 7 Shaldon
Drive, Littleover, Derby DE3 6HZ. Tel: 0332 772985
Press Officer: Peter Joslin, 16 Rangemoor Close,
Mickleover, Derby DE3 5JU. Tel: 0332 516187 (H),
385541 (W)
Coach: Sean Ryan
Club captain (1988–89): Colin Cornfield
Club captain (1989–90): Gordon Stirling
No. of teams: Senior 6, Youth 6, Minis 5
Directions to ground: From Notts or M1 (South).
Approach Derby on A52. Just before City Centre,
take 2nd. exit (straight on) at large roundabout and
get into 2nd lane from the right. Follow the 'inner
rignroad' and signs for Matlock. About 50 yards past
a 'JET' petrol station take the Kedleston Road on the
left (signposted Allestree and Quarndon). 2 miles on
this road and the club is on the left. From other areas
including M1 (North). Get to the junction of A38 and
A52 by the 'Derbyshire Yeoman' pub and large petrol
station. Take the A38 in a North Easterly direction,
keeping Markeaton park on your left. Bear left in
about mile on elevated exit and turn left at the
junction onto Kedleston Road. Continue along this
road for a mile and the club is on the left
Ground capacity: Seating 200, standing 1000+
Clubhouse facilities: Open matchdays, Sunday lunch,
Mon., Thurs., Fri. evenings
Club colours: Black and amber hoops, black socks
and shorts. (*Change colours:* Black, black socks and
shorts)
Floodlights: No
Membership fees: Full £33, Playing £33, Social £2,
Youth £13, 'O'19 Student £20
Ground admission: £1
Programme: No. of editorial pages 4; No. of
advertising pages 8; Price 50p
Programme editor: Peter Joslin, 16 Rangemoore
Close, Mickleover, Derby DE3 5JU
Local newspaper: Derby Evening Telegraph
League: Mid 1
League position (1988–89): 4th
League playing record (1988–89): P 10, W 6, D 0,
L 4, F 156, A 102
Competitions won: Derbyshire R.F.U. K.O. Cup
Final Winners, Dec. 1988. Burton Floodlit 7's
Winners, March 1989. Derbyshire R.F.U. 7's
Winners, May 1989

HEREFORD

P.O. Box 9, Wyeside, Hereford HR4 9UT. Tel: 0432
273410
Founded: 1922
President: John Frederick Escott
Chairman: John Charles Eglington Farr
Secretary: John Allan Butler, 3 Longworth Road,
Tupsley, Hereford HR1 1SP. Tel: 0432 266449 (H),
353881 (W)
Fixtures Secretary: Robert Howe Mason, Merrivale
Farm, Little Birch, Herefordshire HR2 8BA. Tel:
0981 540 032
Press Officer: Geoffrey Clements, 27 Eign Road,
Hereford HR1 2RU. Tel: 0432 273990 (H), 271200
(W)
Club captain (1988–89): Alan John Hill
Club captain (1989–90): Guy Griffiths
No. of teams: Senior 3, Youth 2, Minis 6
Directions to ground: On riverside (Wye) mile above
new bridge
Ground capacity: Standing 3000
Clubhouse facilities: Old School Pavilion, changing
and small bar
Club colours: Red. (*Change colours:* White)

Floodlights: Yes
Membership fees: Full £20, Playing £20, Social £5, Youth £5, Student £5
Ground admission: £2
Programme: No. of editorial pages 4; No. of advertising pages 28; Price £1
Programme editor: Guy Griffiths, 4 Bull Rush Close, Ledbury Road, Hereford
Local newspaper: Hereford Times
League: Mid 1
League position (1988–89): 2nd
League playing record (1988–89): P 10, W 8, D 0, L 2, F 163, A 108
Competitions won: Worcester Floodlit Trophy, April 1989. 4th Round Pilkington cup, February 1989

LEIGHTON BUZZARD

Leighton Road, Stanbridge, Leighton Buzzard, Beds LU7 9HR. Tel: 0525 371322
Founded: 1934/35
President: Harold Burchell
Chairman: Alan Hodey
Secretary: James William McCormack, 15 Neptune Gardens, Leighton Buzzard, Beds LU7 8NW. Tel: 0525 378194 (H), 01–794 2321 (W)
Fixtures Secretary: Alan Hodey, 36 Woodmans Close, Leighton Buzzard, Beds. Tel: 0525 379976
Press Officer: Anthony Guerria, 165 Knaves Hill, Leighton Buzzard, Beds. Tel: 0525 382016
Coach: David Hyde
Club captain (1988–89): John Fraser
Club captain (1989–90): John Fraser
No. of teams: Senior 6, Youth 4, Minis 7
Directions to ground: From North– M1 Junction 13–Woburn– Leighton Buzzard–Stanbridge. From South– M1 Junction 9– A5 through Dunstable–turn off to Tilsworth and Stanbridge. Ground between Stanbridge and Leighton Buzzard
Clubhouse facilities: 5 changing rooms, gymnasium, referee's rooms, Members bar, mainhall and bar, Steward's accommodation
Club colours: Navy/white regular hoops. (*Change colours:* Bottle green)
Nickname: The Buzzards
Floodlights: No
Membership fees: Full £25, Playing £25, Social £5, Youth £5, Student £5
Ground admission: Free
Programme: No. of editorial pages 4; No. of advertising pages 8; Price 25p
Programme editor: Ralph Harper, 99 Townfield Road, Flitwick, Beds MK45 1JG
Local newspapers: Bes & Bucks Observer, The Herald
League: M 2E
League position (1988–89): 1st (promoted)
League playing record (1988–89): P 10, W 8, D 1, L 1
Competitions won: Champions Midlands 2 East

MANSFIELD

Eakring Road, Mansfield, Notts. Tel: 0623 649834
Founded: 1956
President: Ted Lane
Chairman: Byron Edwards
Secretary: Dylan Howells, 273 Nottingham Road, Mansfield, Notts NG18 4SE. Tel: 0623 35722 (H), 0602 691691 ext. 49384 (W)
Fixtures Secretary: Kevin Swithenbank, 40 Summercourt Drive, Ravenshead, Notts. Tel: 0623 793726
Press Officer: Rod Waterhouse, 2 Leadale Crescent, Mansfield Woodhouse, Notts. Tel: 0623 649625
Coach: Dave Doig
Club captain (1988–89): Pete Emberson
Club captain (1989–90): Pete Emberson
No. of teams: Senior 5, Youth 3
Directions to ground: Take A617 S.E. from Mansfield centre; turn left after 1–2 miles at first lights after joining dual carriageway; turn right at 2nd mini-

roundabout after 1 mile onto Eakring Road; ground on right after mile
Ground capacity: No Stand
Clubhouse facilities: Large lounge, large clubroom, 7 changing rooms, 2 sets of showers
Club colours: Blue and white hoops
Floodlights: Training lights only
Membership fees: Full £19
Ground admission: Nil
Programme: No. of editorial pages 2 + 10 pages photographs; No. of advertising pages 8
Programme editor: Byron Edwards, 12 Watson Avenue, Mansfield, Notts
League: Mid 1
League position (1988–89): 6th
League playing record (1988–89): P 10, W 5, D 0, L 5
Competitions won: Winners Notts/Lincs/Derbys County Cup. Winners Notts Colts Cup

NEWARK

The Clubhouse, Kelham Road, Newark-on-Trent, Nottinghamshire. Tel: 0636 702355
Founded: 1919
President: Robert Benbow
Secretary: Edward Hine, Gallowsfield, The Avenue, Newark-on-Trent, Nottinghamshire NG24 1ST. Tel: 0636 703378 (H), 0602 483000 (W)
Fixtures Secretary: Larry Dukes, 47 King Street, Southwell, Notts. Tel: 0636 813542
Club captain (1988–89): Alan King
Club captain (1989–90): David Saxelby
No. of teams: Senior 5, Youth & Minis 11
Directions to ground: From Newark Castle take signs to Mansfield. Clubhouse on right-hand side after 1 mile
Ground capacity: Seating 250, standing 3000
Clubhouse facilities:
Club colours: Royal blue shirts with single white hoop, blue shorts and socks
Floodlights: Yes
Membership fees: Full £20
Ground admission: Nil
Programme: Price 50p
Programme editor: Ken Hunter, 30 Lime Grove, Newark, Notts
Local newspaper: Newark Advertiser
League: M 1
League position (1988–89): 3rd
League playing record (1988–89): P 10, W 7, D 0, L 3
Competitions won: Nottinghamshire County Cup, Tom Ollerhead Cup

PAVIORS

Burnstump Hill, Arnold, Nottingham. Tel: 0602 630384
Founded: 1922
President: R. Rossin
Chairman: M. Sudbury
Secretary: P. Evans, 86B Redhill Road, Arnold, Nottingham. Tel: 0602 269930 (H), 420777 (W)
Fixtures Secretary: L. Hines, 20 Stiles Road, Arnold, Nottingham. Tel: 0602 269061 (H), 492255 (W)
Press Officer: I. Eckloff, 19 Burncroft, West Hallam, Derbys
Club captain (1988–89): M. Lacey
Club captain (1989–90): M. Lacey
No. of teams: Senior 5, Youth 1
Directions to ground: Off A614 4 miles north of Nottingham
Ground capacity: Standing 4000
Clubhouse facilities: Open matchdays and training
Club colours: Green jersey red band
Nickname: 'Pavs'
Floodlights: Yes
Membership fees: Full £25
Programme: Price 50p
Programme editor: P. Sallis
Local newspaper: Nottm. Evening Post
League: M 1
League position (1988–89): 5th

STOCKWOOD PARK

London Road, Luton, Beds. Tel: 0582 28044
Founded: 1946
President: Les Carr
Chairman: Mike Branson
Secretary: Colin Chatwin, 30 Honeygate, Luton LU2 7EP. Tel: 0582 29954 (H), 01–492 8872 (W)
Fixtures Secretary: Rex Poulter, St. Helier, Kings Walden Road, Offley, Hitchen, Herts. Tel: Offley 656 (H), Hitchin 54801 (W)
Press Officer: Mark McKenna, c/o SPRFC, London Road, Luton. Tel: 0582 450779 (H), 572222 (W)
Coach: John Humphreys
Club captain (1988–89): Mark Lovell
Club captain (1989–90): Paul Catling
No. of teams: Senior 6, Youth 5, Minis 5
Directions to ground: M1 to Junction 10, turn left at roundabout, follow signs for Luton Town centre, 1st set of lights, turn left into Stockwood Park. Clubhouse on right
Club colours: Red shirts with yellow band, navy shorts, red socks. (*Change colours:* Yellow)
Nickname: Park
Floodlights: Yes
Membership fees: Full £20, Social £10, Youth £4, Student £4
Ground admission: Nil
Programme: Price Donation
Programme editor: John Howells, 32 Pebblemoor, Edlesborough, Nr. Dunstable, Beds LU62 2HZ
Local newspapers: Herald, Luton News
League: Mid 1
League position (1988–89): 8th
League playing record (1988–89): P 10, W 4, D 1, L 5, F 140, A 167
Competitions won: Hertford Floodlight, Bedfordshire Cup, Runners-up East Midlands

SUTTON COLDFIELD

Walmley Road, Sutton Coldfield. Tel: 021 351 5243
Founded: 1921
President: P. Maxwell-Jones
Chairman: R. Smoldon
Secretary: T. Gallagher, 61 Gorge Road, Sedgley, West Midlands DY3 1LE. Tel: 0902 887605 (H), Bloxwich 710298 (W)
Fixtures Secretary: R. Smoldon, 263 Boldmere Road, Sutton Coldfield. Tel: 021 373 2539
Press Officer: As Secretary
Coach: A. Wilkes
Club captain (1988–89): Kenneth Lewis
Club captain (1989–90): Michael Jenning
No. of teams: Senior 6, Youth & Minis 12
Ground capacity: 3000
Clubhouse facilities: 2 storey, 3 bars, 8 changing rooms
Club colours: Emerald green. (*Change colours:* Blue)
Nickname: Suts
Floodlights: Yes
Membership fees: Full £10, Playing £10, Social £3, Youth 5
Ground admission: Nil
Local newspaper: Sutton Coldfield News
League: Mid 1
League position (1988–89): 1st (promoted)
Competitions won: Midlands Division 1 Winners

WESTLEIGH

Lutterworth Road, Blaby, Leics. Tel: 0533 771010
Founded: 1904
President: B.W. Ball
Chairman: N. Otter
Secretary: R.D. Wain, 12 Talbot Lane, Leicester. Tel: 0533 418139 (W)
Fixtures Secretary: C. Baker, 66 Carisbrooke Road, Leicester. Tel: 0533 708676 (H)
Coach: B. Howell
Club captain (1988–89): L. Clifford

No. of teams: Senior 5, Youth & Minis 5
Directions to ground: A46 from leicester to Lutterworth, leaving Blaby Village on right hand side
Club colours: Black/white. (*Change colours:* Various)
Floodlights: Yes
Membership fees: Playing £25
League: Midlands 1
League position (1988–89): 10th
League playing record (1988–89): P 10, W 1, D 0, L 9, F 102, A 205

KETTERING

Waverley Road, Kettering, Northants. Tel: 0536 85588
Founded: 1875
President: Philip Anthony Croft
Chairman: Patrick Dodson
Secretary: J. David E. Stephens, 8 High Street, Cranford, Kettering, Northants NN14 4AA. Tel: 0536 78737 (H), 513746 (W)
Fixtures Secretary: Robert Bowley, Messuage Farmhouse, 10 Lower Benefield, Peterborough. Tel: 08325 382 (H), 0536 722181 (W)
Press Officer: As Secretary
Coach: Paul Searle
Club captain (1988–89): S.A. Bridgeman
Club captain (1989–90): S.A. Bridgeman
No. of teams: Senior 5, Youth 3, Minis 3
Directions to ground: From A6 through Kettering, left or right turn into Pipers Hill Road, 2nd right into Waverley Road
Ground capacity: Standing 500
Clubhouse facilities: Open matchdays and Tues. and Thurs. evenings. 2 squash courts
Club colours: Blue/white hooped shirts, blue shorts, blue white socks. (*Change colours:* Royal blue)
Floodlights: No
Membership fees: Full £30, Playing £30, Social £5, Youth £15, Student £7
Ground admission: Nil
Programme: No. of editorial pages 2; No. of advertising pages 10; Price 50p
Local newspaper: Evening Telegraph
League: M 2E
League position (1988–89): 4th
League playing record (1988–89): P 10, W 6, D 0, L 4, F 146, A 115
Competitions won: Beach Villas Cup, Bert White Shield

LINCOLN

The Lindum, Wragby Road, Lincoln. Tel: 0522 26592
Founded: 1921
President: Tony F. Beatham
Chairman: Colin Hobbs
Secretary: Brian R. Hunt, 3 St. Giles Avenue, Lincoln LN2 4PE. Tel: 0522 23743 (H), 0427 880431 (W)
Fixtures Secretary: Eion Coulthard, 25 Queensway, Lincoln. Tel: 0522 533666
Press Officer: Sid Gott, Club Steward, The Lindum, Wragby Road, Lincoln. Tel: 0522 26592
Coach: Roger Whittaker
Club captain (1988–89): Mike Wilson
No. of teams: Senior 4, Youth 3, Minis 1
Directions to ground: Top of hill near Cathedral, Wragby Road. Turn into St. Giles Avenue to club
Clubhouse facilities: Bar, committee room, tea/lunch/dining, squash courts
Club colours: White jersey with red collar. (*Change colours:* Red)
Nickname: Imps
Floodlights: Yes (training only)
League: M 2E

League position (1988–89): 7th
League playing record (1988–89): P 10, W 3, D 2,
L 5, F 120, A 138
Competitions won: Losing Finalist Lincolnshire Cup.
Losing Semi-Finalist Lincs Notts Derby Cup

MATLOCK

Cromford Meadows, Cromford, Matlock. Tel:
Wirksworth 2821
Founded: 1926
President: Mike Thornton
Chairman: John G. Lowry
Secretary: Kevin P. Archer, Stoneridge Barn, The
Knoll, Tansley. Tel: 0629 584319 (H), 0332 557032
(W)
Fixtures Secretary: D.J. Pearson
Press Officer: Alan Wragg, Cromford Hill, Cromford.
Tel: Wirksworth 3021
Coach: Dave Pearson
Club captain (1988–89): Mike Pearson
No. of teams: Senior 4, Youth 1, Minis 2
Directions to ground: Off A6, opposite Cromford
Church on Crick Road
Ground capacity: Standing 1000
Clubhouse facilities: Bar/bass, 6 changing rooms/
showers, dining room
Club colours: Royal blue. (Change colours: Royal/
gold/silver quarters)
Floodlights: No
Membership fees: Playing £25, Social £10, Youth £10,
Student £10
Programme: No. of editorial pages 4; No. of
advertising pages 8
Programme editor: As Press Officer
Local newspapers: Derbyshire Times, Matlock
Mercury, Derby Evening Telegraph
League: M 2E
League position (1988–89): 8th
League playing record (1988–89): P 10, W 3, D 1,
L 6, F 100, A 153

MODERNS

Ferryfield, Main Road, Wilford, Nottingham NG2
7AE. Tel: 0602 811374
President: Neil Highfield
Chairman: Brian Walls
Secretary: Jeffrey B.R. Mapp, 57 Chaworth Road,
West Bridgford, Nottingham NG2 7AE. Tel: 0602
814093 (H), 423858 (W)
Fixtures Secretary: Alistair Clarke, 33 Homefield
Avenue, Arnold, Nottingham. Tel: 0602 263865
Press Officer: Gareth Price, 47 Russell Road, Forest
Field, Nottingham. Tel: 0602 781046
Coach: Neil Highfield
Club captain (1988–89): Bill Blakeway
Club captain (1989–90): Bill Blakeway
No. of teams: Senior 4, Junior 2
Directions to ground: From M1 Nottingham (South)
Clifton Bridge – Wilford. From Nottingham over
Trent Bridge, signs for M1 – Wilford
Ground capacity: Standing 5000
Club colours: Cherry/white hoops, white shorts.
(Change colours: Black)
Nickname: Mods
Floodlights: No
Membership fees: Full £15, Social £1, Youth £5,
Student £5
Programme: No. of editorial pages 3; No. of
advertising pages 8–10; Price 20p
Programme editor: As Press Officer
Local newspapers: Nottingham Evening Post
League: Midlands 2E
League position (1988–89): 3rd
League playing record (1988–89): P 34, W 22, D 2,
L 10, F 564, A 331
Competitions won: Notts Shield Winners

PETERBOROUGH

Second Drove, Fengate, Peterborough. Tel: 0733
69413
President: Wilf Saul
Chairman: John West
Secretary: Ian Hamilton, 73 Garton End Road,
Peterborough PE1 4EZ. Tel: 0733 45240 (H), 556431
(W)
Fixtures Secretary: John West, 8 Apsley Way,
Longthorpe, Peterborough PE3 6NE. Tel: 0733
268857 (H), 266201 (W)
Press Officer: Adrian Tasker, 12 Manor House Street,
Peterborough PE1 2TL. Tel: 0733 53778 (H), 265202
ext. 3211 (W)
Coach: Peter Smith
Club captain (1988–89): Peter Hedges
No. of teams: Senior 5
Directions to ground: From Frank Perkins Parkway
(A1139) follow signs to Eastern Industry and Fengate.
At Fengate turn right and first left into Second Drove
Clubhouse facilities: 3 changing rooms (2 for ladies),
bar, lounge, large hall, dining room
Club colours: Red gold silver. (Change colours: Royal
blue)
Nickname: Boro
Floodlights: No
Membership fees: Full £25, Playing £25, Social £5,
Youth £10, Student £10
Local newspapers: Peterborough Evening Telegraph,
Peterborough Standard
League: M 2E
League position (1988–89): 10th
League playing record (1988–89): P 38, W 17, D 1,
L 20, F 665, A 641
Competitions won: East Midlands Cup, April '89.
Hunts Cup, December '88

SCUNTHORPE

Heslam Park, Ashby Road, Scunthorpe, S.
Humberside. Tel: 0724 843013
Founded: 1929
President: Robert J. Webb
Chairman: Not elected yet
Secretary: Alan C. Taylor, Twickenfield, 49A
Moorwell Road, Scunthorpe DN17 2SZ. Tel: 0724
866140 (H), 0472 693473 (W)
Fixtures Secretary: Nigel Cleal, 18 Cheltenham Close,
Bottesford, Scunthorpe. Tel: 0724 856801 (H), 84311,
ext. 2274 (W)
Press Officer: Barry Holmes, 12 Rivelin Crescent,
Scunthorpe. Tel: 0724 872113 (H), 843013 (W)
Coach: Mike Molloy
Club captain (1988–89): Paul Hewitt
Club captain (1989–90): Paul Hewitt
No. of teams: Senior 5 and Colts, Youth 12, 14, 16,
Minis 8, 9, 10, 11
Directions to ground: M181 – A11 to Queens Way
Hotel – Map available from Secretary
Clubhouse facilities: 6–8 changing rooms, bar open
every day, lunch
Club colours: Lincoln green. (Change colours: Royal
blue)
Floodlights: Yes
Membership fees: Full VPs £5, Playing £15, Social £3,
Youth £4.50, Student £10.50
Ground admission: Collection
Programme: No. of editorial pages 6; No. of
advertising pages 10; Price 20p
Programme editor: Ray Wells, 5 Clover Road,
Scunthorpe. Tel: 0724 851799
Local newspaper: Scunthorpe Evening Telegraph/Star
League: NLD 1
League position (1988–89): 1st (promoted)
League playing record (1988–89): P 10, W 9, D 1,
L 0, F 218, A 67
Competitions won: Lincs County Cup, Dec. '88;
Clugston Cup, '88; Lincs County 'Y', Sept. '88; Evans
Cup, Sept. '88; Lincs Merit Table, Notts, Lincs,
Derby League Cup

STEWARTS & LLOYDS

Occupation Road, Corby, Northants. Tel: 0536 400317
President: Charles Veall
Chairman: Robert Russell Morrison
Secretary: Gary Seymour, 1 High Street, Gretton, Nr. Corby, Northants NN17 3DE. Tel: 0536 770415 (H), 202121 ext. 2383 (W)
Fixtures Secretary: Vernon Cook, 20 Tower Hill Road, Corby, Northants. Tel: 0536 741971 (H), 0602 476291 (W)
Press Officer: Dave Murdoch, 12 Deene Close, Corby, Northants NN17 1HY. Tel: 0536 204930 (H), 203381 (W)
Coach: Paul Keating-Rogers
Club captain (1988–89): Paul Bennett
No. of teams: Senior 4, Youth 2, Minis 4
Directions to ground: Follow A6003 from Kettering. Turn right at Corby Town R.F.C. Ground 1 miles (just past the 'Game Bird' pub), turn right into Occupation Road, 200 yds on right
Ground capacity: Standing 500
Clubhouse facilities: Open matchdays, Sundays & Monday and Thursday nights
Club colours: Black shirts, black shorts, black and white hooped socks. (*Change colours:* Red shirts, black shorts, black and white hooped socks)
Floodlights: Yes
Membership fees: Full £13, Social £3
Local newspaper: Evening Telegraph
League: M 2E
League position (1988–89): 6th
League playing record (1988–89): P 10, W 6, D 0, L 4, F 112, A 134
Competitions won: East Northants Cup, Peterborough Evening Telegraph Cup

STONEYGATE

Covert Lane, Scraptoft, Leicester. Tel: 0533 419188
Founded: 1888
President: Michael J. Astill
Chairman: Roger D. Foxon
Secretary: Stephen G. Mounfield, 89 Curzon Avenue, Burstall, Leicester. Tel: 0533 674410 (H), 320202 (W)
Fixtures Secretary: Roger D. Foxon, 33 Buddon Lane, Quorn, Leics. Tel: Quorn 415529 (H), 0533 625564 (W)
Press Officer: Bruce Cooper, Brookview, Main Street, Peatling Parva, Leics. Tel: Peatling Magna 554
Coach: Jon Hall
Club captain (1988–89): David Hope
Club captain (1989–90): Nick Burrows
No. of teams: Senior 5, Youth 2, Minis 4
Directions to ground: A47 East of Leicester. Follow signs for Scraptoft, Covert Lane at junction of Scraptoft Lane and Station Lane, near church
Clubhouse facilities: 2 storey, 6 changing rooms
Club colours: Scarlet and white hoops. (*Change colours:* Red white blue hoops)
Nickname: Gate
Floodlights: Yes (training)
League: M 2E
League position (1988–89): 8th

SYSTON

Fosseway, Syston. Tel: 0533 625707. (New ground Dec 1988: Barkby Road, Queniborough.)
Founded: 1887
President: F.R. Fryer
Chairman: D. Loughran
Coach: E. Walker
Secretary: F.R. Fryer, 1 Festival Avenue, Thurmaston LE4 8JB.
Fixtures Secretary: C. Borderick, 25 Turn Street, Syston. Tel: 0533 007552.
Club captain (1987–88): P. Smith
Club captain (1988–89): D. Rennie
No. of teams: Senior 5. Youth & Minis 5.

Clubhouse: Moving to new ground, Dec. 88, at Barkby Road, Queniborough.
Colours: Navy & saxe blue hoops. (*Change colours:* red)
Floodlights: Yes
Membership: £16
Programme: Free (Editor: E. Wheeler)
Local newspaper: Leicester Mercury
League: Midlands East 2
Final position (1988–89): 2nd
Team Record (1988–89): P 10, W 7, L 3, F 170, A 100, Pts 14

TOWCESTRIANS

Greens Norton Road, Towcester, Northants. Tel: 0327 50141
Founded: 1933
President: John Mayes
Chairman: Brian Stewart
Secretary: Steven Burley, 44 St. Lawrence Road, Towcester, Northants NN12 7DR. Tel: 0327 53932
Fixtures Secretary: As Secretary
Press Officer: Robin Griffin, 5 Fishers Close, Little Billing, Northampton NN3 4SR. Tel: 0604 411571 (H), 405311 (W)
Coach: Robin Griffin
Club captain (1988–89): Steven Yuill
Club captain (1989–90): Steven Yuill
No. of teams: Senior 4, Youth U19, U16, U14, Minis 6
Directions to ground: At the junction of A5 and A43 there is a roundabout. Take Greens Norton Road, ground is mile on right
Clubhouse facilities: Bar, lounge bar, kitchen, changing for 4 teams
Club colours: Maroon shirts with 1 yellow hoop, black shorts. (*Change colours:* Yellow shirts with maroon hoop)
Nickname: 'Tows'
Floodlights: No
Membership fees: Full £12, Playing £12, Social £2, Youth £4, Student £4
Programme: No. of editorial pages 4; No. of advertising pages 12; Price Free
Programme editor: As Press Officer
Local newspapers: Chronicle & Echo, N'pton Post, Towcester & Brackley Advertiser, Northants Citizen
League: M 2E
League position (1988–89): 1st (promoted)
League playing record (1988–89): P 10, W 10, D 0, L 0, F 191, A 50
Competitions won: East Mids./Leics. League Winners. Northampton & District Alliance Cup Winners. Dunstablians Floodlit Winners. Alliance 7-a-Side Winners. N'pton Casuals 7's Winners. N'pton Paget Merit Table Winners

VIPERS

Blaby By-Pass, Whetstone, Leic. Tel: 0533 864777
Founded: 1920
President: Rod Ward
Chairman: Nick Lacey
Secretary: Kelvin Tiday, c/o 40 Howard Road, Leicester, LE2 1XC. Tel: 0533 701623
Fixtures Secretary: Andrew Sewell, 34 Repton Road, Wigston, Leic. Tel: 0533 882341
Press Officer: Steve Solomons, 74 Oastwood Road, Leicester. Tel: 0533 834554
Coach: S. Solomons
Club captain (1988–89): John Woodward
Club captain (1989–90): John Woodward
No. of teams: Senior 5, Youth 1, Minis 6
Directions to ground: To Leic. follow signs for Rugby and Lutterworth
Clubhouse facilities: Full
Club colours: Green black gold. (*Change colours:* County shirts)
Floodlights: No
League: M 2E

League position (1988–89): 5th
Competitions won: County Cup, 2nd Team County Cup, Colts County Cup

MIDLANDS 2 WEST

BEDWORTH

President: Vic Wallis
Chairman: David Hatfield
Secretary: Alan Sheppard, 66 Manor Drive, Bedworth, Warks CV12 0HQ. Tel: 0203 644594
Fixtures Secretary: K. Brown, 20 Rosemary Way, Hinckley LE10 0LN. Tel: 0455 30840
Coach: Ivor Oatridge
Club captain (1988–89): Peter Shillcock
Club captain (1989–90): Colin Griffin
No. of teams: Senior 4, Youth 1, Minis 5
Ground capacity: Standing 500
Club colours: Green shirts, white shorts
Floodlights: No
League: M 2W
League position (1988–89): 2nd
League playing record (1988–89): P 35, W 31, D 1, L 4
Competitions won: Warwickshire Cup

BROMSGROVE

Finstall Park, Finstall Road, Bromsgrove
Founded: 1872
President: R. Weaver
Chairman: A. Finn
Secretary: K.R. Hirst, Worms Ash Farm, Fockbury Lane, Dodford, Bromsgrove, Worcs. Tel: 0527 33087 (H), 221 552 1541 (W)
Fixtures Secretary: D. Harbach, Dolphin Cottage, Middle Road, Wildmoor, Bromsgrove B60 0BX. Tel: 021 453 1527 (H), 9911 (W)
Press Officer: R.J. Dicker, 363 Stourbridge Road, Cats Hill, Bromsgrove B61 9LF. Tel: 0527 71493 (H), 0251 523 0732W)
Coach: D.B. Davies
Club captain (1988–89): A. Perrey
Club captain (1989–90): G. Wright
No. of teams: Senior 6, Youth 2, Minis 9
Directions to ground: From Junc. 4 on M5 → signs to Worcester down A38 via Bromsgrove bypass → at junc. with new road, traffic lights turn left → follow new road to Bromsgrove Station → left and then right for 1 miles
Clubhouse facilities: 1 bar, function room, 4 pitches
Club colours: White, red, black. (*Change colours:* Red)
Floodlights: No
Membership fees: Playing £30, Social £10
Programme: No. of editorial pages 35–40%
League: Mids 2W
League position (1988–89): 8th
League playing record (1988–89): P 10, W 3, D 2, L 5, F 90, A 99

BURTON ON TRENT

Peel Croft, Lichfield Street, Burton on Trent, Staffordshire DE14 3RH. Tel: 0283 64510
Founded: 1870
President: David J. Bowen
Secretary: Alan Wilson, 5 Hornbrook Road, Burton on Trent, Staffordshire DE13 0XE. Tel: 0283 61342
Fixtures Secretary: Philip E. Richard, 20 Olton Road, Mickleover, Derby DE3 5PL. Tel: 0332 516901 (H), 662337 (school hours)
Press Officer: David M. Williams, Walway House, 120 Main Street, Linton, Buton on Trent, Staffordshire DE12 6QA. Tel: 0283 761 494 (H), 45711 (school hours)
Coach: T.B.A.
Club captain (1988–89): Andrew Peach
Club captain (1989–90): Laurence Kenyon

No. of teams: Senior 6, Youth 5, Minis 5
Directions to ground: Just off the Lichfield end of the High Street (B5121) and distinguishable by its ten floodlight pylons from any angle
Ground capacity: 5,000 approx
Clubhouse facilities: Main clubroom with bar, kitchen, changing rooms and lounge
Club colours: Jersey white with black diagonal band over right shoulder shorts white, stockings black with white tops. (*Change colours:* Red jerseys, remainder as above)
Nickname: The Crofters
Floodlights: Yes
Membership fees: Full £10, Playing £25 (£22 if by 31 Oct), Patrons/Patronesses £15, Youth (U17) £3, Student (U19) £5, OAP £5, Ladies £5
Ground admission: Nil (except for County Championship & Staffs Cup [determined by Staffs R.U.])
Programme: No. of editorial pages 2; No. of advertising pages 9; Price Free
Programme editor: D.M. Williams
Local newspaper: Burton Daily Mail, 65–68 High Street, Burton on Trent, Staffs DE14 1LE. Tel: 0283 512345 (Sports Editor: Rex Page)
League: M 2W
League position (1988–89): 6th
League playing record (1988–89): P 10, W 5, D 0, L 5, F 100, A 128

CAMP HILL

Haslucks Green Road, Shirtley, Solihull. Tel: 021 744 4175
Founded: 1893
President: Roger M. Dancey
Chairman: Paul Twiby
Secretary: Anthony A. Mucklow, 51 Shakespeare Drive, Shirley, Solihull B90 2AN. Tel: 021 744 3872 (H), 0203 692222 (W)
Fixtures Secretary: Derek J. Smith, 10B Wakefield Court, Mayfield Road, Birmingham B13 0LQ. Tel: 021 449 4278
Coach: Martin Powis
Club captain (1988–89): John Leyshon
Club captain (1989–90): John Leyshon
No. of teams: Senior 5, Youth 1
Directions to ground: Leave M42 at Junction 4. North on A34 towards Birmingham, approx 3 miles at end of Shirley shopping centre turn left into Haslucks Green Road. Ground mile on left
Clubhouse facilities: Great
Club colours: Maroon and light blue. (*Change colours:* Maroon light blue, white quarters)
Nickname: Camps
Floodlights: Yes (training only)
Membership fees: Full £25, Playing £25, Social £5, Youth £5, Student £5, OAP £5
Programme: No. of editorial pages variable; No. of advertising pages variable; Price 50p
Programme editor: T. Law, 82 Dalbury Road, Birminghamg 28
Local newspaper: Solihull News, Solihull Times
League: NMid 1
League position (1988–89): 1st (promoted)
League playing record (1988–89): P 39, W 31, D 1, L 7
Competitions won: League Champions

DIXONIANS

Wassell Grove Lane, Wassell Grove, Hagley, Worcs. Tel: 0562 882288
Founded: 1913
President: A. Jim Kendrick
Chairman: Malcolm A. Hall
Secretary: Nigel Jeffries, 51 Lightwoods Hill, Warley Woods, West Midlands B67 5EA. Tel: 021 429 1107 (H), 021 233 2500 (W)
Fixtures Secretary: David Hall, 32 Jerrard Drive, Sutton Coldfield, West Midlands B75 7TJ. Tel: 021

378 2839 (H), 021 779 2011 (W)
Press Officer: Ken Brittain, 'The Brambles', Hollywell Lane, Bayton Common, Clows Top, Nr. Kidderminster, Worcs DY14 9NR. Tel: 029922 255 (H), 0905 53335 (W)
Coach: Adrian Miles
Club captain (1988–89): John Larkin
Club captain (1989–90): Graham Jackson
No. of teams: Senior 4
Directions to ground: Junction 3 on M5, A456 to Kidderminster, at 4th island turn right, ground 1 mile on R.H.S.
Ground capacity: Standing 1000
Clubhouse facilities: Bar 150, changing for 6 teams, showers, baths
Club colours: Bottle green with red stripe. (*Change colours:* Maroon)
Floodlights: No
League: Mid 2W
League position (1988–89): 9th
League playing record (1988–89): P 36, W 14, D 3, L 19, F 402, A 533

DUDLEY KINGSWINFORD

Heath Brook, Swindon Road, Wall Heath, West Midlands. Tel: Kingswinford 287006
Founded: 1927
President: Peter W. Hart
Chairman: Graham Robbins
Secretary: David Evans, 156 Common Road, Wombourne, West Midlands WV5 0LX. Tel: 0902 894463 (H), 316327 (W)
Fixtures Secretary: W.R. Jones, 54 Dingle View, Sedley, West Midlands. Tel: 09073 74685
Press Officer: Ian Jones, 27 Holloway Drive, Wombourne, West Midlands. Tel: 0902 898185
Coach: Ian Bletcher
Club captain (1988–89): Mark Lockley
Club captain (1989–90): Mark Lockley
No. of teams: Senior 6, Youth 1, Minis 10
Directions to ground: Just off A449 at Wall Heath, between Wolverhampton and Kidderminster
Ground capacity: Standing 5000
Clubhouse facilities: Bar open every evening and Sunday lunch. Squash courts
Club colours: Cambridge blue and navy hoops. (*Change colours:* Red)
Nickname: D.K.
Floodlights: No
Membership fees: Playing £26, Social £12, Youth £13, Student £13, OAP £12
Programme: No. of editorial pages 1; No. of advertising pages 4; Price 50p
Programme editor: G. Robbins, 79 Highgrove, Ridge Road, Kingswinford, West Midlands
Local newspaper: Express and Star
League: Mid 2W
League position (1988–89): 6th
League playing record (1988–89): P 10, W 5, D 1, L 4, F 120, A 99
Competitions won: North Midlands Cup Winners, March 1989

KERESLEY

Burrow Hill Lane, Corley, Coventry, Warks. Tel: Fillongley 40082
President: John Radford
Chairman: John Magee
Secretary: John Frawley, 37 The Crescent, Keresley, Coventry CU7 8LB. Tel: 0203 337537
Fixtures Secretary: Frank Loftus, 4 Ash Grove, Ash Green, Coventry CU7 9AT. Tel: 367568
Press Officer: Christopher Millerchip, 8 Brookford Avenue, Keresley, Coventry CV6 2GQ. Tel: 7908
Coach: Roy Freemantle
Club captain (1988–89): R. Freemantle
Club captain (1989–90): R. Freemantle

No. of teams: Senior 5, Youth 1, Minis 5
Directions to ground: Situated off the main Bennetts Road North just past Keresley village
Clubhouse facilities: 4 changing rooms, bar/upstairs lounge
Club colours: Royal blue/scarlet/white hoops. (*Change colours:* Dark blue/white)
Nickname: Ks
Floodlights: No
Membership fees: Full £20, Playing £17, Social £6, Youth £8.50
Programme: No. of editorial pages 6; No. of advertising pages 10; Price 50p
Programme editor: Trevor Edwards, 48 Warwick Avenue, Earlsdon, Coventry CV5 5DG
Local newspaper: Coventry Evening Telegraph
League: Mid 2W
League position (1988–89): 1st (promoted)
League playing record (1988–89): P 11, W 10, D 0, L 1, F 243, A 60
Competitions won: Staffs & Warwicks League Winners

NEWBOLD-ON-AVON

Parkfield Road, Rugby, Warwickshire. Tel: 0788 565811
Founded: 1894
President: D.C. Pope
Chairman: P.E. Fereday
Secretary: R. Yapp, 55 Long Furlong, Rugby, Warwickshire CV22 5QT. Tel: 0788 814879 (H), 0203 433515 (W)
Fixtures Secretary: A.R. Spooner, 31 Pantolf Place, Rugby, Warwickshire. Tel: 0788 76672
Press Officer: R. Yapp, 55 Long Furlong, Rugby, Warwickshire CV22 5QT. Tel: 0788 814879 (H), 0203 433515 (W)
Coach: T.B.A.
Club captain (1988–89): John Wallace
Club captain (1989–90): Nigel Davies
No. of teams: Senior 3, Youth 1
Directions to ground: Two miles from M6 Junction 1
Ground capacity: Seating 100, standing Unlimited
Clubhouse facilities: Open mid-week 7.30-11 p.m., Saturday 12 noon-3 p.m./4.30 p.m.-11 p.m., Sundays 12–2 p.m., 7.30-10.30 p.m.
Club colours: Red and black hoops. (*Change colours:* Red)
Floodlights: No
League: Mid 2W
League position (1988–89): 7th
League playing record (1988–89): P 10, W 5, D 0, L 5, F 89, A 121

OLD YARDLEIANS

Tilehouse Lane, Shirley, Solihull, West Midlands. Tel: 021 744 3380
Founded: 1927
President: Colin Thompson
Chairman: Maurice Goode
Secretary: Mick Ison, 28 Quinton Close, Solihull, West Midlands. Tel: 021 743 5311 (H), 021 783 2160 (W)
Fixtures Secretary: Steven Painter, 26 Shrewley Crescent, Marston Green, Birmingham. Tel: 021 779 4192
Press Officer: Ken Collins, 6 Watwood Road, Hall Green, Birmingham. Tel: 021 744 7825
Coach: T.B.A.
Club captain (1988–89): Steve Chinn
Club captain (1989–90): Shannon Killarney
No. of teams: Senior 4, Youth 3
Club colours: Maroon, old gold and green 's. (*Change colours:* Green or yellow)
Nickname: The Y's
Floodlights: No
Membership fees: Full £25, Playing £25, Social £25, Youth £10, Student £10, OAP £10
Ground admission: Nil (Cup games £1 programme)

Programme: No. of editorial pages 19; No. of advertising pages 31; Price £1
Programme editor: Colin Thompson, 85 Harleston Road, Great Barr, Birmingham
Local newspaper: Solihull Times/News, Birmingham Post/Evening Mail and Sunday Mercury
League: Mid 2W
League position (1988–89): 3rd
League playing record (1988–89): P 10, W 6, D 1, L 3, F 114, A 116

STAFFORD

County Ground, Castle Fields, Newport Road, Stafford ST16 1BG. Tel: 0785 211241
Founded: 1876
President: Lord Stafford
Chairman: Ken Bailey
Secretary: Malcolm Boswell, 21 Highfield Grove, Stafford ST17 9RA. Tel: 0785 40209
Fixtures Secretary: D.R. Warbrick, 7 Beech Close, Haughton, Stafford ST18 9HT. Tel: 0785 780 592 (H), 0785 57757 (W)
Press Officer: Martin Rennard, 6 Falmouth Avenue, Stafford. Tel: 0785 663755
Coach: Glyn Featherstone
Club captain (1988–89): G. Williams
Club captain (1989–90): G. Williams
No. of teams: Senior 4, Youth 1, Minis 5
Directions to ground: A518 Newport Road 1 mile on R.H.S. from town centre
Ground capacity: Seating 200, standing 3000
Clubhouse facilities: Lounge and players bar. Open Match days, evenings (excl. Sunday eve.)
Club colours: Black and amber. (*Change colours:* Green)
Floodlights: No
Membership fees: Full £25, Playing £25, Social £5, Youth £5, Student £10, OAP £1, Ladies £1
Ground admission: £1
Programme: No. of editorial pages 2; No. of advertising pages 12; Price Free
Programme editor: S. Skikibi, Clubhouse, Newport Road, Stafford
Local newspaper: Stafford Newsletter

League: Mid 2W
League position (1988–89): 4th
League playing record (1988–89): P 10, W 5, D 2, L 3, F 132, A 102
Competitions won: Staffordshire Senior Cup, Staffordshire Colts Floodlit Cup

WOLVERHAMPTON

Castlecroft Road, Wolverhampton WV3 8NA. Tel: 0902 763900
Founded: 1875
President: Dr. H.A.S. Walker
Chairman: Bob Cheetham
Secretary: S.J. Fraser, 31 Catholic Lane, Sedgley, Dudley DY3 3UF. Tel: 09073 5638 (H), 021–559 6616 (W)
Fixtures Secretary: John Phelps, 92 Woodthorne Road South, Tettenhall, Wolverhampton. Tel: 0902 752208 (H), 791479 (W)
Club captain (1988–89): Clayton Noble
Club captain (1989–90): Clayton Noble
No. of teams: Senior 5, Youth 1, Minis 10
Directions to ground: Behind Castlecroft Hotel, approx. 3 miles from town centre, in the district of Castlecroft
Ground capacity: Seating 250, standing 1500
Clubhouse facilities: Open Saturdays/Sundays plus evenings
Club colours: Black shirts and shorts and socks. (*Change colours:* Black and white hoops)
Nickname: Wolves
Floodlights: No
Membership fees: Full £25, Playing £25, Social £10, Youth £10, Student £5
Ground admission: £1
Programme: No. of editorial pages 1; No. of advertising pages 8; Price 50p
Programme editor: S.J. Fraser (as Secretary)
Local newspapers: Express and Star
League: M 2
League position (1988–89): Bottom (relegated)
League playing record (1988–89): P 10, W 1, D 0, L 9

Harbury's clubhouse in October 1988 after widescale improvements

STAFFORDSHIRE/ WARWICKSHIRE LEAGUE

THE OUTSTANDING achievement of Keresley in winning this league with only one defeat meant promotion for them for a second successive season and a place in Midlands 2 West, but Stoke Old Boys, who qualified for the past season's Pilkington Cup, were out of luck and go down along with last season's Staffordshire Division 1 champions Trentham. Handsworth and Coventry Welsh are the scheduled replacements and it is ironic that Handsworth were relegated in the first season, which shows how far Staffordshire must go to catch up with other county leagues.

STAFFS/WARKS: OFFICIAL

Roger Ellis,
23 Samgoult Close,
Binley, Coventry,
CV3 2LX   (H) 0203 449125

TABLES 1987–88

STAFFORDSHIRE/WARWICKSHIRE

	P	W	D	L	F	A	PTS
Bedworth	10	8	1	1	173	49	17
O Leamingt's	10	6	1	3	120	84	13
Leek	10	6	1	3	90	84	13
Nuneat'n OE	10	6	0	4	106	99	12
O Longton's	10	5	1	4	121	100	11
Stoke OB	10	5	0	5	112	82	10
Newcastle	10	5	0	5	98	111	10
Willenhall	10	4	1	5	140	135	9
Stratford	10	4	0	6	126	102	8
Kenilworth	10	2	0	8	58	195	4
Handsworth	10	1	1	8	72	181	3

TABLES 1988–89

STAFFORDSHIRE/WARWICKSHIRE

	P	W	D	L	F	A	PTS
Keresley	10	9	0	1	213	63	18
Leamington	10	7	0	3	178	88	14
O Leamingtons	10	7	0	3	144	132	14
Stratford	10	6	0	4	141	113	12
Nuneaton OE's	10	5	0	5	132	121	10
Leek	10	4	0	6	149	87	8
N'Castle (Staff)	10	4	0	6	104	115	8
O Longtonian	10	4	0	6	130	150	8
Willenhall	10	4	0	6	100	128	8
Stoke OB's	10	3	0	7	90	148	6
Trentham	10	2	0	8	58	294	4

MIDLANDS DIVISION FIXTURES 1989/90

STAFFORDSHIRE/WARWICKSHIRE

Sat. 9th September (Week 2)
Willenhall v Leek
Tamworth v Coventry Welsh
Newcastle (Staffs) v Stratford-upon-Avon
Handsworth v Leamington
Old Leamingtonians v Nuneaton Old Eds

Sat. 23rd September (Week 4)
Old Longtonians v v Old Leamingtonians
Nuneaton Old Eds v Handsworth
Leamington v Newcastle (Staffs)
Stratford-upon-Avon v Tamworth
Old Longtonians v Willenhall

Sat. 14th October (Week 6)
Leek v Coventry Welsh
Willenham v Stratford-upon-Avon
Tamworth v Leamington
Newcastle (Staffs) v Nuneaton Old Eds
Handsworth v v Old Longtonians

Sat. 28th October (Week 8)
Old Leamingtonians v Handsworth
Old Longtonians v Newcastle (Staffs)
Nuneaton Old Eds v Tamworth
Leamington v Willenhall
Stratford-upon-Avon v Leek

Sat. 11th November (Week 10)
Coventry Welsh v Stratford-upon-Avon
Leek v Leamington
Willenhall v Nuneaton Old Eds
Tamworth v Old Longtonians
Newcastle (Staffs) v Old Leamingtonians

Sat 18th November (Week 11)
Handsworth v Newcastle (Staffs)
Old Leamingtonians v Tamworth
Old Longtonians v Willenhall
Nuneaton Old Eds v Leek
Leamington v Coventry Welsh

Sat. 25th November (Week 12)
Stratford-upon-Avon v Leamington
Coventry Welsh v Nuneaton Old Eds
Leek v Old Longtonians
Willenhall v Old Leamingtonians
Tamworth v Handsowrth

Sat. 13th January (Week 18)
Newcastle (Staffs) v Tamworth
Handsowrth v Willenhall
Old Leamingtonians v Leek
Old Longtonians v Coventry Welsh
Nuneaton O Eds v Stratford-upon-Avon

Sat. 10th March (Week 26)
Leamington v Nuneaton Old Eds
Stratford-upon-Avon v Old Longtonians
Coventry Welsh v Old Leamingtonians
Leek v Handsworth
Willenhall v Newcastle (Staffs)

Sat. 31st March (Week X7)
Tamworth v Willenhall
Newcastle (Staffs) v Leek
Handsworth v Coventry Welsh
Old Leamigtonians v Stratford-upon-Avon
Old Longtonians v Leamington

Sat. 28th April (Week 32)
Nuneaton Old Eds v Old Longtonians
Leamington v Old Leamingtonians
Stratford-upon-Avon v Handworth
Coventry Welsh v Newcastle (Staffs)
Leek v Tamworth

STAFFORDSHIRE/WARWICKSHIRE

COVENTRY WELSH

Burbage Lane, Longford, Coventry. Tel: 0203 360303
Founded: 1947
President: Tom Jones
Chairman: W. Somers
Secretary: M.G. Tainton, 57 Bagworth Road,
Barlestone, Nuneaton, CV13 0EQ. Tel: 0455 292103
Fixtures Secretary: W. Somers, 98 Potters Green,
Walsgrave, Coventry CV2 2AN. Tel: 0203 364569
Press Officer: C. Williams, 173 Goodyears End Lane,
Coventry
Coach: B. Timothy
Club captain (1988–89): Austin Grant
Club captain (1989–90): Les Campbell
No. of teams: Senior 3, Youth 1
Directions to ground: Leave M6 at Junc. 2, follow
signs for Coventry at 2nd roundabout, 3rd exit turn
into Wilson's Lane. 2 miles on at the end of Wilson
Lane turn right into Bedlam Lane, fifty yards turn
right into Burbage Lane
Clubhouse facilities: Changing rooms, bar and lounge,
kitchen area
Club colours: Scarlet jerseys, black shorts, scarlet and
white socks. (*Change colours:* White shirts)
Nickname: The Welsh
Floodlights: No
Membership fees: Full £6, Playing £10, Social £6,
Youth £5, Student £5, OAP £5
Local newspapers: Coventry Evening Telegraph
League: Warwicks 1
League position (1988–89): 1st (promoted)
League playing record (1988–89): P 10, W 10, D 0,
L 0, F 274, A 82
Competitions won: Warwicks League One. Promoted
to Staffs/Warks League for 1989–90 season

HANDSWORTH

430 Birmingham Road, Walsall, W. Mids. Tel: 021
357 6427
Founded: 1887
President: L. Still
Chairman: R. Anderson
Secretary: A. Hardy, 6 Freemount Square, Great
Burr, Birmingham B43 5QT. Tel: 021 358 6612 (H),
021 200 2266 (W)
Fixtures Secretary: L.M. Taylor, 44 Ashfurlong
Crescent, S. Coldfield. Tel: 021 3783530
Coach: J. Yarrall
Club captain (1988–89): T.C. Cartwright
Club captain (1989–90): M. Trace
No. of teams: Senior 4 + Colts, Youth 2, Minis 4
Directions to ground: M6 Junc. 7 → Birmingham Road
to Walsall → club on left adjacent Bell pub
Club colours: Red/white/blue. (*Change colours:* Blue
and white)
Floodlights: No
Membership fees: Playing £15, Social £5
League: Staffs & Warwicks 1
League position (1988–89): 1st
League playing record (1988–89): P 6, W 6, D 0, L 0,
F 140, A 41

LEAMINGTON

Moorefields, Kenilworth Road, Leamington Spa. Tel:
0926 425584
Founded: 1926
President: Maurice Goymer
Secretary: Rod Grinnell, The Old Pump House,
Combroke, Warwick CV35 9HN. Tel: 0926 640699
(H), 0780 51513 (W)
Fixtures Secretary: Peter Payne, Marlborough House,
14 Lillington Road, Leamington Spa, Warks CV32
5YR. Tel: 0926 338380
Press Officer: T.B.A.
Coach: T.B.A.
Club captain (1988–89): Peter Gray

Club captain (1989–90): Peter Gray
No. of teams: Senior 6, Youth 6, Minis 5
Ground capacity: Standing 3000
Clubhouse facilities: Six changing rooms, large club
room, members lounge, physio room
Club colours: Royal blue with single scarlet/gold
hoop. (*Change colours:* Red)
Floodlights: Yes
Membership fees: Full £25, Playing £25, VPs £20,
Youth £5
Ground admission: Optional by programme
Programme: No. of editorial pages 1; No. of
advertising pages 4–6; Price 50p
Programme editor: T.B.A., c/o Secretary
Local newspapers: Leamington Courier, Leamington
Observer
League: Staffs/Warks
League position (1988–89): 2nd
Competitions won: Warwickshire Colts 7's, Old
Halesonians 7's, (Sept. '88), Midland Oak Cup (Oct.
'88), Stars of Tomorrow Tournament U16 (Sept. '88),
Martin Frost Memorial Trophy (Mar. '89), Potterton
Int. U21 Floodlit Cup (Mar. '89), OW's Veteran Cup
(Apr. '89), Eagle Star 7's U14 (Apr. '89)

LEEK

Birchall Playing Fields, Clubhouse, Strangman Street,
Leek. Tel: 0538 383680
Founded: 1923
President: G.F. Bloore
Chairman: A.W. Worth
Secretary: M.J. Clewes, 55 Westwood Park Drive,
Leek ST13 8NW. Tel: 0538 382922 (H), 0782 612669
(W)
Fixtures Secretary: E.J. Birch, 12 Sandy Brook Lane,
Birchall, Leek ST13 5RZ. Tel: 0538 385963
Press Officer: M. Williamson, 3 Elm Close, Leek. Tel:
0538 384374
Coach: D. Hunt
Club captain (1988–89): A. Holland
Club captain (1989–90): P. Bebington
No. of teams: Senior 4, Youth 1, Minis 6
Club colours: Blue white hoops, white shorts
Floodlights: No
Membership fees: Full £5, Playing £5, Youth £2.50
Programme: No. of editorial pages 1; No. of
advertising pages 6; Price –
Programme editor: A. Poole
Local newspapers: Leek Post Times, Sentinel
League: Staffs/Warks
League position (1988–89): 5th
League playing record (1988–89): P 37, W 22, D 0,
L 15, F 797, A 457
Competitions won: North Staffs Junior Cup Winners,
Heckleshield-Lee 7's, Mylechreest Cup Winners,
Staffs Cup Semi-Finalist

NEWCASTLE (STAFFS)

Lilleshall Road, Newcastle-u-Lyme, Staffs. Tel: 0782
617042
Founded: 1947
President: John Whittaker
Chairman: Tony Marsh
Secretary: Bernard Conroy, 237 Fearns Avenue,
Bradwell, Newcastle-u-Lyme ST5 8NN. Tel: 0782
625771 (H), 744824 (W)
Fixtures Secretary: Dave Westrup, 153 Congleton
Road, Sandbach, Cheshire CW11 0SP. Tel: 0270
766538 (H), 766538 (W)
Press Officer: Keith Dale, 14 St. Anthony's Drive,
Westlands, Newcastle-u-Lyme. Tel: 0782 615770 (H),
404230 (W)
Coach: Gerry Rodwell
Club captain (1988–89): Clive Ward
Club captain (1989–90): Mick Wilson
No. of teams: Senior 5, Youth 1, Minis 3
Directions to ground: Leave M6 Junction 15 to
Newcastle, turn left at 1st roundabout, over next
roundabout, right at next roundabout, 2nd road on

left
Clubhouse facilities: 4 changing rooms, ref, lounge, games room, gym
Club colours: Maroon and white hoops, black shorts and socks. (*Change colours:* Blue shirts, black shorts and socks)
Nickname: Castle
Floodlights: Yes
Membership fees: Full £20, Playing £20, Social £7.50, Youth £5, Student £5
Programme: No. of editorial pages 4; No. of advertising pages 24; Price Free
Programme editor: Robin Websdale, 22 Cardington Close, Seabridge, Newcastle-u-Lyme, Staffs
Local newspapers: Evening Sentinel, Newcastle Herald
League: Staffs/Warks
League position (1988–89): 8th
League playing record (1988–89): P 39, W 22, D 0, L 17, F 611, A 441
Competitions won: North Staffs, South Cheshire & Borders Merit Table Winners, Runners-up North Staffs Cup

NUNEATON OLD EDWARDIANS

Weddington Road, Nuneaton. Tel: 0203 386778
Founded: 1910
President: S. Savage
Chairman: R.R. Arnold
Secretary: A.P. Betney, 8 Sunnyside, Hinckky. Tel: 0455 637515
Fixtures Secretary: J. Sparkes, 140 Lutterworth Road, Nuneaton. Tel: 0203 326029
Coach: R. Jones
Club captain (1988–89): M.A. Hall
Club captain (1989–90): M.A. Hall
No. of teams: Senior 5, Colts 1
Directions to ground: On Weddington Road (A444 Burton) going north on left-hand side
Clubhouse facilities: Large brick built structure containing clubroom, six changing rooms for rugby, 4 squash courts, etc.
Club colours: Red and white hoops. (*Change colours:* White)
Floodlights: No
Membership fees: Full £10
Local newspaper: Nuneaton Evening Tribune
League: Staffs/Warks
League position (1988–89): 5th
League playing record (1988–89): P 10, W 5, D 0, L 5, F 132, A 121

OLD LEAMINGTONIANS

The Crofts, Bericote Road, Leamington Spa. Tel: 0926 24991.
Founded: 1931
Secretary: E. Bayliss, 1 Puckerings Lane, Warwick. Tel: Warwick 495373 (H) Coventry 28381 (W).
League: Staffs/Warwicks
Final position (1988–89): 3Rd
League record (1988–89): P 1O, W 7, L 3, F 144, A 132, PTS 14

OLD LONGTONIAN

Roughcote Lane, Caverswall, Stoke-on-Trent. Tel: 0782 394449
Founded: 1953
President: Marshall J. Carson
Chairman: Michael Wheat
Secretary: Terence John Keeling, Checkleybank Farmhouse, Checkley, Stoke-on-Trent ST10 4NF. Tel: 0538 722750 (H), 0332 661422 (W)
Fixtures Secretary: Dr. John R. Till, 174 Stallington Road, Blythe Bridge, Stoke-on-Trent. Tel: 0782 395396 (H), 533121 (W)
Club captain (1988–89): Richard Tams
Club captain (1989–90): Richard Tams

No. of teams: Senior 4, Youth 3
Directions to ground: 6 miles from J14 (M6) or J15 (M6) just off A520 at Caverswall
Clubhouse facilities: 6 changing rooms, 2 clubhouse rooms, gym
Club colours: Black and amber. (*Change colours:* Maroon and gold)
Floodlights: No
Membership fees: Full £25, Playing £25, Social £10, Youth £10, Student £1
Programme: No. of editorial pages 3; No. of advertising pages 8; Price Free
Programme editor: M.J. Wheat, 12 West Avenue, Basford, Newcastle, Staffs
Local newspaper: Evening Sentinel
League: Staffs/Warks
League position (1988–89): 8th
League playing record (1988–89): P 10, W 4, D 0, L 6, F 130, A 150

STRATFORD-UPON-AVON

Pearcecroft, Loxley Road, Stratford-upon-Avon, Warwickshire. Tel: 0789 297796
Founded: 1876
President: Dr. K.J. Holley
Chairman: Roderick Withers
Secretary: Ian Fathers, 61 Loxley Road, Stratford-upon-Avon, Warwickshire CV37 7DP. Tel: 0789 205715 (H), 204278 (W)
Fixtures Secretary: Ron Grant, 4 St. Gregory's Road, Stratford-upon-Avon, Warwickshire. Tel: 0789 66722 (H), 021–502 7116 (W)
Press Officer: Alan Jones, 14 Chapel Street, Wellesbourne, Warks. Tel: 0789 840573
Club captain (1988–89): Paul Gisbourne
Club captain (1989–90): Paul Gisbourne
No. of teams: Senior 4, Youth 4, Minis 7
Directions to ground: South over the Avon via Clopton Bridge, along Tiddington Road, turn right along Loxley Road, turn left into ground after 400 yds before reaching Manor Road
Ground capacity: Seating 200, standing 2000
Clubhouse facilities: 2 bars, function rooms, open match days, Sunday lunch
Club colours: Black and white hoops, white shorts, black socks. (*Change colours:* All black or all white)
Floodlights: Yes
Membership fees: Full £30, Playing £30, Social £18, Youth £18, Student £18, OAP £18
Ground admission: Nil except by Raffle Programme
Programme: No. of editorial pages 10; No. of advertising pages 6; Price Free except when Raffle Prizes are available
Programme editor: Rod Withers, 2 Loxley Road, Stratford-upon-Avon, Warks
Local newspapers: Stratford Herald, Guardian, and Observer
League: Staffs/Warks
League position (1988–89): 4th
League playing record (1988–89): P 10, W 6, D 0, L 4

TAMWORTH

Wigginton Lodge, Wigginton Park, Tamworth, Staffordshire. Tel: 0827 68794
Founded: 1925
President: M.R. Steele-Bodger
Chairman: D. Heaney
Secretary: M. Gibson, 128 Comberford Road, Tamworth, Staffs B79 8PG. Tel: 0827 310148
Fixtures Secretary: D. Heaney, 3 Sunningdale, Amington, Tamworth. Tel: 0827 69801
Press Officer: T. Franks, 16 Shirley Walk, Coton Green, Tamworth, Staffordshire. Tel: 0827 62436
Club captain (1988–89): K. Borthwick
Club captain (1989–90): T. Franks
No. of teams: Senior 5, Youth 3
Club colours: Maroon with black and white band,

black shorts. (*Change colours:* Blue shirts and black shorts)
Floodlights: No
League: Staff/Warks
League position (1988–89): 10th
League playing record (1988–89): P 10, W 1, D 3, L 6

WILLENHALL

Bognor Road, Essington, Staffs. Tel: 0922 405694
Founded: 1963
President: William Simkin
Chairman: Hugh Harris
Secretary: Elfyn Pugh, 9 Five-Fields Road, Willenhall, West Midlands, WV12 4NZ. Tel: 0902 607747 (H), 021–526 4145 (W)
Fixtures Secretary: Geoff Aucott, 21 River Way, Wednesbury, West Midlands. Tel: 021–556 0749
Press Officer: Stuart Fletcher, 12 Sandown Avenue,

Cheslyn Hay, Nr. Walsall. Tel: (0922) 414383
Coach: Eric Field
Club captain (1988–89): Rick Swift
Club captain (1989–90): Rick Swift
No. of teams: Senior 5, Youth 2, Minis 5
Directions to ground: M5 to M54 off M54 Junction 1 towards Wolverhampton for mile. Bognor Road, Essington on left. Along Bognor Road for 1 mile club on right
Ground capacity: Seating Nil, standing 500
Clubhouse facilities: Lounge bar, changing rooms (6 teams), showers, gymnasium
Club colours: Maroon, black shorts. (*Change colours:* Black)
Floodlights: No
League: Staffs/Warks
League position (1988–89): 9th
League playing record (1988–89): P 10, W 4, D 0, L 6
Competitions won: Colts won Staffs Merit Table Under 17 and 14 won Staffs Festival Competition

Both teams pose before the Harbury Silver Jubilee special match

STAFFORDSHIRE LEAGUES

WITH only 17 clubs spread over two divisions this must be one of the weakest county groupings in the whole country and Handsworth with victories in all six matches took the top honours in Division 1, leaving Cannock and Linley with the indignity of dropping to Division 2, where some stiff competition brought promotion to Eccleshall and Wednesbury, who thus ascend after only one season in modest company.

STAFFORDSHIRE OFFICIAL:

Keith Dale
14 St Anthony's Drive,
Newcastle   (H) 0782 615770
Staffs ST5 2JE   (B) 0782 744241 Ext 2230

TABLES 1987–88

STAFFORDSHIRE 1

	P	W	D	L	F	A	PTS
Belgrave	6	6	0	0	94	24	12
Rugeley	6	5	0	1	129	44	10
Burntwood	6	4	0	2	96	57	8
Cannock	6	3	0	3	96	77	6
Linley	6	1	0	5	40	42	2
Wednesbury	6	1	0	5	38	137	2
Wulfrun	6	1	0	5	20	132	2

STAFFORDSHIRE 2

	P	W	D	L	F	A	PTS
Uttoxeter	8	8	0	0	201	27	16
GEC	8	7	0	1	192	38	14
Rubery Owen	8	5	0	3	163	64	10
Michelin	8	4	2	2	77	68	10
Eccleshall	8	4	1	3	82	96	9
W'ton Aston	8	2	1	5	68	93	5
Old Oaks	8	2	0	6	54	143	4
Cheadle	8	2	0	6	49	148	4
St Matthews	8	0	0	8	36	245	0

TABLES 1988–89

STAFFORDSHIRE 1

	P	W	D	L	F	A	PTS
Handsworth	6	6	0	0	140	41	12
Rugeley	6	3	2	1	96	53	8
Uttoxeter	6	3	1	2	39	46	7
Burntwood	6	2	0	4	50	76	4
GEC	6	2	0	4	68	107	4
Cannock	6	2	0	4	44	86	4
Linley	6	1	1	4	52	80	3

STAFFORDSHIRE 2

	P	W	D	L	F	A	PTS
Eccleshall	9	8	0	1	222	52	16
Wednesbury	9	7	0	2	134	38	14
Rubery Owen	9	6	0	3	141	79	12
Michelin	9	5	1	3	87	105	11
Wheaton Aston	9	5	2	2	119	57	10
Old Oaks	9	5	0	4	95	76	10
Wulfrun	9	4	0	5	99	86	8
St. Matthews	9	2	0	7	74	256	4
St. Georges	9	1	0	8	75	156	2
Cheadle	9	0	1	8	57	198	1

MIDLANDS DIVISION FIXTURES 1989/90

STAFFORDSHIRE ONE

Saturday, 23rd September (Week 4)
Trentham v GEC
Eccleshall v Uttoxeter
Rugeley v Wednesbury

Sat. 14th October (Week 6)
Uttoxeter v GEC
Burntwood v Trentham
Eccleshall v Wednesbury

Sat. 28th October (Week 8)
Rugeley v GEC
Uttoxeter v Trentham
Wednesbury v Burntwood

Sat 18th November (Week 11)
GEC v Wednesbury
Burntwood v Eccleshall
Rugeley v Uttoxeter

Sat. 10th March (Week 26)
Trentham v Eccleshall
Burntwood v Rugeley
Wednesbury v Uttoxeter

Sat. 31st March (Week X7)
Eccleshall v Rugeley
Wednesbury v Trentham
GEC v Burntwood

Sat. 28th April (Week 32)
Trentham v Rugeley
Uttoxeter v Burntwood
GEC v Eccleshall

Trentham – back to Staffordshire 1

MIDLANDS DIVISION FIXTURES 1989/90

STAFFORDSHIRE TWO

Sat. 9th September (Week 2)
Cannock v Cheadle
St. Matthews v Rubery Owen
Old Oaks v Wheaton Aston
Michelin v Wulfrun
Sankey Vending v Linley

Sat. 23rd September (Week 4)
Linley v Cannock
Wulfrun v Old Oaks
Rubery Owen v Wheaton Aston
St. Georges v St. Matthews
Michelin v Sankey Vending

Sat. 14th October (Week 6)
Cannock v Michelin
Cheadle v Linley
Wheaton Aston v St. Georges
Rubery Owen v Wulfrun
Sankey Vending v Old Oaks

Sat. 28th October (Week 8)
Cheadle v Michelin
Old Oaks v Cannock
Wulfrun v St. Georges
St. Matthews v Wheaton Aston
Rubery Owen v Sankey Vending

Sat. 11th November (Week 10)
Cannock v Rubery Owen
Old Oaks v Cheadle
Linley v Michelin
Wulfrun v St. Matthews
Sankey Vending v St. Georges

Sat 18th November (Week 11)
Old Oaks v Linley
Cheadle v Rubery Owen
St. Georges v Cannock
Wulfrun v Wheaton Aston
St. Matthews v Sankey Vending

Sat. 25th November (Week 12)
St. Georges v Cheadle
Cannock v St. Matthews
Linley v Rubery Owen
Michelin v Old Oaks
Sankey Vending v Wheaton Aston

Sat. 13th January (Week 18)
St. Georges v Linley
St. Matthews v Cheadle
Wheaton Aston v Cannock
Michelin v Rubery Owen
Wulfrun v Sankey Vending

Sat. 10th March (Week 26)
Cannock v Wulfrun
Wheaton Aston v Cheadle
Linley v St. Matthews
Michelin v St. Georges
Rubery Owen v Old Oaks

Sat. 31st March (Week X7)
St. Georges v Old Oaks
St. Matthews v Michelin
Wheaton Aston v Linley
Cheadle v Wulfrun
Sankey Vending v Cannock

Sat. 28th April (Week 32)
Linley v Wulfrun
Wheaton Aston v Michelin
Old Oaks v St. Matthews
Rubery Owen v St. Georges
Cheadle v Sankey Vending

STAFFORDSHIRE 1

BURNTWOOD

Burntwood Recreation Centre, High Street, Chase Town, Walsall. Tel: 0543 62222
Founded: 1972
President: Harry Cooper
Chairman: Paul Blockley
Secretary: Mansel Thomas, 16 Thorpe Street, Chase Terrace, Walsall WS4 78NE. Tel: 0543 751284
Fixtures Secretary: Martin Steele, 26 Foxhill Close, Heath Hayes, Nr. Cannock, Staffordshire
Press Officer: As Secretary
Club captain (1988–89): Alan Price
Club captain (1989–90): Alan Price
No. of teams: Senior 3, Youth 2
Clubhouse facilities: Shared with Chasetown F.C. at Church Road, Burntwood
Nickname: Nailers
Floodlights: Yes (for training)
Membership fees: Full £12, Playing £12, Social £1, VPs £5 Min., Youth £6, Student £1
Programme editor: As secretary
Local newspapers: Lichfield Mercury, Chase Post, Express & Star
League: Staffs 1
League position (1988–89): 4th
League playing record (1988–89): P 6, W 2, D 0, L 4, F 50, A 76
Competitions won: Loughborough RUFC Youth 7's Plate Winners, Worcester RUFC U16 7's Winners

ECCLESHALL

Drake Hall, Nr. Eccleshall
Founded: 1979
President: A. Rees
Chairman: R. Gibbins
Secretary: P. Rogers, 6 Sherieff's Way, Eccleshall. Tel: 0785 815491
Fixtures Secretary: K. Bott
Press Officer: B. Braithwaite, 4 Badger's Croft, Eccleshall. Tel: 0785 85114
Coach: A. Copeland
Club captain (1988–89): P. Rogers
Club captain (1989–90): P. Winn
Directions to ground: 1 mile north of Eccleshall, follow signs to HM Prison
Club colours: Green/yellow. (*Change colours:* Black with g/y)
Floodlights: No
Membership fees: Full £25, Playing £15
League: Mids Staffs 1
League position (1988–89): 1st
League playing record (1988–89): P 9, W 8, D 0, L 1, F 222, A 52

G.E.C. ST. LEONARDS

G.E.C. St. Leonards Works, Stafford ST17 4LX. Tel: 0875 58070
Founded: 1977
President: M.A. Hughes
Chairman: R.T. English
Secretary: K.J. Richards, 19 Clifton Drive, Kingston-Hill, Stafford ST16 3UZ. Tel: 0875 59873 (H), 223211 ext. 416 (W)
Fixtures Secretary: I. McLeod, 17 St. Augustines Road, Rugeley, Staffordshire. Tel: 0889 579365
Coach: A. Gale and R. Rarrington
Club captain (1988–89): M. Bent
Club captain (1989–90): A. Gale
No. of teams: Senior 3
Directions to ground: M6 Junction 13 take Wolverhampton road into Stafford, take Rickerscote Road to the junction with Lichfeld Road. Turn left over bridge second on right which is St. Leonards Avenue

Clubhouse facilities: Bar
Club colours: Black and gold. (*Change colours:* Yellow)
Nickname: St. Leonards
Floodlights: No
Membership fees: Full £10, Playing £5, Social £5
Local newspapers: Newsletter/Stafford Post
League: Staffs 1
League position (1988–89): 5th
League playing record (1988–89): P 6, W 2, D 0, L 4

RUGELEY

Hagley Park, Rugeley. Tel: 0889 579985
Founded: 1947
President: D. Bishop
Chairman: M.F. Bas
Secretary: N. Evans, 72 Burnthill Lane, Rugeley, Staffs WS15 2HY. Tel: 0889 577819
Fixtures Secretary: A. Jellyman, 23 William Morris Court, Rugeley. Tel: 0889 584493
Press Officer: J. McGuckin, 5 Coalpit Lane, Brereton, Rugeley. Tel: 0889 577794
Coach: S. Barber
Club captain (1988–89): M. Ainger
Club captain (1989–90): W. Williams
No. of teams: Senior 3, Youth 2
Directions to ground: M6 Junction 11 to Cannock, A460 to Rugeley. 2nd left 50 yds on right Rugeley Youth Centre
Ground capacity: Standing Open
Clubhouse facilities: Use Red Lion Inn, Brereton. Open normal pub hours
Club colours: Amber shirts, black shorts, black/amber socks. (*Change colours:* Blue shirts, black shorts, black/amber socks)
Floodlights: No
Membership fees: Full £20, Social £5, Youth £5
Ground admission: Free
Local newspaper: Rugeley Mercury
League: Staff 1
League position (1988–89): 2nd
League playing record (1988–89): P 6, W 3, D 2, L 1, F 96, A 53

TRENTHAM

Oaktree Road, Trentham, Stoke-on-Trent. Tel: 0782 642320
Founded: 1948
President: M.I. Duncan
Chairman: M. West
Secretary: Ms. M. Riley, 23 Kersbrook Close, Trentham, Stoke-on-Trent, ST4 8XL. Tel: 0782 644874
Fixtures Secretary: P.A. Clarke, 11 Porlock Grove, Trentham, Stoke-on-Trent. Tel: 0782 658619
Press Officer: J. Hewitt, c/o Trentham Rugby Club, Oaktree Road, Trentham, Stoke-on-Trent
Club captain (1988–89): M.T. Bezus
Club captain (1989–90): P. Turnock
No. of teams: Senior 3, Youth 1
Directions to ground: M6 Junction 15, A500 to 1st roundabout, A34 South to Trentham Gardens Roundabout, left to Trentham, Oaktree Road mile on R.H.S.
Clubhouse facilities: 4 changing rooms, showers, bar and function room
Club colours: Green and white hoops, black shorts
Floodlights: No (to be erected shortly)
Membership fees: Playing £15, Social £5, Youth £1, Student £1, OAP £1
Local newspaper: Staffordshire Evening Sentinel
League: Staffs
League position (1988–89): 11th
League playing record (1988–89): P 34, W 7, D 3, L 24, F 246, A 643
Competitions won: Losing finalists Staffs 7-a-Side Plate Competition

UTTOXETER

Oldfields Ground, Springfield Road, Uttoxeter. Tel: 0889 564347
President: Steven Brown
Chairman: Graham MacDonald
Secretary: David Ball, 28 Milverton Drive, Uttoxeter, Staffordshire ST14 7RE. Tel: 0889 565935 (H), 0246 435601
Fixtures Secretary: Leslie Humphries, 14 Eaton Road, Rocester, Uttoxeter, Staffs ST14 5LL. Tel: 0889 590604 (H), 593680 (W)
Press Officer: Leslie Humphries, 14 Eaton Road, Rocester, Uttoxeter, Staffs ST14 5LL. Tel: 0889 563718
Coach: G. MacDonald
Club captain (1988–89): Colin Morfitt
No. of teams: Senior 2, Youth 1
Directions to ground: Windsor Park School at Springfield Road
Ground capacity: Standing 500
Clubhouse facilities: Yes
Club colours: Navy blue, yellow orange band (*Change colours:* No)
Floodlights: No
Membership fees: Full £15, Playing £15, Social £10, Youth £7.50, Student £7.50, OAP £5
Local newspaper: Staffordshire Newsletter
League: Staffs 1
League position (1988–89): 3rd
League playing record (1988–89): P 6, W 3, D 1, L 2, F 39, A 46
Competitions won: Owen Cup (Staffs) Final April '89

WEDNESBURY

14 Bridge Street, Wednesbury. Tel: 021 502 2477
Founded: 1921
President: Derek Rogers
Chairman: Robert Slater
Secretary: Peter Hughes, 28 Alder Road, Wednesbury, West Midlands WS10 9PX. Tel: 021 556 5005 (H), 021 366 6303 (W)
Fixtures Secretary: Robert Smith, 31 Doe Bank Road, Ocker Hill, Tipton, W. Mids DY4 0ES. Tel: 021 556 6748
Press Officer: Peter Clemo, 17 Clun Close, Castle View Estate, Tividale. Tel: 0384 53944 (H), 021 556 5522 (W)
Coach: Ian McDermott
Club captain (1988–89): Gary Phillips
Club captain (1989–90): Andrew Price
No. of teams: Senior 2
Directions to ground: Take directions to Wednesbury from Junction 9 on M6. Take 6th turning on left, follow road for approx. one mile. Ground lies to the right on Hydes Road
Clubhouse facilities: Bar, lounge, dining room, kitchen, committee room
Club colours: Black/white hoops. (*Change colours:* Red)
Floodlights: No
League: Staffs 1
League position (1988–89): 2nd
League playing record (1988–89): P 8, W 6, D 0, L 2
Competitions won: Winners of Staffs Sevens Plate Trophy, April 1989. Winners of Handsworth Second Team Trophy, April 1989

STAFFORDSHIRE 2

CANNOCK

Cannock Stadium, Pye Green Road, Cannock.
Founded: 1982
Secretary: C. Webb, 90 Hatherton Road, Cannock, Staffs. Tel: 05435 6105 (H) 021 358 6296 (W).
League: Staffs 2

Final position (1988–89): 6th
League record (1988–89): P 6, W 2, L 4, F 44, A 86, Pts 4

CHEADLE

The Level, Freehay, Cheadle.
Founded: 1983
Secretary: Mrs G.C. Kaminski, 22 Conway Street, Shelton, Stoke-on-Trent, Staffs ST4 2BL. Tel: ?782 415489 (H).
League: Staffs 2
Final position (1988–89):10th

LINLEY

Clough Hall Sports Ground, Kidsgrove, Stoke-on-Trent. Tel: Kidsgrove 5342
Founded: 1962
President: Ronald Tyson
Chairman: David Jennings
Secretary: Alan Hodgkinson, 50 Greenbank Road, Tunstall, Stoke-on-Trent ST6 7EY. Tel: 838201
Fixtures Secretary: Nick Baldie, 47 Becconsall Drive, Coppenhall, Crewe CW1 4RP
Press Officer: Ronald Tyson, 18 Derwent Close, Alsager, Cheshire. Tel: Alsager 87508 (H), 836696 (W)
Coach: David Jennings
Club captain (1988–89): Geoff Morrey
Club captain (1989–90): Malcolm Shepherd
No. of teams: Senior 3, Youth 1 (U16)
Directions to ground: Stoke-on-Trent north to town of Kidsgrove, follow signs to Ski Hut, Kidsgrove
Clubhouse facilities: Change Ski Hut, Kidsgrove/ Drink Red Lion, Goldenhill
Club colours: Green with gold. (*Change colours:* Green and yellow hoops)
Floodlights: No
Membership fees: Full £15, Playing £15, Youth £2, Student £5
Local newspaper: Evening Sentinel
League: Staffs 2
League position (1988–89): 7th (relegated)
League playing record (1988–89): P 6, W 1, D 1, L 4, F 52, A 80

MICHELIN

Mac Sports Centre, Rosetree Avenue, Trent Vale, Stoke-on-Trent. Tel: 0782 642369
President: Terry Forster
Chairman: Mick Yates
Secretary: Bob Beatty, 2 Danemead Close, Meir Park, Stoke-on-Trent, Staffordshire ST3 7XX. Tel: 0782 397731 H, 402814 (W)
Fixtures Secretary: Lawrence Crane, 31 Leveson Street, Longton, Stoke-on-Trent, Staffordshire. Tel: 0782 311021
Press Officer: Paul Clapham, 16 Baltic Close, Trentham, Stoke-on-Trent. Tel: 0782 659791
Coach: Phil Mickleburgh
Club captain (1988–89): Paul Towers
Club captain (1989–90): Phil Ibbs
No. of teams: Senior 2
Directions to ground: Off M6 at Junction 15, straight across 1st. roundabout. About 1 mile further you can see club on left, go off dual carriageway before flyover, turn left, then about 200 yards turn 1st. left, follow road, club on left
Clubhouse facilities: Bar, squash, weight training, athletic track. Open all week
Club colours: Yellow-navy blue hoops with dark blue shorts. (*Change colours:* Navy blue)
Floodlights: No
Membership fees: Full £15, Playing £15, Social £15, Youth £15, Student £7.50, OAP £7.50
Local newspaper: Sentinel
League: Staffs 2
League position (1988–89): 4th
League playing record (1988–89): P 8, W 3, D 1, L 4

OLD OAKS

The Shire Oak School, Walsall Road, Walsall.
Founded: 1983
Secretary: Andy Beswick, 7 Silver Court Gardens, Brownhills, Walsall WS8 6ES. Tel: 0543 377733 (H), 0902 366360 (W).
Club Colours: Scarlet/Royal Blue. (W).
League: Staffs 2
Final position (1988–89): 6th
League record (1988–89): P 9, W 5, L 4, F 95, A 76, Pts 10

RUBERY OWEN

Little Cross Street, Darlaston, West Midlands WS10 8ET. Tel: 021–526 3515
Founded: 1957
Chairman: David Brawn
Secretary: Ian Blake, 32 Crossway Lane, Birmingham B44 8DN. Tel: 021–356 6053 (H), 021–544 5252 ext. 706 (W)
Fixtures Secretary: Jeffery Osborn, 88 Ford Brook Lane, Pelsall, Walsall, West Midlands WS3 4BN. Tel: 0922 684557 (H), 0543 257861 (W)
Coach: Darren Owen
Club captain (1988–89): Jeffery Osborn
Club captain (1989–90): Darren Owen
No. of teams: Senior 4, Youth 1
Directions to ground: M6 Junction 10, towards Wolverhampton, 2nd. left (Lane Arms) then one mile on left
Clubhouse facilities: Yes
Club colours: Red shirts, black shorts, red socks. (*Change colours:* Blue and white hoops)
Floodlights: No
Membership fees: Full £11, Playing £11, Social £5, Youth £3, Student £5, OAP Free
Local newspaper: Wolverhampton Express and Star
League: Staffs 2
League position (1988–89): 3rd
League playing record (1988–89): P 9, W 6, D 0, L 3, F 141, A 79

ST GEORGES

No further information.

ST MATTHEWS

Secretary: I.S. Pritchard, 3 Upfields, Burntwood, Walsall
League: Staffs 2
Final position (1987–88): 9th (bottom)

SANKEY VENDING

Secretary: A.J. Willis, 56 Dimmocks Avenue, Coseley, Bilston, West Midlands. Tel: 021 557 5490

WHEATON ASTON

Wheaton Aston Sports & Social Club, Lapley Road, Wheaton Aston, Stafford. Tel: 0785 840440.
Secretary: K.A. Ingham, 30 Brookhouse Way, Gnosall, Stafford ST20 0HS. Tel: 0785 822904.
League: Staffs 2

WULFRUN

Hilton Main Sports and Social Club, Cannock Road, Wolverhampton, West Midlands. Tel: 0902 732470
Founded: 1963
President: T.B.A.
Chairman: Donald Hargreaves
Secretary: Christopher Withers, 138 Old Park Road, Dudley, West Midlands. Tel: 09073 5472
Fixtures Secretary: Adam Wilkinson, 162 Aldersley Road, Wolverhampton, West Mids. Tel: 0902 758509
Press Officer: John Withers, 9 Gail Park, Bradmore, Wolverhampton. Tel: 0902 343114
Coach: As Press Officer
Club captain (1988–89): J. Withers
Club captain (1989–90): J. Withers
No. of teams: Senior 3
Directions to ground: Adjacent to M54 Junction 1. Follow signs to Wolverhampton, entrance 200 yds on right
Ground capacity: Standing 200
Clubhouse facilities: Bar, clubroom, snooker room
Club colours: Emerald green shirts, black 'V' and trim
Floodlights: No
Membership fees: Full £15, Playing £15, Youth £5, Student £5, OAP Nil
Ground admission: Nil
Local newspaper: Express & Star
League: Staffs 2
League position (1988–89): 6th
League playing record (1988–89): P 37, W 16, D 0, L 21, F 468, A 434

WARWICKSHIRE LEAGUES

COVENTRY WELSH, having failed to head Keresley in 1987–88, now have a chance to emulate their distinguished predecessors as champions of Division 1 by going up again from the Warwickshire/ Staffordshire League. They won Warwickshire 1 with a perfect record in 10 matches played (points difference 274–82), whilst at the bottom of the table GEC (Coventry) and Rugby St. Andrews make way for ambitious Coventry Saracens and Spartans, who both survive a dog-fight in which one point covered the top four teams. Pinley and Standard at the bottom of Division 2 make way for Lanchester Polytechnic (who usually do well in the national Polys cup competitions) and Berkswell and Balsall, who return to higher company after just one season in the basement.

WARWICKSHIRE OFFICIAL:

Roger Ellis,
23 Samgolt Close,
Binley, Coventry,
CV3 2LX   (H) 0203 449125

TABLES 1987–88

WARWICKSHIRE 1

	P	W	D	L	F	A	PTS
Keresley	10	8	2	0	198	63	18
Cov Welsh	10	7	1	2	146	68	15
O Coventrians	10	6	1	3	109	78	13
Trinity Guild	10	6	0	4	154	100	12
GEC Coventry	10	6	0	4	102	128	12
Broad St	10	5	1	4	148	94	11
Rugby St And	10	5	1	4	121	124	11
Dunlop	10	4	1	5	114	124	9
O Wheatleyans	10	3	0	7	59	164	6
Atherstone	10	1	0	9	52	195	2
O Laurentians	10	0	1	9	60	125	1

WARWICKSHIRE 2

	P	W	D	L	F	A	PTS
Manor Park	10	9	0	1	143	63	18
Southam	10	7	0	3	171	73	14
Spartans	1	7	0	3	122	91	14
Cov Saracens	10	6	0	4	171	80	12
Earlsdon	10	6	0	4	110	129	12
Pinley	10	5	1	4	128	110	11
Standard	10	5	1	4	101	106	11
Silhillians	10	4	0	6	120	123	8
Harbury	10	4	0	6	68	143	8
Berks & B'sall	10	1	0	9	66	191	2
Rugby Welsh	10	0	0	10	47	138	0

WARWICKSHIRE 3

	P	W	D	L	F	A	PTS
Coventrians	9	8	0	1	251	54	16
O Warwickians	9	8	0	1	196	45	16
A P Lockheed	9	8	0	1	100	253	16
Shipston-on-S	9	4	1	4	127	69	9
Warwick	9	4	1	4	87	102	9
Alcester	9	3	1	5	75	144	7
Caludon Cas	9	3	1	5	91	195	7
Post Office	9	2	1	6	45	89	5
Shottery	9	2	1	6	82	132	5
Cov Tech	9	0	0	9	30	202	0

TABLES 1988–89

WARWICKSHIRE 1

	P	W	D	L	F	A	PTS
Cov Welsh	10	10	0	0	274	82	20
Trinity Guild	10	6	1	3	172	106	13
O Coventrians	10	6	0	4	130	96	12
Southam	10	6	0	4	132	183	12
Broadstreet	10	5	0	5	155	134	10
O Wheatleyans	10	5	0	5	157	148	10
Kenilworth	10	3	2	5	150	147	8
Dunlop	10	4	0	6	116	159	8
Manor Park	10	4	0	6	120	167	8
GEC Coventry	10	3	1	6	112	149	7
Rugby St And	10	1	0	9	101	248	2

WARWICKSHIRE 2

	P	W	D	L	F	A	PTS
Cov Saracens	10	8	1	1	193	60	17
Spartans	10	8	0	2	226	91	16
Coventrians	10	8	0	2	196	96	16
O Laurentian	10	8	0	2	175	111	16
Harbury	10	5	0	5	123	113	10
Earlsdon	10	4	0	6	125	129	8
Silhillians	10	4	0	6	98	179	8
Atherstone	10	3	1	6	80	122	7
O Warwickian	10	3	0	7	88	178	6
Pinley	10	2	0	8	71	188	4
Standard	10	1	0	9	82	190	2

WARWICKSHIRE 3

	P	W	D	L	F	A	PTS
Lanchester P	8	8	0	0	160	42	16
Berks & B	9	7	1	1	153	63	15
Rugby Welsh	9	7	0	2	191	36	14
Shipston	9	6	1	2	207	77	13
Warwick	9	5	0	4	142	83	10
Claverdon	8	4	0	4	105	65	8
Coventry PO	9	3	0	6	74	125	6
Shottery	9	2	0	7	62	142	4
Alcester	9	1	0	8	33	224	2
Cov Tech	9	0	0	9	33	303	0

MIDLANDS DIVISION FIXTURES 1989/90

WARWICKSHIRE ONE

Sat. 9th September (Week 2)
Old Coventrians v Old Wheatleyans
Trinity Guild v Kenilworth
Stoke Old Boys v Broad Street
Spartans v Manor Park
Dunlop v Coventry Saracens

Sat. 23rd September (Week 4)
Kenilworth v Old Coventrians
Southam v Dunlop
Coventry Saracens v Spartans
Manor Park v Stoke Old Boys
Broad Street v Trinity Guild

Sat. 14th October (Week 6)
Old Coventrians v Broad Street
Old Wheatleyans v Kenilworth
Trinity Guild v Manor Park
Stoke Old Boys v Coventry Saracens
Spartans v Southam

Sat. 28th October (Week 8)
Manor Park v Old Coventrians
Broad Street v Old Wheatleyans
Dunlop v Spartans
Southam v Stoke Old Boys
Coventry Saracens v Trinity Guild

Sat. 11th November (Week 10)
Old Coventrians v Coventry Saracens
Old Wheatleyans v Manor Park
Kenilworth v Broad Street
Stoke Old Boys v Dunlop
Trinity Guild v Southam

Sat 18th November (Week 11)
Southam v Old Coventrians
Coventry Saracens v Old Wheatleyans
Manor Park v Kenilworth
Spartans v Stoke Old Boys
Dunlop v Trinity Guild

Sat. 25th November (Week 12)
Broad Street v Manor Park
Kenilworth v Coventry Saracens
Old Wheatleyans v Southam
Old Coventrians v Dunlop
Trinity Guild v Spartans

Sat. 13th January (Week 18)
Spartans v Old Coventrians
Dunlop v Old Wheatleyans
Southam v Kenilworth
Coventry Saracens v Broad Street
Stoke Old Boys v Trinity Guild

Sat. 10th March (Week 26)
Old Coventrians v Stoke Old Boys
Old Wheatleyans v Spartans
Kenilworth v Dunlop
Broad Street v Southam
Manor Park v Coventry Saracens

Sat. 31st March (Week X7)
Trinity Guild v Old Coventrians
Stoke Old Boys v Old Wheatleyans
Spartans v Kenilworth
Dunlop v Broad Street
Southam v Manor Park

Sat. 28th April (Week 32)
Coventry Saracens v Southam
Manor Park v Dunlop
Broad Street v Spartans
Kenilworth v Stoke Old Boys
Old Wheatleyans v Trinity Guild

MIDLANDS DIVISION FIXTURES 1989/90

WARWICKSHIRE TWO

Sat. 9th September (Week 2)
Atherstone v Coventrians
Harbury v Old Laurentians
Earlsdon v Berkswell & Balsall
Old Warwickians v Silhillians
Rugby St Andrews v GEC Coventry

Sat. 23rd September (Week 4)
Lanchester Polytechnic v Rugby St Andrews
GEC Coventry v Old Warwickians
Silhillians v Earlsdon
Berkswell & Balsall v Harbury
Old Laurentians v Atherstone

Sat. 14th October (Week 6)
Coventrians v Old Laurentians
Atherstone v Berkswell & Balsall
Harbury v Silhillians
Earlsdon v GEC Coventry
Old Warwickians v Lanchester Polytechnic

Sat. 28th October (Week 8)
Rugby St Andrews v Old Warwickians
Lanchester Polytechnic v Earlsdon
GEC Coventry v Harbury
Silhillians v Atherstone
Berkswell & Balsall v Coventrians

Sat. 11th November (Week 10)
Atherstone v GEC Coventry
Coventrians v Silhillians
Old Laurentians v Berkswell & Balsall
Harbury v Lanchester Polytechnic
Earlsdon v Rugby St Andrews

Sat 18th November (Week 11)
Old Warwickians v Earlsdon
Rugby St Andrews v Harbury
Lanchester Polytechnic v Atherstone
GEC Coventry v Coventrians
Silhillians v Old Laurentians

Sat. 25th November (Week 12)
Berkswell & Balsall v Silhillians
Old Laurentians v GEC Coventry
Coventrians v Lanchester Polytechnic
Atherstone v Rugby St Andrews
Harbury v Old Warwickians

Sat. 13th January (Week 18)
Earlsdon v Harbury
Old Warwickians v Atherstone
Rugby St Andrews v Coventrians
Lanchester Polytechnic v Old Laurentians
GEC Coventry v Berkswell & Balsall

Sat. 10th March (Week 26)
Atherstone v Earlsdon
Coventrians v Old Warwickians
Old Laurentians v Rugby St Andrews
Berkswell & Balsall v Lanchester Polytechnic
Silhillians v GEC Coventry

Sat. 31st March (Week X7)
Harbury v Atherstone
Earlsdon v Coventrians
Old Warwickians v Old Laurentians
Rugby St Andrews v Berkswell & Balsall
Lanchester Polytechnic v Silhillians

Sat. 28th April (Week 32)
GEC Coventry v Lanchester Polytechnic
Silhillians v Rugby St Andrews
Berkswell & Balsall v Old Warwickians
Old Laurentians v Earlsdon
Coventrians v Harbury

MIDLANDS DIVISION FIXTURES 1989/90

WARWICKSHIRE THREE

Sat. 9th September (Week 2)
Pinley v Claverdon
Standard v Coventry Tech College
Warwick v Rugby Welsh
Coventry Post Office v Shipston-on-Stour

Sat. 23rd September (Week 4)
Coventry Tech College v Pinley
Shottery v Coventry Post Office
Alcester v Warwick
Rugby Welsh v Standard

Sat. 14th October (Week 6)
Claverdon v Coventry Tech College
Pinley v Rugby Welsh
Standard v Alcester
Warwick v Shipston-on-Stour

Sat. 28th October (Week 8)
Alcester v Pinley
Rugby Welsh v Claverdon
Shottery v Warwick
Shipston-on-Stour v Standard

Sat. 11th November (Week 10)
Pinley v Shipston-on-Stour
Claverdon v Alcester
Coventry Tech College v Rugby Welsh
Standard v Shottery
Warwick v Coventry Post Office

Sat 18th November (Week 11)
Shottery v Pinley
Shipston-on-Stour v Claverdon
Alcester v Coventry Tech College
coventry Post Office v Standard

Sat. 25th November (Week 12)
Rugby Welsh v Alcester
Coventry Tech Coll v Shipston-on-Stour
Claverdon v Shottery
Pinley v Coventry Post Office

Sat. 13th January (Week 18)
Warwick v Standard
Coventry Post Office v Claverdon
Shottery v Coventry Tech College
Shipston-on-Stour v Rugby Welsh

Sat. 10th March (Week 26)
Alcester v Shipston-on-Stour
Rugby Welsh v Shottery
Coventry Tech College v Coventry Post Office
Pinley v Warwick

Sat. 31st March (Week X7)
Standard v Pinley
Warwick v Claverdon
Coventry Post Office v Rugby Welsh
Shottery v Alcester

Sat. 28th April (Week 32)
Shipston-on-Stour v Shottery
Alcester v Coventry Post Office
Coventry Tech College v Warwick
Claverdon v Standard

BROADSTREET

Ivor Preece Field, Brandon Road, Coventry. Tel: 0203 451706 (Caretaker), 453982 (Clubhouse)
Founded: 1929
President: Edward Sheldon
Chairman: Gary Watts
Secretary: Charles McGinty, 14 Glendower Avenue, Whoberley, Coventry CV5 8BE. Tel: 0203 79261 (H), 382167 (W)
Fixtures Secretary: Dave Wilkinson, 4 Court Leet, Binley Woods, Coventry. Tel: 0203 543548
Press Officer: Gary Watts, Capitol Tiles, Eagle Street, Coventry. Tel: 0203 301838 (H), 633336 (W)
Coach: Robert Harcourt
Club captain (1988–89): Simon Buttriss
Club captain (1989–90): Simon Buttriss
No. of teams: Senior 5, Youth 4, Minis 4
Directions to ground: Once approaching Coventry take directions to the Coventry Eastern Bypass. Ground found at the Brandon Village Intersection of the bypass
Clubhouse facilities: 6 dressing rooms, weights room, full catering and bar facilities
Club colours: Red with green and white band, navy shorts. *Change colours:* Green with red and white band, navy shorts
Nickname: The Street
Floodlights: Training lights only
Membership fees: Full £2.50, Playing £2.50, Social £2.50, VPs £10, Youth Free, Student £1.25, OAP Free, Life £50
Ground admission: Free
Programme: No. of editorial pages 4; No. of advertising pages 10; Price Free
Programme editor: Charlie McGinty, 14 Glendower Avenue, Whoberley, Coventry, CV5 8BE
Local newspapers: Coventry Evening Telegraph, Coventry Citizen, Coventry Weekly News
League: Warks 1
League position (1988–89): Mid table
League playing record (1988–89): P 10 , W 5, D 0, L 5

COVENTRY SARACENS

Bredon Avenue, Coventry. Tel: 0203 453557
Founded: 1979
Chairman: B.W. Hancox
Secretary: D.G. Robbins, Mere Anker, Wolds Lane, Wolvey, Hinckley. Tel: 0455 220621 (H), 0203 687167 (W)
Fixtures Secretary: Roger Hancox, 23 Rugby Lane, Streeton-on-Dunsmore, Rugby. Tel: 0203 542252 (H), 687167 (W)
Club captain (1988–89): Brian Craner
Club captain (1989–90): Brian Craner
No. of teams: Senior 3, Youth 5, Minis 5
Clubhouse facilities: Yes
Club colours: Black shirts with red and green 'V', black shorts. (*Change colours:* Blue and white hoops)
Floodlights: No
League: Warwicks 1
League position (1988–89): 1st (promoted)
League playing record (1988–89): P 10, W 8, D 1, L 1

DUNLOP

Burnaby Road, Holbrooks, Coventry
Founded: 1924
President: J. Roberts
Chairman: C. Shaw
Secretary: K.T. Davies, 8 Cheltenham Close, Bedworth, Warks CV12 8TF. Tel: 0203 490138 (H), 666655 (W)
Fixtures Secretary: B. Brown
Press Officer: As Secretary
Coach: P. Dunkley/D. McDonald
Club captain (1988–89): S. Almsby

Club captain (1989–90): J. Pitman
No. of teams: Senior 3, Youth 1
Directions to ground: North Coventry, M6 Junc. 3
Clubhouse facilities: Full
Club colours: Black/amber. (*Change colours:* Bottle green)
Nickname: Dees
Floodlights: No
Membership fees: £1.50 per match
Programme: No. of editorial pages 4; No. of advertising pages 4; Price 50p
Programme editor: As Secretary
League: Mids Warks 1
League position (1988–89): 8th
League playing record (1988–89): P 10, W 4, D 0, L 6, F 116, A 156

KENILWORTH

Glasshouse Lane, Kenilworth, Warwickshire. Tel: 0926 53945
President: J.W. Lynes
Chairman: G. Jordan
Secretary: C.J.S. Pendle, 24 Convent Close, Kenilworth, Warwickshire CU8 2FQ. Tel: 0296 57168 (H), 0203 227331 (W)
Fixtures Secretary: D.C.A. Davies, 33 Fishponds Road, Kenilworth, Warwicks. Tel: 0926 54824
Coach: R. Bennett
Club captain (1988–89): R. Bulow
Club captain (1989–90): M. Bevan
No. of teams: Senior 5, Youth 2, Minis All ages
Club colours: Dark blue/yellow shorts. (*Change colours:* Dark blue shorts)
Floodlights: No
League: Warwicks 1
League position (1988–89): 7th
League playing record (1988–89): P 10, W 3, D 2, L 5

MANOR PARK

Griff & Coton Sports Ground, Heath End Road, Nuneaton, Warks. Tel: 0203 386798
Founded: 1961
President: Alexander Broomfield
Chairman: Chris Taylor
Secretary: Martin D. Broomfield, 75 Hinckley Road, Burbage, Leics LE10 2AF. Tel: 0455 633718 (H), 0806 375338 (W)
Fixtures Secretary: Steve Atkinson, 447 Queen Elizabeth Road, Nuneaton, Warks CV10 9BX. Tel: 0203 394606
Press Officer: Gary 'Elvis' Bonsor, 17 Bracebridge Street, Nuneaton, Warks. Tel: 0203 303080 ext. 6417 (W)
Club captain (1988–89): John 'Jubb' Jenkins
Club captain (1989–90): John 'Jubb' Jenkins
No. of teams: Senior 4
Directions to ground: A444 Nun-Cov at roundabout follow signs for George Elliot Hospital, ground opposite
Ground capacity: 200
Clubhouse facilities: Half share with cricket section of bar and changing rooms. Separate from main sports club.
Club colours: Red and black hoops, black hose. (*Change colours:* Green)
Nickname: The Old Boys
Floodlights: No
Membership fees: Full £10, Playing £10, Youth £5, Student £2.50
Ground admission: Nil
Local newspapers: Nuneaton Evening Tribune, Coventry Evening Telegraph
League: Warwicks 1
League position (1988–89): 8th
League playing record (1988–89): P 10, W 4, D 0, L 6, F 120, A 167

OLD COVENTRIANS

Tile Hill Lane, Coventry. Tel: Coventry 715273
Founded: 1930
President: R.C. Richards
Chairman: J. Over
Secretary: I.M. Thomas, 28 Studland Green,
Coventry. Tel: 0203 611054
Fixtures Secretary: N. Twaite, 43 Ivybridge Road,
Coventry. Tel: 0203 416833
Club captain (1988–89): M. Taylor
Club captain (1989–90): I. Knowles
No. of teams: Senior 4, Minis 2
Directions to ground: Junction of A45 (Coventry
Bypass) and Tile Hill Lane
League: Warwicks 1

OLD WHEATLEYANS

Norman Place Road, Coventry. Tel: Keresley 4888
Founded: 1929
President: A. Potter
Chairman: A. Partridge
Secretary: R. Leigh, 8 Orchard Crescent, Coventry
CV3 6HJ. Tel: 0203 501998 (H), 688918 (W)
Fixtures Secretary: D. Margetts, 2 Rochester Road,
Coventry. Tel: 0203 72952
Press Officer: c/o Secretary
Club captain (1988–89): P. Routledge
Club captain (1989–90): A. Chambers
No. of teams: Senior 4
Club colours: Blue maroon gold
Nickname: Old Wheats
Floodlights: No
Membership fees: Full £30, Youth £12.50, Student
£12.50
Local newspaper: Coventry Evening Telegraph
League: Warwicks 1
League position (1988–89): 6th
League playing record (1988–89): P 37, W 17, D 0,
L 20, F 510, A 516

SOUTHAM

Kineton Road, Southam, Warks. Tel: 0926 813674
Founded: 1963
President: Robert Jones
Chairman: Andrew Mitchell
Secretary: Michael Haville, 11 Banbury Road,
Southam, Warks CV33 0NT. Tel: 0926 814803
Fixtures Secretary: Leighton Tudor Williams, 27
Hillyard Road, Southam, Warks. Tel: 0926 812194
(H), 812560 (W)
Coach: Tim Perkin
Club captain (1988–89): Mark Harvey
No. of teams: Senior 5, Youth 1
Directions to ground: Enter Southam and follow signs
for Kineton/Industrial Estate, continue past Industrial
Estate, Club 400 yd on right
Ground capacity: Standing 500
Clubhouse facilities: Open Tues., Thurs. and Sat.
Club colours: White hoops on navy blue. (*Change
colours:* Blue hoops on white)
Nickname: Dinosaurs
Floodlights: No
Membership fees: Full £15, Playing £15, Social £2,
Youth £1
Programme: No. of editorial pages 2; No. of
advertising pages 1; Price 50p (League and Cup only)
Programme editor: See Secretary
Local newspaper: Leamington Courier
League: Warwick 1
League position (1988–89): 4th

SPARTANS

Coppice Lane, Middleton, Nr. Tamworth,
Staffordshire. Tel: 021–308 5857
Founded: 1960
President: Roger Green

Chairman: Dennis Peel
Secretary: Miss Sarah McGrory, 12 Russell Bank
Road, Four Oaks, Sutton Coldfield, West Midlands
B74 4RE. Tel: 021–353 7365
Fixtures Secretary: Graham Lloyd, 295 Highbridge
Road, Boldmere, Sutton Coldfield, West Midlands
B73 5RB. Tel: 021–354 5818
Press Officer: Julian Whiting, 92 Aldridge Road,
Little Aston, Aldridge, Walsall WS9 0PE
Club captain (1988–89): Tim Rich
Club captain (1989–90): Steve Owen
No. of teams: Senior 4
Directions to ground: By the junction of the A445 and
Coppice Lane, mile on the Coleshill side of the A453
at Bassetts Pole
Clubhouse facilities: Open match days, Tuesday/
Thursday evenings and Sunday lunchtimes
Club colours: Black shirts, black shorts. (*Change
colours:* Red shirts, black shorts)
Floodlights: Yes (training only)
Membership fees: Full £25, Playing £25, Social &
Ladies £5
Ground admission: Free
Local newspapers: Sutton Coldfield News, Sutton
Coldfield Observer
League: Warwick 1
League position (1988–89): 2nd (promoted)
League playing record (1988–89): P 31, W 24, D 1,
L 6, F 703, A 255

STOKE OLD BOYS

Brookvale Avenue, Binley, Coventry. Tel: 0203
453631
Founded: 1921
President: Albert R. Gale
Secretary: G.W. Cousins, 5 Elmore Close, Ernsford
Grange, Coventry, Warwickshire CV3 2QS. Tel: 0203
431010 (H), 402121 ext. 2991 (W)
Fixtures Secretary: R. McArthur, 47 Joseph
Creighton Close, Ernsford Grange, Coventry CV3
2QF. Tel: 0203 450533
Press Officer: As Fixtures Secretary
Coach: R. McArthur
Club captain (1988–89): C. Waite
Club captain (1989–90): M. Elvidge
No. of teams: Senior 4, Youth 2
Directions to ground: Upon request
Clubhouse facilities: Bar/lounge and 4 changing rooms
Club colours: Maroon and white
Floodlights: No
League: Warwicks 1
League position (1988–89): Bottom (relegated)
League playing record (1988–89): P 34, W 12, D 1,
L 21, F 422, A 699

TRINITY GUILD

Rowley Road, Baginton, Nr. Coventry, Warks. Tel:
0203 305928
Founded: 1899
President: G. Bosworth
Chairman: R.W. Wormell
Secretary: Arthur Medlock, 5 Bywater Close,
Coventry. Tel: 0203 414215
Fixtures Secretary: J. Morton, 63 Shirley Road,
Coventry. Tel: 617128
Coach: T. Dingley
Club captain (1988–89): T. Dingley
Club captain (1989–90): T. Dingley
No. of teams: Senior 4, Youth 4
Ground capacity: Seating 8
Club colours: Maroon/old gold/blue. (*Change colours:*
Blue)
Floodlights: Yes (training)
Membership fees: Full £23, Playing £2.50
League: Mids Warks 1
League position (1988–89): 2nd
League playing record (1988–89): P 10, W 6, D 1,
L 3, F 172, A 106

WARWICKSHIRE 2

ATHERSTONE

Ratcliffe Road, Atherstone. Tel: 0827 714934
Founded: 1968
President: J. Stevenson
Chairman: D. Wetton
Secretary: D. Boal, Thurmaston House, 74 South
Street, Atherstone, Warks CV9 1DZ. Tel: 0827
713145
Fixtures Secretary: K. Berry
Coach: J. Burdett
No. of teams: Senior 3, Youth 1
Directions to ground: Drive into town centre, turn at
Midland Bank
Club colours: Black. (*Change colours:* Yellow)
Nickname:
Floodlights: No
Membership fees: Full £5
League: Mids Warks 2
League position (1988–89): 8th
League playing record (1988–89): P 10, W 3, D 1,
L 6, F 80, A 122

BERKSWELL & BALSALL COMMON

Heart of England School, Balsall Common, Warks
Founded: 1982
President: Dr. M. Matthews
Chairman: J. Mayer
Secretary: M.W. Shuter, 99 Kelsey Lane, Balsall
Common, Coventry. Tel: Berkswell 34616
Fixtures Secretary: L. Edwards, 22A Kenilworth
Road. Tel: Berkswell 34119
Coach: S. Staunton
No. of teams: Senior 1
Directions to ground: Heart of England School
Club colours: Red/black. (*Change colours:* Black)
Floodlights: No
Membership fees: Full £15
League: Mids Warks 2
League position (1988–89): 2nd
League playing record (1988–89): P 9, W 7, D 1, L 1,
F153, A 63

COVENTRIANS

Black Pad (off Yelverton Road), Radford, Coventry
CV6 4NW. Tel: 0203 682885
Founded: 1918
President: T.L. Lyon
Secretary: J.H. Parke, 47 High Street, Ryton-on-
Dunsmore, Nr. Coventry CV8 3FJ. Tel: 0203 304394
Fixtures Secretary: J.S. Daniell, 116 Millfarm Park,
Marston Jabbett, Nuneaton, Warwickshire. Tel: 0203
373470
Press Officer: A. Morrall, 7 Partridge Croft, Little
Heath, Coventry CV6 7EY
Coach: M. Cowburn
Club captain (1988–89): Clayton Lee Flick
Club captain (1989–90): Clive Davies
No. of teams: Senior 4
Clubhouse facilities: 4 changing rooms, showers, bar,
lounge
Club colours: Royal blue/white squares; 2nd, 3rd, 4th
XV's Royal blue
Floodlights: No
Membership fees: Full £10
Ground admission: Nil
Local newspaper: Coventry Evening Telegraph
League: Warwick 2
League position (1988–89): Third
League playing record (1988–89): P 10, W 8, D 0,
L 2, F 206, A 96

EARLSDON

Mitchell Avenue, Canley, Coventry. Tel: 0203 464467
Founded: 1905
President: Augustus John Jarvis
Chairman: Robert Price
Secretary: K. Clark, 34 –Cordelia Way, Woodlands,
Rugby CV22 6JW.
Fixtures Secretary: D. Laing, 104 Torbay Road,
Allesley, Coventry CV5 9JL.
Press Officer: Paul Tanney, 132 Lincroft Crescent,
Coventry. Tel: 0203 75612
Coach: Tony Smith
Club captain (1988–89): John Murphy
Club captain (1989–90): John Murphy
No. of teams: Senior 4, Youth 4, Minis 5
Directions to ground: Turn off A45 B'ham/London.
From west turn right at traffic island by Fire Station
on right. Turn right at next traffic island. Turn left at
next traffic island into Mitchell Ave. From east turn
left at traffic island by Fire Station.
Clubhouse facilities: Dressing rooms for 6 teams, 2
shower rooms, bar, club, lounge. Open match days
and 3 evenings per week
Club colours: Red and white hoops. (*Change colours:*
All red or all white)
Floodlights: No
Membership fees: Full £10, Playing £72*, Social £1,
Youth £4, Student £32*. (*Includes playing fees)
Local newspaper: Coventry Evening Telegraph
League: Warwick 2
League position (1988–89): 6th
League playing record (1988–89): P 10, W 4, D 0,
L 6, F 127, A 130

GEC (COVENTRY)

Allard Way. Tel: 0203 451157
Founded: 1925
President: A.G.W. Johnson
Chairman: R.H. McBride
Secretary: R.G. Everitt, 23 Bruntingthorpe Way,
Binley, Coventry CV3 2GD. Tel: 0203 4566570 (H),
636066 ext. 5712 (W)
Fixtures Secretary: G.N. Goodall, 38 Priesthills Road,
Hinckley, Leics LE10 1AJ. Tel: 0455 38742 (H), 0203
452152 ext. 2693 (W)
Press Officer: As Secretary
Coach: C. Rogers, R. Wood, R. Thomas, R. Assinder
Club captain (1988–89): P.J.A. Kelly
Club captain (1989–90): J.W. Cutler
No. of teams: Senior 3
Directions to ground: Off Allard Way, Copsewood,
Coventry
Club colours: Red/blue/green hoops
Floodlights: Yes
Membership fees: Full £10, Social Varies
Local newspaper: Coventry Evening Telegraph
League: Warwick 2
League position (1988–89): 10th (relegated)
League playing record (1988–89): P 32, W 12, D 2,
L 18, F 375, A 455
Competitions won: Easter Tournament Rotterdam,
Holland

HARBURY

Waterloo Fields, Middle Road, Harbour, Leamington
Spa, Warks. Tel: 0926 613462
Founded: 1962
President: J. Bromley
Chairman: Ian Holroyd
Secretary: J. Birkbeck, 22 Campion Terrace,
Leamington Spa, Warks CV32 4SX. Tel: 0926 24053
Fixtures Secretary: Bob New, 139 Cubbington Road,
Leamington. Tel: 0926 25915
Coach: Dye Rogers
Club captain (1988–89): Pepe Pevel
Club captain (1989–90): Pepe Pevell
No. of teams: Senior 3, Youth 8

Directions to ground: A425 and 250 from Leamington Spa to Fosse Way junction, south 1 miles beneath railway bridge, left turn to Harbury
Club colours: Red/white. (*Change colours:* Blue/white)
Floodlights: No
Membership fees: Full £17
League: Mids Warks 2
League position (1988–89): 5th
League playing record (1988–89): P 10, W 5, D 0, L 5, F 123, A 113

LANCHESTER POLYTECHNIC

Secretary: Hwqel Jones, Coventry Polytechnic Students' Union, Priory Street, Coventry 1, West Midlands. Tel: 0203 21167 (W).
Club Colours: Black/Gold.
League: Warwickshire 2
Position (1988–89): 1st (Warwickshire 3 – promoted)
League playing record: P 8, W 8, F 160, A 42, Pts. 16

OLD LAURENTIANS

Lime Tree Avenue, Bilton, Rugby, Warwickshire. Tel: 0788 810855
Founded: 1919
President: O.T. Wooton
Chairman: Joe Keenan
Secretary: Ann Simpson, 24 Cromwell Road, Rugby, Warwickshire CV22 5LP. Tel: 0788 565425
Fixtures Secretary: Ray Roberts, 261 Alwyn Road, Bilton, Rugby, Warwickshire. Tel: 0788 810276
Press Officer: Brian Beckett, 68 Shakespeare Gardens, Rugby, Warwickshire. Tel: 0788 813444
Coach: M. Warwick
Club captain (1988–89): S. Birch
Club captain (1989–90): S. Lennie
No. of teams: Senior 4
Directions to ground: Off Alwyn Road, Bilton, Rugby (A4071)
Clubhouse facilities: 1,000 sq. ft.
Club colours: Maroon/green, gold hoops. (*Change colours:* Blue/gold)
Nickname: O.L.'s
Floodlights: No
Membership fees: Full £20
Programme: No. of editorial pages 1; No. of advertising pages 1; Price 50p (only Home League games)
Programme editor: Ann Simpson, 24 Cromwell Road, Rugby, Warwickshire
Local newspapers: Rugby Advertiser, Rugby Post
League: Warwick 2
League position (1988–89): 4th
League playing record (1988–89): P 10, W 8, D 0, L 2, F 176, A 111

OLD WARWICKIANS

Hampton Road, Warwick. Tel: 0926 496295
Founded: 1929
President: Nor Morris
Chairman: Paul Williams
Secretary: Stef McMahon, 52 Cannon Close, Coventry. Tel: 0203 418489
Fixtures Secretary: Bob Gregory, 8 Tuckwell Close, Stockton, Nr Southam
Coach: Paul Williams
Club captain (1988–89): Terry Bennett
No. of teams: Senior 4
Directions to ground: Birmingham exit (A41) off A46 bypass into Warwick, turn right onto B4095 Hampton Road past Warwick Racecourse (on right). Ground mile on right just after bridge over A46 bypass
Clubhouse facilities: Full
Club colours: Maroon/white. (*Change colours:* Royal blue)
Floodlights: No

Membership fees: Full £15
League: Mids Warks 2
League position (1988–89): 9th
League playing record (1988–89): P 10, W 3, D 0, L 7, F 88, A 178

RUGBY ST. ANDREWS

Hillmorton Grounds, Ashlawn Road, Rugby, Warwickshire. Tel: 0788 542786
President: Alf Reading
Chairman: Mick Robinson
Secretary: Jim Corry, 3 Holme Way, Barby, Nr. Rugby CV 23 8UQ. Tel: 0788 891039 (H), 533404 (W)
Fixtures Secretary: John Hunt, 3 Duke Street, Rugby CV21 2NA. Tel: 0788 74606 (H), 71371 (W)
Press Officer: Brian Humphries, 15 Catesby Road, Rugby. Tel: 0788 78042
Coach: Alan Parish
Club captain (1988–89): Dave Eaton
Club captain (1989–90): Steve Gibson
No. of teams: Senior 4, Youth 3, Minis 4
Directions to ground: From J.18 on M1 follow town centre signs. Fork left at the Paddox Public House. Ground 800 yards on left
Clubhouse facilities: Open matchdays and every evening (excl. Sunday)
Club colours: Sky/navy hoops, navy shorts. (*Change colours:* Green)
Nickname: Saints
Floodlights: No
Local newspaper: Rugby Advertiser
League: Warwick 2
League position (1988–89): 11th (relegated)
League playing record (1988–89): P 10, W 1, D 0, L 9, F 101, A 248

SILHILLIANS

Warwick Road, Copt Heath, Knowle, Solihull, Warwickshire. Tel: 0564 777680
Founded: 1932
President: David N. Green
Chairman: Philip N. Green
Secretary: Paul G. Newby, 8 Ullenhall Road, Knowle, Solihull, West Midlands B93 9JD. Tel: 0564 779559 (H), 021–200 311 (W)
Fixtures Secretary: Graham Loader, 4 Shackleton Drive, Perton, Wolverhampton. Tel: 0902 742695 (H), 0902 353522 (W)
Press Officer: David N. Green, 7 Copt Heath Drive, Knowle, Solihull, West Midlands. Tel: 0564 777669 (H), 0527 510510 (W)
Club captain (1988–89): Alan D. Elliott
Club captain (1989–90): Alan D. Elliott
No. of teams: Senior 3, Youth 1*, Minis 7. (*Trying for new Saturday side)
Directions to ground: Junction M42. Take A41 trunk road towards Knowle and Warwick. Entrance to club and ground 100 yards on left-hand side from motorway roundabout
Clubhouse facilities: Full clubroom, bar and changing facilities
Club colours: Maroon blue and white. (*Change colours:* Blue)
Floodlights: Yes (partial)
League: Warwick 2
League position (1988–89): 7th
League playing record (1988–89): P 8, W 3, D 0, L 5, F 80, A 126

WARWICKSHIRE 3

ALCESTER

Kings Laughton, Nr Alcester, Warwicks.
Founded: 1960
Secretary: M.J. Edwards, 8 Icknield Row, Alcester,

Warwicks. Tel: 0789 764096 (H) 0789 762285 (W).
League: Warwicks 3
Club Colours: Red/Black.

CLAVERDON

Ossetts Hole Lane, Yarningale Common, Claverdon,
Warwicks. Tel: Claverdon 3133
President: Dr. Phillip Reasbeck
Chairman: Lawrence Grove
Secretary: Basil Sayer, The White House, 45 Station
Road, Balsall Common, Coventry CV7 7FN. Tel:
0676 32164 (H), 0203 555266 (W)
Fixtures Secretary: Paul Busby, Avon Croft
Brickyard, The Green, Snitterfield, Warwicks CV39
0JE. Tel: 0789 731423 (H), 730323 (W)
Press Officer: Andy Jones, 10A The White House,
High Street, Henley-in-Arden, Solihull. Tel: 0564
22761 (H), 021–356 6071 (W)
Coach: Mike Reasbeck
Club captain (1988–89): Paul Busby
Club captain (1989–90): Phil Smithers
No. of teams: Senior 3
Directions to ground: Between Warwick and Henley-
in-Arden on the B4096
Clubhouse facilities: Open matchdays
Club colours: Red and white jerseys, white shorts, red
and white socks
Floodlights: Yes
Membership fees: Full £30, Playing £30, Student £15
Local newspapers: Stratford Herald, Solihull News,
Solihull Times
League: Warwick 3
League position (1988–89): 6th
League playing record (1988–89): P 9, W 4, D 0, L 5,
F 108, A 79

COVENTRY POST OFFICE

Telepost Club, Northbrook Road, Coundon,
Coventry. Tel: Keresley 2714
Founded: 1982
President: Bill Ward
Chairman: Keith John Tams
Secretary: Miss Yvette Graham, 251 Telfer Road,
Radford, Coventry CV6 3DS. Tel: Coventry 598378
Fixtures Secretary: Trevor Burnham, 80 Glendower
Avenue, Coventry. Tel: Coventry 74485
Press Officer: Miss Y. Graham, 251 Telfer Road,
Radford, Coventry CV6 3DS. Tel: Coventry 598378
Coach: Damian Morgan
Club captain (1988–89): Ian Croston
Club captain (1989–90): Tim Williams
No. of teams: Senior 2
Directions to ground: Along Coundon Road from city
centre to 'Nugget Public House'. First left, ground at
bottom of hill
Ground capacity: Standing 200
Clubhouse facilities: Sports and social club
Club colours: Red and black hoops, black shorts.
(*Change colours:* Amber and red hoops)
Nickname: Cov Post
Floodlights: Yes (training only)
Membership fees: Full £17.50
Local newspaper: Coventry Evening Telegraph
League: Warwick 3
League position (1988–89): 6th
League playing record (1988–89): P 31, W 11, D 0,
L 20, F 251, A 400

COVENTRY TECHNICAL

Charter Avenue, Canley, Coventry. Tel: 0203 471733
Founded: 1929
President: Robin Riddle
Chairman: Lee Sutton
Secretary: Neil Franklin, 42 Haynestone Road,

Coundon, Coventry CV6 1GJ. Tel: 0203 335560 (H),
668706 (W)
Fixtures Secretary: Brian Sibley, 4 Kimberley Close,
Eastern Green, Coventry CV5 7GL
Press Officer: As Secretary
Coach: Paul Hyslop
Club captain (1988–89): Kevin Prout
Club captain (1989–90): Steve Radford
No. of teams: Senior 2
Clubhouse facilities: Open matchdays and training
evenings
Club colours: Green/yellow/brown hoops. (*Change
colours:* Dark green)
Floodlights: No
League: Warwick 3
League position (1988–89): Bottom
League playing record (1988–89): P 10, W 0, D 0,
L 10, F 42, A 228

PINLEY

The Croft, Wyken, Coventry
Founded: 1950
President: J. Evans
Chairman: T. O'Neil
Secretary: P. Williams, 26 Ferndale Road, Binley
Woods, Coventry CV3 2BG
Fixtures Secretary: J. Brady, 79 Austin Road,
Coventry
Club captain (1988–89): A. Smith
Club captain (1989–90): M. Meade
No. of teams: Senior 3
Directions to ground: The Croft, off Anstey Road
Club colours: Black/red. (*Change colours:* Red)
Floodlights: No
Membership fees: Playing £12, Social £6
League: Warks 2
League position (1988–89): 10th
League playing record (1988–89): P 10, W 2, D 0,
L 8, F 71, A 188

RUGBY WELSH

Alwyn Road, Bilton Council Ground. Tel: 0788
565605
Founded: 1936
President: J. Williams
Chairman: Roy Davies
Secretary: P.J. O'Neill, 66 Wolsey Road, Rugby
CV22 6LW. Tel: 0788 815677 (H), 0203 257372 (W)
Fixtures Secretary: Robin Woerner, 63 Adkinson
Avenue, Dunchurch, Nr. Rugby, Warks CV22 6RQ.
Tel: 0788 811723
Club captain (1988–89): Vincent Ogg
Club captain (1989–90): Liam Price
League: Warwick 3
League playing record (1988–89): P 7, W 5, D 0, L 2

SHIPSTON-ON-STOUR

Mayo Road, Shipston-on-Stour, Warks. Tel: 0608
62107
Founded: 1963
President: Dr. Williams
Chairman: D. Leeson
Secretary: T. Carr, Top Farm, Froglands Lane,
Cleeve Prior, Evesham, Worcs. Tel: 0789 778051 (H),
0666 502641 (W)
Fixtures Secretary: R. Hawkins, Washbrooke,
Ilmington, Shipston-on-Stour, Warks. Tel: Ilmington
216
Club captain (1988–89): R. Flatter
Club captain (1989–90): P. Morris
No. of teams: Senior 3, Youth 1
Club colours: Black. (*Change colours:* Yellow)
Floodlights: No
Membership fees: Full £5, Playing £5
League: Mids Warks 3
League position (1988–89): 4th
League playing record (1988–89): P 9, W 6, D 1, L 2,
F 207, A 77

SHOTTERY

Shottery Field, Stratford-upon-Avon High School,
Alcester Road, Stratford-upon-Avon
President: Clive Hicks
Chairman: Grenville Evans
Secretary: Derek Bowdery, 18 St. Martins Close,
Stratford-upon-Avon, Warwickshire CV37 9W. Tel:
0789 66158 (H), 0926 495321 ext. 4183 (W)
Fixtures Secretary: Andy Fairbrother, 85 Lodge
Road, Stratford-upon-Avon, Warwickshire CV37
9DN. Tel: 0789 67721
Press Officer: As Secretary
Coach: Paul McCoy
Club captain (1988–89): Malcolm Cowell
Club captain (1989–90): Malcolm Cowell
No. of teams: Senior 2
Clubhouse facilities: The Sportsman P.H., Bull Street
Club colours: St. Andrews blue shirts, white shorts,
blue socks. (*Change colours:* Dark blue with gold
hoop)
Floodlights: No
Membership fees: Playing £15, Social £5, Youth £10,
Student £10
Local newspapers: Stratford-upon-Avon Herald,
Stratford Journal
League: Warwicks 3
League position (1988–89): 8th
League playing record (1988–89): P 8, W 2, D 0, L 6,
F 63, A 126

STANDARD

Tile Hill Lane, Canley, Coventry. Tel: 0203 75186.
Founded: 1931
Secretary: P.J. James, 27 Coniston Road, Coventry.
Tel: 0203 77054.
League: Warwicks 3

WARWICK

Hampton Road, Warwick. Tel: 0926 491569
Founded: 1976
President: Bryn Brewster
Chairman: C. Hollins
Secretary: C. Hood
Fixtures Secretary: R. Walters
Press Officer: J. Hough
Coach: C. Hollins
Club captain (1988–89): R. Walters
Club captain (1989–90): D. Halford
No. of teams: Senior 3
Clubhouse facilities: Full
Club colours: Purple/black. (*Change colours:* Black)
Floodlights: No
Membership fees: T.B.A.
League: Mids Warks 3
League position (1988–89): 5th
League playing record (1988–89): P 9, W 5, D 0, L 4,
F 142, A 83

*Action from Harbury's Silver Jubilee match. Notice Martin Green, the former England
coach in the background behind the maul*

NORTH MIDLANDS LEAGUES

THIS past season the North Midands Leagues were increased to 46 teams playing in four divisions and there were some outstanding performances led by Camp Hill, who although losing one match comfortably won the top division and go up to Midlands 2 West. Malvern (promoted in 1988) go down with Old Halesonians and their places go to Aston Old Edwardians (winners of all their 10 Division 2 games) and Ludlow.

West Midlands Police and Veseyans (both promoted in 1987–88) ascend together once again – this time to Division 2 – and they take the places of Bournville and Edwardian, whilst the bottom two Division 3 clubs Kynoch and Ledbury make way for Tenbury and Birchfield, both of whom won 11 of their dozen matches. Edwardian go down for a second successive season, but the competition has generally been good and even Bewdley – right at the bottom of Division 4 – managed one victory.

NORTH MIDLANDS OFFICIAL:

Eric Young,
106 Malvern Road,
Headless Cross,
Redditch,   (H) 0527 42292
Worcs. B97 5DP   (B) 0562 515560

NORTH MIDLANDS LEAGUE TABLES
1987–88/1988–89

TABLES 1987–88

NORTH MIDLANDS 1

	P	W	D	L	F	A	PTS
O Yardleians	10	9	1	0	143	67	19
Whitchurch	10	7	0	3	118	75	14
Kidd'rm'ter	10	6	0	4	135	93	12
Kings Norton	10	6	0	4	124	100	12
Newport	10	5	0	5	144	90	10
Camp Hill	9	5	0	4	111	74	10
Bridgnorth	10	4	1	5	115	99	9
O Halesonians	9	4	1	4	69	112	9
Luctonians	10	3	9	7	80	95	9
Erdington	10	2	1	7	83	144	5
Edwardians	10	1	0	9	34	207	2

NORTH MIDLANDS 2

	P	W	D	L	F	A	PTS
Shrewsbury	10	8	0	2	221	63	16
Malvern	10	7	1	2	143	70	15
Ludlow	10	6	1	3	152	77	13
Woodrush	10	6	0	4	110	85	12
Aston OE	10	5	1	4	138	119	11
Droitwich	10	5	1	4	110	85	11
Telford	10	4	1	5	74	90	9
Pershore	10	4	1	5	80	137	9
Bourneville	10	3	0	7	63	132	6
O Saltleians	10	2	0	8	52	153	4
O Centrals	10	2	0	8	55	187	2

TABLES 1988–89

NORTH MIDLANDS 1

	P	W	D	L	F	A	PTS
Camp Hill	10	9	0	1	216	78	18
Kings Norton	10	7	1	2	153	52	15
Newport	10	7	1	2	124	78	15
Luctonians	10	5	2	3	100	97	12
Shrewsbury	10	4	2	4	117	105	10
Evesham	10	5	0	5	84	135	10
Whitchurch	10	4	1	5	119	120	9
Kidderminster	10	4	1	5	77	105	9
Bridgnorth	10	2	1	7	68	106	5
O Halesonians	10	1	2	7	73	168	4
Malvern	10	1	1	8	97	186	3

NORTH MIDLANDS 2

	P	W	D	L	F	A	PTS
Aston OE	10	10	0	0	258	66	20
Ludlow	10	8	0	2	169	75	16
Woodrush	10	8	0	2	159	81	16
Droitwich	10	6	0	4	147	123	12
Selly Oak	10	6	0	4	120	125	12
Telford	10	5	0	5	123	107	10
Pershore	10	4	0	6	83	130	8
Five Ways	10	4	0	6	84	144	8
Erdington	10	1	1	8	100	132	3
Bournville	10	1	1	8	76	175	3
Edwardian	10	1	0	9	67	228	2

NORTH MIDLANDS 3

	P	W	D	L	F	A	PTS
New Ash Green	10	10	0	0	254	50	20
Five Ways OE	10	9	0	1	172	77	18
B'ham C'Off	9	7	0	2	188	89	14
Old Griffinians	8	6	0	2	117	66	12
B'ham Welsh	9	5	0	4	100	150	10
Warley	9	4	0	5	137	85	8
Redditch	10	4	0	6	110	115	8
Kynoch	10	3	0	7	100	166	6
Ledbury	10	2	1	7	117	227	5
Yardley & Dist	10	1	1	8	78	197	3
Old Moseleian	10	0	0	10	61	212	0

NORTH MIDLANDS 4

	P	W	D	L	F	A	PTS
W Mids Police	9	9	0	0	329	49	18
Veseyians	9	8	0	1	280	53	16
Birchfield	9	6	0	3	165	110	12
Upton	9	6	0	3	98	87	12
Bromyard	9	4	1	4	106	90	9
Tenbury	9	3	1	5	81	190	7
Witton	9	2	0	7	71	158	4
Bewdley	9	2	0	6	28	209	4
B'ham Civ Ser	9	2	0	7	49	159	4
Ross-on-Wye	9	1	0	7	62	164	2

NORTH MIDLANDS 3

	P	W	D	L	F	A	PTS
W Midlands Pol	10	9	0	1	278	67	18
Veseyans	10	8	1	1	228	64	17
Redditch	10	7	0	3	139	93	14
O Centrals	10	5	0	5	121	129	10
O Griffinians	10	5	0	5	107	185	10
Birm City	10	4	1	5	222	125	9
Warley	10	4	0	6	96	125	8
O Saltleians	10	4	0	6	119	153	8
Birm Welsh	10	3	1	6	122	181	7
Kynoch	10	2	1	7	89	216	5
Ledbury	10	2	0	8	47	230	4

NORTH MIDLANDS 4

	P	W	D	L	F	A	PTS
Tenbury	12	11	0	1	284	72	22
Birchfield	12	11	0	1	310	104	22
Oswestry	12	9	0	3	210	124	18
Market Dray	12	7	1	4	149	93	15
Yardley & Dist	12	7	0	5	202	111	14
Upton-on-Sev	12	7	0	5	158	152	14
Bromyard	12	7	0	5	122	210	14
O Moselians	12	5	0	7	141	167	10
Birm'ham CS	12	4	1	7	125	216	9
Ross-on-Wye	12	4	0	8	111	158	8
Witton	12	3	0	9	111	214	6
Thimblemill	12	1	0	11	76	162	2
Bewdley	12	1	0	11	80	296	2

Hereford win the Pilkington Cup battle of the underdogs in Round Three – 10–6 against Tynedale

MIDLANDS DIVISION FIXTURES 1989/90

NORTH MIDLANDS ONE

Sat. 9th September (Week 2)
Evesham v Newport
Worcester v Kings Norton
Luctonian v Kidderminster
Whitchurch v Ludlow
Bridgnorth v Aston Old Edwardians

Sat. 23rd September (Week 4)
Aston Old Edwardians v Evesham
Kings Norton v Bridgnorth
Kidderminster v Worcester
Ludlowv Luctonian
Shrewsbury v Whitchurch

Sat. 14th October (Week 6)
Evesham v Kings Norton
Newport v Aston Old Edwardians
Luctonian v Shrewsbury
Worcester v Ludlow
Bridgnorth v Kidderminster

Sat. 28th October (Week 8)
Kings Norton v Newport
Ludlow v Bridgnorth
Shrewsbury v Worcester
Whitchurch v Luctonian
Kidderminster v Evesham

Sat. 11th November (Week 10)
Evesham v Ludlow
Newport v Kidderminster
Aston Old Edwardians v Kings Norton
Worcester v Whitchurch
Bridgnorth v Shrewsbury

Sat 18th November (Week 11)
Kidderminster v Aston Old Edwardians
Ludlow v Newport
Shrewsbury v Evesham
Whitchurch v Bridgnorth
Luctonian v Worcester

Sat. 25th November (Week 12)
Evesham v Whitchurch
Newport v Shrewsbury
Aston Old Edwardians v Ludlow
Kings Norton v Kidderminster
Bridgnorth v Luctonian

Sat. 13th January (Week 18)
Ludlow v Kings Norton
Shrewsbury v Aston Old Edwardians
Whitchurch v Newport
Luctonian v Evesham
Worcester v Bridgnorth

Sat. 10th March (Week 26)
Evesham v Worcester
Newport v Luctonian
Aston Old Edwardians v Whitchurch
Kings Norton v Shrewsbury
Kidderminster v Ludlow

Sat. 31st March (Week X7)
Shrewsbury v Kidderminster
Whitchurch v Kings Norton
Luctonian v Aston Old Edwardians
Worcester v Newport
Bridgnorth v Evesham

Sat. 28th April (Week 32)
Newport v Bridgnorth
Aston Old Edwardians v Worcester
Kings Norton v Luctonian
Kidderminster v Whitchurch
Ludlow v Shrewsbury

MIDLANDS DIVISION FIXTURES 1989/90

NORTH MIDLANDS TWO

Sat. 9th September (Week 2)
Telford v Malvern
Selly Oak v Pershore
Woodrush v Old Halesonians
Five Ways v Veseyans
Erdington v West Midlands Police

Sat. 23rd September (Week 4)
Pershore v Telford
Old Halesonians v Selly Oak
Veseyans v Woodrush
West Midlands Police v Five Ways
Droitwich v Erdington

Sat. 14th October (Week 6)
Telford v Old Halesonians
Malvern v Pershore
Five Ways v Droitwich
Woodrush v West Midlands Police
Selly Oak v Veseyans

Sat. 28th October (Week 8)
Old Halesonians v Malvern
West Midlands Police v Selly Oak
Droitwich v Woodrush
Erdington v Five Ways
Veseyans v Telford

Sat. 11th November (Week 10)
Telford v West Midlands Police
Malvern v Veseyans
Pershore v Old Halesonians
Woodrush v Erdington
Selly Oak v Droitwich

Sat 18th November (Week 11)
Veseyans v Pershore
West Midlands Police v Malvern
Droitwich v Telford
Erdington v Selly Oak
Five Ways v Woodrush

Sat. 25th November (Week 12)
Telford v Erdington
Malvern v Droitwich
Pershore v West Midlands Police
Old Halesonians v Veseyans
Selly Oak v Five Ways

Sat. 13th January (Week 18)
West Midlands Police v Old Halesonians
Droitwich v Pershore
Erdington v Malvern
Five Ways v Telford
Woodrush v Selly Oak

Sat. 10th March (Week 26)
Telford v Woodrush
Malvern v Five Ways
Pershore v Erdington
Old Halesonians v Droitwich
Veseyans v West Midlands Police

Sat. 31st March (Week X7)
Droitwich v Veseyans
Erdington v Old Halesonians
Five Ways v Pershore
Woodrush v Malvern
Selly Oak v Telford

Sat. 28th April (Week 32)
Malvern v Selly Oak
Pershore v Woodrush
Old Halesonians v Five Ways
Veseyans v Erdington
West Midlands Police v Droitwich

MIDLANDS DIVISION FIXTURES 1989/90

NORTH MIDLANDS THREE

Sat. 9th September (Week 2)
B'ham City Officials v Birchfield
Tenbury v Old Saltleians
B'ham Welsh v Warley
Edwardian v Redditch
Old Centrals v Old Griffinians

Sat. 23rd September (Week 4)
Birchfield v Old Centrals
Old Saltleians v B'ham City Officials
Warley v Tenbury
Redditch v B'ham Welsh
Bourneville v Edwardian

Sat. 14th October (Week 6)
Old Centrals v Old Saltleians
Old Griffinians v Birchfield
B'ham Welsh v Bourneville
Tenbury v Redditch
B'ham City Officials v Warley

Sat. 28th October (Week 8)
Old Saltleians v Old Griffinians
Redditch v B'ham City Officials
Bourneville v Tenbury
Edwardian v B'ham Welsh
Warley v Old Centrals

Sat. 11th November (Week 10)
Old Centrals v Redditch
Old Griffinians v Warley
Birchfield v Old Saltleians
Tenbury v Edwardian
B'ham City Officials v Bourneville

Sat 18th November (Week 11)
Warley v Birchfield
Redditch v Old Griffinians
Bourneville v Old Centrals
Edwardian v B'ham City Officials
B'ham Welsh v Tenbury

Sat. 25th November (Week 12)
Old Centrals v Edwardian
Old Griffinians v Bourneville
Birchfield v Redditch
Old Saltleians v Warley
B'ham City Officials v B'ham Welsh

Sat. 13th January (Week 18)
Redditch v Old Saltleians
Bourneville v Birchfield
Edwardian v Old Griffinians
B'ham Welsh v Old Centrals
Tenbury v B'ham City Officials

Sat. 10th March (Week 26)
Old Centrals v Tenbury
Old Griffinians v B'ham Welsh
Birchfield v Edwardian
Old Saltleians v Bourneville
Warley v Redditch

Sat. 31st March (Week X7)
Bourneville v Warley
Edwardian v Old Saltleians
B'ham Welsh v Birchfield
Tenbury v Old Griffinians
B'ham City Officials v Old Centrals

Sat. 28th April (Week 32)
Old Griffinians v B'ham City Officials
Birchfield v Tenbury
Old Saltleians v B'ham Welsh
Warley v Edwardian
Redditch v Bourneville

MIDLANDS DIVISION FIXTURES 1989/90

NORTH MIDLANDS FOUR

Sat. 9th September (Week 2)
Kynoch v Upton-on-Severn
Ledbury v Ross-on-Wye
Market Drayton v Bewdley
Old Moseleians v Bromyard
Oswestry v Birmingham C S
Yardley and District v Witton

Sat. 23rd September (Week 4)
Witton v Kynoch
Birmingham C S v Yardley and District
Bromyard v Oswestry
Bewdley v Old Moseleians
Ross-on-Wye v Market Drayton
Thimblemill v Ledbury

Sat. 14th October (Week 6)
Kynoch v Birmingham C S
Upton-on-Severn v Witton
Market Drayton v Thimblemill
Old Moseleians v Ross-on-Wye
Oswestry v Bewdley
Yardley and District v Bromyard

Sat. 28th October (Week 8)
Bewdley v Yardley and District
Ross-on-Wye v Oswestry
Thimblemill v Old Moseleians
Ledbury v Market Drayton
Birmingham C S v Upton-on-Severn
Bromyard v Kynoch

Sat. 11th November (Week 10)
Kynoch v Bewdley
Upton-on-Severn v Bromyard
Witton v Birmingham C S
Old Moseleians v Ledbury
Oswestry v Thimblemill
Yardley and District v Ross-on-Wye

Sat 18th November (Week 11)
Bromyard v Witton
Bewdley v Upton-on-Severn
Ross-on-Wye v Kynoch
Thimblemill v Yardley and District
Ledbury v Oswestry
Market Drayton v Old Moseleians

Sat. 25th November (Week 12)
Kynoch v Thimblemill
Upton-on-Severn v Ross-on-Wye
Witton v Bewdley
Birmingham C S v Bromyard
Oswestry v Market Drayton
Yardley and District v Ledbury

Sat. 13th January (Week 18)
Bewdley v Birmingham C S
Ross-on-Wye v Witton
Thimblemill v Upton-on-Severn
Ledbury v Kynoch
Market Drayton v Yardley and District
Old Moseleians v Oswestry

Sat. 10th February (Week 22)
Kynoch v Market Drayton
Upton-on-Severn v Ledbury
Witton v Thimblemill
Birmingham C S v Ross-on-Wye
Bromyard v Bewdley
Yardley and District v Old Moseleians

Sat. 24th February (Week 24)
Ross-on-Wye v Bromyard
Thimblemill v Birmingham C S
Ledbury v Witton
Market Drayton v Upton-on-Severn
Old Moseleians v Kynoch
Oswestry v Yardley and District

Sat. 10th March (Week 26)
Kynoch v Oswestry
Upton-on-Severn v Old Moseleians
Witton v Market Drayton
Birmingham C S v Ledbury
Bromyard v Thimblemill
Bewdley v Ross-on-Wye

Sat. 31st March (Week X7)
Thimblemill v Bewdley
Ledbury v Bromyard
Market Drayton v Birmingham C S
Old Moseleians v Witton
Oswestry v Upton-on-Severn
Yardley and District v Kynoch

Sat. 28th April (Week 32)
Upton-on-Severn v Yardley and District
Witton v Oswestry
Birmingham C S v Old Moseleians
Bromyard v Market Drayton
Bewdley v Ledbury
Ross-on-Wye v Thimblemill

ASTON OLD EDWARDIANS

Sunnybank Avenue, Perry Common, Birmingham
B44 0HP. Tel: 021 373 5746
Founded: 1889
President: Neil Gamble
Chairman: Eric Collis
Secretary: John Silverwood, 120 Brambling,
Wilnecote, Tamworth B77 5PP. Tel: 0827 282164 (H),
0922 614505/8 (W)
Fixtures Secretary: Tony Stafford, 5 Skelton Walk,
Lake View, Northampton NN3 1PU. Tel: 0604 48529
(H), 0789 764021 (W)
Press Officer: Steven Brown, 25 Castleton Road,
Great Barr, Birmingham B42 2RS. Tel: 021 360 4116
(H), 021 706 3300 ext. 2435 (W)
Coach: David Roberts
Club captain (1988–89): Gavin Cairns
Club captain (1989–90): Gavin Cairns
No. of teams: Senior 5, Youth 2
Directions to ground: Sunnybank Avenue is off
College Road A453 travelling away from Birmingham
city centre
Ground capacity: Standing 200
Clubhouse facilities: Clubhouse at ground
Club colours: Red, white and green quartered shirts,
white shorts, green socks. (*Change colours:* White
shirts)
Floodlights: No
Membership fees: Full £22.50, Playing £2.50 match,
Social £5
Programme: No. of editorial pages 4; No. of
advertising pages 8–12
Programme editor: Brian Roberts, 20 Holly Lane,
Erdington, Birmingham B24 9JS
Local newspapers: Sutton Coldfield News, Sutton
Coldfield Observer, Birmingham Post and
Birmingham Evening Mail
League: NMid 2
League position (1988–89): 1st (promoted)
League playing record (1988–89): P 10, W 10, D 0,
L 0, F 255, A 66
Competitions won: North Midlands Cup Semi-
Finalists. Greater Birmingham F.U. Club of the Year

BRIDGNORTH

"The Bull", Bridge Street, Bridgnorth. Tel: 2796.
Founded: 1962
President: E. Davies
Chairman: J. Peake
Coach: B. Greaves
Secretary: J. Peake, 48 Victoria Road, Bridgnorth.
Tel: 0746 766223 (H)
Fixtures Secretary: A. Stoll, The School House,
Vicarage Road, Penn, Wolverhampton. Tel: 0902
332025.
Press Officer: Philip Southall. Tel: 0746 765529.
Club captain (1987–88): J. Price-Jones
Club captain (1988–89): J. Price-Jones
No. of teams: Senior 4. Youth & Minis 8.
Directions to Ground: Find Bridgnorth. Find River
Severn. Club House is next to bridge over River
Severn.
Colours: Black. (*Change colours:* Green)
Membership: £30
Local newspaper: Bridgnorth Journal
League: North Midlands 1
Final position (1988–89): 9th

EVESHAM

Evesham Sports Club, Albert Road, Evesham. Tel:
0386 6469.

Secretary: J.P. Hartley, Nightingale House,
Bishampton, Pershore, Worcs WR10 2NH. Tel: 038
682 325 (H) 03805 54848 (W).
League: North Midlands 1
Final position (1988–89): 6th (bottom)

KIDDERMINSTER CAROLIANS

Marlpool Lane, Kidderminster, Worcs. Tel: 0562
740043
Founded: 1969
President: Oliver Eric Johnson
Chairman: M. Bryce
Secretary: K. Woodham, 20 Comberton Avenue,
Kidderminster. Tel: 0562 515888
Fixtures Secretary: P. Taylor, 1 Falcon Close,
Kidderminster. Tel: 0562 600615
Press Officer: Keith Weston, 62 The Deansway,
Kidderminster, Worcs. Tel: 0562 752012
Coach: A. Higley
Club captain (1988–89): Andy Stookesbury
Club captain (1989–90): John Storey
No. of teams: Senior 5, Youth 1, Minis 7
Directions to ground: Follow signs to Kidderminster
Town Centre, follow signs A442 to Bridgnorth, turn
off A442 into Marlpool Lane at Bull and Bush Public
House
Club colours: Black and gold hoops. (*Change colours:*
Gold)
Floodlights: No
Membership fees: Playing £27
Local newspaper: Kidderminster Shuttle
League: NMid 1
League position (1988–89): 5th
League playing record (1988–89): P 35, W 15, D 1,
L 20, F 497, A 584

KINGS NORTON

Ash Lane, Hopwood, Birmingham B48 7BB. Tel:
021–445 3340
Founded: 1923
President: Graham MacIver
Chairman: Roger Adams
Secretary: Dr. Stephen J. Miskin, 75 Rednal Road,
Kings Norton, Birmingham B38 8DT. Tel: 021–458
3918 (H), 0564 822642 (W)
Fixtures Secretary: Jim Williams, 44 Heaton Road,
Solihull B91 2OX. Tel: 021 705 1257 (H), 021 700
3019 (W)
Press Officer: Roger Adams, 8 Dorchester Drive,
Harborne, Birmingham B17 O5WH. Tel: 021–427
3563
Club captain (1988–89): Bob Boyd
Club captain (1989–90): Bob Boyd
No. of teams: Senior 5, Youth 3, Minis 2
Directions to ground: M42 Junction 2. M42 can be
reached from both M5 and M6. Take directions to
Birmingham on A441. Ash Lane is approx. 400 m
from roundabout on A441, first right before petrol
station. K.N. Club on left side of road
Clubhouse facilities: Open matchdays, Sundays,
Tuesdays and Thursdays
Club colours: Red and gold hooped jersey, white
shorts, red socks
Floodlights: No
Membership fees: Full £20, Playing £20, Assoc. £6,
Youth £10, Student £6, Jun. £6
Programme: No. of editorial pages 12; No. of
advertising pages 8
Programme editor: Pat Dalley, 153 Masshouse Lane,
Kings Norton, Birmingham B38
Local newspapers: Birmingham Post, Birmingham
Evening Mail, Birmingham Daily News, Choice,
Sunday Mercury
League: NMid 1
League position (1988–89): 2nd
League playing record (1988–89): P 10, W 7, D 1,
L 2, F 153, A 52

LUCTONIANS

Mortimer Park, Kingsland, Leominster. Tel: 0568 81 345
Founded: 1948
President: J. Powell
Chairman: P. Burgoyne
Secretary: Hugh Davies, Bell House, Kingsland, Leominster, Herefordshire. Tel: 0568 81 450
Fixtures Secretary: Simon Davies, 48 Wessington Drive, Victoria Park, Hereford. Tel: 0432 272 137 (H), 0594 542421 (W)
Press Officer: David Price, Bryn-y-Coed, 4 Highfield Close, Kingsland, Leominster. Tel: 0568 81 604 (H), 0568 6321 (W)
Club captain (1988–89): Simon Green-Price
Club captain (1989–90): Simon Green-Price
No. of teams: Senior 4, Youth Colts & U15
Directions to ground: Off A44 approx. 4 miles west of Leominster
Ground capacity: Standing 5000
Clubhouse facilities: Clubhouse containing changing rooms, social area and bar
Club colours: Black and white hoops. (*Change colours:* Green)
Floodlights: Yes
League: NMid 1
League position (1988–89): 4th
League playing record (1988–89): P 36, W 19, D 2, L 15

LUDLOW

Linney Fields, Ludlow, Shropshire. Tel: 0584 5762
Founded: 1933
President: Roger Evans
Chairman: Ian Smith
Secretary: Laurie Wallace, 49 Newington Way, Craven Arms, Shropshire SY8 9PU. Tel: 0588 672450 (H), 4465 (W)
Fixtures Secretary: Simon Melvin, Glebe Cottage, Old Downton Farm, Downton, Ludlow, Shropshire. Tel: 056 886 581
Press Officer: Kenny Pritchard, 9 Camp Lane, Ludlow, Shropshire. Tel: 0584 5656
Coach: Philip Norton
Club captain (1988–89): Simon Melvin
Club captain (1989–90): Andrew Jones
No. of teams: Senior 4, Youth 1
Directions to ground: Ask for recreational area below Ludlow Castle on banks of River Teme
Ground capacity: Standing 1000
Clubhouse facilities: Bar/clubroom, showers, 4 changing rooms, etc. Open match days and Tues.
Club colours: Red shirts, black shorts
Floodlights: No
Membership fees: VP Donation Non-Playing £15, Playing £15, Social £10, Youth £6, Student £6
Ground admission: Free
Programme: Free
Programme editor: As Secretary
Local newspapers: Ludlow Advertiser, Shropshire Star, Shropshire Journal
League: NMid 1
League position (1988–89): 2nd (promoted)
League playing record (1988–89): P 10, W 8, D 0, L 2, F 169, A 76
Competitions won: Whitchurch Colts Cup

NEWPORT (SALOP)

The Showground, Forton Road, Newport, Shropshire. Tel: (0952) 810021.
Founded: 1946
President: Gavin Goulson
Chairman: Christopher Cann
Coach: Michael Trumper
Secretary: David Wassell, 54 Ford Road, Newport, Shropshire. Tel: (0952) 820221 (H), (0952) 820202 (B).
Fixtures Secretary: Peter Hardy, 145 Hadlry Park Road, Leegomery, Telford. Tel: (0952) 47358 (H).
(Confirmations) David Vasilionka, 12 Norbroom Drive, Newport. (Tel: (0952) 810755 (H).
Press Officer: M.J. Pollard. Tel: 0952 820202.
Club captain (1988–89): Michael Trumper
No. of teams: Senior 4, Youth & Minis 2.
Directions to Ground: From the Town Centre take A719 Eccleshall Road, turn left (by Showground sign) just past the Ryland's Nursing Home. If approaching the club from the bypass take the A719 into Newport, turn right not far past Plough Farm Nursery.
Clubhouse: There is a good bar and ample changing.
Colours: Shirts maroon & white hoops, white shorts, plain maroon socks.
Floodlights: No
Membership: £20
Programme: We are just starting a programme this year (Editor: Richard Butter Tel: (0952) 47443 (H).
Local newspaper: Newport Advertiser
League: North Mids Division 1
Final position (1988–89): 3rd

SHREWSBURY

Sundorne Castle, Shrewsbury. Tel: 0743 53380
Founded: 1908
President: John Jones
Chairman: Chris MacDonald
Secretary: Mike Willmott, 21 Burton Street, Shrewsbury SY1 2JW. Tel: 0743 231731
Fixtures Secretary: Martin Heiron, Ashford, All Stretton Church, Stretton, Shropshire. Tel: Church Stretton 96 722509
Press Officer: John Edwards, Lower Mill Boarding Kennels, Lower Mill, Pontesford, Shrewsbury. Tel: 0743 790160
Coach: Leighton Jenkins
Club captain (1988–89): Keith Faulkner
Club captain (1989–90): Nick Fox
No. of teams: Senior 4, Youth 2, Minis 4
Directions to ground: North-east of Shrewsbury on B5062 Newport Road
Ground capacity: Standing 500
Clubhouse facilities: Bar, lounge, kitchen, changing rooms
Club colours: Navy blue/light blue hoops, blue shorts. (*Change colours:* Yes)
Floodlights: Yes
Membership fees: Full £23, Playing £23, Social £10, Youth £5, Student £11.50
Programme: No. of editorial pages 4; No. of advertising pages 16; Price 50p
Programme editor: Chris Moxon, 52 Bromley Road, Bicton Heath, Shrewsbury
Local newspapers: Shropshire Star, Shrewsbury Chronicle
League: NMid 1
League position (1988–89): 5th
League playing record (1988–89): P 10, W 4, D 2, L 4
Competitions won: Losing Finalist Shropshire Floodlit Cup

WHITCHURCH

Edgeley Park, Whitchurch, Shropshire. Tel: 0948 3316
Founded: 1936
President: Sam Eccleston
Chairman: John Briggs
Secretary: Neil Prunier, 4 Terrick Mews, Whitchurch, Shropshire SY13 4J2. Tel: 0948 5926 (H), 092575 2109 (W)
Fixtures Secretary: Paul Kaminski, 21 Kingsway, Whitchurch, Shropshire SY13 1H. Tel: 0948 2889 (W)
Press Officer: As Secretary
Coach: Jim Mostyn
Club captain (1988–89): Steve Evans
Club captain (1989–90): Neale Chesters
No. of teams: Senior 4, Youth 1, Minis 6
Directions to ground: South of Whitchurch off Grammar School
Ground capacity: Standing only

Club colours: Red shirts, white shorts. (*Change colours:* Yellow)
Floodlights: No
Membership fees: Full £21
Local newspaper: Whitchurch Herald, Shropshire Star
League: NMid 1
League playing record (1988–89): P 35, W 15, D 5, L 17, F 475, A 378

WORCESTER

Sixways, Pershore Lane, Hindlip, Worcester WR4 0AA. Tel: 0905 51173
Founded: 1871
President: Richard G. Kimberley
Chairman: L. Anthony Lee
Secretary: William John L. Best, 18 Singer Hill, Chawson, Droitwich Spa, Worcestershire. Tel: 0905 774476 (H), 723727 (W)
Fixtures Secretary: Robert Paul, 139 Liverpool Road, Ronkswood, Worcester. Tel: 0905 355565
Press Officer: T.B.A.
Coach: Philip John
Club captain (1988–89): John A.N. Wootten
Club captain (1989–90): Richard Donald Everton
No. of teams: Senior 7, Youth 2, Minis 10
Directions to ground: Junction 6 M5 on to B4538 (Droitwich) 500 yds on left
Ground capacity: Standing Unlimited
Clubhouse facilities: 8 changing rooms, two bars, lounge, etc.
Club colours: Navy blue and gold. (*Change colours:* Red and blue)
Floodlights: Yes
Membership fees: Full £12, Playing £25, Social £9, Youth £10, Student £10
Programme editor: T.B.A.
Local newspaper: Worcester Evening News
League: NMid 1
League position (1988–89): Bottom (relegated)
League playing record (1988–89): P 10, W 1, D 1, L 8
Competitions won: Evesham Sevens

NORTH MIDLANDS 2

DROITWICH

Hanbury Road, Droitwich, Worcestershire. Tel: 0905 770178
Founded: 1972
President: John Culpan
Chairman: Tony Stewart
Secretary: Mark Hodgson, 5 Corbett Street, Droitwich, Worcestershire WR9 6QT. Tel: 0905 770178 (H), 0606 593477 (W)
Fixtures Secretary: Bernard Jones, 27 Hawford Place, Droitwich, Worcestershire. Tel: 0905 772893 (H), 773691 (W)
Press Officer: David Visor, 59 May Tree Hill, Droitwich, Worcestershire. Tel: 0905 770279 (H), 778133 (W)
Club captain (1988–89): David Visor
Club captain (1989–90): Stephen Bradbury
No. of teams: Senior 4, Youth 1, Minis 1
Directions to ground: From M5 Junction 5 take A38 to Droitwich. Turn left at 1st traffic lights to Worcs Road. Left at next traffic lights to Hanbury Road (B4090)
Ground capacity: Standing 200
Clubhouse facilities: 2 bars and 4 changing rooms
Club colours: Yellow and black hoops, black shorts, black socks. (*Change colours:* Orange)
Floodlights: Yes
Membership fees: Full £22.50, Playing £22.50, Social £10, Youth £10, Student £10
Ground admission: Nil
Local newspapers: Droitwich Advertiser, Droitwich Weekly News, Droitwich Evening News
League: NMid 2

League position (1988–89): 4th
League playing record (1988–89): P 32, W 24, D 3, L 5, F 516, A 218

ERDINGTON

Birches Green Playing Fields, Kingsbury Road, Erdington, Birmingham. Tel: 021–373 7567
Founded: 1924
President: Bernard Tinney
Chairman: Ernie Lewis
Secretary: Derek Owen, 129 Bradbury Road, Solihull, West Midlands B92 8AL. Tel: 021–706 4699 (H), 0527 64252 ext. 3307 (W)
Fixtures Secretary: Keith Robinson, 5 Ullenhall Road, Walmley, Sutton Coldfield B76 8QG. Tel: 021–351 2740
Press Officer: Graham Rhodes
Coach: Larry Cahn
Club captain (1988–89): Keith Robinson
Club captain (1989–90): T.B.A.
No. of teams: Senior 4, Minis 2
Directions to ground: Follow Kingsbury Road from Junction 6 of the M6. Cross Bromford Lane, approx. mile on left
Club colours: White shirts with single blue hoop, blue shorts
Floodlights: No
Local newspapers: Birmingham Evening Mail, Sunday Mercury
League: NMid 2
League position (1988–89): 9th
League playing record (1988–89): P 10, W 1, D 1, L 8, F 100, A 132

FIVE WAYS OLD EDWARDIANS

"Masshouse", Ash Lane, Hopwood, Birmingham B48 7BD. Tel: 021–445 4909
Founded: 1892
President: A.G. Boggust
Chairman: Mike Reynolds
Secretary: R.G. Lisseter, 138 Chatsworth Road, Halesown, W. Mids B62 8TH. Tel: 021–559 6549
Fixtures Secretary: P. Hipkiss, 37 The Crescent, Cradley Heath, W. Mids. Tel: 021–550 4280
Coach: M. Collis
Club captain (1988–89): J. Woolley
Club captain (1989–90): J. Woolley
No. of teams: Senior 4
Directions to ground: Junction 2 M42, right at garage in Hopwood, end of Ash Lane
Clubhouse facilities: "Masshouse", 6 changing rooms, 2 baths, shower, large clubhouse upstairs, kitchen, committee room
Club colours: Navy blue and amber. (*Change colours:* White)
Floodlights: No
Membership fees: Full £23.50, Youth £5, Student £5
Ground admission: Nil
Local newspaper: B'ham Evening Mail
League: NMid 3
League position (1988–89): 8th
League playing record (1988–89): P 32, W 12, D 0, L 20, F 258, A 529

MALVERN

Spring Lane, Malvern, Worcs WR14 1AJ. Tel: 0684 53728
Founded: 1934
President: J. Jones
Chairman: C. Willis
Secretary: P.G. Doran, 4 Lansdowne Road, Malvern, Worcs WR14 1HY. Tel: 0684 53072 (H), 892733 (W)
Fixtures Secretary: P. Flanagan, 10 Lower Montpeller Road, W. Malvern, Worcs. Tel: 0684 566918 (H), 575018 (W)
Club captain (1988–89): M. Wolfe

Club captain (1989–90): D. Green
No. of teams: Senior 4, Youth 1
Directions to ground: A449 (Worcester to Malvern) →
traffic light turn → Pickersley Road → 2nd left →
Spring Lane → 1st right
Clubhouse facilities: Full
Club colours: Maroon/blue/gold. (*Change colours:*
Yellow)
Floodlights: Yes (training)
Membership fees: Playing £17.50, Social £10
Programme: No. of editorial pages 4; No. of
advertising pages 8; Price 50p
League: N Mids 2
League position (1988–89): 11th
League playing record (1988–89): P 10, W 1, D 1,
L 8, F 97, A 186

OLD HALESONIANS

Wassell Grove, Hagley, West Midlands. Tel: Hagley
883036
Founded: 1930
President: M. Churchill
Chairman: P. Worsley
Secretary: T. Walters, Bury's Hill, Ounty John Lane,
Stourbridge, West Mids. Tel: Hagley 882363
Fixtures Secretary: D. Cooper, 34 Hyperion Road,
Stourton, Stourbridge, W. Mids. Tel: 0384 422820
Press Officer: Simon Markey, 8 Woods Lane, Quarry
Bank, Lye
Club captain (1988–89): R. Foulds
Club captain (1989–90): K. Dubberley
No. of teams: Senior 5, Youth 2, Minis 8
Directions to ground: From Junction 3 M5 take A456
to Wassell Grove (4 miles)
Clubhouse facilities: 8 changing rooms, showers, bath,
large clubroom and members lounge
Club colours: Royal blue with gold hoop. (*Change
colours:* Red)
Floodlights: No
Membership fees: Full £22, Playing £22, Social £17,
Youth £1.50, Student £1
Local newspapers: Stourbridge News, Halesowen
News, Evening Mail, Express & Star
League: NMid 2
League position (1988–89): 10th (relegated)
League playing record (1988–89): P 10, W 1, D 2,
L 7, F 75, A 168

PERSHORE

Mill Lane, Wyre Piddle, Pershore, Worcs. Tel:
Pershore 554105
Founded: 1963
President: Christopher Askew
Chairman: Stephen Guy
Secretary: Allan Jenkinson, 12 Eltric Road, Claines,
Worcester WR3 7NU. Tel: Worc. 54346
Fixtures Secretary: Robert Bufton, 101 Cornmeadow
Lane, Claines, Worcester. Tel: Worc. 54084 (H), 0386
765200 (W)
Press Officer: Graham Askew, 13 Kilbury Drive,
Worcester. Tel: 350215
Coach: Stephen Llewwellyn
Club captain (1988–89): Charles Hemmings
Club captain (1989–90): Blair Hunter
No. of teams: Senior 4
Directions to ground: Leave M6 Junct. 6 Evesham
Road to Wyre Piddle. Turn right at Stone Cross in
village, follow lane. From Evesham take B4084 to
Wyre Piddle, turn left at Cross
Clubhouse facilities: Bar, showers, changing rooms
Club colours: Black/two scarlet hoops, black shorts,
black/red socks. (*Change colours:* Green shirts)
Nickname: Persh
Floodlights: No
Membership fees: Full £25, Playing £25, Social £5,
Youth £12.50
Local newspapers: Evesham Journal, Evesham
Admag, Worcester Evening News
League: NMid 2

League position (1988–89): 7th
League playing record (1988–89): P 36, W 20, D 1,
L 15, F 435, A 396
Competitions won: Ledbury Veterans Tournament

SELLY OAK

Moor Green Recreation Ground, Holders Lane,
Moseley, Birmingham
Founded: 1964
President: Alan Badsey
Chairman: Gary Dick
Secretary: Mark Spinner, c/o 3 Ashbrook Grove,
Stirchley, Birmingham B30 2XD. Tel: 021 471 4769
(H), 021 233 2001 (W)
Fixtures Secretary: Barry Pearce, 9 Longford Avenue,
Great Barr, Birmingham . Tel: 021 358 4442 (H), 021
360 8500 (W)
Press Officer: Dave Morland, 60 Lulworth Road, Hall
Green, Birmingham B28 8NS. Tel: 021 777 5088 (H),
021 733 1305 (W)
Club captain (1988–89): Andy McGill
Club captain (1989–90): Andy McGill
No. of teams: Senior 4–5
Directions to ground: From Edgbaston County
Ground towards Moseley. At roundabout turn right
along Russell Road, at crossroads turn right down
Moor Green Lane (opp. Reddings Road). Ground is
1st right, Holders Lane
Clubhouse facilities: None
Club colours: Blue and white 3″ hooped jersey, black
shorts, red socks. (*Change colours:* Red shirts)
Floodlights: No
Membership fees: Full £10, Playing £10
Local newspapers: Birmingham Post & Mail, Evening
Mail, Choice
League: NMid 2
League position (1988–89): 5th
League playing record (1988–89): P 10, W 6, D 0,
L 4, F 120, A 125

TELFORD

Town Park, Hinksay Road, Dawley, Telford,
Shropshire TF4 3ND. Tel: 0952 505440
President: Ken R. Reynolds
Chairman: Steven J. Carver
Secretary: Martin C. Dolphin, 10 Canonbie Lea,
Madeley, Telford, Shropshire TF7 5RL. Tel: 0952
684904 (H), 294081 (W)
Fixtures Secretary: Victor Harding, 42 Brookside,
Muxton, Telford, Shropshire TF2 8NJ. Tel: 0952
604414 (H), 754144 ext. 127 (W)
Press Officer: T.B.A.
Club captain (1988–89): Tim Garratt
Club captain (1989–90): T.B.A.
No. of teams: Senior 4, Youth 1
Directions to ground: M6–M54 Junction 4. Follow
signs to Ironbridge until Castlefields roundabout, 4th
exit towards Dawley, 4th turning off island, then 4th
road on the right. Texaco Garage on corner. Hinksay
Road ground approx mile on L.H.S.
Clubhouse facilities: Two pitches
Club colours: Shirts black and gold hoops, black
shorts. (*Change colours:* Light blue shirts)
Floodlights: No
Membership fees: Playing £20, Social £5, Youth £5,
Student £5, OAP £5, VPs £6.50
Local newspapers: Shropshire Star, Telford Journal
League: NMid 2
League position (1988–89): 6th
League playing record (1988–89): P 10, W 5, D 0,
L 5, F 123, A 107

VESEYANS

Little Hardwick Road, Streetly, Sutton Coldfield. Tel:
021 353 5388
Founded: 1928
Chairman: P.J. Laurence
Secretary: Robin Mason, 27 Bishops Road, S.

Coldfield B73 6HX. Tel: 021 354 1680 (H), 021 233 2001 (W)
Fixtures Secretary: S. Mills, 15 High Clare, Cradley Heath, Warley, W. Mids B64 7HT. Tel: 021 550 5430 (H), 0384 230497 (W)
Press Officer: David Jaffa, Bourne & Jaffa, 1 Redditch Road, Kings Norton, Burn B38 8RN. Tel: 021 459 3075
Coach: A. Lane
Club captain (1988–89): J.E.V. Ratlidge
Club captain (1989–90): K. Ward
No. of teams: Senior 4, Youth 1
Directions to ground: A34 Junc. 4
Clubhouse facilities: Full
Club colours: Black/white
Floodlights: No
League: N Mids 2
League position (1988–89): 2nd
League playing record (1988–89): P 10, W 8, D 1,1L 1, F 228, A 64

WEST MIDLANDS POLICE

Tally Ho!, Pershore Road, Edgbaston, Birmingham. Tel: 021 4723201
Founded: 1974
President: Chief Con. G. J. Dear, QPM, LLB, DC
Chairman: Ass. Chief Con. Jones
Secretary: Sup. M.G. Joiner, Chelmsley Wood Police Station, Ceolmund Crescent, Chelmsley Wood, Birmingham B37 5UB. Tel: 021–770 5381
Fixtures Secretary: D. Mason (Sgt.), 63 Scott Road, Solihull, West Midlands B92 2LQ. Tel: 021–706 7182 (H), 021–705 7611 (W)
Press Officer: As Fixtures Secretary
Coach: Insp. I. Darnel
Club captain (1988–89): DC C. Lee
Club captain (1989–90): Gary Haynes
No. of teams: Senior 3
Directions to ground: Next to the Warwickshire County Cricket ground
Clubhouse facilities: Tally Ho!. Tel: 021–472 3201
Club colours: Red top. (*Change colours:* Blue)
Floodlights: No
Local newspapers: Birmingham Post and Mail
League: NMid 3
League position (1988–89): 1st (promoted)
League playing record (1988–89): P 10, W 9, D 0, L 1, F 278, A 67
Competitions won: League Div. 3

WOODRUSH

Icknield Street, Forhill, Birmingham. Tel: 0564 822878
Founded: 1966
President: H.J. Toogood
Chairman: J.C. Johnston
Secretary: R. Caley, 75 Midhurst Road, Kings Norton, Birmingham B30 3RA. Tel: 021 458 4557 (H), 021 455 0601 (W)
Fixtures Secretary: Chris Partridge, The Beeches, Rosewood Drive, Fiery Hill Road, Barnt Green, Bromsgrove
Press Officer: Stan Edwards, 6 Tanwood Close, Callow Hill, Redditch B97 5YU. Tel: 0527 44281
Coach: Ian Smith
Club captain (1988–89): Paul Cox
Club captain (1989–90): Jeff Hughes
No. of teams: Senior 4, Youth 1
Directions to ground: Junc. 3 M42 – Follow B'ham – then Weatheroak – to X-roads. Straight over past K. Norton Golf Club on RT, up to T-junction, left, turn 1st RT into Icknield St. Entrance 200 yds on RT
Clubhouse facilities: Bar/bar lounge/changing rooms. Open Sat./Thurs. evenings
Club colours: Emerald green/white hoops
Floodlights: No
Membership fees: Full £25, Playing £25, Social £3,

Youth £1
Programme editor: S. Peace, 37 Sladepool Farm Road, Maypole, B'ham B14 5DL
Local newspapers: B'ham Evening Mail/Redditch Indicator, Bromsgrove Advertiser
League: NMid 2
League position (1988–89): 3rd
Competitions won: Loughborough 7's, Alcester 7's

BIRCHFIELD

Moor Lane, Witton, Birmingham. Tel: 021–356 2142
Founded: 1957
President: A.J.K. Murphy
Chairman: R. Booth
Secretary: John Wingate, 125 Parkfield Drive, Castle Bromwich, Birmingham B36 9TY. Tel: 021–749 2440 (H), 021–359 0221 (W)
Fixtures Secretary: Roger Booth, 151 Chester Road, Streetly, Sutton Coldfield B74 3NE. Tel: 021 353 9332
Press Officer: David Brain, c/o Secretary (as above)
Coach: David Brain
Club captain (1988–89): Alan Killarney
Club captain (1989–90): Alan Killarney
No. of teams: Senior 4
Directions to ground: A34 out of B'ham towards Walsall, turn off onto A453 (Sutton Coldfield) – this is College Road. Past Halfords Superstore, ground on right. Take next right, Moor Lane
Clubhouse facilities: Large social club
Club colours: Green and black hoops, black socks, shorts. (*Change colours:* Blue shirts)
Floodlights: No
Membership fees: Full £8, Playing £8, Social £3
Local newspapers: Sutton Observer, Birmingham Evening Mail
League: NMid 3
League position (1988–89): 2nd (promoted)
Competitions won: North Midlands Division 4 League Runners-Up

BIRMINGHAM CITY OFFICIALS

Sedeemere Road, Yardley, Birmingham 26. Tel: 021 783 2694.
Founded: 1927
Secretary: T. Dunne, 253 Church Road, Sheldon, Birmingham B26 3TH. Tel: 021 743 0109.
League: North Mids 3

BIRMINGHAM WELSH

Clock Lane, Bickenhill, West Midlands B92 0DX. Tel: 06755 2995
Founded: 1936
President: T.J. Sheen
Chairman: P.W. Gunningham
Secretary: Tony Coates, 11 Fielding Close, Sheepy Meadows, Atherstone, Warwickshire CV9 3FN. Tel: 0827 716629 (H), 0952 290029 ext. 352 (W)
Fixtures Secretary: D.H. (Tony) Thomas, 105 Summerfield Crescent, Edgbaston, Birmingham. Tel: 021 449 2471 (J. Griffiths) (H), 021 632 5881 (J. Griffiths) (W)
Press Officer: As Secretary
Coach: Tony Hockaday
Club captain (1988–89): Dean Allsop
Club captain (1989–90): T.B.A.
No. of teams: Senior 4
Directions to ground: From Junction 6 of M42 follow left-hand lane of A45 towards Birmingham 1000 yds to next roundabout. Turn left towards Bickenhill, ground 800 yds on right
Clubhouse facilities: 2 clubrooms, five changing rooms, indoor training room. Open Tuesday and Thursdays evenings, every Saturday all day and

evening and Sunday lunchtime
Club colours: Red shirts, navy shorts, red socks.
(*Change colours:* Sky blue and navy blue hoops, navy shorts, red socks)
Nickname: 'The Welsh'
Floodlights: Yes (for training area)
Membership fees: Full £20, Playing £20, Social £10, Youth £5, Student £5
Local newspapers: Sunday Mercury, Birmingham Mail, Birmingham Evening Post
League: NMid 3
League position (1988–89): 9th
League playing record (1988–89): P 10, W 3, D 1, L 6, F 122, A 181

BOURNEVILLE

The Pavillion, Heath Road, Bourneville, Birmingham B30 1HH. Tel: 021–458 1711
Founded: 1909
President: Steven George Foley
Chairman: Bill Joyner
Secretary: Steve Hinton, 94 Foredraft Close, Woodgate Valley, Birmingham B30. Tel: 021–421 2676 (H), 021–458 2000 ext. 3230 (W)
Fixtures Secretary: Colin Champken, 94 Wharf Road, Kings Norton, Birmingham B30 3LP. Tel: 021–459 3700
Press Officer: Ian Smith, 97 Quinton Road, Quinton, Birmingham B32. Tel: 021–421 7110
Coach: Barry Richards
Club captain (1988–89): Geoff Bailey
Club captain (1989–90): Steve McMeekan
No. of teams: Senior 4, Youth 1
Directions to ground: To Birmingham, take Bristol Road South, turn off at Bourneville Lane. Playing fields on right 500 yds
Clubhouse facilities: Changing and bar. Banks Brewery
Club colours: Maroon/blue/gold. (*Change colours:* Yellow/white)
Floodlights: No
Membership fees: Full £20, Youth £10, Student £10
League: NMid 3
League position (1988–89): 10th (relegated)
League playing record (1988–89): P 10, W 1, D 1, L 8, F 76, A 175

EDWARDIANS

'The Memorial Ground', Streetsbrook Road, Solihull, West Midlands. Tel: 021–744 6831
Founded: 1882
President: Michael Allport
Secretary: Geoffrey Kearney, 238 Olton Boulevard West, Alcocks Green, Birmingham B11 3HE. Tel: 021 765 4258 (H), 021 357 8282 (W)
Fixtures Secretary: J.G. 'Jim' Bayliss, 48 Westbourne Road, Olton, Solihull. Tel: 021–706 2482
Club captain (1988–89): Paul Stephen Carroll
Club captain (1989–90): John Kelly
No. of teams: Senior 3, Youth U16 & U15
Directions to ground: From M5/M6 follow M42 from either to Junction 3 (Henley/Stratford-upon-Avon/B'ham). Follow A34 signs towards Shirley for approx. 2 miles, turn right at major junction Olton Road. Follow Olton Road to ground
Clubhouse facilities: Changing accommodation, bar, pool table
Club colours: Old gold, claret, navy
Floodlights: Yes
Membership fees: Playing £25, Social £10, Youth £5, Student £10
League: NMid 3
League position (1988–89): Bottom (relegated)
League playing record (1988–89): P 10, W 1, D 0, L 9

OLD CENTRALS

Bourne Vale, Little Hardwick Road, Aldridge, West Mids. Tel: 021 353 2856
Founded: 1913
President: C. Fullard
Chairman: M. Toone
Secretary: M. Harris, 32 Barker Road, Sutton Coldfield, West Mids B74 2NZ
Fixtures Secretary: M. Halloran, 86 Eastern Road, Sutton Coldfield. Tel: 021 355 3770
Coach: M. Chambers
Club captain (1988–89): W. Ward
Club captain (1989–90): W. Ward
No. of teams: Senior 4, Youth & Minis 1
Club colours: Maroon/green/gold
Nickname: C's
Floodlights: Yes
Membership fees: Full £15
League: WMids 3

OLD GRIFFINIANS

Walker Heath Playing Fields, Walker Heath Road, Kings Norton. Tel: 021 458 2408
President: E. FIdgeon
Chairman: A. Scragg
Secretary: T. Burrows, 4 Norman Road, Northfield, Birmingham. Tel: 021 9777295 (H), 7066047 (W)
Fixtures Secretary: M. Langdell, 8 Rectory Road, Northfield, Birmingham. Tel: 021 9758651
Press Officer: As Secretary
Club captain (1988–89): I. James
Club captain (1989–90): P. Weston
No. of teams: Senior 3
Directions to ground: From Kings Norton Green, follow signs for Walkers Heath, R at 1st island and 1st right to playing fields
Ground capacity: Standing 1000
Clubhouse facilities: Full
Club colours: Black. (*Change colours:* Red)
Floodlights: No
Membership fees: Playing £15, Social £7
League: N Mids 3
League position (1988–89): 5th
League playing record (1988–89): P 10, W 5, D 0, L 5, F 107, A 185

OLD SALTLEIANS

Watton Lane, Water Orton, Nr. Birmingham. Tel: 021 748 3380
Founded: 1933
President: Julian Harradence
Secretary: Robert Heighway, 'Amberley', Vicarage Hill, Tanworth in Arden B94 5EA. Tel: 05644 2262 (H), 0905 613191 (W)
Fixtures Secretary: Geoff Phipps, 254 Orphanage Road, Wylde Green, Birmingham B24 0BE. Tel: 021 350 5204
Press Officer: Richard English, 14 The Riddings, Walmley, Sutton Coldfield B76 8RW. Tel: 021 351 2924
Club captain (1988–89): Philip Brugger
Club captain (1989–90): Philip Brugger
No. of teams: Senior 5, Youth 2, Minis 5
Directions to ground: Adjacent M42 at Coleshill. Off A446 turn into Watton Lane, ground at junction of Gilson Road and Watton Lane, Water Orton
Clubhouse facilities: 4 changing rooms, baths, showers, clubroom, lounge, bar, kitchen and stores
Club colours: Red and yellow hoops, blue shorts. (*Change colours:* Green or blue jerseys)
Floodlights: Yes
League: NMid 3
League position (1988–89): 8th
League playing record (1988–89): P 10, W 4, D 0, L 6, F 119, A 153

REDDITCH

Bromsgrove Road, Redditch, Worcs. Tel: 0527 62807
Founded: 1966
President: Archie Moore
Chairman: Russell Johnston
Secretary: Bryn Richards, 29 Ladbrook Close,
Oakenshaw, Redditch B98 7XR. Tel: 0527 42870
Fixtures Secretary: Roger Rees, 2 Wain Close,
Captain's Hill, Alcester, Warwickshire. Tel: 764188
Press Officer: Mack Mason, 4 Morgan Close, Studley,
Warwicks B80 7PB. Tel: 852827
Coach: Noel Pritchard
Club captain (1988–89): Dai Davies
Club captain (1989–90): Jimmy Griffin
No. of teams: Senior 5, Youth 2, Minis 1
Directions to ground: From dual carriageway (A448)
to bridge over carriageway (B4184). Follow Webheath
sign, after Foxlidiate Hotel take 1st left into
Bromsgrove Road (formerly Red Lane). Club is 4th
turning on left
Clubhouse facilities: Evenings and weekends
Club colours: Dark/light blue quarters, blue shorts
and socks. (*Change colours:* Light blue shirts, dark
blue shorts, socks)
Nickname: Kingfishers
Floodlights: No
Membership fees: Playing £20, Social £5
Local newspapers: Redditch Advertiser, Birmingham
Post & Mail
League: NMid 3
League position (1988–89): 3rd
League playing record (1988–89): P 10, W 7, D 0,
L 3, F 142, A 89

TENBURY

Palmers Meadow, Tenbury Wells. H.Q.: c/o The
Sports Club, Worcester Road, Tenbury Wells, Worcs.
Tel: 0584 810456
Founded: 1958
President: John Thomas
Chairman: David James
Secretary: Roger Bowkett, c/o Bowketts (Tenbury)
Ltd., Bromyard Road, Tenbury Wells, Worcs WR15
8DE. Tel: 0584 810351
Fixtures Secretary: Simon Waite, The Cottage, 51
Teme Street, Tenbury Wells, Worcs WR15 8AE. Tel:
0584 811809/810241
Press Officer: As Secretary
Coach: Frank Kitchen
Club captain (1988–89): Patrick James
Club captain (1989–90): Patrick James
No. of teams: Senior 2, Youth 1
Burford (signposted) R.H.S. large building, Hospital,
immediately past, **Directions to ground:** Along A456
from Kidderminster/Worcester, enter next building,
Tenbury Sports Club, Penlu. Sign on Oak Tree.
Change here
Ground capacity: Standing 400–500
Clubhouse facilities: Shared clubhouse with Hockey
Club
Club colours: Green and black squares 1st XV. Green
and black hoops 2nd XV
Floodlights: No
Membership fees: Full £15, Playing £15, Social £5,
Youth £4
Programme: No. of editorial pages 2–5; No. of
advertising pages 4; Price 50p
Programme editor: As Secretary
Local newspapers: Tenbury Advertiser, Berrows News
Worcester
League: NMid 3
League position (1988–89): 1st
League playing record (1988–89): P 12, W 11, D 0,
L 1, F 284, A 72
Competitions won: North Midlands Courage League
Division 4 Winners

WARLEY

Smethwick Cricket Club, Broomfield, Smethwick,
Warley, West Midlands. Tel: 021 558 0084
Founded: 1972
President: Les T. Barnfield
Chairman: Kevin Jordan
Secretary: Peter Jordan, 7 Station Drive, West
Hagley, Worcs DY9 0NX. Tel: 0562 882176 (H), 021
429 6417 (W)
Fixtures Secretary: Peter Davies, 60 Park Road,
Bearwood, Warley, West Midlands. Tel: 021 420 3141
Press Officer: Mick Hancox, 36 Marlborough Road,
Smethwick, Warley, M. Midlands. Tel: 021 429 6647
Coach: Bill Mattocks
Club captain (1988–89): I. Moss
Club captain (1989–90): D. Poole
No. of teams: Senior 4, Youth 1
Clubhouse facilities: Yes
Club colours: Red and white hoops. (*Change colours:*
Blue)
Floodlights: No
Membership fees: Playing £18
League: NMid 3
League position (1988–89): 7th
League playing record (1988–89): P 10, W 4, D 0,
L 6, F 96, A 124

NORTH MIDLANDS 4

BEWDLEY & STOURPORT

'The Rugby Pitch', Walshes Meadow, Stourport-on-
Severn, Worcs
Founded: 198?
President: Colm O'Rouke
Chairman: Glyn McAdam
Secretary: Andrew James Napier, 33 St. John's
Avenue, Kidderminster, Worcs DY11 6AU. Tel: 0562
822717 (H), 021–456 1144 ext. 226 (W)
Fixtures Secretary: Andy Foster, 'Lime Kilns',
Pensax, Worcs WR6 6XM. Tel: 0299 896631
Press Officer: As Secretary
Club captain (1988–89): Steve Owen
Club captain (1989–90): Steve Owen
No. of teams: Senior 2
Directions to ground: From Kidderminster go through
Stourport (taking the Great Witley Road) and take
the first proper turning on left marked Swimming
Pool/Sports Centre. Rugby pitch visible from car park
Clubhouse facilities: Use of Stourport Boat Club and
Stourport Cricket Club
Club colours: Navy blue with yellow 'V'. (*Change
colours:* Yellow with navy blue 'V')
Floodlights: No
Membership fees: Playing £15, Social £5, OAP £2.50
Local newspapers: Kidderminster Shuttle,
Kidderminster Chronicle, Severn Source
League: NMid 4
League playing record (1988–89): P 30, W 11, D 0,
L 19

BIRMINGHAM CIVIL SERVICE

Old Damson Lane, Solihull, West Mids. Tel: 021 779
2136
Founded: 1928
President: Jack Tempest
Chairman: Brian Cole
Secretary: Martin Corfield, 151 Tilehouse Green
Lane, Knowle, Solihull, West Mids B93 9EN. Tel:
0564 773852 (H), 021 233 3401 (W)
Fixtures Secretary: W. Pratt, 3 Warmington Road,
Hollywood, Birmingham B47 5PE. Tel: 0564 822401
Press Officer: Neil Smith, 65 Maywell Drive, Solihull,

West Mids. Tel: 021–705 7983 (H), 021–233 2160 (W)
Coach: David Green
Club captain (1988–89): Mark Howard
Club captain (1989–90): Coleman Flaherty
No. of teams: Senior 4, Youth 1
Directions to ground: Just off Coventry Road (A45) opposite Birmingham International Airport
Clubhouse facilities: Sports club. 2 pitches, training room
Club colours: Red, 1 white hoop jerseys, navy blue shorts
Nickname: Civil Service
Floodlights: No
Membership fees: Full £16, Playing £2.50, Social £8, Youth £8, Student £8, OAP £8
Local newspapers: Solihull Times, Solihull News
League: NMid 4
League position (1988–89): 9th
League playing record (1988–89): P 12, W 4, D 1, L 7, F 125, A 216

BROMYARD

c/o Bromyard Cricket Club. Tel: 0885 488152
Founded: 1981
President: Geraint Williams
Chairman: David W. James
Secretary: Graeme Charters
Fixtures Secretary: Donald A. Wilson. Tel: 08855 232
Coach: D. Redpath
Club captain (1988–89): Ian Ridley
Club captain (1989–90): Andrew Morris
No. of teams: Senior 2
Directions to ground: A465 out of Bromyard to Hereford. Ground is one mile on the right
Clubhouse facilities: Cricket Club
Club colours: Green with gold band. (*Change colours:* Dark blue)
Floodlights: No
Membership fees: Full £14
Local newspaper: Hereford Times
League: NMid 4
League position (1988–89): 7th
League playing record (1988–89): P 12, W 7, D 0, L 5, F 122, A 210

KYNOCH

Holford Drive, Perry Barr, Birmingham. Tel: 021–356 4369
Founded: 1924
President: John Allen
Chairman: John Thompson
Secretary: John K. Ross, 127 Leopold Avenue, Handsworth Wood, Birmingham B20 1EX. Tel: 021 358 3277
Fixtures Secretary: Ray Jones, 11 Alpha close, Balsall Heath, Birmingham B12 9HF. Tel: 021 440 7187
Press Officer: T.B.A.
Coach: Sid Langlands
Club captain (1988–89): Dave Thompson
Club captain (1989–90): Kevin Bolger
No. of teams: Senior 4
Directions to ground: Holford Drive, off Aldridge Road (A453), Perry Barr, B'ham
Ground capacity: Standing 200
Clubhouse facilities: Part of large works sports complex
Club colours: Black and white. (*Change colours:* Red)
Nickname: Kays
Floodlights: Yes (for training and coaching)
Membership fees: Full £10, Playing £10, Social £5, Youth £5, Student £5
Ground admission: Nil
Programme: No. of editorial pages 1 (newsletter twice a season); Price Free
Programme editor: John Horlick, General Secretary, Sports Club, Perry Barr, Birmingham
Local newspaper: Sutton Coldfield Observer
League: NMid 4
League position (1988–89): 10th (relegated)

League playing record (1988–89): P 10, W 2, D 1, L 7, F 89, A 216

LEDBURY

Ross Road Playing Fields, Ledbury
Founded: 1946
President: Trevor Bethell
Chairman: Robert Chapman
Secretary: Ian Stoddart, Richmond Villa, New Street, Ledbury, Herefordshire HR8 2ED. Tel: 0531 4451 (H), 0989 62264 (W)
Fixtures Secretary: Peter Godsall, Moor Court, Stretton Grandison, Ledbury, Herefordshire. Tel: 0531 83408 (W)
Press Officer: John Teale, 34 Oatley Crescent, Ledbury, Herefordshire. Tel: 0531 5523 (H), 4121 (W)
Coach: Wyn Rogers
Club captain (1988–89): Peter Godsall
Club captain (1989–90): Robert Manning
No. of teams: Senior 3
Directions to ground: M5–M50–A417 into Ledbury, turn left after Royal Oak, past Talbot, Ring of Bells, Full Pitcher, on Ross Road out of Ledbury. Playing fields on right on town boundary past by-pass
Clubhouse facilities: Full Pitcher Public House
Club colours: Black and white. (*Change colours:* White)
Nickname: Happy Hoppers
Floodlights: No
Membership fees: Full £20, Playing £20, Youth £10, Student £10
Local newspaper: Ledbury Reporter
League: NMid 4
League position (1988–89): 11th
League playing record (1988–89): P 10, W 2, D 0, L 8, F 47, A 230
Competitions won: Bethell Trophy

MARKET DRAYTON

Greenfields Recreation Ground, Greenlands Lane, Market Drayton, Shropshire
Secretary: Alastair Cooke, 98 Longslow Road, Market Drayton, Shropshire. Tel: 0630 57861 (H)
Press Officer: Secretary
Club colours: Green/black
League: North Midlands 4
League position (1988–89): 4th
League playing record (1988–89): P 12, W 7, D 1, L 4, F 149, A 93

OLD MOSELEIANS

Lugtrout Lane, Solihull, West Midlands. Tel: 021–705 7847
Founded: 1927
President: Pat Shough
Chairman: John Barker
Secretary: John Stefani, 26 Beauchamp Road, Emscote, Warwick CV34 5NU. Tel: 0926 497275 (H), 332525 ext. 5044 (W)
Fixtures Secretary: Mick Fielding, 33 Flora Road, Haymills, Birmingham B25 8BH. Tel: 021 707 7262 (H), 7111 (W)
Press Officer: Richard Lefevre, 4 Kineton Green Road, Olton, Solihull, West Mids. Tel: 021 707 5081 (H), 2008 (W)
Coach: John Barker
Club captain (1988–89): Ugo Muin
Club captain (1989–90): Joseph Smith Jnr.
No. of teams: Senior 3
Directions to ground: A41 to Solihull bypass, signs for Catherine de Barnes, along Field Lane and at the junction of Field Lane and Lugtrout Lane is the Old Moseleians Sports Ground
Clubhouse facilities: Open match days and Sunday lunchtime, Tuesday and Thursday evenings
Club colours: Black shirts with red and white band, black shorts. (*Change colours:* Yellow shirts)

Nickname: 'Mo's'
Floodlights: No
Membership fees: Full £18, Playing £6, Social £6
Ground admission: Nil
Local newspapers: Birmingham Evening Mail, Solihull News, Sports Argus, Sunday Mercury
League: NMid 4
League position (1988–89): 7th
League playing record (1988–89): P 12, W 5, D 0, L 7, F 141, A 167

OSWESTRY

Park Hall, Oswestry. Tel: 0691 2949
Secretary: B.R. Smith, Tan-y-Craig Isa, Rhydhcroesau, Oswestry, Shropshire. Tel: 0691 170375 (H), 4411 (W)
League: North Midlands 4
League position (1988–89): 3rd
League playing record (1988–89): P 12, W 9, D 0, L 3, F 210, A 124

ROSS-ON-WYE

Station Street, Ross-on-Wye. Tel: 0989 63256.
Founded: 1873
Secretary: M. Pearce, 'Uplands', Bromsash, Ross-on-Wye, Herefordshire. Tel: 0989 981 338 (H) 0594 542 421 (W).
League: North Mids 4

THIMBLEMILL

Thimblemill Road, Smethwick, West Midlands. Tel: 021–429 2459
Chairman: Calbirth D. Reynolds
Secretary: Nigel Broadhurst, 10 Moreton Close, Harborne, Birmingham B32 2JN. Tel: 021–427 6134 (H), 021–454 3531 ext. 258 (W)
Fixtures Secretary: Richard Mewis, 156 Hutton Road, Handsworth, Birmingham. Tel: 021–356 9392
Press Officer: Ian Thomas, 35 Warwick Road, Oldbury, West Midlands. Tel: 021–422 3507
Coach: Alan Campbell
Club captain (1988–89): Keith Barbier
Club captain (1989–90): Keith Barbier
No. of teams: Senior 2
Directions to ground: M5 to Junction 3, then A456 towards Birmingham, turn left at second set of traffic lights (Bearwood High Street), then left at first set of traffic lights (Three Shire Oaks Road), then first right (Thimblemill Road), straight on over island. Club entrance 200 yds on left
Clubhouse facilities: Open seven days a week (days/evenings)
Club colours: Green. (Change colours: Blue)
Nickname: The 'Keens'
Floodlights: No
Membership fees: Full £5, Playing £2, Social £10, Youth 50p, Student 50p
Local newspapers: Birmingham Evening Mail, Birmingham Sports Argus
League: NMid 4
League position (1988–89): 12th
League playing record (1988–89): P 12, W 1, D 0, L 11, F 76, A 162

UPTON-UPON-SEVERN

Collinghurst Meadow, Old Street, Upton-upon-Severn, Worcs. Tel: 06846 4445
Founded: 1981
President: Colin Williams
Chairman: Michael Rowley
Secretary: Peter Barker, Tiltridge Farm, Upper Hook Road, Upton-upon-Severn, Worcs WR8 0SA. Tel: 06846 2906 (H), 0684 310001 (W)

Fixtures Secretary: Nigel Banwell, 16 Riverside Close, Upton-upon-Severn, Worcs WR8 0JN. Tel: 06846 2046
Press Officer: Jimmy Campbell, Shippon Cottage, Tower Croft, Bidford on Avon, Warwickshire B50 4DY. Tel: 0789 773070
Coach: Dave Beech
Club captain (1988–89): Phil Humphreys
Club captain (1989–90): Jimmy Campbell
No. of teams: Senior 2
Directions to ground: Opposite church with spire in Upton-upon-Severn
Ground capacity: Standing Unlimited
Clubhouse facilities: Shared with sports club
Club colours: Black and white quarters. (Change colours: Green)
Floodlights: No
Membership fees: Full £18, Playing £18
Local newspaper: Malvern Gazette
League: NMid 4
League position (1988–89): 5th
League playing record (1988–89): P 12, W 7, D 0, L 5, F 158, A 152

WITTON

Ansells Sports & Social Club, Aldridge Road, Birmingham. Tel: 021–356 4296
Founded: 1918
President: Ken Fisher
Chairman: Thomas Creane
Secretary: John Hood, 75 Chingford Road, Kingstanding, Birmingham B44 0BQ. Tel: 021–350 9069 (messages only), 021–359 3051 (W)
Fixtures Secretary: Paul Byrne, 9 Allmyn Drive, Streetly, Birmingham B74 2DE. Tel: 021–353 5190
Club captain (1988–89): Dale Chattaway
Club captain (1989–90): Martin Howard
No. of teams: Senior 3
Clubhouse facilities: Yes
Club colours: Yellow and black hoops
Floodlights: No
Membership fees: Full £15, Social £10
Local newspaper: Sutton & Erdington News
League: NMid 4
League position (1988–89): 11th
League playing record (1988–89): P 12, W 3, D 0, L 9, F 111, A 214

YARDLEY & DISTRICT

Tilehouse Lane, Shirley, Birmingham. Tel: 021 745 9311
Founded: 1971
President: T. Gaiger
Chairman: M. Barnes
Secretary: Joan Thornton, 45 St. Gerrard's Road, Solihull, W. Mids. Tel: 021 7042973
Fixtures Secretary: A. Finam, 61 Gleneagles Road, Yardley, Birmingham. Tel: 021 7837410 (H), 3597174 (W)
Club captain (1988–89): T. Fletcher
Club captain (1989–90): Andy Smith
No. of teams: Senior 3, Youth 1
Clubhouse facilities: Full
Club colours: Gold/royal blue. (Change colours: R. blue)
Floodlights: Yes (training)
Membership fees: Playing £30, Social £15
Programme: Starting 89–90
Programme editor: L. Winters
League: N Mids 4
League position (1988–89): 5th
League playing record (1988–89): P 12, W 7, D 0, L 5, F 202, A 111

NOTTINGHAMSHIRE, LINCOLNSHIRE AND DERBYSHIRE LEAGUES

THE THREE Counties Leagues remained with the same organisation as they had for their first season with 33 clubs in the top three divisions and a further nine teams in the Eastern Section of Division 4 with only eight in the West – a loss of one team from the previous season.

In the top division Scunthorpe were one of the clubs to win a Rugby World & Post Junior Team of the Month award (sponsored by Whitbreads) and they had an outstanding season with a single drawn match the only blot on their record. They comfortably moved on to Midlands 2 East, whilst at the foot of the table the luckless Glossop go down with two teams replacing them from Division 2 – Sleaford and Spalding, the latter going up on points difference from Market Rasen & Louth.

Boston for a second successive season descend and their replacements from Division 3 are Dronfield (winners of all their 10 matches) and Nottinghamshire Police; both clubs had suffered relegation only 12 months earlier, which proves that it pays not to be too discouraged by temporary set-backs. Gainsborough – losers of all their nine matches – are relegated from Division 3 and their Division 4 replacements are Melbourne (West) and Cleethorpes, who won seven of their East matches and drew the other.

There is room in this league organisation for another five clubs, so any ambitious local teams could do well to take a chance. Who knows where it could all end?

NOTTS, LINCS & DERBY: OFFICIAL

Bob Hubbock,
Wadena,
Main Road,
Cutthorpe,
Chesterfield,
Derbyshire   (H) 0246 278734

TABLES 1987–88

NOTTS, LINCS & DERBYS 1

	P	W	D	L	F	A	PTS
Moderns	10	9	0	1	203	40	18
Chesterfield	10	9	0	1	204	55	18
Scunthorpe	10	8	0	2	225	64	16
W Bridgford	10	6	0	4	133	72	12
Southwell	10	5	1	4	120	100	11
Workshop	10	5	0	5	76	134	10
Kesteven	10	4	0	6	48	129	8
Glossop	9	3	0	6	67	113	6
Mellish	9	2	1	6	53	116	5
Boston	10	2	0	8	58	165	4
Grimsby	10	0	0	10	41	240	0

TABLES 1988–89

NOTTS, LINCS & DERBYS 1

	P	W	D	L	F	A	PTS
Scunthorpe	10	9	1	0	218	67	19
Southwell	10	7	0	3	173	87	14
Chesterfield	10	5	1	4	134	89	11
Amber Valley	10	5	1	4	121	107	11
Mellish	10	5	1	4	98	96	11
Kesteven	10	5	0	5	91	127	10
Stamford	10	4	0	6	89	114	8
Worksop	10	3	2	5	64	96	8
West Bridgford	10	4	0	6	99	147	8
East Retford	10	3	1	6	73	146	7
Glossop	10	1	1	8	60	144	3

NOTTS, LINCS, DERBYS 2

	P	W	D	L	F	A	PTS
Amber Valley	10	8	1	1	142	43	17
E Retford	10	8	1	1	144	49	17
Market Rasen	10	7	0	3	105	85	14
Sleaford	9	6	1	2	150	52	13
Spalding	10	6	1	3	137	85	13
Keyworth	10	5	0	3	117	119	10
Casuals	10	4	0	6	80	114	8
Ilkeston	9	3	1	5	90	127	7
Nott'hamians	10	2	0	8	32	165	4
Dronfield	10	1	1	8	72	134	3
Notts Police	10	1	0	9	71	167	2

NOTTS, LINCS, DERBYS 3

	P	W	D	L	F	A	PTS
All Spartans	10	10	0	0	227	29	18
Long Eaton	10	8	0	2	202	61	16
Belper	10	8	0	2	169	55	16
Ashfield Swans	10	6	0	4	104	79	12
Boots	10	5	1	4	87	102	11
NKOB	9	4	1	4	88	93	9
Gainsboro	10	3	1	6	79	141	7
Skegness	10	3	1	6	59	142	7
Rolls-Royce	10	3	0	7	76	77	6
Bakewell	9	1	1	7	26	204	3
Bingham	10	0	1	9	21	155	1

NOTTS, LINCS, DERBYS 4 WEST

	P	W	D	L	F	A	PTS
Ashbourne	7	7	0	0	199	26	14
Hope Valley	8	6	1	1	153	31	13
Buxton	7	5	0	2	186	68	10
Melbourne	8	5	0	3	144	60	10
Leesbrook	7	4	0	3	122	71	8
East Leake	8	3	1	4	99	78	7
Tupton	8	2	0	6	36	187	4
Bolsover	7	1	0	6	47	126	2
Whitwell	8	0	0	8	7	346	0

NOTTS, LINCS, DERBYS 4 EAST

	P	W	D	L	F	A	PTS
Barton	8	7	1	0	180	29	15
Meden Vale	8	6	0	2	154	38	12
Ollerton	7	6	0	1	126	53	12
Yarborough	7	5	1	1	99	30	11
Cleethorpes	8	4	0	4	104	80	8
Rainworth	8	3	0	5	81	72	6
Harworth Coll	8	2	0	6	73	130	4
Bourne	8	1	0	7	26	243	4
Horncastle	8	0	0	8	32	200	0

NOTTS, LINCS, DERBYS 2

	P	W	D	L	F	A	PTS
Sleaford	10	7	1	2	120	63	15
E Spalding	10	6	1	3	148	96	13
Mark Rasen & Lth	10	5	3	2	110	87	13
Ilkeston	10	6	0	4	103	111	12
Nott'ham Cas	10	5	0	5	147	109	10
Nott'hamians	10	5	0	5	116	100	10
Long Eaton	9	4	1	4	88	130	10
Grimsby	10	4	1	5	116	124	9
Keyworth	9	3	2	4	67	88	9
All Spartans	10	2	2	6	87	137	6
Boston	10	1	1	8	63	120	3

NOTTS, LINCS, DERBYS 3

	P	W	D	L	F	A	PTS
Dronfield	10	10	0	0	181	57	20
Notts Police	10	8	0	2	178	78	16
Boots	10	6	1	3	114	76	13
Rolls-Royce	10	6	0	4	136	115	12
Ashbourne	10	5	0	5	111	70	10
Belper	10	5	1	4	130	78	11
Ashfield Swans	9	3	1	5	70	114	9
Barton & Dis	10	4	0	6	87	118	8
N Kesteven	10	3	0	7	86	128	6
Skegness	10	2	1	7	75	165	5
Gainsborough	9	0	0	9	57	226	0

NOTTS, LINCS, DERBYS 4 WEST

	P	W	D	L	F	A	PTS
Melbourne	7	6	0	1	189	63	12
Hope Valley	7	6	0	1	185	78	12
Bakewell M**	6	4	0	2	84	90	10
Leesbrook*	6	4	0	2	104	58	10
Buxton	7	2	0	5	101	95	4
Bolsover	6	2	0	4	39	127	4
Tupton	7	1	0	6	83	168	2
East Leake	6	1	0	5	52	158	2

* 2 points for cancelled game v Bolsover
** 2 points for cancelled game v East Leake

NOTTS, LINCS, DERBYS 4 EAST

	P	W	D	L	F	A	PTS
Cleethorpes	8	7	1	0	241	51	15
Bingham	8	7	0	1	124	40	14
Meden Vale	8	6	1	1	152	47	13
Ollerton & B	8	4	0	4	105	132	8
Yarborough Bees	8	3	0	5	76	95	6
Rainworth	8	3	0	5	103	139	6
Horncastle	8	2	0	6	56	256	4
Harworth Coll	8	1	1	6	113	121	3
Bourne	8	1	1	6	63	153	3

MIDLANDS DIVISION FIXTURES 1989/90

NOTTINGHAMSHIRE, LINCOLNSHIRE & DERBYSHIRE ONE

Sat. 9th September (Week 2)
Chesterfield v Worksop
East Retford v Southwell
Sleaford v West Bridgford
Kesteven v Spalding
Mellish v Stamford

Sat. 23rd September (Week 4)
Spalding v East Retford
Southwell v Sleaford
Stamford v Kesteven
West Bridgford v Chesterfield
Worksop v Amber Valley

Sat. 14th October (Week 6)
Amber Valley v West Bridgford
Chesterfield v Southwell
East Retford v Stamford
Sleaford v Spalding
Kesteven v Mellish

Sat. 28th October (Week 8)
Mellish v East Retford
Spalding v Chesterfield
Southwell v Amber Valley
Stamford v Sleaford
West Bridgford v Worksop

Sat. 11th November (Week 10)
Amber Valley v Spalding
Chesterfield v Stamford
East Retford v Kesteven
Sleaford v Mellish
Worksop v Southwell

Sat 18th November (Week 11)
Kesteven v Sleaford
Mellish v Chesterfield
Spalding v Worksop
Southwell v West Bridgford
Stamford v Amber Valley

Sat. 25th November (Week 12)
Amber Valley v Mellish
Chesterfield v Kesteven
Sleaford v East Retford
West Bridgford v Spalding
Worksop v Stamford

Sat. 13th January (Week 18)
East Retford v Chesterfield
Kesteven v Amber Valley
Mellish v Worksop
Spalding v Southwell
Stamford v West Bridgford

Sat. 10th March (Week 26)
Amber Valley v East Retford
Chesterfield v Sleaford
Southwell v Stamford
West Bridgford v Mellish
Worksop v Kesteven

Sat. 31st March (Week X7)
East Retford v Worksop
Sleaford v Amber Valley
Kesteven v West Bridgford
Mellish v Southwell
Stamford v Spalding

Sat. 28th April (Week 32)
Amber Valley v Chesterfield
Spalding v Mellish
Southwell v Kesteven
West Bridgford v East Retford
Worksop v Sleaford

MIDLANDS DIVISION DIVISION FIXTURES 1989/90

NOTTINGHAMSHIRE, LINCOLNSHIRE & DERBYSHIRE TWO

Sat. 9th September (Week 2)
All Spartans v Glossop
Grimsby v Long Eaton
Ilkeston v Nottinghamians
Keyworth v Market Rasen & Louth
Nottingham Casuals v Nottinghamshire Police

Sat. 23rd September (Week 4)
Long Eaton v All Spartans
Market Rasen & Louth v Ilkeston
Nottinghamians v Grimsby
Glossop v Nottingham Casuals
Nottingham Police v Dronfield

Sat. 14th October (Week 6)
All Spartans v Nottinghamians
Dronfield v Glossop
Grimsby v Market Rasen & Louth
Ilkeston v Keyworth
Nottingham Casuals v Long Eaton

Sat. 28th October (Week 8)
Keyworth v Grimsby
Long Eaton v Dronfield
Market Rasen & Louth v All Spartans
Nottinghamians v Nottingham Casuals
Glossop v Nottinghamshire Police

Sat. 11th November (Week 10)
All Spartans v Keyworth
Dronfield v Nottinghamians
Grimsby v Ilkeston
Nottingham Casuals v Market Rasen & Louth
Nottinghamshire Police v Long Eaton

Sat 18th November (Week 11)
Ilkeston v All Spartans
Keyworth v Nottingham Casuals
Long Eaton v Glossop
Market Rasen & Louth v Dronfield
Nottinghamians v Nottinghamshire Police

Sat. 25th November (Week 12)
All Spartans v Grimsby
Dronfield v Keyworth
Nottingham Casuals v Ilkeston
Glossop v Nottinghamians
Nottinghamshire Police v Market Rasen & Louth

Sat. 13th January (Week 18)
Grimsby v Nottingham Casuals
Ilkeston v Dronfield
Keyworth v Nottinghamshire Police
Market Rasen & Louth v Glossop
Nottinghamians v Long Eaton

Sat. 10th March (Week 26)
Dronfield v Grimsby
Long Eaton v Market Rasen & Louth
Nottingham Casuals v All Spartans
Glossop v Keyworth
Nottinghamshire Police v Ilkeston

Sat. 31st March (Week X7)
All Spartans v Dronfield
Grimsby v Nottinghamshire Police
Ilkeston v Glossop
Keyworth v Long Eaton
Market Rasen & Louth v Nottinghamians

Sat. 28th April (Week 32)
Dronfield v Nottingham Casuals
Long Eaton v Ilkeston
Nottinghamians v Keyworth
Glossop v Grimsby
Nottinghamshire Police v All Spartans

MIDLANDS DIVISION FIXTURES 1989/90

NOTTINGHAMSHIRE, LINCOLNSHIRE & DERBYSHIRE THREE

Sat. 9th September (Week 2)
Ashfield Swans v Skegness
Barton & District v North Kesteven
Belper v Rolls-Royce
Boots Athletic v Ashbourne
Cleethorpes v Melbourne

Sat. 23rd September (Week 4)
Ashbourne v Barton & District
North Kesteven v Belper
Melbourne v Boots Athletic
Rolls-Royce v Ashfield Swans
Skegness v Boston

Sat. 14th October (Week 6)
Ashfield Swans v North Kesteven
Barton & District v Melbourne
Belper v Ashbourne
Boots Athletic v Cleethorpes
Boston v Rolls-Royce

Sat. 28th October (Week 8)
Ashbourne v Ashfield Swans
Cleethorpes v Barton & District
North Kesteven v Boston
Melbourne v Belper
Rolls-Royce v Skegness

Sat. 11th November (Week 10)
Ashfield Swans v Melbourne
Barton & District v Boots Athletic
Belper v Cleethorpes
Boston v Ashbourne
Skegness v North Kesteven

Sat 18th November (Week 11)
Ashbourne v Skegness
Boots Athletic v Belper
Cleethorpes v Ashfield Swans
North Kesteven v Rolls-Royce
Melbourne v Boston

Sat. 25th November (Week 12)
Ashfield Swans v Boots Athletic
Belper v Barton & District
Boston v Cleethorpes
Rolls-Royce v Ashbourne
Skegness v Melbourne

Sat. 13th January (Week 18)
Ashbourne v North Kesteven
Barton & District v Ashfield Swans
Boots Athletic v Boston
Cleethorpes v Skegness
Melbourne v Rolls-Royce

Sat. 10th March (Week 26)
Ashfield Swans v Belper
Boston v Barton & District
North Kesteven v Melbourne
Rolls-Royce v Cleethorpes
Skegness v Boots Athletic

Sat. 31st March (Week X7)
Barton & District v Skegness
Belper v Boston
Boots Athletic v Rolls-Royce
Cleethorpes v North Kesteven
Melbourne v Ashbourne

Sat. 28th April (Week 32)
Ashbourne v Cleethorpes
Boston v Ashfield Swans
North Kesteven v Boots Athletic
Rolls-Royce v Barton & District
Skegness v Belper

MIDLANDS DIVISION DIVISION FIXTURES 1989/90

NOTTINGHAMSHIRE, LINCOLNSHIRE & DERBYSHIRE FOUR EAST

Sat. 9th September (Week 2)
Gainsborough v Bourne
Meden Vale v Yarborough Bees

Sat. 23rd September (Week 4)
Bourne v Bingham
Harworth Colliery v Gainsborough
Yarborough Bees v Horncastle

Sat. 14th October (Week 6)
Bingham v Harworth Colliery
Meden Vale v Ollerton & Bevercoates

Sat. 28th October (Week 8)
Bourne v Harworth Colliery
Ollerton & Bevercoates v Horncastle
Yarborough Bees v Gainsborough

Sat. 11th November (Week 10)
Bingham v Yarborough Bees
Horncastle v Meden Vale

Sat 18th November (Week 11)
Ollerton & Bevercoates v Gainsborough
Yarborough Bees v Bourne

Sat. 25th November (Week 12)
Bingham v Ollerton & Beavercoates
Gainsborough v Meden Vale
Harworth Colliery v Yarborough Bees

Sat. 13th January (Week 18)
Horncastle v Gainsborough
Meden Vale v Bingham
Ollerton & Beavercoates v Bourne

Sat. 10th March (Week 26)
Bingham v Horncastle
Bourne v Meden Vale
Harworth Colliery v Ollerton & Beavercoates

Sat. 31st March (Week X7)
Horncastle v Bourne
Meden Vale v Harworth Colliery

Sat. 28th April (Week 32)
Gainsborough v Bingham
Harworth Colliery v Horncastle
Yarborough Bees v Ollerton Beavercoates

MIDLANDS DIVISION FIXTURES 1989/90

NOTTINGHAMSHIRE, LINCOLNSHIRE & DERBYSHIRE FOUR WEST

Sat. 9th September (Week 2)
Hope Valley v Bolsover
Rainworth v Tupton

Sat. 23rd September (Week 4)
Bolsover v East Leake
Tupton v Leesbrook

Sat. 14th October (Week 6)
Buxton v Bolsover
Hope Valley v Tupton
Leesbrook v Rainworth

Sat. 28th October (Week 8)
Bolsover v Bakewell Mannerians
Rainworth v Hope Valley
Tupton v East Leake

Sat. 11th November (Week 10)
Buxton v Tupton
East Leake v Rainworth
Hope Valley v Leesbrook

Sat 18th November (Week 11)
Leesbrook v East Leake
Rainworth v Buxton
Tupton v Bakewell Mannerians

Sat. 25th November (Week 12)
Bakewell Mannerians v Rainworth
Buxton v Leesbrook
East Leake v Hope Valley

Sat. 13th January (Week 18)
Hope Valley v Buxton
Leesbrook v Bakewell Mannerians

Sat. 10th March (Week 26)
Bakewell Mannerians v Hope Valley
Bolsover v Tupton
Buxton v East Leake

Sat. 31st March (Week X7)
East Leake v Bakewell Mannerians
Rainworth v Bolsover

Sat. 28th April (Week 32)
Bakewell Mannerians v Buxton
Bolsover v Lessbrook

Long Eaton – Notts, Lincs & Derbyshire 1 get ready for battle

NOTTINGHAMSHIRE,
LINCOLNSHIRE & DERBYSHIRE 1

AMBER VALLEY

Palmer Moorwood Recreation Ground, Swanwick,
Derbyshire. Tel: 0773 605072.
Founded: 1967
Secretary: S. Fox Tel: 0246 77251(w)
Club Colours: Amber/Black
League: NLD 1
Final position (1988–89): 4th

CHESTERFIELD

Rugby Field, Sheffield Road, Stonegravels
Chesterfield. Tel: (0246) 232321
Founded: 1920
President: Trevor Pass
Secretary: Peter Ian Jackson, 396 Old Road,
Brampton, Chesterfield, S43 1QF Tel: 0246 568287
(H), 270112 (W)
Fixtures Secretary: P.D. Lourie, 35 Bankfield Road,
Hillsborough, Sheffield. Tel: 0742 342604
Club captain (1988–89): Chris McKee
Club captain (1989–90): Chris McKee
No. of teams: Senior 5, Youth 5, Minis All groups
Directions to ground: A61 from Chesterfield to
Sheffield (not new by-pass. Old A61). One mile from
town centre on left. Car park first left and first left
Ground capacity: Seating small
Clubhouse facilities: Yes
Club colours: Red white hoops, white shorts. (*Change
colours:* Black)
Floodlights: No
League: NLD 1
League position (1988–89): 3rd
League playing record (1988–89): P 10, W 5, D 1,
L 4, F 134, A 91
Competitions won: Colts Derbys Cup

EAST RETFORD

Waterford Board Ground, Ordsall Road, Retford.
Tel: 0777 703243
Founded: 1952
President: Keith Hindle
Chairman: Ron. Shuttleworth
Secretary: Mick Storey, 3 Bankside, Ordsall, Retford,
Notts DN22 7UW. Tel: 0777 707351 (H), (0427) 5571
(W)
Fixtures Secretary: Basil Dudley, 21 Southfall Close,
Ranskill, Retford, Notts. Tel: 0777 818616
Club captain (1988–89): Mick Blackburn
Club captain (1989–90): Not yet appointed
No. of teams: Senior 3
Directions to ground: Ordsall Road is the first turning
on right when approaching from Worksop
Clubhouse facilities: Bar, changing, etc
Club colours: Emerald/amber hoops. (*Change colours:*
Green)
Floodlights: No
League: NLD 1
League position (1988–89): 10th
League playing record (1988–89): P 10, W 3, D 1,
L 7, F 73, A 146

KESTEVEN

Woodnook, Nr. Grantham, Lincs. Tel: 0476 64887
Founded: 1947
President: D.G. Smith
Chairman: P.G. Woods
Secretary: N. Pert, High Street, Ropsley, Grantham.
Tel: 85352 (H), 61631 (W)
Fixtures Secretary: W. Clarke, Oasby Lodge, Oasby,
Nr. Grantham. Tel: 815352 (H), 590244 (W)
Coach: N. Goley
Club captain (1988–89): M. Thornton
Club captain (1989–90): N. Edley
No. of teams: Senior 3, Youth 1, Minis 2

Directions to ground: East Grantham B6403 off
roundabout
Clubhouse facilities: Full
Club colours: Black/white. (*Change colours:* Yellow)
Floodlights: No
Membership fees: Playing £20, Social £20, Student £10
League: N,L&D 1
League position (1988–89): 6th
League playing record (1988–89): P 10, W 5, D 0,
L 5, F 91, A 127

MELLISH

Plains Road, Mapperley, Nottingham NG3 5RT. Tel:
0602 266653
Founded: 1931
President: F. Earnshaw
Chairman: M. Albon
Secretary: P.A. Brook, 5 Grasmere Road, Beeston,
Nottingham. Tel: 0602 255553 (H), 484848, ext 2115/
2626 (W)
Fixtures Secretary: M. Fisher, 8 Lancelot Drive,
Watnak, Nottingham NG16 1JS. Tel: 0602 382933
Press Officer: M. Wrench, 1 Arndale Road,
Sherwood, Nottingham
Coach: P. Bateman
Club captain (1988–89): I. Nicholson
Club captain (1989–90): Not yet known
No. of teams: Senior 4, Youth 3
Directions to ground: On B684 north of Nottingham
Ground capacity: Seating 100, Standing 1,000
Club colours: Black/green/gold
Floodlights: Yes
Membership fees: Full £30, Playing £30, Social £2,
Youth £10, Student £5
Local newspaper: Nottingham Evening Post
League: NLD 1
League position (1988–89): 3rd
League playing record (1988–89): P 10, W 5, D 1,
L 4, F 98, A 96

SLEAFORD

East Road, Sleaford, Lincolnshire. Tel: 0529 303335
Founded: 1979
President: Michael William Laming Brown
Chairman: John Bradwell
Secretary: William Edward Golland, 15/17 Southgate,
Sleaford, Lincs NG34 7SX. Tel: 05295 228 (H), 0529
302271 (W)
Fixtures Secretary: Colin Pearson, 28 Main Street,
South Rauceby, Sleaford, Lincs. Tel: 05298 (H), 0529
302181 (W)
Coach: Colin Davies
Club captain (1988–89): Tony Weldon
Club captain (1989–90): Gess Cocker
No. of teams: Senior 3, Youth 1, Minis 1
Directions to ground: 1 mile east of Sleaford on A153
road to Skegness. Adjacent to Sleaford Eastern
By-pass.
Clubhouse facilities: Bar/shower and changing, etc
Club colours: Jersey – black and red hoops. Shorts –
black. Socks – red
Floodlights: Yes
Membership fees: Full £20, Playing £20, Social £5,
Youth £10, Student £10
Local newspaper: Sleaford Standard, Handley Street,
Sleaford, Lincs
League: NLD 2
League position (1988–89): 1st
League playing record (1988–89): P 10, W 7, D 1,
L 2, F 120, A 63

SOUTHWELL

Park Lane, Southwell, Notts. Tel: 0636 812576
Founded: 1930
President: Michael Elias
Chairman: Bruce Richmond
Secretary: Michael Jones, 31 The Ridgeway,
Farnsfield, Notts. Tel: 0623 883100 (H), 870151 (W)

Fixtures Secretary: David Tinley, Middle Hey, Oxton Hill, Oxton, Southwell, Notts. Tel: 0602 655946
Press Officer: Tony. Morris, c/o Southwell R.U.F.C., Park Lane, Southwell, Notts
Coach: Stuart Butler
Club captain (1988–89): David Hunt
Club captain (1989–90): David Hunt
No. of teams: Senior 5, Youth 4
Directions to ground: On the A612 just south of Southwell
Ground capacity: Standing 2,000
Clubhouse facilities: Bar, lounge, 4 changing rooms, bath and showers
Club colours: Maroon. (*Change colours*: Maroon/white/navy hoops)
Floodlights: Yes
Membership fees: Full £20, Playing £20, Social £5, Youth £10, Student £10, OAP £5
Ground admission: Nil
Local newspaper: Newark Advertiser
League: NLD 1
League position (1988–89): 2nd
League playing record (1988–89): P 33, W 26, D 0, L 7, F 710, A 323

SPALDING

St. Thomas's Road, Spalding, Lincs. Tel: Spalding 5191
Founded: 1923
President: Donald Beecham
Chairman: Brian Stray
Secretary: Stephen Barber, 28 The Terrace, London Road, Spalding, Lincs PE11 2TA. Tel: Spalding 2073 (H), Spalding 4261 (W)
Fixtures Secretary: David Feverhelm, The Cottage, School Lane, Bicker, Boston, Lincs. Tel: Spalding 820695
Press Officer: Brian Stray, Pinchbeck Road, Spalding, Lincs
Club captain (1988–89): Martin Beecham
Club captain (1989–90): Martin Beecham
No. of teams: Senior 3, Youth 1, Minis 1
Directions to ground: Spalding Grammar School Playing Fields, St Thomas's Road, Spalding (near to London Road)
Club colours: Maroon/navy blue hoops. (*Change colours*: Green)
Floodlights: Yes (at Sir Halley Stewart Playing Field, Winfrey Avenue, Spalding)
Membership fees: VPs £5, Playing £15, Youth £2, Student £5
Local newspapers: Lincs Free Press and Spalding Guardian
League: NLD 1
League position (1988–89): 2nd (promoted)
League playing record (1988–89): P 10, W 6, D 1, L 3, F 148, A 96
Competitions won: Promotion gained

STAMFORD

Hambleton Road, Stamford, Lincs. Tel: 0780 52180.
Founded: 1902
Secretary: A.E. Lawrence, 97 Casterton Road, Stamford. Tel: 0780 52689 (H) 0780 64387 (W).
Club colours: Purple/Black/White
League: NLD 1
Final position (1988–89): 7th

WEST BRIDGFORD

Stamford Road, West Bridgford, Nottingham. Tel: Nottingham 232506
Founded: 1939
President: Ken Grundy
Chairman: David Sutton
Secretary: Kim Howells, 117 Mount Pleasant, Keyworth, Nottingham. Tel: Plumtree 4468
Fixtures Secretary: David Pointing, 68 Mona Road, West Bridgford, Nottingham. Tel: Nottingham 821705

Press Officer: Ray Jones, 8 Castle Gardens (off Alderney Street), Castle Boul, Nottingham. Tel: Nottingham 481067 (H), Leics 625624 (W)
Coach: R. Studholme
Club captain (1988–89): Kim Howells
Club captain (1989–90): John Frankland
No. of teams: Senior 5, Youth 1
Directions to ground: From Trent Bridge follow road towards Melton Mowbray through two sets of traffic lights. Take 6th turning off to the right. Follow Stanford Road to end. Ground opposite Willow Tree Pub
Club colours: Black and red/gold stripes, black shorts and socks
Floodlights: Yes
Membership fees: Full £17.50, Social £5, Youth £5, Student £10
Local newspaper: Nottingham Evening Post
League: NLD 1
League position (1988–89): 8th
League playing record (1988–89): P 33, W 11, D 0, L 22, F 351, A 608

WORKSOP

Stubbing Meadows, Studding Lane, Worksop, Notts. Tel: 0909 484247
Founded: 1898
President: Ken Thompson
Chairman: Fred Baguley
Secretary: John H. Gibson, 3 Chatsworth Road, Worksop S81 0LQ. Tel: 0909 482439
Fixtures Secretary: Kevin Hughes, 36 Woodland Drive, Worksop, Notts. Tel: 0909 484067
Press Officer: Mark Cox, 184 Netherton Road, Worksop. Tel: 0909 473731
Coach: Alan (Jack) Billam
Club captain (1988–89): Stuart Vardy
Club captain (1989–90): Stuart Vardy
No. of teams: Senior 4 + Vets, Youth U19s, U16s
Directions to ground: Travel A57 Worksop by-pass, if travelling north look to right for rugby posts, if travelling south look to left, between roundabouts, Old Mill Pub on one, G.R. Stein Refractories on other
Ground capacity: Seating: 80 approx., Standing: Unlimited
Clubhouse facilities: Function room, lounge, meeting room, 8 changing, club room (open match day Sundays, all eves)
Club colours: Black/white hoops, black shorts, black/white hooped socks. (*Change colours*: Black/emerald hoops, blue, and white shirts)
Floodlights: No
Membership fees: Full £25, Playing £25, Social £4.50, Youth £6.25, Student £6.25, OAP Free
Ground admission: Free
Programme: No. of editorial pages 4; No. of advertising pages 4; Price 20p
Programme editor: Mark Cox, 184 Netherton Road, Worksop, Notts
Local newspapers: Worksop Trader, Worksop Guardian, Worksop Star
League: NLD 1
League position (1988–89): 8th
League playing record (1988–89): P 10, W 3, D 2, L 5, F 64, A 96
Competitions won: Retford Pub Sevens Plate, Worksop Club 7s Invitation Shield

NOTTINGHAMSHIRE, LINCOLNSHIRE & DERBYSHIRE 2

ALL SPARTANS

Sutton Lawns
Founded: 1980
Chairman: Victor Wilkes
Secretary: Graham Usher, 85 Sherwood Road, Rainworth, Mansfield, Notts. Tel: 0623 797815
Fixtures Secretary: Victor Wilkes, 87 Bancroft Lane,

Mansfield, Notts. Tel: 0623 647773
Press Officer: Neil Edson, 5 Burns Street, Mansfield,
Notts. Tel: 0623 657726
Coach: M. Revel
Club captain (1988–89): J. Higgins
Club captain (1989–90): J. Higgins
No. of teams: Senior 2
Directions to ground: Ground is on Sutton Lawn, off
Station Road, Sutton-in-Ashfield
Clubhouse facilities: Mansfield Hosiery Mills Sports &
Social Club
Club colours: Navy blue and broad amber hoop.
(*Change colours*: Blue and amber hoops)
Nickname: Spartans
Floodlights: No
Membership fees: Playing £15, Social £5
Local newspaper: Mansfield Chad
League: NLD 2
League position (1988–89): 9th
League playing record (1988–89): P 10, W 2, D 2, L 6

DRONFIELD

Gosforth School, off Carr Lane, Dronfield
Woodhouse, Nr. Sheffield. Tel: Sheffield 890931
President: Doug Dearden
Chairman: Mike Smallcross
Secretary: Bob Machin, 2 Hatton Close, Dronfield,
Woodhouse, Nr. Sheffield S18 5RW. Tel: 0246 411453
(H), 0709 522103 (W)
Fixtures Secretary: Steve Broadhead, Prospect Road,
Bradway, Sheffield S17. Tel: Sheffield 620098
Press Officer: Steve Bertram, Wentworth Road,
Dronfield Woodhouse, Nr. Sheffield. Tel: 0246 410898
Coach: Greg Colbourne
Club captain (1988–89): Carl Pass
Club captain (1989–90): Carl Pass
No. of teams: Senior 4, Youth 4, Minis 5
Club colours: Red/black hooped shirts, black shorts.
(*Change colours:* Blue shirts, black shorts)
Floodlights: No
Membership fees: Full £20, Playing £20, Social £10,
Student £1
Local newspapers: Sheffield Star, Derbyshire Times
League: NLD 2
League position (1988–89): 1st (promoted)
League playing record (1988–89): P 10, W 10, D 0,
L 0, F 181, A 57
Competitions won: NLD 2 Winners

GLOSSOP

Hargate Hill Lane, Charlesworth, Glossop,
Derbyshire
Founded: 1973
President: S. Stephens
Chairman: B. Thompson
Secretary: G. HArtman, The Salt Box, Brookbottom,
Strines, Stockport SFK12 3AY
Fixtures Secretary: G. Collyer. Tel: 0457 464553
Press Officer: B. Thompson, 11 Old Road, Tintwistle,
Hadfield via Hyde, Cheshire. Tel: 0457 44841
Coach: M. Kirkshaw
Club captain (1988–89): M. Kirkshaw
Club captain (1989–90): M. Kirkshaw
No. of teams: Senior 5, Youth 2
Directions to ground: A57 Manchester-Sheffield Road,
A627 to Marple. Ground is 1 mile on right-hand side
Clubhouse facilities: Full
Club colours: Navy/black. (*Change colours:*
Black/green)
Floodlights: No
Membership fees: Full £25, Playing £25, Social £5
League: NLD 2
League position (1988–89): 11th
League playing record (1988–89): P 10, W 1, D 1,
L 8, F 60, A 144

GRIMSBY

Springfield Road, Scartho, Grimsby, S. Humberside.
Tel: 0472 78594
Founded: 1885
President: William Boyers
Chairman: Eric Macklam
Secretary: Joe Byrom, 57 Langton Road, Holton-le-
Clay, Grimsby, S. Humberside DN36 5BA. Tel: 0472
825190 (H), 840441 (W)
Fixtures Secretary: Alistair Blair, 7 Chadwell Springs,
Waltham, Grimsby, S. Humberside. Tel: 0472 827470
Press Officer: William Boyers, 11 Summerfield
Avenue, Waltham, Grimsby, S. Humberside. Tel:
0472 822054
Coach: Alistair. Blair
Club captain (1988–89): Trevor Hunderson
Club captain (1989–90): Alan Parkin
No. of teams: Senior 3, Youth 2, Minis 1
Directions to ground: R.T. at College of Technology
into Scartho Road, roundabout take Waltham Road
600 yds R.T. into Springfield Road, 200 yds on right
Ground capacity: Standing 300–400
Clubhouse facilities: Clubhouse, bar, changing rooms,
3 pitches
Club colours: Royal blue jersey, white shorts.
(*Change colours:* Red jersey)
Floodlights: No
Membership fees: Playing £15 + VAT, Social
£7.50 + VAT, Youth £5, Student £5
Programme: No. of editorial pages 40; No. of
advertising pages 20; Price Free
Programme editor: D. Foulkes, 18 Amesbury
Avenue, Grimsby, S. Humberside
Local newspaper: Grimsby Evening Telegraph
League: NLD 2
League position (1988–89): 6th
League playing record (1988–89): P 10, W 4, D 1,
L 5, F 94, A 122

ILKESTON

Gallows Inn Field, Ilkeston. Tel: Ilkeston 323088
Founded: 1926
President: David. Cufflin
Chairman: Bill Bailey
Secretary: Ean Wykes, 8 Carman Close, Watnall,
Notts, NG16 1JX. Tel: 0602 384307 (H), 384093 (W)
Fixtures Secretary: David French, 73 Cedar Street,
Derby DE3 1GE. Tel: Derby 371275
Press Officer: Bill Bailey, 38 Derby Road, Eastwood,
Notts. Tel: 0773 768452
Club captain (1988–89): Terry Keely
Club captain (1989–90): Ian Meyrick
No. of teams: Senior 4
Directions to ground: Approach from Nottingham
Road, Ilkeston
Club colours: Emerald green and white hoops.
(*Change colours:* Red)
Nickname: The Elks
Floodlights: No
Membership fees: Full £18, Playing £18, Social £5,
Youth £5, Student £5
League: NLD 2
League position (1988–89): 4th
League playing record (1988–89): P 10, W 6, D ?,
L 4, F 103, A 111

KEYWORTH

The Pavillion, Willoughby Lane, Widmerpool, Notts.
Tel: 06077 5579
Founded: 1976
President: C. Geoffrey Brooks
Chairman: Kevin A. Price
Secretary: Joe Wolanin, 11 Mickleden Close,
Castleview, The Meadows, Nottingham NG2 1LE.
Tel: 0602 865599 (H), 865599 (W)
Fixtures Secretary: Joe Wolanin, 11 Mickleden Close,
Castleview, The Meadows, Nottingham NG2 1LE.
Tel: 0602 865599 (H), 865599 (W) (Temporary)
Press Officer: Joe Wolanin, 11 Mickleden Close,
Castleview, The Meadows, Nottingham NG2 1LE.
Tel: (0602) 865599 (H), 865599 (B) (Temporary)

Coach: Ian Hartland/Terry Baker
Club captain (1988–89): Ian Hartland
Club captain (1989–90): Ian Hartland
No. of teams: Senior 4 + Vets
Clubhouse facilities: Bar, pool table, snack bar, music. Open match days, training
Club colours: Black with 2 gold hoops, black shorts and socks. (*Change colours*: Gold with 2 black hoops or red shirts)
Floodlights: No
Membership fees: Full £20, Playing £20, Social £5, Youth £10, Student £10
Local newspapers: Nottingham Evening Post, South Notts Advertiser
League: NLD 2
League position (1988–89): 9th
League playing record (1988–89): P 9, W 3, D 2, L 4, F 67, A 88

LONG EATON

West Park, Long Eaton. Tel: 0602 460907
Founded: 1961
President: Don Mackintosh
Chairman: Michael Grant
Secretary: Stephen Bradford, 9 Elm Avenue, Long Eaton, Notts NG10 ALR. Tel: 0602 733533 (H), 691300 (W)
Fixtures Secretary: Andy Potter, 296 Bennett Street, Long Eaton, Notts. Tel: 0602 725932
Press Officer: Chris Brookes, 4 Ilkeston Road, Sandiacre, Notts.
Coach: Russ Burton
Club captain (1988–89): Peter Podboraczynski
Club captain (1989–90): Rob Beekin
No. of teams: Senior 3
Directions to ground: J25 M1/A52. Follow signs 'Long Eaton', turn right at island, straight on next island, ground mile on left
Clubhouse facilities: Open match days, Sunday lunch and Wednesday evening
Club colours: Blue shirts/black shorts. (*Change colours*: Black/white 2 in. hoops)
Floodlights: No
Membership fees: Full £15, Playing £15, Social £1
Local newspapers: Long Eaton Advertiser, Nottingham Evening Post, Derby Telegraph
League: NLD 2
League position (1988–89): 7th
League playing record (1988–89): P 36, W 16, D 2, L 18, F 483, A 548

MARKET RASEN & LOUTH

Willingham Road, Market Rasen. Tel: 0673 843162.
Founded: 1950
Secretary: B.N. Harper, Nongoby, Church Lane, Manby, Louth, Lincs LN11 8HL. Tel: 0507 82318 (H).
Club colours: Scarlet/Emerald
League: NLD 2
Final position (1988–89): 3rd

NOTTINGHAMIANS

Adbolton Lane, West Bridford, Nottinghamshire. Tel: 0602 811372
Founded: 1971 as an open club [was Old Nottinghamians]
President: David Culm
Secretary: Guy Barnes, 19 Main Street Lowdham, Notts. Tel: 0602 663847
Fixtures Secretary: G. Bareford, 8 Osborne Close, Sandiacre, Notts. Tel: 0602 391011
Press Officer: M. Ford, 62 Main Street, Asfordby, Melton Mowbray, Leicestershire. Tel: M. Mowbray 812384
Coach: Dr Barry Page
Club captain (1988–89): P. Renshaw

Club captain (1989–90): To be appointed
No. of teams: Senior 4
Directions to ground: Next to the National Water Sports Centre, Holme Pierrepont
Clubhouse facilities: Bar/committee room/lounge/ kitchen. Below changing and showers
Club colours: Purple/black/white hoops. (*Change colours*: Purple
Floodlights: No
Membership fees: Full £20, Student £15
Programme: Produced for 'special' matches only.
Programme editor: L. Darlaston, 15 Bluecoat Close, Nottingham
Local newspaper: Nottingham Evening Post
League: NLD 2
League position (1988–89): 6th
League playing record (1988–89): P 10, W 5, D 0, L 5, F 116, A 100
Competitions won: Oakham RFC Seven-a-Side Competition, April 1989

NOTTINGHAM CASUALS

Canal Side, Meadow Road, Beeston, Notts. Tel: 0602 250135
Founded: 1922
President: J.V. Grealy
Chairman: I. Lowndes
Secretary: A. Moll, 2 Egerton Drive, Stapleford, Nottingham NG9 8HE. Tel: 0602 392005
Fixtures Secretary: Danny Smith, 20 Flixton Road, Kimberley, Notts NG16 2TJ. Tel: 0602 384831
Coach: Lech Kluk
Club captain (1988–89): M. Boxshall
Club captain (1989–90): Mark Haylett
No. of teams: Senior 4
Directions to ground: Approach Beeston on A6005 from Long Eaton. Go Past Notts RFC on right, next traffic lights turn right. Follow this road until meet canal, go over canal bridge, turn left, 100 yards on right
Club colours: Maroon and white
Floodlights: Yes for training
Membership fees: £15
Local newspaper: Nottingham Evening Post
League: NLD 2
League position (1988–89): 5th
League playing record (1988–89): P 10, W 5, D 0, L 5, F 147, A 109

NOTTINGHAM CONSTABULARY

c/o Hugh Grundy, 6 Coopers Green, Wollaton, Nottingham NG8 2RP. Tel: 0602 250135
Founded: 1960
President: Chief Con. R. Hadfield
Chairman: Christopher Fox
Secretary: Hugh Grundy, 6 Coopers Green, Wollaton, Nottingham NG8 2RP. Tel: 0602 289473 (H), 672244 (W)
Fixtures Secretary: Martin Hewitt, 10 The Mount, Redhill, Nottingham NG5 8LU. Tel: 0602 204996 (H), 420999 (W)
Coach: C. Fox
Club captain (1988–89): Peter Bradshaw
Club captain (1989–90): Peter Bradshaw
No. of teams: Senior 2
Directions to ground: Take A6005 from Nottingham-Long Eaton, turn into Station Road, over Beeston Railway Bridge. Follow road to canal, take small bridge over canal, turn left, ground 100 yds on right
Clubhouse facilities: Notts Casuals RFC. Canal Side Beeston
Club colours: Black shirts and shorts, green socks. Gold collar, cuffs, numbers. (*Change colours:* Gold)
Floodlights: No
Membership fees: Full £7.50, Playing £1

Local newspaper: Nottingham Evening Post
League: NLD 2
League position (1988–89): 2nd (promoted)
League playing record (1988–89): P 10, W 8, D 0, L 2, F 178, A 78

NOTTINGHAMSHIRE, LINCOLNSHIRE & DERBYSHIRE 3

ASHBOURNE

The Recreation Ground, Ashbourne, Derbyshire
Founded: 1934
President: Fred Bates
Chairman: Paul D. King
Secretary: Stephen Jones, 34 Lambourne Avenue, Ashbourne, Derbyshire DE6 1BP. Tel: 0335 43819 (H), 43821 (W)
Fixtures Secretary: Fred Bates, 5 Spencer Close, Ashbourne, Derbyshire. Tel: 0335 43440 (H), 42701 (W)
Club captain (1988–89): Andrew Keeling
Club captain (1989–90): Andrew Keeling
No. of teams: Senior 3, Youth U19
Directions to ground: Ask anybody
Club colours: Dark blue/old gold hoops, blue shorts. (*Change colours*: Black)
Floodlights: No
Membership fees: Full £15, Playing £15, Youth £5, Student £5
Local newspaper: Ashbourne News Telegraph
League: NLD 3
League position (1988–89): 6th
League playing record (1988–89): P 32, W 13, D 0, L 19
Competitions won: Quarter final 3 Counties Cup

ASHFIELD SWANS

Ashfield School, Sutton Road, Kirkby-in-Ashfield, Notts. Tel: 0623 752314
Founded: 1972
Chairman: Ron Fazey
Secretary: Stephen Trainer, 14 King Street, Kirkby-in-Ashfield, Notts NG17 8AG. Tel: 0602 652341 ext. 231 (W)
Fixtures Secretary: Neil Johnson, 6 Searwood Avenue, Kirbby-in-Ashfield, Notts. Tel: 0623 553991 (H), 511111 ext. 206 (W)
Press Officer: Pat Orrell, 8 Elder Street, Skegby, Sutton-in-Ashfield, Notts. Tel 0623 517472
Coach: Craig Musgrove
Club captain (1988–89): Robert Sawyer
Club captain (1989–90): Robert Sawyer
No. of teams: Senior 2
Directions to ground: M1 Junction 28, join A38 to Mansfield 2nd set of lights, turn right onto Sutton road. Ground yards on your right (Ashfield School)
Club colours: Red/black hoops. (*Change colours*: Amber/black hoops)
Nickname: Swans
Floodlights: No
League: NLD 3
League position (1988–89): 7th
League playing record (1988–89): P 9, W 3, D 1, L 5, F 70, A 114

BARTON & DISTRICT

Mill Lane, Barrow-on-Humber, South Humberside
Founded: 1963
President: T. (Jack) Binks
Chairman: Perry Pounds
Secretary: D.J.C. (Jon) Bain, 'The Chimneys', Barton Road, Wrawby, Brigg, South Humberside, DN20 8SH. Tel: 0652 557861 (H), 0724 280280 ext. 2463 (W)
Fixtures Secretary: Tim P.R. Phipps, 16–18 Frances Street, Scunthorpe, South Humberside. Tel: 0652 32373 (H), 0724 847888 (W)

Press Officer: Tim Ensor. Tel: 0652 660028
Club captain (1988–89): M. Meaker
Club captain (1989–90): John Kearney
No. of teams: Senior 2, Youth 1
Directions to ground: Into Barrow from Barton-on-Humber, right at mini roundabout, next right into Mill Lane
Club colours: Red and white hoops. (*Change colours*: Black and white)
Floodlights: No
Membership: Full £20, Playing £20
League: NLD 3
League position (1988–89): 6th

BELPER

Eyes Meadow, Duffield
Founded: 1975
Chairman: Paul Melhuish
Secretary: Mike Ryan, 6 Oakwood Drive, Oakwood, Derby, DE2 2LE. Tel: 0302 665377 (H), 0602 282261 (W)
Fixtures Secretary: Roger Morgan, 1 Bone Mill Cottages, Bargate Road, Belper. Tel: 0773 826308
Press Officer: Jon Agyeman, 113 City Road, Chester Green, Derby
Coach: Paul Teager
Club captain (1988–89): Rob Parker
Club captain (1989–90): Rob Parker
No. of teams: Senior 3
Directions to ground: Take A6 to north of Derby. Follow signs for Eyes Meadow, between Building Society Headquarters and Kennings Garage. Follow signs, alongside railway
Clubhouse facilities: Duffield CC Pavilion
Club colours: Black white hooped shirts, black shorts, black socks with white/red trim. (*Change colours*: All black)
Floodlights: No
Membership fees: Full £20
Local newspapers: Belper News, Evening Telegraph
League: NLD 3
League playing record (1988–89): P 32, W 14, D 3, L 15, F 422, A 382

BOOTS ATHLETIC

Lady Bay Pavilion, Lady Bay, West Bridgford, Nottingham. Tel: 0602 822392
Founded: 1928
President: A. Bramham
Chairman: B. Richmond
Secretary: N. Sleigh, 70 Chetwynd Road, Toton, Notts. Tel: 0602 720918 (H), 592340 (W)
Fixtures Secretary: Tom Miller, 22 Promenade, Nottingham. Tel: 598053
Coach: Neil Malik
Club captain (1988–89): Trevor Sills
Club captain (1989–90): Trevor Sills
No. of teams: Senior 3
Directions to ground: Follow signs from Nottingham A52 to Grantham, turn right after Trent Bridge, left at next traffic lights
Club colours: Dark and light blue. (*Change colours:* Maroon)
Floodlights: No
Membership fees: Full £3.50
League: N,L&D 3
League position (1988–89): 3rd
League playing record (1988–89): P 10, W 6, D 1, L 3, F 114, A 76

BOSTON

Great Fen Road, Wyberton, Boston PE21 7PB. Tel: 0205 62683
Founded: 1927
President: S.B. Julian
Chairman: S.B. Julian
Secretary: R.G. Clark, 41 Spilsby Road, Boston, Lincs PE21 9NX. Tel: 0205 62040

Fixtures Secretary: N.R. Borden, Halltoft hall Lane, Algarkirk, Nr. Boston PE20 2HG. Tel: 0205 460845 (H), 820747 (W)
Coach: J.D. Sneddon
Club captain (1988–89): S.G. Dunlop
No. of teams: Senior 3
Directions to ground: On the main Boston-Slehford Road about 3 miles from centre of Boston
Club colours: Blue/white. (*Change colours:* Red)
Floodlights: No
Membership fees: Playing £17
League: N,L&D 3
League position (1988–89): 11th
League playing record (1988–89): P 10, W 1, D 1, L 8, F 63, A 120

CLEETHORPES

Taylors Avenue, Cleethorpes
Founded: 1979
Chairman: C.S. Marks
Secretary: S. Regan, 75 Poplar Road, Cleethorpes. Tel: 0472 691285
Fixtures Secretary: J. Walsham, 9 Queenmary Avenue, Cleethorpes. Tel: 0472 42628
Club captain (1988–89): R. Benefer
Club captain (1989–90): M. Debnam
No. of teams: Senior 2
Club colours: Blue yellow hoops
Floodlights: No
Membership fees: Full £2
Local newspaper: Grimsby Evening Telegraph
League: NLD 4 East
League position (1988–89): 1st (promoted)
League playing record (1988–89): P 9, W 8, D 1, L 0
Competitions won: Notts, Lincs & Derbys Div. 4 East

MELBOURNE

Melbourne Recreation Ground, Cockshut Lane, Melbourne, Derby.
Founded: 1983
Secretary: Paul Sheldrake, 41 Redmires Drive, Chellaston, Derbys. DE7 1XF. Tel: 0332 704683(H), 0942 670707(W)
Club colours: Bottle Green/White
League: NLD 3
Final position (1988–89): 1st (NLD 4 West)

NORTH KESTEVEN

Hykeham PFA Pavilion Club, Newark Road, North Hykeham, Lincoln. Tel: 0522 680193
President: Dr. Nick Huntley
Chairman: Malc Ross
Secretary: Kevin Flynn, 20 Stenigot Close, Doddington Park, Lincoln LN6 3PB. Tel: 0522 692409
Fixtures Secretary: Nigel Thomas, 376 Newark Road, Lincoln. Tel: 0522 541544
Coach: Ray Bing
Club captain (1988–89): Paul Cartland
Club captain (1989–90): Graham Wilson
No. of teams: Senior 3
Directions to ground: Behind Memorial Hall, Newark Road, North Hykeham, Lincoln
Clubhouse facilities: Bar, kitchen, changing block, weights room
Club colours: Shirts: black with white, red and green hoops. Shorts: black
Floodlights: No
Membership fees: Full £15, VPs £6, Youth Free
Local newspaper: Lincolnshire Echo
League: NLD 3
League position (1988–89): 9th
League playing record (1988–89): P 10, W 3, D 0, L 7, F 86, A 128

ROLLS-ROYCE

Merrill Way, Allenton, Derby. Tel: 0332 249167

Founded: 1943
President: Phil Ruffles
Chairman: Toby Broome
Secretary: Toby Broome, 11 Lavender Row, Darley Abbey, Derby DE3 1DF. Tel: 0332 552285 (H), 249295 (W) (Acting)
Fixtures Secretary: Steve Roome, 14 Tailby Drive, Willington, Derbyshire DE6 6YB. Tel: 0283 701308 (H), 0602 732291 (W)
Press officer: Dave Thompson, 533 Stenson Road, Littleover, Derby DE3 7LP. Tel: 0322 775582 (H), 249188 (W)
Coach: John Currie
Club captain (1988–89): Mike Crawshaw
Club captain (1989–90): David Cross
No. of teams: Senior 3
Directions to ground: The ground is situated on the south of Derby's outer ring road – the A5111. The ground can be located at the rear of the Moorways International Athletics Stadium
Clubhouse facilities: Two pitches, eight changing rooms, separate clubhouse on site
Club colours: Maroon and skyblue hoops, black shorts. (*Change colours:* Navy blue shirts, black shorts)
Floodlights: No
League: NLD 3
League position (1988–89): 4th
League playing record (1988–89): P 10, W 6, D 0, L 4, F 136, A 115
Competitions won: Rolls-Royce Company Sevens Tournament held every September. Rolls-Royce hosted the Derbyshire Sevens in April 1989

SKEGNESS

Wainfleet Road Playing Fields, Skegness. Tel: 0754 5699
Founded: 1950
President: G.R. Bell
Chairman: B. Major
Secretary: Alan Hawkes, South View Farm, East Keal, Spilsby, Lincs PE23 4AY. Tel: 0790 52788 (H), 52176 (W)
Fixtures Secretary: Peter Halliday, 58 Beresford Avenue, Skegness. Tel: 0754 4225 (H), 5107 (W)
Press Officer: Simon Hatch, Virginia Cottage, Hanby Lane, Welton-le-Marsh, Skegness. Tel: 0754 85329 (H), 85329 (W)
Coach: Eamon Boyd Reavey
Club captain (1988–89): Andy Archer
Club captain (1989–90): Andy Archer
No. of teams: Senior 2
Directions to ground: Wainfleet/Boston A52 out of Skegness
Clubhouse facilities: Two changing, showers, kitchen, bar
Club colours: Blue and white. (*Change colours:* Light blue)
Nickname: Seasiders
Floodlights: No
Membership fees: Full £12, Playing £12, Social £2, Youth £5, Student £5, OAP £2
Local newspapers: Skegness News, Lincolnshire Standard
League: NLD 3
League position (1988–89): 10th
League playing record (1988–89): P 10, W 2, D 1, L 7, F 75, A 165
Competitions won: Skegness Veterans (Over 35) Plate Competition 1988

NOTTINGHAMSHIRE, LINCOLNSHIRE & DERBYSHIRE 4E

BINGHAM

Bingham Sports Centre, The Banks, Bingham. Tel: Bingham 38628.
Founded: 1971

Secretary: K.H. Bartsch, 14 Sherwood Grove, Bingham, Nottingham NG13 8RG. Tel: Bingham 39008 (H) 0533 663086 (W).
Club colours: Red/Green
League: NLD 4 East
Final position (1988–89): 2nd

BOURNE
West Road, Bourne
Founded: 1987
President: A. Cooke
Chairman: R.I. Johnson
Secretary: A.D. Lock, The Nags Head, Market Place, Bourne, Lincolnshire PE10 9EF. Tel: 0778 422095 (H), 0978 422095 (W)
Fixtures Secretary: A. Rowe, 54 North Road, Bourne, Lincolnshire. Tel: 0778 424353 (H), 424353 (W)
Press Officer: S. Woodcock, 44 West Street, Bourne. Tel: 0778 426408
Coach: Glynn James
Club captain (1988–89): M. Hempstead
No. of teams: Senior 2
Directions to ground: A515 (Melton) from town centre 1 mile, left-hand side, one field back
Ground capacity: Standing Unlimited
Clubhouse facilities: Pub
Club colours: Navy/gold circlet
Floodlights: No
Membership fees: Playing £15
Ground admission: Nil
Local newspaper: Stamford & Rutland Mercury
League: NLD 4E
League position (1988–89): Bottom
League playing record (1988–89): P 40, W 8, D 4, L 28, F 239, A 594

GAINSBOROUGH
Rose Leisure Club, N. Warren Road, Gainsborough, Lincs. Tel: 0427 2915
Founded: ????
President: A. Hancock
Chairman: Guy Marsden
Secretary: M. Yates, 7 South Dale Close, Weirton-in-Lindsey, Gainsborough. Tel: 0652 648084
Fixtures Secretary: A. List
Press Officer: Tony Goode
Coach: Len Davis
Club captain (1988–89): Ian Robinson
Club captain (1989–90): T. Goode
No. of teams: Senior 2
Directions to ground: Over rivery by bridge, left 1st set of T-lights → thro' town → N. Warren Road → Rose Leisure Club
Clubhouse facilities: Full
Club colours: Black. (*Change colours:* Yellow)
Floodlights: No
Membership fees: Playing £17, Social £4
League: N,L&D 4E
League position (1988–89): 11th
League playing record (1988–89): P 9, W 0, D 0, L 9, F 57, A 226

HARWORTH COLLIERY
Recreation ground, Scrooby Road, Bircotes.
Founded: 1986
Chairman: Bill Jackson
Coach: T. Wilkinson
Secretary: Chris Shail, 157 Scrooby Road, Bircotes, Doncaster DN11 8AD
Fixtures Secretary: As above
Club captain (1988–89): Terry Wilkinson
No. of teams: Senior 1
Directons to Ground: 2 miles Sth of Bantry on A614, turn right to Bircotes ground mile on left.
Colours: Royal blue & White
Floodlights: No
Admission: none
Membership: £5
Programme: 30p (Editor: Chris Shail)
Local newspaper: Worksop Guardian

HORNCASTLE
St. Lawrence School, Bowl Alley Lane, Horncastle, Lincs. Tel: 06582/2365.
Founded: 1985
President: Philip Sharpe
Chairman: Bill Laing
Coach: Trevor Francis (RFU coach)
Secretary: Trevor Francis, 54 Langton Hill, Horncastle, Lincs LN9 5AH. Tel: 06582/2325.

Fixtures Secretary: As above
Club captain (1988–89): David Middlebrook
No. of teams: Senior 1
Directions to Ground: From traffic lights on the main Lincoln/Skegness road travel 200 yds towards Skegness; turn left onto Stanhope Road; 100 yds on the tright is Bowl Alley Lane; ground 200 yds on the left.
Clubhouse facilities: On premises of St. Lawrence School, but separate building.
Colours: Green with inverted yellow "V".

Floodlights: No
Membership: £15
Local newspaper: Horncastle News & Horncastle Standard
League: Notts, Lincs, Derbys East 4

MEDEN VALE
Welbeck Colliery Pitch, Meden Vale, Mansfield.
Founded: 1980
Secretary: Garry Blake, 36 Rutland Close, Warsop, Notts, NG20 0DY. Tel: 0623 846335(H).
Colours: Black/White
League: N. L. D. 4 East
Final Position: (1988–89): 3rd

OLLERTON
Ollerton Recreation Centre, Dukeries Complex, Main Road, Boughton, Newark, Notts. Tel: 0623 862469
Founded: 1983
Chairman: Bob Murray
Secretary: David Price, 10 The Brambles, Walesby, Newark, Notts. Tel: 0623 860871
Fixtures Secretary: David Price, 10 The Brambles, Walesby, Newark, Notts. Tel: 0623 860871
Press Officer: As above
Coach: Tommy Galloway
Club captain (1988–89): Colin Boyles
Club captain (1989–90): Jeff Raine
No. of teams: Senior 2
Directions to ground: A614 roundabout, take A6075 through New Ollerton, turn left opposite 'Blue Tit' Pub. on B6387 for mile, then turn left into Ollerton Recreation Centre
Ground capacity: Seating none, standing a lot
Clubhouse facilities: 'Plough' in Ollerton (11 a.m.–11 p.m.)
Club colours: Yellow and blue hoops. (*Change colours:* Black)
Floodlights: No
League: NLD 4 East
League position (1988–89): 4th
League playing record (1988–89): P 8, W 4, D 0, L 4, F 105, A 132

YARBOROUGH BEES
Yarborough Sports Centre, Lincoln. Tel: 24228
Founded: 1976
President: P. Mitchell
Chairman: H. Sampson
Secretary: D. Stobie, 131 Newark Road, N. Hykeham, Lincs LN6 5QT. Tel: 689449

Fixtures Secretary: R. Payne, Disney Pace Hotel, Eastgate, Lincoln LN2 4AA. Tel: Linc 38881
Coach: H. Sampson
Club captain (1988–89): Z. Gray
Club captain (1989–90): A. Gray
No. of teams: Senior 1
Directions to ground: A15 uphill Lincoln, Yarborough Sports Centre
Club colours: Maroon/amber
Floodlights: No
Membership fees: Full £10
League: N,L&D 4E
League position (1988–89): 5th
League playing record (1988–89): P 8, W 3, D 0, L 5, F 76, A 94

NOTTINGHAMSHIRE, LINCOLNSHIRE & DERBYSHIRE 4W

BAKEWELL MANNERIANS

The Showground
Secretary: A. J. Hall, 70 Moorhall Estate, Bakewell, Derbyshire DE4 1FT. Tel: 062981 2363(H)
Colours: Dark Blue/Light Blue/White
League: NLD 4 W
Final position (1988–89): 3rd.

BOLSOVER

Bolsover School
Founded: 1982
President: Gerald Weeden
Chairman: Gerald Weeden
Secretary: Ken Dudhill, 32 Sandhills Road, Bolsover, Chesterfield, Derbyshire S44 6EY. Tel: 0246 826738 (H), 250108 (W)
Fixtures Secretary: Gerald Weeden, 55 Station Road, Bolsover, Chesterfield, Derbyshire. Tel: 0246 824076
Press Officer: Geoff Davis, 41 Castle Lane, Bolsover, Chesterfield, Derbyshire. Tel: 0246 824593
Coach: Ian Richardson
Club captain (1988–89): Chris Smith
Club captain (1989–90): Pete East
No. of teams: Senior 1
Clubhouse facilities: None
Club colours: White/navy/gold hoops, navy shorts
Floodlights: No
Membership fees: Full £10, Playing £10, Social £5
League: NLD 4 West
League position (1988–89): 6th
League playing record (1988–89): P 6, W 2, D 0, L 4, F 39, A 127

BUXTON

Fairfield Centre, Victoria Road, Buxton, Derbyshire
Founded: 1927
President: David N. Robinson
Chairman: Alan Wells
Secretary: Gary Lomas, 45 Windsor Road, Buxton, Derbyshire SK17 7NS. Tel: 0298 3972 (H), 2844 (W)
Fixtures Secretary: Patrick Leahy, 39 Brown Edge Road, Buxton, Derbyshire SK17. Tel: 0298 70455
Coach: Howard Graham
Club captain (1988–89): Keith Beevers
Club captain (1989–90): Mark Guyer
No. of teams: Senior 2, Minis 5
Clubhouse facilities: Bar, seating, etc.
Club colours: Blue, gold red hoops. (*Change colours:* Multi-colour shirts)
Floodlights: No
Membership fees: Playing £20, Social £2
Local newspaper: Buxton Advertiser
League: NLD 4 West
League position (1988–89): 5th
League playing record (1988–89): P 31, W 16, D 0, L 15, F 392, A 310

EAST LEAKE

Harry Carlton School, East Leake. Tel: 0509 852956
Founded: 1977/78
President: Colin Fearn
Chairman: Graham Hey
Secretary: Andrew Noble, 46 Rydal Avenue, Loughborough, Leics LE11 3RX. Tel: 0509 215859
Fixtures Secretary: Alan Sharkey, 13 Eastham Road, Arnold, Nottingham. Tel: 0602 205640
Press Officer: John Pears, Pinecroft, Church Lane, Widmerpool, Notts. Tel: 0602 372892
Coach: Anthony Taylor
Club captain (1988–89): Paul Johnson
Club captain (1989–90): Paul Johnson
No. of teams: Senior 2
Directions to ground: mile from centre of the village, East Leake Leisure Centre, off Lantern Lane
Clubhouse facilities: Nags Head Public House
Club colours: Maroon and white hooped shirts and socks, black shorts. (*Change colours:* Maroon shirts, black shorts)
Floodlights: No
Membership fees: Full £10, Playing £5, Student £5
Local newspaper: Loughborough Echo
League: NLD 4 West
League position (1988–89): 8th
League playing record (1988–89): P 34, W 17, D 1, L 15, F 528, A 469

HOPE VALLEY

Hollowford Lane, Castleton, Derbyshire. Tel: 0433 20247
Founded: 1979
President: J.E. Mason
Chairman: Richard Gray
Secretary: Mrs. Tracey Gale, Castle View, Goosehill, Castleton, Derbyshire S30 2WD. Tel: 0433 21384
Fixtures Secretary: Paul Holwell, Peak Hotel, Castleton, Derbyshire. Tel: 0433 20247 (H), 20247 (W)
Press Officer: Ian Dawson, 'Adyar', Jaggers Lane, Hathersage, Sheffield. Tel: 0433 50533
Coach: Colin Field
Club captain (1988–89): Perry Gale
Club captain (1989–90): Perry Gale
No. of teams: Senior 2
Directions to ground: A625 out of Sheffield to Castleton, after Peak Hotel take first right into Back Lane. Ground 600 yards on right
Ground capacity: Standing 400
Clubhouse facilities: Shower and changing facilities. Hospitality at Peak Hotel
Club colours: Purple/green/white hoops, white shorts, green socks. (*Change colours:* Green shirts, white shorts, green socks)
Nickname: Valley
Floodlights: No
Membership fees: Full £25, Playing £25, Social £5, Youth £10, Student £10
Programme: No. of editorial pages variable; No. of advertising pages variable; Price 50p
Programme editor: Ian Dawson, 'Adyar', Jaggers Lane, Hathersage, Sheffield
Local newspapers: Derbyshire Times, Sheffield Star, Matlock Mercury, Buxton Advertiser
League: NLD 4 W
League position (1988–89): 2nd
League playing record (1988–89): P 7, W 6, D 0, L 1
Competitions won: Runner-up Courage Clubs Championship NLD Div. 4 West

LEESBROOK ASTERDALE

Asterdale Club, Borrowash Road, Spondon, Derby. Tel: 668656 (previously Leesbrook R.F.C.)
Founded: 1978

President: Leigh Woodside
Chairman: Mike Wilson
Secretary: Neil Buckler, 27 Wollaton Road, Chaddesden, Derby DE2 4HX. Tel: 674470
Fixtures Secretary: Leigh Woodside, 1 South Drive, Chaddesden, Derby. Tel: 673872
Press Officer: Conor Campbell, 242 Stenson Road, Sunnyhill, Derby. Tel: 763899
Coach: Paul Swannick
Club captain (1988–89): Peter Albon
Club captain (1989–90): Peter Albon
No. of teams: Senior 1
Directions to ground: The A6005 from Derby to Notts, turn left opposite Bemrose Printing into Borrowash Road. Club on the right
Clubhouse facilities: Showers, bar, pool, snooker, darts. Live music and function room
Club colours: Emerald green, sky blue, white and black quarters. (*Change colours:* Black)
Floodlights: No
Local newspaper: Derby Evening Telegraph
League: NLD 4W
League position (1988–89): 3rd
League playing record (1988–89): P 6, W 4, D 0, L 2, F 104, A 57
Competitions won: Derbyshire Sevens Finalists, 1989

RAINWORTH

League: N.L.D. 4 East
Secretary: E. W. Bramwell, Trecarmar, 41 Beaulah Road, Kirby-in-Ashfield, Notts.
Final position (1988–89): 6th

TUPTON

Recreation Ground, Northwide, Tupton, Nr. Chesterfield, Derbyshire
Founded: 1970
President: K. Aires
Chairman: R. Mellor
Secretary: B.A. Wakefield
Fixtures Secretary: R. Wilks. Tel: 270387
Club captain (1988–89): M. Thackery
Club captain (1989–90): M. Thackery
No. of teams: Senior 1
Directions to ground: On A61
Club colours: Royal blue/gold. (*Change colours:* Bright yellow)
Floodlights: No
League: N,L&D 4W
League position (1988–89): 7th
League playing record (1988–89): P 7, W 1, D 0, L 6, F 83, A 168

Scunthorpe – Notts, Lincs & Derbyshire champions for 1988–89. Photo: Scunthorpe Evening Telegraph

EAST MIDLANDS/ LEICESTERSHIRE LEAGUE

THE STRUGGLE at the top of this feeder league for Midlands 2 East was won by Towcestrians, whose 100 percent record left them two points clear of Wellingborough, who had themselves only been promoted the previous season. A strong defence was the champions' greatest asset as they conceded only 50 points. The basement positions were both filled by teams relegated from Midlands 2 East in 1987–88 – Loughborough and Wigston being the sad victims of humiliation and they must go even lower next season to play their league rugby.

EAST MIDLANDS/LEICS: OFFICIAL

Mike Bracey,
White Lodge,
Park Road,
Toddington,
Dunstable,   (H) 05255 4251
Beds. LU5 6AB   (B) 021 328 6866

TABLES 1987–88

EAST MIDLANDS/LEICS 1

	P	W	D	L	F	A	PTS
Stewart & Lloyd	10	9	0	1	213	45	18
Towcestrians	10	9	0	1	153	37	18
Luton	10	6	0	4	70	85	12
Long Buckby	10	5	0	5	141	106	10
N'hampton Trin	10	5	0	5	107	75	10
Bedford Ath	10	5	0	5	92	120	10
Oadby Wygg	10	4	0	6	75	107	8
O N'hamptons	10	4	0	6	70	137	8
Sth Leicester	10	3	0	7	55	166	6
Melton Mowbray	10	0	0	10	70	178	0

TABLES 1988–89

EAST MIDLANDS/LEICS

	P	W	D	L	F	A	PTS
Towcestrians	10	0	0	0	191	50	20
Wellingborough	10	9	0	1	217	74	18
Aylestone St J	10	6	1	3	134	110	13
Long Buckby	10	6	0	4	147	113	12
Belgrave	10	4	2	4	165	163	10
Bedford Ath	10	4	1	5	123	126	9
Northampton T	10	4	0	6	133	143	8
Luton	10	4	0	6	107	124	8
Oadby-Wygg	10	3	0	7	100	180	6
Loughborough	10	2	0	8	79	182	4
Wigston	10	1	0	9	83	214	2

Peterborough – winners of the East Midlands County Cup after beating Stockwood Park in the final on 30th April 1989 (15–13). Players (l to r): (Back Row): S. Britten, R. Paton, D. Griffin, J. Nugetn, T. French, T. Meston, D. Grierson, A. Croson, D. Kitching, B. Morley (rep); (Front Row): J. Sismey, S. Flemming, I. Fowler, P. Hodges (captain), D. O'Donoghue, M. Harris, A. Jones (rep.)

MIDLANDS DIVISION FIXTURES 1989/90

EAST MIDLANDS/LEICESTER LEAGUE

Sat. 9th September (Week 2)
Biggleswade v Northampton Trinity
Hinckley v Aylestone St. James
Long Buckby v Bedford Athletic
Lutterworth v Oadby-Wyggestonians
Wellingborough v Belgrave

Sat. 23rd September (Week 4)
Aylestone St. James v Lutterworth
Belgrave v Hinckley
Luton v Biggleswade
Northampton Trinity v Wellingborough
Oadby-Wyggestonians v Long Buckby

Sat. 14th October (Week 6)
Bedford Athletic v Oadby-Wyggestonians
Hinckley v Northampton Trinity
Long Buckby v Aylestone St. James
Lutterworth v Belgrave
Wellingborough v Luton

Sat. 28th October (Week 8)
Aylestone St. James v Bedford Athletic
Belgrave v Long Buckby
Biggleswade v Wellingborough
Luton v Hinckley
Northampton Trinity v Lutterworth

Sat. 11th November (Week 10)
Bedford Athletic v Belgrave
Hinckley v Biggleswade
Long Buckby v Northampton Trinity
Lutterworth v Luton
Oadby-Wyggestonians v Aylestone St. James

Sat 18th November (Week 11)
Belgrave v Oadby-Wyggestonians
Biggleswade v Lutterworth
Luton v Long Buckby
Northampton Trinity v Bedford Athletic
Wellingborough v Hinckley

Sat. 25th November (Week 12)
Aylestone St. James v Belgrave
Bedford Athletic v Luton
Long Buckby v Biggleswade
Lutterworth v Wellingborough
Oadby-Wyggestonians v Northampton Trinity

Sat. 13th January (Week 18)
Biggleswade v Bedford Athletic
Hinckley v Lutterworth
Luton v Oadby-Wyggestonians
Northampton Trinity v Aylestone St. James
Wellingborough v Long Buckby

Sat. 10th March (Week 26)
Aylestone St. James v Luton
Bedford Athletic v Wellingborough
Belgrave v Northampton Trinity
Long Buckby v Hinckley
Oadby-Wyggestonians v Biggleswade

Sat. 31st March (Week X7)
Biggleswade v Aylestone St. James
Hinckley v Bedford Athletic
Luton v Belgrave
Lutterworth v Long Buckby
Wellingborough v Oadby-Wyggestonians

Sat. 28th April (Week 32)
Aylestone St. James v Wellingborough
Belgrave v Biggleswade
Bedford Athletic v Lutterworth
Northampton Trinity v Luton
Oadby-Wyggestonians v Hinckley

EAST MIDLANDS AND LEICESTERSHIRE

AYLESTONE ST. JAMES

Covert Lane, Scraptoft, Leicester. Tel: 0533 419202
President: Malcolm Webb
Chairman: Roger Price
Secretary: John Fenton, Nook Farm, Church Lane,
Ratby, Leics. Tel: 0533 386860 (H), 663391 (W)
Fixtures Secretary: Richard Hickson, 12 Springdale
Road, Thurmaston, Leics. Tel: 693745
Coach: Kingsley Harmer
Club captain (1988–89): J. Mitchelson
Club captain (1989–90): J. Mitchelson
No. of teams: Senior 5, Youth 2
Directions to ground: A47 east of Leicester, T-lights
Station Lane/Scraptoft Church
Clubhouse facilities: Full
Club colours: Red
Nickname: Dimmies
Floodlights: Yes (training)
Membership fees: Full £20
League: EMids/Leics
League position (1988–89): 3rd
League playing record (1988–89): P 10, W 6, D 1,
L 3, F 134, A 110

BEDFORD ATHLETIC

Putnoe Woods, Wentworth Drive, Putnoe, Bedford,
Beds. Tel: 0234 50874
Founded: 1908
President: Ron Cox
Chairman: Nic Davies
Secretary: David Warren, Bedford Athletic,
Wentworth Drive, Putnoe, Bedford
Fixtures Secretary: John Ross, 63 Avon Drive,
Brickhill, Bedford, Beds. Tel: 0234 43157 (H), 225116
(W)
Press Officer: Derek Norman, 3 Poplar Avenue,
Putnoe, Bedford, Beds. Tel: 0234 262325
Coach: P. Wheeler
Club captain (1988–89): Paul McGuckian
Club captain (1989–90): Paul McGuckian
No. of teams: Senior 5–6, Youth 1
Directions to ground: A47 East of Leicester, T. lights
Station Lane–Scraptoft to Scraptoft Church
Clubhouse facilities: Open matchdays, Tues., Thurs.,
Sun.
Club colours: 4 in. black and white hoops. (*Change
colours:* Black)
Nickname: The Ath
Floodlights: No
Membership fees: Full £15, Playing £15, Social £5,
Youth £5, OAP Donation
Ground admission: Free
Programme: No. of editorial pages 3; No. of
advertising pages 6; Price 30p
Programme editor: D. August, 22 Brookfield Road,
Bedford
Local newspapers: Bedford on Sunday, Beds Times,
Bedford Express
League: EMid/Leics
League position (1988–89): 6th
League playing record (1988–89): P 36, W 11, D 4,
L 21, F 385, A 535

BELGRAVE

Belgrave Pastures, Thurcaston Road, Leicester. Tel:
Leic. 663033
President: John Law
Chairman: Roger Broughton
Secretary: John Goddard, 16 Birstall Road, Birstall,
Leics. Tel: 0533 677383 (H), 677383 (W)
Fixtures Secretary: Kevin Hick, 3 Coplow Crescent,
Syston, Leicester. Tel: 0533 608617
Coach: David Cort
Club captain (1988–89): Bob Kyle

Club captain (1989–90): Mick Quilter
No. of teams: Senior 4
Directions to ground: Abbey Lane/Thurcaston Road
interchange
Club colours: Red and black hoops. (*Change colours:*
Green)
Floodlights: No
League: EMid/Leics
League position (1988–89): 5th
League playing record (1988–89): P 10, W 4, D 2,
L 4, F 165, A 163

BIGGLESWADE

Langford Road, Biggleswade, Beds. Tel: 0767 312463
Founded: 1949
President: John Jordan
Chairman: Jack Chisholm
Secretary: Mike Williams, 8 Laurel Way, Ickleford,
Hitchin, Herts SG5 3UP. Tel: 0462 54782 (H), 01–867
7478 (W)
Fixtures Secretary: Roy Caulfield, 76 Winston
Crescent, Biggleswade, Beds. Tel: 0767 316106
Press Officer: Rob Bakewell, The Old School House,
Waresley, Beds. Tel: 0767 50067
Coach: Mick Buck
Club captain (1988–89): Grant Ingle
Club captain (1989–90): Grant Ingle
No. of teams: Senior 5, Youth 4, Minis 5
Directions to ground: 1 miles out of Biggleswade on
A6001 Biggleswade to Henlow Road
Ground capacity: Standing 500+
Clubhouse facilities: Main clubroom and lounge bar, 4
squash courts, 2 tennis courts. Bar open every evening
and lunchtimes Sat. and Sun.
Club colours: Navy with red hoop. (*Change colours:*
Green)
Nickname: Biggy
Floodlights: Yes (training only)
Membership fees: Full £25, Playing £25, Social £5,
Youth £5, Student Neg.
Ground admission: Free (but collection on Cup and
League games)
Programme: No. of editorial pages 4; No. of
advertising pages 2; Price 20p (League and Cup games
only)
Programme editor: Jack Chisholm, Speeds Farm,
Beadlow, Shefford, Beds
Local newspaper: Biggleswade Chronicle
League: EM 1
League position (1988–89): 1st (promoted)
League playing record (1988–89): P 36, W 28, D 0,
L 8, F 694, A 323
Competitions won: East Midlands Division 1 Winners,
Huntingdon Floodlit Tournament. Colts:
Bedfordshire League

HINCKLEY

Leicester Road, Hinckley. Tel: 0455-615010.
Founded: 1893
President: R.S. Palmer
Chairman: D.J. Barratt
Coach: A. Ottey
Secretary: G. March, Tinkers Cuss, Sharnford, Leics.
Tel: 045527-2380.
Fixtures Secretary: G. Targett, 14 Grange Drive,
Burbage, Hinckley.
Club captain (1987–88): P. Adams
Club captain (1988–89): P. Green
No. of teams: Senior 2
Directions to Ground: Left hand side of A47 towards
Leicester.
Colours: Black & Amber.
Floodlights: Yes
Admission: Collection
Membership: £10
Local newspaper: Hinckley Times
League: East Mids/Leics
Final position 11th Midlands 2 East)
Competitions won: 5 times winners of Leicestershire
Cup – twice runners up.

LONG BUCKBY

Station Road, Long Buckby, Northampton. Tel: L.B. 842222
Founded: 1875
President: G.G. Tebbitt
Chairman: P.K. Spokes
Secretary: P.J. Osborne, Ashthorne, Tegton Road, Ravensthorpe, Northampton. Tel: North. 770772 (H), Daventry 705785 (W)
Fixtures Secretary: S. Ruddlesden, 37 Rockhill Road, Long Buckby, Northampton. Tel: L.B. 842933
Press Officer: M. York, 9 Watts Way, Long Buckby, Northampton. Tel: L.B. 842726
Club captain (1988–89): M. Dickens
Club captain (1989–90): M. Dickens
No. of teams: Senior 4, Youth 1, Minis 7
Directions to ground: From west via Daventry. From north via A5, A45 or M1. From east via Market Harborough/Kettering. From south via Northampton on M1. From centre of village 500 m down Station Road
Ground capacity: Standing 500
Clubhouse facilities: Large bar, separate lounge. Open match days and Sundays, Mondays, Wednesdays
Club colours: Emerald Green. (*Change colours:* White)
Floodlights: Yes
Membership fees: Full £7.50, Playing £7.50, Social £1, Youth £2, Student £2, OAP £1
Programme: No. of editorial pages 2; No. of advertising pages 4; Price Free
Programme editor: M. York, 9 Watts Way, Long Buckby
Local newspapers: Daventry Weekly Express, Northampton Chronicle and Echo, Rugby Advertiser
League: EMid/Leics
League position (1988–89): 4th
League playing record (1988–89): P 10, W 6, D 0, L 4, F 175, A 126

LUTON

Newlands Road, Luton, Beds. Tel: 0582 20355
Founded: 1931
President: David T.P. Shane
Chairman: Neil Foster
Secretary: Richard John, 37 Byron Crescent, Flitwick, Beds MK45 1PY. Tel: 0525 716560
Fixtures Secretary: Andy Ross, 17 Tomlinson Avenue, Luton, Beds. Tel: 0582 668098
Press Officer: Hughie Byrne, 7 Ailsworth Road, Luton, Beds. Tel: 0582 575522 (H), 422387 (W)
Coach: Bryn Hughes
Club captain (1988–89): John Long
Club captain (1989–90): T.B.A.
No. of teams: Senior 6, Youth 2
Directions to ground: M1 Junction 10. Right at roundabout on A1081, 500 yds right turn into Newland Road, 600 yds on left
Clubhouse facilities: Open lunchtimes and evenings (except Sunday)
Club colours: Green with red hoop and white bands. (*Change colours:* White)
Floodlights: Yes
Local newspapers: Citizen, Herald, Luton News
League: E Mid/Leics
League position (1988–89): 8th
League playing record (1988–89): P 10, W 4, D 0, L 6, F 107, A 124

LUTTERWORTH

Ashby Lane, Bitteswell, Nr. Lutterworth, Leics. Tel: 0455 557329
Founded: 1873
President: M. Ross
Chairman: M. Ross
Secretary: C. Hudson, Mason & Browns Cottage, Ashby Parva, Lutterworth. Tel: 0455 209053
Fixtures Secretary: C. Payne, Cowder Ghyll, Shawell, Lutterworth

Club captain (1988–89): R. Tranter
Club captain (1989–90): R. Tranter
No. of teams: Senior 4, Youth + Minis 8
Directions to ground: North from Lutterworth on A426 towards Leicester, approx. 1 miles out of Lutterworth, left turn signposted Ashby Parva
Clubhouse facilities: Full
Club colours: Red/green/white. (*Change colours:* Blue)
Floodlights: No
Membership fees: Full £15
Programme: Price Free
Programme editor: M.J. Ross
League: EMids/Leics
League position (1988–89): 1st
League playing record (1988–89): P 9, W 9, D 0, L 0, F 198, A 19

NORTHAMPTON TRINITY

Dallington Park, Northampton. Tel: 0604 515521. Abbey Street, Northampton. Tel: 0604 583706
Founded: 1960
President: G. Grimshaw
Chairman: H. Cooke
Secretary: P.W. Collyer, 3 School Lane, Quinton, Northampton. Tel: 0604 863456 (H), 0438 745745 (W)
Fixtures Secretary: I. Billson. Tel: 0604 880070
Club captain (1988–89): J. Sharpe
No. of teams: Senior 4, Youth 2
Directions to ground: Next to Express Life Tower off Weedon Road, Northampton
Club colours: Emerald green/red/white
Floodlights: No
Membership fees: Playing £18
Programme: Price Free
Programme editor: As Secretary
League: EMids/Leics
League position (1988–89): 7th
League playing record (1988–89): P 10, W 4, D 0, L 6, F 133, A 143

OADBY-WYGGESTONIANS

Wigston Road, Oadby, Leicester. Tel: 0533 714848
Founded: 1888
President: Peter Bayley
Chairman: Martin Bromley
Secretary: Jim Kilgallen, 75 Leicester Road, Oadby, Leicester. Tel: 0533 713987 (H), 532999 (W)
Fixtures Secretary: Neil Bromley, 38 Wintersdale Road, Leicester. Tel: 0533 414856
Press Officer: Neil Jones, 62 Hollow Road, Anstey, Leicester. Tel: 0533 365245 (H), 871313 (W)
Coach: John Thawley
Club captain (1988–89): Neil Jones
Club captain (1989–90): Neil Jones
No. of teams: Senior 4, Youth 1, Minis 4
Directions to ground: On A5096 halfway between Oadby (A6) and Wigston (A50)
Clubhouse facilities: 4 changing rooms. Totally refurbished bar-lounge 1988
Club colours: Black, white, gold hoops. (*Change colours:* White)
Floodlights: No
League: EMid/Leics
League position (1988–89): 8th

WELLINGBOROUGH

Cut Throat Lane, Gt. Doddington, Wellingborough. Tel: 0933 222260
Founded: 1897
President: James Saxby
Chairman: Malcolm Carter

Secretary: Thomas Meyer, 16 Gray Close, Earls Barton, Northampton NN6 0PT. Tel: 0604 811151 (H), 0733 558781 (W)
Fixtures Secretary: Melvin Carter, 4 Fir Tree Grove, Bozeat, Wellingborough. Tel: 0933 663909
Press Officer: David Fairheard, c/o Clubhouse. Tel: 0933 673920
Coach: John Matthews
Club captain (1988–89): Richard Langley
Club captain (1989–90): Richard Langley
No. of teams: Senior 4, Youth 2, Minis 4
Directions to ground: A45 from Northampton. B573

turning Earls Barton/Great Doddington. Left turn in Great Doddington to Wilby. Ground on rt. hand side
Clubhouse facilities: Match day, Sunday, 3 evenings
Club colours: White/red
Floodlights: No
Membership fees: Full £17, Social £5, Youth £8.50, Student £3.50
Local newspaper: Evening Telegraph
League: EMid/Leics
League position (1988–89): 2nd
League playing record (1988–89): P 10, W 9, D 0, L 1, F 217, A 74

Stockwood Park – winners of the Hertford Floodlit Cup 1988–89

Stockwood Park winning the Bedfordshire Cup Final against Leighton Buzzard (16–3).

LEICESTERSHIRE LEAGUES

ONCE again Leicestershire only managed two leagues, but the numbers had increased to 18 clubs – 10 in the top division with eight in the other – and there was some keen competition before Lutterworth – by winning all their nine matches with only 19 points conceded – edged out the higher-scoring Market Bosworth to gain promotion. The two promoted teams from Division 2 in 1987–88 failed to sustain their progress and return down the ladder to be replaced by Old Newtonians (relegated in 1987–88) and Burstall Community College – the former having won all seven matches played with a points differential of 211–38 which was excellent going. At the foot of the table Shepshed – a new team in the league – had the misfortune to lose all its games and one hopes that they will follow the example of Oakham and persist, since the latter won four of their matches having lost everything in 1987–88.

LEICESTERSHIRE: OFFICIAL

Dennis Stewart,
87 Greengate Lane,
Birstall,
Leics. LE4 3JG   (H) 0533 675981

TABLES 1987–88

LEICESTERSHIRE 1

	P	W	D	L	F	A	PTS
Belgrave	8	8	0	0	149	65	16
Coalville	8	7	0	1	134	63	14
O Bosworthians	8	5	0	3	150	88	10
Lutterworth	8	4	1	3	98	71	9
West Leics	8	3	1	4	82	140	7
Market Bros	8	3	0	5	78	80	6
Ibworth	8	3	0	5	45	97	6
O Ashbeians	8	1	0	7	83	126	2
Old Newtonians	8	1	0	7	73	162	2

LEICESTERSHIRE 2

	P	W	D	L	F	A	PTS
New Parks	5	4	0	1	86	32	8
Aylestonians	5	4	0	1	79	34	8
Anstey	5	3	0	2	95	65	6
Birstall	5	2	0	3	91	36	4
Burbage	5	2	0	3	49	83	4
Oakham	5	0	0	5	14	164	0

TABLES 1988–89

LEICESTERSHIRE 1

	P	W	D	L	F	A	PTS
Lutterworth	9	9	0	0	198	19	18
M Bosworth	9	8	0	1	234	39	16
O Bosworthians	9	7	0	2	169	94	14
Coalville	9	6	0	3	115	52	12
Melton Mowbray	9	4	0	5	76	124	8
Kibworth	9	3	1	5	109	113	7
S Leicester	9	3	0	6	101	173	6
W Leicester	9	2	0	7	79	186	4
Aylestonians	9	1	1	7	58	183	3
New Parks OB	9	0	2	7	53	209	2

LEICESTERSHIRE 2

	P	W	D	L	F	A	PTS
O Newtonians	7	7	0	0	211	38	14
Birstall Comm	7	6	0	1	160	58	12
O Ashbeians	7	5	0	2	157	56	10
Oakham	7	4	0	3	93	61	8
Anstey	7	2	1	4	86	90	5
Burbage	7	2	1	4	49	148	5
Braunston	7	1	0	6	57	160	2
Shepshed	7	0	0	7	34	236	0

MIDLANDS DIVISION FIXTURES 1989/90

LEICESTERSHIRE DIVISION ONE

Sat. 9th September (Week 2)
Melton Mowbray v Coalville
Market Bosworth v Kibworth
Loughborough v Wigston
Old Bosworthians v South Leicester
West Leicester v Old Newtonians

Sat. 23rd September (Week 4)
Old Newtonians v Birstall
Coalville v Old Bosworthians
Kibworth v Melton Mowbray
South Leicester v Loughborough
Wigston v West Leicester

Sat. 14th October (Week 6)
Birstall v Wigston
Loughborough v Coalville
Old Bosworthians v Kibworth
Melton Mowbray v Market Bosworth
West Leicester v South Leicester

Sat. 28th October (Week 8)
South Leicester v Birstall
Coalville v West Leicester
Kibworth v Loughborough
Market Bosworth v Old Bosworthians
Wigston v Old Newtonians

Sat. 11th November (Week 10)
Birstall v Coalville
West Leicester v Kibworth
Loughborough v Market Bosworth
Old Bosworthians v Melton Mowbray
Old Newtonians v South Leicester

Sat 18th November (Week 11)
Kibworth v Birstall
Coalville v Old Newtonians
Melton Mowbray v Loughborough
Market Bosworth v West Leicester
South Leicester v Wigston

Sat. 25th November (Week 12)
Birstall v Market Bosworth
Wigston v Coalville
Old Newtonians v Kibworth
Loughborough v Old Bosworthians
West Leicester v Melton Mowbray

Sat. 13th January (Week 18)
Melton Mowbray v Birstall
Coalville v South Leicester
Kibworth v Wigston
Market Bosworth v Old Newtonians
Old Bosworthians v West Leicester

Sat. 10th March (Week 26)
Birstall v Old Bosworthians
South Leicester v Kibworth
West Leicester v Loughborough
Wigston v Market Bosworth
Old Newtonians v Melton Mowbray

Sat. 31st March (Week X7)
Loughborough v Birstall
Kibworth v Coalville
Market Bosworth v South Leicester
Melton Mowbray v Wigston
Old Bosworthians v Old Newtonians

Sat. 28th April (Week 32)
Birstall v West Leicester
Coalville v Market Bosworth
Old Newtonians v Loughborough
South Leicester v Melton Mowbray
Wigston v Old Bosworthians

MIDLANDS DIVISION FIXTURES 1989/90

LEICESTERSHIRE DIVISION TWO

Sat. 23rd September (Week 4)
Aylestone Athletic v Burbridge
Anstey v South Wigston
Aylestonians v Braunstone
New Parks v Oakham
Old Ashbeians v Shepshed

Sat. 14th October (Week 6)
South Wigston v Aylestone Athletic
Braunstone v Anstey
Oakham v Aylestonians
Burbage v Old Ashbeians
Shepshed v New Parks

Sat. 28th October (Week 8)
Aylestone Athletic v Old Ashbeians
Anstey v Oakham
Aylestonians v Shepshed
South Wigston v Braunstone
New Parks v Burbage

Sat. 11th November (Week 10)
Braunstone v Aylestone Athletic
Shepshed v Anstey
Burbage v Aylestonians
Old Ashbeians v New Parks
Oakham v South Wigston

Sat 18th November (Week 11)
Anstey v Burbage
Aylestone Athletic v New Parks
Aylestoaians v Old Ashbeians
Braunstone v Oakham
South Wigstone v Shepshed

Sat. 25th November (Week 12)
Old Ashbeians v Anstey
Oakham v Aylestone Athletic
New Parks v Aylestonians
Shepshed v Braunstone
Burbage v South Wigston

Sat. 13th January (Week 18)
Aylestone Athletic v Aylestoaians
Anstey v New Parks
Brauntone v Burbage
Oakham v Shepshed
South Wigston v Old Ashbeians

Sat. 10th March (Week 26)
Aylestonians v Anstey
Shepshed v Aylestone Athletic
Old Ashbeians v Braunstone
Burbage v Oakham
New Parks v South Wigston

Sat. 31st March (Week X7)
South Wigston v Aylestonians
Aylestone Athletic v Anstey
Braunstone v New Parks
Shepshed v Burbage
Oakham v Old Ashbeians

BIRSTALL COMMUNITY

Birstall Community College, Wanlip Lane, Birstall, Leicestershire
Founded: 1957
President: Malcolm Cooper
Chairman: Dennis Sewart
Secretary: Rodney Offley, 41 Town Green Street, Rothley, Leicestershire. Tel: 0533 302503 (H), 531291 (W)
Fixtures Secretary: Jeremy Cross, 9 Foxglove Close, East Goscote, Leicestershire. Tel: 0533 601543 (H), 776503 (W)
Press Officer: Andrew Reed, 4 Hawthorn Avenue, Birstall, Leicestershire. Tel: 0533 675489
Coach: Geoffrey Payne
Club captain (1988–89): Brian Cox
Club captain (1989–90): Richard Pearce
No. of teams: Senior 3
Directions to ground: Leicester A6 north, 3 miles Birstall, A6 1 mile turn R. (sign B673 Syston). 1st R. Wanlip village through college campus drive on right
Ground capacity: Standing Open
Clubhouse facilities: Lounge and bar
Club colours: Green/black/white hoops
Floodlights: No
League: Leics 1
League position (1988–89): 2nd
League playing record (1988–89): P 7, W 6, D 0, L 1, F 160, A 58

COALVILLE

Memorial Ground, Broomleys Road. Tel: 812059.
Founded: 1902
Secretary: G.H. Gadsby, 172 Ashburton Road, Hugglescote, Leicester. Tel: 0530 31949 (H) 0530 61052 (W).
Colours: Navy/Amber/Red.
League: Leics 1
Final position (1988–89): 4th

KIBWORTH

Up to 1.10.89: 89 Gores Lane, Market Harborough. As from 1.10.89: Northampton Road, Market Harborough, Leicestershire. Tel: 0858 64210
Founded: 1923
President: K.R.D. Wiggins
Chairman: J.B. Morris
Secretary: D.R. Coe, 114 Harborough Road, Desborough, Northants. Tel: 0536 761637 (H), 402551 ext. 3104 (W)
Fixtures Secretary: H.J. Smith, 1 Elm Drive, Market Harborough. Tel: 0858 63924 (H), 632090 (W)
Press Officer: Jim Knights, 12 Farndon Road, Market Harborough. Tel: 0858 644676 (H), 62408 (W)
Coach: Coaching panel
Club captain (1988–89): Clive M. Giles
Club captain (1989–90): Ross Clarkson
No. of teams: Senior 4, Youth 1, Minis (U8-U15) 6
Directions to ground: Re. Northampton Road: Follow Northampton signs out of town. Ground situated on R.H. side between cemetery and golf club
Clubhouse facilities: Open matchdays evenings
Club colours: Black. (*Change colours:* Blue and white hoops)
Nickname: "Kibby"
Floodlights: Yes (at Northampton Road Ground)
Membership fees: Full £20, Playing £20, Social £10, Youth £10, Student £10, OAP £10
Programme: No. of editorial pages 4; No. of advertising pages 16; Price Free
Programme editor: David R. Coe, 114 Harborough Road, Desborough, Northants
Local newspapers: Harborough Mail, Harborough Post, Leicester Mercury, Evening Telegraph
League: Leics 1
League position (1988–89): 6th
League playing record (1988–89): P 9, W 4, D 1, L 4

LOUGHBOROUGH

Derby Road Playing Fields, Derby Road, Loughborough, Leicestershire. Tel: 0509 216093
President: Les G. Moseley
Chairman: John F.G. Charles
Secretary: Cmdr. Patrick Talbot, 11 Kirkstone Drive, Loughborough, Leicestershire LE11 3RN. Tel: 0509 239393 (H), 0533 487000 (W)
Fixtures Secretary: David Jacques, 2 Nursery Lane, Quorn, Leicestershire. Tel: 0509 413308 (H), 0602 830331 (W)
Press Officer: Jason Whowell, Highfield, Whitcroft's Ulverscroft, Leicester LE6 0QE. Tel: 0533 707502 (H), 0664 66120 (W)
Coach: Alan Waters
Club captain (1988–89): Alan Shephard
Club captain (1989–90): David Barnett
No. of teams: Senior 5, Youth 2, Minis 10
Directions to ground: Heading north along A6 out of Loughborough turn right at Derby Road Industrial Estate and follow signs to Derby Road Playing Fields
Clubhouse facilities: Baths/showers, clubroom, extensive bar/lounge
Club colours: Navy blue and old gold. (*Change colours:* Old gold shirts)
Nickname: The "Borough"
Floodlights: No
Membership fees: Full £23, Playing £23, Social £10, Youth £10, Student £10, OAP £5
League: Leics 1
League position (1988–89): 10th
League playing record (1988–89): P 10, W 2, D 0, L 8

MARKET BOSWORTH

Cadeby Lane, Cadeby, Nuneaton, Warks
Founded: 1965
President: Kenneth W. Coleman
Chairman: Robert Jarvis
Secretary: Steven Stokes, 126 Charnwood Road, Barwell, Leics LE9 8FL. Tel: 0455 46421
Fixtures Secretary: Paul Spencer, 10 Beaumont Avenue, Hinckley, Leics. Tel: 0455 30804
Coach: Brian Godfrey
Club captain (1988–89): Steven Moore
Club captain (1989–90): Steven Moore
No. of teams: Senior 3, Youth 4, Minis 1
Directions to ground: Take the road to Cadeby out of Market Bosworth for mile
Clubhouse facilities: Clubroom, kitchen, 4 changing rooms, showers, toilets
Club colours: Gold blue white. (*Change colours:* Blue)
Floodlights: Yes
Membership fees: Full £10, Playing £10, Social £5, Youth £5, Student £5, OAP £5
Local newspapers: Hinckley Times, Leicester Mercury
League: Leics 1
League position (1988–89): 2nd
League playing record (1988–89): P 35, W 25, D 2, L 8, F 591, A 250

MELTON MOWBRAY

All England Ground, Saxby Road, Melton Mowbray. Tel: 0664 63342
Chairman: Vivian Carlick
Secretary: Robert Goldthorpe, 14 Kirk Hill, Bingham, Notts N613 8FF. Tel: 0949 37638 (H), 0602 419866 (W)
Fixtures Secretary: Malcolm Crane, 56 Ferneley Crescent, Melton Mowbray, Leics. Tel: 0664 67988
Coach: Jim Kempin
Club captain (1988–89): Tony Middleton
Club captain (1989–90): James Severn
No. of teams: Senior 4, Youth 1, Minis 5
Club colours: Maroon and white
Floodlights: No
Membership fees: Full £20, Playing £20, Social £5, Youth £7.50

Local newspaper: Melton Times
League: Leics 1
League position (1988–89): 5th
League playing record (1988–89): P 9, W 4, D 0, L 5, F 76, A 124

OLD BOSWORTHIANS

Hinkley Road, Leicester, Forest East, Leics. Tel: 0533 387136
Founded: 1955
President: P. Penny
Chairman: M. Willcox
Secretary: G.D. Spendlove-Mason, Croft House Farm, Newton Harcourt, Leics LE8 0Fn. Tel: 0537 592965 (H), 0533 557803 (W)
Fixtures Secretary: C. Hughes, 97 Rosslyn Road, Whitick, Leics. Tel: Coalville 34493 (H), Lough 611011 ext. 4102 (W)
Coach: R. Merrick
Club captain (1988–89): J. Coulthurst
No. of teams: Senior 4, Youth 3+
Directions to ground: Go west on the A47 out of Leics, pass over M1, 1 mile on right
Club colours: Navy. (*Change colours:* Navy and sky blue)
Nickname: Old Bos
Floodlights: No
Membership fees: Full £5
League: Mids Leics 1
League position (1988–89): 3rd
League playing record (1988–89): P 9, W 7, D 0, L 2, F 169, A 94

OLD NEWTONIANS

Hinckley Road (A47), Leicester Forest East, Leicester. Tel: 0533 392389
Founded: Originally 1904, re-formed 1928
President: James Weir
Chairman: Graham Corns
Secretary: Geoff Clark, 250 Wigston Lane, Aylestone, Leicester LE2 8DH. Tel: 832309 (H), 833461 (W)
Fixtures Secretary: Alan Massey, 314 Scraptoft Lane, Leicester. Tel: 0533 413928
Press Officer: Trevor Catcheside, 25 Stanhope Road, Wigston, Leicester. Tel: 0533 884995
Coach: P. Frost/B. Taylor
Club captain (1988–89): P. Frost
Club captain (1989–90): P. Frost
No. of teams: Senior 4, Youth 4, Minis 2
Directions to ground: From Leicester A47 towards Hinckley after 1 mile past Red Cow pub on right. towards Leicester from Hinckley A47 approx. 1 mile past Bull's Head pub on right
Clubhouse facilities: Open matchdays, Sunday lunch, Tuesday, Thursday
Club colours: Navy with red/green/white central bands (shirt), navy shorts. (*Change colours:* Red with navy/green/white central bands)
Nickname: "Newts"
Floodlights: No
Membership fees: Full £18, Playing £2.50 per match, Social £12 (Ground), Youth £10
Local newspapers: Leicester Mercury, Leicester Mail, Leicester Trader
League: Leics 1
League position (1988–89): 1st (promoted)
League playing record (1988–89): P 7, W 7 D 0, L 0, F 211, A 38
Competitions won: Leicestershire Div. II Champions, John Hill Cup Winners (15-a-side Competition)

SOUTH LEICESTER

Welford Road, Wigston Magna, Leicester LE8 1TE. Tel: 0533 882066
Founded: 1919
President: Frank Brewin
Chairman: John Gunby
Secretary: Richard Dowdall, 4 Bodmin Avenue,

Wigston Magna, Leicester LE8 2HB. Tel: 0533 885606
Fixtures Secretary: Scott Kirkpatrick, 47 Horsewell Lane, Wigston Magna, Leicester, LE8 2HQ. Tel: 0885021
Press Officer: M. McNeil
Club captain (1988–89): Robert Rayner
Club captain (1989–90): Tim Cooke
No. of teams: Senior 4+Colts, Youth 5, Minis 4
Directions to ground: Take Leicester ring road to A50 (Welfor Road). Travel trhough Wigston. Club is by final roundabout
Clubhouse facilities: Lounge, bar, six changing rooms, baths
Club colours: Green and white hoops
Nickname: South
Floodlights: Partial
Membership fees: Full £35
Local newspaper: Leicester Mercury
League: Leics 1
League position (1988–89): 7th
League playing record (1988–89): P 9, W 3, D 0, L 6

WEST LEICESTER

78A Granby Street, Leicester LE1 1DJ. Tel: 0533 540634
Founded: 1962
President: Geoff Topley
Chairman: Barry Bell
Secretary: Richard Pittom, 98 Grace Road, Aylestone Park, Leicester LE2 8AZ. Tel: 0533 834373 (H), 536725 (W)
Fixtures Secretary: Richard Bee, 47 Wilmington Road, Leicester. Tel: 0533 823658
Press Officer: As Secretary
Coach: Peter Poysor
Club captain (1988–89): Peter Poyser
Club captain (1989–90): Peter Poyser
No. of teams: Senior 3
Directions to ground: Narborough Road, opposite 'The Braunstone' public house, 1 miles from the M1/M69 junction. Follow signs for city centre
Clubhouse facilities: 2 bars
Club colours: Red shirts, white shorts
Nickname: West
Floodlights: No
Membership fees: Full £25, Playing £25, Social £15, Youth £15, Student £15, OAP £15
Local newspaper: Leicester Mercury
League: Leics 1
League position (1988–89): 8th
League playing record (1988–89): P 33, W 7, D 1, L 25

WIGSTON

Leicester Road, Countesthorpe, Leicester. Tel: 0533 771153
President: John Tipper
Chairman: Keith Jones
Secretary: Steve Benton, 5 Ramsdean Avenue, Wigston, Leicester LE8 1DX. Tel: 0533 889381 (H), 556776 (W)
Fixtures Secretary: Charles Hill, 7 Florence Avenue, South Wigston, Leicester. Tel: 0533 783274
Press Officer: John Nicholson, 7 The Farmway, Braunstone, Leicester. Tel: 0533 895773
Coach: John Nicholson
Club captain (1988–89): Steve Jordan
Club captain (1989–90): Ian Kedie
No. of teams: Senior 4, Youth 3
Directions to ground: Head for South Wigston, take Countesthorpe directions, ground on left-hand side
Ground capacity: Standing 3000
Clubhouse facilities: Open matchdays, Tues./Thurs eves., Sunday lunchtimes
Club colours: Black with amber, purple, white silver band. (*Change colours:* Purple)
Floodlights: No
Membership fees: Playing £15, Social £10

Local newspapers: Leiceser Mercury, Oadby & Wigston Mail, Oadby & Wigston Post
League: Leics 1
League position (1988–89): 11th (relegated)
League playing record (1988–89): P 10, W 1, D 0, L 9, F 83, A 214

LEICESTERSHIRE 2

ANSTEY
Link Road, Anstey, Leicester
Founded: 1980
President: George Dowling
Chairman: Frank Johnson
Secretary: Terry Everley, 287 Leicester Road, Markfield, Leicester LE6 0RH. Tel: 0530 243458 (H), 0509 268739 (W)
Fixtures Secretary: David Worrall, 72A Forest Gate, Anstey, Leicester. Tel: 0533 351321
Coach: Martin Ball
Club captain (1988–89): Robert Pearson
Club captain (1989–90): Robert Pearson
No. of teams: Senior 2, Minis 3
Directions to ground: A50 from Leicester. Right into Gynsill Lane, left into Anstey Lane and village, right in The Nook, left into link road. Ground behind Anstey Martins School
Clubhouse facilities: None
Club colours: Black. (*Change colours:* Red)
Floodlights: No
Membership fees: Full £15, Playing £15, Social £5, Youth £5, Student £5, OAP £5
Local newspaper: Leicester Mercury
League: Leics 2
League position (1988–89): 5th

AYLESTONE ATHLETIC
Victoria Park, Leicester
President: Jack Grimbley
Secretary: Alan Lee, 146 Dorset Avenue, South Wigston, Leicestser LE8 2WF. Tel: Leicester 0783246
Fixtures Secretary: Tom Clay, 56 Cranfield Road, Leicester. Tel: 834364
Press Officer: As Secretary
Coach: Michael Sarson
Club captain (1988–89): M. Sarson
Club captain (1989–90): R. Bentley
No. of teams: Senior 1
Directions to ground: The park is on the A6, 1 mile south of Leicester
Clubhouse facilities: Storks Head pub, Welford Road. Bar and food
Club colours: Scarlet and navy hoops. (*Change colours:* Scarlet)
Floodlights: No
Membership fees: Full £10, Playing £10, Student £6
Local newspaper: Leicester Mercury
League: Leics 2
League playing record (1988–89): P 26, W 10, D 2, L 14, F 278, A 374

AYLESTONIANS
Knighton Lane East, Leicester. Tel: Leics 834899.
Founded: 1921
Secretary: K. Moffoot, 1 Eton Close, Knighton, Leicester LE2 3TZ. Tel: Leics 701177 (H) Coalville 813111 (W).
Colours: Red/white/Blue/Navy
League: Leicestershire 2
Final position (1988–89): 9th (Div. 1)

BRAUNSTONE TOWN
Mossdale Meadows, The Kingsway, Braunstone, Leicester.
President: Haydn Pareth Evans-Hughes
Chairman: Ian Wright

Secretary: Philip Steven Clarke, 47 Bramcote Road, Wigston Fields, Leicester LE8 1DB. Tel: 0533 881952(H), 04557 2441 ext. 3722 (W)
Fixtures Secretary: Paul Whetton, 70 Henley Crescent, Braunstone, Leicester. Tel: 0533 890197 (H), 750999 (W)
Press Officer: Ian Wright, 97 Ravenhurst Road, Leicester LE3 2PW. Tel: 0533 897033
Coach: Peter Tyers
Club captain (1988–89): Nigel Tyers
Club captain (1989–90): Nigel Tyers
No. of teams: Senior 2
Club colours: Amber shirts, black shorts, amber socks
Floodlights: No
League: Leics 2
League position (1988–89): 7th
League playing record (1988–89): P 7, W 1, D 0, L 6

BURBAGE
John Cleveland College, Butt Lane, Hinckley, Leics LE10 1LD. Tel: Hinckley 632183
Founded: 1983
President: John R. Thomas
Chairman: John Gamble
Secretary: Lynda K. Murphy, 65 Hereford Close, Barwell, Leicestershire LE9 8HS. Tel: 0455 43998
Fixtures Secretary: B. Slater, 52 Marigold Drive, Burbage. Also R. Sansome, 190 Brookside, Burbage. Tel: 0455 30010
Coach: John Gamble
Club captain (1989–90): Michael Birchall
No. of teams: Senior 3
Directions to ground: Through Hinckley (A47), right turning into Butt Lane
Clubhouse facilities: Public house. Changing facilities at college
Club colours: Emerald green and white hoops, black shorts and socks
Nickname: Burbage Beagles
Floodlights: Yes
Membership fees: Full £5
Local newspaper: Hinckley Times
League: Leics 2
League position (1988–89): 6th
League playing record (1988–89): P 7, W 2, D 1, L 4

NEW PARKS OLD BOYS
No further information.

OAKHAM
The Showground, Barleythorpe Road, Oakham, Rutland. Tel: 0572 724206
Founded: 1923
President: Richard T. Watson M.R.C.V.S.
Chairman: Jeffrey T. Dale
Secretary: S. John Manby, Valley View, 1 East Lane, Ridlington, Nr. Oakham, Rutland LE15 9AN. Tel: 0572 822728 (H), 0533 899555 (W)
Fixtures Secretary: Peter Bateman, 26 Well Street, Langham, Nr. Oakham, Rutland. Tel: 0572 756143
Press Officer: Charles Mason, 5 Pleasant Terrace, Adderley Street, Uppingham, Rutland. Tel: 0572 821178
Coach: Stan Boles
Club captain (1988–89): Charles Mason
Club captain (1989–90): Charles Mason
No. of teams: Senior 3, Minis 5
Directions to ground: Take road to Langham out of Oakham and ground is on the showground on the right-hand side when leaving Oakham
Ground capacity: Standing 500+
Clubhouse facilities: Bar, darts, TV, singing
Club colours: Black and amber. (*Change colours:* Variable)
Floodlights: No
Membership fees: Full £20, Playing £20, Social £4, Youth £5, Student £10
Local newspapers: Rutland & Stamford Mercury,

Rutland Times, Leicester Mercury
League: Leics 2
League position (1988–89): 4th
League playing record (1988–89): P 7, W 4, D 0, L 3, F 93, A 61

OLD ASHBEIANS

New Field, Lower Packington Road, Ashby-de-la-Zouch, Leics. Tel: 0530 413992
President: D.E. Herbert, B.A.
Chairman: J. Little
Secretary: A. Porter, 26 Swallowdale, Thringstone, Leics. Tel: 0530 222137 (H), 021 772 3701 (W)
Fixtures Secretary: P. Clewes, 49 Lower Packington Road, Ashby-de-la-Zouch
Coach: I. Sharpe/T. Beales
Club captain (1988–89): A. Jackson
No. of teams: Senior 3, Youth 5+
Directions to ground: South of Ashley, via Lower Packington Road, off A453
Club colours: Maroon and sky
Floodlights: No
Membership fees: Full £25
League: Mids Leics 2
League position (1988–89): 3rd
League playing record (1988–89): P 7, W 5, D 0, L 2, F 157, A 56

SHEPSHED

Hindleys College Sports Ground, Forest Street, Shepshed, Leicester. Tel: 0509 506175
President: Brian Saley
Chairman: Raymond W.P. Short
Secretary: Alan K. Fossey, 24 Tetbury Drive, Shepshed, Leicester LE12 9NF. Tel: 0509 508787 (H),

0530 36300 (W)
Fixtures Secretary: Raymond W.P. Short, 40D Loughborough Road, Shepshed, Leicester LE12 9DN. Tel: 0509 503592 (H), 506175 (W)
Press Officer: Neil Parry (Social Secretary), Holborn House, 76 Charnwood Road, Shepshed, Leics. Tel: 0509 504780
Coach: T.B.A.
Club captain (1988–89): David 'Griff' Griffiths
Club captain (1989–90): David 'Griff' Griffiths
No. of teams: Senior 2
Directions to ground: M1 Junction 23, A512 to Shepshed, right at first traffic lights into Leicester Road, after mile immediately after petrol station right into Forest Street. Ground at college 300 yards on right
Ground capacity: Standing 1000+
Clubhouse facilities: Richmond Arms P.H., Forest Street, Shepshed
Club colours: Scarlet shirts, black shorts. (*Change colours:* Black shirts and shorts)
Floodlights: No
Membership fees: Full £15, Playing £15, Social £5, Student £8
Local newspapers: Shepshed/Loughborough Echo, Leicester Mercury
League: Leics 2
League position (1988–89): 8th
League playing record (1988–89): P 7, W 0, D 0, L 7, F 34, A 236

SOUTH WIGSTON

New team in Leicestershire. No records available.

Ollerton line up before Notts, Lincs & Derbyshire 4 East action

EAST MIDLANDS LEAGUES

THE EAST Midlands had only 28 teams durng the past season, the Third Division fielding only six clubs and the ambitious Biggleswade took the top honours with only one defeat to go up to the East Midlands/Leicestershire League. Only one club is relegated from the division and the unlucky team is St. Neots, who were strong promotion candidates only a year ago. An adjustment in the leagues means promotion from Division 2 for Wellingborough OG, relegated only 12 months earlier, and Corby, whilst again only one team from Division 2 goes down – Cutler Hammer after a sad campaign being the unlucky ones. They make way for Bedford Swifts and Deeping, another team which has bounced back after being relegated from higher company. The leagues could benefit from some new recruits as the usual trend is for more teams or – at least – the status quo.

EAST MIDLANDS: OFFICIALS

(One)
Terry Burwell,
4 Teal Close,
Ladybridge,   (H) 0604 31870
Northampton   (B) 0604 761217

(Two/Three)
Paul Adams,
323A Bedford Road, Kempston,
Bedfordshire MK42 8QB   (H) 0234 853390

TABLES 1987–88

EAST MIDLANDS 1

	P	W	D	L	F	A	PTS
Wellingboro'	10	8	1	1	198	55	17
St Neots	10	7	0	3	210	107	14
Biggleswade	10	7	0	3	133	102	14
N'ton BBOB	10	6	1	3	114	79	13
N'Pton O Scts	10	5	0	5	117	101	10
Ampthill	10	5	0	5	129	122	10
Huntingdon	10	5	0	5	100	95	10
Daventry	10	4	0	6	82	152	8
Rushden	10	3	0	7	84	137	6
W'ingboro OG	10	3	0	7	79	156	6
Dunstablians	10	1	0	9	64	204	2

EAST MIDLANDS 2

	P	W	D	L	F	A	PTS
N'ton Mens O	10	9	0	0	308	63	20
Brackley	10	7	1	2	205	68	15
Corby	10	7	0	3	140	70	14
N'ton Casuals	10	7	0	3	146	101	14
St Ives	9	5	0	4	99	46	10
Oundle	10	4	0	6	86	154	8
Vauxhall	10	4	0	6	97	199	8
Cutler Hammer	10	3	1	6	68	134	7
Colworth H	9	3	0	6	74	155	6
O Wellburian	10	2	0	8	47	229	4
Deeping	10	1	0	9	83	131	2

EAST MIDLANDS 3

	P	W	D	L	F	A	PTS
Bedford Qns	8	8	0	0	292	34	16
Westwood	8	6	0	2	159	63	12
Bugbrooke	8	6	0	2	139	66	12
N'ton Hthns	8	5	0	3	65	75	10
Bedford Swifts	8	3	0	5	123	106	6
RAF Bedford	8	3	0	5	104	123	6
Potton	8	2	0	6	69	151	4
Bretton	8	2	0	6	37	284	4
Ramsey	8	1	0	7	69	155	2

TABLES 1988–89

EAST MIDLANDS 1

	P	W	D	L	F	A	PTS
Biggleswade	10	9	0	1	213	76	18
Ampthill & D	10	7	1	2	192	104	15
N'hampton Mens	10	6	1	3	142	111	13
N'hampton Sc'ts	10	6	0	4	121	116	12
Rushden & High	10	5	0	5	140	112	10
O No'hamptians	10	5	0	5	128	131	10
Huntingdon & D	10	3	2	5	98	115	8
N'hampton Boys	10	3	1	6	110	141	7
Brackley	10	2	2	6	96	171	6
Daventry	10	2	2	6	113	221	6
St Neots	10	2	1	7	73	128	5

EAST MIDLANDS 2

	P	W	D	L	F	A	PTS
Wellingboro OG	10	8	1	1	176	71	17
Corby	10	7	1	2	256	52	15
Dunstablians	10	7	1	2	181	78	15
N'hampton Cas	10	7	0	3	154	109	14
Westwood	10	5	1	4	113	121	11
Colworth House	10	5	0	5	126	133	10
Bedford Qns	10	5	0	5	140	152	10
Oundle	10	3	1	6	93	134	7
St Ives	10	2	1	7	72	162	5
Vauxhall	10	2	0	8	83	151	4
Cutler Hammer	10	1	0	9	37	268	2

EAST MIDLANDS 3

	P	W	D	L	F	A	PTS
Bedford Swifts	5	5	0	0	147	36	10
Deepings	5	4	0	1	58	21	8
Bugbrooke	5	3	0	2	78	58	6
O W'ingburians	5	1	0	4	41	69	2
N'mpton Heath	5	1	0	4	35	85	2
Potton	5	1	0	4	42	132	2

MIDLANDS DIVISION FIXTURES 1989/90

EAST MIDLANDS ONE

Sat. 9th September (Week 2)
Brackley v Northampton Mens Own
Daventry v Corby
Rushden/Higham v Northampton BBOB
O Northamptonians v N'hampton O Scouts
Ampthill v Huntingdon

Sat. 23rd September (Week 4)
Huntingdon v Brackley
Northampton Old Scouts v Ampthill
Northampton BBOB v O Northamptonians
Corby v Rushden/Higham
Wellingborough OG v Daventry

Sat. 14th October (Week 6)
Brackley v Northampton Old Scouts
Northampton Mens Own v Huntingdon
Rushden/Higham v Wellingborough OG
Old Northamptonians v Corby
Ampthill v Northampton BBOB

Sat. 28th October (Week 8)
Corby v Ampthill
Wellingborough OG v O Northamptonians
Daventry v Rushden/Higham
N'hampton O Scouts v N'hampton Mens Own
Northampton BBOB v Brackley

Sat. 11th November (Week 10)
Brackley v Corby
N'hampton Mens Own v N'hampton BBOB
Huntingdon v Northampton Old Scouts
Old Northamptonians v Daventry
Ampthill v Wellingborough OG

Sat 18th November (Week 11)
Northampton BBOB v Huntingdon
Corby v Northampton Mens Own
Wellinborough OG v Brackley
Daventry v Ampthill
Rushden/Higham v Old Northamptonians

Sat. 25th November (Week 12)
Brackley v Daventry
N'hampton Mens Own v Wellingb'rough OG
Huntingdon v Corby
N'hampton Old Scouts v N'hampton BBOB
Ampthill v Rushden/Higham

Sat. 13th January (Week 18)
Corby v Northampton Old Scouts
Wellingborough OG v Huntingdon
Daventry v Northampton Mens Own
Rushden/Higham v Brackley
Old Northamptonians v Ampthill

Sat. 10th March (Week 26)
Northampton Mens Own v Rushden/Higham
Brackley v Old Northamptonians
Huntingdon v Daventry
Northampton Old Scouts v Wellingborough OG
Northampton BBOB v Corby

Sat. 31st March (Week X7)
Wellingborough OG v Northampton BBOB
Daventry v Northampton Old Scouts
Rushden/Higham v Huntingdon
Old Northamptonians v Northampton Mens Own
Ampthill v Brackley

Sat. 28th April (Week 32)
Northampton Mens Own v Ampthill
Huntingdon v Old Northamptonians
Northampton Old Scouts v Rushden/Higham
Northampton BBOB v Daventry
Corby v Wellingborough OG

MIDLANDS DIVISION FIXTURES 1989/90

EAST MIDLANDS TWO

Sat. 9th September (Week 2)
Bedford Queens v Dunstablians
St Neots v Deepings
St Ives v Bedford Swifts
Oundle v Colworth House
Westwood v Vauxhall Motors

Sat. 23rd September (Week 4)
Vauxhall Motors v Bedford Queens
Colworth House v Westwood
Bedford Swifts v Oundle
Deepings v St Ives
Northampton Casuals v St Neots

Sat. 14th October (Week 6)
Bedford Queens v Colworth House
Dunstablians v Vauxhall Motors
St Ives v Northampton Casuals
Oundle v Deepings
Westwood v Bedford Swifts

Sat. 28th October (Week 8)
Colworth House v Dunstablians
Bedford Swifts v Bedford Queens
Deepings v Westwood
Northampton Casuals v Oundle
St Neots v St Ives

Sat. 11th November (Week 10)
Bedford Queens v Deepings
Dunstablians v Bedford Swifts
Vauxhall Motors v Colworth House
Oundle v St Neots
Westwood v Northampton Casuals

Sat 18th November (Week 11)
Bedford Swifts v Vauxhall Motors
Deepings v Dunstablians
Northampton Casuals v Bedford Queens
St Neots v Westwood
St Ives v Oundle

Sat. 25th November (Week 12)
Bedford Queens v St Neots
Dunstablians v Northampton Casuals
Vauxhall Motors v Deepings
Colworth House v Bedford Swifts
Westwood v St Ives

Sat. 13th January (Week 18)
Deepings v Colworth House
Northampton Casuals v Vauxhall Motors
St Neots v Dunstablians
St Ives v Bedford Queens
Oundle v Westwood

Sat. 10th March (Week 26)
Bedford Queens v Oundle
Dunstablians v St Ives
Vauxhall Motors v St Neots
Colworth House v Northampton Casuals
Bedford Swifts v Deepings

Sat. 31st March (Week X7)
Northampton Casuals v Bedford Swifts
St Neots v Colworth House
St Ives v Vauxhall Motors
Oundle v Dunstablians
Westwood v Bedford Queens

Sat. 28th April (Week 32)
Dunstablians v Westwood
Vauxhall Motors v Oundle
Colworth House v St Ives
Bedford Swifts v St Neots
Deepings v Northampton Casuals

MIDLANDS DIVISION FIXTURES 1989/90

EAST MIDLANDS THREE

Sat. 9th September (Week 2)
Bugbrooke v Cutler Hammer
N'hampton Heathens v Old Wellingburians
Potton v Beds Police

Sat. 23rd September (Week 4)
Cutler Hammer v Northampton Heathens
Old Wellingburians v Potton
Beds Police v Bugbrooke

Sat. 14th October (Week 6)
Bugbrooke v Northampton Heathens
Potton v Cutler Hammer
Old Wellingburians v Beds Police

Sat. 28th October (Week 8)
Cutler Hammer v Old Wellingburians
Potton v Bugbrooke
Beds Police v Northampton Heathens

Sat. 11th November (Week 10)
Bugbrooke v Old Wellingburians
Northampton Heathens v Potton
Cutler Hammer v Beds Police

Sat 18th November (Week 11)
Cutler Hammer v Bugbrooke
Old Wellingburians v Northampton Heathens
Beds Police v Potton

Sat. 25th November (Week 12)
Northampton Heathens v Cutler Hammer
Potton v Old Wellingburians
Bugbrooke v Beds Police

Sat. 13th January (Week 18)
Northampton Heathens v Bugbrooke
Cutler Hammer v Potton
Beds Police v Old Wellingburians

Sat. 10th March (Week 26)
Old Wellingburians v Cutler Hammer
Bugbrooke v Potton
Northampton Heathens v Beds Police

Sat. 28th April (Week 32)
Old Wellingburians v Bugbrooke
Potton v Northampton Heathens
Beds Police v Cutler Hammer

EAST MIDLANDS ONE

AMPTHILL

Dillingham Park, Woburn Road, Ampthill, Bedford.
Tel: 0525 403303
Founded: 1951 (originally 1881)
President: R. Dillingham
Chairman: B. Clark
Secretary: R.G. Churchill, The Bungalow, Park
Gardens, Bletchley, Milton Keynes MK3 6HT. Tel:
0908 677577
Fixtures Secretary: P. New, 39 Station Road,
Ampthill, Bedford. Tel: 0525 404945 (H), 403431 (W)
Press Officer: As Fixtures Secretary
Coach: G. McElroy
Club captain (1988–89): Peter Nouch
Club captain (1989–90): Richard Sheard
No. of teams: Senior 5, Youth 5, Minis 5
Directions to ground: West of Ampthill Town Centre,
opposite Ampthill Park
Ground capacity: Open
Clubhouse facilities: Two storey, brick built
Club colours: Maroon/amber. (*Change colours:*
Maroon)
Floodlights: No
Membership fees: Full £25, Playing £25, Social £3,
Youth £1, Student £1, OAP £1
Ground admission: Nil
Local newspapers: Ampthill/Flitwick Times & Express
League position (1988–89): 2nd
League playing record (1988–89): P 31, W 20, D 2,
L 9, F 674, A 421
Competitions won: Stockwood Park Sevens, Winners
1989. Loughboro Colts Sevens, Winners 1989

BRACKLEY

Pavilions Way, Brackley, Northants. Tel: 0280 700685
President: D. Vernon
Chairman: J. Hartley
Secretary: N. Hooper, Ingrams Cottage, Hinton-in-
the-Hedges, Brackley, Northants NN13 5NE. Tel:
0280 703563 (H). 0295 57150 (W)
Fixtures Secretary: R. Grant, 1 The Square, Aynho,
Oxon. Tel: Croughton 810819 (H)
Coach: N. Johnson
Club captain (1988–89): C. Page
Club captain (1989–90): C. Page
No. of teams: Senior 3
Directions to ground: From Brackley take the
Banbury Road, after mile turn left into Pavilions
Way. Entrance to ground on left after mile
Club colours: Blue. (*Change colours:* Red)
Floodlights: No
Membership fees: Full £18
League: East Midlands 1
League position (1988–89): 9th
League playing record (1988–89): P 10, W 2, D 2,
L 6, F 96, A 111

CORBY

Northern Park, Rockingham Road, Corby, Northants.
Tel: 0536 204466
Founded: 1958
President: William Douglas Wetherall
Chairman: Leslie Alan Smith
Secretary: Arthur George Portman, 2 Teesdale Road,
Corby, Northants NN17 1LN. Tel: 0536 69288
Fixtures Secretary: Alan Johnson, 4 Great Easton
Road, Caldecott, Mk. Harborough, Leics. Tel: 0536
771079
Press Officer: Anthony Bebb, 1 Uist Walk, Corby,
Northants. Tel: 0536 62206
Coach: John Smith
Club captain (1988–89): Anthony Bebb
Club captain (1989–90): Anthony Bebb
No. of teams: Senior 3, Youth 1, Minis 3
Directions to ground: Situated at junction of A6003/
A6116 near Rockingham Castle
Clubhouse facilities: Yes

Club colours: Scarlet/white hoops. (*Change colours:*
Scarlet or bottle green)
Floodlights: No
League: EMid 2
League position (1988–89): 2nd (promoted)
League playing record (1988–89): P 11, W 7, D 1,
L 2, F 252, A 56

DAVENTRY

Stefen Hill, Western Avenue, Daventry, Northants.
Tel: 0327 703802
Founded: 1968
President: Bill Tyson
Chairman: John Bell
Secretary: Geoff Buck, 'Reckfield', London Road,
Daventry, Northants, NN11 4DA. Tel: 0327 703401
(H), 709462 (W)
Fixtures Secretary: Graham Woodliffe, Checkley
Cottage, Chapel Street, Charwelton, Daventry,
Northants NN1 6YU. Tel: 0327 61461 (H), 709137
(W)
Press Officer: John Bell, Berryfields Farm, Daventry,
Northants. Tel: 0788 890320 (H), 890320 (W)
Coach: Vic Wilton
Club captain (1988–89): Clive Hill
Club captain (1989–90): Clive Hill
No. of teams: Senior 3, Colts 1, Minis 4
Directions to ground: M1 Junction 15: Take the A45
to Daventry, upon reaching Daventry you come to a
roundabout (adjacent is the Penguin Hotel). Take the
2nd exit and then the 3rd road on the left. Ground is
immediately on the left
Ground capacity: Standing 2000
Clubhouse facilities: Open all day Saturday, Sunday
lunchtime and every evening
Club colours: All black. (*Change colours:* Red shirts)
Nickname: 'All Blacks'
Floodlights: Yes (training area only)
Membership fees: Full £15, Playing £15, Social £5,
Youth £5, Student £5, OAP £5
Ground admission: Free
Programme: No. of editorial pages 3; No. of
advertising pages 5; Price Free
Programme editor: As Secretary
Local newspapers: Daventry Weekly Express,
Daventry Post
League: EMid 1
League position (1988–89): 10th
League playing record (1988–89): P 10, W 2, D 2,
L 6, F 113, A 221

HUNTINGDON & DISTRICT

The Racecourse, Brampton, Huntingdon
Founded: 1935
President: Sam Raby
Chairman: Nick Whitbey
Secretary: John Bishop, 2 Willow Close, Little
Paxton, Huntingdon, Cambs. Tel: 0480 72468
Fixtures Secretary: Jerry Adams, 21 Chapel Street,
Alconbury, Huntingdon. Tel: 0480 891032 (H), 57344
(W)
Coach: Trevor Fowler
Club captain (1988–89): Andrew Bragg
Club captain (1989–90): Andrew Bragg
No. of teams: Senior 4
Directions to ground: Follow signs to Brampton
Racecourse
Club colours: Emerald green shirts, blue shirts.
(*Change colours:* Blue shirts)
Nickname: The Stags
Floodlights: Yes
Local newspapers: Hunts Post, Cambridge Evening
News
League: EMid 1
League position (1988–89): 7th
League playing record (1988–89): P 10, W 3, D 2, L 5
Competitions won: Royston Sevens

NORTHAMPTON B.B.O.B.

St. Andrews Mill, St. Andrews Road, Semilong, Northampton, NN. Tel: 0604 32460
Founded: 1933
President: Keith Allen
Secretary: Sally Jeffery, as above. Tel: 0604 717947
Fixtures Secretary: Gordon Lines, 84 Sherwood Avenue, Spring Park, Northampton, NNZ 8TD. Tel: 0604 845198 (H), 766311 (W)
Press Officer: As Fixtures Secretary
Club captain (1988–89): Sidney Feasey
Club captain (1989–90): Robert Willix
No. of teams: Senior 4
Directions to ground: Leave M1 at Junction 15, follow dual carriageway, leave at 2nd exit for Northampton at (A428) Bedford Road roundabout (near Casuals R.F.C.). Members coming into Northampton from the East of the area should also make for this Bedford Road roundabout (A428). Leave roundabout in direction of Town Centre, at 2nd. set of traffic lights turn right (after turning Hospital on right), go straight through next 3 sets of lights, at fourth set go across, bearing slightly to left into Grafton Street, at next traffic lights turn right into St. Andrew's Road, ground and clubhouse 300 yards on left
Clubhouse facilities: Bar, lounge, two changing rooms
Club colours: Navy with light blue and maroon hoops. (*Change colours:* Red)
Floodlights: Yes
Membership fees: Full £15, Playing £1.50, Social £3, Student £1
Local newspapers: Chronicle & Echo, Post, Citizen
League: EMid 1
League position (1988–89): 8th
League playing record (1988–89): P 10, W 3, D 1, L 6, F 110, A 141

NORTHAMPTON MEN'S OWN

Stoke Road, Ashton, Northampton. Tel: 0604 862463
Founded: 1922
President: James Attwood
Chairman: Robert Bunting
Secretary: David R. Edwards, 1A Landcross Drive, Abington Vale, Northampton NN3 3NA. Tel: 0604 28972 (H), 252837 (W)
Fixtures Secretary: Ernie Dalby, 39 Forest Road, Piddington, Northampton NN7 2DA. Tel: 0604 870609 (H), 255427 (W)
Press Officer: James Attwood, Miles Well House, 90 Lumbertubs Lane, Northampton. Tel: 0604 44638
Coach: John Wilson
Club captain (1988–89): Andrew Morris
Club captain (1989–90): Andrew Morris
No. of teams: Senior 5–6, Youth 1, Minis 1
Directions to ground: M1 Junc. 15 A508 to village of Roade. Pass through, after one mile turn left at crossroads to Ashton. 700 yds on right
Ground capacity: Standing 2000
Clubhouse facilities: Three pitches, ample parking, two bars, entertainment room, kitchen, committee room
Club colours: White-blue hoops
Nickname: The Own
Floodlights: No
Membership fees: Full £12.50, Playing £12.50, Social £3, Youth £2
Ground admission: Nil
Programme: No. of editorial pages 2; No. of advertising pages 6–8; Price 50p
Programme editor: As Press Officer
Local newspapers: Chronicle & Echo, Northants Post, Citizen
League position (1988–89): 3rd
League playing record (1988–89): P 39, W 28, D 2, L 9, F 681, A 342
Competitions won: Ball of Month Competition

NORTHAMPTON OLD SCOUTS

Rushmore Road, Northampton. Tel: 0604 33639.
Founded: 1927
Secretary: D. Walsh, 14 Berry Close, Rothersthorpe, Northampton NN7 3JQ. Tel: 0604 831455, 0327 71100.
Fixtures Secretary: K.D. Shurville, 41 Churchill Avenue, Northampton. Tel: 0604 494374.
League: East Mids 1
Final position (1988–89): 45th

OLD NORTHAMPTONIANS

Billing Road, Northampton. Tel: 0604 34045
President: B. Liddington
Chairman: J. Bull
Secretary: K.R. Newton, 73 Cavendish Drive, Langlands, Northampton NN3 3HL. Tel: 0604 32036 (H), 766333 (W)
Fixtures Secretary: A. Deathe, 11 Hallam Close, Moulton, Northampton. Tel: 0604 42161
Press Officer: K.R. Newton, 73 Cavendish Drive, Langlands, Northampton NN3 3HL. Tel: 0604 32036 (H), 766333 (W)
Coach: M. Lee
Club captain (1988–89): A. Hodgson
Club captain (1989–90): A. Hodgson
No. of teams: Senior 4, Youth 2
Directions to ground: Junction 15 M1 – off ring road signposted Kettering/Wellingborough, pass Old Scouts RFC on left-hand side, turn left at lights. Ground 200 yards on right-hand side
Clubhouse facilities: Open matchdays and evenings
Club colours: Cardinal, navy and gold hoops
Nickname: The ON's
Floodlights: Yes (training only)
Membership fees: Full £25, Playing £22, Social £14, Youth £5
Programme: No. of editorial pages 2; No. of advertising pages 5; Price Free
Programme editor: A. Hodgson, 146 Charnwood Avenue, Northampton
Local newspapers: Northants Post and the Chronicle & Echo
League: EMid 1
League position (1988–89): 6th
League playing record (1988–89): P 10, W 5, D 0, L 5, F 128, A 131

RUSHDEN AND HIGHAM

Manor Park, Bedford Road, Rushden, Northants. Tel: 0933 312071
Founded: 1959
President: Malcolm Wright
Chairman: Brian Ward
Secretary: Steve Miles, 9 Grange Road, Little Cransley, Kettering, Northants. Tel: 0536 790429 (H), 0604 235410 (W)
Fixtures Secretary: Colin Stringer, 18 Paddocks Road, Rushden, Northants. Tel: 0933 58481
Press Officer: Steve Miles, 9 Grange Road, Little Cransley, Kettering, Northants. Tel: 0536 790429 (H), 0604 235410 (W)
Club captain (1988–89): Gordon Riding
Club captain (1989–90): Martin Garley
No. of teams: Senior 4, Youth 2, Minis 4
Directions to ground: On main A6, Bedford side of Rushden. On left travelling to Bedford and right from Bedford
Clubhouse facilities: Clubhouse and changing rooms
Club colours: Black and white hoops. (*Change colours:* Yellow)
Floodlights: No
Membership fees: Full £20, Playing £20, Social £13,

Youth £10, Mini £4, Junior £5
Local newspapers: Evening Telegraph, Northants
Post, Citizen and Leader
League: EMid 1
League position (1988–89): 5th
League playing record (1988–89): P 10, W 5, D 0,
L 5, F 140, A 112

WELLINGBOROUGH OLD GRAMMARIANS

Memorial Sports Ground, Sanders Road, Finedon
Road Industrial Estate, Wellingborough, Northants.
Tel: 0933 79316. Clubhouse: 0933 226188
Founded: 1938
President: Ged Eady
Chairman: Dick Bedells
Secretary: Kevin McDonald, 17 Second Avenue,
Wellingborough, Northants NN8 3PX. Tel: 0933
72526 (H), 72222 (W)
Fixtures Secretary: Paul Bush, 33 Newtown Road,
Little Irchester, Nr. Wellingborough, Northants. Tel:
0933 441663 (H), 222741 (W)
Press Officer: Nick Groom, 9 Dene Close,
Wellingborough. Tel: 0933 676739 (H), 0604 38268
(W)
Coach: Peter Mankiewicz
Club captain (1988–89): Dick Petty
Club captain (1989–90): Nick Groom
No. of teams: Senior 4, Youth 3
Directions to ground: From A45 follow signs to
Finedon Road Industrial Estate. From entry
roundabout take Sanders Road. Ground mile on
right
Ground capacity: Standing Unlimited
Clubhouse facilities: 46 Oxford Street,
Wellingborough. Normal Licensing hours
Club colours: Claret and white hoops. (*Change
colours:* Claret solid)
Nickname: Old Boys
Floodlights: Yes (training only)
Membership fees: Full £2
Programme: No. of editorial pages 1; No. of
advertising pages 4; Price Nil
Programme editor: Dick Petty, 3 Easy Street,
Stannick
Local newspaper: Evening Telegraph
League: EMid 1
League position (1988–89): 1st (promoted)
League playing record (1988–89): P 10, W 8, D 1, L 1
Competitions won: I.J. Nicholas Memorial Trophy.
East Midlands Divisio 2 Courage Club Champions

EAST MIDLANDS 2

BEDFORD QUEENS

Allen Park, Old Ford End Road, Queens Park,
Bedford. Tel: 0234 271172
President: Ray Mann
Chairman: Simon Lousada
Secretary: Tony Davis, 49 Gratton Road, Queens
Park, Bedford. Tel: 0234 325179
Fixtures Secretary: Ian Mortimer, 14 Palmerston
Street, Bedford. Tel: 0234 219219 (H), 0234 840356
(W)
Press Officer: Simon Lousada, 102 High Street,
Kempston. Tel: 0908 582240 (H), 0234 840356 (W)
Coach: Richard Millard
Club captain (1988–89): Geoff Janes
Club captain (1989–90): Simon Pierce-Roberts
No. of teams: Senior 3
Clubhouse facilities: Open matchdays
Club colours: Maroon and white hooped shirts, navy
shorts. (*Change colours:* All maroon shirts)
Floodlights: No
Membership fees: Full £15, Playing £15, Social £10,
Youth £5, Student £5, OAP £5
Local newspapers: Beds on Sunday, Beds Times,
Bedford Herald, Bedford Express & Citizen

League position (1988–89): 6th
League playing record (1988–89): P 10, W 5, D 0,
L 5, F 140, A 152

BEDFORD SWIFTS

Newnham Athletics Track, Barkers Lane, Bedford.
Tel: 0234 54606
Founded: 1950
President: Michael Cotter
Chairman: James Clark
Secretary: Trevor N. Stewart, 64 Ravensden Road,
Renhold, Bedford MK41 0JY. Tel: 0234 771828
Fixtures Secretary: Stanley Davidson, 26 Thornton
Street, Kempston, Bedford. Tel: 0234 857529
Press Officer: Steven Tuner, 17 Swift Close, Bedford.
Tel: 0234 272700 (H), 44231 (W)
Coach: Eamon Quinn
Club captain (1988–89): Noel Hinchliffe
Club captain (1989–90): Noel Hinchliffe
No. of teams: Senior 4–5
Directions to ground: From A1 North and South
follow A428 west towards Northampton/Birmingham.
Follow signs left turn to Milton Keynes, Luton and
M1 South. Ground 200 yards on left
Clubhouse facilities: Shared with Bedford Athletics
Club. Open matchdays and Tuesday and Thursday
evenings
Club colours: Gold/royal blue hoop shirts, navy
shorts, socks. (*Change colours:* Gold shirts)
Floodlights: No
Membership fees: Full £15
Local newspaper: Bedfordshire Times and Express
(1988–89): 1st (promoted)
League playing record (1988–89): P 7, W 7, D 0, L 0,
F 480, A 60
Competitions won: East Midlands 3 League

COLWORTH HOUSE

Unilever Research, Colworth House, Sharnbrook,
Beds. Tel: 0234 222221
Founded: 1964
President: Dr. D. Osborne
Chairman: S. Williamson
Secretary: S. Dyks, Unilever Research, Section 912,
Colworth House, Sharnbrook, Beds. Tel: 0933 56966
(H), 0234 222798 (W)
Fixtures Secretary: G. Stock, Unilever Research,
Section 922, Colworth House, Sharnbrook, Beds. Tel:
0933 650418 (H), 0234 222660 (W)
Coach: D. Woodhead
Club captain (1988–89): S. Dyks
Club captain (1989–90): B. Kasteel
No. of teams: Senior 3
Directions to ground: Leave Rushden on A6-Bedford,
after 6 miles turn into Sharnbrook, at URL Colworth
signs, follow sports field directions
Clubhouse facilities: Colworth House Sports and
Social Club
Club colours: Emerald/green black. (*Change colours:*
Red/black)
Floodlights: No
Membership fees: Included in match fees (£3 per
game) + £1 social club fee
Local newspapers: Bedfordshire Times, Rushden
Evening Telegraph
League position (1988–89): 6th
League playing record (1988–89): P 10, W 5, D 0,
L 5, F 126, A 133

DEEPINGS

Linchfield Road, Deeping St. James, Peterborough.
Tel: 0778 345228
Founded: 1983
President: Graham D. Cox
Chairman: David K. Evans
Secretary: Brian E. Kirby, 14 Halfleet, Market
Deeping, Peterborough PE6 8DB. Tel: 0778 343048
(H), 0733 68989 ext. 4173 (W)
Fixtures Secretary: Peter Ward, 14 Manor Way,
Deeping St. James, Peterborough. Tel: 0778 343489

Press Officer: David Morgan, 18 Clover Road, Market Deeping, Peterborough. Tel: 0778 345549
Coach: Chris Davies
Club captain (1988–89): Mark Whitehead
Club captain (1989–90): Mark Whitehead
No. of teams: Senior 2, Youth 1
Directions to ground: Spalding Road from Market Deeping. Turn left at crossroads just before footbridge over road, then immediately right through gate
Clubhouse facilities: Clubroom and four changing rooms
Club colours: Yellow green and black hoops, black shorts and socks. (*Change colours:* White)
Floodlights: Yes (for training only)
Membership fees: Full £10, Playing £15, Youth £2, Student £7.50
Local newspapers: Peterborough Evening Telegraph, Stamford Mercury
League position (1988–89): 2nd (promoted)
League playing record (1988–89): P 5, W 4, D 0, L 1, F 58, A 21
Competitions won: Promotion from Division 3. Plate Winners, Oundle 7's

DUNSTABLIANS

Bidwell Park, Houghton Regis, Dunstable, Beds LU5 6JP. Tel: 0582 866555
Founded: 1948
President: Ross Barrington
Chairman: Norman Cook
Secretary: Paul Freeman, 19 Preston Road, Toddington, Dunstable, Beds. Tel: 05255 4550 (H), 0234 328111 (W)
Fixtures Secretary: William Thompson, 1 Bibshall Crescent, Dunstable. Tel: Dunstable 602209 (H), Luton 842323 ext. 306 (W)
Press Officer: See Fixtures Secretary
Coach: Philip Brown
Club captain (1988–89): Martin Morris
Club captain (1989–90): Philip Brown
No. of teams: Senior 4, Youth 3, Minis 5
Directions to ground: Junction 12 M1, through Toddington, ground on 'S' bend, entering Houghton Regis
Ground capacity: Standing 500
Clubhouse facilities: 2 bars, 6 changing rooms
Club colours: Red, silver and black. (*Change colours:* Black)
Floodlights: Yes
Membership fees: Full £17.25, Playing £17.25, Social £11.50
Local newspapers: Dunstable Gazette, Herald, Citizen
League: EMid 2
League position (1988–89): 3rd
League playing record (1988–89): P 10, W 7, D 1, L 2, F 181, A 78

NORTHAMPTON CASUALS

Rush Mills House, Bedford Road, Northampton. Tel: 0604 36716
Founded: 1922
President: M.D. Askew
Chairman: J.T. Wearing
Secretary: S.M. Tee, 41 Gresham Drive, West Hunsbury, Northampton. Tel: 0604 701685 (H), 0203 412029 (W)
Fixtures Secretary: M.D. Askew, Rush Mills House, Bedford Road, Northampton. Tel: 0604 846959 (H), 581131 (W)
Press Officer: T.B.A.
Coach: T.B.A.
Club captain (1988–89): P.D. Horrocks
Club captain (1989–90): P.D. Horrocks
No. of teams: Senior 4, Youth 1, Minis 4
Directions to ground: From A45 ringroad take A428 Bedford exit, head towards Bedford. Entrance to ground is 500 yds on right

Clubhouse facilities: 2 bars, changing rooms for 6 teams, physio room
Club colours: Black with an amber band. (*Change colours:* Yellow shirts, black shorts and socks)
Nickname: The 'Ks'
Floodlights: No
Membership fees: Full £15, Playing £15, Social £5, Youth £3, Student £1
Local newspaper: Northampton Chronicle and Echo
League: EM 2
League position (1988–89): 4th
League playing record (1988–89): P 10, W 7, D 0, L 3, F 141, A 94

OUNDLE

Occupation Road, Oundle, Northants. Tel: Oundle 73101
Founded: 1986
President: Haydn Adams
Chairman: Graham Snelling
Secretary: Roger Smith, 6 Pheasant Way, Yaxley, Peterborough, Cambs. Tel: 0733 242344 (H), 68989 (W)
Fixtures Secretary: Nigel Howe, Highgate House, Bulwick, Nr. Corry, Northants. Tel: 078 085285
Press Officer: As Fixtures Secretary
Coach: Terry Cobner
Club captain (1988–89): Terry Curtis
Club captain (1989–90): Terry Curtis
No. of teams: Senior 3, Youth 3, Minis All ages
Directions to ground: Enter Oundle at eastern end of bypass roundabout over bridge, turn right at garage on bend, first right, 40 m right onto track leading to club
Clubhouse facilities: Changing for 6 teams, bar, kitchen, toilets, etc.
Club colours: Black with red and white hoops. (*Change colours:* Maroon)
Nickname: Owls
Floodlights: Yes (training only)
Membership fees: Full £15, *Playing £3, Social £5, *Youth 50p, *Student £1.50 (* Payed on a weekly basis)
Local newspapers: Kettering & Peterborough Evening Telegraph, Stamfor Mercury
League: EMid 2
League position (1988–89): 8th
League playing record (1988–89): P 10, W 3, D 1, L 6, F 81, A 138

ST. IVES (CAMBS.)

St. Ivo Outdoor Centre, California Road, St. Ives, Cambs. Tel: 0408 65485
Founded: 1976
President: Jim Murdoch
Chairman: Percy Walker
Secretary: Peter Reeve, 7 Aragon Close, Buckden, Huntingdon, Cambs PE18 9TY. Tel: 0480 811272 (H), 433433 (W)
Fixtures Secretary: Brian Paynter, 218 Ramsey Road, St. Ives, Huntingdon, Cambs PE17 6QZ. Tel: 0480 67511 (H), 433433 (W)
Press Officer: As Fixtures Secretary
Coach: Gareth Phillips
Club captain (1988–89): Steve Smith
Club captain (1989–90): Andy Frear
No. of teams: Senior 3, Youth 2
Directions to ground: From West (Huntingdon) on A1123, 300 m past '40' sign turn left into Hill Rise. Go 250 m, second left is California Road. St. Ivo Outdoor Centre is at far end
Clubhouse facilities: Shared use of public sports centre and bar
Club colours: Royal blue shirts, socks, black shorts. (*Change colours:* Scarlet shirts)
Floodlights: No
Local newspapers: Cambridge Evening News, Hunts Post, St. Ives Weekly News
League: EMid 2
League position (1988–89): 9th

ST. NEOTS
The Common, St. Neots, Cambs. Tel: 0480 74285
Founded: 1936
President: V.J. Ibbett
Chairman: C.D. Owen
Secretary: P.S. Townsend, 9 Staughton Place, Eaton Socon, St. Neots, Cambs PE19 3PH. Tel: 0223 62222
Fixtures Secretary: K. Sanford, 36 Avenue Road, St. Neots, Cambs. Tel: 0480 72812
Club captain (1988–89): T. Ibbett
Club captain (1989–90): R. Thompson
No. of teams: Senior 4, U8's–Colts
Directions to ground: East of A1, North through town on St. Neots Common
Clubhouse facilities: Clubhouse and changing rooms adjacent to pitch
Club colours: Light blue with dark blue hoop. (*Change colours:* Red)
Nickname: Saints
Floodlights: No
Membership fees: Full £19.85, Social £5, Youth £9.95
Local newspaper: St. Neots Weekly News
League: EM 2
League position (1988–89): Bottom (relegated)
League playing record (1988–89): P 38, W 14, D 2, L 22, F 396, A 497

VAUXHALL MOTORS
Branche Estate, Osbourne Road, Luton. Tel: 0582 454785.
Founded: 1926
Secretary: K. I. Munn, 5 Stoneleigh Close, Bramingham Park,
Luton, Beds. Tel: Luton 508781 (H) Luton 21122 (W).
Colours: Gold/Blue
League: East Mids 2
Final position: (1988–89): 10th

WESTWOOD
APV Baker, Westfield Road, Peterborough PE3 6TA. Tel: 0733 262000
Founded: 1944
President: M.J. Mason
Chairman: R. Barnett
Secretary: M. Marjoram, 57 Uplands, Werrington, Peterborough PE4 5AF. Tel: 0733 77369
Fixtures Secretary: M. Stevenson, 78 Apsley Way, Longthorpe, Peterborough. Tel: 261497
Club captain (1988–89): R. Swinscoe
Club captain (1989–90): R. Swinscoe
No. of teams: Senior 3
Directions to ground: Westfield Road, Peterborough, located at rear of APV Baker Ltd.
Club colours: Red/white. (*Change colours:* Black)
Floodlights: No
League: E Mids 2
League position (1988–89): 5th
League playing record (1988–89): P 5, W 1, D 4, L 0, F 113, A 121

EAST MIDLANDS 3

BEDFORDSHIRE POLICE
Police H.Q., Woburn Road, Kempston, Bedford. Tel: 0234 841212 (new club)
President: Chief Con. Bedfordshire Police
Chairman: Chief Supt. Marlow
Secretary: Robert Dover, 36 West Hill, Dunstable LU6 3PW. Tel: 0582 664913 (H), 0234 841212 ext. 365 (W)
Fixtures Secretary: As Secretary
Club captain (1989–90): P. MaCarthy, Police Station, Luton
No. of teams: Senior 1
Directions to ground: From Junction 13 M1 A421 to Bedford/Kempston. The H.Q. building and ground being the first building on the left in Kempston
Clubhouse facilities: Bar, changing rooms, showers
Club colours: Red shirts/black shorts. (*Change colours:* Red/yellow/blue hooped shirts)
Floodlights: No
League: EMid 3 (new entrant)

BUGBROOKE
Pilgrims Lane, Bugbrooke, Northants
Founded: 1976
President: John Sexton
Chairman: Glyn Francis
Secretary: James Peel, 42 Martel Close, St. Giles Park, Duston, Northampton NN5 6HA. Tel: 0604 587327 (H), 0480 52552 (W)
Fixtures Secretary: Graham Cooper, 2 The Anvil, Bugbrooke, Northants, NN7 3PX. Tel: 0604 830955
Press Officer: As Secretary
Coach: Dick Parker
Club captain (1988–89): Neil Sturdy
Club captain (1989–90): T.B.A.
No. of teams: Senior 3, Youth 1
Directions to ground: Bugbrooke situated on B4525 between the A45 and A5. Pilgrims Lane on left of High Street as leaving the village. Ground at end of the lane
Clubhouse facilities: Open matchdays and training sessions
Club colours: Bottle green and amber shirt variations. (*Change colours:* Bottle green shorts and socks)
Nickname: The Badgers (1st XV), The Goats (2nd XV)
Floodlights: No
Membership fees: Full £10, Playing £10, Social £5, Youth £5, Student £5, OAP £5, Life £30
Local newspapers: Northampton Chronicle & Echo, Northants Citizen, Northants Post
League: EM 3
League position (1988–89): 3rd
League playing record (1988–89): P 5, W 3, D 0, L 2, F 78, A 58

CUTLER HAMMER
High Street, Kempston, Beds. Tel: 0234 852499
Founded: 1922
President: Ken Porter
Chairman: Barry Williams
Secretary: Will Hunt, 5 Vyne Close, Kempston, Beds MK42 8RM. Tel: 0234 852072 (H), 0525 404305 (W)
Fixtures Secretary: Brian Edmunds, 50 Littledale Street, Kempston, Beds. Tel: 0234 854032 (H), 0525 404305 (W)
Press Officer: Bob Short, Flat 6, 36 Linden Road, Bedford. Tel: 0234 218741
Club captain (1988–89): Mark Ouke
Club captain (1989–90): Bob Fairbrother
No. of teams: Senior 3
Directions to ground: Ask for the King William pub in Kempston. We are 800 yds past this pub on the corner of the road to Bromham
Clubhouse facilities: Concert room, bar
Club colours: Black/red quarters. (*Change colours:* Black/red hoops)
Nickname: Igranic
Floodlights: No
Membership fees: Full £14
Local newspapers: Beds Express, Times, Herald, Beds on Sunday
League: EM 3
League position (1988–89): Bottom (relegated)
League playing record (1988–89): P 30, W 10, D 0, L 20, F 348, A 562

NORTHAMPTON HEATHENS

The Racecourse, East Park Parade, Northampton.
Tel: 0604 39250/38277
Founded: 1920
President: Bernard Alcock
Chairman: Keith Collier
Secretary: Derek Hodgkinson, 5 Pine Trees, Weston Favell, Northampton NN3 3ET. Tel: 0604 416442 (H), 01–481 8521 (W)
Fixtures Secretary: Derek Hodgkinson, 5 Pine Trees, Weston Favell, Northampton NN3 3ET. Tel: 0604 416442 (H), 01–481 8521 (W)
Press Officer: As Fixtures Secretary
Club captain (1988–89): Geoff Lovell
Club captain (1989–90): Geoff Lovell
No. of teams: Senior 3
Directions to ground: On main road to Kettering leaving Northampton town centre
Clubhouse facilities: 'Bat & Wicket', Bailiff Street. Tel: 0604 38277
Club colours: Black 3"/amber " hoop shirts, black shorts, black socks with amber tops
Floodlights: No
Membership fees: Full £15, Social £7.50, Youth £7.50, Student £7.50
Local newspapers: Chronicle & Echo, Northants Post, Northampton Citizen
League: EM 3
League position (1988–89): 5th
League playing record (1988–89): P 5, W 1, D 0, L 4, F 35, A 85
Competitions won: Barry Shaw Memorial Cup

OLD WELLINGBURIAN

O.W. Sports Ground, The Embankment, Wellingborough, Northants. Tel: Wellingborough 225922
Founded: 1981

President: Gordon W. Flex
Chairman: John Beales
Secretary: Mrs. Deborah Pearson, 48 Wellingborough Road, Rushden, Northants. Tel: Rushden 53926
Fixtures Secretary: Antony G. Field, 3 Shelley Road, Wellingborough, Northants NN8 3DA. Tel: Wellinborough 673327 (H), Northampton 769171 (W)
Press Officer: As Secretary
Coach: T.B.A.
Club captain (1988–89): Timothy J.R. Gordon
Club captain (1989–90): Timothy J.R. Gordon
No. of teams: Senior 2–3
Directions to ground: A45 to Wellinborough, come off slip road, straight over 2 roundabouts (heading towards station), this brings you on to the Embankment, follow road round bend and we are on the left
Ground capacity: Standing Unlimited
Clubhouse facilities: Open 7 days a week
Club colours: Bottle green and gold hoops or maroon, black shorts, maroon socks. (*Change colours:* Maroon or green and gold hoops)
Nickname: The OW's
Floodlights: No
Membership fees: Full £20, Playing £20, Social As donation, Student £10
Ground admission: Nil
Local newspapers: Wellingborough Evening Telegraph and Wellingborough Post
League: EMid 3
League position (1988–89): 3rd
League playing record (1988–89): P 5, W 1, D 0, L 4

POTTON

League: East Mids 3
Secretary: A. Kirk, 18 Astwich Road, Srotfield, Herts.
Final position (1988–89): 6th

Ampthill – East Midlands 1 – 1988–89. (Back row – l to r): B. Clark, S. Peacey, P. Argent, G. Whitehall, J. Wilkinson, T. Willison, M. Tanner, R. Beasley, N. Hollick, A. Teague, G. McIlroy, D. Dillingham; (front row): S. Billoux, L. Clark, I. Burgess, P. Nouch, D. Hardy, N. Randall, D. Day, N. Regan.

*The top colts team in the South-West – unbeaten Wootton Bassett with the Dorset &
Wilts Colts Shield. They won all 24 matches played, scoring 767 points against 79*

*Hucclecote Old Boys – Gloucestershie Three. No. 8 Peter Greenwood – 12 times a try
scorer – feeds flanker Brian Dobbins (lefvt). Photo: J.E. Ring*

SOUTH-WEST DIVISION

The formula of the first season was maintained in the South West with the two top divisions followed by the two regional sections and then two strong feeder leagues in the West Country, where the main counties have their own leagues, whereas to the East of the division counties combine to produce strongly competitive sections.

A total of 26 leagues now compete in the area.

Through this system it can be seen that the traditional junior teams are moving up the ladder to bid for higher status, but none were quite good enough to prevent a former senior club – Clifton – from gaining promotion so that they can try their luck to regain former glories in higher company. At the same time clubs, which a were not always taken seriously by senior sides, must now be taken very seriously indeed and the Pilkington Cup results this coming season may well confirm the threat they pose to the "big boys".

SOUTH-WEST DIVISION STRUCTURE

TO AREA LEAGUE SOUTH

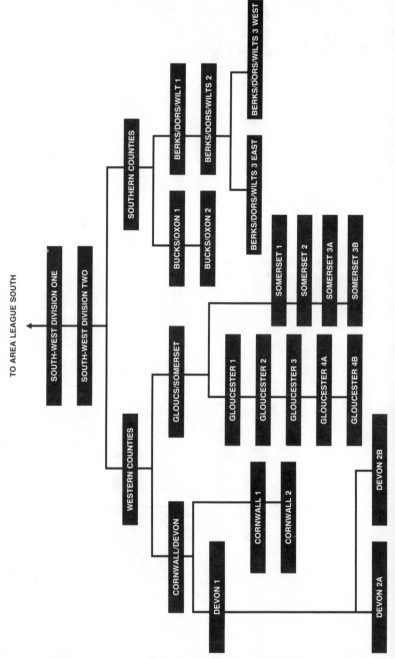

SOUTH WEST DIVISION COURAGE CLUBS CHAMPIONSHIP RULES

These Rules are in addition to and not in substitution for the Regulations as laid down by the R.F.U.

PLAYER REGISTRATION

a) Each Club at the beginning of each season will hold the Player Registration Form for each of the Club's players.

b) The Registration Form will contain the following information:
i Name of Player.
ii Player's Address.
iii Player's Date and Place of Birth.
iv Club played for by Player in previous Season.
v Date of leaving previous Club.

c) The Registration Form will be signed by both the Player and the Club Secretary.

d) The Club will keep the Registration Forms for all its Players on file at the Club's premises.

e) For all League games each Club will make available for its opponents its Team List (including replacements).

f) The Away Club, if it so wishes, may ask to check the Home Teams Registration File after the match.

g) On the occasion of an away match the visiting Club will arrange for an Official to carry the Club's file of Players Registration Forms so that they are available for inspection by the Home Club Officials, if required.

h) In the event of a dispute a Club may request its League Secretary to check the Player Registration File of its opponents. This will be done by the League Secretary passing a copy of the Team List for the fixture to the Leagues Committee of the appropriate Constituent Body who will carry out the check. Such a request will be subject to a leavy of £10.00 to cover expenses payable in advance to the Divisional administration.

i) A player leaving his Club will inform his Club Secretary and ask for his Registration Form which he will then pass to his new Club.

j) Club Secretaries may not withhold a Player's Registration form and will be responsible for retaining a copy within the Club's Registration File.

k) Players must be informed at the beginning of each season that they cannot be registered with more than one Club for League Rugby purposes.

REGISTRATION

All Clubs wishin to compete in the Courage Clubs Championship will register with the Rugby Football Union on the form supplied and by the date required each Season. Courage monies will not be paid to Club's who fail to register.

CLUBS SUSPENDED FOR DISCIPLINARY REASONS

a) Any Club, which is suspended by its County Constituent Body from playing Rugby Union football for disciplinary reasons, will not be permitted to re-arrange any League fixtures falling within the period of the suspension.

b) The opponents of any such Club with League fixtures scheduled during the period of the suspension will be credited with the Competition points for such matches. No match points will be awarded.

FAILURE TO FULFIL FIXTURES

a) Courage Clubs Championship Regulation 11 will apply.

b) In the event of a Club failing to fulfil a League fixture, the South West Division Leagues Committee will award the Competition points to the non-offending Club. No match points will be awarded to either side.

POSTPONED MATCHES

Club Secretaries are reminded that, in the event of a postponement of any League match, they should immediately inform the First Eleven Sports Agency on (0734) and their appropriate League Secretary. They should subsequently inform the Agency and the League Secretary of the rearranged date for the postponed match.

ADMINISTRATION INSTRUCTIONS

A SOUTH WEST DIVISION ONE AND DIVISION TWO
i) Home Clubs will telephone the First Eleven Sports Agency on (0734) 861593 before 4.45 pm on each League Saturday with the match result.
ii) The Home Club in each game will complete a results card and post it first class to their League Secretary by first post Monday.

B WESTERN AND SOUTHERN COUNTIES LEAGUES
i) Home Clubs will telephone the First Eleven Sports Agency on (0734) 861593 before 4.45 pm on each League Saturday with the match result.
ii) The Home Club in each game will complete a results card and post it first class to their appropriate League Secretary by first post Monday.

C TWO-COUNTIES LEAGUES

i) Home Clubs will telephone the First Eleven Sports Agency on (0734) 861593 before 4.45 pm and 5.00 pm on each League Saturday with the match result.

ii) The Home Club in each game will complete a results card and post it first class to their appropriate League Secretary by first post Monday.

D COUNTY LEAGUES

i) Home Clubs will telephone the First Eleven Sports Agency on (0734) 861593 before 5.00 pm and 6.00 pm on each League Saturday with the match result.

ii) The Home Club in each game will complete a results card and post it first class to their appropriate League Secretary by first post Monday.

E TELEPHONE MESSAGES

The Club Official responsible for telephoning-in the match result should confine the telephone message to:–
Match between (HOME TEAM) and (AWAY TEAM)

HOME Team (POINTS) – Away Team (POINTS)
The Administrator will repeat back the message.

FINES

Club Secretaries are reminded that they are responsible for their Club's compliance with the Rules for Notification of Results and should ensure that these are complied with on each League Saturday. Failure to do so will result in the application of a Fine of £5.00 on each occasion when there is a failure to omply with the requirements either by phone or card. It is essential for the continuing success of the Courage Clubs Competition that results are phoned-in within the laid-down periods and confirmed by cards. Clubs receiving Fine notices from their League Secretaries should ensure payment within 28 days of the date of the match, otherwise disciplinary action against the Club may be taken.

PLAYER REGISTRATION

These Rules applicable to Player Registration in the South West Division R.F.U. are the same as those applicable in Season 1988/89 – viz:–

a) Each Club at the beginning of each season will hold the Player Registration Form for each of the Club's players.

b) The Registration Form will contain the following information:–
i Name of Player.
ii Player's Address.
iii Player's Date and Place of Birth.
iv Club played for by Player in previous Season.
v Date of leaving previous Club.

c) The Registration Form will be signed by both the Player and the Club Secretary.

d) The Club will keep the Registration Forms for all its Players on file at the Club's premises.

e) For all League games each Club will make available for its opponents its Team List (including replacements).

f) The Away Club, if it so wishes, may ask to check the Home Teams Registration File after the match.

g) On the occasion of an away match the visiting Club will arrange for an Official to carry the Club's file of Players Registration Forms so that they are available for inspection by the Home Club Officials, if required.

h) In the event of a dispute a Club may request its League Secretary to check the Player Registration File of its opponents. This will be done by the League Secretary passing a copy of the Team List for the fixture to the Leagues Committee of the appropriate Constituent Body who will carry out the check. Such a request will be subject to a levy of £10.00 to cover expenses payable in advance to the Divisional administration.

i) A player leaving his Club will inform his Club Secretary and ask for his Registration Form which he will then pass to his new Club.

j) Club Secretaries may not withhold a Player's Registration form and will be responsible for retaining a copy within the Club's Registration File.

k) Players must be informed at the beginning of each season that they cannot be registered with more than one Club for League Rugby purposes.

It is not necessary to register every player in the Club, only those players who are, or are likely to be, in the Club's First XV squad, should be registered initially. Subsequently it may be necessary to register any other players who are selected for Courage League matches.

IT IS VITAL THAT ALL CLUBS AND PLAYERS COMPLY WITH THE RULES FOR PLAYER REGISTRATION AND ELIGIBILITY.

CHAIRMAN:

Dr Victor Phillips,
Barlowena
Alexandra Road,
Illogan,
Cornwall –TR16 4EN   (H) 0209 842660

SOUTH WEST ADMINISTRATION
OFFICER:

c/o First Eleven Sports Agency,
P.O. Box 11,
Reading,
Berks RG6 3DT   0734 861593

RFU REPRESENTATIVE:

Stan Oswin,
Manor Farmhouse,
Appleton,
Abingdon,   (H) 0865 862954
Oxon, OX13 5JR   (B) 0865 244661

SOUTH AND SOUTH-WEST MEDIA CONTACTS

BBC TV WEST:

Broadcasting House,
Whiteladies Road,
Bristol BS8 2LR   0272 732211

TELEVISION SOUTH WEST:

Derry's Cross,
Plymouth,
Devon PL1 2Sp   0752 663322

GWR:

PO Box 2000, Watershed,
Canons Road,
Bristol BS99 7SN   0272 279900

DEVONAIR:

35/37 St. David's Hill,
Exeter,
Devon EX4 4DA   0392 30703

HTV WEST:

Television Centre,
Bath Road,
Bristol BS4 3HG   0272 778366

PLYMOUTH SOUND:

Earl's Acre,
Alma Road,
Plymouth PL3 4HX   0752 227272

BBC RADIO BRISTOL:

3 Tyndalls Park Road,
Clifton,
Bristol BS8 1PP   0272 741111

BBC TV SOUTH WEST:

Seymour Road,
Wannamead,
Plymouth   0752 229201

BBC RADIO CORNWALL:

Phoenix Wharf,
Truro,
Cornwall TR1 1UA   0872 75421

BBC RADIO DEVON:

PO Box 100,
Walnut Gardens,
Exeter EX4 4DB   0392 215651

TWO COUNTIES RADIO:

5/7 Southcote Street,
Bournemouth,
Dorset BH1 3LR   0202 294881

SEVERN SOUND:

Old Talbot House,
67 Southgate Street,
Gloucester Gl1 2DQ   0452 423791

BBC RADIO OXFORD:

242 Banbury Road,
Oxford OX2 7DW   0865 311444

SOUTHERN SOUND:

Radio House, Franklin Road,
Portslade-by-Sea,
Sussex BN4 255   0273 430111

GWR RADIO (SWINDON):

Lime Kiln Studios,
Wootton Bassett,
Swindon SN4 7EX   0793 853222

BATH AND WEST EVENING CHRONICLE:

33 Westgate Street,
Bath BA1 1EW   0225 444044

BOURNEMOUTH EVENING ECHO:

Richmond Hill,
Bournemouth BH2 6HH   0202 24601

WESTERN DAILY PRESS AND EVENING POST:

Temple Way,
Bristol –BS99 7HD   0272 260080

GLOUCESTERSHIRE ECHO:

1 Clarence Parade,
Cheltenham GL50 3NZ   0242 526261

DORSET EVENING ECHO:

57 St. Thomas Street,
Weymouth DT4 8EQ   0305 784804

EXPRESS AND ECHO:

160 Sidwell Street,
Exeter EX4 6RS   0392 73051

THE CITIZEN:

St. John's Lane,
Gloucester GL1 2AT   0452 424442

OXFORD MAIL:

Newspaper House,
Osney Mead, Oxford   0865 244988

WESTERN EVENING HERALD AND MORNING NEWS:

Leicester Harmsworth House,
65 New George Street,
Plymouth PL1 1RE   0752 266626

READING EVENING POST:

Tessa Road,
Reading RG1 8NS   0734 575833

EVENING ADVERTISER:

Newspaper House,
100 Victoria Road,
Swindon SN1 3BE   0793 28144

HERALD EXPRESS:

Harmsworth House,
Barton Hill Road,
Torquay TQ1 1BD   0803 21313

GLOUCESTER CITIZEN:

0452 424442

SOUTH WEST LEAGUES

The threat posed by some emerging clubs was fought off by Clifton, who beat the challenge of High Wycombe only on points difference after a thrilling campaign, which also involved Berry Hill, promoted only the previous season and the bane of London Welsh in cup matches. Promoted Reading also had a thoroughly satisfactory season in the top divisional league, but for Bridgwater & Albion it was a tragic campaign as they lost all 10 matches (many heavily) and went down along with unlucky Torquay Athletic, whose points difference was inferior to those of Oxford and Maidenhead.

To take their places come Matson, who lost only one of 10 matches and have long posed threats to the best, and Brixham, who ran them close, but the sad fate of relegation befell Launceston (recently Cornwall's top club side) and the Devon & Cornwall Constabulary. Although competition is strong in the West they must return soon. It is interesting, however, to see how well teams from the unfashionable areas of Berkshire, Buckinghamshire and Oxfordshire are faring. Danger here?

CO-ORDINATING SECRETARY SOUTH-WEST DIVISION ONE & TWO:

J.D. Wooldridge,
16 Grange Drive,
Durleigh, Bridgwater,
Somerset TA6 7LL   (H) 0278 422009

SOUTH WEST ADMINISTRATION OFFICER:

c/o First Eleven Sports Agency,
P.O. Box 11
Reading
Berks RG6 3DT   0734 861593

TABLES 1987–88

SOUTH WEST DIVISION ONE

	P	W	D	L	F	A	PTS
Redruth	10	8	0	2	213	102	16
High Wycombe	10	8	0	2	1557	89	16
Maidenhead	10	7	0	3	197	121	14
Torquay	10	7	0	3	156	117	14
Clifton	10	6	0	4	210	112	12
Taunton	10	4	1	5	99	122	9
Oxford	10	4	1	5	115	152	9
Weston	10	4	0	6	146	107	8
Bridgwater	10	3	0	7	98	154	6
St Ives	10	2	0	8	90	189	4
Bournemouth	10	1	0	9	63	280	2

SOUTH WEST DIVISION TWO

	P	W	D	L	F	A	PTS
Berry Hill	10	10	0	0	290	102	20
Reading	10	7	1	2	146	75	15
Barnstaple	10	7	0	3	123	97	14
Brixham	10	5	0	5	142	135	10
Cinderford	10	5	0	5	135	145	10
Launceston	10	4	0	6	125	159	8
Abbey	10	4	0	6	94	148	8
D & C Const	10	3	1	6	126	175	7
Henley	10	3	1	6	109	164	7
Devonport S	10	2	0	8	140	157	4

TABLES 1988–89

SOUTH WEST DIVISION ONE

	P	W	D	L	F	A	PTS
Clifton	10	9	0	1	237	76	18
High Wycombe	10	9	0	1	168	85	18
Berry Hill	10	8	0	2	214	100	16
Taunton	10	6	0	4	154	136	12
Reading	10	5	0	5	144	146	10
St Ives	10	5	0	5	110	139	10
Weston	10	4	0	6	188	183	8
Maidenhead	10	3	0	7	159	148	6
Oxford	10	3	0	7	141	211	6
Torquay	10	3	0	7	97	177	6
Bridgwater	10	0	0	10	53	264	0

SOUTH WEST DIVISION TWO

	P	W	D	L	F	A	PTS
Matson	10	9	0	1	244	81	18
Brixham	10	8	0	2	250	74	16
Cinderford	10	7	0	3	156	97	14
Barnstaple	10	6	0	4	114	96	12
Henley	10	6	0	4	137	163	12
Abbey	10	4	1	5	150	158	9
Newbury	10	4	0	6	102	134	8
Redingensians	10	3	1	6	110	176	7
Bournemouth	10	3	0	7	60	177	6
Launceston	10	2	0	8	120	160	4
D & C Cons	10	2	0	8	93	220	4

Plympton of Devon 2A are about to field 16 players – or not?

Berry Hill lose out to Lydney in the 1988 Gloucestershire Cup. But not this latest season!

SOUTH WEST DIVISION FIXTURES 1989/90

SOUTH WEST ONE

Sat. 9th September (Week 2)
Berry Hill v Brixham
Weston v Matson
Stroud v High Wycombe
Taunton v Maidenhead
St Ives v Oxford

Sat. 23rd September (Week 4)
Matson v Berry Hiill
Reading v St Ives
Oxford v Taunton
Maidenhead v Stroud
High Wycombe v Weston

Sat. 14th October (Week 6)
Brixham v Matson
Berry Hill v High Wycombe
Weston v Maidenhead
Stroud v Oxford
Taunton v Reading

Sat. 28th October (Week 8)
Maidenhead v Berry Hill
High Wycombe v Brixham
St Ives v Taunton
Reading v Stroud
Oxford v Weston

Sat. 11th November (Week 10)
Matson v High Wycombe
Brixham v Maidenhead
Berry Hill v Oxford
Weston v Reading
Stroud v St Ives

18th November (Week 11)
Reading v Berry Hill
Oxford v Brixham
Maidenhead v Matson
Taunton v Stroud
St Ives v Weston

Sat. 25th November (Week 12)
High Wycombe v Maidenhead
Matson v Oxford
Brixham v Reading
Berry Hill v St Ives
Weston v Taunton

Sat. 13th January (Week 18)
Taunton v Berry Hill
St Ives v Brixham
Reading v Matson
Oxford v High Wycombe
Stroud v Weston

Sat. 10th March (Week 26)
Maidenhead v Oxford
High Wycombe v Reading
Matson v St Ives
Brixham v Taunton
Berry Hill v Stroud

Sat. 31st March (Week X7)
Weston v Berry Hill
Stroud v Brixham
Taunton v Matson
St Ives v High Wycombe
Reading v Maidenhead

Sat. 28th April (Week 32)
Oxford v Reading
Maidenhead v St Ives
High Wycombe v Taunton
Matson v Stroud
Brixham v Weston

SOUTH WEST DIVISION FIXTURES 1989/90

SOUTH WEST TWO

Sat. 9th September (Week 2)
Abbey v Barnstaple
Redingensians v Bournemouth
Newbury v Banbury
Gordon League v Cinderford
Henley v Bridgwater

Sat. 23rd September (Week 4)
Bournemouth v Abbey
Torquay v Henley
Bridgwater v Gordon League
Cinderford v Newbury
Banbury v Redingensians

Sat. 14th October (Week 6)
Barnstaple v Bournemouth
Abbey v Banbury
Redingensians v Cinderford
Newbury v Bridgwater
Gordon League v Torquay

Sat. 28th October (Week 8)
Cinderford v Abbey
Banbury v Barnstaple
Henley v Gordon League
Torquay v Newbury
Bridgwater v Redingensians

Sat. 11th November (Week 10)
Bournemouth v Banbury
Barnstaple v Cinderford
Abbey v Bridgwater
Newbury v Henley
Redingensians v Torquay

18th November (Week 11)
Torquay v Abbey
Bridgwater v Barnstaple
Cinderford v Bournemouth
Gordon League v Newbury
Henley v Redingensians

Sat. 25th November (Week 12)
Banbury v Cinderford
Bournemouth v Bridgwater
Abbey v Henley
Redingsinsians v Gordon League
Barnstaple v Torquay

Sat. 13th January (Week 18)
Gordon League v Abbey
Henley v Barnstaple
Torquay v Bournemouth
Bridgwater v Banbury
Newbury v Redingensians

Sat. 10th March (Week 26)
Cinderford v Bridgwater
Bournemouth v Henley
Barnstaple v Gordon League
Banbury v Torquay
Abbey v Newbury

Sat. 31st March (Week X7)

Redingensians v Abbey
Newbury v Barnstaple
Gordon League v Bournemouth
Henley v Banbury
Torquay v Cinderford

Sat. 28th April (Week 32)
Cinderford v Henley
Banbury v Gordon League
Bridgwater v Torquay
Bournemouth v Newbury
Barnstaple v Redingensians

SOUTH WEST 1

BERRY HILL

Lakers Road, Berry Hill, Coleford, Glos GL16 7LY.
Tel: 0594 33295
Founded: 1889
President: R. Jenkins
Chairman: R. Powell
Secretary: T. Baldwin, Hill Bring, Joyford Hill,
Coleford, Glos. Tel: 0594 32539
Fixtures Secretary: G. Goddard, 71A Cheltenham
Road, Gloucester. Tel: 0454 306749
Coach: T.B.A.
Club captain (1988–89): Jeff Powell
Club captain (1989–90): Jeff Powell
No. of teams: Senior 5, Youth 1, Minis 6
Directions to ground: Directions to nearest town
Coleford then road signs for Berry Hill
Ground capacity: Standing 2000
Club colours: Black/amber. (*Change colours:
Red/white*)
Floodlights: Yes
Membership fees: Playing £5, Social £2
Programme: Price Free
League: South West 1
League position (1988–89): 3rd
League playing record (1988–89): P 10, W 8, D 0,
L 2, F 214, A 100

BRIXHAM

Astley Park, Brixham. Tel: 0803 882162
Founded: 1874
President: Eric Crow, FCA
Chairman: Raymond Gardner
Secretary: Bob Houston, 'St. Cloud', Cliff Park Road,
Gooderington, Paignton. Tel: 0803 550427 (H), 0392
52155 ext. 2715 (W)
Fixtures Secretary: (Rugby) – Danny Irvine, BEM, 1
Great Rea Road, Brixham IQ5 9SW. Tel: 0803
882219 (H), 0804 2337(W)
Press Officer: Tony Brooks, 33 Penpath Road,
Brixham. Tel: 08045 3989 (H), 08045
3989 (W)
Coach: David Wiggans
Club captain (1988–89): Ian Griffin
Club captain (1989–90): Terry Maggs
No. of teams: Senior 4, Youth 2, Minis 4
Directions to ground: Follow road signs for Torbay,
then follow signs for Brixham. On entering town turn
right at traffic lights in centre of town. Follow this
road to next traffic lights, turn left up Rea Barn Hill.
Ground is at the top of the hill opposite Police Station
Ground capacity: Seating 300, standing 5000
Clubhouse facilities: Two storey building incorporating
main bar area, lounge bar, players bar and reception
room. Open 11 a.m. to 3 p.m. daily, 5 p.m. to
11 p.m. daily, 12 p.m. to 3 p.m. Sunday, 11 a.m. to
11 p.m. Saturdays
Club colours: Black with 6" chest band. (*Change
colours:* White, red or orange)
Nickname: 'The Fishermen'
Floodlights: Yes
Membership fees: Full £8, Playing £10, Social £2,
Youth £3, Student £3, OAP £8
Ground admission: OAP £1.50, Youth £1
Programme: No. of editorial pages 7; No. of
advertising pages 9; Price (included in admission)
Programme editor: Norman Marler, 3 Southdown
Close, Brixham. Tel: 08045 3795
Local newspapers: Western Morning News, Herald
Express, Weekender and Brixham News
League: SW 1
League position (1988–89): 2nd (promoted)
League playing record (1988–89): P 10, W 8, D 0,
L 2, F 250, A 74
Competitions won: South West Runners-Up, Devon
Sevens Winners

HIGH WYCOMBE

Kingsmead Road, High Wycombe, Bucks. Tel: 0493
24407
Founded: 1929
President: James Clayton Rivett
Chairman: Jeremy Cook
Secretary: Don Dickerson, 3 Talbot Avenue, High
Wycombe, Bucks HP13 5HZ. Tel: 0494 32024 (H),
441211 (W)
Fixtures Secretary: Terry Baker, 5 Orhcard Way,
Hollier Green, High Wycombe, Bucks. Tel: 0494
713047 (H), 33333 (W)
Press Officer: Dudley Scott, 32 Kings Ride, Penn,
Bucks. Tel: Penn 3399
Club captain (1988–89): Curtis Roddick
Club captain (1989–90): David Cheeswright
No. of teams: Senior 9, Youth 6, Minis 10
Directions to ground: A40 from East: Turn left into
Station Road, Loudwater and right into Kingsmead
Road. A40 from West: Turn
right into Abbey Barn Road (by Wycombe Marsh
Papermill) and left into Kingsmead Road. Ground 1
mile on left
Ground capacity: Standing Unlimited
Clubhouse facilities: Two storey, all usual facilities
Club colours: Green/white/black hoops, black shorts.
(*Change colours:* All black)
Floodlights: Yes
Membership fees: Playing £25, Life VPs £75, VPs £10,
Youth £2, Student £5, Playing (18–21 yrs.) £10
Ground admission: Nil
Programme: No. of editorial pages variable; No. of
advertising pages variable; Price 59p
Programme editor: D.H. Dickerson, 3 Talbot
Avenue, High Wycombe, Bucks HP13 5HZ
Local newspapers: Bucks Free Press, The Star, The
Observer
League: SW 1
League position (1988–89): 2nd
League playing record (1988–89): P 37, W 30, D 0,
L 17, F 734, A 294
Competitions won: Buckinghamshire County
Champions, winners of Bucks Sevens, Staines Floodlit
Sevens, Oxford County Sevens Plate Competition,
Abingdon Sevens Plate Competition, Phoenix 15-a-
Side Competititon won by 3rd XV. Winners of
Pennanians Athletics Competition. Winners of Trevor
Thomas Cup

MAIDENHEAD

Braywick Park, Maidenhead. Tel: 0628 29663
Founded: 1922
Secretary: J. Hayden. Tel: 0628 231239
Fixtures Secretary: A.G. Cowen, 31 Furze Platt
Road, Maidenhead, Berks. Tel: 0628 29327 (H), 0865
246681 (W)
No. of teams: Senior 4, Youth 11+
Directions to ground: From town centre take road to
Windsor (A423). Ground is 1 mile on left. From M4
take exit top Maidenhead Central, left at 1st
roundabout. Ground is mile on right
Ground capacity: Standing 2000+
Clubhouse facilities: Full
Club colours: Violet/magenta/black
Nickname: Maids
Floodlights: No
Programme: Price Donation
League: SW 1
League position (1988–89): 8th
League playing record (1988–89): P 10, W 3, D 0,
L 7, F 159, A 148

MATSON

Redwell Road, Matson, Gloucester. Tel: 0452 28963
Founded: 1957
President: Hayden Jones
Chairman: Brian Peart
Secretary: Gilbert Locke, 39 Oxmoor, Abbeydale,

Gloucester GL4 9XW. Tel: 0452 419587 (H), 712802 (W)
Fixtures Secretary: Colin Thornton, 43 Brimsome Meadow, Highnam, Gloucester. Tel: 0452 503768 (H), 711101 (W)
Press Officer: Mark Bishop, 9 Sivell Close, Longford, Gloucester. Tel: 0452 26671 (H), 0836 771525 (W)
Coach: Glyn Rowlands
Club captain (1988–89): Rod Correia
Club captain (1989–90): Tony Bebber
No. of teams: Senior 4
Directions to ground: Off eastern ringroad on B4073, after 1 ½ miles turn right into Matson (club is near Dry Ski Slope)
Ground capacity: Standing 4000
Clubhouse facilities: 3 bars, dancehall, 4 changing rooms, large weights room, skittle alley and lounge. Open 7 days
Club colours: Black shirt, white shorts. (*Change colours:* Black/white hoops)
Floodlights: Yes (sufficient for training)
Membership fees: Full £10, Playing £10, Social £3, Youth £3, Student £3, OAP £5
Ground admission: Nil
Programme: No. of editorial pages 3; No. of advertising pages 8; Price 30p
Programme editor: Stan Green, 27 Winsley Road, Matson, Gloucester
Local newspaper: Citizen
League: SW 1
League position (1988–89): 1st (promoted)
League playing record (1988–89): P 10, W 9, D 0, L 1, F 229, A 81
Competitions won: South West Div. 2 League Winners, North Glos. Combination Senior Cup

OXFORD

Southern By-Pass, North Hinksey, Oxford. Tel: 0865 243984
Founded: 1909
President: Brian Deane
Chairman: David Bagnall
Secretary: Ronald Martin, Pantiles, 22 Didcote Road, Long Wittenham, Oxon OX14 4PZ . Tel: 086730 7528
Fixtures Secretary: Roger Whitfield, 3 Henwood Drive, Wootton, Boars Hill, Oxford. Tel: 0865 739136 (H), 023587 551 (W)
Press Officer: Richard Tyrrell, 159 Banbury Road, Kidlington, Oxford. Tel: 0865 77366
Coach: John Gunter
Club captain (1988–89): Roy Davies
Club captain (1989–90): Steve Lazenby
No. of teams: Senior 3
Directions to ground: Turn left at North Hinksey off A34 going south towrds Abingdon/Newbury
Ground capacity: Seating 150
Clubhouse facilities: Main bar, lounge, hall, 2 squash courts
Club colours: Green, black, silver. (*Change colours:* Green)
Floodlights: Yes
Membership fees: Full £10 (VP), Playing £25, Social £5, Student £12.50, OAP £4
Ground admission: By programme
Programme: No. of editorial pages 8; No. of advertising pages 10; Price 50p
Programme editor: Richard Tyrrell, 159 Banbury Road, Kidlington, Oxford
Local newspaper: Oxford Mail
League: SW 1
League position (1988–89): 9th
League playing record (1988–89): P 10, W 3, D 0, L 7, F 141, A 211
Competitions won: 3rd Round Pilkington Glass Comp. Oxford County Cup, March '89. Oxford RFC Courage Floodlit Cup.

ST. IVES

Alexandra Road, St. Ives, Cornwall. Tel: 0736 795346

Founded: 1887
President: Edwin Trewhella
Chairman: Nicholas A. Simpson
Secretary: Michael Gee, Suhaili, 7 Hellesvean Close, St. Ives, Cornwall TR26 2HQ. Tel: 0736 797168
Fixtures Secretary: As Secretary
Press Officer: As Secretary
Coach: Roger Corin-Kevin Trudeeca
Club captain (1988–89): Ian Deacon
Club captain (1989–90): Ian Deacon
No. of teams: Senior 3, Youth 1, Minis + Juniors 7
Directions to ground: From A30 take coach route/holiday route to St. Ives via B3311 to B3306, turn left at first mini roundabout
Ground capacity: Standing 5000
Clubhouse facilities: 4 bars. Oen every night
Club colours: Navy shirts, white shorts. (*Change colours:* White with navy hoop)
Nickname: The Haves
Floodlights: Yes
Membership fees: Full £10, Playing £13, Social £3, Youth £5, Student £5, OAP £5
Ground admission: £1
Programme: No. of editorial pages 11; No. of advertising pages 12; Price 10p
Programme editor: As Secretary
Local newspapers: St. Ives Times & Echo
League: South West 1
League position (1988–89): 6th
League playing record (1988–89): P 38, W 24, D 0, L 14, F 617, A 416

READING

Holme Park, Sonning Lane, Sonning, Nr. Reading, Berkshire RG11 0ST. Tel: 0734 696592/690030
Founded: 1898
President: Colin Barrett
Chairman: Graham Ethelston
Secretary: Mike Wickson, 21 Lunds Farm Road, Woodley, Reading A65 4PZ. Tel: 0734 695999 (H), 475022 (W)
Fixtures Secretary: Bob Pendleton, 1 Green Croft Gardens, Reading. Tel: 0734 580014
Press Officer: Lorcan P. Mullally, 35 Western Elms Avenue, Reading RG3 2AL. Tel: 0374 572357 (H), 475022 (W)
Coach: Jeff Owen
Club captain (1988–89): Ian Turrell
Club captain (1989–90): Paul Guttridge
No. of teams: Senior 6, Youth 3, Minis 3
Directions to ground: Signposted from A4 trunkroad two miles east of Reading. Situated opposite Reading Cricket and Hockey Club and next to Reading Blue Coat School
Ground capacity: Seating 120, standing 500
Clubhouse facilities: 3 bars, 2 function rooms, 8 changing rooms, weights room, 2 squash courts, 3 pitches
Club colours: Myrtle and white hoops, blue shorts, green stockings. (*Change colours:* Blue jerseys with white collars, shorts or stockings)
Nickname: Berkshire Wanderers
Floodlights: Yes (training only)
Membership fees: Full £11 (p.m.), Playing £9 (p.m.), Social £2 (p.a.), Youth £6 (p.m.), Student £6 (p.m.), OAP (£1.25 p.a.)
Ground admission: £1 or donation for programme on Sundays
Programme: No. of editorial pages 4–8; No. of advertising pages 8; Price inc. admission
Programme editor: As Press Officer
Local newspapers: Reading Evening Post and Reading Chronicle
League: SW 1
League position (1988–89): 5th
League playing record (1988–89): P 10, W 5, D 0, L 5, F 144, A 146
Competitions won: Berkshire Cup, March '89. Twickenham R.F.C. Sevens, April '89 and Abbey (Reading) Floodlit Sevens, April '89

STROUD

Fromehall Park, Stroud, Glos. Tel: 045376 3019
Founded: 1873
President: C.G. Woodruff
Chairman: W.J. Silverthorne
Secretary: N.F. Hall, 1 Elm Terrace, Foxmoor Lane, Ebley, Stroud, Clos. Tel: Stonehowe (045382) 4321
Fixtures Secretary: R.J. Hillier, Marijon, Paganhill Lane, Stroud, Glos. Tel: Stroud 045376 4381
Press officer: D.W. Reed. Tel: 0452 728264
Club captain (1988–89): A. Dix
Club captain (1989–90): J. Perrins
Directions to ground: A46, 1 mile south of Stroud at Golden Cross
Ground capacity: Seating 4000, Standing 100
Clubhouse facilities: Clubroom, 3 bars, changing rooms, 2 squash courts
Club colours: Blue and white hoops. (*Change colours:* All blue)
Floodlights: No
Membership fees: Between £5 (social) to £20 (patron)
Ground admission: £1
Programme: Price 20p
Programme editor: As Secretary
Local newspaper: Stroud News & Journal
League: South West 1
League position (1988–89): 9th
League playing record (1988–89): P 40, W 18, D 1, L 21

TAUNTON

Priory Bridge Road, Taunton, Somerset. Tel: 0823 275670
Founded: 1875
President: George Babbage
Chairman: Michael Newport
Secretary: John Reid MacHoney, 35 Bramley Road, Taunton, Somerset TA1 2XJ. Tel: 0823 272533
Fixtures Secretary: Danny Ward, 9 Bridge Close, Taunton. Tel: 0823 335037
Press Officer: Eric Coombes, re. Directory
Coach: John Cooling/Nicholas Hunt
Club captain (1988–89): Michael Reece
Club captain (1989–90): Michael Reece
No. of teams: Senior 3, Youth 1, Minis 4
Directions to ground: Take Junction 25 for Taunton on the motorway, travel under the motorway, past the Crest Hotel, straight across three roundabouts into Priory Bridge Road. Ground on the right
Ground capacity: Standing 3000
Clubhouse facilities: Club, dance hall, 3 bars
Club colours: Black white crimson stripe. (*Change colours:* Black/white)
Floodlights: Yes
League: SW 1

WESTON-SUPER-MARE

The Recreation Ground, Drove Road, Weston-Super-Mare, Avon. Tel: 0934 623118 (public)
Founded: 1875
President: Dr. G.W.J. Papworth
Chairman: R.C. Crocker
Secretary: Roy H. Main, 77 Pleshey Close, Weston-Super-Mare, Avon BS22 9DH. Tel: 0934 417864 (H), 625643 (W)
Fixtures Secretary: As Secretary
Press Officer: As Secretary
Coach: Richard Hazzard
Club captain (1988–89): Paul Tincknell
Club captain (1989–90): Tim Whittle
No. of teams: Senior 3, Youth 1, Minis 4
Directions to ground: M5 Junction 21 exit. Follow A370 new Bristol road into Locking Road, left at traffic lights, over railway bridge onto roundabout, 4th exit entrance to Recreation Ground
Ground capacity: Seating 499, standing 6000
Clubhouse facilities: Large clubhouse, committee room, lounge bar, skittle alley

Club colours: Royal blue. (*Change colours:* Red)
Floodlights: Yes
Membership fees: T.B.D.
Ground admission: £1
Programme: No. of editorial pages 4; No. of advertising pages 4; Price 10p
Programme editor: As Secretary
Local newspapers: Weston Mercury
League: SW 1
League position (1988–89): 7th
League playing record (1988–89): P 10, W 4, D 0, L 6, F 188, A 183

SOUTH WEST 2

ABBEY

Roschill, Peppard Road, Emmer Green, Reading, Berks. Tel: 0734 722881
Founded: 1956
President: A. Young
Chairman: M. Lee
Secretary: P. Loveridge, 1 Clifton Park Road, Caversham, Reading, Berks. Tel: 0734 477427
Fixtures Secretary: P. Carroll, 24 Harrogate Road, Caversham, Reading, Berks. Tel: 0734 482257
Coach: T.B.A.
Club captain (1988–89): A. Lester
Club captain (1989–90): S. Smith
No. of teams: Senior 6, Youth and Minis 9
Directions to ground: From Reading town centre follow signs to Peppard and Sonning Common. Club on left after 2–3 miles
Clubhouse facilities: Open Saturdays during season and training nights
Club colours: Navy blue with white and green hoops
Floodlights: Yes
Membership fees: Playing £22, VPs £20, Joint £25, Youth £7
Ground admission: Nil
Local newspapers: Reading Chronicle & Evening Post
League: SW 2
League position (1988–89): 6th
League playing record (1988–89): P 10, W 4, D 0, L 6, F 150, A 158

BANBURY

Founded: 1925
President:
Chairman:
Secretary: . Tel: Ban 711582 (H), 52535 ext. 230 (W)
Fixtures Secretary: 0295 66777 (W)
Coach:
Club captain (1988–89): Martin Court
Club captain (1989–90): Richard Fox
No. of teams: Senior 5, Youth 4, Minis 3
Directions to ground:
Clubhouse facilities:
Club colours: . (*Change colours:*)
Floodlights: No
Membership fees: VPs £9, Playing £20, Social £1, Youth £9, Student £9
Ground admission: Free
Programme: No. of editorial pages 2; No. of advertising pages 4; Price Free
Programme editor: B. Gilkes, 12 Burlington Gardens, Banbury, Oxon
Local newspapers: Banbury Guardian, Oxford Mail
League: South West 2
League position (1988–89): 1st

BARNSTAPLE

Founded: 1877
President: F. C. Passmore
Chairman: E. Parsley
Coach: Tony Stevens
Secretary: B. C. Williams, 'The Mews', Whiddon

Park, Landkey Road, Barnstaple. Tel: 79289. Ex 329La.
Fixtures Secretary: A. Wasley, 39 St Mary's Road, Barnstaple. Tel: 71553.
Club captain (1988–89): Ian Innes
Club captain (1989–90): Ian Innes
No. of teams: Senior 3, Youth & Minis 5
Directions to ground: From town square follow Braunton signs. Turn left into Pottington Road at traffic lights in Rolle Street.
Ground capacity: 3000–4000. Stand 500
Clubhouse facilities: 2 bars, dining room, kitchen.
Club colours: Red shirts, white shorts. (*Change colours:* White or brown)
Nickname: 1st XV – Chiefs
Floodlights: No
Admission: £1
Membership fees: £10 playing, £10 VP
Ground admission:
Programme: 20p (Editor: B. C. Williams)
Local newspapers: N. Devon Journal
League: SW2

BOURNEMOUTH

Chapel Gate, Parley, Hurn, Christchurch, Dorset. Tel: 0202 580842
Founded: 1893
President: A.J. Thorne
Chairman: N.R.E. Yeoman
Secretary: M.B. Wilkes, 15/17 Lansdowne Road, Bournemouth, Dorset BH1 1RZ. Tel: 0202 35168 (H), 297555 (W), 27511 (F)
Fixtures Secretary: J. Arthur, 62 Iddesleigh Road, Bournemouth, Dorset. Tel: 0202 292676 (H), 687424 (W)
Press Officer: N.R.E. Yeoman, 28 Dorset Lake Avenue, Lilliput, Poole, Dorset. Tel: 0202 707629 (H), 692308 (W)
Coach: Stuart O'Donnell
Club captain (1988–89): Rodney Clayton
Club captain (1989–90): T.B.A.
No. of teams: Senior 7, Youth 2, Minis 3
Directions to ground: North of Bournemouth immediately adjacent Bournemouth International Airport
Ground capacity: Standing 250
Clubhouse facilities: 2 bars, function/dining room, squash courts, skittle alley, 10 changing rooms, treatment/first aid room
Club colours: Yellow and black. (*Change colours:* Red)
Floodlights: No
Membership fees: Full £25, Playing £25, Social £12, Youth £6, Student £15
Ground admission: Nil
Programme: Price 50p
Programme editor: As Press Officer
Local newspapers: Bournemouth Evening Echo, Advertiser and Street Life
League: SW 2
League position (1988–89): 9th
League playing record (1988–89): P 10, W 3, D 0, L 7, F 60, A 177
Competitions won: Dorset VII's Competition

BRIDGWATER & ALBION

The Broadway, Bridgwater. Tel: 0278 423900
President: T.B.A.
Chairman: T.B.A.
Secretary: Anthony Pomeroy, 'Hafod-y-Gân', Newton Road, North Petherton, Somerset TA6 6SN. Tel: 0278 662181 (H), 455631 (W)
Fixtures Secretary: Ralph Sealey, 12 Capes Close, Bridgwater. Tel: 0278 444757 (H), 428500 (W)
Press Officer: As Secretary
Coach: Jeff Davies
Club captain (1988–89): Anthony Harris

Club captain (1989–90): Anthony Harris
No. of teams: Senior 3, Youth 1, Minis 4
Directions to ground: From M5 to J.23 follow A38 to roundabout at junction A38/39, follow A39. Ground entrance 100 yds on left
Ground capacity: Seating 550, Standing 2000
Clubhouse facilities: Two bars and reception hall
Club colours: Red/black/gold. (*Change colours:* Gold)
Floodlights: Yes
Programme: Price 20p
Programme editor: M. Derrick, c/o B & A R.F.C.
Local newspaper: Bridgwater Mercury
League: South West 2
League position (1988–89): Bottom
League playing record (1988–89): P 10, W 0, D 0, L 10

CINDERFORD

Recreation Ground, Dockham Road, Cindeford, Glos. Tel: 0594 22673
Founded: 1886
President: Robert Henry Beavis
Chairman: K. Morse
Secretary: Mrs. M. Beavis, 5 Abbots Road, Cinderford, Glos. Tel: 0594 23779
Fixtures Secretary: J. Gazzard, 1 Wedgewood Crescent, Cinderford, Glos. Tel: 0594 22333
Press Officer: R. Allen, 14 Heywood Road, Cinderford, Glos. Tel: 0594 26301
Coach: Dennis Hargreaves
Club captain (1988–89): D. Richards
Club captain (1989–90): N. Worgan
No. of teams: Senior 4, Youth 5
Directions to ground: Bus station at the centre of the town
Ground capacity: Seating 300, standing 4000
Clubhouse facilities: Licensed. Open weekdays
Club colours: Red, black and amber. (*Change colours:* Red)
Nickname: Cindy
Floodlights: Yes
Membership fees: Full £5, Playing £5, Social £3, Youth £3, OAP 50p
Ground admission: £1
Programme: No. of editorial pages 4; No. of advertising pages 6; Price £1
Programme editor: J. Wood, Splinters, II Buckshaft Road, Cinderford, Glos GL14 3DN
Local newspapers: 3 Forest of Dean newspapers
League: SW 2
League position (1988–89): 3rd
League playing record (1988–89): P 34, W 24, D 3, L 7, F 434, A 261

GORDON LEAGUE

Hempstead Lane, Gloucester. Tel: 0542 303434
Founded: 1888
President: Mayor of Gloucester
Chairman: John Emery
Secretary: John Wakefield, 1 Berry Lawn, Wheatway, Gloucester. Tel: 0542 303434 (H), 0542 28431 (W)
Fixtures Secretary: Howard Williams, 62 Escourt Road, Gloucester. Tel: 20913
Coach: Paul Red
Club captain (1988–89): Steven Artus
Club captain (1989–90): Steven Artus
Directions to ground: Map supplied to visiting teams
Ground capacity: Seating 1500, Standing 150
Clubhouse facilities: New
Club colours: White/red. (*Change colours:* Red)
Floodlights: Yes (training)
Membership fees: Full £10
Ground admission: 50p
Programme editor: Terry Phillips
League: SW 2
League position (1988–89): 1st
League playing record (1988–89): P 10, W 10, D 0, L 0, F 218, A 80

HENLEY

Dry Leas, Marlow Road, Henley-on-Thames, Oxon.
Tel: 0491 574499
Founded: 1930
President: Sidney W. Lewington
Chairman: Noel P. North
Secretary: Peter J. Allen, 8 St. Katherine's Road,
Henley-on-Thames, Oxon. Tel: 0491 575154
Fixtures Secretary: A.W.M. Cooke, 86 Makins Road,
Henley-on-Thames, Oxon. Tel: 0491 575789 (H),
01–636 3422 ext. 220 (W)
Press Officer: G.M.W. French, 1 Western Road,
Henley-on-Thames, Oxon. Tel: 0491 572795
Coach: G. Horner
Club captain (1988–89): M. Poulson
Club captain (1989–90): M. Duffellen
No. of teams: Senior 6, Youth 1, Minis 9
Directions to ground: 100 yds on left-hand side from
the mini roundabout/junction of A4155 and A423
Clubhouse facilities: Bar, toilets, kitchen
Club colours: Gold dark blue and green hoops, blue
shorts, green socks. (*Change colours:* Dark green)
Floodlights: No
Membership fees: Full £20, Playing £20, Social £10,
Youth £5, Student £5
Programme: No. of editorial pages 2; No. of
advertising pages 8; Price 50p
Local newspaper: Henley Standard
League: SW 2
League position (1988–89): 5th
League playing record (1988–89): P 10, W 6, D 0,
L 4, F 137, A 161

NEWBURY

Pinchington Lane, Newbury, Berks. Tel: 0635 40103
President: R.M. Tucker
Chairman: G.J. Wickens
Secretary: L.A. Sugden, Brook Cottage, Boxford,
Newbury, Berks. Tel: 6488 38607 (H), 0635 521212
(W)
Fixtures Secretary: A. Boyer, 11 Christopher Court,
Boundary Road, Newbury. Tel: 40574
Press Officer: C. Whittaker, Burton House,
Burghclere, Newbury. Tel: B 300 (H), N 41911 (W)
Coach: E.J. Cripps
Club captain (1988–89): R. King
Club captain (1989–90): R. King
No. of teams: Senior 4 + Evetts, Youth U17–U8
Directions to ground: A34 Newbury bypass, south of
town
Clubhouse facilities: 2 bars, 3 team changing rooms
Club colours: D blue/l blue. (*Change colours:* Red)
Floodlights: No
Membership fees: Playing £8, Social £5
Ground admission: 50p
Programme: No. of editorial pages 4; No. of
advertising pages 6–8; Price 50p (included in
admission)
Programme editor: A. Boyer
Local newspapers: Newbury Weekly News, Reading
Evening Post
League position (1988–89): 7th
League playing record (1988–89): P 10, W 4, D 0,
L 6, F 102, A 134

REDINGENSIANS

Old Bath Road, Sonning, Berks. Tel: 0734 695259
Founded: 1924
President: W.J. Bennett
Chairman: G. Bruce
Secretary: J.H. Cook, 95 Century Court, Grove End
Road, London NW8 9LD. Tel: 01–289 1887 (H),
01–628 4981 (W)
Fixtures Secretary: V.W. Bowen, 9 Hawthorn Way,
Sonning, Berks. Tel: 0734 696415 (H), 0235 864824
(W)
Press Officer: K.G. Davis, 16 Penwood Heights,
Burghclere, Newbury, Berks. Tel: 0635 253827
Coach: R.L. Vaughan
Club captain (1988–89): S.L. Hunt
Club captain (1989–90): A.T. Lynch
No. of teams: Senior 6, Youth 3, Minis 9
Directions to ground: On A4 to the east of Reading
Clubhouse facilities: Excellent
Club colours: Light blue, dark blue and white hoops.
(*Change colours:* Red)
Nickname: The 'R's'
Floodlights: No
League: SW 2
League position (1988–89): 7th
League playing record (1988–89): P 33, W 14, D 2,
L 17, F 519, A 509

TORQUAY

Recreation Ground, Seafront, Torquay. Tel: 0803
23842
Founded: 1875
President: Bryan Lang
Chairman: Barney Bettesworth
Secretary: Ken Evans, 15 Broadstone Park Road,
Torquay. Tel: 0803 606233
Fixtures Secretary: Malcolm Baker, 'Trevaunance',
Barton Hill Road, Torquay. Tel: 0803 36542
Coach: Chris Edwards
Club captain (1988–89): Kevin Butterworth
Club captain (1989–90): John Widdecombe
No. of teams: Senior 3, Colts 1 (U10–U16) & Minis
Directions to ground: Ground close to sea front
Torquay, adjacent to Grand Hotel and railway station
Ground capacity: Seating 5000, standing 400
Clubhouse facilities: Main bar, president's lounge,
dining room, kitchen, toilets – North end of stand
Club colours: Black and white hoops. (*Change
colours:* Red)
Floodlights: No
Membership fees: Full £18, Playing £15, OAP £15
Ground admission: 1.50
Programme: No. of editorial pages 8; Price 20p
Programme editor: Richard Harris, Narrowater,
Hampton Avenue, Torquay
Local newspaper: Torbay Herald Express
League: SW 1
League position (1988–89): 10th (relegated)
League playing record (1988–89): P 10, W 3, D 0,
L 7, F 97, A 177

WESTERN COUNTIES LEAGUES

For many seasons Gordon League have been a tough proposition for even the top senior sides and their position in the Western Counties League was a false one, which they proved by running away with the title – and gaining promotion to South West 2 in the process – with all 10 matches won and a points differential of 218–80. Two Devon teams also go down – Devonport Services and Crediton with the latter out of their class last season and the former suffering a second successive descent mainly because in spite of their Plymouth location they are unable to call on the top services players, who find their way into the squads of top clubs such as Plymouth Albion. That is "progress" and there is not much that can be done about it.

OVERALL RESPONSIBILITY FOR
GLOUCESTERSHIRE, SOMERSET,
DEVON, CORNWALL:

Michael Gee,
Suhaili,
7 Hellesvane Close,
St. Ives,
Cornwall TR6 7HQ   0736 797168

TABLES 1987–88

WESTERN COUNTIES

	P	W	D	L	F	A	PTS
Matson	10	9	1	0	343	58	19
Gordon Lge	10	6	2	2	213	80	14
Clevedon	10	6	1	3	150	118	13
Truro	10	6	0	4	111	178	12
O Redcliffs	10	5	0	5	144	138	10
Newquay Hor	10	4	1	5	107	160	9
Okehampton	10	3	2	5	103	127	8
Cirencester	10	4	0	6	76	124	8
Tiverton	10	3	1	6	74	121	7
Av & Som Con	10	3	0	7	79	193	6
Sidmouth	10·	2	0	8	79	182	4

TABLES 1988–89

WESTERN COUNTIES

	P	W	D	L	F	A	PTS
Gordon League	10	10	0	0	218	80	20
Avonmouth Old Boys	10	7	0	3	162	112	14
Cirencester	10	6	1	3	124	109	13
Clevedon	10	5	1	4	136	95	11
Okehampton	10	5	1	4	109	78	11
Tiverton	10	5	0	5	109	143	10
Old Redcliffians	10	4	0	6	108	113	8
Truro	10	3	1	6	89	130	7
Newquay Hornets	10	3	1	6	101	152	7
Devonport Services	10	3	0	7	139	198	6
Crediton	10	1	1	8	87	162	3

Weston-super-Mare (plain shirts) attack in South-West 1.

SOUTH WEST DIVISION FIXTURES 1989/90

WESTERN COUNTIES

Sat. 9th September (Week 2)
Avonmouth OB v Cirencester
Truro v Clevedon
Launceston v Dev & Cwll Const
Tiverton v Old Culverhaysians
Penryn v Newquay Hornets

Sat. 23rd September (Week 4)
Newquay Hornets v Launceston
Clevedon v Avonmouth OB
Okehampton v Penryn
Dev & Cwll Const v Tiverton
Old Culverhaysians v Truro

Sat. 14th October (Week 6)
Cirencester v Clevedon
Truro v Dev & Cwll Const
Avonmouth OB v O Culverhaysians
Tiverton v Newquay Hornets
Launceston v Okehampton

Sat. 28th October (Week 8)
Penryn v Launceston
Dev & Cwll Const v Avonmouth OB
O Culverhaysians v Cirencester
Okehampton v Tiverton
Newquay Hornets v Truro

Sat. 11th November (Week 10)
Cirencester v Dve & Cwll Const
Clevedon v O Culverhaysians
Avonmouth OB v Newquay Hornets
Truro v Okehampton
Tiverton v Penryn

18th November (Week 11)
Okehampton v Avonmouth OB
Newquay Hornets v Cirencester
Dev & Cwll Const v Clevedon
Launceston v Tiverton
Penryn v Truro

Sat. 25th November (Week 12)
Truro v Launceston
Culverhaysians v Dev & Cwll Const
Clevedon v Newquay Hornets
Cirencester v Okehampton
Avonmouth OB v Penryn

Sat. 13th January (Week 18)
Launceston v Avonmouth OB
Penryn v Cirencester
Okehamnpton v Clevedon
Newquay H v Culverhaysians
Tiverton v Truro

Sat. 10th March (Week 26)
Cirencester v Launceston
Dev & Cwll Const v Newquay Horn.
Culverhaysians v Okehampton
Clevedon v Penryn
Avonmouth OB v Tiverton

Sat. 31st March (Week X7)
Tiverton v Cirencester
Launceston v Clevedon
Okehampton v Dev & Cwll Const
Truro v Avonmouth OB
Penryn v O Culverhaysians

Sat. 28th April (Week 32)
O Culverhaysians v Launceston
Newquay Hornets v Okehampton
Dev & Cwll Const v Penryn
Clevedon v Tiverton
Cirencester v Truro

WESTERN COUNTIES 1

AVONMOUTH OLD BOYS

Barracks Lane, Avonmouth, Bristol. Tel: 829093
Founded: 1987
President: W.A. Baker
Chairman: Rodney Kennett
Secretary: Mrs. Patricia Chilcott, 448 Portway, Shirehampton, Bristol BS11 9UA. Tel: 829753 (H), 823741 (W)
Fixtures Secretary: Mal Rowlands, 420 Portway, Shirehampton, Bristol. Tel: 0824235
Press Officer: Fred Amphlett, 24 Nigel Park, Shirehampton, Bristol. Tel: 826854
Coach: Graham Rich
Club captain (1988–89): Richard Thayer
Club captain (1989–90): Derek Hone
No. of teams: Senior 4, Youth 2, Minis 3 (U9, 10, 11)
Directions to ground: Exit M5 Junction 18, take immediate left turn at exit on roundabout, then second left opposite shops, continue for 200 yds
Ground capacity: Standing 3000
Clubhouse facilities: Double storey brick construction with car park
Club colours: Black with red hoops. (*Change colours:* Cherry and white hoops)
Nickname: Bacon Porkers
Floodlights: No
Membership fees: Full £15, Playing £15, Social £3
Programme: No. of editorial pages 11; No. of advertising pages 11; Price 30p
Programme editor: Clive Scorrer, Rugby Club, Barracks Lane, Avonmouth
Local newspaper: Bristol Evening Post
League: Western Counties
League position (1988–89): 2nd
League playing record (1988–89): P 10, W 7, D 0, L 3, F 162, A 112

CIRENCESTER

The Whiteway, Cirencester, Glos. Tel: 0285 654434
Founded: 1948
President: Tegid Pugh
Chairman: John Sawyer
Secretary: Peter Davies, 1 Sawyers Close, Minety, Malmesbury, Wilts SN16 9QS. Tel: 0666 860482 (H), 0285 654875 (W)
Fixtures Secretary: Tony Weighell, Garden Cottage, Somerford Keynes, Glos. Tel: 0285 861488 (H), 651271 (W)
Press Officer: As Secretary
Coach: Dennis Woolrich
Club captain (1988–89): David Weaver
Club captain (1989–90): Peter Tuck
No. of teams: Senior 4, Youth 2, Minis 4
Directions to ground: Positioned at traffic lights (Grove Lane and The Whiteway) on main Gloucester to Swindon Road (A419) within mile of centre of Cirencester
Ground capacity: Standing 200+
Clubhouse facilities: Two bars, function room
Club colours: Red and black hoops. (*Change colours:* Green)
Floodlights: Yes (for training)
Membership fees: Full £15, Playing £15, Social £5, Youth £7.50, Student £7.50, OAP £5
Programme: No. of editorial pages 2; No. of advertising pages 5; Price 50p
Programme editor: J. Sawyer, 36 Courtbrook, Fairford, Glos
Local newspaper: The Wilts & Glos Standard
League: Western Counties
League position (1988–89): 3rd
League playing record (1988–89): P 33, W 25, D 2, L 6, F 580, A 270
Competitions won: 1st and 2nd XV's won their respective local Combination Cups

CLEVEDON

Coleridge Vale Playing Fields, Clevedon. Tel: 0272 877772
Founded: 1921
President: O.R.L. Taylor
Chairman: R.W.J. Newton
Secretary: R.G. Legge, 2 Kingston Avenue, Clevedon, Avon. Tel: 0272 874624
Fixtures Secretary: O.R.L. Taylor, 40 Ash Hayes Drive, Naksea, Bristol
Coach: H. Jones
Club captain (1988–89): D. Hussey
No. of teams: Senior 4, Youth 7+
Directions to ground: M5 Junc. 20, 1st and 2nd r'about, leave at 12 o'clock roadway junction. At lights turn left, take next left, take 2nd left. Ground in front
Club colours: Royal blue/gold. (*Change colours:* Royal blue)
Floodlights: No
Membership fees: Playing £13.50, Social £3
Programme: Price 50p
Programme editor: Sue Davis
League: Western Counties
League position (1988–89): 4th
League playing record (1988–89): P 10, W 5, D 1, L 4, F 136, A 95

DEVON & CORNWALL POLICE

Police HQ, Middlemoore, Exeter. Tel: 0392 52101
Founded: 1971
President: Chief Supt. J. Evans
Chairman: Supt. J. Essery
Secretary: Det. Con. I. Nain, Police Station, Heavitree Road, Exeter. Tel: 0392 68485 (H), 52101 (W)
Fixtures Secretary: Chris Mucker, Police Station, Tywardreath, Cornwall. Tel: 0726 812262 (H), 66930 (W)
Club captain (1988–89): I. Main
Club captain (1989–90): T.B.A.
No. of teams: Senior 1
Directions to ground: M5 to Exeter. Take city road, Police HQ 1 mile from M5
Clubhouse facilities: None
Club colours: Black and white hoops, black shorts, red socks
Floodlights: No
League: Western Counties
League position (1988–89): Bottom (relegated)
League playing record (1988–89): P 33, W 10, D 0, L 23, F 432, A 594
Competitions won: Mayflower Sevens

LAUNCESTON

Polson, Launceston, Cornwall. Tel: 0566 3406
President: Rev. M. James
Chairman: David H. Baker
Secretary: Stuart G. Towers, 7 Trecarn Close, Launceston, Cornwall PL15 7LN. Tel: 0566 5447
Fixtures Secretary: Mervyn Yeo, Whiterow Farm, Lewdown, Okehampton, Devon. Tel: Lewdown 230
Press Officer: Jeremy Fry, c/o Thorne Farm, Broadwood, Lanson. Tel: 025 63009
Coach: Ian Davies
Club captain (1988–89): Jon O'Neil
Club captain (1989–90): John Dunstan
No. of teams: Senior 3, Youth 1, Minis 7
Directions to ground: A30 to Launceston, right turn for Polson off main road. Ground mile
Club colours: All black with white trim on collars and socks. (*Change colours:* Blue and white hoops)
Floodlights: Yes
Membership fees: Full £10, Playing £10, Social £1, Student £5
Ground admission: £1

Programme: No. of editorial pages 1; No. of advertising pages 10; Price Free
Local newspapers: Cornish & Devon Post, Western Morning News
League: Western Counties

NEWQUAY HORNETS

Newquay Sports Centre, Tretherras Road, Newquay, Cornwall. Tel: 0637 875533
Founded: 1933
President: R. Edwards
Chairman: S. Dunn
Secretary: R.T. Delbridge, "Thurso", Cubert, Newquay 7R8 5HB. Tel: 0637 830441
Fixtures Secretary: C.R. Roberts, 18 St Annes Road, Newquay. Tel: 874568 (H)
Coach: F.R. Barnett
Club captain (1988–89): K. Wheeldon
Club captain (1989–90): K. Wheeldon
No. of teams: Senior 3, Youth 1, Minis 1
Directions to ground: Hewer Road for 1 mile, left along Chester Road, first left Whitegate Road, left to Sports Centre.
Ground capacity: Standing 1000's
Clubhouse facilities: 2 bars
Club colours: Green/white. (*Change colours:* Royal blue and white)
Floodlights: Yes, training
Membership fees: Full £200, Playing £100
Programme: No. of editorial pages 3; No. of advertising pages 6; Price 50p
Programme editor: R. Edwards
League: Western Counties SW
League position (1988–89): 9th
League playing record (1988–89): P 10, W 3, D 1, L 6, F 101, A 152

OKEHAMPTON

Oaklands Showfield, Okehampton. Tel: 0837 52508
Founded: 1884
President: Eric Chowings
Chairman: Russell Thomas
Secretary: Ted Cann, 11 Exeter Road, Okehampton, Devon EX20 1NN. Tel: 0837 52759 (H), 53338 (W)
Fixtures Secretary: Bryan Hucker, The Brackens, South Zeal, Nr. Okehampton. Tel: 0837 840428
Press Officer: Eddie Williamson, Ashbury House, Northlew, Nr. Okehampton. Tel: 0837 87351
Club captain (1988–89): Nick Holliday
Club captain (1989–90): Martyn Cox
No. of teams: Senior 3, Youth 4
Directions to ground: Hatherleigh Road, Okehampton
Ground capacity: Seating 250, standing 1000
Clubhouse facilities: Bar, dining area
Club colours: Maroon and amber hoops. (*Change colours:* Maroon)
Nickname: The Okes
Floodlights: No
Membership fees: Playing £7.50, Social £2.50, Youth £5, Student £2.50, OAP £2.50
Ground admission: £1 (League games only)
Programme: No. of editorial pages 3; No. of advertising pages 25; Price £1
Programme editor: Edward Hawkins, 103 Crediton Road, Okehampton, Devon. Tel: 0837 52473
Local newspapers: Okehampton Times, Western Morning News
League: Western Counties
League position (1988–89): 4th
League playing record (1988–89): P 10, W 5, D 1, L 4, F 106, A 75

OLD CULVERHAYSIANS

Old Fosse Road, Odd Down, Bath. Tel: 0225 832081
President: Tony Bond
Chairman: Maurice Cooper
Secretary: Terry Shore, 54 Edgeworth Road, Kingsway, Bath BA2 2LU. Tel: 0225 29979 (H),

795885 (W)
Fixtures Secretary: Robin Barnfield, 72 Edgeworth Road, Kingsway, Bath. Tel: 0225 330122
Press Officer: Dick Stevens, 43 Inverness Road, East Tiverton, Bath BA 3RX. Tel: Bath 22433 (H), 312791 (W)
Coach: Haydn Davies/George Norman/Robin Barnfield
Club captain (1988–89): Derek gimson
Club captain (1989–90): Nick Chandler
No. of teams: Senior 3, Youth 6
Directions to ground: From Bristol take Combe Down Road, turn left by Clarks Factory. From Radstock, turn left just as you enter city boundary
Ground capacity: Standing 1000
Clubhouse facilities: Good sized with bar, kitchen, hall, changing rooms, showers
Club colours: Black. (*Change colours:* Amber)
Nickname: Old C's or C's
Floodlights: No
Membership fees: Full £5, Playing £5, Social £2.50, Youth 0, Student £1, OAP £2.50
Ground admission: Nil
Local newspapers: Bath & Wilts Evening Chronicle and Bristol Evening Post
League: Gloucester/Somerset
League position (1988–89): 1st (promoted)
League playing record (1988–89): P 10, W 10, D 0, L 0, F 217, A 79
Competitions won: League

PENRYN

The Memorial Ground, Kernick Road, Penryn, Cornwall. Tel: 72239
Founded: 1872
President: Cyril Vanstone
Chairman: Dr. D. Shier
Secretary: Mrs. S.A. Head, 8A Lambs Lane, Falmouth, Cornwall TR11 2JL. Tel: 0326 319811
Fixtures Secretary: K. Loft, 6 Belle Vue, Penryn TR10 9LB. Tel: 72862
Coach: David Thomas
Club captain (1988–89): Mark Smith
Club captain (1989–90): Mark Smith
No. of teams: Senior 3, Youth 2, Minis (U8's–U14's)
Directions to ground: From Truro keep to Falmouth signs, at Treluswell turn of ffor Penryn (A39) up through town towards estate. Well sign posted
Ground capacity: Seating 400
Clubhouse facilities: 2 bars plus changing rooms
Club colours: Red and black hoops. (*Change colours:* Black)
Nickname: The Borough
Floodlights: No
Membership fees: Full £3.50, Playing £10, VPs £10, OAP £2
Ground admission: £1
Programme: No. of editorial pages 2; No. of advertising pages 4; Price 20p
Programme editor: As Secretary
Local newspapers: The Packet, The Leader, The West Briton
League: Devon/Cornwall
League position (1988–89): 1st (promoted)
League playing record (1988–89): P 37, W 24, D 0, L 13, F 631, A 425
Competitions won: Penryn R.F.C. Easter 7's (Plate Winners)

TIVERTON

Coronation Field, Bolham Road, Tiverton, Devon. Tel: 0884 252271
Founded: 1868
President: George Burt
Chairman: Steve Andrews
Secretary: Mike Heard, 6 Norwood Road, Tiverton, Devon. Tel: 0884 258600 (H), 0392 272957 (W)
Fixtures Secretary: Keith Sutton, 43 Belmont Road, Tiverton, Devon. Tel: 0884 255199

Coach: John Hughes
Club captain (1988–89): Phil Cole
Club captain (1989–90): Richard Cruse
No. of teams: Senior 3, Youth 1, Minis 3
Directions to ground: M5 Junction 27, North Devon link road, left at first roundabout, club 400 yards on right by footbridge
Ground capacity: Seating 200
Clubhouse facilities: 2 bars, multi-gym, gas. Open each evening and weekend lunchtimes
Club colours: Light and dark blue hoops. (*Change colours:* Yellow)
Nickname: Tivvy
Floodlights: Yes
Membership fees: Full £10, Playing £10, Social £3.50, Youth £3, Student 50p, OAP £2
Programme: No. of editorial pages 4; No. of advertising pages 12; Price 50p
Programme editor: Geoff Bulley, 2 Besley Close, Tiverton, Devon
Local newspapers: Tiverton Gazette, Mid Devon Star
League: Western Counties
League position (1988–89): 5th
League playing record (1988–89): P 10, W 5, D 0, L 5, F 109, A 143

TRURO

St. Clements Hill, Truro, Cornwall. Tel: 0872 74750
Founded: 1920

President: Jack W.E. Edwards
Chairman: David Matthews
Secretary: Greg O.F. Oldrieve, Chydavas, Idless, Truro, Cornwall TR4 9QS. Tel: 0872 42091 (H), 71033 (W)
Fixtures Secretary: Chris Richards, 7 Treneoweth Estate, North Country, Redruth TR16 4AQ. Tel: 0209 218042
Press Officer: As Secretary
Coach: G. Baines
Club captain (1988–89): Steve Caruana
Club captain (1989–90): Steve Caruana
No. of teams: Senior 3, Youth 2, Minis 1
Directions to ground: From A30 signposted to Truro, on entering Truro take first exit at first roundabout. Club on right at top of hill
Clubhouse facilities: Bar
Club colours: Blue/amber
Floodlights: No
Membership fees: Full £10, Playing £10, Social £3, Youth £5, Student £5
Ground admission: £1
Programme: No. of editorial pages 2; No. of advertising pages 2; Price 5p
Programme editor: As Secretary
Local newspapers: West Briton
League: Western 6
League position (1988–89): 7th
League playing record (1988–89): P 10, W 3, D 1, L 6, F 89, A 129

SOUTHERN COUNTIES LEAGUE

After threatening a breakthrough for some time Banbury won the league after a stern tussle with Aylesbury and it will be interesting to see how they fare in South West 2, where they will play in the coming season. A large pack will be no disadvantage to them. In the coming season one of the Dorset clubs – Swanage & Wareham or Wimborne – could well be the front runners for promotion, or perhaps Marlow will finally live up to the promise they have shown for so many seasons in the county cup competitions. Oxford Marathon, who narrowly survived in 1987–88, had no such luck this time and lost all their 10 matches to go down.

OVERALL RESPONSIBILITY FOR
BERKS., BUCKS., OXON., DORSET AND
WILTS.:

Trevor Palm, Esq,
13 Dolesford Road,
Aylesbury,   (H) 0296 81847
Bucks.   (O) 0753 33233

TABLES 1987–88

SOUTHERN COUNTIES

	P	W	D	L	F	A	PTS
Redingensian	10	8	0	2	159	80	16
Swindon	10	7	1	2	162	66	15
Wimborne	10	7	0	3	175	95	14
Marlow	10	7	0	3	135	78	14
Oxford OB	10	6	0	4	142	82	12
Aylesbury	10	5	1	4	156	110	11
Banbury	19	4	1	4	129	111	9
Windsor	10	3	2	5	86	144	8
Bletchley	10	3	0	7	76	176	6
Oxford Mara	10	1	1	8	66	257	3
Bracknell	9	1	1	9	63	150	0

TABLES 1988–89

SOUTHERN COUNTIES

	P	W	D	L	F	A	PTS
Banbury	10	8	1	1	242	92	17
Aylesbury	10	8	0	2	192	69	16
Swanage & Wareham	10	7	0	3	146	79	14
Wimborne	10	7	0	3	145	98	14
Marlow	10	6	1	3	140	102	13
Swindon	10	5	1	4	152	127	11
Oxford Old Boys	10	5	0	5	147	144	10
Windsor	10	3	0	7	108	154	6
Bletchley	10	3	0	7	73	188	6
Slough	10	1	1	8	119	189	3
Oxford Marathan	10	0	0	10	42	264	0

Old Culverhaysians – stalwarts of Western Counties League. Photo: Wessex Newspaper, Bath.

SOUTHERN COUNTIES FIXTURES 1989/90

Sat. 9th September (Week 2)
 Aylesbury v Bracknell
 Swanage & Wareham v Chiltern
 Swindon v Marlow
 Wimborne v Slough
 Windsor v Bletchley

Sat. 23rd September (Week 4)
 Slough v Windsor
 Marlow v Wimborne
 Chiltern v Swindon
 Oxford Old Boys v Swanage & Wareham
 Bletchley v Aylesbury

Sat. 14th October (Week 6)
 Aylesbury v Slough
 Bracknell v Bletchley
 Swindon v Oxford Old Boys
 Wimborne v Chiltern
 Windsor v Marlow

Sat. 28th October (Week 8)
 Slough v Bracknell
 Marlow v Aylesbury
 Chiltern v Windsor
 Oxford Old Boys v Wimborne
 Swanage & Wareham v Swindon

Sat. 11th November (Week 10)
 Aylesbury v Chiltern
 Bracknell v Marlow
 Bletchley v Slough
 Wimborne v Swanage & Wareham
 Windsor v Oxford Old Boys

18th November (Week 11)
 Marlow v Bletchley
 Chiltern v Bracknell
 Oxford Old Boys v Aylesbury
 Swanage & Wareham v Windsor
 Swindon v Wimborne

Sat. 25th November (Week 12)
 Aylesbury v Swanage & Wareham
 Bracknell v Oxford Old Boys
 Bletchley v Chiltern
 Slough v Marlow
 Windsor v Swindon

Sat. 13th January (Week 18)
 Chiltern v Slough
 Oxford Old Boys v Bletchley
 Swanage & Wareham v Bracknell
 Swindon v Aylesbury
 Wimborne v Windsor

Sat. 10th March (Week 26)
 Aylesbury v Wimborne
 Bracknell v Swindon
 Bletchley v Swanage & Wareham
 Slough v Oxford Old Boyx
 Marlow v Chiltern

Sat. 31st March (Week X7)
 Oxford Old Boys v Marlow
 Swanage & Wareham v Slough
 Swindon v Bletchley
 Wimborne v Bracknell
 Windsor v Aylesbury

Sat. 28th April (Week 32)
 Bracknell v Windsor
 Bletchley v Wimborne
 Slough v Swindon
 Marlow v Swanage & Wareham
 Chiltern v Oxford Old Boys

SOUTHERN COUNTIES

AYLESBURY

Ostler's Field, Brook End, Weston Turville,
Aylesbury, Bucks. Tel: 0296 612556
Founded: 1931
President: Geoffrey Cowen
Chairman: John Rose
Secretary: Rowland Langdon, Ivy Cottages, Halton
Village, Aylesbury, Bucks HP22 5NS. Tel: 0296
622562 (H), 625011 (W)
Fixtures Secretary: David Furby, Yew Tree Cottage,
Stockaway, Weedon, Aylesbury, Bucks. Tel: 0296
641289
Coach: Martin Poste
Club captain (1988–89): Huw Stone
Club captain (1989–90): Huw Stone
No. of teams: Senior 6, Youth 6, Minis 5
Directions to ground: On north side of road between
Weston Turville and Aston clinton. South by
Aylesbury
Ground capacity: Seating 300, standing 2000
Clubhouse facilities: Large clubroom and 2 bars
Club colours: Magenta and black. (*Change colours:*
White)
Nickname: Ducks
Floodlights: No
Membership fees: Playing £25, Social £10, Youth £8,
Student £7
Programme: No. of editorial pages 1; No. of
advertising pages 4
Programme editor: As Secretary
Local newspaper: Bucks Herald
League: Southern Counties
League position (1988–89): 2nd
League playing record (1988–89): P 31, W 17, D 0,
L 14, F 467, A 368
Competitions won: Blake Sevens, Galway, Ireland,
Easter '89

BLETCHLEY

Manor Fields, Bletchley, Bucks. Tel: 0908 72298
Founded: 1946/47
President: Norman Anderson
Chairman: Robin Bowen-Williams
Secretary: Jim Dewhurst, 2 St. Pauls Road, Bletchley,
Bucks. Tel: 0908 77020
Coach: Martin Robson
Club captain (1988–89): Tim Rawles
Club captain (1989–90): Peter Garrett
No. of teams: Senior 4, Youth 1
Directions to ground: M1 or A5 to Bletchley, head for
Fenny Stratford, turn into Aylesbury Street, 400 yds
mini roundabout, straight over next left, over hump-
back bridge to ground
Club colours: Maroon/white hoops
Floodlights: Yes
League: Southern Counties
League position (1988–89): 9th
League playing record (1988–89): P 30, W 11, D 0,
L 19

BRACKNELL

Lily Hill, London Road, Bracknell. Tel: 0344 424013
Founded: 1955
President: J.R. Dance
Chairman: M. Dixon
Secretary: A. Gooch, 15 Denmark Road, Reading.
Tel: 0734 872306
Fixtures Secretary: N. Featherstone, 25 Claverdon,
Bracknell. Tel: 0344 422471
Coach: G. Parsons
Club captain (1988–89): C. Vaal
Club captain (1989–90): C. Vaal
No. of teams: Senior 8, Youth and Minis 9
Clubhouse facilities: Open matchdays, lunchtimes and
evenings
Club colours: Green/gold/black. (*Change colours:*

Black)
Floodlights: No
Membership fees: Full £20, Playing £12, Social £3,
Youth £3, Student £3, OAP £1
Programme: No. of editorial pages 2; No. of
advertising pages 9; Price 30p
Local newspapers: Evening Post, Evening Mail
League: Southern Counties
League position (1988–89): 1st (promoted)
League playing record (1988–89): P 10, W 10, D 0,
L 0, F 222, A 59

CHILTERN

Weedon Lane, Amersham, Bucks. Tel: 0494 725161
Founded: 1924
President: Brian Arbib
Chairman: Stan Griffiths
Secretary: Peter Jallan, Greenhaven, 20 Green Lane,
Chesham Bois, Bucks MP6 5LQ. Tel: 0494 725588
Club captain (1988–89): Alex Pegley
Club captain (1989–90): Alex Pegley
No. of teams: Senior 6, Youth 6, Minis 15
Directions to ground: Turn left at first mini
roundabout after Boot & Slipper pub on Amersham
to Chesham road (A416), signposted to Hyde Heath.
Take 3rd left (Weedon Lane). Clubhouse is in cul-de-
sac 300 yards along Weedon Lane on right
Ground capacity: Standing 2000
Club colours: Claret and white hoops
Floodlights: Yes
Membership fees: £30
Local newspapers: Bucks Examiner, Bucks Advertiser
League: Southern Counties
League position (1988–89): 1st
League playing record (1988–89): P 33, W 20, D 1,
L 12

MARLOW

Riverwoods Drive, Marlow, Bucks. Tel: 06284 3911
Founded: 1948
President: Peter Charles Trunkfield
Chairman: Michael Lewins
Secretary: Robin John Gates, St. Jasual, Wheeler
End, Lane End, High Wycombe, Bucks. Tel: 0494
881089 (H), 450171 (W)
Fixtures Secretary: Andrew Sanderson, 26 Dedmere
Court, Marlow, Bucks. Tel: 06284 71731 (H), 0628
74811 (W)
Press Officer: David Sumpter, Little Dene, Handleton
Common, Lane End, Nr. High Wycombe, Bucks.
Tel: 0494 881632 (H), 06284 890190 (W)
Coach: Ian Coull
Club captain (1988–89): Richard Smart
Club captain (1989–90): John Watson
No. of teams: Senior 6 + Colts, Youth 5, Minis 5
Directions to ground: Into Marlow from bypass, into
Marlow to top of High Street, down High Street, left
just before bridge, turn right at Marlow Donkey pub,
down to T-junction, turn left all way along to club car
park
Ground capacity: Standing 2000–3000
Clubhouse facilities: Members bar, large function
room/bar, multi-gym training room, bath, showers,
kitchens, 10 changing rooms
Club colours: Black and white ringed shirts, black and
white topped stockings. (*Change colours:* White
shirts)
Floodlights: No
Membership fees: Full £22, Playing £22, Social £12,
Youth £5, Student £5
Ground admission: Only charged for Cup games
Programme: No. of editorial pages 2; No. of
advertising pages 2; Price 50p
Programme editor: As Press Officer
Local newspapers: Bucks Free Press, Maidenhead
Advertiser, Maidenhead Gazette
League: SW Southern Counties
League position (1988–89): 5th
League playing record (1988–89): P 10, W 6, D 1,
L 3, F 140, A 102

OXFORD OLD BOYS

Marston Ferry Road, Marston, Oxford. Tel: 0865
52813
Founded: 1963
Secretary: D. Williams, 206 Woodstock Road,
Oxford, OX2 7NH. Tel: 0865 54528
Fixtures Secretary: T. Whitelow, 41 Church Hill
Road, Cowley, Oxford. Tel: 0865 716381
No. of teams: Senior 5, Youth 3, Minis 3
League: Southern Counties
League position (1988–89): 7th
League playing record (1988–89): P 10, W 5, D 0,
L 5, F 147, A 144

SLOUGH

Upton Court Park, Slough, Berks. Tel: Slough 22107
Founded: 1928
Secretary: S. Webb, 8 Chestnut Avenue, Wokingham,
Berks RG11 2UU. Tel: 0734 789040 (H), 0344 86666
(W)
Fixtures Secretary: M. Carter, 65 Wavell Road,
Maidenhead, Berks. Tel: 0628 25640
Club colours: Green/white
League: Southern Counties
League position (1988–89): 10th
League playing record (1988–89): P 10, W 1, D 1,
L 8, F 119, A 189

SWANAGE AND WAREHAM

Bestwall, Wareham, Dorset. Tel: 09295 2224
Founded: 1953
President: John R. Procter
Chairman: Jim Woolley
Secretary: John M. Hopkins, 'Sospan', Greenclose
Lane, Wimborne, Dorset BH21 2AL. Tel: 0202
886804
Fixtures Secretary: As Secretary
Press Officer: John Constable, 16 Worgret Road,
Wareham, Dorset. Tel: 09295 3033 (H), 0202 292333
ext. 3548 (W)
Coach: Hefin Thomas
Club captain (1988–89): John Strange
Club captain (1989–90): John Strange
No. of teams: Senior 4 (U19), Youth (U14, U16),
Minis (U8, U10, U12)
Directions to ground: Town centre Wareham, turn
into East Street at traffic lights, travel to the end, turn
left into ground
Ground capacity: Standing 2000
Clubhouse facilities: Presidents room, clubroom, six
changing rooms, referees room, showers
Club colours: Maroon (plain), white shorts. (*Change
colours:* White, maroon hoops)
Nickname: 'Swans'
Floodlights: No
Membership fees: Full £20, Playing £20, Youth match
fee, OAP £5
Local newspaper: Evening Echo
League: Southern Counties
League position (1988–89): 3rd
League playing record (1988–89): P 34, W 26, D 0,
L 8, F 682, A 306
Competitions won: Dorset and Wilts Cup Winners,
Lytchett Minster R.F.C. 7's Winners

SWINDON

Greenbridge Road, Swindon. Tel: 0793 21148
Founded: 1895
President: R. Nash

Chairman: I.I. Pantzig
Coach: L. Morgan
Secretary: W.M. Hillyard, 12 Fitzroy Road, Swindon.
Tel: 611925.
Fixtures Secretary: H. Evans, The Close, High Street,
Warborough, Swindon. Tel: 790432.
Club captain (1988–89): T. Brant
No. of teams: Senior 4.
Directions to Ground: Greenbridge Road off Darcan
Way – by W.H. Smith Distribution Centre.
Clubhouse: 2/3 bars and hall.
Colours: Blue, amber shirts. (*Change colours:* Cherry,
white hoops).
Floodlights: Yes, training only
Membership: £25 rugby, £5 social
Local newspaper: Evening Advertiser
League: Southern Counties

WIMBORNE

Leigh Park, Wimborne, Dorset. Tel: 0202 882602
Founded: 1950
President: T. Eill
Chairman: D. Mitchell
Secretary: G. Emery, 4 River Close, Wimborne,
Dorset. Tel: 0202 888830 (H), 885211 (W)
Fixtures Secretary: D. Beck, 112 Wareham Road,
Corfe Mullen, Wimborne, Dorset. Tel: 0202 693205
Press Officer: G. Robinson
Coach: M. Heffield
Club captain (1988–89): A. Symes
Club captain (1989–90): A. Symes
No. of teams: Senior 6, Youth and Minis 6
Directions to ground: Approach Wimborne on A31
from east, one mile from town centre turn left into
Gordon Road, ground 100 yds ahead
Clubhouse facilities: Two bars
Club colours: Black. (*Change colours:* Black and
white hoops)
Floodlights: No
League: Southern Counties
League position (1988–89): 4th
League playing record (1988–89): P 10, W 7, D 0,
L 3, F 145, A 98
Competitions won: Dorset & Wilts Second XV
Knockout Cup

WINDSOR

Home Park, Datchet Road, Windsor, Berks. Tel:
0753 860807
Founded: 1922
President: Bob Deeley
Chairman: Will Beckett
Secretary: Martin Unsworth, 7 Fairlight Avenue,
Windsor, Berks. Tel: 0753 855555 (W)
Fixtures Secretary: Bill Manger, 127 Springfield Road,
Windsor, Berks. Tel: 0753 869943
Press Officer: Andy Dingley, 20 Ricardo Road, Old
Windsor, Berks
Coach: John Jackson
Club captain (1988–89): Andy Dingley
Club captain (1989–90): Dick Munro
No. of teams: Senior 7, Youth 5, Minis 6
Directions to ground: Opposite Windsor Castle
Ground capacity: Standing 3000+
Clubhouse facilities: 2 clubhouses
Club colours: Green/gold/maroon/black 's. (*Change
colours:* Green/black/red hoops)
Floodlights: No
League: Southern Counties
League position (1988–89): 8th
League playing record (1988–89): P 35, W 15, D 0,
L 20, F 414, A 580
Competitions won: Slough Express Floodlit Cup

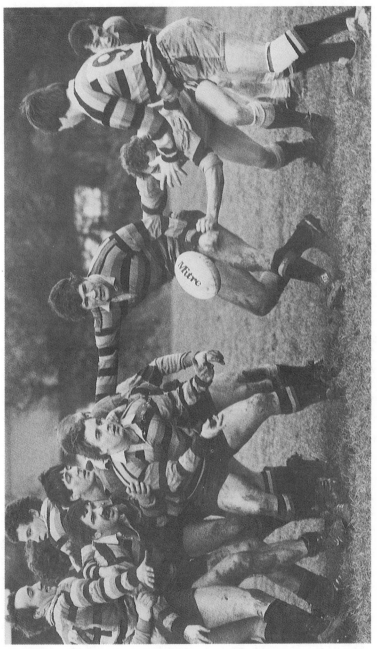

Cornish action from Saltash in the Duchy's Division One

CORNWALL & DEVON LEAGUE

Penryn were only a point off the leaders last time out, but this time they made no mistake by losing only one game and finishing a cool six points ahead of their nearest challengers. They also scored 261 points and will relish the challenge of the Western League. No fewer than four clubs are listed for relegation with three of them from Devon – Exeter Saracens (on points difference), Paignton and Exmouth. Cornwall lose bottom club Hayle from this league, which was probably less exciting than some others – so dominant were Penryn.

In fact, it is not easy to forecast a winner for the coming season, although there are several well enough known teams on parade.

CORNWALL AND DEVON AND ALL
DEVON LEAGUES: OFFICIAL

Geoff Simpson,
108 Pattinson Drive,
Mainstone, Plymouth,
Devon PL6 8RU   (H) 0752 707432

TABLES 1987–88

CORNWALL & DEVON LEAGUE

	P	W	D	L	F	A	PTS
Crediton	10	9	0	1	232	65	18
Exmouth	10	9	0	1	187	64	18
Penryn	10	8	1	1	191	67	17
Penzance/Newlyn	10	7	1	3	166	111	13
Falmouth	10	6	0	4	110	140	12
Paignton	10	5	0	5	156	157	10
Teignmouth	10	4	0	6	112	176	8
Bideford	10	3	0	7	160	153	6
Hayle	10	2	1	7	107	157	5
St Austell	10	1	1	8	69	193	3
Newton Abbot	10	0	0	10	31	238	0

TABLES 1988–89

CORNWALL & DEVON LEAGUE

	P	W	D	L	F	A	PTS
Penryn	10	9	0	1	261	64	18
Teignmouth	10	6	0	4	146	106	12
Falmouth	10	6	0	4	116	117	12
Sidmouth	10	6	0	4	104	123	12
Bideford	10	5	0	5	141	138	10
Illogen Park	10	5	0	5	84	105	10
Penzance & Newlyn	10	5	0	5	120	147	10
Exeter Saracens	10	5	0	5	81	123	10
Paignton	10	4	0	6	114	152	8
Exmouth	10	2	0	8	130	134	4
Hayle	10	2	0	8	108	196	4

CORNWALL & DEVON LEAGUE FIXTURES 1989/90

Sat. 9th September (Week 2)
Bideford v Exeter Saracens
Penzance-Newlyn v Devonport Services
Sidmouth v Falmouth
Teignmouth v Crediton
Wadebridge Camels v Illogan Park

Sat. 23rd September (Week 4)
Crediton v Bideford
Devonport Services v Sidnouth
Falmouth v Teignmouth
Illogan Park v Penzance-Newlyn
Plymouth CS v Wadebridge Camels

Sat. 14th October (Week 6)
Bideford v Falmouth
Exeter Saracens v Crediton
Penzance-Newlyn v Plymouth CS
Sidmouth v Illogan Park
Teignmouth v Devonport Services

Sat. 28th October (Week 8)
Devonport Services v Bideford
Falmouth v Exeter Saracens
Illogan Park v Teignmouth
Plymouth Cs v Sidmouth
Wadebridge Camels v Penzance-Newlyn

Sat. 11th November (Week 10)
Bideford v Illogan Park
Crediton v Falmouth
Exeter Saracens v Devonport Services
Sidmouth v Wadebridge Camels
Teignmouth v Plymouth CS

18th November (Week 11)
Devonport Services v Crediton
Illogan Park v Exeter Saracens
Penzance-Newlyn v Sidmouth
Plymouth CS v Bideford
Wadebridge Camels v Teignmouth

Sat. 25th November (Week 12)
Bideford v Wadebridge Camels
Crediton v Illogan Park
Exeter Saracens v Plymouth CS
Falmouth v Devonport Services
Teignmouth v Penzance-Newlyn

Sat. 13th January (Week 18)
Illogan Park v Falmouth
Penzance-Newlyn v Bideford
Plymouth CS v Crediton
Sidmouth v Teignmouth
Wadebridge Camels v Exeter Saracens

Sat. 10th March (Week 26)
Bideford v Sidmouth
Crediton v Wadebridge Camels
Devonport Services v Illogan Park
Exeter Saracens v Penzance-Newlyn
Falmouth v Plymouth CS

Sat. 31st March (Week X7)
Penzance-Newlyn v Crediton
Plymouth CS v Devonport Services
Sidmouth v Exeter Saracens
Teignmouth v Bideford
Wadebridge Camels v Falmouth

Sat. 28th April (Week 32)
Crediton v Sidmouth
Devonport Services v Wadebridge Camels
Exeter Saracens v Teignmouth
Falmouth v Penzance-Newlyn
Illogan Park v Plymouth CS

CORNWALL & DEVON

BIDEFORD

King George's Field, Bideford, Devon. Tel: 02372 74049
Founded: 1926
President: John Tucker
Chairman: Hugh Jones
Secretary: Bernard Ridd, Higher Benton, Bratton Fleming, Devon. Tel: Brayford 298
Fixtures Secretary: R.J. Ovenell, Meadow Farm, Langtree, Devon. Tel: Langtree 232
Press Officer: Lester Bird, c/o Bideford R.F.C.
Coach: Simon Berry
Club captain (1988–89): Nick Giddy
Club captain (1989–90): Mark Priest
No. of teams: Senior 3, Youth 1, Minis 4
Directions to ground: Right over Bideford old bridge, right again, follow bank past Kingsley Statue
Ground capacity: Seating 400, standing 2000
Clubhouse facilities: Main club bar, lounge bar, kitchen, toilets, changing rooms
Club colours: Red and white hoops. (*Change colours:* White or blue and white hoops)
Nickname: Biddy
Floodlights: Yes
Membership fees: Full £5, Playing £20, Social £5, Youth £7.50 OAP £5
Ground admission: £1
Programme: No. of editorial pages 1; No. of advertising pages 6; Price Free
Programme editor: John Driffield, 5 North Avenue, Broadlands, Bideford. Tel: Bideford 78184
Local newspaper: North Devon Journal
League: Devon/Cornwall
League position (1988–89): 5th
League playing record (1988–89): P 10, W 5, D 0, L 5, F 141, A 138

CREDITON

Blagdon, Exhibition Road, Crediton EX17 1BY. Tel: 03632 2784
Founded: 1878
President: J.C. Hayes
Chairman: H.W. Wadsworth
Secretary: P.H. Gibbings, South Coombe, Cheriton Fitpaine, Crediton EX17 4HP. Tel: 03636 413
Fixtures Secretary: Capt. K.S. Pitt R.N., Tannery Farm, Bow, Nr. Crediton, Devon. Tel: 03633 230
Press Officer: J.C. Hayes, 13 Brookside Crescent, Exeter EX4 8NF. Tel: 0392 66534
Coach: T.J. Crocker/B. Steer
Club captain (1988–89): M.J. Leyman
Club captain (1989–90): V. Steer
No. of teams: Senior 3, Youth 1 (Colts), Minis 6 (12–17)
Directions to ground: M5 – A377 Exeter to Crediton ground on A3072 (Crediton-Tiverton road)
Ground capacity: Seating 250, standing 1200
Clubhouse facilities: Two storey, changing rooms, showers (lower floor), bar, lounge/diner (upper floow) and squash court
Club colours: Black and amber. (*Change colours:* Amber)
Nickname: Kirton
Floodlights: No
Membership fees: Full £7, Playing £8.50, Social £1, Youth £1, Student 50p
Ground admission: £1
Programme: No. of editorial pages 2; No. of advertising pages 9; Price £1
Programme editor: As Press Officer
Local newspapers: Express & Echo, Western Morning News, Sunday Independent, Crediton Country Courier
League: Devon/Cornwall
League position (1988–89): Bottom (relegated)
League playing record (1988–89): P 10, W 1, D 1, L 8, F 87, A 162

FALMOUTH

Founded: 1873
President: B.F. Smales
Chairman: T.B.A.
Secretary: E. Nicholls, 4 Elm Grove Cottages, Arwenack Avenue, Falmouth. Tel: 314618
Fixtures Secretary: D. Chatterton, 5 Treworder Road, Truro, Cornwall. Tel: 72970
Press Officer: Bunny Williams, 18 Grove Hill Crescent, Falmouth. Tel: 313453
Coach: P. Smith
Club captain (1988–89): Neil Blight
Club captain (1989–90): Neil Blight
No. of teams: Senior 2, Colt 1, Minis 1
Directions to ground: Main road into Falmouth, along Dracaena Avenue. Ground at end of avenue
Ground capacity: Seating 8000–10,000, standing 600
Clubhouse facilities: Two bars, general facilities
Club colours: Black and white. (*Change colours:* Red and navy blue)
Floodlights: No
Membership fees: Full £7, Playing £7, Social £2, Youth £1, Student £1, OAP £21
Ground admission: £1
Programme: No. of editorial pages 1; No. of advertising pages 2; Price Free
Programme editor: Roger Mead, c/o Falmouth R.F.C.
Local newspaper: Falmouth Packet
League: Devon/Cornwall
League position (1988–89): Joint 2nd
League playing record (1988–89): P 10, W 6, D 0, L 4, F 116, A 117

DEVONPORT SERVICES

Rectory Field, Second Avenue, Devonport, Plymouth. Tel: 0752 561065. Tel: 0752 561065
Founded: 1919
President: I. White
Chairman: Cmdr. Craig, D.S.C., R.N.
Secretary: Cmdr. R.W. 'Tommy' Tucker, R.N., 8 Tamerton Close, Holly Park, Plymouth PL5 4JX. Tel: 703404 (H), 552037 (W)
Fixtures Secretary: Mrs. C. Bartlett-Horwood, 36 Fordhill, Stoke. Tel: Ply 558271
Press Officer: Lt. Mike Cheetham, HMS Raleigh, Tor Point, East Cornwall
Coach: Dennis Brown
Club captain (1988–89): Jim Martin
Club captain (1989–90): Steve Jones
No. of teams: Senior 3, Youth 1
Directions to ground: Follow signs to centre of Plymouth → thro' Royal Parade → directly along Union Street → over Stonehouse Bridge → 1st right and 1st right again into Rectory Road → under low tunnel and 2nd on left
Ground capacity: Seating 2000, Standing 400
Clubhouse facilities: Bar
Club colours: N blue. (*Change colours:* Red)
Nickname: Services
Floodlights: Yes
Membership fees: Full £12, Social £6 (members of Armed Forces)
Programme: Price 20p–£1
League: Cornwall/Devon
League position (1988–89): 10th
League playing record (1988–89): P 10, W 3, D 0, L 7, F 139, A 198

EXETER SARACENS

Exhibition Fields, Summer Lane, Whipton, Exeter. Tel: 0392 66993
Founded: 1953
President: David Mortimore
Chairman: William (Bill) Cormack
Secretary: Robert W. (Jack) Buchanan, 72 Sylvan Road, Pennsylvania, Exeter, EX4 6HA. Tel: 0392 430804 (H), 433641 (W)

Fixtures Secretary: Peter Blackmore, 1 Yieux Close,
Behindhayes, Otterton, Budleigh Salterton. Tel:
Colaton Raleigh 67777 (H), 0395 264373 (W)
Press Officer: Gordon King, 28 Hanover Road,
Exeter. Tel: 0392 431323 (H), 68891 (W)
Coach: T.B.A.
Club captain (1988–89): Mike Flavin
Club captain (1989–90): Andy Kift
No. of teams: Senior 5, Youth 1, Minis 5
Directions to ground: From city centre take Pinhoe
Road. At Whipton Shops turn left into Summer Lane
under railway bridge. Ground on right
Ground capacity: Seating 200, standing 2000+
Clubhouse facilities: Open match days
Club colours: Red shirts, black shorts. (*Change
colours:* Black shirt with red/white hoop)
Nickname: Sarries
Floodlights: Yes (training lights)
Membership fees: Full £10, Playing £10, Social £6,
Youth £2, Student £6, OAP £6
Ground admission: £1 Cup games, generally free
Programme: Price £1 (not regularly produced)
Programme editor: G. King, 28 Hanover Road,
Exeter
Local newspapers: Express and Echo
League: D 1
League position (1988–89): 8th
League playing record (1988–89): P 10, W 5, D 0,
L 5, F 81, A 123

ILLOGAN PARK

Paynters Lane End, Illogan, Redruth, Cornwall.
Founded: 1967
Chairman: T. May
Coach: T. May
Secretary: I. Collett, Paynters Lane End, Illogan,
Redruth, Cornwall.
Fixtures Secretary: G. Nicholls, 3 Railway Villas,
Barncoose, Redruth, Cornwall.
Team secretary: B. Sullivan
Club captain (1988–89): M. Downing
Clubhouse: Good facilities.
Colours: Yellow shirts, one thick blacck hoop. Black
shorts.
Nickname: "Park"
Floodlights: No
Local newspaper: The Cornishman
League: Cornwall 1

PENZANCE & NEWLYN

Alexandra Road, Penzance, Cornwall. Tel: 0736
64227
Founded: 1945
President: Alvin Williams
Chairman: Cecil Dunn
Secretary: Mike Dorey, 'Bollowal', Parade Passage,
Penzance, Cornwall TR18 4SW. Tel: 0736 68426
Fixtures Secretary:
Coach: Paul Greaves
Club captain (1988–89): Dave Elliott
Club captain (1989–90): T.B.A.
No. of teams: Senior 2, Youth & Minis 7
Directions to ground: Take Harbour Road on entering
Penzance, go along Promenade and turn right at
roundabout by Beachfield Hotel
Ground capacity: Seating 6000, standing 700
Clubhouse facilities: Open every evening and
lunchtime, weekends and bank holidays
Club colours: Black/red/white. (*Change colours:*
Black)
Nickname: The Pirates
Floodlights: Yes
Membership fees: Full £12 (including social
membership)
Ground admission: 70p
Programme: Price 10p
Programme editor: Phil Westren
Local newspaper: Devon & Cornwall
League: Devon/Cornwall

PLYMOUTH CIVIL SERVICE

C.S.S.A., Beacon Down, Recreation Road, Peverell,
Plymouth. Tel: 0702303
Founded: 1928
President: T. Butler
Chairman: M. Welsford
Secretary: B. Attis, 4 The Lawns, Torpoint,
Cornwall. Tel: 0752 815024
Fixtures Secretary: S. Brown, 1 Westways Close,
Staddiscombe, Plymouth. Tel: 0752 492216
Press Officer: As Secretary
Coach: R. Jewel/A. Newman
Club captain (1988–89): B. Attis
Club captain (1989–90): G. Keane
No. of teams: Senior 2
Directions to ground: Contact Fixture Secretary
Ground capacity: Standing 2000
Clubhouse facilities: Civil Service Club
Club colours: Red and white hoops. (*Change colours:*
Plain blue or plain red)
Floodlights: No
Membership fees: Full £10, Playing £10, Social £5
Local newspaper: Western Evening Herald
League: D 1
League position (1988–89): 1st
League playing record (1988–89): P 37, W 32, D 1,
L 4, F 846, A 293
Competitions won: Lockie Cup, R.N.E.C. Cup, Ellis
Cup

SIDMOUTH

Blackmore Field, Heydons Lane, Sidmouth. Tel: 0395
516816
Founded: 1884
President: Brian Thomas
Chairman: Derek Marchant
Secretary: David Salter, 5 Barrington Mead,
Sidmouth EX10 8EW. Tel: 0395 513678
Fixtures Secretary: Terry O'Brien, 2 Rivulet Cottages,
Sidford, Sidmouth. Tel: 0395 577403
Coach: Tim Smith
Club captain (1988–89): Bob Smith
Club captain (1989–90): Bob Smith
No. of teams: Senior 3, Youth 2, Minis 3
Directions to ground: A3052 from M5. Turn right at
Bowd Inn, straight on for approx. 2 miles, straight
across mini roundabout then second left and first left
Ground capacity: Seating 150, standing 600
Clubhouse facilities: 2 bars
Club colours: Green. (*Change colours:* Navy blue)
Nickname: Evergreens
Floodlights: No
Ground admission: £1
Programme: No. of editorial pages 1; No. of
advertising pages 4
Local newspaper: Sidmouth Herald
League: Devon/Cornwall
League position (1988–89): 4th
League playing record (1988–89): P 10, W 6, D 0,
L 4, F 104, A 123

TEIGNMOUTH

Lower Bitton Sports Ground, Bitton Park Road,
Teignmouth TQ14. Tel: 0626 774714
Founded: 1874
President: John R. Rowland
Chairman: Alan S. Norsworthy
Secretary: Maureen O. Powell, Leyden, 6 Fourth
Avenue, Teignmouth TQ14 9OR. Tel: 0626 774950
Fixtures Secretary: Brian Abrahams, 16 Gloucester
Road, Teignmouth. Tel: 0776346
Press Officer: John Ware
Coach: Douglas Attwell
Club captain (1988–89): David Tidball
Club captain (1989–90): David Tidball
No. of teams: Senior 3, Youth 2, Minis 3

Directions to ground: From east: Through town towards torquay, bottom of hill opposite Talbot Hotel. From west: As entering town opposite Talbot Hotel
Club colours: Red, white and black hoops, white shorts. (*Change colours:* Black shirts, white shorts)
Nickname: Teigns
Floodlights: Yes
Programme: Price included in ground position
League: Devon/Cornwall
League position (1988–89): 2nd
League playing record (1988–89): P 10, W 6, D 0, L 4, F 146, A 106

WADEBRIDGE CAMELS

Molesworth Field, Egloshaule, Wadebridge, Cornwall
Founded: 1955
President: Peter Richards
Chairman: Mike Howells
Secretary: John Owen, 5 Valley View, Wadebridge. Tel: 020881 3453
Fixtures Secretary: Mike Richards, 115 Egloshaule Road, Wadebridge. Tel: 020881 2519
Press Officer: Mark Richards, Perlees Farm, St.

Breock, Wadebridge, Cornwall. Tel: 020881 2848 (H), 0726 860308 (W)
Coach: T.B.A.
Club captain (1988–89): Chris Taylor
Club captain (1989–90): Chris Taylor
No. of teams: Senior 2, Youth 2
Directions to ground: Opposite Egloshaule Church
Ground capacity: Standing touchline perimeter
Clubhouse facilities: Open matchdays and training, evenings
Club colours: Chocolate and gold. (*Change colours:* Red and green hoops)
Nickname: Camels
Floodlights: Yes (training only)
Membership fees: Full £10, Playing £10, Social £2.50, Youth £2.50, Student £2.50
Ground admission: £1
Local newspaper: Cornish Guardian
League: C 1
League position (1988–89): 1st
League playing record (1988–89): P 39, W 27, D 1, L 11, F 529, A 351
Competitions won: Cornwall League Division 1, 2 J&B Hat Trick Awards

CORNWALL LEAGUES

IN a change from the procedure elsewhere in the system the Division 2 clubs (all six of them) met each other twice and Stithians – relegated in 1987–88 without a win – emerged on top with only one defeat to go up along with St. Just, who lost twice after also suffering relegation last time out. Lankelly and St. Agnes (the latter promoted in 1987–88) go down without ever having seriously threatened anything else, but at the top Wadebridge Camels are promoted as champions – two points ahead of St. Austell, who thus fail to go up after one season.

CORNWALL All Leagues: OFFICIAL

Mrs. Beverley Davis,
8 Penrose Road,
Helston,
Cornwall TR13 8TP   0326 563744

TABLES 1987–88

CORNWALL 1

	P	W	D	L	F	A	PTS
Illogan Park	10	9	1	0	163	61	19
Wadebridge	10	8	1	1	200	89	17
Saltash	10	7	2	1	171	85	16
Helston	10	6	0	4	166	80	12
Liskeard	10	5	1	4	129	87	11
Bude	10	4	2	4	105	90	10
St. Agnes	10	4	1	5	131	120	9
Bodmin	10	4	0	6	128	126	8
Redruth Alb	10	3	0	7	93	154	6
St. Just	10	1	0	9	41	310	2
Stithians	10	0	0	10	49	174	0

CORNWALL 2

	P	W	D	L	F	A	PTS
Veor	4	3	0	1	34	19	6
Lankelly	4	2	1	1	37	39	5
Redruth GSOB	4	2	0	2	41	25	4
Roseland	4	2	0	2	21	45	4
RAF S Mawgan	4	0	1	3	16	21	1

TABLES 1988-89

CORNWALL 1

	P	W	D	L	F	A	PTS
Wadebridge C	10	8	1	1	198	75	17
St. Austell	10	7	1	2	194	68	15
Liskeard & L	10	6	2	2	153	57	14
Saltash	10	6	0	4	118	81	12
Helston	10	5	1	4	170	78	11
Bude	10	4	2	4	147	82	10
Redruth Alb	10	4	2	4	82	174	10
Bodmin	10	4	0	6	128	143	8
Veor	10	3	1	6	90	104	7
Lankelly	10	2	0	8	55	349	4
St. Agnes	10	0	2	8	87	211	2

CORNWALL 2

	P	W	D	L	F	A	PTS
Stithians	10	9	0	1	177	26	18
St. Just	10	8	0	2	164	55	16
Roseland	10	5	0	5	73	131	10
Redruth GSOB	10	4	0	6	1131	70	8
Perranporth	10	0	2	8	34	131	4
RNAS Culdrose	10	2	0	8	41	186	4

SOUTH WEST DIVISION FIXTURES 1989/90

CORNWALL ONE

Sat. 9th September (Week 2)
Bodmin v Bude
Stithians v Helston
Veor v Hayle
Saltash v Liskeard Looe
St Austell v Redruth Albany

Sat. 23rd September (Week 4)
Helston v Bodmin
St Just v St Austell
Redruth Albany v Saltash
Liskeard Looe v Veor
Hayle v Stithians

Sat. 14th October (Week 6)
Bude v Helston
Bodmin v Hayle
Stithians v Liskeard Looe
Veor v Redruth Albany
Saltash v St Just

Sat. 28th October (Week 8)
Liskeard Looe v Bodmin
Hayle v Bude
St Austell v Saltash
St Just v Veor
Redruth Albany v Stithians

Sat. 11th November (Week 10)
Helston v Hayle
Bude v Liskeard Looe
Bodmin v Redruth Albany
Stithians v St Just
Veor v St Austell

Sat 18th November (Week 11)
St Just v Bodmin
Redruth Albany v Bude
Liskeard Looe v Helston
Saltash v Veor
St Austell v Stithians

Sat. 25th November (Week 12)
Hayle v Liskeard Looe
Helston v Redruth Albany
Bude v St Just
Bodmin v St Austell
Stithians v Saltash

Sat. 13th January (Week 18)
Saltash v Bodmin
St Austell v Bude
St Just v Helston
Redruth Albany v Hayle
Veor v Stithians

Sat. 10th March (Week 26)
Liskeard Looe v Redruth Albany
Hayle v St Just
Helston v St Austell
Bude v Saltash
Bodmin v Veor

Sat. 31st March (Week X7)
Stithians v Bodmin
Veor v Bude
Saltash v Helston
St Austell v Hayle
St Just v Liskeard Looe

Sat. 10th March (Week 26)
Redruth Albany v St Just
Liskeard Looe v St Austell
Hayle v Saltash
Helston v Veor
Bude v Stithians

SOUTH WEST DIVISION FIXTURES 1989/90

CORNWALL TWO

Sat. 23rd September (Week 4)
Camborne School of Mines v RAF St. Mawgan
RNAS Culdrose v St. Agnes
Roseland v St. Day
Lankelly v Redruth GSOB

Sat. 14th October (Week 6)
RAF St. Mawgan v Lankelly
Camborne School of Mines v Redruth GSOB
St. Day v RNAS Culdrose
St. Agnes v Roseland

Sat. 28th October (Week 8)
Redruth GSOB v RAF St. Mawgan
RNAS Culdrose v Lankelly
Roseland v Camborne School of Mines
St. Day v St. Agnes

Sat. 11th November (Week 10)
Camborne School of Mines v St. Agnes
Lankelly v Roseland
RAF St. Mawgan v RNAS Culdrose
Redruth GSOB v St. Day

Sat. 25th November (Week 12)
RNAS Culdrose v Redruth GSOB
Roseland v RAF St. Mawgan
St. Agnes v Lankelly
St. Day v Camborne School of Mines

Sat. 13th January (Week 18)
Camborne School of Mines v RNAS Culdrose
Lankelly v St. Day
RAF St. Mawgan v St. Agnes
Redruth GSOB v Roseland

Sat. 10th March (Week 26)
Lankelly v Camborne School of Mines
Roseland v RNAS Culdrose
St. Agnes v Redruth GSOB
St. Day v RAF St. Mawgan

CORNWALL 1

BODMIN

Cliffden Park, Bodmin, Cornwall.
Founded: 1969
Secretary: A. Cornish, 7 Whitestone Crescent,
Bodmin, Cornwall. Tel: Bodmin 2174.
League: Cornwall 1

BUDE

Bencoolen Meadow, Bude, Cornwall. Tel: 0288 4795
Founded: 1966
President: I. Opie
Chairman: E. Gent
Secretary: Sue Courtenay, 7 Cedar Grove, Bude,
Cornwall. Tel: 0288 3076
Fixtures Secretary: J. Boundy
Club captain (1988–89): M. Fry
Club captain (1989–90): P. Cholwill
No. of teams: Senior 2, Youth 1
Directions to ground: Left Kings Hill and R at
bottom, signposted
Clubhouse facilities: Bar
Club colours: Maroon/blue
Floodlights: No
League: Cornwall 1
League position (1988–89): 6th
League playing record (1988–89): P 10, W 4, D 2,
L 4, F 147, A 82

HAYLE

Memorial Park, Hayle, Cornwall. Tel: 0736 753320.
Tel: 0736 753320
Founded: 1877
President: Lt. Cdr. R. Coombe
Chairman: M. Trathen
Secretary: P. Yendell, Fairview Cottage, Coldsithney,
Nr. Penzance. Tel: 0736 710955
Fixtures Secretary: M. Doney, 2 Bohelland Way,
Penryn, Cornwall. Tel: 0326 77370
Coach: T.B.A.
Club captain (1988–89): B. Gibson
No. of teams: Senior 2, Youth 1
Directions to ground: Eastern side of Hayle, adjoining
A30
Ground capacity: Standing 1000+
Clubhouse facilities: Full
Club colours: Green/black/white
Nickname: Lions
Floodlights: Yes
Membership fees: Playing £10, Social £3
Ground admission: 80p
League: Cornwall 1
League position (1988–89): 11th
League playing record (1988–89): P 10, W 2, D 0,
L 8, F 108, A 196

HELSTON

Clodgey Lane, Helston. Tel: 0326 573423
Founded: 1964
President: R.G.W Sanders
Chairman: D.W. Wearne
Secretary: P.R.A. Collins, Chyreen, Cadgwith,
Helston, Cornwall. Tel: 0326 290754 (H), 0209 714851
(W)
Fixtures Secretary: B.A. Davis, 8 Penrose Road,
Helston. Tel: 0326 563744 (H), 0209 215620 (W)
Press Officer: As Secretary
Coach: Ian Jones
Club captain (1988–89): Scott Yelland
Club captain (1989–90): T.B.A.
No. of teams: Senior 2, Youth and Minis 5
Directions to ground: Off Clodgey Lane, opposite
Glenhaven Caravan Park at Helston Cricket Club
entrance
Clubhouse facilities: Open matchdays, Sunday

lunchtime, Tues. and Thurs. evenings
Club colours: Navy and white hoops. (*Change
colours:* Green and blue hoops)
Floodlights: No
Membership fees: Full £7, Playing £7, Social £2,
Youth £2, Student £2, OAP £1
Ground admission: Nil
Local newspapers: Packet and West Briton
League: C 1
League position (1988–89): 4th
League playing record (1988–89): P 37, W 21, D 3,
L 13, F 705, A 622
Competitions won: Cornwall Plate Competition, 1988

LISKEARD-LOOE

Lux Park, Liskeard, Cornwall. Tel: 0579 42665
Founded: 1956
President: J.W.W. Smith
Chairman: Robin Stephens
Secretary: Geoff Collings, Little Polscoe, Lostwithiel.
Tel: 0208 873201
Fixtures Secretary: As Secretary
Coach: Chris Hocking
Club captain (1988–89): Ian Strang
Club captain (1989–90): Micheal Liston
No. of teams: Senior 3, Youth and Minis 7
Directions to ground: Leave A38 to A390, follow signs
to Liskeard Sports Centre
Clubhouse facilities: Shared Liskeard Sports Club
Club colours: Red and black hoops. (*Change colours:*
Black)
Floodlights: No
Membership fees: Playing £10, VPs £12
Local newspapers: Cornish Times, Western Morning
News
League: C 1
League position (1988–89): 3rd
League playing record (1988–89): P 34, W 14, D 3,
L 16, F 441, A 397

REDRUTH ALBANY

Clubhouse, 2 Station Hill, Trewirgie, Redruth. Tel:
0209 216945
Founded: 1928/29
President: N.J. Goldsworthy
Chairman: Nigel Barnes
Secretary: W.J. Rogers, 'Pencoys', Roskear,
Camborne, Cornwall. Tel: 0209 714102
Fixtures Secretary: Colin Johns, 'Colaine', Strawberry
Lane, Redruth, Cornwall. Tel: 0209 218886 (H),
216375 (W)
Press Officer: As Secretary
Coach: Alan Mitchell
Club captain (1988–89): Alan Mitchell
Club captain (1989–90): T.B.A.
No. of teams: Senior 2
Clubhouse facilities: 2 bars, pool, darts, discos
Club colours: Royal blue. (*Change colours:* Blue and
white quarters)
Nickname: The Blues
Floodlights: Yes (partial)
Membership fees: Full £6, Playing £4, Social £2
Local newspapers: Camborne & Redruth Packet,
West Briton
League: C 1
League position (1988–89): 7th
League playing record (1988–89): P 39, W 21, D 3,
L 15, F 494, A 562

SALTASH

Moorland Lane, Burraton, Saltash, Cornwall. Tel:
0752 847227
Founded: 1969
President: E.J. Jacket
Chairman: R.A. Dickerson
Secretary: R. Morcumb, 22 Fairmead Mews, Saltash,
Cornwall. Tel: 0752 849514
Fixtures Secretary: W.T. Ryan, 15 Fairmead Mews,

Saltash, Cornwall PL12 4JR. Tel: 0752 843565
Press Officer: J. Nicholls, 13 Caernarvon Gardens,
Beacon Park, Plymouth, Devon. Tel: 0752 781541
Coach: D. Jackson
Club captain (1988–89): J. Greiner
Club captain (1989–90): K. Horsham
No. of teams: Senior 3, Youth 1, Minis 1–2
Directions to ground: A38, follow old Liskeard Road
'til Ploughboy Inn, turn into Moorlands Lane
Clubhouse facilities: Open Tues./Thurs. evenings;
Sat./Sun. lunchtimes/Sat. evenings
Club colours: Black/red/amber. (*Change colours:*
Red)
Nickname: 'Ashes'
Floodlights: No
Membership fees: Full £7.50, Playing £5, Social £2.50
Local newspapers: Saltash Journal, West Evening
Herald
League: C 1
League position (1988–89): 4th
League playing record (1988–89): P 10, W 6, D 0, L 4
Competitions won: Runners-Up Plate Competititon
(Ply. Comb. Sevens)

ST. JUST

Turnpike Road, Treyeseal, St. Just in Penwith,
Cornwall. Tel: 0736 788593
Founded: 1967
President: R. Hamer
Chairman: T. Thomas
Secretary: R. Warren, Sheldon, Tredavoe Lane,
Newlyn, Cornwall TR18 5DN. Tel: 0736 62986
Fixtures Secretary: P. Whiteman, Ashmoore Cottage,
Kelynack, Nr. St. Just. Tel: Penz 788150
Club captain (1988–89): E. Leah
Club captain (1989–90): I. Boyns
No. of teams: Senior 2, Minis 1
Directions to ground: Penzance → signposted to St.
Just
Club colours: Black. (*Change colours:* Black and
white striped)
Floodlights: No
Membership fees: Full £2, Playing £5
Ground admission: Nil
Programme: No. of editorial pages 2; No. of
advertising pages 6
League: Cornwall 2
League position (1988–89): 2nd
League playing record (1988–89): P 10, W 8, D 0,
L 2, F 164, A 55

ST. AUSTELL

Tregorrick Lane, St. Austell, Cornwall. Tel: St.
Austell 67846
President: Ivor Price
Chairman: Christopher Owen
Secretary: G. David Brain, c/o E.D. Brain & Co.
(Solicitors), 9A Fore Street, St. Austell, Cornwall
PL25 5PX. Tel: 0726 6811 (W)
Fixtures Secretary: Clive Jago, Greenholm, 5 Creed
Lane, Grampound, Cornwall. Tel: 0726 882614 (H),
64322 (School)
Press Officer: Bernie Shepherd, 28 Parkengear Vean,
Probus, Truro TR2 4JT. Tel: 0726 883317
Coach: Nigel Allen/Richard Lamb
Club captain (1988–89): Robert Daniels
No. of teams: Senior 2, Youth 1
Directions to ground: Main Plymouth to Truro road
(A390;, bypass to St. Austell, turn left onto
Porthpean Road, second right into Tregorrick Lane
opposite Duporth Holiday Camp entrance
Ground capacity: Seating 400, standing 5000
Clubhouse facilities: Two bars, restaurant, stewards'
accommodation, sauna, weights room, etc.
Club colours: Red and white 4″ hoops. (*Change
colours:* Dark blue and light blue 4″ hoops)
Nickname: The Saints
Floodlights: Yes (to two pitches)
Membership fees: VPs £15, Playing £12, Social £10,

Youth £5 (to be ratified at A.G.M.)
Programme editor: As Press Officer
Local newspapers: Cornish Guardian, Sunday
Independent, Western Morning News
League: C 1
League position (1988–89): 2nd

STITHIANS

Stithians, Truro, Cornwall
Founded: 1890
President: R.W. Hosen
Chairman: W.J. Burley
Secretary: T.J. Knight, New Road, Stithians, Truro,
Cornwall
Fixtures Secretary: C. Burley, 54 Colins Park,
Stithians, Truro. Tel: 0209 860148
Club captain (1988–89): R. Strick
Club captain (1989–90): T. Strick
No. of teams: Senior 1
Directions to ground: Opposite village church
Ground capacity: Seating 50, Standing 2000
Club colours: Maroon
Floodlights: No
Membership fees: Full £5, Playing £5
League: Cornwall 1
League position (1988–89): 1st
League playing record (1988–89): P 10, W 9, D 0,
L 1, F 177, A 26

VEOR

Wheal Gerry, Cliff View Road, Camborne, Cornwall
Founded: 1969
President: Robert Goldby
Chairman: Jack Mankee
Secretary: Bert Barber, 86 Dolcoath Road,
Camborne, Cornwall TR14 8RP. Tel: 0209 710593
(H), 0752 665951 (W)
Fixtures Secretary: Paul Pascoe, 18 Condurrow Road,
Beacon, Camborne, Cornwall. Tel: 0209 716535 (H),
0872 74282 (W)
Press Officer: As Secretary
Coach: Tracy Bassett
Club captain (1988–89): Nigel Dunstan
No. of teams: Senior 1
Directions to ground: Turn off A30 Camborne bypass
at Camborne signpost and follow Camborne signs.
Turn right at traffic lights at bottom of hill, turn right
again (just before pedestrian crossing). Follow North
Roskear Road for approx. mile then turn right at x-
roads after T.A. Centre. Ground 100 yds on right,
opposite school
Clubhouse facilities: Red Jackets Inn, Trevewson
Street, Camborne
Club colours: All black, amber 'V'. (*Change colours:*
Amber shirts, black shorts)
Floodlights: No
League: C 1
League position (1988–89): 9th
League playing record (1988–89): P 10, W 3, D 1,
L 6, F 90, A 104

CORNWALL 2

CAMBORNE SCHOOL OF MINES

The Memorial Ground, Boundervean Lane,
Peaponds, Camborne. Clubhouse: Tel: 0209 712186
(new entry)
Founded: 1878
Chairman: W. Andy Neil
Secretary: Dr. C. Victor Phillips, Barlowena,
Alexandra Road, Illogan, Redruth, Cornwall TR16
4EN. Tel: 0209 842660 (H), 71486600000 (W)
Fixtures Secretary: As Secretary
Club captain (1988–89): Ben Cantellow
Club captain (1989–90): Simon Village

No. of teams: Senior 2
Directions to ground: via Camborne-Helston Road, turn right off Pendarves Road to Boundervean Lane
Ground capacity: Seating 150
Clubhouse facilities: Bars, etc.
Club colours: Navy gold and white hoops. (*Change colours:* Navy gold and white quarters)
Nickname: CSM R.F.C.
Floodlights: No
Membership fees: Full £5, Playing £5
Local newspapers: West Briton, Packet Series Weekly, Sunday Independant, Western Morning News
League: SW Cornwall 2

LANKELLY-FOWEY

Lankelly Farm, Lankelly Lane, Fowey, Cornwall. Tel: 0726 833350
Founded: 1968
President: James W. Lewis
Chairman: Christopher S. Biggs
Secretary: James W. Lewis, 'Polmear', 62 Esplanade, Fowey, Cornwall PL23 1JA. Tel: 0726 833464
Fixtures Secretary: Nigel Dennis, 32 Allen Vale, Gypsy Lane, Liskeard, Cornwall. Tel: 0579 47678
Press Officer: As Secretary
Coach: Brian Monk/Tony Francis
Club captain (1988–89): Andrew Rees
Club captain (1989–90): Nigel Dennis
No. of teams: Senior 1
Directions to ground: Turn right into Lankelly Lane at entrance to Fowey opposite Cotswold Garage
Clubhouse facilities: King of Prussie, on town quay, Fowey
Club colours: Navy blue and white hoops, black shorts. (*Change colours:* Yellow)
Nickname: Kelly
Floodlights: No
Membership fees: Full £10, Playing £10, Youth £5, Student £5
Ground admission: Collection
Local newspapers: Cornish Guardian, Cornish Times
League: C 2
League position (1988–89): 10th (relegated)
League playing record (1988–89): P 10, W 2, D 0, L 8, F 55, A 349

RAF ST. MAWGAN

RAF St. Mawgan, Newquay, Cornwall. Tel: Newquay 872201
President: Wg. Cdr. Spalding
Chairman: Flt. Lt. Aunger
Secretary: Sac. C. Palmer, RAF St. Mawgan
Fixtures Secretary: Cpl. Cheadle, RAF St. Mawgan
Club captain (1988–89): Cpl. Barraclough
Club captain (1989–90): Sac. Blanken
No. of teams: Senior 1
Directions to ground: On RAF St. Mawgan Station itself
Club colours: Light/dark blue hoop. (*Change colours:* Red/blue/yellow hoops)
Floodlights: No
Membership fees: £5
Local newspaper: Cornish Guardian
League: Cornwall 2

REDRUTH GS OBs

Clijan Croft, Redruth. Tel: 216586
Founded: 1958
President: Joan Mercer
Chairman: Ewart Thomas
Secretary: A.P. Lay, 27 Bosvean Road, Shortlanesend, Truro. Tel: 0872 75481 (H), 0209 216842 (W)
Fixtures Secretary: Alan Wetheralt
Coach: K.C. Bawden/A. Parsons
Club captain (1988–89): Nigel Mitchell
No. of teams: Senior 1

Directions to ground: From Redruth centre follow signs to Falmouth, after mile go over traffic lights at Trefusis Arms. Groun on R after 300 yds down Wheal Trefusis
Clubhouse facilities: Council owned
Club colours: Red/black. (*Change colours:* Green)
Floodlights: No
League: Cornwall 2
League position (1988–89): 4th
League playing record (1988–89): P 10, W 4, D 0, L 6, F 113, A 70

RNAS CULDROSE

Sports Field, RNAS Culdrose, Helston, Cornwall. Tel: Helston 574121 ext. 7167
Secretary: P.T.I. I/C Rugby, Sports Centre, RNAS Culdrose
Fixtures Secretary: As Secretary
Press Officer: P.R.O., RNAS Culdrose
Coach: P.T.I. I/C Rugby
Club captain (1989–90): T.B.A.
No. of teams: Senior 1
Club colours: Red. (*Change colours:* Blue)
Floodlights: No
Local newspapers: Helston Packet, West Briton
League: S 2
League position (1988–89): 6th
League playing record (1988–89): P 30, W 13, D 1, L 16, F 445, A 461

ROSELAND

Philleigh, Truro, Cornwall. Tel: 0872 58254
Founded: 1971
President: Des Sinnott
Chairman: David Thomas
Secretary: Chris Thomas, Parton Vrane, Gerrans Portscatho, Truro, Cornwall TR2 5ET. Tel: 0872 58495 (H), 58495 (W)
Fixtures Secretary: Colin Trerise, Omega, West End, Blackwater, Truro, Cornwall. Tel: 0872 560248 (H), 742820 (W)
Press Officer: Tony Conlay, 2 Well Street, Tregony, Truro, Cornwall. Tel: 0872 53574
Coach: Roger Grove
Club captain (1988–89): Humphrey Stobart
Club captain (1989–90): Caarl Old
No. of teams: Senior 1
Directions to ground: Follow signs from Truro for St. Mawes, then Philleigh
Clubhouse facilities: Roseland Inn
Club colours: Navy and scarlet hoops. (*Change colours:* White)
Floodlights: No
Membership fees: Full £5
Local newspapers: West Briton
League: C 2
League position (1988–89): 3rd
League playing record (1988–89): P 35, W 15, D 0, L 20, F 375, A 485

ST. AGNES

Ground: Wheal Butson, St. Agnes. Clubhouse: Enys Park, St. Agnes. Tel: 0872 553673
Founded: 1972
President: G. Jones
Chairman: M. Watts
Secretary: P. Carson, 22 Polstain Road, Threemilestone, Truro. Tel: 0872 75479 (H), 74242 ext. 246 (W)
Fixtures Secretary: M. Watts, Trevalunace Point Hotel, St. Agnes. Tel: 0872 553275
Coach: Dai Morgan
Club captain (1988–89): C. Blackmore
Club captain (1989–90): A. Dawe
No. of teams: Senior 2, Youth 1
Directions to ground:
Clubhouse facilities: Shared facility with St. Agnes Sports Club. 4 changing rooms and bar area

Club colours: Red and black hoops. (*Change colours:* Blue and black hoops)
Floodlights: No
Membership fees: Full £11, Playing £11, Student £6
Local newspapers: West Briton and West Briton

Argus
League: C 1
League position (1988–89): Bottom (relegated)
League playing record (1988–89): P 10, W 0, D 2, L 8, F 87, A 211

Helston of Cornwall 1 – 1988–89.

DEVON LEAGUES

AGAIN there were 27 clubs in the Devon Leagues with 11 at the top, nine in Devon 2 "A" and another seven in 2 "B". Plymouth Civil Service lost only one match in the top flight and are promoted with a two point margin over South Molton. Four teams go down, including last season's Division 2 winners Devonport HSOB along with Plymouth Argaum (on points difference from Old Technicians), Honiton and Kingsbridge.

Only one team goes up from Division 2A (Prince Rock, who were relegated only last time out) – and only one team goes up from "B" and the lucky ones are Topsham with five wins out of six and a creditable 154 points scored.

DEVON LEAGUES OFFICIAL:

Geoff Simpson,
108 Pattinson Dive,
Mainstone,
Plymouth,
Devon PL6 8RU   0752 707432

TABLES 1987–88

DEVON 1

	P	W	D	L	F	A	PTS
Exeter Sars	10	10	0	0	107	66	20
Plymouth C Ser	10	8	0	2	167	95	16
Ivybridge	9	7	0	2	191	73	14
Totnes	10	6	1	3	148	113	13
Honiton	10	5	1	4	153	139	11
S Molton	10	4	1	5	159	97	9
Kingsbridge	10	3	1	6	90	150	7
Plymouth A	10	3	1	6	123	224	7
O Technicians	9	3	0	6	66	116	6
Prince Rock	10	1	3	6	62	151	5
Ilfracombe	10	0	0	10	46	188	0

DEVON 2A

	P	W	D	L	F	A	PTS
DHSOB	8	6	1	1	152	51	13
Victoria	8	6	0	2	56	32	12
Jesters	8	6	0	2	56	32	12
Plymouth YM	8	4	1	3	65	63	9
OPO	7	3	2	2	81	41	8
OPM	8	4	0	4	112	123	8
St. Columba	8	3	0	5	78	97	6
Tamar Sara	8	1	0	7	47	123	2
Plymouth	7	0	0	7	37	150	0

DEVON 2B

	P	W	D	L	F	A	PTS
Cullompton	6	5	0	1	92	38	10
Dartmouth	6	4	0	2	134	59	8
Tavistock	6	4	0	2	94	36	8
Salcombe	6	4	0	2	94	71	8
Topsham	6	2	1	3	74	86	5
Withycombe	6	1	0	5	16	100	2
N Taunton	6	0	1	5	30	144	1

TABLES 1988-89

DEVON 1

	P	W	D	L	F	A	PTS
Plymouth CS	10	9	0	1	235	86	18
S Molton	10	8	0	2	263	119	16
Ivybridge	10	7	0	3	191	88	14
Cullompton	10	7	0	3	199	122	14
New Abbot	10	7	0	3	168	124	5
Totnes	10	6	0	4	159	113	12
O Technicians	10	3	0	7	106	93	6
Plymouth A	10	3	0	7	110	299	6
Honiton	10	2	1	7	114	194	5
Devonport HSOB	10	1	1	8	84	292	3
Kingsbridge	10	1	0	9	96	195	2

DEVON 2A

	P	W	D	L	F	A	PTS
Prince Rock	8	8	0	0	182	38	16
Jesters	8	7	0	1	89	62	14
Victoria	8	5	0	3	127	82	10
O Public Oaks	8	5	0	3	89	72	10
O Plymouth & M	8	4	0	4	100	86	8
Tamar Sar	8	3	0	5	80	148	6
St. Columba	8	2	0	6	71	93	4
Plymouth YMCA	8	1	0	7	64	137	2
Plympton	8	1	0	7	32	116	2

DEVON 2B

	P	W	D	L	F	A	PTS
Topsham	6	5	0	1	154	50	10
Tavistock	6	4	11	1	113	36	9
Ilfracombe	6	4	1	1	74	48	9
Withycombe	6	3	0	3	94	53	6
N Tawton	6	2	0	4	75	86	4
Salcombe	6	2	0	4	40	134	4
Dartmouth	6	0	0	6	47	190	0

SOUTH WEST DIVISION FIXTURES 1989/90

DEVON ONE

Sat. 9th September (Week 2)
Cullompton v Paignton
Newton Abbot v Prince Rock
South Molton v Ivybridge
Topsham v Old Technicians
Totnes v Exmouth

Sat. 23rd September (Week 4)
Exmouth v Cullompton
Ivybridge v Totnes
Old Technicians v Newton Abbot
Plymouth Argaum v Topsham
Prince Rock v South Molton

Sat. 14th October (Week 6)
Cullompton v Ivybridge
Newton Abbot v Plymouth Argaum
Paignton v Exmouth
South Molton v Old Technicians
Totnes v Prince Rock

Sat. 28th October (Week 8)
Ivybridge v Paignton
Old Technicians v Totnes
Plymouth Argaum v South Molton
Prince Rock v Cullompton
Topsham v Newton Abbot

Sat. 11th November (Week 10)
Cullompton v Old Technicians
Exmouth v Ivybridge
Paignton v Prince Rock
South Molton v Topsham
Totnes v Plymouth Argaum

Sat 18th November (Week 11)
Newton Abbot v South Molton
Old Technicians v Paignton
Plymouth Argaum v Cullompton
Prince Rock v Exmouth
Topsham v Totnes

Sat. 25th November (Week 12)
Cullompton v Topsham
Exmouth v Old Technicians
Ivybridge v Prince Rock
Paignton v Plymouth Argaum
Totnes v Newton Abbot

Sat. 13th January (Week 18)
Newton Abbot v Cullompton
Old Technicians v Ivybridge
Plymouth Argaum v Exmouth
South Molton v Totnes
Topsham v Paignton

Sat. 10th March (Week 26)
Cullompton v South Molton
Exmouth v Topsham
Ivybridge v Plymouth Argaum
Paignton v Newton Abbot
Prince Rock v Old Technicians

Sat. 31st March (Week X7)
Newton Abbot v Exmouth
Plymouth Argaum v Prince Rock
South Molton v Paignton
Topsham v Ivybridge
Totnes v Cullompton

Sat. 28th April (Week 32)
Exmouth v South Molton
Ivybridge v Newton Abbot
Old Technicians v Plymouth Argaum
Paignton v Totnes
Prince Rock v Topsham

SOUTH WEST DIVISION FIXTURES 1989/90

DEVON TWO A

Sat. 9th September (Week 2)
DHSOB v Jesters
Plymstock v Plymouth YMCA
St. Columba v OPO
Tamar Saracens v OPM
Victoria v Plympton

Sat. 23rd September (Week 4)
OPM v DHSOB
OPO v Tamar Saracens
Plymouth YMCA v St. Columba
Plympton v Plymstock
Victoria v Jesters

Sat. 14th October (Week 6)
DHSOB v OPO
Jesters v OPM
Plymstock v Victoria
St. Columba v Plympton
Tamar Saracens v Plymouth YMCA

Sat. 28th October (Week 8)
OPM v Victoria
OPO v Jesters
Plymouth YMCA v DHSOB
Plympton v Tamar Saracens
Plymstock v St. Columba

Sat. 11th November (Week 10)
DHSOB v Plympton
Jesters v Plymouth YMCA
OPM v OPO
Tamar Saracens v Plymstock
Victoria v St. Columba

Sat 18th November (Week 11)
Plymouth YMCA v OPM
Plympton v Jesters
Plymstock v DHSOB
St. Columba v Tamar Saracens
Victoria v OPO

Sat. 25th November (Week 12)
DHSOB v St. Columba
Jesters v Plymstock
OPM v Plympton
OPO v Plymouth YMCA
Tamar Saracens v Victoria

Sat. 13th January (Week 18)
Plymouth YMCA v Victoria
Plympton v OPO
Plymstock v OPM
St. Columba v Jesters
Tamar Saracens v DHSOB

Sat. 10th March (Week 26)
DHSOB v Victoria
Jesters v Tamar Saracens
OPM v St. Columba
OPO v Plymstock
Plymouth YMCA v Plympton

SOUTH WEST DIVISION FIXTURES 1989/90

DEVON TWO B

Sat. 14th October (Week 6)
Dartmouth v Honiton
North Tawton v Withycombe
Salcombe v Kingsbridge
Tavistock v Ilfracombe

Sat. 28th October (Week 8)
Ilfracombe v Dartmouth
Kingsbridge v Tavistock
North Tawton v Salcombe
Withycombe v Honiton

Sat. 11th November (Week 10)
Dartmouth v Kingsbridge
Honiton v Ilfracombe
Tavistock v North Tawton
Withycombe v Salcombe

Sat 18th November (Week 11)
Ilfracombe v Withycombe
Kingsbridge v Honiton
North Tawton v Dartmouth
Salcombe v Tavistock

Sat. 25th November (Week 12)
Dartmouth v Salcombe
Honiton v North Tawton
Ilfracombe v Kingsbridge
Tavistock v Withycombe

Sat. 13th January (Week 18)
North Tawton v Ilfracombe
Salcombe v Honiton
Tavistock v Dartmouth
Withycombe v Kingsbridge

Sat. 10th March (Week 26)
Dartmouth v Withycombe
Honiton v Tavistock
Ilfracombe v Salcombe
Kingsbridge v North Tawton

DEVON 1

COLLOMPTON

Stafford Park, Knowle Lane, Cullompton, Devon.
Tel: 0884 32480
Founded: 1892
President: Lester Neale
Chairman: Ian Wood
Secretary: Tony Lindsell, Kirkdale, Stoneyford,
Cullompton EX15 1NU. Tel: 0884 38884 (H), 0803
217752 (W)
Fixtures Secretary: Terry Radmore, Cider Press
Cottage, Ashill, Cullompton. Tel: 0884 40817
Press Officer: As Fixture Secretary
Club captain (1988–89): Phil Sanders
Club captain (1989–90): Martin Dyke
No. of teams: Senior 3
Directions to ground: Tiverton side of town
Clubhouse facilities: New clubhouse. Lounge and
functions rooms
Club colours: Red and black hoops. (*Change colours:*
Blue)
Floodlights: Yes (for training)
League: D 1
League position (1988–89): 4th
League playing record (1988–89): P 10, W 7, D 0,
L 3, F 199, A 122

EXMOUTH

Imperial Recreation Ground, Royal Avenue,
Exmouth, Devon. Tel: (0395 2623665)
Founded: 1873
President: L. Mogridge
Chairman: M. England
Secretary: N. Harris, 14 Phillipps Avenue, Exmouth.
Tel: 263414 (H), 0392 215201 (W)
Fixtures Secretary: G. Williams, 11 Sunwine Place,
Exmouth. Tel: Ex 271373
Press Officer: As Secretary
Club captain (1988–89): Chris Witkies
Club captain (1989–90): Niall Thurlow
No. of teams: Senior 3, Youth 1, Minis 8
Directions to ground: Exeter Junc. on M5, to
Exmouth, Exeter Road, 1 set traffic lights, past
Exmouth Town F.C., roundabout → right → 2nd
roundabout → right. Club on left 50 yds
Ground capacity: Seating 150
Clubhouse facilities: 3 bars
Club colours: Heliothrope/white. (*Change colours:*
Plain heliothrope)
Floodlights: No
Membership fees: Full £15, Playing £11
Programme: No. of editorial pages 4; No. of
advertising pages 4; Price 50p
Programme editor: R. Holman, Nutwell Court,
Lympstone, Exmouth
League: Devon 1
League position (1988–89): 10th
League playing record (1988–89): P 10, W 2, D 0,
L 8, F 130, A 134

IVYBRIDGE

Cross-in-Hand, Exeter Road, Ivybridge, Devon. Tel:
0752 894392
Founded: 1975
President: Alan W. Knight
Chairman: Pete Keenan
Secretary: Bob Thomas, 41 Rue St. Pierre, Ivybridge,
Devon PL21 0HZ. Tel: 0752 894295 (H), 0392 57364
(W)
Fixtures Secretary: Gary Aldridge, 99 Cleave Drive,
Ivybridge, Devon. Tel: 0752 893773 (H), 668040 (W)
Coach: John Borrill
Club captain (1988–89): Sheumais Webster
Club captain (1989–90): Sheumais Webster
No. of teams: Senior 3, Youth 2, Minis 8
Directions to ground: Take old A38 into Ivybridge
village where you will find the club at the eastern end

of the village
Ground capacity: Standing 500
Clubhouse facilities: Open match days and evening
except Sunday/Monday
Club colours: Green, white and black. (*Change
colours:* Blue)
Nickname: Ives
Floodlights: No
Membership fees: Full £12, Playing £12, Social £7,
Youth £5, Student £5, OAP £7
Ground admission: Free
Local newspapers: Western Morning News, Plymouth
Evening Herald, South Hams Gazette
League: D 1
League position (1988–89): 3rd
League playing record (1988–89): P 38, W 30, D 0,
L 8, F 979, A 308
Competitions won: Devon Junior Cup, April '89.
Salcome Sevens, March '89. Launceston Floodlit Cup,
March '89

NEWTON ABBOT

"Rocherhayes" Kingsteignton Road, Newton Abbot,
Devon. Tel: 0626 5415.
Founded: 1873
President: Watts
Chairman: R. Burgin
Secretary: R. Baker.
Fixtures Secretary: As Secretary
Press Officer: G. Hooper, 39 Wilton Way, Abbots,
Kerswell. Tel: N.A. 69791
Coach: C. Pomeroy
Club captain (1989–90): M. Beavis
No. of teams: Senior 3, Youth 1
Directions to ground: A38 from Exeter, ground opp.
Newton Racecourse
Ground capacity: Seating 150, Standing 4000
Clubhouse facilities: bars, dining room
Club colours: White. (*Change colours:* Black,
maroon, gold)
Floodlights: No
Membership fees: Full £19, Playing £10
Ground admission: Nil
Programme: No. of editorial pages 1; No. of
advertising pages 2; Price 50p
Programme editor: As Press Officer
League: Devon 1
League position (1988–89): 5th
League playing record (1988–89): P 10, W 7, D 0,
L 3, F 168, A 124

OLD TECHNICIANS

Weston Mill, Ferndale Road, Plymouth. Tel: 0752
363352
Founded: 1932
President: John Boasden
Chairman: Roger Ninnis
Secretary: Terry Carney, 2 Jedburgh Crescent, Ham
Estate, Plymouth PL2 2NY. Tel: 0752 364884
Fixtures Secretary: David Coombes, 19 Beaconfield
Road, Beacon Park, Plymouth PL2 3LD. Tel: 0752
561612
Press Officer: R. Ninnis, 48 Sycamore Drive,
Torpoint, Cornwall
Coach: Ray Hancock
Club captain (1988–89): Sammy Matts
Club captain (1989–90): Sammy Matts
No. of teams: Senior 3, Youth 1
Directions to ground: Plymouth Parkway, Devonport
then turn off, turn left at 1st set of traffic lights, 50 yds
up the road
Clubhouse facilities: Bar, changing rooms, gym
Club colours: Black with white circlets. (*Change
colours:* Red)
Floodlights: No
League: D 1
League position (1988–89): 7th
League playing record (1988–89): P 10, W 3, D 0,
L 7, F 106, A 93

Competitions won: Eddie Jones Plate (Runners-Up Lockie Cup), Prince Rock Sevens Winner, Ply. Combination Sevens Runner-Up, Pedrick Cup Winners (2nd's)

PAIGNTON

Queens Park, Queens Road, Paignton. Tel: 557715
Founded: 1873
President: T. Ward
Chairman: M. Bagge
Secretary: K.A.P. Ferris, 129 Torquay Road, Paignton TQ3 2SG. Tel: 0803 526532
Fixtures Secretary: G. Platt, 72 Osney Crescent, Paignton. Tel: 0803 521646
Press Officer: A. Vanstone, 38 Piller Avenue, Brixham. Tel: 4889
Coach: N. Thomas/N. Harries
Club captain (1988–89): Andy Baker
Club captain (1989–90): Morley Benstead
No. of teams: Senior 2, Youth 1, Minis 2
Directions to ground: Town centre
Ground capacity: Seating 50, standing 3000
Clubhouse facilities: Under stand lounge
Club colours: Red white hoops. (*Change colours:* Blue black hoops)
Floodlights: No
League: Devon/Cornwall
League position (1988–89): 3rd from bottom
League playing record (1988–89): P 10, W 4, D 0, L 6, F 114, A 152

PLYMOUTH ARGAUM

Bickleigh Down, Roborough, Nr. Plymouth. Tel: 0752 772156
Founded: 1887
President: Thomas K. Hitchins
Chairman: T.B.A.
Secretary: T.B.A.
Fixtures Secretary: W. Annandale, 68 Reservoir Road, Elburton, Plymouth. Tel: 0752 402254
Press Officer: Michael Pike, 24 Frenskam Avenue, Glenholt, Plymouth PL6 7JN. Tel: 0752 778538 (H), 362294 (W)
Club captain (1988–89): Brian Willcocks
Club captain (1989–90): Dave Johnson
No. of teams: Senior 3, Youth 1
Directions to ground: Leave Plymouth on Tavistock (A386) road past the George Hotel. After passing Tesco Superstore 1st turn to right into Bickleigh Down Lane, then 300 yards up the lane
Clubhouse facilities: Large clubhouse, kitchen, dining area, 5 changing and referees room
Club colours: Black/white/green hoops. (*Change colours:* Blue)
Floodlights: Yes
League: D 1
League position (1988–89): 6th (relegated)

PRINCE ROCK

Founded: 1964
President: Dave Bishop
Chairman: Les Perkin
Secretary: Rob Hibbs, 23 Lydcot Walk, Eggbuckland, Plymouth, Devon PL6 5LL. Tel: 0752 780184
Fixtures Secretary: Les Fowden, 1 Hayes Road, Oreston, Plymouth. Tel: 405018
Press Officer: Dave Arnott, 6 Vine Gardens, Milehouse, Plymouth. Tel: 564674
Coach: Reg Perkin
Club captain (1988–89): Gary Weight
Club captain (1989–90): Reg Perkin
No. of teams: Senior 2
Directions to ground: A38 Marsh Mills roundabout. Head for Saltash 2nd junction A386 towards Tavistock, 1 mile on right Seaton Barracks
Club colours: Gold
Nickname: Rockey's
Floodlights: No

Membership fees: Full £10, Playing £10, Social £10
Local newspaper: Evening Herald
League: D 1
League position (1988–89): 1st (promoted)
League playing record (1988–89): P 31, W 19, D 0, L 12, F 444, A 309
Competitions won: Devon 2A Winners

SOUTH MOLTON

Furze Bray, Station Road, South Molton, DEvon. Tel: 07695 2024
Founded: 1935
President: Gerald Kingdon
Chairman: Christopher Kingdon
Secretary: Peter Snow, 4 Gwythers, South Molton, Devon EX36 4A2. Tel: 07695 3027 (H), 3204 (W)
Fixtures Secretary: Dennis Cronk, Old Rectory, Rose Ash, South Molton, Devon. Tel: 07697 402
Press Officer: Robert Holmes, Woods, Ash Mill, South Molton, Devon. Tel: 07697 340
Coach: David Butt/Tim Francis
Club captain (1988–89): Paul Berry
Club captain (1989–90): Paul Berry
No. of teams: Senior 3, Youth 1
Directions to ground: Take North Molton Road out of South Molton. Approx. 800 yards on right is Unicorn Park. Just as you reach the bend at the far end of this pitch turn left to find clubhouse and our second pitch about 200 yards on left
Club colours: All black. (*Change colours:* Gold shorts)
Nickname: Blacks
Floodlights: No
Membership fees: Full £10
Local newspapers: North Devon Journal Herald, North Devon Advertiser, South Molton Gazette
League: D 1
League position (1988–89): 2nd
League playing record (1988–89): P 10, W 8, D 0, L 2, F 263, A 119

TOPSHAM

The Bonfire Field, Exeter Road, Topsham, Exeter, Devon. Tel: 0392 873651
Founded: Re-founded 1982
President: Paul Pirongs
Chairman: Clive Pascoe
Secretary: Geoffrey Hogg, 22 Newcourt Road, Topsham, Exeter, Devon EX3 0BT. Tel: 0392 874129 (H), 77977 (W)
Fixtures Secretary: Paul Pirongs, The Dutch House, The Strand, Topsham, Exeter, Devon. Tel: 0392 877347 (H), 0626 52655 (W)
Press Officer: As Secretary
Coach: Terry Doyle
Club captain (1988–89): Jerry Alford
Club captain (1989–90): Phil Symons
No. of teams: Senior 3
Directions to ground: Follow signs to Topsham. Bonfire Field is on left as entering Topsham from Exeter just before Pretty's Garage
Club colours: Light and dark blue hoops. (*Change colours:* Red)
Floodlights: No
Membership fees: Full £15, Playing £15, Social £15
Programme editor: Dick Corbett-Winder, The Old School House, Martinstown, Dorchester, Dorset
Local newspapers: Express and Echo, Exmouth Journal
League: D 2B
League position (1988–89): 1st (promoted)
League playing record (1988–89): P 6, W 5, D 0, L 1, F 154, A 53
Competitions won: Devon League 2B

TOTNES

The Borough Park, Totnes, Devon. Tel: 0803 863746
Founded: 1889

President: Brian Perring
Chairman: Colin Taylor
Secretary: Miss Jackie Pantry, 50 Punchards Down, Follaton, Totnes, Devon TQ9 5FD. Tel: 0803 864581 (H), 864282 (W)
Fixtures Secretary: Roger Lang, 42 The Carrions, Totnes, Devon TQ9 5XX. Tel: 0803 864516
Coach: Charles Williamson
Club captain (1988–89): Andrew Pearson
Club captain (1989–90): Andrew Pearson
No. of teams: Senior 2, Youth 2
Directions to ground: Adjacent to Totnes Railway Station
Clubhouse facilities: Full bar, food, changing facilities
Club colours: Royal blue/white
Floodlights: No
Nickname: Blues
Membership fees: Full £10, Playing £10, Social £10, Youth £5, Student £5, OAP £5
Ground admission: Nil
Local newspapers: Totnes Times Gazette, Herald Express, Torquay
League: D 1
League position (1988–89): 6th
League playing record (1988–89): P 10, W 6, D 0, L 4, F 159, A 113

DEVON 2A

DEVONPORT HIGH SCHOOL OLD BOYS

Devonport High School for Boys, Paradise Road, Millbridge, Plymouth
Founded: 1927
Secretary: Ian K. Robertson, 69 Merrivale Road, Beacon Park, Plymouth PL2 2RW. Tel: 0752 559377 (H), 553795 (W)
Fixtures Secretary: Geoffrey K. Simpson, 108 Pattinson Drive, Mainstone, Plymouth. Tel: 0752 707432 (H), 563001 (W)
Press Officer: As Secretary
Coach: T.B.A.
Club captain (1988–89): Walker S. Lapthorne
Club captain (1989–90): T.B.A.
No. of teams: Senior 1
Club colours: Green black and white irregular hoops. (*Change colours:* Red shirts)
Floodlights: No
Membership fees: Full £20
Local newspaper: Western Evening Herald
League: D 1
League position (1988–89): 10th
League playing record (1988–89): P 10, W 1, D 1, L 8

JESTERS

Marsh Meadows, Lower Leigham, Plym Valley, Plymouth, Devon
Founded: 1953
President: Louis Quinn
Chairman: Micheal Edwards
Secretary: Frank Thomas, 8 Powderham Road, Hartley Vale, Plymouth PL3 5SF. Tel: 701987
Coach: Martin Finlay
Club captain (1988–89): Mark Pascoe
Club captain (1989–90): Timothy Smale
No. of teams: Senior 2
Directions to ground: Off Marsh Mills roundabout. Head towards Plympton, take 1st left, 2nd right, then 2nd right again
Clubhouse facilities: Bath and changing, drinking at Lopes Arms, Roboroog, Plymouth
Club colours: Red yellow black white, black shorts and stockings
Nickname: Jesters
Floodlights: No
Membership fees: Full £15, Playing £2
Local newspapers: Evening Herald, South Hams

Gazette
League: D 1
League position (1988–89): 2nd
League playing record (1988–89): P 8, W 7, D 0, L 1, F 89, A 62

OLD PLYMOTHIAN AND MANNAMEADIAN

Bickleigh Down Lane, Roborough, Plymouth. Tel: 0752 772156
Founded: 1926
President: P. Organ
Chairman: E.C. Keast
Secretary: E.J. Bolster, 22 Carlton Close, Lower Compton, Plymouth, Devon. Tel: 0752 223908
Fixtures Secretary: G.A. Wesley, 13 Hill Park Crescent, Mutley, Plymouth, Devon. Tel: 0752 600797
Club captain (1988–89): Chris Furnival/Alex Brooks
Club captain (1989–90): Alex Brooks
No. of teams: Senior 1
Directions to ground: A386 from Plymouth towards Tavistock. Turn right at Roborough sign, take immediate second left and follow lane 1 mile to clubhouse on right
Ground capacity: Standing 200
Clubhouse facilities: Open match days
Club colours: Claret and blue hoops, black shorts, claret and blue socks. (*Change colours:* Red)
Nickname: OPM's
Floodlights: No
Membership fees: Full £10, Playing £10
Local newspapers: Western Evening Herald, Western Morning News and Sunday Independent
League: D 2A
League position (1988–89): 5th
League playing record (1988–89): P 26, W 12, D 2, L 12

OLD PUBLIC OAKS

King George IV Playing Fields, Elburton, Plymouth
Founded: 1927
President: D.M. Barrett
Chairman: W. Pinhey
Secretary: R.W. Ward, 48 Gifford Terrace Road, Motley Plain, Plymouth, Devon. Tel: 224466 (H), 673505 (W)
Fixtures Secretary: G.H. Matthews, 25 Colwill Road, Mainstone, Plymouth. Tel: 707363
Press Officer: J. McConnell, 10 Alton Road, North Hill, Plymouth. Tel: 674615
Club captain (1988–89): I. Colley
Club captain (1989–90): K. Potter
No. of teams: Senior 2
Directions to ground: Take A379 Plymouth to Kingsbridge Road from Plymouth centre, turn left at 3rd roundabout into Haye Road. Ground 200 yds on right
Clubhouse facilities: RAFA Club, Ormington Terrace, Mutley, Plymouth
Club colours: Green and gold unequal hoops, black shorts. (*Change colours:* Solid green and black shorts)
Nickname: The Oaks
Floodlights: Yes
Membership fees: Full £15, Playing £15, Youth £7.50, Student £7.50
Local newspapers: Western Evening Herald, Western Morning News, Sunday Indepdent
League: D 2A
League position (1988–89): 4th
League playing record (1988–89): P 8, W 5, D 0, L 3, F 84, A 79

PLYMOUTH YMCA

Burrington School, Honicknowle, Plymouth
Founded: 1910
President: D. Libbey
Chairman: D. Padfield

Coach: A. Pyle
Secretary: Mrs J. Pyle, 5 Dudley Road, Plympton, Plymouth. Tel: 345853
Fixtures Secretary: S. Briggs, 16 Holland Road, Peverel, Plymouth. Tel: 261663
Club captain (1988–89): J. Lee
No. of teams: Senior 1
Colours: Black with red hoop
Floodlights: No
Local newspaper: Western Evening Herald & Sunday Independent
League: Devon 2A

PLYMPTON

George IV Playing Fields, Elburton, Nr. Plymouth
Founded: 1977
President: Steve Smith
Chairman: George Anthony Bardwell
Secretary: Robert Carter, 26 Molesworth Road, Plympton, Plymouth, Devon. Tel: 335770
Fixtures Secretary: Tony Peter Willoughby, 38 Princess Avenue, Plymstock, Plymouth. Tel: 402955
Press Officer: George Anthony Bardwell, 7 Higher Brook Park, Woodlands Ivybridge, Devon PL21 9UA. Tel: Ply. 896671
Coach: George Antony Bardwell
Club captain (1988–89): Alan Dibble
Club captain (1989–90): Alan Dibble
No. of teams: Senior 1
Directions to ground: From Plymouth. Kingsbridge Road, cross Plym estuary, turn left at third roundabout, 200 m on right
Clubhouse facilities: 'The Foresters' Public House, Plympton
Club colours: Red chest band on white. (*Change colours:* Navy blue)
Floodlights: No
Membership fees: Full £18, Playing £2.50, Social £9
Ground admission: Nil
Local newspapers: Plymouth Evening Herald, Sunday Independent
League: D 2A
League position (1988–89): =Bottom
League playing record (1988–89): P 8, W 1, D 0, L 7, F 32, A 116

PLYMSTOCK

King George V, Elburton, Plymouth
President: Mark Jewell
Chairman: Martin 'Sid' Kernick
Secretary: Roy Eyers, 16 Winnow Close, Staddiscombe, Plymouth, Devon PL9 9RZ. Tel: Ply 491105 (H), 775851 ext. 256 (W)
Fixtures Secretary: Nigel Higginson, 8 Goosewell Park Road, Plymstock, Plymouth. Tel: Ply 401108 (H), 492560 (W)
Press Officer: Bob Hunter, 58 Kitter Drive, Staddiscombe, Plymouth, Devon PL9 9RZ
Coach: Kieran Thorne
Club captain (1988–89): Lee Grant
Club captain (1989–90): Lee Grant
No. of teams: Senior 1
Directions to ground: Take Kingsbridge Road from Plymouth. 3 miles from Laira Bridge prior to Elburton Hotel turn left at roundabout then 150 yds on right
Clubhouse facilities: Bar
Club colours: Royal blue shirts, white shorts
Floodlights: No
Membership fees: Full £15, Playing £15, Social £10, Youth £5, Student £5, OAP Free
Local newspapers: Western Morning News, Evening Herald
League: Devon 2A
League position (1988–89): First entry
League playing record (1988–89): P 31, W 21, D 5, L 5, F 585, A 208

ST COLUMBA

Defiance Field, Torpoint, Devon.
Founded: 1927
Secretary: P.C. Summers, 112 Rochford Crescent, Ernesette, Plymouth PL5 2Q.Tel: 0752 362785 (H), 0752 552986 (W).
League: Devon 2A

TAMAR SARACENS

Tamar Valley Sports & Social Club, Ernesettle lane, Ernesettle, Plymouth, Devon. Tel: 0752 363080
Founded: 1973
President: Wayne D'Oliviera
Chairman: Stephen Leeson
Secretary: Kevin McDermottroe, 8 Pinewood Close, Plympton, Plymouth, Devon PL7 3DW. Tel: 0752 344633 (H), 364341 (W)
Fixtures Secretary: Paul Morgan, 8 Bramfield Close, Austin Farm Estate, Eggbuckland, Plymouth. Tel: 0752 787932
Press Officer: Mike 'Nigger' Ryeland, c/o Secretary
Coach: Steve Leeson
Club captain (1988–89): Gary Richardson
Club captain (1989–90): Gary Richardson
No. of teams: Senior 2
Directions to ground: A38 towards Liskeard. Take St. Budeaux sliproad through two roundabouts towards Ernesettle. Drive 300 yards down Ernesettle Lane. Club is on the right
Clubhouse facilities: Weekends and evenings
Club colours: Black shirts with red hoops. (*Change colours:* Red shirts with green hoops)
Nickname: Saracens or Saras
Floodlights: Yes
Membership fees: Full £5, Playing £2
Ground admission: Nil
Local newspapers: Plymouth Evening Herald and Western Morning News
League: D 2A
League position (1988–89): 5th
League playing record (1988–89): P 8, W 3, D 0, L 5

VICTORIA

27 Hooe Road, Plymstock, Plymouth, Devon. Tel: 0752 405196
Founded: 1981
President: Barry John
Chairman: Ray Purchase
Secretary: Jean M. Pardy, 25 Longacre, Woodford, Plympton, Devon PL7 4RQ. Tel: 0752 344081
Fixtures Secretary: Dave Cranswick, 90 Lalebrick Road, Hooe, Plymouth, Devon. Tel: 0752 407448 (H), 56377 ext. 2253 (W)
Press Officer: Steve Sargent, 49 Lower Park Drive, Staddiscombe, Plymouth PL9 9DA. Tel: 0752 408744
Coach: John Lang
Club captain (1988–89): Paul Tottman
Club captain (1989–90): Steve Sargent
No. of teams: Senior 1
Directions to ground: King George V Playing Fields, Standerhayes Road, Elburton, Plymouth
Club colours: All black. (*Change colours:* Yellow)
Floodlights: No
Nickname: The Vic
Local newspaper: Western Evening Herald
League: D 2A
League position (1988–89): 3rd
League playing record (1988–89): P 8, W 5, D 0, L 3, F 124, A 82

DEVON 2B

DARTMOUTH

Dartmouth Community College, Milton Lane,

Dartmouth, Devon. Tel: 08043 3994.
Founded: 1952
Secretary: Ms J. Evans, 58A Victoria Road,
Dartmouth, Devon TD6 9DZ. Tel: 08043 3311 (H).
08043 4921 (W).
League: Devon 2B

HONITON

All Hallows Playing Fields, Honiton, Devon. Tel:
0404 41239
Founded: 1883
President: G.J. George
Chairman: G. 'Hovis' Brown
Secretary: J.E. Rice, 2 Fouracres Close, Offwell,
Honiton, Devon EX14 9SX. Tel: 040483/492 (H),
0392 516551 (W)
Fixtures Secretary: K. Clark, Millhouse, Millhayes,
Stockland, Honiton, Devon. Tel: 040488/249
Press Officer: As Fixture Secretary
Coach: N. Huggett
Club captain (1988–89): D. McGrath
Club captain (1989–90): D. McGrath
No. of teams: Senior 2, Youth 1, Minis 1
Directions to ground: Next to Swimming Pool and
Sports Hall behind church, Honiton High Street
Clubhouse facilities: Bar open match days and
evenings
Club colours: Red amber and black hoops. (*Change
colours:* Yellow shirts)
Floodlights: No
Membership fees: Full £10, Playing £16, Social £10,
Youth £3, Student £3, OAP £10
Programme: No. of editorial pages 0; No. of
advertising pages 7; Price Donations
Programme editor: S. Noar, Deer Park Hotel,
Western Honiton, Devon
Local newspapers: Honiton Pulman and East Devon
News
League: D 2B
League position (1988–89): 9th (relegated)
League playing record (1988–89): P 41, W 16, D 2,
L 23, F 579, A 678

ILFRACOMBE

Brimlands, Ilfracombe. Tel: 0271 64249
Founded: 1887
President: R.C. Beer
Chairman: A. Beer
Secretary: J. Kift, Highcroft, Shaftsboro, Lee,
Ilfracombe. Tel: 0271 62797
Fixtures Secretary: J. Williams, 5 Castle Hill Villas,
Ilfracombe. Tel: 0271 65198
Club captain (1988–89): D. Hutchings
Club captain (1989–90): W. Freestone
No. of teams: Senior 2, Minis 3
Directions to ground: From A361 Barnstaple, thro'
High Street, Coombe Martin Road, 1 miles and on
left
Clubhouse facilities: Bar, dining room, 3 changing
rooms
Club colours: Blue/white. (*Change colours:* White)
Floodlights: No
Membership fees: Full £3, Playing £10
Programme: No. of editorial pages 1; No. of
advertising pages 2; Price 50p
League: Devon 2B
League position (1988–89): 3rd
League playing record (1988–89): P 6, W 4, D 1, L 1,
F 74, A 48

KINGSBRIDGE

High House, Kingsbridge, Devon. Tel: 0548 2051.
Founded: 1889
Secretary: P. Edwards, 8 Camperdown Road,
Salcombe, Devon.
League: Devon 1

NORTH TAWTON

The Butts, Barton Street, North Tawton
Founded: 1885
President: J. Avery
Chairman: M. Thwaites
Secretary: Gillian M. Hoggins, The Old Forge, North
Street, North Tawton, Devon EX20 2DE. Tel: 938
782516
Fixtures Secretary: Jem Ions, 2 Bal Lane, Mary Tavy,
Tavistock PL19 9PD. Tel: 994 81700 (H), 0752 346441
(W)
Coach: M. Thwaites
Club captain (1988–89): R. Tidball
Club captain (1989–90): D. Quick
No. of teams: Senior 2
Ground capacity: Standing 500
Clubhouse facilities: Two changing rooms and bar
area
Club colours: Black and amber hoops. (*Change
colours:* Amber)
Nickname: Tawts
Floodlights: No
Membership fees: Full £12, Playing £12, Social £10
Ground admission: Nil
Local newspapers: Express and Echo
League: D 2B
League position (1988–89): 4th
League playing record (1988–89): P 34, W 15, D 0,
L 19, F 410, A 443

SALCOMBE

Twomeads, Camperdown Road, Salcombe, Devon.
Tel: 0548 842639
Founded: 1888
President: Kenneth John Richards M.B.E.
Chairman: Charles Allen
Secretary: Shirley Hobbs, National & Provincial
Building Society, 46 Fore Street, Kingsbridge, Devon
TQ7 1NY. Tel: 0548 6248 (H), 6301 (W)
Fixtures Secretary: Peter Kemp, 6 Bonaventure
Close, Onslow Road, Salcombe, Devon. Tel: 054884
2492
Coach: Roger Taylor
Club captain (1988–89): Pete Kemp
Club captain (1989–90): Charley Fraser
No. of teams: Senior 2, Youth 3, Minis 2
Ground capacity: Seating 150, standing 1000
Clubhouse facilities: Clubhouse, bar, kitchen,
telephone, recreation area
Club colours: Red/white. (*Change colours:* White with
red band)
Floodlights: Yes
League: D 2B
League position (1988–89): 5th
League playing record (1988–89): P 5, W 2, D 0, L 3
Competitions won: Havill Plate, April '89

TAVISTOCK

Mary Tavy Playing fields, Tavistock, Devon
Founded: 1971
President: W. Oliver
Chairman: R. Watson
Secretary: J. Lawson, 4 Mount Ford, Tavistock,
Devon PL19 8EB
Fixtures Secretary: Cedric John Sutton, 121 Plymouth
Road, Tavistock, Devon PL19 9DT. Tel: 0822 615829
(H), 0509 43818 ext. 206 (W)
Coach: K. Oliver
Club captain (1988–89): J. Wakem
Club captain (1989–90): T.B.A.
No. of teams: Senior 2, Youth and Minis 6
Directions to ground: Alongside main road in centre
of Mary Tavy village, 3 miles east of Tavistock on
A386.
Ground capacity: Standing 300
Clubhouse facilities: Being built '88/'89
Club colours: Red shirts, black shorts, red socks.
(*Change colours:* Black shirts)

Floodlights: No
Membership fees: Social £13
Local newspapers: Tavistock Times and Gazette
League: D 2B

WITHYCOMBE

Rugby, Football & Recreation Club, Raleigh Park, Hulham Road, Exmouth, Devon. Tel: 0395 266762
Founded: 1924
President: Mrs Joan Rowsell-Pryce
Chairman: R.E. Jones
Secretary: D.M. Josey, 2 Larch Close, Marley Gardens, Exmouth, Devon EX8 5NQ. Tel: 0395 275038
Fixtures Secretary: D.J. Field, "The Bishop Blaize", The Quay, Exeter, Devon. Tel: 0392 214499

Club captain (1988–89): H. Symons
No. of teams: Senior 2
Directions to Ground: From Exeter, M5 junction 30, take A376 to Exmouth at box junction *before* first traffic lights, turn left into Hulham Road. Ground is 200 yds on right (on bend)
Ground capacity: 2,000. Stand, 50
Clubhouse: Clubroom, lounge, large changing rooms, cloakrooms, weights room
Colours: Emerald green & black hoops. (*Change colours*: Yellow)
Nickname: The Withies
Floodlights: No
Admission: Free. (Collection)
Membership: £5
Local newspaper: Exmouth Journal & Exmouth Herald
League: Devon 2B

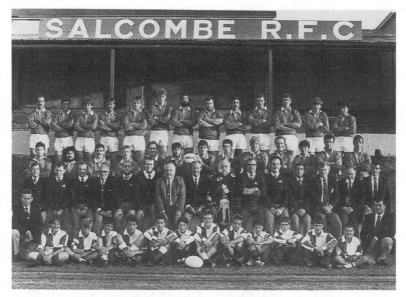

Salcombe of Devon 2B – 1988–89. Photo: South Hams Newspapers.

GLOUCESTER/SOMERSET LEAGUES

OLD CULVERHAYSIANS lost one of their 11 games in Somerset 1 in 1987–88, but this time in the next league up they were only required to play 10 games and won them all for a 207–82 points differential, which was not as good as that of Combe Down, who lost one and drew one to finish second and miss out on promotion for a second successive season. At the foot of the table Minehead go down to Somerset 1 and one team each from Gloucestershire 1 (Drybrook) and Somerset 1 (Frome) go up. Avon & Somerset Police, who were relegated last season from the Western Counties League, managed a mid-table position in less testing company, but Spartans, who were promoted from Gloucester 1 in 1988, had a satisfactory first season in higher company by finishing fourth and they could be real challengers next season, when Old Culverhaysians will hope to do even better and gain their hat-trick of promotions.

GLOUCESTER AND SOMERSET:
OFFICIAL

Bill Bishop,
Hellwellyn,
1 Wiltshire Place,
Kingswood,

Bristol BS15 4XA

(H) 0272 575729
(O) 0272 352017

TABLES 1987–88
GLOUCESTER/SOMERSET

	P	W	D	L	F	A	PTS
Avon OB	10	9	0	1	304	90	18
Combe Down	9	8	0	1	178	85	16
Coney Hill	10	7	0	3	193	89	14
Whitehall	10	7	0	3	196	104	14
Cleve	10	4	1	5	146	127	9
Keynsham	10	4	1	5	137	118	9
Midsomer Noe	10	4	0	6	151	171	8
Gordano	10	4	0	6	85	133	8
Minehead	10	3	0	7	94	197	6
Tredworth	9	2	0	7	38	154	4
St. Brendans	10	1	0	9	76	330	2

TABLES 1988–89
GLOUCESTER/SOMERSET

	P	W	D	L	F	A	PTS
O Culverhaysians	10	10	0	0	209	82	20
Combe Down	10	8	1	1	243	83	17
Midsomer Nor	10	7	0	3	120	110	14
Spartans	10	6	2	3	178	84	13
Coney Hill	10	6	0	4	89	71	12
Av & Som Pol	10	5	1	4	110	99	11
Keynsham	10	3	0	7	108	161	6
Whitehall	10	3	0	7	82	175	6
Cleve	10	2	1	7	76	94	5
Gordano	10	2	0	8	82	189	4
Minehead	10	1	0	9	84	231	2

SOUTH WEST DIVISION FIXTURES 1989/90

GLOUCESTERSHIRE/SOMERSET LEAGUE

Sat. 9th September (Week 2)
A & S Police v Cleve
Frome v Keynsham
Spartans v Drybrook
Old Redcliffians v Coney Hill
Whitehall v Combe Down

Sat. 23rd September (Week 4)
Combe Down v A & S Police
Coney Hill v Whitehall
Drybrook v Old Redcliffians
Keynsham v Spartans
Midsomer Norton v Frome

Sat. 14th October (Week 6)
A & S Police v Coney Hill
Cleve v Combe Down
Spartans v Midsomer Norton
Old Redcliffians v Keynsham
Whitehall v Drybrook

Sat. 28th October (Week 8)
Coney Hill v Cleve
Drybrook v A & S Police
Keynsham v Whitehall
Midsomer Norton v Old Redcliffians
Frome v Spartans

Sat. 11th November (Week 10)
A & S Police v Keynsham
Cleve v Drybrook
Combe Down v Coney Hill
Old Redcliffians v Frome
Whitehall v Midsomer Norton

Sat 18th November (Week 11)
Drybrook v Combe Down
Keynsham v Cleve
Midsomer Norton v A & S Police
Frome v Whitehall
Spartans v Old Redcliffians

Sat. 25th November (Week 12)
A & S Police v Frome
Cleve v Midsomer Norton
Combe Down v Keynsham
Coney Hill v Drybrook
Whitehall v Spartans

Sat. 13th January (Week 18)
Keynsham v Coney Hill
Midsomer Norton v Combe Down
Frome v Cleve
Spartans v A & S Police
Old Redcliffians v Whitehall

Sat. 10th March (Week 26)
A & S Police v Old Redcliffians
Cleve v Spartans
Combe Down v Frome
Coney Hill v Midsomer Norton
Drybrook v Keynsham

Sat. 31st March (Week X7)
Midsomer Norton v Drybrook
Frome v Coney Hill
Spartans v Combe Down
Old Redcliffians v Cleve
Whitehall v A & S Police

Sat. 28th April (Week 32)
Cleve v Whitehall
Combe Down v Old Redcliffians
Coney Hill v Spartans
Drybrook v Frome
Keynsham v Midsomer Norton

AVON & SOMERSET CONSTABULARY

Kings Weston Sports Ground, Napier Miles Road, Kings Weston, Bristol. Tel: 0272 828307.
Founded: 1935
Secretary: B. Gardiner, "Hillsley", Bleadon Road, Bleadon, Weston-Super-Mare, Avon. Tel: 0934 812020 (H). 0934 25411 (W)

CLEVE

Bromley Heath Road, Downend, Bristol BS16 6HY. Tel: 560323
Founded: 1922
President: E.B. Reakes
Chairman: P. Warne
Secretary: R. Pocock, 44 Spring Hill, Kingswood, Bristol BS15 1XT. Tel: 0272 611079 (H), 290215 (W)
Fixtures Secretary: R.T. Reed, 56 Keys Avenue, Horfield, Bristol. Tel: 690258
Press Officer: As Secretary
Club captain (1988–89): J. Tasker
Club captain (1989–90): G. Coombes
No. of teams: Senior 3, Youth 1, Minis 4
Directions to ground: Leave M4 for M32, come off roundabout to Kingswood. Ground is 1 mile on right-hand side
Clubhouse facilities: Players bar, dance hall, 4 changing rooms
Club colours: Maroon. (*Change colours:* Orange)
Floodlights: Yes
Membership fees: Full £15
Local newspapers: Evening Post, Observer
League: Gloucester/Somerset
League position (1988–89): 8th
League playing record (1988–89): P 9, W 2, D 1, L 6

COMBE DOWN

Holly's Corner, North Road, Combe Down, Bath. Tel: Bath 832075
Founded: 1896
President: Roger Wilcox
Chairman: Roger Hillman
Secretary: Peter Langley, 7 Ivy Grove, Bath BA2 1AP. Tel: Bath 318431 (H), Bath 338616 (W)
Fixtures Secretary: Wynford Bailey, 3 Keels Hill, Peasedown St. John, Nr. Bath. Tel: Radstock 34845
Press Officer: John Heal, 3 Gladstone Place, Combe Down, Bath. Tel: Bath 837903
Club captain (1988–89): Bob Gay
Club captain (1989–90): Bob Gay
No. of teams: Senior 3, Youth 1, Minis 1
Directions to ground: Exeter Road out of Bath – Wells Road, Wellsway, left at St. Martins Hospital, left at the Glasshouse Garage, 1 mile further on left past MOD (Foxhill)
Ground capacity: Standing 1000
Clubhouse facilities: Bar/clubroom,/kittle alley
Club colours: Black and amber. (*Change colours:* Amber)
Floodlights: Yes
Membership fees: Full £10, Playing £10, Social £3, Youth £5, OAP £3
Ground admission: Collection (£1 Cup games)
Programme: No. of editorial pages 4; No. of advertising pages 4 (Cup games)
Programme editor: As Press Officer
Local newspapers: Bath Chronicle & Herald
League: Gloucester/Somerst
League position (1988–89): 2nd
League playing record (1988–89): P 10, W 8, D 1, L 1
Competitions won: Somerset Cup Finalist. Bath Combination (1st Team Cup) Winners. Bath Combination (2nd Team Cup) Winners

CONEY HILL

Coney Hill, Gloucester. Tel: 306239
Founded: 1949
President: T. Brinkworth
Chairman: J. Barrett
Secretary: K. Stokes, 1 Stanway Road, Coney Hill, Gloucester. Tel: 410899
Fixtures Secretary: B. Dix, Coney Hill. Tel: 306239
Coach: W. Hall
Club captain (1988–89): P. Mansel
No. of teams: Senior 4
Club colours: Amber/black
Floodlights: No
Membership fees: Playing £8, Social £3
League: Gloucs/Som
League position (1988–89): 5th
League playing record (1988–89): P 10, W 6, D 0, L 4, F 89, A 71

DRYBROOK RFC

Mannings, Drybrook, Blos. Tel: 0594 542595
Founded: 1893
President: Clifford Davies
Chairman: Jeffrey Tate
Secretary: Glyn Tingle, Southview, Hazel Hill, Drybrook, Glos. Tel: 0594 543294 (H), 542769 (W)
Fixtures Secretary: Paul Mason, 29 Carisbrook Gardens, Mitcheldean, Glos. Tel: 0594 543948
Press Officer: As Fixtures Secretary
Coach: Peter Jones
Club captain (1988–89): Alan Miles
Club captain (1989–90): Alan Miles
No. of teams: Senior 5, Youth 1, Minis 1
Directions to ground: A40 from Gloucester, turn right to Huntley, turn left toward Monmouth, turn right at Mitcheldean into Drybrook
Clubhouse facilities: Lounge, bar, function room
Club colours: Green with black and white band. (*Change colours:* Black and white hoops)
Floodlights: No
League: Gloucester/Somerset
League position (1988–89): 1st (promoted)
Competitions won: Forest of Dean Combination Cup, Courage League Glos Div. 1 Drybrook Sevens

FROME

Clubhouse: The Pavilion, The Showground, Frome. Tel: 0373 65382. Ground: Gypsy Lane Playing Fields, Frome. Tel: 0373 62506
Founded: 1883
President: P.E. Quick
Chairman: J. Twigger
Secretary: D.J. Rose, 140 High Street, Chapmanslade, Westbury, Wilts BA13 4AP. Tel: 0373 88647
Fixtures Secretary: P. Lovatt, The Bath Arms, Horningsham, Wilts. Tel: Maiden Bradley 308
Press Officer: G. Barrow, 4 Valley View, Rodden. Tel: 0373 73551 (H), Trowbridge 766451 (W)
Coach: D. Fuszard
Club captain (1988–89): D. Kelly
Club captain (1989–90): K. Hewton
No. of teams: Senior 4, Youth 4, Minis 5
Ground capacity: Standing 500
Clubhouse facilities: Bar, clubroom, lounge, kitchen, toilets, showers
Club colours: Red black white hoops. (*Change colours:* Red black)
Floodlights: No
Membership fees: Full £12.50, Playing £15, Social £2, Youth £3, Student £2
Programme: No. of editorial pages 7; No. of advertising pages 3; Price 50p
Programme editor: G. Jones, 172 Whatcombe Road, Frome. Tel: 0373 73217 (H), Melksham 703036 (W)
Local newspaper: Somerset Standard
League: S 1
League position (1988–89): 1st (promoted)

League playing record (1988–89): P 36, W 28, D 2, L 6, F 846, A 283
Competitions won: Somerset Division 1, 1988/89

KEYNSHAM

The Crown Fields, Bristol Road, Keynsham, Bristol. Tel: 0272 867879
Founded: 1923
President: D.E. Cockbaine
Chairman: R. Palmer
Secretary: W.R. Harwood, 3 Windrush Road, Keynsham, Bristol BS18 1QL. Tel: 0272 862323
Fixtures Secretary: A.J. Oxenham, 54 Rock Road, Keynsham, Bristol. Tel: 0272 867334
Coach: R. Miller
Club captain (1988–89): J. Clark
Club captain (1989–90): J. Clark
No. of teams: Senior 4, Youth 6, Minis 3
Directions to ground: From Bristol follow A4 to Keynsham. From Bath follow A4 to Keynsham, through town centre and follow signs to Bristol
Club colours: Amber/black
Floodlights: No
League: Gloucester/Somerset
League position (1988–89): 7th
League playing record (1988–89): P 37, W 19, D 0, L 18

MIDSOMER NORTON

Norton Down Playing Field, Midsomer Norton. Tel: 0761 412827
Founded: 1936
President: D. Lyons
Chairman: R. Ladd
Secretary: M. Carter, 16 Redfield Road, Midsomer Norton. Tel: 0761 418745 (H), 0225 314400 (W)
Fixtures Secretary: R. Ladd, 5 Wood View, Wells Road, Hallatrow, Bristol BS18 5ED. Tel: 0761 53451
Coach: P. Helps
Club captain (1988–89): S. Pratt
Club captain (1989–90): S. Pratt
No. of teams: Senior 5, Youth 4
Directions to ground: B3139 off A367
Club colours: Scarlet. (*Change colours:* Emerald green)
Floodlights: Yes
Membership fees: Full £20, Playing £1.50
League: Gloucs/Som
League position (1988–89): 3rd
League playing record (1988–89): P 10, W 7, D 0, L 3, F 120, A 110

SPARTANS

St. Catherines Meadow, Cattle Market Complex, St. Oswald Road, Gloucester. Tel: 0452 410552
Founded: 1927
President: C. Teague
Chairman: S. Manley
Secretary: S. Martin, 120 Oxford Road. Tel: 26518
Fixtures Secretary: S. Lodge, 61 Armscroft Road,

Gloucester. Tel: 305515
Club captain (1988–89): P. Brown
Club captain (1989–90): R. Gough
Club colours: Red/black shorts. (*Change colours:* Green)
Floodlights: No
Membership fees: Full £10, Playing £10, Social £2
League: Gloucs/Som
League position (1988–89): 4th
League playing record (1988–89): P 10, W 6, D 1, L 3, F 178, A 84

OLD REDCLIFFIANS

Stockwood Lane, Brislington, Bristol. Tel: 0272 778501
Founded: 1918
President: A.A. Johnson
Chairman: K. Warren
Secretary: C.V. Heybyrne
Fixtures Secretary: R. Yandell, 5 High Street, Portbury, Bristol. Tel: Pill 3444
Press Officer: J. Rice. Tel: 0272 712212
Coach: M. Fry
Club captain (1988–89): L. Yandell
Club captain (1989–90): L. Yandell
No. of teams: Senior 5, Youth 4, Minis 2
Directions to ground: Bath Road out of Bristol → traffic lights → Stockwood Road mile r-hand side
Clubhouse facilities: Bar
Club colours: Red/black. (*Change colours:* Blue)
Floodlights: No
Membership fees: Full £5+£5, Playing £1.50
Programme: Special occasions only
League: Western Counties
League playing record (1988–89): P 10, W 4, D 0, L 6, F 108, A 113

WHITEHALL

Foundry Lane, Speedwell, Bristol. Tel: 0272 659636
Founded: 1934
President: C. Scott
Chairman: J. Lewis
Secretary: T. Hickey, 47 Berkley Road, Fishponds, Bristol. Tel: 657305
Fixtures Secretary: A. Furgeson, 8 Stoneleigh Road, Knowle, Bristol. Tel: 72898
Press Officer: M. Tomlin. Tel: 583192
Coach: B. Hesford
Club captain (1988–89): M. Hickey
Club captain (1989–90): M. Tomlin
No. of teams: Senior 4–5, Youth 3
Clubhouse facilities: 3 bars
Club colours: Green/gold
Floodlights: Yes
Membership fees: Full £15, Social £5
League: Gloucs/Som
League position (1988–89): 8th
League playing record (1988–89): P 10, W 3, D 0, L 7, F 82, A 175

GLOUCESTERSHIRE LEAGUES

THE TOP teams in the four divisions – the first three with 11 clubs each and the fourth with a dozen – all had unblemished records, starting with Drybrook in Division 1, whose perfect record (196–42 points difference) meant a second successive miss for Dings Crusaders, beaten on points difference last time round. Old Colstonians go down and with the top league being increased to a dozen clubs two sides replace them from Division 2 – Gloucester Old Boys (promoted from Division 3 in 1987–88) and Cheltenham North (relegated from Division 1 last time). The Gloucester side won all its 10 matches (252–63), but at the bottom Cheltenham Civil Service won only one match and go down to be replaced by Frampton Cotterrell (another team with 10 unblemished victories) and Thornbury, who lost but once.

Chosen Hill FP at the foot of the table descend and again two sides from Division 4 take their plce, the successful teams being Bristol Telephones (defeated once in 11 fixtures) and Hucclecote Old Boys, also only defeated once but runners-up on points difference. Dowty and Old Colthamians drew their match and lost all their other games!

GLOUCESTERSHIRE ALL LEAGUES: OFFICIAL

Nick Healey,
98 London Road,
Gloucester GL1 3PG   0452 24917

TABLES 1987–88

GLOUCESTERSHIRE 1

	P	W	D	L	F	A	PTS
Spartans	10	9	0	1	275	61	18
Dings Crusad	10	9	0	1	153	65	18
Drybrook	10	6	0	4	182	95	12
Longlevens	10	6	0	4	124	134	12
O Patesians	10	5	1	4	152	112	11
O Colstonian	10	5	1	4	75	112	11
St. Mary's OB	10	4	1	5	92	112	9
Widden	10	4	1	5	92	112	9
Bream	10	2	1	7	109	154	5
Cheltenham N	10	2	0	8	71	146	4
Bristol Sara	10	0	0	10	41	273	0

GLOUCESTERSHIRE 2

	P	W	D	L	F	A	PTS
N Bristol	10	9	1	0	148	54	19
Saintbridge	10	7	2	1	159	69	16
Ashley Down	10	6	2	2	189	93	14
Chelt Sara	10	6	1	3	120	79	13
Cotham Park	10	5	1	4	120	124	11
O Cryptians	10	4	1	5	95	160	9
Barton Hill	10	4	0	6	87	102	9
Chelt'ham CS	10	3	1	6	87	123	7
Brockworth	10	3	0	7	147	130	6
Dursley	10	3	0	7	90	180	6
Cainscross	10	0	1	9	42	170	1

TABLES 1988-89

GLOUCESTERSHIRE 1

	P	W	D	L	F	A	PTS
Drybrook	10	10	0	0	196	42	20
Dings Crusad	10	7	1	2	155	113	15
N Bristol	10	7	0	3	161	113	14
Widden OB	10	6	1	3	168	117	13
Longlevens	10	5	0	5	154	116	10
Saintbridge FP	10	3	2	5	109	122	8
O Patesians	10	3	0	7	133	140	6
Bream	10	3	0	7	116	166	6
Tredworth	10	1	1	8	75	192	3
O Colstonians	10	0	0	10	29	230	0

GLOUCESTERSHIRE 2

	P	W	D	L	F	A	PTS
Gloucester OB	10	10	0	0	252	63	20
Cheltenham N	10	0	0	1	188	75	18
O Bristolians	10	7	1	2	145	92	15
Ashley D OB	10	6	1	3	136	121	13
Bristol Sara	10	5	0	5	115	148	10
Cheltenham Sara	10	4	0	6	102	133	8
O Cryptians	10	3	0	7	101	146	6
Barton Hill	10	3	0	7	84	138	6
Brockworth	10	3	0	7	96	152	6
Cotham Pk	10	3	0	7	115	181	6
Chelt'ham CS	10	1	0	9	74	159	2

GLOUCESTERSHIRE 3

	P	W	D	L	F	A	PTS
O Bristolian	10	10	0	0	157	60	20
Gloster OB	10	9	0	1	352	43	18
Chipping Sod	10	8	0	2	173	91	16
Frampton Cot	10	6	0	4	176	115	12
Thornbury	10	4	1	1	127	131	9
Kingswood	10	4	0	6	73	161	8
Tewsbury	10	3	0	7	94	168	6
Chosen Hill	10	3	0	7	73	188	6
Painswick	10	3	0	7	101	226	6
Gloster CS	10	2	1	7	79	154	5
Bishopston	10	2	0	8	99	167	4

GLOUCESTERSHIRE 4

	P	W	D	L	F	A	PTS
Smiths	10	8	1	1	125	82	17
O Elizabeth	10	8	0	2	136	63	16
Bristol Tels	10	7	0	3	162	66	14
Broad Plain	10	6	1	3	121	76	13
All Blues	10	6	1	3	133	94	13
Aretians	10	6	0	4	88	76	12
BAC	10	5	0	5	138	99	10
Hucclecote	10	4	0	6	99	78	8
Newent	10	2	1	7	73	137	5
O Cothamians	10	0	1	9	46	160	1
Minchin'ton	10	0	1	9	36	226	1

GLOUCESTERSHIRE 3

	P	W	D	L	F	A	PTS
Frampton Cott	10	10	0	0	281	63	20
Thornbury	10	9	0	1	296	66	18
Dursley	10	6	1	3	128	92	13
Chipping Sod	10	5	0	5	182	77	10
Tewkesbury	10	4	2	4	114	174	10
Painswick	10	3	2	5	90	128	8
O Elizabethans	10	4	0	6	94	180	8
Cainscross	10	4	0	6	76	183	8
Smiths Ind	10	3	0	7	83	228	6
Kingswood	10	2	1	7	86	182	5
Chosen Hill FP	10	2	0	8	79	136	4

GLOUCESTERSHIRE 4

	P	W	D	L	F	A	PTS
Bristol Tele	11	10	0	1	295	66	20
Hucclecote OB	11	10	0	1	270	70	20
Bishopston	11	7	1	3	242	90	15
Aretians	11	7	0	4	166	84	14
Newent	11	7	0	4	191	184	14
Brist Aero Co	11	6	0	5	174	142	12
Minchinhampton	11	5	1	5	201	160	11
Gloucester CS	11	5	0	6	149	131	10
Broad Plain	11	5	0	6	124	152	10
All Blues	11	2	0	9	123	263	4
Old Cothamians	11	0	1	10	54	308	1
Dowty	11	0	1	10	76	415	1

Old Elizabethans – runners-up in Bristol Combination sevens. Photo: Brendon Studio, Beaminster.

SOUTH WEST DIVISION FIXTURES 1989/90

GLOUCESTERSHIRE DIVISION ONE

Sat. 9th September (Week 2)
Bream v North Bristol
Old Patesians v Longlevens
St. Mary's OB v Cheltenham North
Tredworth v Dings Crusaders
Widden Old Boys v Saintbridge FP

Sat. 23rd September (Week 4)
Dings Crusaders v Widden Old Boys
Cheltenham North v Tredworth
Longlevens v St. Mary's OB
Gloucester OB v Old Patesians
Saintbridge FP v Bream

Sat. 14th October (Week 6)
Bream v Dings Crusaders
North Bristol v Saintbridge FP
St. Mary's OB v Gloucester OB
Tredworth v Longlevens
Widden Old Boys v Cheltenham North

Sat. 28th October (Week 8)
Dings Crusaders v North Bristol
Cheltenham North v Bream
Longlevens v Widden Old Boys
Gloucester OB v Tredworth
Old Patesians v St. Mary's OB

Sat. 11th November (Week 10)
Bream v Longlevens
North Bristol v Cheltenham North
Saintbridge FP v Dings Crusaders
Tredworth v Old Patesians
Widden Old Boys v Gloucester OB

Sat 18th November (Week 11)
Cheltenham North v Saintbridge FP
Longlevens v North Bristol
Gloucester OB v Bream
Old Patesians v Widden Old Boys
St. Mary's OB v Tredworth

Sat. 25th November (Week 12)
Bream v Old Patesians
North Bristol v Gloucester OB
Saintbridge FP v Longlevens
Dings Crusaders v Cheltenham North
Widden Old Boys v St. Mary's OB

Sat. 13th January (Week 18)
Longlevens v Dings Crusaders
Gloucester OB v Saintbridge FP
Old Patesians v North Bristol
St. Mary's OB v Bream
Tredworth v Widden Old Boys

Sat. 10th March (Week 26)
Bream v Tredworth
North Bristol v St. Mary's OB
Saintbridge FP v Old Patesians
Dings Crusaders v Gloucester OB
Cheltenham North v Longlevens

Sat. 31st March (Week X7)
Gloucester OB v Cheltenham North
Old Patesians v Dings Crusaders
St. Mary's OB v Saintbridge FP
Tredworth v North Bristol
Widden Old Boys v Bream

Sat. 28th April (Week 32)
North Bristol v Widden Old Boys
Saintbridge FP v Tredworth
Dings Crusaders v St. Mary's OB
Cheltenham North v Old Patesians
Longlevens v Gloucester OB

GLOUCESTERSHIRE DIVISION TWO

Sat. 9th September (Week 2)
Ashley Down OB v Barton Hill
Old Colstonians v Cheltenham Saracens
Thornbury v Frampton Cotterell
Old Cryptians v Bristol Saracens
Old Bristolians v Brockworth

Sat. 23rd September (Week 4)
Bristol Saracens v Old Bristolians
Frampton Cotterell v Old Cryptians
Cheltenham Saracens v Thornbury
Cotham Park v Old Colstonians
Brockworth v Ashley Down OB

Sat. 14th October (Week 6)
Ashley Down OB v Bristol Saracens
Barton Hill v Brockworth
Thornbury v Cotham Park
Old Cryptians v Cheltenham Saracens
Old Bristolians v Frampton Cotterell

Sat. 28th October (Week 8)
Bristol Saracens v Barton Hill
Frampton Cotterell v Ashley Down OB
Cheltenham Saracens v Old Bristolians
Cotham Park v Old Cryptians
Old Colstonians v Thornbury

SOUTH WEST DIVISION FIXTURES 1989/90

Sat. 11th November (Week 10)
Ashley Down OB v Cheltenham Saracens
Barton Hill v Frampton Cotterell
Brockworth v Bristol Saracens
Old Cryptians v Old Colstonians
Old Bristolians v Cotham Park

Sat 18th November (Week 11)
Frampton Cotterell v Brockworth
Cheltenham Saracens v Barton Hill
Cotham Park v Ashley Down OB
Old Colstonians v Old Bristolians
Thornbury v Old Cryptians

Sat. 25th November (Week 12)
Ashley Down OB v Old Colstonians
Barton Hill v Cotham Park
Brockworth v Cheltenham Saracens
Bristol Saracens v Frampton Cotterell
Old Bristolians v Thornbury

Sat. 13th January (Week 18)
Cheltenham Saracens v Bristol Saracens
Cotham Park v Brockworth
Old Colstonians v Barton Hill
Thornbury v Ashley Down OB
Old Cryptians v Old Bristolians

Sat. 10th March (Week 26)
Ashley Down OB v Old Cryptians
Barton Hill v Thornbury
Brockworth v Old Colstonians
Bristol Saracens v Cotham Park
Frampton Cotterell v Cheltenham Saracens

Sat. 31st March (Week X7)
Cotham Park v Frampton Cotterell
Old Colstonians v Bristol Saracens
Thornbury v Brockworth
Old Cryptians v Barton Hill
Old Bristolians v Ashley Down OB

Sat. 28th April (Week 32)
Barton Hill v Old Bristolians
Brockworth v Old Cryptians
Bristol Saracens v Thornbury
Frampton Cotterell v Old Colstonians
Cheltenham Saracens v Cotham Park

GLOUCESTERSHIRE DIVISION THREE

Sat. 9th September (Week 2)
Cainscross v Chipping Sodbury
Smiths Industries v Old Elizabethans
Painswick v Dursley
Tewkesbury v Cheltenham CS
Hucclecote OB v Bristol Telephones

Sat. 23rd September (Week 4)
Cheltenham CS v Hucclecote OB
Dursley v Tewkesbury
Old Elizabethans v Painswick
Kingswood v Smiths Industries
Bristol Telephones v Cainscross

Sat. 14th October (Week 6)
Cainscross v Cheltenham CS
Chipping Sodbury v Bristol Telephones
Painswick v Kingswood
Tewkesbury v Old Elizabethans
Hucclecote OB v Dursley

Sat. 28th October (Week 8)
Cheltenham CS v Chipping Sodbury
Dursley v Cainscross
Old Elizabethans v Hucclecote OB
Kingswood v Tewkesbury
Smiths Industries v Painswick

Sat. 11th November (Week 10)
Cainscross v Old Elizabethans
Chipping Sodbury v Dursley
Bristol Telephones v Cheltenham CS
Tewkesbury v Smiths Industries
Hucclecote OB v Kingswood

Sat 18th November (Week 11)
Dursley v Bristol Telephones
Old Elizabethans v Chipping Sodbury
Kingswood v Cainscross
Smiths Industries v Hucclecote OB
Painswick v Tewkesbury

Sat. 25th November (Week 12)
Cainscross v Smiths Industries
Chipping Sodbury v Kingswood
Bristol Telephones v Old Elizabethans
Cheltenham CS v Dursley
Hucclecote OB v Painswick

Sat. 13th January (Week 18)
Old Elizabethans v Cheltenham CS
Kingswood v Bristol Telephones
Smiths Industries v Chipping Sodbury
Painswick v Cainscross
Tewkesbury v Hucclecote OB

SOUTH WEST DIVISION FIXTURES 1989/90

Sat. 10th March (Week 26)
Cainscross v Tewkesbury
Chipping Sodbury v Painswick
Bristol Telephones v Smiths Industries
Cheltenham CS v Kingswood
Dursley v Old Elizabethans

Sat. 31st March (Week X7)
Kingswood v Dursley
Smiths Industries v Cheltenham CS
Painswick v Bristol Telephones
Tewkesbury v Chipping Sodbury
Hucclecote OB v Cainscross

Sat. 28th April (Week 32)
Chipping Sodbury v Hucclecote OB
Bristol Telephones v Tewkesbury
Cheltenham CS v Painswick
Dursley v Smiths Industries
Old Elizabethans v Kingswood

GLOUCESTERSHIRE DIVISION FOUR

Sat. 23rd September (Week 4)
Dowty v Chosen Hill F.P.
Gloucester CS v All Blues
Minchinhampton v Old Richians
Bristol Aero v Bishopston
Broadplain v Aretians
Old Cothamians v Tetbury

Sat. 28th October (Week 8)
All Blues v Minchinhampton
Chosen Hill F.P. v Gloucester CS
Old Richians v Newent
Aretians v Old Cothamians
Bishopston v Broadplain
Tetbury v Southmead

Sat. 11th November (Week 10)
Gloucester CS v Dowty
Minchinhampton v Chosen Hill F.P.
Newent v All Blues
Broadplain v Bristol Aero
Old Cothamians v Bishopston
Southmead v Aretians

Sat. 25th November (Week 12)
All Blues v Old Richians
Chosen Hill F.P. v Newent
Dowty v Minchinhampton
Aretians v Tetbury
Bishopston v Southmead
Bristol Aero v Old Cothamians

Sat. 13th January (Week 18)
Minchinhampton v Gloucester CS
Newent v Dowty
Old Richians v Chosen Hill F.P.
Old Cothamians v Broadplain
Southmead v Bristol Aero
Tetbury v Bishopston

Sat. 10th March (Week 26)
Chosen Hill F.P. v All Blues
Dowty v Old Richians
Gloucester CS v Newent
Bishopston v Aretians
Bristol Aero v Tetbury
Broadplain v Southmead

Sat. 31st March (Week X7)
All Blues v Dowty
Newent v Minchinhampton
Old Richians v Gloucester CS
Aretians v Bristol Aero
Southmead v Old Cothamians
Tetbury v Broadplain

GLOUCESTERSHIRE 1

BREAM

High Street, Bream, Nr. Lydney, Glos GL15 6JG.
Tel: 0594 562320
Founded: 1878
President: D. Watkins
Chairman: M. Dunn
Secretary: J. Grail, 31 Highbury Road, Bream, Nr.
Lydney, Glos GL15 6EF. Tel: 0594 562737 (H),
562320 (W)
Fixtures Secretary: T. Evans, High Bank, White Croft
Road, Glos. Tel: 562242
Club captain (1988–89): J. Thomas
Club captain (1989–90): R. Macey
No. of teams: Senior 4
Directions to ground: 3 miles off A48 from Lydney
Clubhouse facilities: 3 bars
Club colours: Red/black. (*Change colours:*
Blue/white)
Membership fees: Full £3, Playing £3
Ground admission: 50p
League: Gloucs 1
League position (1988–89): 9th
League playing record (1988–89): P 10, W 3, D 0,
L 7, F 116, A 166

CHELTENHAM NORTH

Stone Road, Bishops Cleeve, Nr. Cheltenham. Tel:
024267 5968
Founded: 1905
President: P.K. Wheatley
Chairman: A.L. Rogers
Secretary: A.D. Page, 22 Fairfield Avenue,
Leckhampton, Cheltenham. Tel: 510932 (H), 0452
411477 (W)
Fixtures Secretary: P. Shand, 96 Netherwood
Gardens, Cheltenham. Tel: 574962
Press Officer: As Secretary
Coach: R. Davies, L. Dick
Club captain (1988–89): S. Gourlay
Club captain (1989–90): S. Gourlay
No. of teams: Senior 4
Directions to ground: Take A435 out of Cheltenham
to Bishops Cleeve and take road to Glos. County
Council Tip. Groun on L.H.S.
Ground capacity: Standing 500
Clubhouse facilities: 377 High Street, Cheltenham
Club colours: Black with red hoop. (*Change colours:*
Black or yellow)
Floodlights: Yes (training purposes)
Membership fees: Full £10
Local newspaper: Gloucestershire Echo
League: Gloucester 2
League position (1988–89): 2nd (promoted)
League playing record (1988–89): P 10, W 9, D 0,
L 1, F 193, A 70
Competitions won: Cheltenham Senior Cup Winners

DINGS CRUSADERS

Lanseer Avenue, Lockleaze, Bristol. Tel: 691367
Founded: 1897
President: Graham Backes
Chairman: Floyd Waters
Secretary: Graham Troote, 50 Kipling Road, Filton,
Bristol BS7 0QR. Tel: 694141
Fixtures Secretary: Terry Webb, 50 Monks Park
Avenue, Horfield BS7 0UH. Tel: 692749
Press Officer: Robert Stevens, 4 Fonthill Way, Bitton.
Tel: 329129
Club captain (1988–89): Gary Peters
Club captain (1989–90): Gary Peters
No. of teams: Senior 5
Directions to ground: M4 or M5 to M32 to Filton.
Turn left at King George VI pub, turn left at
Fellowship pub, cross over railway bridge, turn left
into Landseer Avenue ground

Ground capacity: Seating 200, standing 300–400
Clubhouse facilities: Bar, food
Club colours: Royal blue and black
Nickname: Dings
Floodlights: Yes
Membership fees: Full £10, Playing £1.50
Local newspapers: Western Daily Press, Evening Post
League: Gloucester 1
League position (1988–89): 2nd
Competitions won: Evening Post Merit Table 1988/89
Winners

GLOUCESTER OLD BOYS

Memorial Playing Field, Failand, Bristol. Tel: 0272
392137
Founded: 1904
President: Gilbert A. Roberts
Chairman: Arnold F. Sinclair
Secretary: . Tel: 0452 27658 (H), 302088 (W)
Fixtures Secretary: Richard Potterton, 35 Corcorde
Drive, Westbury-on-Trym, Bristol. Tel: 505104
Club captain (1988–89): Russ Ellis
Club captain (1989–90): Kevin Hale
No. of teams: Senior 3
Directions to ground: Off Beggar Bush Lane near
Redwood Lodge Country Club
Clubhouse facilities: 2 bars, skittle alley, 3 changing
rooms
Club colours: Maroon/amber/green hoops. (*Change
colours:* Maroon)
Nickname: B's
Floodlights: No
Membership fees: Full £10, Playing £10, Social £2.50
Local newspaper: Bristol Evening Post
League: Gloucester 2
League position (1988–89): 1st
League playing record (1988–89): P 10, W 10, D 0,
L 0, F 252, A 63

LONGLEVENS

Longford Lane, Longlevens, Gloucester. Tel: 0452
306880
Founded: 1954
President: David T. Foyle
Chairman: Kenneth D. Hending
Secretary: Colin F. Dunford, 66 Estcourt Road,
Gloucester GL1 3LG. Tel: 0452 22795 (H), 411666
(W)
Fixtures Secretary: Mark J. Dunford, 66 Estcourt
Road, Gloucester GL1 3LG. Tel: 0452 22795
Press Officer: Adrian Richings, 77 Oxtalls Way,
Longlevens, Gloucester. Tel: 0452 301969
Coach: John Watkins
Club captain (1988–89): John Norman
Club captain (1989–90): Mark Glanville
No. of teams: Senior 4, Youth 3, Colts 1
Directions to ground: Tewkesbury Road (A38) from
Gloucester and turn right into Longford Lane. Or M5
Junction 11 Golden Valley bypass to Cheltenham
Road, second traffic lights turn right into church Road
and Longford Lane
Clubhouse facilities: Open every evening and Sunday
lunchtime
Club colours: Red. (*Change colours:* Blue)
Nickname: 'Levens
Floodlights: Yes (for training only)
Membership fees: Full £5, Playing £5, Social £2.50,
Student £2.50, OAP £50p
Local newspapers: The Citizen and Gloucester Journal
League: Gloucester 1
League position (1988–89): 5th
League playing record (1988–89): P 10, W 5, D 0,
L 5, F 156, A 116
Competitions won: Gloucestershire County Colts Cup

NORTH BRISTOL

Oaklands, Almondsbury, Bristol. Tel: 0454 612740
Founded: 1933
President: Charles Hill
Chairman: Ken Rendell
Secretary: C.H. Hill, 7 Keinton Walk, Henbury, Bristol BS10 7EE. Tel: 0272 508123
Fixtures Secretary: Derek Kettlewell, 227 Gloucester Road, Patchway, Bristol BS12 5AD. Tel: 0454 613418. Tel: 0272 296268
Press Officer: As Secretary
Coach: David Martin
Club captain (1988–89): John Harris
Club captain (1989–90): Derek Miles
No. of teams: Senior 5, Youth 3
Directions to ground: M5 Junction 16
Clubhouse facilities: Clubroom, lounge, treatment room, showers, changing for 6 teams
Club colours: Red and light blue stripes. (*Change colours:* Emerald green)
Nickname: North
Floodlights: Yes (two pitches)
Membership fees: Full £10 + £2 per game
Local newspapers: Bristol Evening Post and Gloucestershire Gazette
League: Gloucester 1
League position (1988–89): 4th
League playing record (1988–89): P 10, W 7, D 0, L 3, F 163, A 113

OLD PATESIANS

Everest Road, Leckhampton, Cheltenham, Glos. Tel: 0242 524633
Founded: 1913
President: David Powell
Chairman: David Harper
Secretary: Meurig Richards, 8 The Lawns, Gotherington, Cheltenham, Glos. Tel: 0242 672758
Fixtures Secretary: Robin Beckley, 'Waverley', Western Road, Cheltenham, Glos. Tel: 0242 576042
Press Officer: As Secretary
Club captain (1988–89): Paul Morris
Club captain (1989–90): Paul Keegan
No. of teams: Senior 5, Youth 1, Minis 2
Directions to ground: From M5 into Cheltenham via Gloucester Road, meet Old Bath Road, left into Everest Road
Ground capacity: Standing Unlimited
Clubhouse facilities: Open every evening, Sat./Sun. lunchtime
Club colours: Magenta, white, navy irregular hoops. (*Change colours:* Yellow)
Nickname: Old Pats
Floodlights: No
Membership fees: Full £15, Playing £15, Social £5, Youth £7.50, Student £7.50, OAP £5
Local newspaper: Gloucester Echo
League: Gloucester 1
League position (1988–89): 7th
League playing record (1988–89): P 10, W 3, D 0, L 7, F 133, A 135
Competitions won: Cheltenham Combination Junior Cup Winners, Cheltenham Combination 7-a-Side Winners

SAINTBRIDGE

Saintbridge Sports Centre, Painswick Road, Gloucester, Glos. Tel: Glos. 303768
Founded: 1937
President: John Smith
Chairman: Martin Slatter
Secretary: Stephen Fritchley, 7 Saintbridge Close, Gloucester, Glos. Tel: Glos. 22690 (H), Glos. 306387 (W)
Fixtures Secretary: Stuart Slatter, 40 Eagle Way, Heron Park, Gloucester. Tel: Glos. 411142
Press Officer: Alan Locke, c/o Club
Coach: T.B.A.
Club captain (1988–89): J. Roberts
Club captain (1989–90): R. Creese

No. of teams: Senior 4, Youth 4
Directions to ground: Take A435 out of Cheltenham to Bishops Cleeve and take road to Stoke Orhcard, on right 1 mile
Clubhouse facilities: 3 changing rooms, 3 bars, function room
Club colours: Navy blue, royal blue and gold rings
Nickname: Old Cents
Floodlights: No
Membership fees: Full £10
Local newspapers: Citizen
League: Gloucester 1
League position (1988–89): 7th
League playing record (1988–89): P 10, W 3, D 2, L 5

ST. MARY'S OLD BOYS

Combination Ground, Northway, Filton, Bristol. Tel: 0272 2326029
Founded: 1898
President: J.H. White
Chairman: D. Portlock
Secretary: Mrs. L. Collins, 18D Belment Road, St. Andrews, Bristol BS6 5AS. Tel: 0272 249879
Fixtures Secretary: G. Jelfs
Press Officer: M. Mansfield
Club captain (1988–89): A. Lathrope
Club captain (1989–90): S. Cooke
No. of teams: Senior 4, Minis 1
Clubhouse facilities: Bar, skittle alley
Club colours: Emerald green and black. (*Change colours:* Black)
Floodlights: Yes (for training sessions)
League: Gloucester 1
League position (1988–89): 3rd
Competitions won: Bristol Combination Cup

TREDWORTH

The Lannett, King Edwards Avenue, Gloucester.
Founded: 1904
Secretary: R.–E. Bowhett, Kingston House, 5 Landsown Road, Gloucester GL2 3IW. Tel: 0452 593893.
Fixtures Secretary: 1904
League: Gloucester/Somerset.

WIDDEN OLD BOYS

Memorial Ground, Tuffley Avenue, Gloucester. Tel: 0452 34080.
Founded: 1922
Secretary: A. Lane, 13 Tuffley Avenue, Gloucester GL1 5LS. Tel: 9452 504226.
League: Gloucestershire 1

ASHLEY DOWN OLD BOYS

Lockleaze Combination Ground, Bonnington Walk, Bristol
President: Sidney Grant
Chairman: Mike Delderfield
Secretary: John Bennett, 307 Ashley Down Road, St. Andrews, Bristol BS7 9BG. Tel: 0272 243734 (H), 797291 (W)
Fixtures Secretary: Patrick Dono, 28 St. Aidans Road, Hanham, Bristol BS5 3RT. Tel: 0272 679649
Press Officer: Colin Vincent, c/o Ashley Down Road, St. Andrews, Bristol BS7 9BG. Tel: 0272 243734 (H), 797291 (W)
Coach: Barry Cole
Club captain (1988–89): Andy Weston
Club captain (1989–90): Ashley Williams
No. of teams: Senior 4, Youth 1
Directions to ground: From the north, turn right at

second junction of M32 two miles turn left Filton Avenue (King George VI pub). One mile turn left at Fellowship pub into Bonnington Walk. mile left into gate of ground
Clubhouse facilities: Bar (3 miles from ground)
Club colours: White with purple circlet. (*Change colours:* Maroon)
Floodlights: No
Membership fees: Full £10, Playing £2, Social £3, Student £3, OAP £3
Local newspapers: Bristol Evening Post, Western Daily Press
League: Glos 2
League position (1988–89): 4th
League playing record (1988–89): P 10, W 6, D 0, L 4, F 70, A 80

BARTENHILL O.B.

Founded: 1908
President: Jim Pruett
Chairman: John Moran
Secretary: Donald Edward Blackmore, 31 Battens Lane, St. George, Bristol BS5 8TG. Tel: Bristol 611754 (H), 362682 (W)
Fixtures Secretary: Paul Uppington, 18 Easton Close, Fishponds, Bristol. Tel: 650340
Press Officer: R. Andrews, 30 High Street, Staple Hill, Bristol. Tel: 566307
Club captain (1988–89): Andrew Powell
Club captain (1989–90): Mark Hughes
No. of teams: Senior 4, Youth 4
Directions to ground: Follow signs for Fishponds when leaving M32
Club colours: White with cherry band
Nickname: The Barts
Floodlights: No
Membership fees: Full £10
Local newspaper: Bristol Evening Post
League: South West/Gloucs 2

BRISTOL SARACENS

Station Road, Cribbs Causeway, Bristol. Tel: 0272 500037
Founded: 1896
President: H.A. Hill
Chairman: D.J. Preen
Secretary: A.E. Swash, 6 Downs Road, Westbury-on-Trym, Bristol BS9 3TX. Tel: 0272 629047 (H), 232181 (W)
Fixtures Secretary: C. Matthews, 6 Wellington Drive, Henleaze, Bristol BS10 5ET. Tel: 0272 243696 (H), 0454 419008 (W)
Press Officer: As Secretary
Club captain (1988–89): P. Naish
Club captain (1989–90): Peter Naish
No. of teams: Senior 4, Youth 4
Directions to ground: On M5 junction south of M5/M4 Interchange, 800 yds towards Bristol centre on right
Clubhouse facilities: 2 bars, dressing rooms
Club colours: Myrtle green/white hoop shirts, black shorts. (*Change colours:* Blue/yellow hoops)
Floodlights: Yes
League: Gloucester 2
League position (1988–89): 5th

BROCKWORTH

Mill Lane, Brockworth, Gloucester. Tel: Glos. 862556
Founded: 1975
President: David Morgan
Chairman: Brian Webber
Secretary: Joanne Farrington, 6 Westfield Avenue, Brockworth, Gloucester. Tel: 613576
Fixtures Secretary: John Ford, Pomona, St. Georges Road, Brockworth, Gloucester
Coach: Crayton Phillips
Club captain (1988–89): Gary Weston
Club captain (1989–90): Gary Weston

No. of teams: Senior 3, Youth 1
Directions to ground: From Gloucester turn left opposite the Flying Machine public house, straight over roundabout, first turning on right, second turning on left on the hill
Ground capacity: Standing 5000
Clubhouse facilities: Large function room, bar, changing rooms and shower
Club colours: Black shirt with white V, white shorts, socks black with white tops. (*Change colours:* Black/white hoops)
Nickname: Badgers
Floodlights: No
Membership fees: Full £12, Playing £12, Social £6, Youth £5, Student £5, OAP £1
Programme: No. of editorial pages 1; No. of advertising pages 0
Programme editor: D. Alden, 27 Boverton Drive, Brockworth, Gloucester
Local newspapers: The Citizen and Gloucestershire Echo
League: Gloucester 2
League position (1988–89): 7th

COTHAM PARK

Beggar Book Lane, Failand, Bristol.
Founded: 1901
Secretary: J. Crocker, Grove House, Tennessee Grove, Henleaze, Bristol. Tel: 0272 424885 (H). 0272 292227 (W).
League: Gloucestershire 2

CHELTENHAM SARACENS

Club, 18 Swindon Road, Cheltenham, Gloucester. Tel: 0242 520529
Founded: 1975
President: Harry Attwood
Chairman: Tony Pates
Secretary: Colin Wheeler, c/o Bredon School, Pull Court, Bushley, Nr. Tewkesbury, Gloucestershire GL20 6AN. Tel: 0684 294119 (H), 293156 (W)
Fixtures Secretary: Alan Biggs, 17 Swanswell Drive, Benhall, Cheltenham, Gloucestershire. Tel: 0242 571819
Coach: Colin Wheeler
Club captain (1988–89): Dermot Walsh
Club captain (1989–90): Chris Whitelow
No. of teams: Senior 3, Youth 1
Directions to ground: M5 Junc. 10. A40 to Cheltenham, across 1st roundabout, left at 2nd roundabout (by G.H.C.Q.). Follow round to the right around square traffic island (road in front of shops). Gates to K.G.V. facing at the 'T' junction at the end of this road
Clubhouse facilities: Town centre (large sports and social club)
Club colours: Blue with gold circlet. (*Change colours:* Yellow)
Nickname: Saras
Floodlights: No
Membership fees: Full £7, Playing £7, Social £3, Youth £5, Student £5
League: Gloucester 2

FRAMPTON COTTERELL

School Road, Frampton Cotterell, Bristol
Founded: 1973
President: D. Mayer
Chairman: T.N. Knight
Secretary: N. Smith, 16 The Land, Coalpit Heath, Bristol BS17 2LJ. Tel: 0454 775113 (H), 617888 (W)
Fixtures Secretary: D. Pritchard, 84 Beesmoor, F. Cotterell, Bristol. Tel: 0454 774293
Press Officer: B. Smith, 3 Fire Engine Way, F.

Cotterell, Bristol. Tel: 0454 776300
Club captain (1988–89): T. Draisey
Club captain (1989–90): B. Glastonbury
No. of teams: Senior 4–5, Youth 3, Minis 3
Directions to ground: Signs to F. Cotterell
Club colours: Green/black. (*Change colours:* Red)
Floodlights: Yes (training)
League: Gloucs 2
League position (1988–89): 1st
League playing record (1988–89): P 10, W 10, D 0, L 0, F 281, A 63

OLD BRISTOLIANS

Memorial Playing Field, Failand, Bristol. Tel: 0272 392137
Founded: 1925
President: Garth Morris
Chairman: Trevor Harris
Secretary: Nicholas Noble, 7 North Street, Nailsea, Bristol BS19 2NP. Tel: 0272 856070 (H), 294271 (W)
Fixtures Secretary: Richard Potterton, 35 Concorde Drive, Westbury-on-Trym, Bristol. Tel: 0272 505104
Press Officer: As Secretary
Coach: Garth Morris
Club captain (1988–89): Ray Jones
Club captain (1989–90): Richard Berry
No. of teams: Senior 4, Youth 1
Directions to ground: Off Beggar Bush Lane, near Redwood Lodge Country Club
Ground capacity: Standing Yes
Clubhouse facilities: 2 bars, men's and women's changing rooms. Open 3 nights per week
Club colours: Maroon, amber and green hoops. (*Change colours:* Maroon)
Nickname: OB's
Floodlights: Yes (for training only)
Membership fees: Full £25, Playing £25, Social £5, Youth £5, Student £5, OAP £5
Local newspaper: Bristol Evening Post
League: Gloucester 2
League position (1988–89): 3rd
League playing record (1988–89): P 10, W 7, D 1, L 2, F 145, A 92
Competitions won: Gloucester III Champions, 1988

OLD COLSTONIANS

New Road, Stoke Gifford, Bristol BS12 6QW. Tel: 0272 690009
Founded: 1902
President: Michael Humphries
Chairman: David Muir
Secretary: 1 Samian Way, Stoke Gifford, Bristol BS12 6UQ. Tel: 0272 791688 (H), 223324 (W)
Fixtures Secretary: Ian Parks, 4 Woodmans Vale, Chipping Sodbury, Bristol BS17 6DL. Tel: 0454 311080 (H), 0272 717436 (W)
Press Officer: John Griffiths
Coach: Steve Lewis
Club captain (1988–89): Simon Pomphrey
Club captain (1989–90): Martin Cutts
No. of teams: Senior 4, Youth 2
Directions to ground: From M5 follow signs to Parkway Station. Gound is mile past station on right-hand side beyond roundabout
Clubhouse facilities: Bar, changing rooms
Club colours: Blue, black and old gold hoops
Floodlights: No
Membership fees: Full £15, Playing £2, Social £5
Local newspapers: Bristol Evening Post, Western Daily Press
League: Gloucester 2
League position (1988–89): 11th (relegated)
League playing record (1988–89): P 10, W 0, D 0, L 10

OLD CRYPTIANS

Memorial Ground, Tuffley Avenue, Gloucester. Tel: 0452 20052

Founded: 1925
President: D.S.R. Perks
Chairman: R. Hannaford
Secretary: K.N. Bendall, 53 Southfield Road, Gloucester GL4 9UG. Tel: 0452 501481
Fixtures Secretary: D.L. Howell, 255C Stroud Road, Gloucester. Tel: 0452 414010 (H), 425611 (W)
Press Officer: As Secretary
Coach: E. Stephens
Club captain (1988–89): H. Sutton
Club captain (1989–90): H. Sutton
No. of teams: Senior 4, Youth 1
Directions to ground: Off Bristol Road to Tuffley Avenue. Ground 1 mile on right (before Stroud Road)
Ground capacity: Standing 500
Clubhouse facilities: Lounge, public bar, 2 changing rooms, showers, mens and ladies toilets
Club colours: Maroon, yellow and black. (*Change colours:* Green and white)
Nickname: Old C's
Floodlights: Yes
Local newspaper: Citizen
League: Gloucester 2
League position (1988–89): 7th
League playing record (1988–89): P 10, W 3, D 0, L 8

THORNBURY

Coopers Farm, Newton, Rockhampton Road, Thornbury, Bristol. Tel: 0454 2096
Founded: 1963
President: Cliff Barrington
Chairman: John Arrowsmith
Secretary: Gordon Dykes, 42 Maple Avenue, Thornbury, Bristol. Tel: 0454 5451
Fixtures Secretary: Maurice Carling, 57 Ashgrove, Thornbury, Bristol BS12 1BH. Tel: 0454 415083 (H), 0453 810451 ext. 2100 (W)
Club captain (1988–89): Ken Rivers
Club captain (1989–90): Ken Rivers
No. of teams: Senior 5, Youth 3, Minis 4
Directions to ground: 1 mile north of Thornbury on Rockhampton Road
Clubhouse facilities: 2 bars, function room
Club colours: Amber and black hoops. (*Change colours:* Blue or red)
Nickname: Thorns
Floodlights: No
Membership fees: Full £20, Playing £20, Social £5, Youth £10, Student £10, Mini £6
Local newspapers: Gazette & Evening Post
League: Gloucester 3
League position (1988–89): 2nd (promoted)
League playing record (1988–89): P 11, W 10, D 0, L 1, F 296, A 66

BRISTOL TELEPHONE AREA

Founded: 1961
President: Sid Clarke
Chairman: Dave C. Rees
Secretary: Shaun W. Partridge, 9 Gages Road, Kingswood, Bristol BS15 2UQ. Tel: 0272 605757 (H), 296368 (W)
Fixtures Secretary: Steve Cowell, 13 Graitney Close, Cleeve, Bristol BS19 4NJ. Tel: 0934 832440
Press Officer: As Secretary
Coach: Steve O'Reilly
Club captain (1988–89): Steve O'Reilly
Club captain (1989–90): Steve O'Reilly
No. of teams: Senior 3
Directions to ground: Follow A37 (Wells Road) for approx. 4 miles from city centre. Turn left at Black Lion Pub in Whitchurch Village. Ground is approx.

mile on right
Clubhouse facilities: One bar, home and away
changing rooms, showers and bath, hot food. Bar
open Wednesday nights after training and match days
Club colours: Red, white and blue hoops. (*Change
colours:* Maroon)
Nickname: Phones or Teles
Floodlights: Yes (training only)
Membership fees: Full £10, Playing £10, Social £5,
Youth Free, Student Free, OAP Free
Local newspaper: Bristol Evening Post
League: Gloucester 3
League position (1988–89): 1st (promoted)
League playing record (1988–89): P 11, W 10, D 0,
L 1
Competitions won: Gloucestershire Division IV
Champions

CAINSCROSS

Victory Park, Cainscross, Stroud, Gloucestershire.
Tel: 04536 6707.
Founded: 1894
Secretary: S. Mynett, 118 Orchard Road. Ebley,
Stroud, Gloucestershire GL5 4UA. Tel: 045382 2566
(H).
League: Gloucestershire 2

CHELTENHAM CIVIL SERVICE

Civil Service Sports Ground, Tewkesbury Road,
Cheltenham, Glos. Tel: 0242 680424
Founded: 1947
President: Bill Collins
Chairman: David Townsend
Secretary: Brian Didlick, 66A Clarence Street,
Cheltenham, Glos GL50 3LE. Tel: 0242 221491 ext.
2479 (W)
Fixtures Secretary: Geoff Hardy, 3 Cudnall Street,
Charlton Kings, Cheltenham, Glos. Tel: 0242 523958
(H), 680424 (W)
Press Officer: David Townsend, 65 Read Way,
Bishops Cleeve, Cheltenham, Glos. Tel: 0242 676381
(H), 221491 ext. 3186 (W)
Coach: Paul Beard
Club captain (1988–89): Neil Evans
Club captain (1989–90): Mark Sheridan
No. of teams: Senior 3–4, Youth 1
Directions to ground: About 2 miles from centre of
Cheltenham on main Cheltenham to Tewkesbury
Road (A4019)
Clubhouse facilities: Shared clubhouse at Civil Service
Sports Ground
Club colours: Navy blue. (*Change colours:* Red)
Nickname: Service
Floodlights: No
Membership fees: Full £5, Playing £5, Social £5
Local newspaper: Gloucester Echo
League: Gloucester 3
League position (1988–89): 11th
League playing record (1988–89): P 32, W 11, D 2,
L 19, F 420, A 475

CHIPPING SODBURY

'The Ridings', Wickwar Road, Chipping Sodbury,
Bristol, Avon. Tel: 0454 312852
Founded: 1952
President: Harry Price
Chairman: Mike Groom
Secretary: Alan Richards, 12 Tyning Close, Yate,
Bristol, Avon. Tel: 0454 311185 (H), 0272 508919 (W)
Fixtures Secretary: Clive Fry, 50 Stanshawes
Crescent, Yate, Bristol. Tel: 0454 321848
Press Officer: As Secretary
Club captain (1988–89): Colin Edgar
Club captain (1989–90): Colin Edgar
No. of teams: Senior 4, Youth 1

Directions to ground: Take road from Chipping
Sudbury High Street to Wickwar
Clubhouse facilities: Bar, darts, pool
Club colours: Black. (*Change colours:* Green)
Floodlights: Yes
League: Gloucester 3
League position (1988–89): 3rd
League playing record (1988–89): P 35, W 19, D 1,
L 15

DURSLEY

Stinchcombe Stragglers, Dursley. Tel: 0453 3693
Founded: 1953
President: Jack Heaven
Chairman: Geoff Reynolds
Secretary: John Darlaston, Winrush, Field Lane,
Dursley, Glos GL11 6JF. Tel: 0453 3135 (H), 810451
(W)
Fixtures Secretary: David Weeks, The Cottages,
Elmcote Lane, Cambridge, Dursley, Glos. Tel: 0453
89850 (H), 316000 (W)
Press Officer: As Fixtures Secretary
Coach: Stuart Freeman
Club captain (1988–89): Kevin Tudor
Club captain (1989–90): Kevin Tudor
No. of teams: Senior 3
Directions to ground: From Dursley direction Wotton-
u-Edge to Stinchcombe
Clubhouse facilities: Tuesdays and Thursday evening,
match days
Club colours: Maroon and amber. (*Change colours:* 1
Amber, 2 Navy blue)
Floodlights: Yes (training only)
Membership fees: Full £15, Playing £15, Social £5,
Student £7.50
Local newspapers: Dursley Gazette
League: Gloucester 3
League position (1988–89): 3rd
League playing record (1988–89): P 10, W 6, D 1,
L 3, F 128, A 92

HUCCLECOTE OLD BOYS

Pineholt Club, Hucclecote Road, Hucclecote,
Gloucester
Founded: 1970
President: H.K. Richards
Chairman: Michael Zeal
Secretary: John E. Ring, 9 Conway Road,
Hucclecote, Gloucester GL3 3PD. Tel: 0452 618920
Fixtures Secretary: Colin W. Bevan, 2 Watermead
Cottages, Green Street, Brockworth, Glos GL3 4RR.
Tel: 0452 863689
Press Officer: Clark Kent, 9 Conway Road,
Hucclecote, Gloucester GL3 3PD. Tel: 0452 618920
Coach: Anthony A. Wainwright
Club captain (1988–89): Tony Parsloe
Club captain (1989–90): Steve Parsloe
No. of teams: Senior 3, Minis 1
Directions to ground: At the Crosshands roundabout
Brockworth on the A46 head west towards
Gloucester. Next roundabout take road to
Hucclecote. Travel 250 yds, Pineholt Club on left
Ground capacity: Seating 12, standing 2000
Clubhouse facilities: Excellent cuisine
Club colours: Amber shirts, black shorts and socks.
(*Change colours:* Bottle green shirts)
Nickname: 'Cote'
Floodlights: Yes (training only)
Membership fees: Full £5, Playing £5, Social £5,
Youth Free, Student Free, OAP £5
Ground admission: Free
Local newspapers: The Citizen, Western Daily Press
League: Gloucester 3
League position (1988–89): =1st (promoted)
League playing record (1988–89): P 11, W 10, D 0,
L 1, F 270, A 70

KINGSWOOD

Church Avenue Playing Field, London Road, Warmley, Nr. Bristol. Tel: 0272 675001
Founded: 1954
President: Harry Watkins Snr.
Chairman: Dave Paget
Secretary: Roger Clease, 166 Mounthill Road, Kingswood, Bristol BS15 2SX. Tel: 0272 615948
Fixtures Secretary: Graham Jury, 21 North Field Road, Hanham, Nr. Bristol. Tel: 0272 679459
Press Officer: Rob Wey, 35 Kelston Grove, Kingswood, Bristol BS15. Tel: 0272 676326
Coach: Chris Cooper
Club captain (1988–89): Mark Phillips
Club captain (1989–90): Mark Phillips
No. of teams: Senior 3
Directions to ground: Off A420 midway between Midland Spinner P.H. and Griffin Inn
Clubhouse facilities: Open every Saturday through season, Tues. and Thurs. evening all year
Club colours: Sky blue/chocolate brown
Nickname: 'Kings'
Floodlights: No
Membership fees: Full £20, Non-Playing £10, Social £7.50, Full-time Students & Unwaged 50% of above
Ground admission: Nil
Local newspapers: South Gloucestershire Gazette, Bristol Observer, Bristol Independent, Kingswood Gazette
League: Gloucester 3
League position (1988–89): 3rd
League playing record (1988–89): P 302 W 10, D 1, L 21

OLD ELIZABETHANS

Severn Road, Hallen, Bristol. Tel: 0272 591072
Founded: 1932
President: David Perkins
Chairman: Charlie H. Howard
Secretary: David Langdon, 13 Gloucester Street, Wootton-under-Edge, Glos GL12 7DN. Tel: 0453 845349 (H), 0272 668431 (W)
Fixtures Secretary: Charlie H. Howard, 10 Priory Road, Portbury, Nr. Bristol BS20 9TH. Tel: 0275 813551 (H), 0272 290777 ext. 6469 (W)
Press Officer: Nick Duffin, 4 Birdale Crescent, Henbury, Birstol BS10 7NU. Tel: 0272 507157 (H), 290599 (W)
Club captain (1988–89): David Langdon
Club captain (1989–90): Peter Lindsay
No. of teams: Senior 3
Directions to ground: Take A5 to Junction 17, take A4018 to Bristol. At roundabout take 3rd exit at T-junction, go right then first right again. Turn left at mini roundabout, follow road for 1 mile. Ground is on the left 400 yds after crossroads with King William IV pub on right
Clubhouse facilities: Bar, 2 changing rooms, showers, Car park
Club colours: Old gold, white and blue hoops, navy blue shorts, sock as shirts. (*Change colours:* Black shirts)
Nickname: Old E's
Floodlights: No
Membership fees: Full £15, Playing £15, Social £2, Student £15, OAP £2
Programme: No. of editorial pages 10; No. of advertising pages 16; Price Free on membership (Handbook)
Programme editor: As Fixtures Secretary
Local newspapers: Bristol Evening Post, Western Daily Press
League: Gloucester 3
League position (1988–89): 7th
League playing record (1988–89): P 10, W 4, D 0, L 6, F 100, A 180
Competitions won: Chipping Sudbury Sevens Winners, April 1989. Bristol Combination Sevens Runners-Up, April 1989

PAINSWICK

Broadham Fields, Stroud Road, Painswick.
Headquarters: The Recreation field, Painswick, Glos.
Tel: Painswick 813861
Founded: 1872
President: Dr. Jim Hoyland
Chairman: Laurie Steele
Secretary: Adrian Bressington, c/o Martin Hayward, 12 White Horse Lane, Painswick, Stroud, Glos. Tel: Pains. 812592 (H), Stroud 2387 (W)
Fixtures Secretary: Martin Hayard, 12 White Horse Lane, Painswick, Stroud, Glos GL6 6XT. Tel: Pains. 812582 (H), Stroud 2387 (W)
Press Officer: Ian Hogg, 8 Upper Washwell, Painswick, Stroud, Glos. Tel: Pains. 812505
Coach: Ian Dunbar
Club captain (1988–89): Steve Townsend
Club captain (1989–90): Steve Townsend
No. of teams: Senior 3
Clubhouse facilities: Showers, changing quarters and bar. Open match days, Sundays, Tuesdays and Fridays
Club colours: Cherry and white
Nickname: 'Wicks'
Floodlights: No
Local newspapers: Stroud News & Journal, The Citizen
League: Gloucester 3
League position (1988–89): 6th
League playing record (1988–89): P 10, W 3, D 2, L 5

SMITHS (INDUSTRIES)

The Newlands, Eveshaw Road, Bishops Cleeve, Cheltenham, Glos
Founded: 1952
President: J.H. Sykes
Chairman: Robert W. Ellis
Secretary: Gerald D. Owen, Jasmine Cottage, 79 Station Road, Bishops Cleeve, Cheltenham, Glos. Tel: 0242 676345 (H), 0242 673333 ext. 2454 (W)
Fixtures Secretary: Roger Brennan, 'Driftwood', Shutter Lane, Gotherington, Cheltenham, Glos. Tel: 0242 673902 (H), 221311 (W)
Press Officer: Gerald Owen, 79 Station Road, Bishops Cleeve, Cheltenham. Tel: 0242 676345 (H), 673333 ext. 2454 (W)
Club captain (1988–89): Peter Crossland
Club captain (1989–90): Henry Peters
No. of teams: Senior 3
Directions to ground: 2 miles north of Cheltenham on A435
Clubhouse facilities: Smiths Industries Sports & Social Club
Club colours: White with blue hoop, black shorts. (*Change colours:* Blue with white hoop)
Floodlights: No
League: Gloucester 3
League position (1988–89): 9th
League playing record (1988–89): P 38, W 15, D 1, L 22, F 236, A 310

TEWKESBURY

64A High Street, Tewkebury, Gloucestershire. Tel: 0684 294364
Founded: 1955
President: John Hall
Chairman: Reg Bull
Secretary: Michael Slatter, Cleeve Cottage, Bushley, Tewkesbury, Glos GL20 6HP. Tel: 0684 293200 (H), 296182 (W)
Fixtures Secretary: Brian Woodard, 41 Gravel Walk, Tewkesbury, Glos
Press Officer: Brian Williams, Cornerways Nursery, Twyning, Nr. Tewkesbury, Glos. Tel: 0684 293561 (H), 293561 (W)
Coach: A. Davies
Club captain (1988–89): T. Rhoden
Club captain (1989–90): S. McHardy

No. of teams: Senior 3
Directions to ground: Left off A38 going toward Gloucester
Ground capacity: Standing 1000
Clubhouse facilities: Bar, changing rooms
Club colours: Black and amber. (*Change colours:* Yellow)
Floodlights: No
Membership fees: Full £12, Playing £12, Social £2, Youth £6, Student £6, OAP £2
Local newspapers: Gloucestershire Echo and Tewkesbury Ad. Mag.
League: Gloucester 3
League position (1988–89): 7th
League playing record (1988–89): P 10, W 6, D 0, L 4, F 198, A 236

GLOUCESTERSHIRE 4A

CHOSEN HILL FORMER PUPILS

Brookfield Road, Churchdown, Glos. Tel: 0452 712384
Founded: 1971
President: A. Winwood
Chairman: Arthur Nield
Secretary: Mick Reid, 212 Cheltenham Road East, Churchdown, Glos GL3 1AL. Tel: 0452 856312
Fixtures Secretary: Ian Yeates, 20 Westover Court, Churchdown, Glos. Tel: 0452 713502
Press Officer: As Secretary
Coach: Rog Windo
Club captain (1988–89): Duncan MacRae
Club captain (1989–90): Duncan MacRae
No. of teams: Senior 3, Colts 1
Directions to ground: Midway between Gloucester and Cheltenham. Head for Churchdown village, clubhouse adjacent to M5 motorway bridge
Clubhouse facilities: Dressing rooms, bar, 2 pitches adjacent to club
Club colours: Myrtle green and white. (*Change colours:* White)
Floodlights: Yes (training lights)
Membership fees: Full £10, Playing £10, Social £5, Youth £5, Student £5
Local newspapers: Gloucester Citizen and Cheltenham Echo
League position (1988–89): 11th
League playing record (1988–89): P 10, W 2, D 0, L 8, F 79, A 126

DOWTY

Dowty Sports Ground, Staverton, Near Gloucester. Tel: 0452 714567
Secretary: D.F. Harwood, South Cottage, Twyning, Tewkesbury, Glos. Tel: 0242 533231 (W)
Club colours: Blue/white
League: Gloucestershire 4A

GLOUCESTER ALL BLUES

The Oxleaze, Westgate, Gloucester. Tel: 0452 306984
President: Eddy Cumming
Chairman: Mike Dangerfield
Secretary: Graham Redding, 28 Knowles Road, Tredworth, Gloucester GL1 4TW. Tel: 0452 410307 (H), 22225 (W)
Fixtures Secretary: Mike Heath, 35 Didmore Close, Hardwick, Gloucester. Tel: 0452 728159
Press Officer: G. Redding, 28 Knowles Road, Gloucester. Tel: 410307 (H), 22225 (W)
Club captain (1988–89): Rob Miltaggart
Club captain (1989–90): Rob Miltaggart
No. of teams: Senior 3
Directions to ground: Out of Gloucester on S. Wales

road, over Westgate River bridge then first left directly over bridge
Clubhouse facilities: 4 changing/shower/bath, bar
Club colours: Blue. (*Change colours:* Light blue, dark blue hoops)
Floodlights: No
League: Gloucester 4
League position (1988–89): 6th

GLOUCESTER CIVIL SERVICE

Estcourt Road, Gloucester. Tel: 0452 28317
Secretary: A.J. Apperley, 327B, Stroud Road, Gloucester, Glos. Tel: 0452 28733 (H). 418588 Ext 2053 (W)
Club colours: Amber/black
League: Gloucestershire 4A

MINCHINHAMPTON

Chalford Sports & Social Club, Highfield, Chalford Hill, Nr. Stroud, Glos. Tel: 0453 882714
Founded: 1982
President: Denis Mason
Chairman: Roger Entwhistle
Secretary: Robert Edmonds, Woodlands Cottage, 205 Slad Road, Stroud, Glos. Tel: 0453 766662 (H), 0452 308989 (W)
Fixtures Secretary: George Cansino, 17 Tetbury Street, Minchinhampton, Nr. Stroud, Glos. Tel: 0453 885006
Club captain (1988–89): Pat Milston
Club captain (1989–90): Clive Sluter
No. of teams: Senior 2, Minis 3
Directions to ground: Approx. 4 miles from Stroud on A419, turn left at Chalford Church, up hill mile, right at crossroads, bear left at next crossroads, across junction, mile, left at next junction
Clubhouse facilities: Bar. Open matchdays
Club colours: Green/white hoops
Nickname: 2nd XV 'The Rams'
Floodlights: Yes (training only)
Membership fees: Full £10, Playing £1
Local newspaper: Stroud News & Journal
League: Glos 4A
League position (1988–89): 5th
League playing record (1988–89): P 10, W 5, D 1, L 4

NEWENT

Recreation Ground, Watery Lane, Newent, Glos
Founded: 1970
President: M. Poole
Chairman: R. Everest
Secretary: P. Dawe, Sunny Lodge, Culver Street, Newent, Glos. Tel: 0531 822161 (H), 021–377 7000 (W)
Fixtures Secretary: D. Nottingham, Belmont Annex, Glebe Road, Newent. Tel: 0531 821798
Club captain (1988–89): S. Turner
Club captain (1989–90): N. Montague
No. of teams: Senior 3, Youth 1
Directions to ground: A40 through Gloucester, follow signs to Newent (Ross Road)
Clubhouse facilities: Capacity 100. Bar, darts and pool table
Club colours: Green and gold. (*Change colours:* Gold and green)
Floodlights: No
Membership fees: Full £15, Playing £10, Social £3.50, Student £3.50
Local newspapers: Citizen
League: Gloucester 4
League position (1988–89): 4th
League playing record (1988–89): P 10, W 5, D 0, L 5, F 153, A 158

OLD RICHIANS

Sandyleaze, Longlevens, Gloucester. Tel: 0452 24649
President: Keith D. Ray
Chairman: Gerald Stone
Secretary: Clive Bishop, Flat 2, 20 Alexandra Road, Gloucester GL1 3DR
Fixtures Secretary: David A. Carter, 55 Paygrove Lane, Longlevens, Gloucester GL2 0BA. Tel: 0452 500424
Press Officer: As Fixtures Secretary
Coach: Robert Gough
Club captain (1988–89): Paul Wood
Club captain (1989–90): James Byrne
No. of teams: Senior 4, Youth 5, Minis 5
Directions to ground: 3 miles off Junction 11 M5 to roundabout, straight over 200 yds traffic lights, turn left into Nine Elms Road, 4th turning left into Oaklease, 1st left into Sandyleaze, 300 yds to clubhouse
Clubhouse facilities: 2 spacious changing rooms, showers, large players bar and large lounge bar
Club colours: Royal blue and gold hoops. (*Change colours:* Blue)
Nickname: 'Rich's'
Floodlights: No
Membership fees: Full £13, Playing £10, Social £3 family, Youth £3, Student £2, OAP £1
Local newspaper: Gloucester Citizen
League: Gloucester 4
Competitions won: Drybrook Sevens Winners, Sept '88

ARETIANS

The Clubhouse, Station Road, Little Stoke, Bristol. Tel: 0454 621004
Founded: 1961
President: Martin Dart
Chairman: Colin Luton
Secretary: Paul Pritchard, 25 Kewstoke Road, Stoke Bishop, Bristol. Tel: 0272 683595 (H), 027581 3497 (W)
Fixtures Secretary: David Bawles, Thyme Cottage, Webbs Heath, Warmley, Bristol. Tel: 0272 675641
Press Officer: As Secretary
Coach: Chris Williams
Club captain (1988–89): Kim Hazeldine
Club captain (1989–90): Kim Hazeldine
No. of teams: Senior 4, Youth 3, Minis 2
Directions to ground: At BAC/Rolls-Royce flyover on A38 at Filton take Yate/Winterbourne Road, first left after railway bridge
Clubhouse facilities: 2 bars, dining facilities, 4 changing rooms, multigym
Club colours: Black. (*Change colours:* Blue and white hoops)
Floodlights: No
Membership fees: Full £20, Playing £20, Social £5, Youth £3, Student £3
Local newspaper: Bristol Evening Post
League: Gloucester 4
League position (1988–89): 4th
League playing record (1988–89): P 11, W 7, D 0, L 4, F 166, A 84

BISHOPSTON

Bonnington Walk, Lockleaze, Bristol. Tel: 0272 691916
Founded: 1894
President: T.R. Dowell
Chairman: R. Burge
Secretary: D.G.J. Hockley, 21 Pinewood Close, Westbury-on-Trym, Bristol. Tel: 0272 623509 (H), 291031 (W)
Fixtures Secretary: J.P. Hucker, 10 Teresa Avenue, Bishopston, Bristol. Tel: 0272 246442

Club captain (1988–89): S. Oakley
Club captain (1989–90): S. Oakley
No. of teams: Senior 4, Youth 1, Minis 1
Directions to ground: M4/M5 interchahnge into A38 Gloucester Road, left into Toronto Road at lights, straight across Filton Avenue, left past railway bridge
Clubhouse facilities: Licensed clubhouse
Club colours: Red with black hoops. (*Change colours:* Black and white hoops)
Nickname: Bish
Floodlights: No
Newspaper: Bristol Evening Post
League: Gloucester 4B
League position (1988–89): 3rd
League playing record (1988–89): P 11, W 7, D 1, L 3

BAC

Sports Pavilion, Southmead Road, Bristol. Tel: 0272 692507
Founded: 1921
President: G.J. Pearce
Chairman: I.M. Gibson
Secretary: C. Evans, 3 Third Avenue, Northville, Bristol BS7 0RS. Tel: 0272 696766 (H), 366047 (W)
Fixtures Secretary: K. Robinson, Holybank, Stockwood Vale, Keynsham, Bristol. Tel: 0272 863586
Press Officer: Martin Lawlor, 22 Ashwell Close, The Coots, Stockwood, Bristol
Coach: Peter Dawber
Club captain (1988–89): Andrew Plummer
Club captain (1989–90): David Lawrence
No. of teams: Senior 4
Directions to ground: From M4/M5 motorway junction take A38 south for about 2 miles then at roundabout close to British Aerospace Works take right fork and find ground on right about 1 mile
Club colours: Red, white and blue hoops. (*Change colours:* Red)
Nickname: Aero
Floodlights: No
Membership fees: Full £1, Playing £1
Local newspaper: Filton & Patchway Gazette
League: Gloucester 4
League playing record (1988–89): P 10, W 5, D 0, L 5, F 153, A 124

BROAD PLAIN

Bonnington Walk, Lockleaze, Bristol. Clubhouse: Clement St. Easton, Bristol BS2 9EQ. Tel: 552782
Founded: 1909
President: Jack Shean
Chairman: Roy Palfrey
Secretary: Ivan Gregory, 7 Luxton Street, Easton, Bristol BS5 0HT. Tel: 540706 (H), 552782 (W)
Fixtures Secretary: John Daveridge, 115 Ravenhill Road, Knowle, Bristol. Tel:771823
Coach: John White
Club captain (1988–89): John White
Club captain (1989–90): Robert Slocombe
No. of teams: Senior 3, Youth 1
Directions to ground: Bonnington Walk, Lockleaze off Filton Avenue, Bristol
Clubhouse facilities: 2 bars, 2 skittle alleys, outside hard court
Club colours: Blue/maroon/gold. (*Change colours:* Gold)
Nickname: Plainers
Floodlights: Yes (portable)
Membership fees: Full £5, Playing £5, Social £5, Youth £3.75, Student £3.75, OAP £2
Local newspapers: Bristol Evening Post, Western Daily Press
League: Gloucester 4
League position (1988–89): 7th
League playing record (1988–89): P 10, W 5, D 0, L 5, F 126, A 154

OLD COTHAMIANS

The New Pavilion, Northway, Filton, Bristol. Tel:
0272 790260
Founded: 1924
President: D. Pratton
Chairman: J. Pinches
Secretary: J.P. Clevely, 7 Latton Road, Horfield,
Bristol BS7 0UX. Tel: 692978 (H), 363020 (W)
Fixtures Secretary: J. Pinches, 135 Sefton Park Road,
Bristol 7
Press Officer: As Secretary
Coach: J. Tyler
Club captain (1988–89): K. Hanham
Club captain (1989–90): P. Russel
No. of teams: Senior 1
Nickname: Old Cot's
Membership fees: Full £10, Playing £10, Social £10,
Youth £5, Student £5, OAP Free
Local newspapers: Evening Post, Bristol Journal,
Bristol Observer, Western Daily Press
League position (1988–89): =Bottom
League playing record (1988–89): P 29, W 2, D 2,
L 25, F 198, A 298

SOUTHMEAD

The Greenway Centre, Doncaster Road, Southmead,
Bristol, BS10 5PY. Tel: (0272) 503335
President: Geoffrey Williams
Chairman: Barry Jakes
Secretary: David Thomas Jones. 12 Westover
Gardens, Westbury on Trym, Bristol, BS9 3LE,
Avon. Tel: (0272) 502988 (H), Bath 832936 Ext 44
(W)
Fixtures Secretary: Michael Haddow. 20 Braydon
Avenue, Littlemore, Bristol, Avon. Tel: 614019
Press Officer: David Thomas Jones. As above
Coach: Michael Davies
Club Captain (1988–89): Colin Attwell
Club Captain (1989–90): Colin Attwell
No. of teams: Senior 3

Club facilities: New club in progress
Club Colours: Dark Blue/Emerald/
Membership fees: Full £10, Playing £10
Ground admission: Nil
League: Gloucestershire 4B

TETBURY

Recreation Ground, Tetbury, Glos
Chairman: David Hugh Hobbs
Secretary: Sue Dyer, 34 Bartley Croft, Tetbury, Glos
GL8 8ER. Tel: 0666 503077 (H), 0666 503467 (W)
Fixtures Secretary: David Hugh Hobbs, 34 Bartley
Croft, Tetbury, Glos GL8 8ER. Tel: 0666 503077 (H),
503467 (W)
Press Officer: Barry Dean, Conygar Road, Tetbury,
Glos. Tel: 0666 503057 (H), 822001 (W)
Coach: Chris Short
Club captain (1988–89): Chris Robins
Club captain (1989–90): David Barnes
No. of teams: Senior 2
Directions to ground: Enter Tetbury from any
direction and then ask for the Recreation Ground
Ground capacity: Standing 1000
Clubhouse facilities: Showers and changing near pitch.
Use of local pub after match
Club colours: Black with single amber hoop across
shirt. (*Change colours:* Black yellow and red hoops)
Nickname: Dolphins
Floodlights: No
Membership fees: Full £10, Playing £10, Social £5,
Youth £5, Student £5, OAP £5
Ground admission: Nil
Local newspaper: Wilts & Gloucester Standard,
Cirencester
League: South West/Gloucestershire 4B
League playing record (1988–89): P 34, W 18, D 2,
L 14, F 652, A 392

SOMERSET LEAGUES

FOR the latest season the Somerset Leagues consisted of 32 clubs – two more than last time – with a top league of 10 and two others of 11 each. Frome, runners-up in 1987–88, this time had one draw as their only blemish and they go up to the Western League, but Oldfield Old Boys finished only a point behind and gave them a run for their money. Only one team go down from this section, the unlucky ones being St. Brendans Old Boys, who descend for a second successive season and were unable to add to the solitary Gloucestershire/Somerset win of 1987–88. Also down are Burnham and their replacements are Avondale and Yeovil, who were separated by only one point with the former (promoted for a second successive season) in top place.

At the foot of League 2 Wellington (for a second season running) and Westland (promoted only last time) go down, the former having won only once in two seasons and the latter with a blank sheet on this occasion. Wiveliscombe won 11 games in the campaign and had an astonishing points differential (459–50) to win Division 3 from the other promoted side Tor, whose only defeat was at the hands of the champions. Wincanton's record in two seasons in the league shows not a single win – only a draw in 1987–88.

SOMERSET ONE:

Bill Bishop,
Hellwellyn, 1 Wiltshire Place,
Kingswood, Bristol   (H) 0272 575729
Avon BS15 4XA   (O) 0272 352017

SOMERSET LEAGUES TWO & THREE:

Clive Macdonald,
8 Sycamore Drive,
Crewkerne,   (H) 0460 76136
Somerset TA18 7BT   (B) 0460 75685

TABLES 1987–88

SOMERSET 1

	P	W	D	L	F	A	PTS
O Culverhays	11	10	0	1	205	77	20
Frome	11	8	2	1	200	47	18
Oldfield OB	11	8	0	3	235	101	16
Walcott OB	11	8	0	3	223	126	16
O Sulians	11	6	2	3	151	94	14
N Petherton	11	4	2	5	121	94	10
Yatton	11	4	1	6	149	158	9
Burnham	11	4	1	6	78	140	9
Hornets	11	4	0	7	136	149	8
Yeovil	11	4	0	7	108	144	8
Crewkerne	11	2	0	9	58	218	4
Wellington	11	0	0	11	39	355	0

SOMERSET 2

	P	W	D	L	F	A	PTS
St. Bernadet	10	9	0	1	160	72	18
Bristol Harl	10	7	2	1	209	62	16
Avon	10	6	1	3	120	102	13
Blagdon	10	5	0	5	140	156	10
Wells	10	4	1	5	132	112	9
Winscombe	10	4	1	5	85	89	9
Imperial	10	4	1	5	84	121	9
Stothert & P	10	4	0	6	70	81	8
Bath OE	10	4	0	6	126	148	8
Chard	10	4	0	6	99	150	8
Cheddar Val	10	1	0	9	67	199	2

SOMERSET 3

	P	W	D	L	F	A	PTS
Avondale	9	8	1	0	221	45	17
Westland	9	7	2	0	135	58	16
Backwell	9	5	0	4	213	92	10
Tor	9	5	0	4	152	100	10
O Ashtonians	9	5	0	4	144	118	10
Morganians	9	5	0	4	113	89	10
Chew Valley	9	3	2	4	163	99	8
Bath CS	9	3	0	6	103	166	6
Castle Cary	9	2	2	7	62	142	2
Wincanton	9	0	1	8	43	440	1

TABLES 1988-89

SOMERSET 1

	P	W	D	L	F	A	PTS
Frome	10	9	1	0	226	69	19
Oldfield OB	10	9	0	1	299	93	18
St. Bernadettes	10	6	1	3	178	140	13
O Sulians	10	5	1	4	172	78	11
Hornets	10	5	0	5	153	134	10
Bristol Harls	10	4	2	4	124	144	10
Yatton	10	4	1	5	113	148	9
Walcot OB	10	4	0	6	122	116	8
N Petherton	10	4	0	6	128	161	8
Burnham	10	2	0	8	94	202	4
St. Brendans OB	10	0	0	10	61	425	0

SOMERSET 2

	P	W	D	L	F	A	PTS
Avondale	11	10	0	1	181	107	20
Yeovil	11	9	1	1	170	110	19
Avon	11	7	1	3	185	142	15
Imperial	11	6	2	3	149	102	14
Bath OEs	11	6	0	5	151	117	12
Stothert & P	11	5	1	5	179	138	11
Crewkerne	11	5	1	5	115	132	11
Wells	11	5	0	6	144	120	10
Winscombe	11	5	0	6	130	148	10
Blagdon	11	4	0	7	127	157	8
Wellington	11	1	0	10	90	170	2
Westland	11	0	0	11	76	254	0

SOMERSET 3

	P	W	D	L	F	A	PTS
Wiveliscombe	11	11	0	0	459	50	22
Tor	11	10	0	1	236	57	20
Backwell	11	9	0	2	243	100	18
Chard	11	8	0	3	272	90	16
O Ashtonians	11	7	0	4	207	107	14
Bath Civ Ser	11	5	1	5	194	116	11
Cheddar	11	4	1	6	108	194	9
Aller	11	3	0	8	120	254	6
Castle Cary	11	3	0	8	88	175	6
Morganians	11	3	0	8	81	197	6
Chew Valley	11	2	0	9	90	335	4
Wincanton	11	0	0	11	47	470	0

SOUTH WEST DIVISION FIXTURES 1989/90

SOMERSET ONE

Sat. 9th September (Week 2)
Avondale v Bristol Harlequins
Old Sulians v Oldfield
Walcot v Minehead
Yeovil v Hornets
Yatton v Gordano

Sat. 23rd September (Week 4)
Gordano v Avondale
Hornets v Yatton
Minehead v Yeovil
Oldfield v Walcot
St. Bernadette's v Old Sulians

Sat. 14th October (Week 6)
Avondale v Hornets
Bristol Harlequins v Gordano
Walcot v St. Bernadette's
Yeovil v Oldfield
Yatton v Minehead

Sat. 28th October (Week 8)
Hornets v Bristol Harlequins
Minehead v Avondale
Oldfield v Yatton
St. Bernadette's v Yeovil
Old Sulians v Walcot

Sat. 11th November (Week 10)
Avondale v Oldfield
Bristol Harlequins v Minehead
Gordano v Hornets
Yeovil v Old Sulians
Yatton v St. Bernadette's

Sat 18th November (Week 11)
Minehead v Gordano
Oldfield v Bristol Harlequins
St. Bernadette's v Avondale
Old Sulians v Yatton
Walcot v Yeovil

Sat. 25th November (Week 12)
Avondale v Old Sulians
Bristol Harlequins v St. Bernadette's
Gordano v Oldfield
Hornets v Minehead
Yatton v Walcot

Sat. 13th January (Week 18)
Oldfield v Hornets
St. Bernadette's v Gordano
Old Sulians v Bristol Harlequins
Walcot v Avondale
Yeovil v Yatton

Sat. 10th March (Week 26)
Avondale v Yeovil
Bristol Harlequins v Walcot
Gordano v Old Sulians
Hornets v St. Bernadette's
Minehead v Oldfield

Sat. 31st March (Week X7)
St. Bernadette's v Minehead
Old Sulians v Hornets
Walcot v Gordano
Yeovil v Bristol Harlequins
Yatton v Avondale

Sat. 28th April (Week 32)
Bristol Harlequins v Yatton
Gordano v Yeovil
Hornets v Walcot
Minehead v Old Sulians
Oldfield v St. Bernadette's

SOUTH WEST DIVISION FIXTURES 1989/90

SOMERSET TWO

Sat. 9th September (Week 2)
Avon v Bath O.E.
Tor v St. Brendans O.B.
Stothert & Pitt v Crewkerne
Wells v Burnham-on-Sea
Winscombe v North Petherton
Imperial v Wiveliscombe

Sat. 23rd September (Week 4)
North Petherton v Avon
Burnham-on-Sea v Winscombe
Crewkerne v Wells
St. Brendans O.B. v Stothert & Pitt
Imperial v Tor
Wiveliscombe v Bath O.E.

Sat. 14th October (Week 6)
Avon v Burnham-on-Sea
Bath O.E. v North Petherton
Stothert & Pitt v Imperial
Wells v St. Brendans O.B.
Winscombe v Crewkerne
Tor v Wiveliscombe

Sat. 28th October (Week 8)
Burnham-on-Sea v Bath O.E.
Crewkerne v Avon
St. Brendans O.B. v Winscombe
Imperial v Wells
Tor v Stothert & Pitt
Wiveliscombe v North Petherton

Sat. 11th November (Week 10)
Avon v St. Brendans O.B.
Bath O.E. v Crewkerne
North Petherton v Burnham-on-Sea
Wells v Tor
Winscombe v Imperial
Stothert & Pitt v Wiveliscombe

Sat 18th November (Week 11)
Crewkerne v North Petherton
St. Brendans O.B. v Bath O.E.
Imperial v Avon
Tor v Winscombe
Stothert & Pitt v Wells
Wiveliscombe v Burnham-on-Sea

Sat. 25th November (Week 12)
Avon v Tor
Bath O.E. v Imperial
North Petherton v St. Brendans O.B.
Burnham-on-Sea v Crewkerne
Winscombe v Stothert & Pitt
Wells v Wiveliscombe

Sat. 13th January (Week 18)
St. Brendans O.B. v Burnham-on-Sea
Imperial v North Petherton
Tor v Bath O.E.
Stothert & Pitt v Avon
Wells v Winscombe
Wiveliscombe v Crewkerne

Sat. 10th March (Week 26)
Avon v Wells
Bath O.E. v Stothert & Pitt
North Petherton v Tor
Burnham-on-Sea v Imperial
Crewkerne v St. Brendans O.B.
Winscombe v Wiveliscombe

Sat. 31st March (Week X7)
Imperial v Crewkerne
Tor v Burnham-on-Sea
Stothert & Pitt v North Petherton
Wells v Bath O.E.
Winscombe v Avon
Wiveliscombe v St. Brendans O.B.

Sat. 28th April (Week 32)
Bath O.E. v Winscombe
North Petherton v Wells
Burnham-on-Sea v Stothert & Pitt
Crewkerne v Tor
St. Brendans O.B. v Imperial
Avon v Wiveliscombe

SOUTH WEST DIVISION FIXTURES 1989/90

SOMERSET THREE A

Sat. 9th September (Week 2)
Backwell v Bath Civil Service

Sat. 23rd September (Week 4)
Blagdon v Backwell

Sat. 14th October (Week 6)
Backwell v Cheddar Valley
Bath Civil Service v Blagdon

Sat. 28th October (Week 8)
Cheddar Valley v Bath Civil Service
Chew Valley v Backwell

Sat. 11th November (Week 10)
Backwell v Old Ashtonians
Bath Civil Service v Chew Valley
Blagdon v Cheddar Valley

Sat 18th November (Week 11)
Chew Valley v Blagdon
Old Ashtonians v Bath Civil Service
South West Gas v Backwell

Sat. 25th November (Week 12)
Bath Civil Service v South West Gas
Blagdon v Old Ashtonians
Cheddar Valley v Chew Valley

Sat. 13th January (Week 18)
Old Ashtonians v Cheddar Valley
South West Gas v Blagdon

Sat. 10th March (Week 26)
Cheddar Valley v South West Gas
Chew Valley v Old Ashtonians

Sat. 31st March (Week X7)
South West Gas v Chew Valley

Sat. 28th April (Week 32)
Old Ashtonians v Southwest Gas

SOMERSET THREE B

Sat. 9th September (Week 2)
Aller v Castle Cary

Sat. 23rd September (Week 4)
Chard v Aller

Sat. 14th October (Week 6)
Aller v Morganians
Castle Cary v Chard

Sat. 28th October (Week 8)
Morganians v Castle Cary
Wellington v Aller

Sat. 11th November (Week 10)
Aller v Westland
Castle Cary v Wellington
Chard v Morganians

Sat 18th November (Week 11)
Wellington v Chard
Westland v Castle Cary
Wincanton v Aller

Sat. 25th November (Week 12)
Castle Cary v Wincanton
Chard v Westland
Morganians v Wellington

Sat. 13th January (Week 18)
Westland v Morganians
Wincanton v Chard

Sat. 10th March (Week 26)
Morganians v Wincanton
Wellington v Westland

Sat. 31st March (Week X7)
Wincanton v Wellington

Sat. 28th April (Week 32)
Westland v Wincanton

AVONDALE

Bathford Playing Fields, Bathford, Bath, Avon. Tel:
0225 858295
Founded: 1883
President: George Atchison
Secretary: Peter J. Kilmister, 33 West Park Road,
Corsham, Wiltshire. Tel: 0249 72906 (H), 0249 443322
(W)
Fixtures Secretary: Steven Vowles, 25 Mills Road,
Melksham, Wiltshire. Tel: 0225 333852 (H), 766451 (W)
Press Officer: As Secretary
Club captain (1988–89): Andrew Ball
Club captain (1989–90): Andrew Ball
No. of teams: Senior 3, Youth 1
Directions to ground: From Bath take the A4 London
Road to Bathford, fork right at the roundabout
towards Bradford on Avon, fork left at 'The Crown',
turn left opposite 'The Inn'
Clubhouse facilities: Clubroom, bar, changing rooms,
kitchen
Club colours: Navy blue and white. (*Change colours:*
Red)
Nickname: The 'Vale
Floodlights: Yes (training only)
Membership fees: Full £2, Playing £2, Social £2,
Youth £1, Student £1, OAP £1
Ground admission: By collection/donation
Local newspaper: Bath & West Evening Chronicle

BRISTOL HARLEQUINS

'Valhalla', Broomhill Road, Brislington, Bristol. Tel:
721650
Founded: 1926
President: Valentino Sidoli
Chairman: Stephen Croot
Secretary: Peter J. Broome, 1 Ketch Road, Lower
Knowle, Bristol 3. Tel: 713815 (H), 721261 (W)
Fixtures Secretary: Ted Morrison, 4 Lowbourne,
Whitchurch, Bristol. Tel: 832580
Press Officer: Richard Fisher, 20 Rookery Road,
Knowle, Bristol. Tel: 715543
Coach: Peter Sams
Club captain (1988–89): Sean Mason
Club captain (1989–90): Andrew Crocker
No. of teams: Senior 4, Youth 1, Minis 1
Directions to ground: From A4 (Bath) turn right into
Emery Road, then 1st right into Broomhill Road, 3rd
entrance on right
Clubhouse facilities: Yes
Club colours: Blue black and white. (*Change colours:*
White)
Nickname: Quins
Membership fees: Full £5, Playing £10, Social £5

GORDANO

Caswell Lane, Portbury, Bristol. Tel: 0272 8813486
Founded: 1970
Secretary: M.H. Pritchard, 32 Drakes Way,
Portishead, Bristol BS20 9XA. Tel: 0272 845893 (H).
266091 Ext 248 (W)
League: Somerset 1
League position (1988–89): 8th

HORNETS

Hutton Moor Lane, Weston-S-Mare. Tel: 0934 621433
Founded: 1962
President: F.L.P. Costeloe
Chairman: David Pollard
Secretary: Brian Collard, 8 Waywide, Worle, Weston-
S-Mare, Avon BS22 9BL. Tel: 0934 622570
Fixtures Secretary: Tim Garnor, Stoneyways, The
Batch, Churchill, Nr. Weston-S-Mare. Tel: 0934
852192
Press Officer: As Secretary

Coach: Paul Issacson
Club captain (1988–89): Nick Mager
Club captain (1989–90): Lester Gaulton
No. of teams: Senior 5, Youth 6, Minis 5
Directions to ground: Follow main road into Weston,
turn left at traffic lights, Mac's Garage, over bridge.
Ground on left at bottom
Clubhouse facilities: Full
Club colours: Black and amber. (*Change colours:*
Amber)
Floodlights: Yes (partial)
Membership fees: Full £20, Playing £20, Social £10,
Youth £10, Student £10, OAP £5
Local newspapers: Weston Mercury and Evening Post
Competitions won: Somerset Colts, 1988–89

MINEHEAD BARBARIANS

Tom Stewart field, Ellicombe, Minehead. Tel: 0643
5662
Founded: 1946
President: Malcolm Appleton
Chairman: David Bodley
Secretary: Malcolm Parslow, Ladbrook, The
Holloway, Minehead TA24 5TP. Tel: 0643 2101
Fixtures Secretary: Mike Turner, 4 Wristland Road,
Watchet TA4. Tel: 0984 31170
Club captain (1988–89): Tim Campbell
Club captain (1989–90): David Hurley
No. of teams: Senior 3, Youth 2, Minis 6
Directions to ground: Beside A39, mile before
Minehead from Williton turn off at roundabout signed
Ellicombe
Clubhouse facilities: Modern building, changing
rooms, showers, 2 bars, hall, function room
Club colours: Black and white hoops. (*Change
colours:* Red or blue)
Floodlights: No

OLDFIELD OLD BOYS

Shaft Road, Combe Down, Bath. Tel: 0255 834135
Founded: 1951
President: David R. Griffin
Chairman: Anthony Sweet
Secretary: Steve Godwin, 12 Lime Grove Gardens,
Bath, Avon Ba2 4HE. Tel: 0225 318612 (H), 01–833
0395 (W)
Fixtures Secretary: Barry Quintin, 10 Gordon Road,
Peasdown St. John, Radstock, Nr. Bath. Tel:
Radstock 33308
Press Officer: Richard Millard, Oldfield Clubhouse,
Lower Bristol Road, Bath. Tel: 0225 311575
Coach: Chris Lilley
Club captain (1988–89): Chris Lilley
Club captain (1989–90): Chris Lilley
No. of teams: Senior 5, Youth 6
Directions to ground: Follow signs for University then
ask for Shaft Road, Combe Down
Ground capacity: Standing 500
Clubhouse facilities: Bar, skittle alley
Club colours: Maroon gold hoops. (*Change colours:*
Maroon)
Nickname: Oldfield
Floodlights: Yes (partial)
Membership fees: Full £10, Playing £10, Social £3,
Youth £3, Student £Free, OAP £Free
Ground admission: 50p (Cup games only)
Programme: No. of editorial pages 1; No. of
advertising pages 2
Programme editor: E.A. Sweet, 14 Cedric Road, Bath

OLD SULIANS

Lansdown Road, Bath, Avon. Tel: 0225 310201
Founded: 1926
President: J. Trude
Chairman: P. Beach
Secretary: A. Slee, 8 Heathfield Close, Weston, Bath.

Tel: 0225 317256
Fixtures Secretary: M. Bailey, 32 Napier Road,
Weston, Bath. Tel: 0225 314060
Coach: J. Wrigley
Club captain (1988–89): M. Self
Club captain (1989–90): J. Wrigley
No. of teams: Senior 4, Youth 1
Directions to ground: From centre of city, take
London Road to Lansdown Road, travel up hill for 2
miles approx., pass M.O.D. buildings. Ground on
left, 100 yds
Ground capacity: Standing 500–750
Clubhouse facilities: Large showers, 2 large changing
rooms, referees room, bar and clubroom
Club colours: Red band on blue. (*Change colours:*
Green or white)
Nickname: Sus
Floodlights: Yes (training purposes only)
Membership fees: Full £7

ST. BERNADETTES OLD BOYS

Hengrove Park, Bamfield, Whitchurch, Bristol. Tel:
0272 891500
Founded: 1964
President: James Gallagher
Chairman: Micheal Trevor Woore
Secretary: Sean Broad, 25 Blakeney Road, Patchway,
Bristol BS12 5LY. Tel: 0272 698031
Fixtures Secretary: Brian John Murphy, 4 Rookery
Way, Whitchurch, Bristol BS14 0DT. Tel: 0272
837702
Club captain (1988–89): Kevin Crehan
Club captain (1989–90): Kevin Crehan
No. of teams: Senior 4, Youth 2
Directions to ground: Leave M at J18, follow signs for
Bristol Airport until you reach Parson Street BR
Station, then follow signs for Hartcliffe & Whitchurch
Sports Centre. Club behind running track of sports
centre
Clubhouse facilities: Lounge bar, showers, three
changing rooms. Catering facilities
Club colours: Green and blue hoops. (*Change*
colours: Red)
Nickname: The Lords of Lourdes
Floodlights: No
Membership fees: Full £10, Playing £1.50, Social £5,
Youth £5

WALCOT OLD BOYS

Albert Field, Lansdown, Bath. Tel: Bath 330199
Founded: 1882
President: P. Blackmore
Chairman: J. Wride
Secretary: Keith Jones, 14 Canterbury Road, Oldfield
Park, Bath BA2 3LG. Tel: Bath 27045 (H), 0249
712051 (W)
Fixtures Secretary: John Gifford, 131 Lymore
Avenue, Oldfield Park, Bath. Tel: Bath 28524
Press Officer: As Secretary
Coach: R. Hookway
Club captain (1988–89): M. Brown
Club captain (1989–90): J. Williams
No. of teams: Senior 4, Youth 1
Clubhouse facilities: Yes
Club colours: Black and white hoops. (*Change*
colours: Red)
Floodlights: Yes
Membership fees: Full £6, Playing £6, Social £3,
Youth £2, Student 50p, OAP 50p

YATTON

North End Road, Yatton. Tel: 832085
Founded: 1968
President: Roy Screen
Chairman: Tony Leigh
Secretary: Graham Goodhind, 8 Binhay Road, Yatton

BS19 4HD. Tel: Yatton 835434
Fixtures Secretary: Richard Scott, 49 Henley Park,
Yatton, Bristol BS19 4JJ. Tel: 0934 834174
Coach: Terry Brooks
Club captain (1988–89): Jonathan Crew
Club captain (1989–90): Jonathan Crew
No. of teams: Senior 4, Youth and Minis 5
Directions to ground: J20 (M5) left at roundabout, left
to Yatton at next roundabout
Ground capacity: Standing 300
Clubhouse facilities: Open matchdays, sundays and
training nights
Club colours: Black and amber. (*Change colours:*
Green)
Floodlights: No
Membership fees: Full £17.50, Playing £17.50, Social
£5, Youth £5, Student £3.50, OAP £3.50
Ground admission: Nil
Local newspaper: Weston Mercury
League: S 1
League position (1988–89): 7th
League playing record (1988–89): P 31, W 13, D 3,
L 15

YEOVIL

Johnson Park, Yeovil, Somerset. Tel: 0935 74433
Founded: 1875
President: George Habberfield
Chairman: Victor J. Jenkins
Secretary: Robert Elsmore Johnson, 55 Westbourne
Grove, Yeovil, Somerset BA20 2DG. Tel: 0935 28458
(H), 75291 ext. 232 (W)
Fixtures Secretary: Steve Greenn, 72A Wessex Road,
Yeovil, Somerset. Tel: 0935 26024
Press Officer: As Secretary
Coach: Jeff Green
Club captain (1988–89): Andy Jarvis
Club captain (1989–90): Adrian Radford
No. of teams: Senior 2, Youth 2, Minis 2
Directions to ground: A303 then A37 (ground to the
north side of Yeovil), Ilchester Road turning close to
the Pickety Witch p/h
Ground capacity: Standing 2000
Clubhouse facilities: 2 bars and function room. Open
daily
Club colours: Blue/yellow hoops. Colts: Red (*Change*
colours: White)
Floodlights: Yes
Membership fees: Full £12 (paid by club), Social £1
Ground admission: Free

SOMERSET 2

AVON

Hicks Field, London Road, Bath. Tel: 0225 852446
Founded: 1925
President: Ray Hicks
Chairman: Steve Bird
Secretary: Chris Lander, 63 Lansdown View,
Twerton, Bath BA2 1BQ. Tel: 0225 314408
Fixtures Secretary: Chris Perry, 32 Gainsborough
Gardens, Bath. Tel: 0225 319633 (H), 26366 (W)
Club captain (1988–89): Mike Mallon
Club captain (1989–90): Chris Nicholson
No. of teams: Senior 4, Youth 1
Directions to ground: A4 London Road out of Bath,
200 yds past Lambridge traffic lights, right turn down
steep track 50 yds before garage
Ground capacity: Seating 100, Standing 2000
Club colours: Black shirts with narrow amber hoops
Floodlights: Yes (training lights)
Membership fees: Full £12, Playing £12, Social £12,
Youth £6, Student £6

BATH OLD EDWARDIANS

K.E.S. Playing Fields, Bathampton, Bath, Avon. Tel: 0225 62354
Founded: 1926
President: Peter Boyce
Chairman: Richard Caudle
Secretary: Peter Merchant, 28 Longfellow Avenue, Bath, Avon. Tel: 0225 313450 (H), 0793 512636 (W)
Fixtures Secretary: As Secretary
Press Officer: As Secretary
Club captain (1988–89): Graham Corp
Club captain (1989–90): T.B.A.
No. of teams: Senior 2
Directions to ground: A46 London Road, Bathampton toll Bridge, past The George at Bathamptom on your right over bridge, ground on left
Club colours: Maroon, blue and gold hoops, blue shorts, maroon socks
Floodlights: Yes

BURNHAM ON SEA

BASC Sports Ground, Stoddens Road, Burnham on Sea, Somerset. Tel: 0278 788355
President: F. Cross
Chairman: M. O'Farrell
Secretary: Chris Garner, Brendon Cottage, Church Road, East Brent, Somerset. Tel: 0278 76078
Fixtures Secretary: Gareth Berry, 86 Burnham Road, Highbridge, Burnham on Sea
Coach: Graham Watts
Club captain (1988–89): Peter Gaylard
Club captain (1989–90): Peter Gaylard
No. of teams: Senior 4, Youth 1
Directions to ground: Junc. 22 M5, follow signs to BASC Sports Ground
Ground capacity: Seating 120, Standing 1000+
Clubhouse facilities: Full
Club colours: R blue/white. (*Change colours:* R blue)
Floodlights: Yes (training)
Membership fees: Playing £20
Programme editor: John Clist/Michael O'Farrell

CREWKERNE

Henhayes, Crewkherne, Somerset. Tel: 0460 76422
Founded: Re-formed 1975
President: Pat MacCready
Chairman: John Williams
Secretary: Clive MacDonald, 8 Sycamore Drive, Crewherne, Somerset TA18 7BT. Tel: 0460 76136 (H), 75685 (W)
Fixtures Secretary: John Davies, Old School House, Drimpton, Beaminster, Dorset. Tel: 0308 68388 (H), 0935 24544 (W)
Press Officer: As Secretary
Coach: George Cooper
Club captain (1988–89): Trevor Boyer
Club captain (1989–90): Trevor Boyer
No. of teams: Senior 2, Youth 1
Directions to ground: Adjoining main car park in the centre of town
Clubhouse facilities: Shared with other sports clubs
Club colours: Scarlet and black hoops. (*Change colours:* Cambridge blue)
Nickname: Crew
Floodlights: No
Membership fees: VPs £15 min., Playing £16, Student £4
Ground admission: Nil
Programme editor: As Secretary

IMPERIAL

Imperial Athletic Club, West Town Lane, Knowle, Bristol. Tel: 0272 777210
Founded: 1905
Chairman: Roger Osgood

Secretary: Howard Walton, 1 Rushmoor Grove, Backwell, Bristol BS19 3BW. Tel: 027 5833405 (H), 641111 ext. 2641 (W)
Fixtures Secretary: Nic Thatcher, 1 Kingscourt Close, Whitchurch, Bristol. Tel: 0272 836861
Press Officer: Roy Leitch, 19 Wellsford Road, Stapleton, Bristol. Tel: 0272 518762
Club captain (1988–89): Martin Wilcox
Club captain (1989–90): Kevin Hickory
No. of teams: Senior 4, Youth 4, Minis 2
Directions to ground: 3 miles south of Bristol on A37-Wells Road
Club colours: Myrtle green and amber. (*Change colours:* Red)
Floodlights: No
League: S 2
League position (1988–89): 4th

NORTH PETHERTON

Beggars Brook, North Petherton, Somerset. Tel: 0278 663028.
Founded: 1893
Secretary: G. G. Williams, 83 Greenacre, Wembdon, Bridgwater, Somerset TA6 7RF. Tel: 0278 457186.
Colours: Black/White
League: South-West Somerset 1

ST. BRENDANS OLD BOYS

Northway, Filton, Bristol. Tel: 0272 692793
Founded: 1964
President: Mike Titcomb
Chairman: Mike Witts
Secretary: John Franklin, 49 Farm Road, Milton, Weston-S-Mare, Avon BS22 8BE. Tel: 0934 627926 (H), 0392 58201 (W)
Fixtures Secretary: George Wysocki, 17 Newlyn Avenue, Stoke Bishop, Bristol, Avon BS22 8BE. Tel: 0272 685851
Press Officer: Sean Wills (through Secretary)
Coach: Frank Piekarski
Club captain (1988–89): Gurvane Davies
Club captain (1989–90): Adam Wills
No. of teams: Senior 4, Youth 6, Minis 3
Directions to ground: Junction 16 M5 – A38 towards Bristol. Flyover at Rolls-Royce factory, 1st left after factory entrance. Filton runway on right
Clubhouse facilities: Bar. Open Tuesdays, matchdays (Sat. and Sun.)
Club colours: Maroon and old gold. (*Change colours:* Maroon)
Nickname: The Saints
Floodlights: No
Membership fees: Full £1, Playing £2 wk., Youth £1 wk., Student £1 wk., Ass. Neg.
Local newspapers: Bristol Evening Post, Western Daily Press
League: S 2
League position (1988–89): Bottom (relegated)

STOTHERT & PITT

Founded: 1906
Chairman: I. Guy
Secretary: R.V. Garraway, 2 Westfield Park South, Lower Weston, Bath BA1 3HT. Tel: Bath 316863
Fixtures Secretary: B. Gibbs, 114 Newton Road, Bath. Tel: Bath 330455
Press Officer: Thomas Humphries, 30 Rivers Street, Bath
Coach: Alan Gore
Club captain (1988–89): Thomas Humphreys
Club captain (1989–90): Thomas Humphreys
No. of teams: Senior 3
Directions to ground: Bristol side of Bath, situated on A4 road
Ground capacity: Standing 200

Clubhouse facilities: Changing rooms, showers and bar
Club colours: Blue/black/amber. (*Change colours:* Blue)
Nickname: 'Cranes'
Floodlights: No
Membership fees: Full £6, Playing £6, Social £6, Youth £6, Student £6, OAP £6
Ground admission: Nil
Local newspapers: Bath & Wilts Evening Chronicle

TOR

Lowerside Park, Lowerside Lane, Glastonbury. Tel: 0458 31360
Founded: 1954
President: David Sparks
Chairman: Brian Harbinson
Secretary: Jon Whittock, Shapwick Manor, Shapwick, Bridgewater TA7 9NJ. Tel: 0458 210591 (H), 210384 (W)
Fixtures Secretary: Keith Elver, 170 Strode Road, Street
Press Officer: Janet Graham
Club captain (1988–89): Jerry Morse
Club captain (1989–90): Geoff Calder
No. of teams: Senior 2, Youth 2, Minis 4
Directions to ground: Take Wells Road out of Glastonbury, cemetery on right, opposite take Lowerside Lane on left, through housing estate. Ground and clubhouse is on the right-hand side
Clubhouse facilities: 2 storey building, 2 bars, skittle alley. Open on training nights and match days
Club colours: Maroon
Floodlights: No
Membership fees: Full £7, Playing £25, Social £7, VPS £25, Youth £5, Student £5, Mini £5
Local newspapers: Central Somerset Gazette

WELLS

The Portway, Wells. Tel: 0749 72823 (callbox)
Founded: 1876 (inaugurated)
President: Richard D. Draper
Chairman: Terry Western
Secretary: Michael F.P. Dennis, 2 Bilbury Lane, Glastonbury, Somerset BA6 8LX. Tel: 0458 34625
Fixtures Secretary: Ray MaCarthey, 26 Elm Close, Wells. Tel: 0749 77582
Club captain (1988–89): Rob Norman
No. of teams: Senior 3, Youth 2, Minis 2
Directions to ground: Leave Wells on A361 Weston-S-Mare at top of hill, about mile from town turn right at Charter Way. Signpost 'Wells R.F.C.'
Clubhouse facilities: 6 changing rooms, bar, skittle alley, darts, pool
Club colours: Black and white hoops. (*Change colours:* Blue shirts)
Floodlights: Yes (training only)
Membership fees: Full £3
Ground admission: Donations

WINSCOMBE

Longfield Recreation Ground, Winscombe, Avon. Tel: Winscombe 2720
Founded: 1962
President: Stephen Hart
Chairman: Geoff News
Secretary: Jamie Ware, Little Acre, Dolberrow, Churchill, Bristol, Avon BS19 5NS. Tel: 0934 852323
Fixtures Secretary: Adrian Ellis, 30 Wimblestone Road, Winscombe, Somerset. Tel: Winscombe 3087
Coach: David Howles
Club captain (1988–89): Mark Badger
Club captain (1989–90): Mark Badger
No. of teams: Senior 3, Youth 9, Minis 3
Directions to ground: 10 miles south of Bristol on A38. Turn right into Sidcot signposted to Winscombe, turn left at 'Asleys' at sharp right bend, 1st right into rec.
Clubhouse facilities: All

Club colours: Black. (*Change colours:* Red)
Floodlights: No
Membership fees: Playing £20

WIVELISCOMBE

Founded:
President:
Chairman:
Secretary:
Fixtures Secretary:
Press Officer:
Coach: Jerry Winter
Club captain (1988–89): Peter Stone
Club captain (1989–90): Peter Stone
No. of teams: Senior 3, Youth 2
Directions to ground:
Ground capacity: Seating 000, standing 000
Clubhouse facilities:
Club colours: . (*Change colours:*)
Floodlights: No
Membership fees: Full £ , Playing £ , Social £ , Youth £ , Student £ , OAP £
Ground admission: 00p
Programme: No. of editorial pages ; No. of advertising pages ; Price   p
Programme editor:

SOMERSET 3A

BACKWELL

Rodney Road, Backwell, Bristol
Founded: 1972
President: Alan Peters
Chairman: Paul Henley
Secretary: Andrew Nelson, 51 Westway, Nailsea, Bristol BS19 1EF. Tel: 0272 851340
Coach: ???
Club captain (1988–89): Paul Flower
No. of teams: Senior 3, Youth 2, Minis 5
Directions to ground: A370 Bristol to Weston, enter Backwell, turn into Rodney Road. Club positioned at end of Rodney Road
Ground capacity: Seating 12,000, standing 18,000
Clubhouse facilities: Fully plumbed, outside toilets
Club colours: Black with white band. (*Change colours:* Red)
Nickname: The Ravens
Floodlights: Yes
Membership fees: Full £12, Playing £12, Social £3, Youth £6, Student £6, OAP £6
Ground admission: £1.50
Programme: No. of editorial pages 20; No. of advertising pages 10; Price 75p
Programme editor: Alastair Cooke

BATH C.S.

CS Club, Claverton Down, Bath. Tel: 0225 832403
Founded: 1947
President: W. Chippendale
Chairman: C. Trout
Secretary: B. Clough, Ground Floor Flat, Linsley House, Beechen Cliff Road, Bath BA2 4QR. Tel: 0272 290566
Fixtures Secretary: As Secretary
Coach: R. McCullough
Club captain (1988–89): A. Pike
Club captain (1989–90): A. Pike
No. of teams: Senior 3
Directions to ground: M4 take main A36 to Bath, signs to Bath until sign for A367 Exeter & Coombe Down. Follow A367 past Uni and ground on left
Club colours: N blue/cardinal red/gold. (*Change colours:* Red)
Floodlights: No
Membership fees: Playing £12, Social £1

BLAGDON

The Mead, Brighton. Tel: 0761 62696
President: A. Addicott
Chairman: D. Slin
Secretary: N. Williams, 16 Stockton Close,
Whitchurch, Bristol. Tel: 0272 833796 (H), 636289
(W)
Fixtures Secretary: W. fitzpatrick, 2 The Linxs,
Cheddar
Coach: M. Badgar
Club captain (1988–89): I. Simmonds
Club captain (1989–90): I. Simmonds
No. of teams: Senior 3
Directions to ground: A365 at Blagdon between Bath
and Weston-Super-Mare
Clubhouse facilities: Village club
Club colours: Green. (*Change colours:* Blue)
Floodlights: Yes
Membership fees: Playing £5

CHEDDAR VALLEY

Sharpham Road, Cheddar, Somerset. Tel: 0934
743623.
Founded: 1963
Secretary: E. -. M. Roberts, 1 Brimridge Road,
Winscombe, Avon. Tel: 093 484 372 (H), 0272 333179
(B).
League: Somerset 2
Final position (1987–88): 11th

CHEW VALLEY

Lobbingtons, Chew Stoke, Bristol. Tel: 643622
Founded: 1968
President: P. Markham
Chairman: V. Pritchard
Fixtures Secretary: Martin Wooding, 91 Silver Street,
Chew Magna. Tel: 3332170
Press Officer: Peter Anthony Townson, 8 Chapel
Road, Bishopsworth, Bristol. Tel: 643622
Coach: Duncan Smith
Club captain (1988–89): Sam Broderick
Club captain (1989–90): Peter Townson
No. of teams: Senior 2, Youth 1
Directions to ground: The ground is betwen Chew
Magan and Chew Stoke
Ground capacity: Seating 400, standing 500
Clubhouse facilities: Pelican pub
Club colours: Green
Nickname: Africa Korps
Floodlights: Yes

OLD ASHTONIANS

Ashton Park School, Blackmore Lane, Bower
Ashton, Bristol. Tel: 0272 28385.
Founded: 1963
Secretary: M. Cox, "Lyndale", Wick Road,
Brislington, Bristol BS4 4HV. Tel: 0272 773025 (H),
0272 731191 (B).
League: Somerset 3

SOUTH WEST GAS (BRISTOL)

The Beeches, Broomhill Road, Braslington, Bristol.
Tel: 0272 777848 (new club)
President: Michael Garland
Chairman: Andrew Goven
Secretary: Andrew Hibbett, 26 Weare Court, Canada
Way, Baltic Wharf, Bristol. Tel: 0272 276061
Fixtures Secretary: Glenn Forde, 133 Talbot Road,
Braslington, Bristol BS4 2NU. Tel: 0272 721794 (H),
267044 (W)
Press Officer: As Fixtures Secretary
Coach: Ivor Sobey
Club captain (1988–89): Stephen Arnold

Club captain (1989–90): Stephen Arnold
No. of teams: Senior 2
Directions to ground: Take A4 Bristol-Bath road, to
Braslington, into Emery Road, at traffic lights, then
1st right into Broomhill Road. The Beeches is the
second gateway on right-hand side
Ground capacity: Seating 6, Standing 500
Clubhouse facilities: Large function room, players bar,
squash, tennis courts
Club colours: Blue and white hoops. (*Change colours:*
Maroon)
Floodlights: No
Membership fees: Full £15, Playing £5, Social £5

ALLER

West Fields, Langport, Taunton, Somerset. Tel:
Langport 252687
President: K. Male
Chairman: Jim Morris
Secretary: Jim Selway, Riggiston Farm, Walton, Nr.
Street, Somerset BA16 9RN. Tel: Ashcott 210236
Fixtures Secretary: Mark Edwards, Underhill Farm,
Low Ham, Langport TA10 9DO. Tel: Langport
251368
Press Officer: Patrick Robinson. Tel: 0823 69727
Coach: Bruce Williams
Club captain (1988–89): Neal Daniels
Club captain (1989–90): Kevin Cox
No. of teams: Senior 2, Minis 1
Directions to ground: 100 yds south of A378 –
Taunton end of Curry River
Clubhouse facilities: Changing rooms, shower, bar,
kitchen, pool table
Club colours: Green/red hoops
Floodlights: Yes (training only)

CASTLE CARY

Brook House Field, Alhampton, C. Cary, Somerset.
Tel: 0963 51178
Founded: 1888
President: B.J.A. Croffield
Chairman: B. Knock
Secretary: M.J. Armson, Brookhampton Cottage, N.
Cadbury, Yeovil, Somerset BA22 7DA. Tel: 0963
40648 (H), 0749 3300 ext. 2313 (W)
Fixtures Secretary: C. Watts, 15 Woodford Green,
Ansford, C. Cary. Tel: 0963 50162
Press Officer: P.J. Hardy, Brooklyn, N. Cardbury,
Yeovil, Somerset. Tel: 0963 402620
Coach: J. Cranmer
Club captain (1988–89): N. Knight
Club captain (1989–90): N. Knight
No. of teams: Senior 2
Directions to ground: Outskirts of C. Cary
Clubhouse facilities: Bar
Club colours: Red/black. (*Change colours:* Blue)
Floodlights: No
Membership fees: Playing £15, Social £9, Youth £6

CHARD

Ground Park Road, Chard, Somerset. Tel: 04606
2495
Founded: 1878
President: R.W. Morgan
Chairman: J.V. Baker
Secretary: N.J. Urch, 2 South View, Listers Hill,
Ilminster, Somerset TA19 0EJ. Tel: 0460 54295 (H),
0935 702913 (W)
Fixtures Secretary: 27 Norrington Way, Lordleaze
Estate, Chard. Tel: 0460 61140
Press Officer: Mike Berry, 27 Halcombe, Chard,
Somerset
Club captain (1988–89): Rob Baker
Club captain (1989–90): Alan Mear
No. of teams: Senior 3, Youth 6, Minis 1

Directions to ground: off Chard High Street
Ground capacity: Standing 1000
Clubhouse facilities: Yes
Club colours: REd, black, gold. (*Change colours:* Red)
Floodlights: No
Membership fees: Full £20, Playing £20
Local newspapers: Chard and Ilminster News

MORGANIANS

Clubhouse, Chedzoy Lane, Bridgwater. Tel: 0278 423434
Founded: 1923
President: Stuart Vinecombe
Chairman: Gary Bohot
Secretary: Geoff Presdee, 66 Woodbury Road, Bridgwater, Somerset TA6 7LJ. Tel: 0278 451366
Fixtures Secretary: David Bryant, 14 Norfolk Close, Bridgwater, Somerset. Tel: 427411
Press Officer: As Secretary
Coach: David Bryant
Club captain (1988–89): M. Derewicz
Club captain (1989–90): T.B.A.
No. of teams: Senior 2
Directions to ground: A39 out of Bridgwater, first right over motorway bridge
Clubhouse facilities: Hall, lounge, skittle alley, 2 changing rooms, shower/bath block
Club colours: Navy with red and gold bands. (*Change colours:* Red)
Nickname: Morgs
Floodlights: No
Membership fees: Full £12

WELLINGTON

The Athletic Ground, Corams Lane, Wellington. Tel: Wellington 3758
Founded: 1874
President: G.E. Sprague
Chairman: A.H. Trott
Secretary: B.K. Colman, Meadowside, Mantle Street, Wellington, Somerset TA21 8BG. Tel: Wellington 3307 (H), Taunton 333451 ext. 5121 (W)
Fixtures Secretary: G.R. Vickery, 7 Seymour Street, Wellington. Tel: Wellington 4695 (H), Taunton 335166 (W)
Press Officer: A.H. Trott, 7 Sylvan Road, Wellington. Tel: Wellington 2191
Coach: R.D. Burton
Club captain (1988–89): A.W. Terry
Club captain (1989–90): J. Dunbar
No. of teams: Senior 3, Youth 1, Minis 7
Directions to ground: Next to Sports Centre
Ground capacity: Standing 3000+

Clubhouse facilities: Lounge bar, members bar and function room (catering for 200+)
Club colours: Red and black. (*Change colours:* Blue)
Nickname: Sergemen
Floodlights: No
Membership fees: Full £12, Playing £10, Social £5, Youth £2, Student £5, OAP £5
Ground admission: Contribution
Programme editor: B.K. Colman, Meadowside, Mantle Street, Wellington, Somerset TA21 8BG
Local newspapers: Welllington Weekly News, Somerset County Gazette

WESTLAND

Bunford Lane, Yeovil. Tel: 0935 74297
Founded: 1954
President: P. Holland
Chairman: D. Thompson
Secretary: Keith Biggin, 121 Mudford Road, Yeovil, Somerset. Tel: 0935 73731 (H), 75222 (W)
Press Officer: P.E. Paul
No. of teams: Senior 3, Minis 3
Club colours: Maroon/sky blue
League: Som 2
League position (1988–89): 11th
League playing record (1988–89): P 11, W 0, D 0, L 11, F 76, A 254

WINCANTON

Hale Farm, Cucklington, Wincanton, Somerset
President: J. Heyes
Chairman: J. Bastable
Secretary: P. Wright, 64 High Street, Wincanton, Somerset BA9 9JF. Tel: 0963 34294
Fixtures Secretary: A. Wright, 64 High Street, Wincanton, Somerset BA9 9JF. Tel: 0963 34294 (H), 0935 814946 (W)
Press Officer: Julian Ohlsen, The Flat, 6 High Street, Wincanton, Somerset. Tel: 0963 33420
Club captain (1988–89): Ray Holder
Club captain (1989–90): Ray Holder
No. of teams: Senior 1, Youth 1
Directions to ground: Turn off High Street at top end of town and take Common Road. After bypass bridge turn left then follow signs to Cucklington. On approach to Cucklington turn right, 100 yds on right
Clubhouse facilities: Open evenings
Club colours: Black and amber
Floodlights: No
Membership fees: Full £7.50, Playing £7.50, Social £3.50, Youth £1, Student £3.50
Local newspapers: Western Gazette, Somerset Star

BERKS, DORSET & WILTS LEAGUES

AFTER an initial season, in which 22 clubs took part in only two divisions, these leagues were increased by a further 14 teams, divided by geography into two third divisions with each having a team promoted.

In the top division Bracknell, bottom of the Southern League in 1987–88, won all their 10 matches (222–59) and are promoted, whilst in contrast the luckless Marlborough go down after losing all 10 games (68–423). Taking their place in the top flight are North Dorset and Puddletown who both managed nine wins and lost only once, although the former had a better points difference (242–76).

Minety, although winning two games, are the only team to descend and two teams ascend from the third divisions – Melksham (East) and Westbury (West), the latter edging out both Warminster and Dorset Institute on points difference in an exciting first campaign. This county grouping would seem to be quite a success story and it is good to see that the "chopping blocks" of 1987–88 – Hungerford – won three of their 10 games this time and conceded only 167 points in the process to stay in Division 2.

BERKS, DORSET AND WILTS:

Tony Bott,
Kew House,
Anchor Road,
Calne,
Wilts. SN11 8DI   (H) 0249 813021

Reading's celebrations after they retained the Berkshire Cup against Maidenhead (8–4).

TABLES 1987–88

BERKS, DORSET & WILTS 1

	P	W	D	L	F	A	PTS
Swanage & W	9	8	0	1	266	31	16
Devizes	9	8	0	1	254	72	16
Dorchester	9	7	0	2	108	42	14
Sherborne	9	6	0	3	160	34	12
Weymouth	9	6	0	3	198	79	12
Wootton Bas	9	3	0	6	174	141	6
REME A'bfld	9	3	0	6	117	155	6
Aldermaston	9	2	0	7	64	180	4
Marlborough	9	2	0	7	57	258	4
Hungerford	9	0	0	9	22	428	0

BERKS, DORSET & WILTS 2

	P	W	D	L	F	A	PTS
Chippenham	11	10	0	1	302	74	20
Corsham	11	10	0	1	265	52	20
Puddleton	11	8	0	3	176	82	16
Supermarine	11	8	0	3	128	108	16
N Dorset	11	7	0	4	232	84	14
Lychett Min	11	5	0	6	170	143	10
Poole	11	5	0	6	147	142	10
Oakmedians	11	4	0	7	86	166	8
Trowbridge	11	3	0	8	91	220	6
Bradford	11	3	0	8	84	216	6
Minety	11	2	0	9	70	193	4
Swindon Col	11	1	0	10	49	320	2

TABLES 1988-89

BERKS, DORSET & WILTS 1

	P	W	D	L	F	A	PTS
Bracknell	10	10	0	0	222	59	20
Dorchester	10	9	0	1	256	64	18
Sherborne	10	7	0	3	350	71	14
Chippenham	10	6	0	4	157	126	12
Devizes	10	5	0	5	230	100	10
Wootton Bass	10	5	0	5	140	116	10
Weymouth	10	5	0	5	95	157	10
Corsham	10	4	0	6	89	148	8
REME A'fld	10	3	0	7	128	209	6
Aldermaston	10	1	0	9	65	327	2
Marlborough	10	0	0	10	68	423	0

BERKS, DORSET & WILTS 2

	P	W	D	L	F	A	PTS
N Dorset	10	9	0	1	242	76	18
Puddletown	10	9	0	1	176	75	18
Trowbridge	10	7	0	3	247	86	14
Supermarine	10	5	1	4	96	76	11
Lytchet Min	10	5	1	4	171	121	11
Swindon Coll	10	4	0	6	76	148	8
Poole	10	4	0	6	99	171	8
Bradford-on-Av	10	3	0	7	149	123	6
Hungerford	10	3	0	7	109	167	6
Oakmedians	10	3	0	7	83	259	6
Minety	10	2	0	8	29	131	4

BERKS, DORSET & WILTS 3E

	P	W	D	L	F	A	PTS
Melksham	6	5	1	0	221	30	11
Berks Sh Hall	6	5	1	0	138	47	11
Colerne	6	3	1	2	84	48	7
Tadley	6	1	2	3	52	101	4
Thatcham	6	2	0	4	31	81	4
Amesbury	6	1	1	4	43	101	3
Calne	6	1	0	5	38	199	2

BERKS, DORSET & WILTS 3W

	P	W	D	L	F	A	PTS
Westbury	6	5	0	1	258	40	10
Warminster	6	5	0	1	135	67	10
Dorset In	6	5	0	1	93	40	10
Portcastrians	6	2	0	4	51	72	4
Bridport	6	2	0	4	69	187	4
Blandford	6	1	0	5	67	88	2
Plessey	6	1	0	5	48	227	2

SOUTH WEST DIVISION FIXTURES 1989/90

BERKS, DORSET & WILTS ONE

Sat. 9th September (Week 2)
Aldermaston v Devizes
Sherborne v Chippenham
Corsham v Puddletown
Weymouth v North Dorset
Wootton Bassett v Dorchester

Sat. 23rd September (Week 4)
North Dorset v Wootton Bassett
Puddletown v Weymouth
Chippenham v Corsham
REME Arborfield v Sherborne
Dorchester v Aldermaston

Sat. 14th October (Week 6)
Aldermaston v North Dorset
Devizes v Dorchester
Corsham v REME Arborfield
Weymouth v Chippenham
Wootton Bassett v Puddletown

Sat. 28th October (Week 8)
North Dorset v Devizes
Puddletown v Aldermaston
Chippenham v Wootton Bassett
REME Arborfield v Weymouth
Sherborne v Corsham

Sat. 11th November (Week 10)
Aldermaston v Chippenham
Devizes v Puddletown
Dorchester v North Dorset
Weymouth v Sherborne
Wootton Bassett v REME Arborfield

Sat 18th November (Week 11)
Puddletown v Dorchester
Chippenham v Devizes
REME Arborfield v Aldermaston
Sherborne v Wootton Bassett
Corsham v Weymouth

Sat. 25th November (Week 12)
Aldermaston v Sherborne
Devizes v REME Arborfield
Dorchester v Chippenham
North Dorset v Puddletown
Wootton Bassett v Corsham

Sat. 13th January (Week 18)
Chippenham v North Dorset
REME Arborfield v Dorchester
Sherborne v Devizes
Corsham v Aldermaston
Weymouth v Wootton Bassett

Sat. 10th March (Week 26)
Aldermaston v Weymouth
Devizes v Corsham
Dorchester v Sherborne
North Dorset v REME Arborfield
Puddletown v Chippenham

Sat. 31st March (Week X7)
REME Arborfield v Puddletown
Sherborne v North Dorset
Corsham v Dorchester
Weymouth v Devizes
Wootton Bassett v Aldermaston

Sat. 28th April (Week 32)
Devizes v Wootton Bassett
Dorchester v Weymouth
North Dorset v Corsham
Puddletown v Sherborne
Chippenham v REME Arborfield

SOUTH WEST DIVISION FIXTURES 1989/90

BERKS, DORSET & WILTS TWO

Sat. 9th September (Week 2)
Bradford-on-Avon v Hungerford
Poole v Westbury
Melksham v Marlborough
Supermarine v Lytchet Minster
Swindon College v Trowbridge

Sat. 23rd September (Week 4)
Lytchet Minster v Swindon College
Marlborough v Supermarine
Westbury v Melksham
Oakmedians v Poole
Trowbridge v Bradford-on-Avon

Sat. 14th October (Week 6)
Bradford-on-Avon v Lytchet Minster
Hungerford v Trowbridge
Melksham v Oakmedians
Supermarine v Westbury
Swindon College v Marlborough

Sat. 28th October (Week 8)
Lytchet Minster v Hungerford
Marlborough v Bradford-on-Avon
Westbury v Swindon College
Oakmedians v Supermarine
Poole v Melksham

Sat. 11th November (Week 10)
Bradford-on-Avon v Westbury
Hungerford v Marlborough
Trowbridge v Lytchet Minster
Supermarine v Poole
Swindon College v Oakmedians

Sat 18th November (Week 11)
Marlborough v Trowbridge
Westbury v Hungerford
Oakmedians v Bradford-on-Avon
Poole v Swindon College
Melksham v Supermarine

Sat. 25th November (Week 12)
Bradford-on-Avon v Poole
Hungerford v Oakmedians
Trowbridge v Westbury
Lytchet Minster v Marlborough
Swindon College v Melksham

Sat. 13th January (Week 18)
Westbury v Lytchet Minster
Oakmedians v Trowbridge
Poole v Hungerford
Melksham v Bradford-on-Avon
Supermarine v Swindon College

Sat. 10th March (Week 26)
Bradford-on-Avon v Supermarine
Hungerford v Melksham
Trowbridge v Poole
Lytchet Minster v Oakmedians
Marlborough v Westbury

Sat. 31st March (Week X7)
Oakmedians v Marlborough
Poole v Lytchet Minster
Melksham v Trowbridge
Supermarine v Hungerford
Swindon College v Bradford-on-Avon

Sat. 28th April (Week 32)
Hungerford v Swindon College
Trowbridge v Supermarine
Lytchet Minster v Melksham
Marlborough v Poole
Westbury v Oakmedians

SOUTH WEST DIVISION FIXTURES 1989/90

BERKS, DORSET & WILTS
THREE EAST

Sat. 23rd September (Week 4)
  Calne v Amesbury
  Thatcham v Minety

Sat. 14th October (Week 6)
  Berks Sh. Hall v Calne
  Amesbury v Colerne

Sat. 28th October (Week 8)
  Colerne v Berks Sh. Hall
  Minety v Tadley

Sat. 11th November (Week 10)
  Calne v Colerne
  Amesbury v Minety
  Tadley v Thatcham

Sat 18th November (Week 11)
  Tadley v Amesbury
  Minety v Berks Sh. Hall
  Thatcham v Colerne

Sat. 25th November (Week 12)
  Calne v Minety
  Berks Sh. Hall v Tadley
  Amesbury v Thatcham

Sat. 13th January (Week 18)
  Thatcham v Berks Sh. Hall
  Tadley v Calne
  Minety v Colerne

Sat. 10th March (Week 26)
  Amesbury v Berks Sh. Hall
  Colerne v Tadley
  Calne v Thatcham

BERKS, DORSET & WILTS
THREE WEST

Sat. 23rd September (Week 4)
  Dorset Inst. v Blandford

Sat. 14th October (Week 6)
  Bridport v Dorset Inst.
  Blandford v Plessey

Sat. 28th October (Week 8)
  Portcastrians v Blandford
  Plessey v Bridport

Sat. 11th November (Week 10)
  Dorset Inst. v Plessey
  Bridport v Portcastrians
  Blandford v Warminster

Sat 18th November (Week 11)
  Warminster v Bridport
  Portcastrians v Dorset Inst.

Sat. 25th November (Week 12)
  Plessey v Portcastrians
  Dorset Inst. v Warminster

Sat. 13th January (Week 18)
  Warminster v Plessey

Sat. 10th March (Week 26)
  Blandford v Bridport
  Portcastrians v Warminster

BERKS, DORSET & WILTS 1

ALDERMASTON

Aldermaston Recreational Society Avenue,
Aldermaston, Reading, Berks RG7 4PR. Tel: 0734
814111
Founded: 1954
Chairman: Derek Griggs
Secretary: Dr. D. McGinnes, 11 Rowan Close,
Tadley, Hants RG26 6RP. Tel: 0734 3213 (H), 4111
ext. 6394 (W)
Fixtures Secretary: Arthur Cuss, 153 Winchester
Road, Basingstoke. Tel: 0256 24159
Coach: Ian Titley
Club captain (1988–89): Terry Francis
No. of teams: Senior 4, Youth 1 + Minis
Club colours: Scarlet. (*Change colours:* White)
Floodlights: No
League: B,D&W 1
League position (1988–89): 10th
League playing record (1988–89): P 10, W 1, D 0,
L 9, F 65, A 327

CHIPPENHAM

Birch Grove, Chippenham, Wilts. Tel: 0249 656390
Founded: 1929
President: Frank Osborne
Chairman: Rod Turvey
Secretary: John Wakefield, 46 Langley Road,
Chippenham, Wilts SN15 1DB. Tel: 0249 651677 (H),
0272 617248 (W)
Fixtures Secretary: Geoff Millard, 11 Murray Walk,
Melsham, Wilts. Tel: Melksham 702469
Press Officer: Brian Reid, 53 Westcroft, Chippenham,
Wilts. Tel: 0249 655777
Coach: Mark Coombs
Club captain (1988–89): Mark Prangle
Club captain (1989–90): Brian Reid
No. of teams: Senior 4, Youth 1, Minis 3
Directions to ground: Take B4069 out of Chippenham
towards Lyneham. Birch Grove is opposite the
Westinghouse factory gates
Ground capacity: Standing 300
Clubhouse facilities: Bar, lounge, kitchen, changing
rooms
Club colours: Black and white hoops, black shorts.
(*Change colours:* Red)
Floodlights: Yes (training only)
Local newspapers: Chippeham News, Wiltshire
Gazette & Herald
League: SW BD&W
League position (1988–89): 4th
League playing record (1988–89): P 32, W 17, D 0,
L 15

CORSHAM

Corsham Sports Clubhouse, Station Road, Corsham,
Wilts SN13 9LU. Tel: 0249 713929
Founded: 1964
President: John Gordon Wiltshire
Chairman: Keith Jones
Secretary: Frederick Thomas Trahair, M.B.E., 5
Penleigh Close, Corsham, Wilts SN13 9LE. Tel: 0249
714468
Fixtures Secretary: Peter Kaljusco, 7 Penleigh Close,
Corsham, Wilts SN13 9LE. Tel: 0249 712344
Press Officer: Sean McDonald, Corsham R.F.U., The
Clubhouse, Station Road, Corsham SN13 9LU. Tel:
0249 712205
Coach: Michael O'Shea
Club captain (1988–89): John Beazer
Club captain (1989–90): John Beazer
No. of teams: Senior 1, Youth 2
Directions to ground: Lacock Road, mile east of
Methuen Arms Hotel, Corsham
Ground capacity: Standing 500
Clubhouse facilities: Bar
Club colours: Red and white hoops, black shirts

Floodlights: Yes
Membership fees: Full £10+, Playing £2.50, Social £15
Ground admission: 00p
Programme: No. of editorial pages 0; No. of
advertising pages 15; Price £1 (Handbook only)
Programme editor: Sean McDonald
Local newspaper: Bath & Wilts Evening Chronicle
League: BDW 1
League position (1988–89): 8th
League playing record (1988–89): P 10, W 4, D 0,
L 6, F 89, A 148

DEVIZES

Sports Club, London Road, Devizes, Wilts. Tel:
Devizes 3763
Founded: 1931
President: David Gent
Chairman: Michael Gaiger
Secretary: M.J. Maundrell, Manor House, Calstone,
Calne, Wilts SN11 8PY. Tel: 0249 812373
Fixtures Secretary: D. Gaiger, 67 Queens Road,
Devizes, Wilts. Tel: Devizes 2480
Press Officer: T.B.A.
Coach: T.B.A.
Club captain (1988–89): John Bathe
Club captain (1989–90): T.B.A.
No. of teams: Senior 3, Youth 1, Minis 6
Directions to ground: Leave the town on the London
Road (A361). On reaching hump-back bridge over
canal turn left (sharp) into Sports Club. Signboard:
Cricket, Rugby, Tennis Clubs
Clubhouse facilities: Changing rooms, clubroom,
lounge, kitchen, skittles, bar billiards
Club colours: Black and white hoop. (*Change colours:*
Irish green)
Nickname: 'Vizes'
Floodlights: No
Membership fees: Full £20, Playing £20, Social £15,
Youth £5
Local newspaper: Wiltshire Gazette & Herald
League: BDW 1
League position (1988–89): 5th
League playing record (1988–89): P 10, W 5, D 0,
L 5, F 230, A 100

DORCHESTER

Coburg Road, Dorchester. Tel: 0305 65692
Founded: 1934
President: Elfet Mills
Chairman: Nigel Jones
Secretary: Simon Meyers, 12 Manor Road,
Dorchester, Dorset DT1 2AU. Tel: 0305 66343 (H),
64774 (W)
Fixtures Secretary: Hugh Meyers, 27 Victoria Road,
Dorchester, Dorset. Tel: 0305 65877 (H), 64774 (W)
Press Officer: As Fixtures Secretary
Coach: Garry Knowles
Club captain (1988–89): Eddie Taylor
Club captain (1989–90): T.B.A.
No. of teams: Senior 3, Youth 2, Minis 4
Directions to ground: Take the Weymouth Road out
of Dorchester, turn right towards Maiden Castle, take
1st right in Maud Road, take 4th L.H. turning
(Coburg Road). the ground is about 1/3 mile on L.H.
side
Clubhouse facilities: 6 changing rooms, 3 pitches, 2
bars, function hall and kitchen
Club colours: Green and white hoops. (*Change
colours:* Blue shorts)
Floodlights: Yes
Membership fees: Full £10, Playing £10, Social £5,
Youth £5, Student £5
Local newspaper: Dorset Evening Echo
League: BDW 1
League position (1988–89): 2nd
League playing record (1988–89): P 10, W 9, D 0,
L 1, F 257, A 66

NORTH DORSET

Slaughtergate, Wyke. Clubhouse and facilities South
Street, Gillingham, Dorset. Tel: Gillingham 2748
Founded: 1951
President: Maj. P. Stoop
Chairman: Chris Brickell
Secretary: Jane Stickland, Preston Cottage, Wyke,
Gillingham, Dorset. Tel: 07476 2438 (H), 07476 4141
(W)
Fixtures Secretary: Dr. R. Jones, Hatherley, Long
Cross, Shaftesbury, Dorset. Tel: Shaftesbury 3733
Press Officer: J. Spicer, Plot 36, Wyke Manor Road,
Gillingham, Dorset. Tel: Gillingham 4871 (H), Mere
869166 (W)
Coach: T.B.A.
Club captain (1988–89): Mark Sampson
Club captain (1989–90): Mark Sampson
No. of teams: Senior 3–4, Youth 1, Minis 3
Directions to ground: Wincanton Road from
Gillingham – mile on right signposted: Trevor
Stickland Memorial Ground (Clubhouse and changing
rooms, South Street, Gillingham)
Clubhouse facilities: Car park, changing rooms, bar
Club colours: Emerald green shirt/navy shorts.
(*Change colours:* Yellow)
Floodlights: No
Membership fees: Playing £12.50, Social £2
League: BDW 2
League position (1988–89): 1st
League playing record (1988–89): P 10, W 9, D 0,
L 1, F 242, A 76

PUDDLETOWN

Greenfields, Piddlehinton, Dorchester, Dorset. Tel:
0305 848808
Founded: 1974
President: Sir J. Spicer, M.P.
Chairman: E. Dury, M.B.E., R.E.
Secretary: A.R.Foot, Booham Farm, Buckland
Newton, Dorchester, Dorset. Tel: 03005 511 (H), 360
(W)
Fixtures Secretary: P. Smeeth, London Close,
Piddlehinton, Dorchester, Dorset. Tel: 03004 310
Press Officer: D.H.J. Foot, West Dibberford Farm,
Beaminster, Dorset. Tel: 0308 68229
Coach: P. Talbot
Club captain (1988–89): P. Talbot
No. of teams: Senior 2
Directions to ground: Off B3143 4 miles from
Dorchester, 1 mile Piddlehinton
Ground capacity: Standing Unlimited
Clubhouse facilities: Bar, changing rooms, showers,
etc.
Club colours: Red. (*Change colours:* White)
Nickname: Peckers
Floodlights: No
Membership fees: Full £20, Playing £20, Social £5,
Youth £10
Local newspaper: Dorset Evening Echo
League position (1988–89): 2nd
League playing record (1988–89): P 10, W 9, D 0,
L 1, F 176, A 75

REME (ARBOURFIELD)

Garrison Sports Club, School fo Electronic
Engineering, Arborfield, Reading, Berks. Tel: 0734
760421 Extn. 344
Secretary: Capt. D.R. Prowse, School of Electronic
Engineering, Arborfield, Reading, Berks. Tel: 0734
410105 (H) 0374 760421. Extn 2341 (W)

SHERBORNE

The Terrace, Sherborne, Dorset
Founded: 1980
Secretary: S. Hill, Wescot, Westbury, Sherborne,
Dorset. Tel: 0935 813663.

Press Officer: P. Rushton. Tel: 0258 72274.
Colours: Black
League: Berks/Dorset/Wilts 1

WEYMOUTH

Monmouth Avenue, Weymouth, Dorset DT3 5HZ.
Tel: Weymouth 778889
Founded: 1872
President: W.M.C. Whittle, J.P.
Chairman: J.H. Parker
Secretary: G. Barber, 23 Purbeck Close, Weymouth.
Tel: 778531
Fixtures Secretary: R.E. Foyle, 12 Powys Close,
Dorchester. Tel:66144
Coach: P. Absolom
Club captain (1988–89): H. Mason
Club captain (1989–90): H. Mason
No. of teams: Senior 4, Youth and Minis 2
Directions to ground: Down Dorchester Road, straight
across roundabout on Ring Cross railway bridge, next
left at Olds Garage
Clubhouse facilities: 4 changing rooms plus usual
facilities
Club colours: Light blue/navy
Nickname: Sea Horses
Floodlights: No
Membership fees: Full £15
Local newspaper: Dorset Evening Echo
League: BDW 1

WOOTTON BASSETT

Rylands Field, Stoneover Lane, Wootton Bassett,
Wiltshire. Tel: 0793 851425
Founded: 1971
President: Ritchard Bradley
Chairman: Mike Leighfield
Secretary: Hamish Keith, 25 Briars Close, Wootton
Bassett, Wiltshire. Tel: 0793 850985 (H), 615601 (W)
Fixtures Secretary: Jim Brierly, 25 Broad Town Road,
Broad Town, Swindon, Wiltshire
Club captain (1988–89): Kevin Griffiths
No. of teams: Senior 4, Youth 3, Minis 3
Directions to ground: Junction 16 M4 to Wootton
Bassett, turn right first roundabout and first left to
Stoneover Lane
Ground capacity: Standing 400
Clubhouse facilities: Car park, two pitches, clubhouse,
changing, etc.
Club colours: Black. (*Change colours:* White)
Floodlights: No
Local newspaper: Evening Advertiser
League: BDW 1
League position (1988–89): 4th
League playing record (1988–89): P 8, W 4, D 0, L 4
Competitions won: Dorset & Wilts Colt Winners

BERKS, DORSET & WILTS 2

BRADFORD ON AVON

Founded: 1982
Secretary: J.W. Brockbank, 17 Whitehill, Bradford on
Avon, Wilts. Tel: 02216 3803 (H). 02216 3911 (W).
League: Berks, Dorset, Wilts 2

HUNGERFORD

50 High Street, Hungerford, Berks
Secretary: C. Dowse, 38 Dunn Crescent, Kintbury,
Nr. Newbury, Berks. Tel: 0488 58896
Directions to ground: Ground is near cricket club off
Bulpitt Lane
Ground capacity: Standing Ample
Floodlights: No
League: B.D&W 2
League position (1988–89): 9th

League playing record (1988–89): P 10, W 3, D 0,
L 7, F 109, A 167

LYCHETT MINSTER

Lytchett Park, Lytchett Minister, Poole, Dorset.
Founded: 1981
President: R. Castleton
Chairman: Bryan Hobson
Secretary: Andrea Wilson, Linden Lea, Wimborne
Road, Lytchett, Matravers, Poole, Dorset BH16 6HQ
Fixtures Secretary: Mark Hobson, Broonheyes,
Beacon Hill, Poole. Tel: 0202 623287
Press Officer: Juliette Dennett, 10 Gravel Lane,
Charlton Marshall, Blandford. Tel: Blandford
94459439
Coach: Gordon Glover and Steve Matthews
Club captain (1988–89): Bob Cullen
Club captain (1989–90): Bob Cullen
No. of teams: 3
Directions to ground: Next to Parish Church in
Lytchett Minister village
Clubhouse facilities: Clubhouse
Club colours: Red and Blue Hoops (*Change colours:
Red*)
Membership fees: Playing £15, Social £10, Youth £5,
Student £5, O. A. P. 10
Programme: No. of editorial pages 12; No. of
advertising pages 4; price 20p
Programme editor: Gordon glover. 20 Violet Farm
Close, Corte Mullen, Wimborne. Tel: 0202 698678
Local newspaper: Bournemouth Evening Echo
League: Berks/Dorset/Wilts II
League position (1988–89): 5th
League playing record (1988–89): P 36, W 20, D 3,
L 13, F 544, A 454

MARLBOROUGH

The Common, Marlborough, Wilst. Tel: 0672 54717.
Founded: 1967
Secretary: N.P. Ludlow, 10 Sawden Close,
Hungerford, Berks RG17 0LB. Tel: 0488 82159 (H).
0488 83334 (W).
Fixtures Secretary: A. Thomas, 2 Dando Drive,
Marlborough, Wilts. Tel: 0672 52296.
League: Berks, Dorset and Wilts/1
Press Officer: A. Stone. Tel: 0672 52417
Colours: Amber/Black

MELKSHAM

Secretary: M. Moore, 50 Addisson Road, Melksham,
Wilts. Tel: 0225 707446
League: Berks/Dorset/Wilts 2

OAKMEDIANS

White Farm, Ensbury Park, Slades Farm Road,
Bournemouth, Dorset.
Founded: 1963
Secretary: Miss S. Bennett, 63 Stewart Road,
Charminster, Bournemouth, Dorset. Tel: 0202 36757
(H), 0202 572271. Extn. 255 (W).

POOLE

Turlin Moor, Hamworthy, Poole, Dorset. Tel: 0202
687170
Founded: 1963
President: Mayor of Poole
Chairman: P. Quinn
Secretary: John Wateridge, 8 Harness Close,
Wimborne, Dorset BH21 2UF. Tel: 0202 889105 (H),
524111 (W)
Fixtures Secretary: Graham Sellars, 18 Plantation
Road, Poole, Dorset. Tel: 0202 658375
Press Officer: As Fixtures Secretary
Coach: Richard Dowding
Club captain (1988–89): Ian Appleton

Club captain (1989–90): Martin Holloway
No. of teams: Senior 3, Youth 3, Minis 4
Directions to ground: Upton to Poole A350 right into
Turlin Moor after Sherry and Haycock Building
Supplies
Clubhouse facilities: Bar. Open match days, mini/
youth sessions, training
Club colours: Amber and blue hoops. (*Change
colours:* Blue)
Nickname: Dolphins
Floodlights: No
Membership fees: Full £15, Playing £15, Social £5,
Youth £5, Student £5, OAP £5
Local newspaper: Bournemouth Evening Echo
League: BDW 2
League position (1988–89): 6th
League playing record (1988–89): P 10, W 4, D 0,
L 6, F 99, A 171

SUPERMARINE

Highworth Road, South Marston, Swindon, Wilts.
Tel: 0793 824828
Founded: 1951
President: Mike Atwell
Chairman: Sam Smyth
Secretary: Paul Ferris, 13 Sandgate, Stratton Street,
Margaret, Swindon, Wilts SN3 4HH. Tel: 0793 826233
(H), 514514 ext. 2262 (W)
Fixtures Secretary: Steve Bartlett, 148 Windrush,
Highworth, Nr. Swindon, Wilts. Tel: 0793 764794
Press Officer: Steve Menham, 6 Cabot Drive, Grange
Park, Swindon, Wilts. Tel: 0793 875865
Coach: T.B.A.
Club captain (1988–89): Cyril Randall
Club captain (1989–90): Cyril Randall
No. of teams: Senior 3, Youth 4, Minis 6
Directions to ground: Situated off the main Swindon-
Highworth Road, 4 miles from Highworth
Clubhouse facilities: Lounge bar, function hall,
snooker, pool, darks, skittles
Club colours: Light/dark blue hoops. (*Change colours:*
Red)
Nickname: Vickers
Floodlights: Yes (training only)
Membership fees: Full £5, Playing £2, Social £11.50,
Youth Half, Student Half, OAP Free
Ground admission: Nil
Programme: No. of editorial pages 0; No. of
advertising pages 16 (Club Handbook – no
programmes)
Programme editor: Mike Atwell, 12 Volpe Close,
Grange Park, Swindon, Wilts
Local newspaper: Evening Advertiser
League: BDW 2
League position (1988–89): 4th
League playing record (1988–89): P 10, W 5, D 1,
L 4, F 96, A 76

SWINDON COLLEGE

Merton Fields, Merton Avenue, Swindon, Wilts.
Founded: 1964
Secretary: I. McHenry, 37 Weedon Road, Stratton,
St. Margaret, Swindon, Wilts SN3 4EG. Tel: 0793
828954 (H) 0793 616161. Extn. 2912 (W)

TROWBRIDGE

Green Lane, Ashton Park, Trowbridge, Wilts. Tel:
0225 761389
Founded: 1931
President: Ray Matthews
Secretary: Peter Riddiford, Pepperacre Lane,
Trowbridge. Tel: 753764
Fixtures Secretary: Bryn Parfitt, 60 Paxcroft Way,
Ashton Park, Trowbridge. Tel: 764953
Press Officer: Neil Fleming, 9 Avonvale Road,
Trowbridge. Tel: 761760
Coach: David Sullivan
Club captain (1988–89): Keith Morris

Club captain (1989–90): 'Billy' Chidlow
No. of teams: Senior 3, Youth 1
Directions to ground: Take West Ashton Road out of Trowbridge, take left turning (Green Lane), go to far end
Clubhouse facilities: Bar and changing rooms
Club colours: Light blue, dark blue and gold
Floodlights: No
League: BDW 2
League position (1988–89): 3rd
League playing record (1988–89): P 10, W 7, D 0, L 3, F 247, A 86
Competitions won: Dorset & Wilts Plate Competition, April '89

WESTBURY

Leighton Sports Ground, Wellhead Lane, Westbury, Wilts. Tel: 0373 826438
Founded: 1980
President: Dennis Cooke
Chairman: Maj. Colin Scragg
Secretary: Mark Knott, 4 Studland Park, Westbury, Wilts BA13 3HL. Tel: 0373 823479 (H), 822666 (W)
Fixtures Secretary: As Secretary
Press Officer: Malcolm Sadler, 'Brownhills', Bratton Road, Westbury. Tel: 0373 822392
Coach: Craig Hibbert
Club captain (1988–89): Steven Hinton
Club captain (1989–90): Mark Ball
No. of teams: Senior 2, Youth 1
Directions to ground: Warminster Road (A350), turn into Wellhead Lane opposite Cedar Hotel. Ground is 300 m on left
Ground capacity: Standing 500
Clubhouse facilities: Brand new opening Summer 1989. Large bar, skittles, 2 squash courts attached. Open every evening
Club colours: Green/black hoops. (*Change colours:* Blue/white hoops)
Floodlights: No (training lights, powerhouse scrummaging machine)
Membership fees: Playing £10, Social £3, Youth £3, Student £3, OAP £3
Programme: No. of editorial pages 2; No. of advertising pages 1; Price Donation
Programme editor: As Secretary
Local newspapers: Wiltshire Times, Baths & Wilts Evening Chronicle
League: BDW 2
League position (1988–89): 1st (promoted)
League playing record (1988–89): P 6, W 5, D 0, L 1, F 258, A 40

BERKS, DORSET & WILTS 3W

BLANDFORD

Larksmead, Blandford, Dorset
President: Dr. Ian Wilson
Chairman: Dr. John Evans
Secretary: Adrian Adams, Blandford Rugby Club, 53A East Street, Blandford, Dorset. Tel: 0258 53514
Fixtures Secretary: David Stringer, 21 Damory Street, Blandford, Dorset. Tel: 0258 56954
Press Officer: As Secretary
Coach: Sid Soqo
Club captain (1988–89): Steve Crocker
Club captain (1989–90): Steve Crocker
No. of teams: Senior 2
Directions to ground: Take the Salisbury road out of Blandford, turn right opposite the cemetery into Larksmead, then take first left
Ground capacity: Standing 4000
Clubhouse facilities: Open matchdays and evenings
Club colours: Gold, brown, red, white. (*Change colours:* White)
Nickname: The Bulldogs
Floodlights: Yes
Membership fees: Full £10, Playing £10, Social £3,

Youth £5, Student £5, OAP £5
Ground admission: Nil
Local newspapers: Dorset Evening Echo, Bournemouth Evening Echo, Western Gazette
League: BDW 3E
League position (1988–89): 6th
League playing record (1988–89): P 6, W 1, D 0, L 5, F 67, A 88
Competitions won: Lytchett 7's Plate Winners 1989

BRIDPORT

Bridport Leisure Centre, Brewery Fields, Skilling Hill Road, Bridport, Dorset DT6 5LN. Tel: 0308 27464
President: George Morgan
Chairman: Malcolm Heaver
Secretary: Richard Salt, 5 Downes Street, Bridport, Dorset OT6 3JR. Tel: 0308 22236 (W)
Fixtures Secretary: John Greig, 94 West Bay Road, Bridport, Dorset. Tel: 0308 56692 (H), 24600 (W)
Press Officer: Philip Moores. Tel: 0308 27266
Coach: Joe Seogalutze
Club captain (1989–90): Peter Wyrill
No. of teams: Senior 2, Youth 1, Minis 1
Club colours: Dark blue
Floodlights: Yes (training lights only)
League: BDW 3

DORSET INSTITUTE

Meyrick Park, Braidley Road, Bournemouth
Secretary: Dai Dower, DIHE, Wallisdown Road, Poole, Dorset BH12 5BB. Tel: 0202 768892 (H). 524111 Ext 5012 (W)
Press Officer: As Secretary
Club colours: Royal blue/navy/white
League: Berks/Dorset/Wilts 3 West

THE OLD PORTCASTRIANS

Cricket Pavilion, Meryick Park, Bournemouth. Tel: 0202 294990
President: Maxwell James Kennedy
Chairman: Gary Fretton
Secretary: Howard Larkin, 68 Redhill Drive, Endsbury Park, Bournemouth BH10 6AN. Tel: 302 466
Fixtures Secretary: Stuart May, 62 Bridport Road, Parkstone, Poole, Dorset. Tel: 730 864
Press Officer: Andy Hansford, 80 Stamford Road, South Bourne, Bournemouth, Dorset
Club captain (1988–89): Jonathan Fretton
Club captain (1989–90): Andy Hansford
No. of teams: Senior 1
Directions to ground: Right at Bournemouth Square, first right to Meryick Park
Clubhouse facilities: Bar
Club colours: Yellow/blue/red hoops
Floodlights: Yes
Membership fees: Full £5
Local newspaper: Bournemouth Evening Echo
League: BDW 3
League playing record (1988–89): P 6, W 2, D 0, L 4, F 51, A 72

PLESSEY CHRISTCHURCH

Grange Road, Somerford, Christchurch, Dorset
Chairman: D.J. Ward
Secretary: T.B.A., c/o Dave Ward, Plessey Defence Systems, Grange Road, Somerford, Christchurch, Dorset. Tel: 0202 48611 (H), 404664 (W)
Fixtures Secretary: David Tilley, 44 Tweedale Road, Bournemouth, Dorset B49 3LN. Tel: 0202 526074 (H), 404652 (W)

Press Officer: Steven Lidgbird, 184 Hillview Road, Ensbury Park, Bournemouth BH10 5BS. Tel: 0202 515394 (H), 404390 (W)
Club captain (1988–89): David Ward
Club captain (1989–90): Les Wilson
No. of teams: Senior 1
Directions to ground: From the east: out of Forest on A35, past Little Chef, first exit of next roundabout, 4th exit off next roundabout, back up dual carriageway, take first left into Grange Road
Ground capacity: Standing Unlimited
Clubhouse facilities: Open after matches and evenings
Club colours: Black and white hoops. (*Change colours:* Black, red and yellow hoops)
Floodlights: No
League: BDW 3W
League position (1988–89): Bottom
League playing record (1988–89): P 6, W 1, D 0, L 5, F 48, A 227

WARMINSTER

Sambourne Road, Warminster, Wilts. Tel: 0985 219019
President/Chairman: Tom Carroll
Secretary: Tony Holton, 6 Hillside Park, Westbury, Wilts BA13 3UQ. Tel: 0373 826502 (H), 0272 584121 (W)
Fixtures Secretary: D. Morrison, 16 Foxley Close, Warminster, Wilts
Press Officer: As Secretary
Club captain (1988–89): P. Dyton
Club captain (1989–90): A. Evans
No. of teams: Senior 2, Minis 6
Clubhouse facilities: Yes
Club colours: Blue/gold. (*Change colours:* Green/white strip)
Floodlights: Yes
League position (1988–89): 2nd
League playing record (1988–89): P 35, W 20, D 2, L 13

BERKS, DORSET & WILTS 3E

AMESBURY

League: Berks/Dorset/Wilts 3 East
No further information available

BERKSHIRE SHIRE HALL

Royal County of Berkshire Sports & Social Club, Sonning Lane, Sonning, Nr. Reading. Tel: 0734 691340
President: Cameron Kirk
Chairman: Keith Laws
Secretary: Trevor Keable, 9 Newport Road, Reading, Berks RL1 8EA. Tel: Reading 500324 (H), Slough 31201 (W)
Fixtures Secretary: David Croft, 16 Delamere Road, Earley, Reading RG6 1AP. Tel: 0734 67609 (H), 0276 29131 (W)
Press Officer: Mike Painter, 10 Wroxham Road, Woodley. Tel: 0734 442048
Coach: Steve Watson
Club captain (1988–89): Sandy Wieliczko
Club captain (1989–90): David Norris
No. of teams: Senior 2
Directions to ground: A4 out of Reading (off M4 Junction 10 – M329 towards Reading hitting A4). Towards London, follow dual carriageway up hill. Major roundabout, garage on let, Volvo Garage on island. Take 1st left (A4) over bridge, 1st left. Club signposted (we are 2nd right, opposite school)
Clubhouse facilities: Bar, showers, communal bath
Club colours: Blue and yellow hoops, black shirts, blue socks with gold top. (*Change colours:* Royal blue)

Floodlights: No
League: BDW 3E
League position (1988–89): 2nd
League playing record (1988–89): P 6, W 5, D 1, L 0, F 138, A 47

CALNE

Recreation Ground, Anchor Road, Calne. Tel: 0249 812206
President: Anthony Brent Russell
Chairman: Christopher Robinson
Secretary: Tom W. Gerken, 38 Duncan Street, Calne, Wilts SN11 9BU. Tel: 0249 816471 (H), 0272 276026 (W)
Fixtures Secretary: Mark Anthony Richardson, 81 Oaklands, Chippenham. Tel: 0249 659909
Club captain (1989–90): Sean Riches
No. of teams: Senior 2
Directions to ground: Off A4 in centre of town
Club colours: Blue with single red and white hoop. (*Change colours:* Red)
Floodlights: No
Membership fees: Full £15, Playing £15, Social £15, Youth £8, Student £8
League: BDW 3E
League position (1988–89): Bottom
League playing record (1988–89): P 6, W 1, D 0, L 5, F 38, A 199

COLERNE

c/o RAF Rudloe Manoe (own ground puchaed with target date for playing Sept. '90)
President: Rev. Roger Clifton, B.A., F.C.A.
Chairman: Simo Rogers
Secretary: David Stirling, 1 Grocyn Close, Colerne, Nr. Chippenham, Wilts SN14 8DZ. Tel: 0225 742007 (H), 08696 6044 (W)
Fixtures Secretary: As Secretary
Press Officer: As Secretary
Coach: Geoff Willis
Club captain (1988–89): John Hutchinson
Club captain (1989–90): Paul Alford
No. of teams: Senior 2
Clubhouse facilities: Colerne Liberal Club (target completion date for own clubhouse Sept. '89)
Club colours: All black. (*Change colours:* Red shirts, black shorts)
Floodlights: No
Membership fees: Full £25, Playing £10, Social £5, Youth £5, Student £5, OAP £5
Ground admission: Nil
Local newspaper: Bath and West Evening Chronicle
League: BDW 3E
League position (1988–89): 3rd
League playing record (1988–89): P 6, W 3, D 1, L 2, F 84, A 48

MINETY

Minety Playing Fields, Silver Street, Minety. Tel: 0666 860802
Founded: 1972
President: Mark Wallington
Chairman: Peter Gifford
Secretary: Judith Brown, 61 Bristol Street, Malmesbury, Wiltshire SN16 0AZ. Tel: 0666 822828
Fixtures Secretary: Ian Ormanroyd, 50 North Walk, Cricklade, Swindon. Tel: Swindon 751670
Press Officer: John Butler, 9 melford Walk, Swindon, Wiltshire. Tel: Swindon 497215
Coach: John Butler
Club captain (1988–89): Tny Kemp
Club captain (1989–90): Graeme Brown
No. of teams: Senior 3, Minis 1
Directions to ground: Chippenham, Malmesbury taking the Cricklade Road out for 6 miles to Minety
Clubhouse facilities: Bar, 4 changing rooms, toilets, skittle alley
Club colours: Green and purple hoops

Floodlights: No
Membership fees: Full £12, Playing £12, Social £6, Youth £6, Student £6, OAP £6
Local newspapers: Evening Advertiser, Wilts Gazette, Wilts & Glos Standard
League: BDW 3E
League position (1988–89): Bottom (relegated)
League playing record (1988–89): P 10, W 2, D 0, L 8, F 29, A 101

TADLEY

Hurst Community School, Braughurst, Hants. Tel: Tadley 71611
Chairman: Frank Jose
Secretary: Roy Mears, 7 Maple Grove, Tadley, Basingstoke, Hants RG26 6ND. Tel: 0734 815104
Fixtures Secretary: As Secretary
Press Officer: Derek Alston, Tadley, Basingstoke, Hants. Tel: 0734 816564
Coach: Bruce Surey
Club captain (1988–89): Derek Alston
Club captain (1989–90): Bruce Surey
No. of teams: Senior 2
Directions to ground: M4 Junction 12. Follow A340 to Tadley/Basingstoke, 2nd roundabout 3rd exit turn left at crossroads. Ground 1 mile on left. Alternative: M3 Junction 6. Follow A340 Tadley, Aldermaston, 2nd roundabout straight across, turn left at crossroad. Ground 1 mile on left
Clubhouse facilities: Wellington Arms Public House, Baughurst, Hants
Club colours: Black with amber hoop
Nickname: Tad's

Floodlights: No
Membership fees: Full £5, Playing £5, Social £2.50
Local newspapers: Newbury Weekly News, Basingstoke Gazette
League: BDW 3E
League position (1988–89): 4th
League playing record (1988–89): P 6, W 1, D 2, L 3, F 52, A 101

THATCHAM

The Kennet School, Stoney Lane, Thatcham
Chairman: P. Walker
Secretary: J. Short, 105 Sagecroft Road, Thatcham. Tel: 0635 60383
Fixtures Secretary: S. McNab
Press Officer: Roy Bloom
No. of teams: Senior 2, Youth 6
Directions to ground: A4 Bath Road, towards Newbury → left at junc. prior to The Plough pub → Stoney Lane → school on left
Clubhouse facilities: Bar
Club colours: Blue and red quarters. (*Change colours:* Blue)
Floodlights: No
Membership fees: Full £15, Playing £13
Ground admission: Nil
Programme: 1 × A4 sheet Price Free
League: B,D&W 3E
League position (1988–89): 4th
League playing record (1988–89): P 6, W 2, D 0, L 4, F 31, A 81

BUCKS AND OXON LEAGUES

ONE club from the 1987–88 season had dropped out as a result of no team being relegated from Southern Counties to replace promoted Slough and this time Chiltern, although losing two games, finished in top spot with a margin of three points over the challengers after a most competitive season. One point covered the next five teams and even the two relegated teams – Witney and Buckingham – won two matches and were by no means disgraced.

The promoted teams from Division 2 are Cholsey, winners of all nine games for a points differential of 178 to 40, and Olney (points difference a thundering 285–57), who finished well ahead of the field, whilst sadly at the foot of the table the only point gained each by Chesham and Chipping Norton came in the match they played against each other – and drew! That point was Chesham's first in the league and meant a rise of one place from 1987–88!

BUCKS AND OXON LEAGUES:

Humphrey Pocock,
10 Laceys Drive,
Hazlemere,
High Wycombe,   (H) 0494 713879
Bucks.   (O) 0895 36471

TABLES 1987–88

BUCKS & OXON 1

	P	W	D	L	F	A	PTS
Slough	11	10	1	0	162	61	21
Bicester	11	9	0	2	210	78	18
Chiltern	11	7	0	4	169	85	14
Littlemore	11	6	1	4	134	124	13
Grove	11	5	1	5	157	99	11
Beaconsfield	11	5	1	5	108	112	11
Chinnor	11	5	1	5	89	109	11
Pennanians	11	4	1	6	115	128	9
Witney	11	4	1	6	91	113	9
Buckingham	11	4	0	7	119	175	8
Abingdon	11	2	0	9	67	241	4
Didcot	11	1	1	9	56	152	3

BUCKS & OXON 2

	P	W	D	L	F	A	PTS
Drifters	9	7	1	1	203	51	15
Milt Keynes	9	7	0	2	168	56	14
Olney	9	7	0	2	158	54	14
Wheatley	9	7	0	2	144	63	14
Phoenix	9	5	1	3	143	78	11
Cholsey	9	4	0	5	78	122	8
Gosford AB	9	3	0	6	111	123	6
Chipping Ntn	9	2	0	7	87	114	4
Harwell	9	2	0	7	116	223	4
Chesham	9	0	0	9	33	357	0

TABLES 1988-89

BUCKS & OXON 1

	P	W	D	L	F	A	PTS
Chiltern	10	8	0	2	164	84	16
Littlemoor	10	6	1	3	155	63	13
Pennanians	10	6	1	3	116	110	13
Beaconsfield	10	6	0	4	158	95	12
Chinnor	10	6	0	4	160	109	12
Bicester	10	6	0	4	158	133	12
Drifters	10	4	1	5	99	113	9
Grove	10	3	2	5	101	145	8
Milt Keynes	10	3	0	7	101	150	6
Witney	10	2	1	7	99	192	5
Buckingham	10	2	0	8	104	221	4

BUCKS & OXON 2

	P	W	D	L	F	A	PTS
Cholsey	9	9	0	0	178	40	18
Olney	9	8	0	1	285	57	16
Wheatley	9	6	0	3	129	55	12
Didcot	9	6	0	3	161	99	12
Abingdon	9	5	0	4	98	99	10
Gosford A Bs	9	4	0	5	116	104	8
Phoenix	9	4	0	5	111	132	8
Harwell	9	2	0	7	54	252	4
Chesham	90	0	1	8	71	178	1
Chipping Ntn	9	0	1	8	46	233	1

SOUTH WEST DIVISION FIXTURES 1989/90

BUCKS & OXON ONE

Sat. 9th September (Week 2)
Beaconsfield v Bicester
Milton Keynes v Grove
Olney v Drifters
Oxford Marathon v Cholsey
Pennanians v Chinnor

Sat. 23rd September (Week 4)
Cholsey v Pennanians
Drifters v Oxford Marathon
Grove v Olney
Littlemoor v Milton Keynes
Chinnor v Beaconsfield

Sat. 14th October (Week 6)
Beaconsfield v Cholsey
Bicester v Chinnor
Olney v Littlemoor
Oxford Marathon v Grove
Pennanians v Drifters

Sat. 28th October (Week 8)
Cholsey v Bicester
Drifters v Beaconsfield
Grove v Pennanians
Littlemoor v Oxford Marathon
Milton Keynes v Olney

Sat. 11th November (Week 10)
Beaconsfield v Grove
Bicester v Drifters
Chinnor v Cholsey
Oxford Marathon v Milton Keynes
Pennanians v Littlemoor

Sat 18th November (Week 11)
Drifters v Chinnor
Grove v Bicester
Littlemoor v Beaconsfield
Milton Keynes v Pennanians
Olney v Oxford Marathon

Sat. 25th November (Week 12)
Beaconsfield v Milton Keynes
Bicester v Littlemoor
Chinnor v Grove
Cholsey v Drifters
Pennanians v Olney

Sat. 13th January (Week 18)
Grove v Cholsey
Littlemoor v Chinnor
Milton Keynes v Bicester
Olney v Beaconsfield
Oxford Marathon v Pennanians

Sat. 10th March (Week 26)
Beaconsfield v Oxford Marathon
Bicester v Olney
Chinnor v Milton Keynes
Cholsey v Littlemoor
Drifters v Grove

Sat. 31st March (Week X7)
Littlemoor v Drifters
Milton Keynes v Cholsey
Olney v Chinnor
Oxford Marathon v Bicester
Pennanians v Beaconsfield

Sat. 28th April (Week 32)
Bicester v Pennanians
Chinnor v Oxford Marathon
Cholsey v Olney
Drifters v Milton Keynes
Grove v Littlemoor

SOUTH WEST DIVISION FIXTURES 1989/90

BUCKS & OXON TWO

Sat. 9th September (Week 2)
Abingdon v Chesham
Witney v Gosford AB
Phoenix v Didcot
Wheatley v Buckingham

Sat. 23rd September (Week 4)
Didcot v Wheatley
Gosford AB v Phoenix
Harwell v Witney
Chipping Norton v Abingdon

Sat. 14th October (Week 6)
Abingdon v Buckingham
Chesham v Chipping Norton
Phoenix v Harwell
Wheatley v Gosford AB

Sat. 28th October (Week 8)
Buckingham v Chesham
Didcot v Abingdon
Harwell v Wheatley
Witney v Phoenix

Sat. 11th November (Week 10)
Abingdon v Gosford AB
Chesham v Didcot
Chipping Norton v Buckingham
Wheatley v Witney

Sat 18th November (Week 11)
Didcot v Chipping Norton
Gosford AB v Chesham
Harwell v Abingdon
Phoenix v Wheatley

Sat. 25th November (Week 12)
Abingdon v Witney
Chesham v Harwell
Chipping Norton v Gosford AB
Buckingham v Didcot

Sat. 13th January (Week 18)
Gosford AB v Buckingham
Harwell v Chipping Norton
Witney v Chesham
Phoenix v Abingdon

Sat. 10th March (Week 26)
Abingdon v Wheatley
Chesham v Phoenix
Chipping Norton v Witney
Buckingham v Harwell
Didcot v Gosford AB

Sat. 31st March (Week X7)
Harwell v Didcot
Witney v Buckingham
Phoenix v Chipping Norton
Wheatley v Chesham

Sat. 28th April (Week 32)
Chipping Norton v Wheatley
Buckingham v Phoenix
Didcot v Witney
Gosford AB v Harwell

BUCKS & OXON 1

BEACONSFIELD

Oak Lodge Meadow, Windsor End, Beaconsfield.
Tel: 0494 63783
Founded: 1953
President: N. Hickman
Chairman: A. Batty
Secretary: P. Badman, Southways, Burkes Crescent,
Beaconsfield. Tel: 0494 63509
Fixtures Secretary: A. Batty, 43 Lakes Lane,
Beaconsfield. Tel: 0494 63471
Coach: M. Wood
Club captain (1988–89): S. Wall
Club captain (1989–90): S. Wall
No. of teams: Senior 6, Youth 10 + Minis
Directions to ground: M40 follow signs to
Beaconsfield, turn left in centre of town
Club colours: Green/yellow. (*Change colours:*
Blue/white)
Floodlights: Yes
Membership fees: Playing £36
League: Bucks & Oxon 1
League position (1988–89): 4th
League playing record (1988–89): P 10, W 6, D 0,
L 4, F 158, A 95

BICESTER

Oxford Road, Bicester, Oxfordshire. Tel: 0869 241000
Founded: 1948
President: Roger Smith
Chairman: Tom Coker
Secretary: Jack Gomarsall, Cottage on the Green,
Hethe, Bicester, Oxon OX6 9EU. Tel: 0869 7752 (H),
246733 (W)
Fixtures Secretary: George Davies, 166 Barry
Avenue, Bicester, Oxon. Tel: 0869 241993
Club captain (1988–89): Dave Spencer
Club captain (1989–90): Dave Spencer
No. of teams: Senior 5, Youth 2, Minis 5
Club colours: Red, amber, chocolate hoops
Floodlights: No
League: Bucks/Oxon 1

CHINNOR

The Pavilion, Kingsey Road, Thame, Oxon. Tel:
084421 3735
Founded: 1963
President: Joseph Slinger
Chairman: Kevin Robinson
Secretary: Neil Gardham, c/o K. Robinson, Pathways,
10 The Rise, Kingston Blount, Oxon OX9 4RD. Tel:
0844 53428 (H), 0491 41077 (W)
Fixtures Secretary: N.K. Robinson, Pathways, 10 The
Rise, Kingston Blount, Oxon OX9 4RY. Tel: 0844
53428 (H), 0491 410779 (W)
Press Officer: P. Fincken, 1 Foster Close, Aylebury,
Bucks. Tel: 0296 434367 (H), 01–702 4251 (W)
Coach: B. Ward
Club captain (1988–89): B. Evans
Club captain (1989–90): J. Mark
No. of teams: Senior 6, Youth 2, Minis 3
Directions to ground: To Thame, southern bypass at
intersection to road to Princes Risborough
Ground capacity: Standing 1000
Clubhouse facilities: 8 changing rooms, lounge and
social areas
Club colours: Black and white hoops. (*Change
colours:* White)
Floodlights: No
Membership fees: Full £30, Playing £30, Youth £10,
Student £10
League: Bucks Oxon 1
League position (1988–89): 3rd
League playing record (1988–89): P 34, W 22, D 1,
L 11, F 646, A 341

CHOLSEY

Hithercroft Road, Wallingford, Oxon. Tel: 0491
35044
Founded: 1967
Secretary: D. Haynes, 20 Hambledon Drive,
Wallingford, Oxon OX10 0PQ. Tel: 0491 35578 (H),
0727 26766 (W)
Fixtures Secretary: R. Hodgson, 11 Anthony Hill
Road, RAF Benson, Wallingford, Oxon. Tel: 0491
39975
Club colours: Black/amber
League: Bucks & Oxon 1
League position (1988–89): 1st
League playing record (1988–89): P 9, W 9, D 0, L 0,
F 178, A 40

DRIFTERS

Farnham Common Sports Club, One Pin Lane,
Farnham Common, Bucks SL2 3QY. Tel: Farnham
Common 4190
Founded: 1963
President: L.C. Clark
Chairman: G.H.A. Lewis
Secretary: Glenn Charles Miller, c/o Farnham
Common Sports Club, One Pin Lane, Farnham
Common, Bucks SL2 3QY. Tel: 0628 29715 (H), 0753
654000 (W)
Fixtures Secretary: Roger Ellis, c/o Farnham
Common Sports Club. Tel: Bracknell 59902 (H),
01–562 5694 (W)
Press Officer: Chris Ashton, c/o Farnham Common
Sports Club. Tel: 0753 692099 (H), 01–679 1899 (W)
Club captain (1988–89): Patrick Spellman
Club captain (1989–90): Patrick Spellman
No. of teams: Senior 3
Directions to ground: From the M40 or M4 take the
A355. One Pin Lane is approx. 1 miles outside
Farnham Common heading towards M40
Ground capacity: Standing 200
Clubhouse facilities: Open 7 days a week
Club colours: Black and magenta. (*Change colours:*
Red)
Floodlights: No
Membership fees: Full £38, Playing £38, Social £12,
Youth £19, Student £19
Local newspapers: Slough Observer, Slough, Windsor
& Eton Express
League: Bucks/Oxon 1
League position (1988–89): 7th
League playing record (1988–89): P 30, W 16, D 2,
L 12, F 373, A 285

GROVE

Grove Recreation Ground, Cane Lane, Grove,
Wantage, Oxon. Tel: 02357 67041
Founded: 1972
President: E.A. Prosser
Chairman: Rodger Williams
Secretary: Steve Hopkins, 35 Mill Road, Abingdon,
Oxon OX14 SN2. Tel: 0235 32273
Fixtures Secretary: Alan Davies, 23 Cameron
Avenue, Abingdon, Oxon. Tel: 0235 33568
Coach: T.B.A.
Club captain (1988–89): Bob Hallam
Club captain (1989–90): Duncan Nicholl
No. of teams: Senior 4, Youth 2, Minis 2
Directions to ground: Main road from Oxford to
Wantage. Take 2nd Grove turn second left into Cane
Lane. Groundon left 200 yds.
Club colours: Red, white blue
Floodlights: No
Membership fees: Full £15
Local newspaper: Wantage Herald
League: Bucks/Oxon 1
League position (1988–89): 8th
League playing record (1988–89): P 36

LITTLEMORE

Littlemore R.F.C., Peers School, Sandy Lane (West),
Littlemore, Oxford OX4 5JY. Tel: 0865 715776
Founded: 1978
President: Kevin Heffernan
Chairman: Noel Heffernan
Secretary: Charles Bowler, Hillside, Elm Drive,
Garsington, Oxon OX9 9AG. Tel: 086736 766 (H),
985 6427 (W)
Fixtures Secretary: Carl Wright, 91 Alice Smith
Square, Littlmore, Oxford OX4 4NQ. Tel: 0865
770301
Press Officer: Tim Stevens, 34 Eastern Avenue,
Littlemore, Oxford OX4 4QS. Tel: 0865 779886
Coach: L. Evans
Club captain (1988–89): J. Kennedy/C. Wright
Club captain (1989–90): C. Wright
No. of teams: Senior 2, Minis 2
Directions to ground: On reaching Oxford join the
Oxford ring-road system heading towards Cowley and
the Austin-Rover roundabout. Next take the A4142
south, under a road bridge, then left at a turning
marked Peer school Sports & Arts Centre. First right
on a long drive to the car park
Ground capacity: Standing 2000
Clubhouse facilities: Open Monday to Friday
evenings, lunch-time, afternoon evenings, match day
Saturdays. Sunday lunchtime and evenings
Club colours: White shirts, white shorts, royal blue
socks. (*Change colours:* Royal blue shirts, white
shorts, royal blue socks)
Nickname: 'More', 'The Whites'
Floodlights: Yes (for training purposes only)
Membership fees: Playing £15, Social £5, Youth £7.50,
Student £7.50
Ground admission: Free
Programme: No. of editorial pages 2; No. of
advertising pages 2; Price Free
Programme editor: As Press Officer
Local newspapers: Oxford Mail, Oxford Times,
Oxford Star, Oxford Journal
League: Bucks/Oxon 1
League position (1988–89): 2nd
League playing record (1988–89): P 32, W 24, D 1,
L 7, F 636, A 249
Competitions won: Runners-Up in Bucks/Oxon
League 1, Runners-Up Diespeker Oxfordshire Merit
Table

MILTON KEYNES

Field Lane, Greenleys, Wolverton, Milton Keynes.
Tel: 0908 313858
Founded: 1895
President: Jeff Butterfield
Chairman: John Silk
Secretary: Peter Hemingway Acting Secretary), 6
Malvern Drive, Hilltop, Stony Stratford, Milton
Keynes MK11 2AE. Tel: 0908 564931 (H), 01–863
5611 ext. 2474 (W)
Fixtures Secretary: Verryl H. Wilcox, 8 Caxton Road,
Wolverton, Milton Keynes. Tel: 0908 313083
Press Officer: As Secretary
Coach: T.B.A.
Club captain (1988–89): Rick White
Club captain (1989–90): Paul Earnshaw
No. of teams: Senior 4, Youth 3, Minis 4
Directions to ground: Lies between Stony Stratford
and Wolverton in the north-west corner of Milton
Keynes, adjacent to the A5 trunk road
Ground capacity: Standing 500
Clubhouse facilities: Open weekends and evenings
during the week
Club colours: Black with a single white band around
the chest
Nickname: 'Wolves'
Floodlights: Yes (training only)
Membership fees: Full £20, Playing £20, Social £5,
Youth £5, Student £5, OAP £5
Local newspapers: Milton Keynes Citizen, Herald,

Mirror
League: Bucks/Oxon 1
League position (1988–89): 9th

OLNEY

Recreation Ground, East Street, Olney, Bucks. Tel:
0234 712880
Founded: 1877
President: Leslie Fairey
Chairman: 'Manny' Howkins
Secretary: Stuart Parkin, West View Farm, Olney,
Bucks MK46 5EX. Tel: 0234 713165 (H), 711792 (W)
Fixtures Secretary: Robert Taylor, 24 Elmea Drive,
Olney, Bucks. Tel: 0234 712110 (H), 0604 765895 (W)
Press Officer: Des Coltman, Rosary Cottage, Tapp
Yard, Stoke Goldington, Bucks. Tel: 94 55455 (H),
0296 688632 (W)
Coach: Tony Carter
Club captain (1988–89): R. Morel
Club captain (1989–90): T.B.A.
No. of teams: Senior 5, Youth 3, Minis 5
Directions to ground: Entering Olney from Newport
Pagnell turn right at Market Square, then left into
East Street. Approx. 400 yards turn right into
Recreation Ground car park
Clubhouse facilities: Large clubroom and members
lounge, garden, baths, showers and 4 changing rooms
Club colours: Cerise and French grey. (*Change
colours:* Blue)
Floodlights: Yes (training)
Membership fees: Full £20, Playing £10, Social £1,
Youth £1, Student £2.50
Ground admission: 00p
Programme: No. of editorial pages 4; No. of
advertising pages 1
Programme editor: Des Coltman, Rosary Cottage,
Tap Yard, Stoke Goldington, Bucks
Local newspapers: Milton Keynes Herald, Milton
Keynes Citizen
League: Bucks/Oxon 2
League position (1988–89): 2nd
League playing record (1988–89): P 9, W 8, D 0, L 1,
F 285, A 57
Competitions won: Lewis Shield Winners, April '89

OXFORD MARATHON

Horspath Road, Cowley, Oxford. Tel: 0865 775765
Founded: 1948
President: W. Franklin
Chairman: K. Hearn
Secretary: A. Barson, 97 Oxford Road, Garsington,
Oxford OX9 9AD. Tel: 0865 36540
Fixtures Secretary: R. Reynolds, 2 The Orchard,
Badswell Lane, Appleton, Abingdon, Oxon. Tel:
0865 863765
Coach: G. Williams
Club captain (1988–89): G. Williams
Clubhouse facilities: Full
Club colours: Navy/amber. (*Change colours:* Red)
Nickname: Maras
Floodlights: Yes (training)
Membership fees: Playing £15
League: Bucks & Oxon 1
League position (1988–89): 11th
League playing record (1988–89): P 10, W 0, D 0,
L 10, F 42, A 264

PENNANIANS

Farnham Park Sports Field, Farnham Royal, Bucks.
Tel: 02814 6252
Founded: No
President: T.B.A.
Chairman: Richard Thomas
Secretary: M.A. Bartlett, 14 Adam Close,
Bishopswood Lane, Baughurst, Hants RG26 5HG.
Tel: 07356 3867
Fixtures Secretary: Dave Watson, 40 St. Andrews
Way, Cippenham, Slough, Berks. Tel: Burnham

66098
Press Officer: Ray Spencer, 79 Burgett Road, Slough,
Berks. Tel: Slough 38109
Coach: T.B.A.
Club captain (1988–89): Nigel Pyefinch
Club captain (1989–90): T.B.A.
No. of teams: Senior 3
Directions to ground: From M4 Exit 6 towards
Beaconsfield A355, through Farnham Royal, 200 yds
right into Farnham Park
Clubhouse facilities: At present extending
Club colours: Black with two white bands through
chest. (*Change colours:* White black collar/cuffs)
Nickname: Penns
Floodlights: No (training lights)
Membership fees: Full £25, Playing £25, Social £10,
Youth £10, Student £10, OAP £10
Local newspapers: Slough Observer, Slough Express
League: Bucks/Oxon 1
League position (1988–89): =2nd
League playing record (1988–89): P 10, W 6, D 1,
L 3, F 116, A 110

BUCKS AND OXON 2

ABINGDON

Lambrick Way, Abingdon, Oxon
President: G. Dimond
Chairman: R. Simpson
Secretary: K. Sykes, 24 Segsbury Road, Wantage,
Oxon OX12 9XP. Tel: 0235 769320 (H), 0491 35351
(W)
Fixtures Secretary: Contact Clubhouse
Press Officer: C. Mole, 26 High Street, Drayton, Nr.
Abingdon, Oxon. Tel: Ab 31507
Coach: Dr. N. Crosley
Club captain (1988–89): Dr. N. Crosley
Club captain (1989–90): Dr. N. Crosley
No. of teams: Senior 4
Directions to ground: Drayton and Sutton Coldfield
Road out of Abingdon → over r'about → 2nd left
(Preston Road) → Lambrick Way mile on right and
signposted to Abingdon Marina
Clubhouse facilities: 2 bars
Club colours: Green/yellow. (*Change colours:* Green)
Floodlights: No
Membership fees: Full £17.50, Playing £17.50, Social
£5
League: Bucks & Oxon 2
League position (1988–89): 5th
League playing record (1988–89): P 9, W 5, D 0, L 4,
F 98, A 99

BUCKINGHAM

Moreton Road, Buckingham, Bucks. Tel: 0280 815474
Founded: 1933
President: R.A. Smith
Chairman: E. Curtis
Secretary: F.M. Gemmell, 22 Elmfields, Winslow,
Bucks. Tel: 0296 714640 (H), 393123 ext. 2388 (W)
Fixtures Secretary: F.A.W. Smith, 10 Mare Leys,
Buckinghamshire. Tel: 0280 815634
Press Officer: As Fixture Secretary
Coach: Clive Martin/Tony Grant
Club captain (1988–89): Jack Evershed
Club captain (1989–90): Will Abbott
No. of teams: Senior 4
Directions to ground: From centre of buckingham
(Market Square) follow A413 to Towcester and
ground is on left on edge of town, one mile from town
centre
Clubhouse facilities: Open training evenings, Sat.
lunch./eve., Sun. lunch.
Club colours: . (*Change colours:*)
Floodlights: No
Membership fees: Full £25
Local newspapers: Slough Express and Slough
Observer

League: Bucks/Oxon 1
League position (1988–89): 11th
League playing record (1988–89): P 10, W 2, D 0, L 8

CHESHAM

Chess Valley Sports and Leisure Association, The
Moor, Chesham, Bucks
Founded: 1981
President: Frederick William Kerr
Chairman: Neil Page
Secretary: Peter Wharton, 41 Glenister Road,
Chesham, Bucks. Tel: 0494 783659
Fixtures Secretary: Richard King, 75 Darvell Drive,
Chesham, Buckinghamshire. Tel: 0494 786056
Club captain (1988–89): Barry Bowd
Club captain (1989–90): Peter Gent
No. of teams: Senior 3
Directions to ground: From Amersham: Upon
entering Chesham turn right at the first roadabout,
continue for 600 yds. Chess Valley Sports and Leisure
Association (Chesham Swimming Pool) is on the right
Clubhouse facilities: Chesham Cricket Club
Club colours: Claret/blue hoops. (*Change colours:*
White)
Nickname: Stags
Floodlights: No
Membership fees: Full £20, Playing £20, Social £10,
Youth £10, Student £10, OAP £10
Ground admission: Nil
Local newspapers: Bucks Examiner, Bucks Advertiser
League: Bucks/Oxon 2
League position (1988–89): 9th

CHIPPING NORTON

Greystones, Burford Road, Chipping Norton, Oxon.
Tel: Chipping Norton 3968.
Founded: 1975
Secretary: R. Hemmings, Cotswold Cresent, Chipping
Norton, Oxon. Tel: 0608 2078.
Colours: Red/Black.
League: Bucks & Oxon 2

DIDCOT

Edmonds Park, Park Road, Didcot, Oxon OX11
8QX, c/o Youth Centre. Tel: 0235 812332
Founded: 1955
President: James Turner
Chairman: John 'Yorkie' Fleming
Secretary: John Kilcznski, 46 Slade Road, Didcot,
Oxon OX11 7AT. Tel: 0235 815582 (H), 813435 (W)
Fixtures Secretary: Martin Llewellyn, 54 Lloyd Road,
Didcot, Oxon OX11 8JT. Tel: 0235 813634
Press Officer: As Secretary
Coach: Martin Llewellyn
Club captain (1988–89): Simon Beard
Club captain (1989–90): Steve Thomas
No. of teams: Senior 2, Youth 1, Minis 1
Directions to ground: Ask for Didcot Youth Centre
Clubhouse facilities: Bar on matchdays only
Club colours: Red/white hooped jerseys, white shorts,
black socks
Floodlights: No
Membership fees: Full £7.50, Playing £7.50, Social
£7.50
League: Bucks/Oxon 2

GOSFORD ALL BLACKS

Langford Lane, Kidlington, Oxford. Tel: Kidlington
3994
Founded: 1956
President: John O'Shea
Chairman: Paul Willats
Secretary: Alan Smith, 28 Great Close Road,
Yarnton, Oxon. Tel: 08675 71037 (H), 0865 742742

(W)
Fixtures Secretary: David Outhie, Langford Lane, Kidlington, Oxford. Tel: 0993 702261
Press Officer: Martin Cook, Langford Lane, Kidlington, Oxford
Club captain (1988–89): Alan Smith
Club captain (1989–90): Gary Coleman
No. of teams: Senior 3
Directions to ground: From Oxford take road to Woodstock, turn right at signpost to Airport. Club is opposite entrance to Airport
Clubhouse facilities: Standard
Club colours: Black. (*Change colours:* Black and yellow)
Floodlights: No
League: Bucks/Oxon 2
League position (1988–89): 6th
League playing record (1988–89): P 9, W 4, D 0, L 5, F 116, A 104

HARWELL

Social Club, A.E.R.E. Harwell, Chilton, Oxon. Tel: 0235 834331
Founded: 1947
President: Brian A. Arnold
Chairman: Gary Daluzvieira
Secretary: Colin Bartlett, 66 Upthorpe Drive, Wantage, Oxon. Tel: Wantage 67596 (H), 0235 24141 ext. 2419 (W)
Fixtures Secretary: Brian L. Flanders, Old Cross House, Coscote, Didcot, Oxon OX11 0NP. Tel: 0235 816523 (H), 0865 340471 (W)
Press Officer: T.B.A.
Coach: T.B.A.
Club captain (1988–89): Nigel Cook
Club captain (1989–90): Douglas Bosley
No. of teams: Senior 3
Directions to ground: A34 north/south come off at Chilton (south) or Milton (north) on to A4130 to main gate at A.E.R.E. Harwell site
Ground capacity: Standing 300
Clubhouse facilities: A.E.R.E. Social Club, 3 bars, dining hall, games room, air hall
Club colours: Navy/light blue/white hoops, blue shorts and socks. (*Change colours:* All blue)
Floodlights: No
League: Bucks/Oxon 2
League position (1988–89): 8th
League playing record (1988–89): P 9, W 2, D 0, L 7, F 54, A 252

PHOENIX

Institute Road, Taplow, Bucks. Tel: 0628 664319
Founded: 1963
President: Peter Carr
Chairman: Steve Rafferty
Secretary: Andrew Underwood, 708 Bath Road, Taplow, Bucks. Tel: 0628 663011 (H), 01–589 8100 (W)
Fixtures Secretary: Steve Turner, 20 Balmoral Close, Cippenham, Slough, Berks. Tel: 0628 661660
Press Officer: Nigel Duffett, 213 Trelawney Avenue, Langley, Slough, Berks. Tel: 0735 45345 (H), 0753 842088 (W)
Coach: Steve Rafferty
Club captain (1988–89): Steve Turner
Club captain (1989–90): Steve Turner
No. of teams: Senior 4
Directions to ground: M4 Exit Junction 7, A4 head towards Maidenhead, over crossroads, over roundabout, next right, first left after bridge
Clubhouse facilities: Open Tues., Thurs. and Sat. evening and and Sun. lunch.
Club colours: Red and black. (*Change colours:* Black)
Floodlights: Yes (training only)
Membership fees: Full £25, Playing £25, Social £15, Student £5
Local newspapers: Slough Express, Slough Observer, Maidenhead Advertiser
League: Bucks/Oxon 2
League playing record (1988–89): P 33, W 15, D 1, L 17, F 444, A 485

WHEATLEY

Founded: 1971
Secretary: Paul Willmott, 12 Orchard Close, Wheatley, Oxford OX9 1US. Tel: 08677 2972 (H), 4311 (W).
Press Officer: R. Cosier. Tel: 08677 3502.
Colours: Purple/White
League: Bucks & Oxon 2

WITNEY

Tel: 0993 771043
President: John Jackson
Chairman: Danny Crump
Secretary: T.B.A., Clubhouse, Witney Road, Hailey, Witney, Oxon OX8 5XX
Fixtures Secretary: F. Cobb, 41 Hill Crescent, Finstock, Oxford. Tel: Ramsden 422
Press Officer: David Gardner. Tel: 0993 779222
Club captain (1988–89): D. Wicks
Club captain (1989–90): T.B.A.
No. of teams: Senior 4, Youth 1, Minis 3
Directions to ground: Charlbury Road out of Witney, on left-hand side just before Hailey village
Club colours: Blue and black hoops. (*Change colours:* Sky blue)
Floodlights: No
League: Bucks/Oxon 2

Old Millhillians of Middlesex 1 – 1988–89.

Plenty of energetic players and there is also a ball. Wisbech show the way.

LONDON AND SOUTH EAST DIVISION

THE LONDON & South East Division now has 34 leagues covered by seven county groupings topped off by an elite first division, two second divisions and four third divisions – the latter two categories being regional. That was the same organisation that prevailed in the opening season of leagues, but the extra clubs now mean that this area is the biggest in the whole Courage Leagues "set-up", although it still remains to be seen whether it is the strongest and that can only be proved if Basingstoke, who won the London Division 1 title narrowly from Sutton & Epsom, can survive in Area League South as Ealing – most unluckily – failed to do.

Other divisions may be short on quantity, but both the North and the South West may make justifiable claims to being superior in terms of quality at this level, so results in the National Divisions and, particularly, in Area League South will be watched with interest along with the Pilkington Cup efforts of such as Ealing, Ruislip, Old Alleynians, Worthing, Cheshunt and others. On their efforts will the area be judged.

LONDON & SOUTH EAST DIVISION STRUCTURE

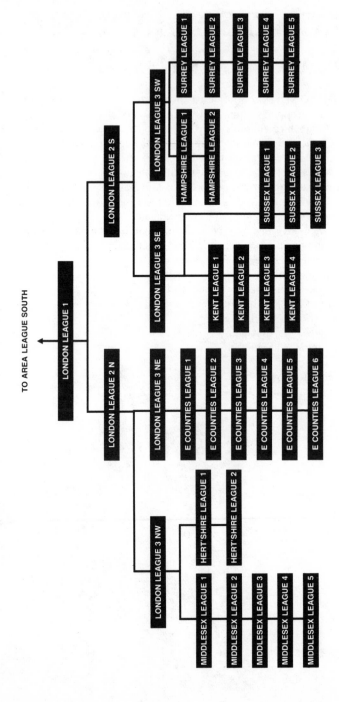

TO AREA LEAGUE SOUTH

LONDON LEAGUE 1

LONDON LEAGUE 2 N

LONDON LEAGUE 2 S

LONDON LEAGUE 3 NW

LONDON LEAGUE 3 NE

LONDON LEAGUE 3 SE

LONDON LEAGUE 3 SW

MIDDLESEX LEAGUE 1
MIDDLESEX LEAGUE 2
MIDDLESEX LEAGUE 3
MIDDLESEX LEAGUE 4
MIDDLESEX LEAGUE 5

HERT'SHIRE LEAGUE 1
HERT'SHIRE LEAGUE 2

E COUNTIES LEAGUE 1
E COUNTIES LEAGUE 2
E COUNTIES LEAGUE 3
E COUNTIES LEAGUE 4
E COUNTIES LEAGUE 5
E COUNTIES LEAGUE 6

KENT LEAGUE 1
KENT LEAGUE 2
KENT LEAGUE 3
KENT LEAGUE 4

SUSSEX LEAGUE 1
SUSSEX LEAGUE 2
SUSSEX LEAGUE 3

HAMPSHIRE LEAGUE 1
HAMPSHIRE LEAGUE 2

SURREY LEAGUE 1
SURREY LEAGUE 2
SURREY LEAGUE 3
SURREY LEAGUE 4
SURREY LEAGUE 5

LONDON & SOUTH EAST DIVISION COMPETITION SUB-COMMITTEE COURAGE CLUBS CHAMPIONSHIP RULES

1.   These Rules shall be in addition to the Courage Clubs Championship Regulations and shall be read in conjunction with the Administrative Instructions.

2. ORGANISING COMMITTEE

The Competition shall be organised by the Competition Sub-Committee of the Rugby Football Union who have delegated to the London & South East Division (Competition Sub-committee) powers to organise Divisional Leagues within the Division.

The Divisional Competition Sub-Committee has requested the Constituent Bodies within the Division to administer County Leagues in accordance with these Rules.

3. STRUCTURE

Promotion from the London & South East Division League One and the South & South West Division League One shall be to the RFU Area League South. The London & South East Division Leagues below League One shall be League Two North and League Two South. Promotion from League Two North and League Two South shall be to League One.

The London & South East Division Leagues below League Two North and League Two South shall be League Three North-East, League Three North-West, League Three South-East and League Three South-West. Promotion from League Three North-East and League Three North-West shall be to League Two North and promotion from League Three South-East and League Three South-West shall be to League Two South.

Each Constituent Body shall have a first County League and other such lower Leagues as may be required for the allocated Clubs entered in the Competition.

Promotion from Hertfordshire League One and Middlesex League One shall be to League Three North-West; from Eastern Counties League One shall be to League Three North-East; from Kent League One and Sussex League One shall be to League Three South-East;

and from Hampshire League One and Surrey League One shall be to League Three South-West.

Each League shall comprise not more than eleven clubs except that, in Leagues below County league One, the number may be more or less, subject to the approval of the Divisional Competition Sub-committee.

4. PROMOTION AND RELEGATION

Where a County League below League One comprises more than eleven clubs at the inauguration of the Competition, promotion and relegation shall be implemented to ensure that such Leagues shall continue to comprise not more than the same number of Clubs as in the preceding season. Entry to and resignation from the lowest League may vary the number of Clubs in that League.

5. ELIGIBILITY – PLAYERS

All Clubs entering the Competition shall, by the date of the first League match in each season, prepare a list of bone fide regular playing members with particulars of the date on which they became members. Such list shall be altered and amended, where necessary, on the date of each League match. This list shall be available for inspection at the premises of the Club to members of the organising committee of the League.

Each Club shall keep a record of the names of players and replacements in each League match on the team sheets provided, such lists being available for inspection together with the membership records.

Where it is found that a competing Club has played an ineligible player in a League match; that club shall forfeit any Championship points won in the match and have any match points scored by them deducted.

6. PLAYING OF MATCHES

League matches shall be played on the dates laid down in the fixture lists by the organising committee of the League in accordance with Regulation 6(a). Only weather conditions would normally provide a reason for not so playing but a club may appeal to its League Secretary for dispensation where circumstances, totally beyond the control of the club and its members, prevail.

7. POSTPONED MATCHES

In the event of a League match having to be postponed for an acceptable reason, BOTH Clubs have a responsibility for its re-arrangement. Both clubs shall individually notify their League Secretary of the re-arranged date within FOURTEEN days after the date of the postponed fixture. All post-poned matches shall be played as soon as poss-ible, but, in any event, not later than 31st March in any season.

In the absence of a notification of a mutually acceptable re-arranged date within the time specified, the League Secretary shall have the power to direct the clubs to play on a particular date.

8. FAILURE TO FULFIL FIXTURES

Failure to comply with rules 6 and 7 above may render the offending Club liable to be placed bottom of its League and have all its results removed from the League records.

9. NOTIFICATION OF RESULTS

a. The home club shall notify the appropriate officer of the League, as defined in the Admi-nistrative Instructions, of the result of a League match by telephone by the time stated in the Administrative Instructions.
b. Both clubs shall confirm, in writing on the cards provided, to the appropriate officer of the League, the result of each match played, together with the score, in accordance with the Administrative Instructions.

Failure to comply with 9(a) shall incur an immediate fine of £25 for the first and second offence which shall be paid within 28 days of the notification of the fine. Failure to notify on the third and subsequent occasions and/or fai-lure to pay the fine within the period stated shall result in the Club being deducted two Championship points.

10. DISPUTES AND TRANSGRESSIONS

Any matters in disptue or any transgression of the Competition Rules, the Divisional Rules and/or the Administrative Instructions shall be reported immediately to the Officer of the Lea-gue named in the list of Divisional Officers and the Administrative Instructions.

In addition to those penalties particularly speci-fied in Rules 8 and 9, failure to comply with the RFU Regulations and Competition Rules, the Divisional Rules and/or the Administrative Instructions may result in the imposition of monetary fines, loss of Competition points and dismissal from the Competition according to the gravity of the offence.

A Club may appeal against a decision of the Officer of the League. The Club shall, within seven day sof the decision being notified, request the Constituent Body Competition Committee to reconsider the ruling. If the Club is still not satisfied it may, within a further seven days, appeal to the Divisional Compe-tition Secretary who shall arrange a formal hearing. A final right of appeal is then available to the Rugby Football Union as defined in the RFU Regulations.

LONDON AND SOUTH EAST DIVISION COMPETITION SUB-COMMITTEE

CHAIRMAN:

W.C. Hawkins,
89 Blackheath Park,
Blackheath,
London SE3 0EU   (H) 01 852 7317

SECRETARY:

M.A. Ward,
3 Rookery Close,
Oulton Broad,   (H) 0502 566169
Lowestoft   (O) 0603 666961
Suffolk NR33 9NZ   Fax: 0502 501135

EASTERN COUNTIES:

F.A.G. Ford,
'Fairhaven',
36 Haynes Road,
Hornchurch   (H) 04024 57807
Essex RM11 2HT   (O) 04023 45533

HAMPSHIRE:

Lt Col D. McF. Hathorn,
3 Broomacres
Fleet, Aldershot,
Hampshire,   (H) 0252 621565

HERTFORDSHIRE:

D.J. Williams,
7 Sadlers Way, Hertford,   (H) 0992 586744
Hertfordshire SG14 2DZ   (O) 0438 726481

KENT:

R. Tennant,
57 Boveney Road,
Forest Hill, London SE23 3NL
(H) 01 699 9025

MIDDLESEX:

J.P.D. Mallinson,,
70 Park Road,
London W4 3HL   (H) 01 994 6540

SURREY:

H. Brady,
16 Selwood Terrace,
London SW7 3QG   (H) 01 370 1078

SUSSEX:

P. Sealey,
2 Cedars Close,
Uckfield,   (H) 0825 3293
Sussex TN22 1JA   (O) 0732 863868

CO-OPTED:

A.T.T. Street,
27 Chaucer Court,
Laun Road,
Guildford,
Surrey GU2 5DB   (H) 0483 575742

The Telephone number of the East India Club, where most of the meetings of the Sub-Committee will be held, is 01 930 1000.

LONDON AND SOUTH EAST DIVISION R.F.U. COMPETITION SUB-COMMITTEE REPLACEMENTS

EASTERN COUNTIES:

M.J. Stott,
Brick Kiln Farm,
North Walsham,
Norfolk   (H) 0692 403096

MIDDLESEX:

D. Gershlick,
20A The Avenue,
Potters Bar,   (H) 0707 44433
Herts EN6 1EB   (O) 01 453 1047

HAMPSHIRE:

J. Boyle,
Holly Bush Farm,
Ramsdell,
Basingstoke,
Hants RG16 5SL   (H) 0256 850043

SURREY:

A. Titheridge,
Treave House,
Beech Hill,
Mayford,
Woking,   (H) 04862 69902
Surrey GU22 0SB   (O) 01 580 4528

HERTFORDSHIRE:

C. Pool,
24 Firs Walk,
Tewin Wood,
Welwyn,   (O) 01 609 8004
Hertfordshire AL6 0NZ   (H) 0438 79469

SUSSEX:

A.E. Parker,
34 Marine Crescent,
Goring by Sea,
Worthing,
Sussex BN12 4JF   (H) 0903 44464

KENT:

O.S. Kverndal,
Christopher House,
Station Road,
Sidcup,   (H) 0959 34267
Kent DA15 7BS   (O) 01 300 7744

LONDON AND THE SOUTH EAST MEDIA CONTACTS

BBC ESSEX:

198 New London Road,
Chelmsford,
Essex CM2 9XB   0245 262393

ESSEX RADIO:

Radio House, Clifftown Road,
Southend-on-Sea,
Essex SS1 1SX   0702 333711

BBC RADIO CUMBRIA:

Hilltop Heights,
London Road,
Carlisle CA1 2NA   0228 31661

BBC RADIO JERSEY:

Broadcasting House,
Rouge Bouillion,
St Helier,
Jersey   0534 70000

BBC RADIO SOLENT:

South Western House,
Canute Road,
Southampton,
Hants SO9 4PJ   0703 631311

OCEAN SOUND:

Whittle Avenue,
Segensworth West, Fareham,
Hants PO15 5PA   04895 89911

BBC TV SOUTH:

South Western House,
Canute Road,
Southampton,
Hants SO9 1PF   0703 226201

TVS TELEVISION:

Television Centre,
Southampton,
Hants SO9 5HZ   0703 834274

INVICTA RADIO:

15 Station Road East,
Canterbury,
Kent CT1 2RB   0227 67661

BBC RADIO KENT:

Sunpier,
Chatham,
Kent ME4 4EZ   0634 830505

GREATER LONDON RADIO:

35A Marylebone High Street,
London W1A 4LG   01 224 2424

LBC:

Communications House,
Gough Square,
London EC4P   01 353 1010

CAPITAL RADIO:

Euston Tower,
London NW101 388 1288

RADIO ORWELL:

Electric House,
Lloyds Avenue,
Ipswich   0473 216971

SAXON RADIO:

Long Brackland,
Bury St Edmunds,
Suffolk 1IP33 1JY   0284 701511

THAMES TELEVISION:

Television Centre, City Road,
Newcastle-Upon-Tyne
NE1 2AL   091 261 0181

BBC RADIO NEWCASTLE:

306–316 Euston Road,
London NW1   01 387 9494

LONDON WEEKEND TELEVISION:

South Bank TV Centre,
London SE1   01 261 3434

EVENING STAR AND EAST ANGLIAN DAILY TIMES:

30 Lower Brook Street,
Ipswich,
Suffolk IP4 1AN   0473 230023

KENT MESSENGER:

New Hythe Lane,
Larkfield,
Maidstone ME20 6SG   0622 717880

EASTERN DAILY PRESS AND EASTERN EVENING NEWS:

Prospect House,
Rouen Road,
Norwich, NR1 1RE   0603 628311

THE NEWS:
The News Centre,
Hilsea,
Portsmouth PO2 9SX   0705 664488

EVENING ECHO:

Newspaper House,
Chester Hall Lane,
Basildon, Essex   0268 522792

SOUTHERN EVENING ECHO:

45 Above Bar,
Southampton SO9 7BA   0703 634134

SURREY ADVERTISER:

Martyr Road,
Guildford GU1 4LQ   0483 571234

CAMBRIDGE EVENING NEWS:

51 Newmarket Road,
Cambridge CB5 8EJ   0223 358877

PETERBOROUGH EVENING TELEGRAPH:

Telegraph House,
57 Priestgate,
Peterborough PE1 1JW   0735 555111

EVENING POST (KENT):

395 High Street,
Chatham,
Kent ME4 4PG   0634 830600

BBC RADIO NORFOLK:

Surrey Street,
Norwich NR1 3PA   0603 617411

BBC RADIO SUSSEX:

Marlborough Place,
Brighton BN1 1TU   0273 680231

COUNTY SOUND RADIO:

The Friary,
Guildford,
Surrey GU1 4YX   0483 505566

EVENING ARGUS:

89 North Road,
Brighton BN1 4AU   0273 606799

LONDON LEAGUES

AGAIN there were seven top leagues consisting of 77 clubs and these were divided into a top, elite competition, two regional second divisions and four (also regional) third divisions. This meant at the end of the season that there were 10 ecstatic clubs and 17 aching hearts.

Basingstoke go up from the top division after a "cliff-hanger" with Sutton & Epsom. Both won eight of their 10 matches, drawing one and losing one, but the Hampshire team had a vastly superior points difference even though the Surrey club won their last match at relegated Dartfordians 41–12. Also down are Guildford & Godalming and Ipswich, the latter owing to the demotion from Area League South of an extra team. Basingstoke's success was their second in successive seasons and their progress will be followed with great interest.

Ascending from the two second divisions are Cheshunt (North) and Old Alleynians (South); both also won their respective county cups – Herts and Surrey – and Alleynians also won a Rugby World & Post junior club of the Month award, whilst neither was hard pressed to win their sections. Down go several clubs – from the North Upper Clapton (for a second successive season) and Hertford and from the South Purley, promoted last season, Old Reigatian and K.C.S. Old Boys.

They make way for Eton Manor (10 unblemished matches in League 3 NE and an outstanding 369–55 points differential), Finchley (on points difference from Bishop's Stortford in 3 North West and their second successive rise), Old Colfeians (comfortably in 3SE) and Alton, who lost only one match in League 3 South West. Going down to the county leagues are Ipswich YMCA (3NE), Letchworth (3NW), Hendon (3NW), pointless Harrow (3NW), Old Dunstonians (3SE), Gosport (3SW), Eastleigh (3SW), Winchester (3SW) and Jersey (3SW). At least none of them were descending for a second successive season, but Gosport have the galling experience of having been promoted from Hampshire 1 last season and now being sent down after finishing eighth in an 11 team league.

OFFICERS:

LONDON LEAGUE ONE:

MA. Ward, Esq.,
3 Rookery Close,
Oulton Broad,
Lowestoft,   (H) 0502 566169
Suffolk NR33 9NZ   (O) 0603 617411

LONDON LEAGUE TWO NORTH:

M.A. Ward, Esq.,
3 Rookery Close,
Oulton Broad,
Lowestoft,   (H) 0502 566169
Suffolk NR33 9NZ   (O) 0603 617411

LONDON LEAGUE TWO SOUTH:

M.A. Ward, Esq.,
3 Rookery Close,
Oulton Broad,
Lowestoft,   (H) 0502 566169
Suffolk NR33 9NZ   (O) 0603 617411

LONDON LEAGUE THREE
NORTH-EAST:

F.A.G. Ford, Esq.,
'Fairhaven',
36 Haynes Road,   (H) 04024 57807
Hornchurch, Essex RM11 2HT
                                         (O) 04023 45533

LONDON LEAGUE THREE
NORTH-WEST:

J.P.D. Mallinson, Esq.,
70 Park Road,
London W4 3HL   (H) 01 944 6540

LONDON LEAGUE THREE
SOUTH-EAST:

P. Sealey, Esq.,
2 Cedars Close,
Uckfield,   (H) 0825 3293
Sussex TN22 1JA   (O) 0732 863868

LONDON LEAGUE THREE
SOUTH-WEST:

Miss E. Morris
29 Mullens House,
Chartfield Avenue,
Putney,
London SW15 6DA   (H) 01 788 5738

LONDON DIVISIONS

TABLES 1987–88

LONDON 1

	P	W	D	L	F	A	PTS
Ealing	10	9	0	1	198	60	18
Ruislip	10	7	0	3	182	68	14
Lewes	10	6	0	4	120	87	12
Ipswich	10	6	0	4	97	103	12
O. Gayton's	10	5	0	5	99	122	10
Dartfordians	10	5	0	5	90	159	10
Sutton & Eps	10	4	1	5	108	110	9
Guild & God	10	4	0	5	100	104	8
US Portsm'th	10	3	1	6	100	128	7
Esher	10	3	1	6	68	133	7
Upr Clapton	10	1	1	8	53	141	3

LONDON 2N

	P	W	D	L	F	A	PTS
N Walsham	9	7	0	2	180	72	14
Grasshoppers	9	6	1	2	134	121	13
Norwich	9	6	0	3	109	63	12
Cheshunt	9	5	1	3	160	93	11
Thurrock	9	5	1	3	118	59	11
Woodford	9	5	0	4	135	104	10
O. Albanians	9	2	2	5	94	121	6
O Mer Taylors	9	2	2	5	112	167	6
Hertford	9	2	2	5	47	112	6
St. Marys Hos**	9	0	1	8	46	223	–1

West London Institute withdrawn – all results void
**2 points deducted – breach of rules

LONDON 2S

	P	W	D	L	F	A	PTS
Basingstoke	10	8	0	2	253	89	16
O Mid Whits	10	8	0	2	176	113	16
Worthing	10	7	0	3	171	117	14
Camberley	10	7	0	3	139	122	14
O Alleynian	10	6	0	4	157	80	12
Gravesend	10	5	0	5	97	180	12
O Brockleians	10	4	0	6	100	137	8
K.C.S. O.B.	10	3	1	6	108	187	7
O Reigatian	10	3	0	7	71	133	6
Portsmouth	10	2	1	7	98	142	5
O Juddian	10	1	0	9	123	193	2

LONDON 3NE

	P	W	D	L	F	A	PTS
Barking	10	8	1	1	204	61	17
Eton Manor	10	8	0	2	171	76	16
W. Norfolk	10	6	1	3	115	108	13
Colchester	10	6	0	4	126	94	12
O Westcliffians	10	5	2	3	149	118	12
Chingford	10	5	0	5	117	96	10
Ipswich YMCA	10	4	0	6	100	122	8
Saffron Wal	10	4	0	6	91	117	8
O Cantabrigian	10	4	0	6	99	130	8
Brentwood	10	2	0	8	75	196	4
Bury St. Ed	10	1	0	9	61	190	2

TABLES 1988-89

LONDON 1

	P	W	D	L	F	A	PTS
Basingstoke	10	8	1	1	238	98	17
Sutton & Ep	10	8	1	1	165	80	17
Ruislip	10	8	0	2	181	94	16
N Walsham	10	6	0	4	165	105	12
Lewes	10	6	0	4	167	116	12
Streatham/Croy	10	5	0	5	139	135	10
O Gaytonians	10	5	0	5	154	154	10
US Portsm'th	10	3	1	6	110	113	7
Ipswich	10	2	1	7	98	163	5
Guildford & God	10	2	0	8	80	189	4
Dartfordians	10	0	0	10	30	280	0

LONDON 2N

	P	W	D	L	F	A	PTS
Cheshunt	10	8	1	1	243	110	17
B. Stortford	10	6	1	3	177	104	13
Norwich	10	6	1	3	182	120	13
O Albanians	10	6	0	4	121	91	12
Barking**	10	7	0	3	113	103	12
Grasshoppers	10	6	0	4	111	138	12
O. Merchant T	10	4	0	6	76	125	8
Thurrock	10	3	1	6	107	122	7
Woodford	10	3	0	7	143	162	6
U Clapton	10	3	0	7	89	134	6
Hertford	10	1	0	9	44	210	2

LONDON 2S

	P	W	D	L	F	A	PTS
O Alleynians	10	9	0	1	224	64	18
Worthing	10	7	1	2	186	66	15
O Mid Whits	10	6	1	3	121	109	13
Camberley	10	6	1	3	123	112	13
Gravesend	10	5	0	5	127	115	10
Tun Wells	10	5	0	5	116	116	10
Esher	10	4	0	6	77	180	8
O Brockleians	10	3	1	6	84	157	7
Purley	10	3	0	7	99	139	6
K.C.S. O.B.	10	2	2	6	96	147	6
O Reigatian	10	2	0	8	72	120	4

LONDON 3NE

	P	W	D	L	F	A	PTS
Eton Manor	10	10	0	0	369	55	20
Chingford	10	8	0	2	200	104	16
Cambridge	10	6	0	4	272	86	12
W Norfolk	10	6	0	4	215	138	12
O Westcliffians	10	6	0	4	167	98	12
Met. Pol., Ching	10	5	0	5	168	131	10
O Cantabrians	10	5	0	5	147	116	10
Brentwood	10	5	0	5	153	217	10
Colchester	10	3	0	7	190	125	6
Saffron Wal	10	1	0	9	65	375	2
Ipswich Y.M.C.A.	10	0	0	10	24	525	0

LONDON 3NW

	P	W	D	L	F	A	PTS
B. Stortford	10	9	0	1	192	72	18
Hendon	10	8	0	2	166	89	16
Letchworth	10	7	1	2	120	76	15
Tabard	10	7	1	2	104	87	15
Fullerians	10	6	0	4	159	98	12
O Kingsburian	10	5	0	5	169	115	10
Mill Hill	10	4	1	5	107	104	9
Harrow	10	2	1	7	77	156	5
Bacavians	10	2	0	8	70	140	4
Twickenham	10	2	0	8	47	177	4
Old Paulines	10	1	0	9	65	162	2

LONDON 3SE

	P	W	D	L	F	A	PTS
Tunbridge Wells	10	7	2	1	169	106	16
Beckenham	10	7	1	2	106	77	15
O Colfeians	10	6	1	3	148	115	13
Westcombe Pk	10	5	2	3	149	77	12
Crawley	10	5	0	5	116	108	10
Horsham	10	5	0	5	104	123	10
E Grinstead	10	4	1	5	109	99	9
O Dunstonians	10	4	1	5	95	113	9
O Beccehams	10	4	0	6	84	110	8
Gill Anchorian	10	3	1	6	78	122	7
Canterbury	10	0	1	9	59	177	1

LONDON 3SW

	P	W	D	L	F	A	PTS
Purley	10	9	0	1	228	67	18
Alton	10	7	0	3	187	96	14
O Walcountians	10	7	0	3	133	102	14
Eastleigh	10	6	0	4	170	95	12
O Emanuel	10	6	0	4	133	106	12
Jersey	10	5	0	5	168	121	10
O Whitgiftians	10	5	0	5	90	117	10
Winchester**	10	4	0	6	126	142	8
Guy's Hos	10	3	0	7	149	161	6
Warlingham	10	3	0	7	102	165	6
Trojans	10	0	0	10	43	369	0

**12 match points deducted – ineligible player.

LONDON 3NW

	P	W	D	L	F	A	PTS
Finchley	10	8	0	2	156	40	16
Tabard	10	8	0	2	162	88	16
Mill Hill	10	6	2	2	136	89	14
Kingsburians	10	7	0	3	122	81	14
St. Mary's Hos	10	6	1	3	130	110	13
H. Hempstead	10	3	2	5	135	104	8
Bacavians	10	3	2	5	110	140	8
Fullerians	10	4	0	6	127	169	8
Letchworth	10	3	1	6	117	171	7
Hendon	10	3	0	7	84	128	6
Harrow	10	0	0	10	61	220	0

LONDON 3SE

	P	W	D	L	F	A	PTS
O Colfeians	10	9	0	1	183	81	18
Westcombe Pk	10	7	1	2	143	119	15
Crawley	10	6	0	4	135	79	12
Beckenham	10	6	0	4	129	102	12
O Beccehams	10	6	0	4	117	113	12
Old Juddian	10	5	2	3	131	132	12
Charlton Pk	10	6	0	4	116	130	12
E Grinstead	10	2	1	7	92	154	5
Horsham	10	2	0	8	123	128	4
Bognor	10	2	0	8	94	121	4
O Dunstonian	10	2	0	8	64	168	4

LONDON 3SW

	P	W	D	L	F	A	PTS
Alton	10	9	0	1	207	71	18
O Guildfordians	10	8	0	2	231	66	16
O Walcountians	10	6	0	4	152	102	12
O Emanuel	10	6	0	4	111	127	12
Portsmouth$**	9	6	0	3	109	109	10
O Whitgifts	10	5	0	5	85	166	10
Guy's Hos	10	4	0	6	157	113	8
Gosport	10	3	0	7	118	142	6
Eastleigh	10	3	0	7	72	141	6
Winchester	10	3	0	7	69	178	6
Jersey**	9	1	0	8	42	166	2

** = Match postponed through weather – not required to be replayed due to travel problems.
$ = 2 Championship points and match points deducted under Divisional Rule 5 – ineligible player.

LONDON & SOUTH EAST DIVISION FIXTURES 1989/90

LONDON LEAGUE ONE

Sat. 14th October (Week 6)
Ealing v North Walsham
Cheshunt v Streatham & Croydon
Old Alleynians v Sutton & Epsom
Lewes v Ruislip
U.S. Portsmouth v Old Gaytonians

Sat. 14th October (Week 6)
Old Gaytonians v Ealing
Ruislip v U.S. Portsmouth
Sutton & Epsom v Lewes
Streatham & Croydon v Old Alleynians
Sidcup v Cheshunt

Sat. 28th October (Week 8)
Ealing v Ruislip
North Walsham v Old Gaytonians
Old Alleynians v Sidcup
Lewes v Streatham & Croydon
U.S. Portsmouth v Sutton & Epsom

Sat. 11th November (Week 10)
Ruislip v North Walsham
Sutton & Epsom v Ealing
Streatham & Croydon v U.S. Portsmouth
Sidcup v Lewes
Cheshunt v Old Alleynians

Sat 18th November (Week 11)
Ealing v Streatham & Croydon
North Walsham v Sutton & Epsom
Old Gaytonians v Ruislip
Lewes v Cheshunt
U.S. Portsmouth v Sidcup

Sat. 25th November (Week 12)
Sutton & Epsom v Old Gaytonians
Streatham & Croydon v North Walsham
Sidcup v Ealing
Cheshunt v U.S. Portsmouth
Old Alleynians v Lewes

Sat. 13th January (Week 18)
Ealing v Cheshunt
North Walsham v Sidcup
Old Gaytonians v Streatham & Croydon
Ruislip v Sutton & Epsom
U.S. Portsmouth v Old Alleynians

Sat. 27th January (Week 20)
Streatham & Croydon v Ruislip
Sidcup v Old Gaytonians
Cheshunt v North Walsham
Old Alleynians v Ealing
Lewes v U.S. Portsmouth

Sat. 10th February (Week 22)
Ealing v Lewes
North Walsham v Old Alleynians
Old Gaytonians v Cheshunt
Ruislip v Sidcup
Sutton & Epsom v Streatham & Croydon

Sat. 24th February (Week 24)
Sidcup v Sutton & Epsom
Cheshunt v Ruislip
Old Alleynians v Old Gaytonians
Lewes v North Walsham
U.S. Portsmouth v Ealing

Sat. 10th March (Week 26)
North Walsham v U.S. Portsmouth
Old Gaytonians v Lewes
Ruislip v Old Alleynians
Sutton & Epsom v Cheshunt
Streatham & Croydon v Sidcup

LONDON & SOUTH EAST DIVISION FIXTURES 1989/90

LONDON LEAGUE TWO NORTH

Sat. 23rd September (Week 4)
Ipswich v Norwich
Old Merchant Taylors v Finchley
Grasshoppers v Eton Manor
Barking v Woodford
Bishop's Stortford v Thurrock

Sat. 14th October (Week 6)
Thurrock v Ipswich
Woodford v Bishop's Stortford
Eton Manor v Barking
Finchley v Grasshoppers
Old Albanians v Old Merchant Taylors

Sat. 28th October (Week 8)
Ipswich v Woodford
Norwich v Thurrock
Grasshoppers v Old Albanians
Barking v Finchley
Bishop's Stortford v Eton Manor

Sat. 11th November (Week 10)
Woodford v Norwich
Eton Manor v Ipswich
Finchley v Bishop's Stortford
Old Albanians v Barking
Old Merchant Taylors v Grasshoppers

Sat 18th November (Week 11)
Ipswich v Finchley
Norwich v Eton Manor
Thurrock v Woodford
Barking v Old Merchant Taylors
Bishop's Stortford v Old Albanians

Sat. 25th November (Week 12)
Eton Manor v Thurrock
Finchley v Norwich
Old Albanians v Ipswich
Old Merchant Taylors v Bishop's Stortford
Grasshoppers v Barking

Sat. 13th January (Week 18)
Ipswich v Old Merchant Taylors
Norwich v Old Albanians
Thurrock v Finchley
Woodford v Eton Manor
Bishop's Stortford v Grasshoppers

Sat. 27th January (Week 20)
Finchley v Woodford
Old Albanians v Thurrock
Old Merchant Taylors v Norwich
Grasshoppers v Ipswich
Barking v Bishop's Stortford

Sat. 10th February (Week 22)
Ipswich v Barking
Norwich v Grasshoppers
Thurrock v Old Merchant Taylors
Woodford v Old Albanians
Eton Manor v Finchley

Sat. 24th February (Week 24)
Old Albanians v Eton Manor
Old Merchant Taylors v Woodford
Grasshoppers v Thurrock
Barking v Norwich
Bishop's Stortford v Ipswich

Sat. 10th March (Week 26)
Norwich v Bishop's Stortford
Thurrock v Barking
Woodford v Grasshoppers
Eton Manor v Old Merchant Taylors
Finchley v Old Albanians

LONDON & SOUTH EAST DIVISION FIXTURES 1989/90

LONDON LEAGUE TWO SOUTH

Sat. 23rd September (Week 4)
Gravesend v Tunbridge Wells
Old Colfeians v Old Mid-Whitgiftians
Camberley v Guildford & Godalming
Alton v Dartfordians
Esher v Old Brockleians

Sat. 14th October (Week 6)
Old Brockleians v Gravesend
Dartfordians v Esher
Guildford & Godalming v Alton
Old Mid-Whitgiftians v Camberley
Worthing v Old Colfeians

Sat. 28th October (Week 8)
Gravesend v Dartfordians
Tunbridge Wells v Old Brockleians
Camberley v Worthing
Alton v Old Mid-Whitgiftians
Esher v Guildford & Godalming

Sat. 11th November (Week 10)
Dartfordians v Tunbridge Wells
Guildford & Godalming v Gravesend
Old Mid-Whitgiftians v Esher
Worthing v Alton
Old Colfeians v Camberley

Sat 18th November (Week 11)
Gravesend v Old Mid-Whitgiftians
Tunbridge Wells v Guildford & Godalming
Old Brockleians v Dartfordians
Alton v Old Colfeians
Esher v Worthing

Sat. 25th November (Week 12)
Guildford & Godalming v Old Brockleians
Old Mid-Whitgiftians v Tunbridge Wells
Worthing v Gravesend
Old Colfeians v Esher
Camberley v Alton

Sat. 13th January (Week 18)
Gravesend v Old Colfeians
Tunbridge Wells v Worthing
Old Brockleians v Old Mid-Whitgiftians
Dartfordians v Guildford & Godalming
Esher v Camberley

Sat. 27th January (Week 20)
Old Mid-Whitgiftians v Dartfordians
Worthing v Old Brockleians
Old Colfeians v Tunbridge Wells
Camberley v Gravesend
Alton v Esher

Sat. 10th February (Week 22)
Gravesend v Alton
Tunbridge Wells v Camberley
Old Brockleians v Old Colfeians
Dartfordians v Worthing
G'ford & Godalming v O M'-Whitgiftians

Sat. 24th February (Week 24)
Worthing v Guildford & Godalming
Old Colfeians v Dartfordians
Camberley v Old Brockleians
Alton v Tunbridge Wells
Esher v Gravesend

Sat. 10th March (Week 26)
Tunbridge Wells v Esher
Old Brockleians v Alton
Dartfordians v Camberley
Guildford & Godalming v Old Colfeians
Old Mid-Whitgiftians v Worthing

LONDON & SOUTH EAST DIVISION FIXTURES 1989/90

LONDON LEAGUE THREE NORTH WEST

Sat. 23rd September (Week 4)
Upper Clapton v Bacavians
Kingsburians v Mill Hill
Welwyn v Fullerians
Hemel Hempstead v Tabard
Hertford v St. Mary's Hospital

Sat. 14th October (Week 6)
St. Mary's Hospital v Upper Clapton
Tabard v Hertford
Fullerians v Hemel Hempstead
Mill Hill v Welwyn
Twickenham v Kingsburians

Sat. 28th October (Week 8)
Upper Clapton v Tabard
Bacavians v St. Mary's Hospital
Welwyn v Twickenham
Hemel Hempstead v Mill Hill
Hertford v Fullerians

Sat. 11th November (Week 10)
Tabard v Bacavians
Fullerians v Upper Clapton
Mill Hill v Hertford
Twickenham v Hemel Hempstead
Kingsburians v Welwyn

Sat 18th November (Week 11)
Upper Clapton v Mill Hill
Bacavians v Fullerians
St. Mary's Hospital v Tabard
Hemel Hempstead v Kingsburians
Hertford v Twickenham

Sat. 25th November (Week 12)
Fullerians v St. Mary's Hospital
Mill Hill v Bacavians
Twickenham v Upper Clapton
Kingsburians v Hertford
Welwyn v Hemel Hempstead

Sat. 13th January (Week 18)
Upper Clapton v Kingsburians
Bacavians v Twickenham
St. Mary's Hospital v Mill Hill
Tabard v Fullerians
Hertford v Welwyn

Sat. 27th January (Week 20)
Mill Hill v Tabard
Twickenham v St. Mary's Hospital
Kingsburians v Bacavians
Welwyn v Upper Clapton
Hemel Hempstead v Hertford

Sat. 10th February (Week 22)
Upper Clapton v Hemel Hempstead
Bacavians v Welwyn
St. Mary's Hospital v Kingsburians
Tabard v Twickenham
Fullerians v Mill Hill

Sat. 24th February (Week 24)
Twickenham v Fullerians
Kingsburians v Tabard
Welwyn v St. Mary's Hospital
Hemel Hempstead v Bacavians
Hertford v Upper Clapton

Sat. 10th March (Week 26)
Bacavians v Hertford
St. Mary's Hospital v Hemel Hempstead
Tabard v Welwyn
Fullerians v Kingsburians
Mill Hill v Twickenham

LONDON & SOUTH EAST DIVISION FIXTURES 1989/90

LONDON LEAGUE THREE NORTH EAST

Sat. 23rd September (Week 4)
Met. Police, Chigwell v Romford & G.P.
Old Cantabrigians v Brentwood
Harlow v Saffron Walden
Cambridge v Chingford
West Norfolk v Westcliff

Sat. 14th October (Week 6)
Westcliff v Met. Police, Chigwell
Chingford v West Norfolk
Saffron Walden v Cambridge
Brentwood v Harlow
Colchester v Old Cantabrigians

Sat. 28th October (Week 8)
Met. Police, Chigwell v Chingford
Romford & G.P. v Westcliff
Harlow v Colchester
Cambridge v Brentwood
West Norfolk v Saffron Walden

Sat. 11th November (Week 10)
Chingford v Romford & G.P.
Saffron Walden v Met. Police, Chigwell
Brentwood v West Norfolk
Colchester v Cambridge
Old Cantabrigians v Harlow

Sat 18th November (Week 11)
Met. Police, Chigwell v Brentwood
Romford & G.P. v Saffron Walden
Westcliff v Chingford
Cambridge v Old Cantabrigians
West Norfolk v Colchester

Sat. 25th November (Week 12)
Saffron Walden v Westcliff
Brentwood v Romford & G.P.
Colchester v Met. Police, Chigwell
Old Cantabrigians v West Norfolk
Harlow v Cambridge

Sat. 13th January (Week 18)
Met. Police, Chigwell v Old Cantabrigians
Romford & G.P. v Colchester
Westcliff v Brentwood
Chingford v Saffron Walden
West Norfolk v Harlow

Sat. 27th January (Week 20)
Brentwood v Chingford
Colchester v Westcliff
Old Cantabrigians v Romford & G.P.
Harlow v Met. Police, Chigwell
Cambridge v West Norfolk

Sat. 10th February (Week 22)
Met. Police, Chigwell v Cambridge
Romford & G.P. v Harlow
Westcliff v Old Cantabrigians
Chingford v Colchester
Saffron Walden v Brentwood

Sat. 24th February (Week 24)
Colchester v Saffron Walden
Old Cantabrigians v Chingford
Harlow v Westcliff
Cambridge v Romford & G.P.
West Norfolk v Met. Police, Chigwell

Sat. 10th March (Week 26)
Romford & G.P. v West Norfolk
Westcliff v Cambridge
Chingford v Harlow
Saffron Walden v Old Cantabrigians
Brentwood v Colchester

LONDON & SOUTH EAST DIVISION FIXTURES 1989/90

LONDON LEAGUE THREE SOUTH EAST

Sat. 23rd September (Week 4)
Charlton Park v Bognor
Old Juddian v Hove
East Grinstead v Westcombe Park
Crawley v Beckenham
Horsham v Gillingham Anch.

Sat. 14th October (Week 6)
Gillingham Anch. v Charlton Park
Beckenham v Horsham
Westcombe Park v Crawley
Hove v East Grinstead
Old Beccehamians v Old Juddian

Sat. 28th October (Week 8)
Charlton Park v Beckenham
Bognor v Gillingham Anch.
East Grinstead v Old Beccehamians
Crawley v Hove
Horsham v Westcombe Park

Sat. 11th November (Week 10)
Beckenham v Bognor
Westcombe Park v Charlton Park
Hove v Horsham
Old Beccehamians v Crawley
Old Juddian v East Grinstead

Sat 18th November (Week 11)
Charlton Park v Hove
Bognor v Westcombe Park
Gillingham Anch. v Beckenham
Crawley v Old Juddian
Horsham v Old Beccehamians

Sat. 25th November (Week 12)
Westcombe Park v Gillingham Anch.
Hove v Bognor
Old Beccehamians v Charlton Park
Old Juddian v Horsham
East Grinstead v Crawley

Sat. 13th January (Week 18)
Charlton Park v Old Juddian
Bognor v Old Beccehamians
Gillingham Anch. v Hove
Beckenham v Westcombe Park
Horsham v East Grinstead

Sat. 27th January (Week 20)
Hove v Beckenham
Old Beccehamians v Gillingham Anch.
Old Juddian v Bognor
East Grinstead v Charlton Park
Crawley v Horsham

Sat. 10th February (Week 22)
Charlton Park v Crawley
Bognor v East Grinstead
Gillingham Anch. v Old Juddian
Beckenham v Old Beccehamians
Westcombe Park v Hove

Sat. 24th February (Week 24)
Old Beccehamians v Westcombe Park
Old Juddian v Beckenham
East Grinstead v Gillingham Anch.
Crawley v Bognor
Horsham v Charlton Park

Sat. 10th March (Week 26)
Bognor v Horsham
Gillingham Anch. v Crawley
Beckenham v East Grinstead
Westcombe Park v Old Juddian
Hove v Old Beccehamians

LONDON & SOUTH EAST DIVISION FIXTURES 1989/90

LONDON LEAGUE THREE SOUTH WEST

Sat. 23rd September (Week 4)
Guy's Hospital v Old Emanuel
K.C.S. O.B. v Old Guildfordians
Dorking v Old Walcountians
Purley v Portsmouth
Old Reigatian v Old Whitgiftians

Sat. 14th October (Week 6)
Old Whitgiftians v Guy's Hospital
Portsmouth v Old Reigatian
Old Walcountians v Purley
Old Guildfordians v Dorking
Southampton v K.C.S. O.B.

Sat. 28th October (Week 8)
Guy's Hospital v Portsmouth
Old Emanuel v Old Whitgiftians
Dorking v Southampton
Purley v Old Guildfordians
Old Reigatian v Old Walcountians

Sat. 11th November (Week 10)
Portsmouth v Old Emanuel
Old Walcountians v Guy's Hospital
Old Guildfordians v Old Reigatian
Southampton v Purley
K.C.S. O.B. v Dorking

Sat 18th November (Week 11)
Guy's Hospital v Old Guildfordians
Old Emanuel v Old Walcountians
Old Whitgiftians v Portsmouth
Purley v K.C.S. O.B.
Old Reigatian v Southampton

Sat. 25th November (Week 12)
Old Walcountians v Old Whitgiftians
Old Guildfordians v Old Emanuel
Southampton v Guy's Hospital
K.C.S. O.B. v Old Reigatian
Dorking v Purley

Sat. 13th January (Week 18)
Guy's Hospital v K.C.S. O.B.
Old Emanuel v Southampton
Old Whitgiftians v Old Guildfordians
Portsmouth v Old Walcountians
Old Reigatian v Dorking

Sat. 27th January (Week 20)
Old Guildfordians v Portsmouth
Southampton v Old Whitgiftians
K.C.S. O.B. v Old Emanuel
Dorking v Guy's Hospital
Purley v Old Reigatian

Sat. 10th February (Week 22)
Guy's Hospital v Purley
Old Emanuel v Dorking
Old Whitgiftians v K.C.S. O.B.
Portsmouth v Southampton
Old Walcountians v Old Guildfordians

Sat. 24th February (Week 24)
Southampton v Old Walcountians
K.C.S. O.B. v Portsmouth
Dorking v Old Whitgiftians
Purley v Old Emanuel
Old Reigatian v Guy's Hospital

Sat. 10th March (Week 26)
Old Emanuel v Old Reigatian
Old Whitgiftians v Purley
Portsmouth v Dorking
Old Walcountians v K.C.S. O.B.
Old Guildfordians v Southampton

LONDON 1

CHESHUNT

Rosedale, Andrews Lane, Cheshunt, Herts. Tel: 0992 23983
Founded: 1952
President: David Bird
Chairman: Roger Bradbury
Secretary: Philip Wash, as above or 'Wynchlows', 91 High Street, Hunsdon, Ware, Herts SG12 8NJ. Tel: 027984 2263 (H), 01–588 9956 (W)
Fixtures Secretary: Martin Budd, 66 Pickets Lock Lane, Edmonton N9 0AX. Tel: 01–803 5668
Press Officer: Peter Goodwin, 20 Wavell Close, Cheshunt, Herts EN88 0LA. Tel: 0992 33161
Coach: Stephen Dowling/David Perkins
Club captain (1988–89): Simon King
Club captain (1989–90): Simon King
No. of teams: Senior 6, Youth/Colts 1
Directions to ground: M25 Junction 25, north on Cambridge Road, left at first roundabout (approx. mile), straight on at next 2 roundabouts, then 1st left. In all approx. 3 miles from M25
Ground capacity: Standing 1000+
Clubhouse facilities: Two bars. Open evenings and Sat./Sun. lunch
Club colours: Green and white hooped shirts, white shorts, red socks
Floodlights: No
Membership fees: Full £50, Playing £40, Social £15, Youth £20, Student £20, OAP £25
Ground admission: By programme on 1st XV home match days
Programme: No. of editorial pages 2–4; No. of advertising pages 8–10; Price £1
Programme editor: As Press Officer
Local newspapers: Lea Valley Mercury, Cheshunt Telegraph
League: London 1
League position (1988–89): 1st (promoted)
League playing record (1988–89): P 34, W 27, D 2, L 5, F 782, A 321
Competitions won: Courage League London North Division

EALING

Berkeley Avenue, Greenford, Middlesex. Tel(01-422-0868.
Founded: 1871
Secretary: C.R. Benjamin, "Kenilworth", 30 Woodville Road, Ealing, London W5. Tel: 01-997-5967 (H), 01-507-5167 (B).
Fixtures Secretary: P. Monteith, 65 Pinner Hill Road, Pinner, Middlesex. Tel: 01-429-3009 (H), 01-638-1001 (B).
Colts Secretary: W. Taylor, 435 Whitton Avenue, West Greenford, Middlesex. Tel: 01-864-6542 (H).
League: London 1

LEWES

Stanley Turner Ground, Kingston Road, Lewes, East Sussex. Tel: 0273 473732
Founded: 1930
President: Dick Rees
Chairman: Graham Thompson
Secretary: Phil Clark, 5 Cleve Terrace, Lewes, E. Sussex BN7 1JJ. Tel: 0273 476672 (H), 01–239 6101 (W)
Fixtures Secretary: Ken Gordon, Lynsted, Coopers Green, Uckfield, Sussex. Tel: Buxted 2440
Press officer: As Secretary
Coach: Terry Powell
Club captain (1988–89): Paul Taylor
Club captain (1989–90): Bob Jackson
No. of teams: Senior 5, Youth 4
Directions to ground: Ground is on the Lewes-Newhaven Road, just over the bypass. Ground cannot be reached from the bypass itself

Club colours: Royal blue and white hoops. (*Change colours:* Red)
Floodlights: No
Membership fees: Full £22.50, Playing £22.50, Social £10, Youth £10, Student £10
Local newspapers: Sussex Express, Evening Argus (Brighton)
League: London 1
League position (1988–89): 5th

NORTH WALSHAM

Norwich Road, Scottow, Nr North Walsham. Tel: 06929 461
Founded: 1962
President: Alan Jackson
Chairman: Chris Lockhart
Secretary: George Howard, 152 Cromer Road, Norwich, Norfolk NR6 6XA. Tel: 0603 404786
League Contact: Joe Hodges, Church View, Town Street, Hickling, Norwich. Tel: 069261 318 (H). Wroxham 2715 (W)
Fixtures Secretary: As League Contact
Press Officer: Maurice Boyd, Orchard End, Little Plumstead, Norwich. Tel: 0603 712614
Coach: Dave Brunton
Club captain (1988–89): Rupert Emblem
Club captain (1989–90): Simon Rossi
No. of teams: Senior 5, Youth 4, Minis 5+
Directions to ground: Take B1150 off the Norwich Ring Road – signed North Walsham. Through Horstead and Cottishall (7 miles) to Scottow (2 miles further) About 3 miles from North Walsham the ground is on the left just after the Three Horse shoes Public House and just beyond some council houses also on the left. 'The Horse shoes' is on a crossroads and on the right. In all the ground is about 9 miles from the Norwich Ring Road
Ground capacity: Standing unlimited
Clubhouse facilities: Bar, kitchen, toilets, changing rooms, gymnasium (under construction)
Club colours: Green and black. (*Change colours:* White or red)
Floodlights: Training lights only
Membership fees: Playing £30, Social £5, Youth £5, Student £3,4,5, VP £10
Programme: No. of editorial pages 4; No. of advertising pages 8 (varies); Price: Free
Programme editor: As Press Officer
Local newspapers: North Norfolk News, Estern Evening News, Eastern Daily Press
League: London 1
League position (1988–89): 4th
League playing record (1988–89): P 10, W 6, D 0, L 4, F 165, A 105
Competitions won: Pilkington Cup – reached the 2nd round. Norfolk Cup Finalists. Eastern Counties Cup Winners. U.13 County Cup Winners. U.19 County Cup Finalists

OLD ALLEYNIANS

Dulwich Common, London, SE21 7HA. Tel: 01 693 2402
Founded: 1898
President: A. Verity – Master of Dulwich College
Chairman: E.S.J. Sutton
Secretary: Robert Crow, 13 Gable Court, Lawrie Park Avenue, Sydenham, London SE26 6HR. Tel: 01 778 2868 (H). 703 5400 Ext 229 (W)
League Contact: D.R. Branscombe, 9 Rockwell Gardens, Dulwich Wood Park, London SE19 1HW. Tel: 01 670 3188
Fixtures Secretary: R.A. Jackman, 28 Kingsfield Avenue, Harrow, Middlesex HA2 6AT. Tel: 01 427 8600
Press Officer: Mike Hayhoe, 12 Dirdene Grove, Epsom, Surrey KT17 4BA. Tel: 03727 28153. Or contact Secretary as above
Coach: F.R.F. Wilson
Club captain (1988–89): Peter Ashworth

Club captain (1989–90): Peter Ashworth
No. of teams: Senior 6
Directions to ground: On South Circular opposite
Dulwich Park
Clubhouse facilities: 2 Bars, tea room, balcony
Club colours: Dark blue, light blue, black. (*Change
colours:* White)
Floodlights: No
Membership fees: Full £40, Playing £40, Social £10,
Youth £27, Student £12
Local newspapers: South London Press
League: London 1
League position (1988–89): 1st in London 2S
League playing record (1988–89): P 35, W 30, D 0,
L 5, F 810, A 230
Competitions won: Courage League London 2 South,
Surrey Cup, Combined London Old Boys British Car
Auctions Merit Table Central Division, reached last
16 of Middlesex Sevens, Rugby World Junior Club of
the Month – April 1989

OLD GAYTONIANS

South Vale, Sudbury Hill, Harrow, Middlesex. Tel:
01 423 4133
Founded: 1934
President: J.W. Carroll
Chairman: J.H. Rigby
Secretary: A.P. Usher, 9 Paynesfield Road, Bushey
Heath, Herts WD2 1PQ. Tel: 01 950 2956
League Contact: B. Kennett, 102 Cleveland Road,
London W13 0EL. Tel: 01 998 2879
Fixtures Secretary: J. Brake, 14 Foxes Way, Warwick,
Warwickshire CV3 468X. Tel: 0926 494408
Coach: Robert Williams
Club captain (1988–89): Steve Rigby
Club captain (1989–90): Paul Minihan
No. of teams: Senior 5, Youth 1
Directions to ground: Piccadilly Line to Sudbury Hill
Station. Turn left, Ground in road opposite the
'Rising Sun'. By road: South Vale is a turning off
Greenford Road (A4127). Opposite the Rising Sun
Club colours: White jerseys with broad band of light
blue, chocolate and green; white shorts. (*Change
colours:* Dark green)
Floodlights: No
Membership fees: Full £28, Youth £7.50, Student
£7.50
Programme: No. of editorial pages 2; No. of
advertising pages 8; Price 50p
Programme editor: Glyn Rees, 38 Capel Road,
Bushey, Herts.
Local newspapers: Harrow Observer
League: London 1
League position (1988–89): 7th
League playing record (1988–89): P 10, W 5, D 0,
L 5, F 154, A 154
Competitions won: Hertford Floodlit Sevens

RUISLIP

West End Road, Ruislip, Middlesex. Tel: 08956 33102
Founded: 1936
President: J.R. Andrews
Chairman: S.W. Harrison
Secretary: Mark Hearn
League Contact: Geoffrey Sykes, 11 Ivy Close,
Eastcote Pinner, HA5 1PU
Fixtures Secretary: As League Contact
Press Officer: M.A. Searls, 16 Park Way,
Rickmansworth, Herts. Tel: 0923 773903 (H). 01 621
1922 (W)
Club captain (1988–89): Simon Warren
Club captain (1989–90): Paul Howells
No. of teams: Senior 5, Youth 6, Minis 5
Club colours: Maroon and white. (*Change colours:*
White)
Floodlights: No
Local newspapers: Ruislip Gazette
League: London 1
League position (1988–89): 3rd

League playing record (1988–89): P 10, W 8, D 0,
L 2, F 181, A 94
Competitions won: Middlesex County Colts Cup

SIDCUP

Sydney Road, Sidcup, Kent. Tel: 01–300 2336
Founded: 1883
President: Brian J. Bennett
Secretary: Derek A. Ash. 282A High Street,
Orpington, Kent BR6 0ND. Tel: 01–464 0953 (H),
0689 25674 (W)
Fixtures Secretary: Alan J. Brown, 213 Broad Walk,
Blackheath, London SE3 8NG. Tel: 01–853 7734
Press Officer: Brian T. Tuley, 1 Priestlands, Park
Road, Sidcup, Kent DA15 7HR. Tel: 01–300 2887
(H), 01–401 2849 (W)
Coach: Malcolm J. Leamon
Club captain (1988–89): Philip M. Dwyer
Club captain (1989–90): Paul C. Bensley
No. of teams: Senior 6, Youth 3, Minis & Juniors 8
Directions to ground: From A20 take A222, turn left
at Police Station, turn left into Sydney Road
Ground capacity: Seating 200
Clubhouse facilities: 2 bars, hall, 2 committee rooms,
squash courts, medical room, changing rooms and
toilets
Club colours: White, maroon monogram. (*Change
colours:* Maroon shirts/white shorts)
Nickname: Cup
Floodlights: No
Membership fees: Playing £40, Social £10, Youth £10,
OAP £5, Ladies £5
Ground admission: By programme
Programme: No. of editorial pages Variable; No. of
advertising pages Variable
Programme editor: As Press Officer
Local newspapers: Sidcup Times, News Shopper
League: London 1
League position (1988–89): 11th (relegated)
League playing record (1988–89): P 10, W 0, D 0,
L 10, F 74, A 268
Competitions won: Giro Kent Cup Runners-Up

STREATHAM & CROYDON

159 Brigstock Road, Thornton Heath. Tel: 01 684
1502
League Contact: R. Towers, 24 Ernest Grove,
Beckenham, Kent BR3 3JF. Tel; 01 658 2333
Club colours: Cardinal Red/white
League: London 1
League position (1988–89): 6th

SUTTON & EPSOM

Cuddington Court, Rugby Lane, West Drive, Cheam,
Surrey. Tel: 01–642 0280
Founded: 1881
President: E. Justin St. J. Thomas
Secretary: John C. Evans, Garden House, 4 College
Avenue, Epsom, Surrey KT17 4HN. Tel: 03727 29891
(H), 01–247 7666 (W)
Fixtures Secretary: R.E.G. Caines, 5 Shirley Road,
Wallington, Surrey. Tel: 01–647 7464
Press Officer: John Ashton, 86 Wickham Avenue,
Cheam, Surrey. Tel: 01–644 9664
Coach: Clive Marshall
Club captain (1988–89): Roland Cheall
Club captain (1989–90): Geoffrey Green
No. of teams: Senior 7, Youth 5, Minis Many
Directions to ground: Convenient to M25 and A3,
near Ewell bypass
Ground capacity: Seating 400 approx., Standing 2000
approx.
Clubhouse facilities: 2 bars, tearoom
Club colours: Black and white hoops, black shorts and
socks. (*Change colours:* Light blue)
Floodlights: Yes (training only)

Membership fees: Life £75, Playing £40, Social £15, Youth £25, Student £20, OAP £15
Programme: No. of editorial pages 4; No. of advertising pages 6–8
Programme editor: As Press Officer
Local newspapers: Epsom & Ewell Herald, Sutton Herald, Advertiser and Guardian Group
League: London 1
League position (1988–89): 2nd
League playing record (1988–89): P 10, W 8, D 1, L 1
Competitions won: Surrey Vets Cup, Surrey U16 and U14 Cups

UNITED SERVICES PORTSMOUTH

Burnaby Road, Portsmouth. Tel: 0705 825394
Founded: 1882
President: Captain Mike O'Reilly RN
Chairman: Commander Jeff Roberts RN
Secretary: Lt. Cdr. Dick Mittins RN, 60 Privett Road, Gosport, Hants. Tel: 0705 587543 (H). 822351 Ext 85700 (W)
League Contact: Commander Jed Stone RN, 7 Fairthorne Gardens, Gosport, Hants. Tel: 0705 583097 (H). 822351 Ext 45148 (W)
Fixtures Secretary: As League Contact
Press Officer: Mr Ken Edwards, USRFC, Burnaby Road, Portsmouth. Tel: 0705 861897
Coach: Warrant Officer Willie Febree
Club captain (1988–89): Petty Officer John Hirst
Club captain (1989–90): Petty Officer Dusty Miller
No. of teams: Senior 3, Youth 1
Directions to ground: From end of M275 follow tourist signs to 'Historic Ships'. RN Sports Grounds are to side of main Portsmouth to Waterloo railway line
Ground capacity: Seating 400
Clubhouse facilities: 2 Bars
Club colours: Royal blue/scarlet hoops. (*Change colours:* Navy blue)
Floodlights: No
Membership fees: Full £10, Playing £10, Social £10, Youth £5
Ground admission: Nil
Programme: No. of editorial pages 1-2; No. of advertising pages 0; Price 50p
Programme editor: As League Contact/Fixture Secretary
Local newspapers: Portsmouth News
League: London 1
League position (1988–89): 8th
League playing record (1988–89): P 27, W 12, D 1, L 14, F 363, A 350
Competitions won: Fifth in Tandem Computers Seven Counties Merit Table (Played 9 Won 6)

LONDON 2 NORTH

BARKING

Goresbrook Park, Gale Street, Dagenham, Essex
Founded: 1931
President: Bill Jones
Chairman: Ron Rust
Secretary: Jim Marner, 239 Wingletye Lane, Hornchurch, Essex RM11 3BL. Tel: 040 24 51723 (H). 0708 858252 (W)
League Contact: As Secretary
Fixtures Secretary: Graham Comley, 26 Beltings Road, Harold Wood, Essex. Tel: 040 23 46482
Coach: Tim Wright
Club captain (1988–89): Tim Reader
Club captain (1989–90): Tim Reader
No. of teams: Senior 4, Youth 2
Directions to ground: 1) From Dartford Tunnel take A13 towards London, past Ford Works, take 4th junction off next roundabout back onto other side of A13 dual carriageway. Clubhouse is 800m on left. 2) From M11, take A406 to A12 and A13. Follow road

to end, and turn left onto A13 towards Dartford Tunnel. Clubhouse is 4 miles on left
Club colours: Cardinal and gray. (*Change colours:* No)
Membership fees: Full £25, Playing £25, Social £7.50, Youth £7.50, Student £7.50, OAP Nil
League: London 2N
League position (1988–89): 5th
Competitions won: Essex Cup Winners

BISHOP'S STORTFORD

Silver Leys, Hadham Road, Bishop's Stortford, Hertfordshire. Tel: 0279 652092
Founded: 1920
President: Les Clarke
Chairman: Bev Clarke
Secretary: John B. Robinson, 193 Heath Row, Bishop's Stortford, Herts. CM23 5BX. Tel: 0279 657104 (H). 0582 24182 (W)
League Contact: As Secretary
Fixtures Secretary: Mrs Jenny Lancey, 41 Appleton Fields, Bishop's Stortford, Herts. Tel: 0279 651061
Press Officer: Phil Docherty, 10 Standrums, Great Dunmow, Essex. Tel: 0371 4978
Club captain (1988–89): Gordon Campbell
Club captain (1989–90): Gordon Campbell
No. of teams: Senior 6, Youth Colts +3, Minis 5
Directions to ground: A120 from west – at first roundabout on Bishop's Stortford Bypass, straight on to town centre, ground is mile on left. All other directions join BS Bypass (A120) to last roundabout, turn left then as above
Ground capacity: Standing unlimited
Club colours: Royal blue and white. (*Change colours:* No)
Floodlights: No
League: London 2N
League position (1988–89): 2nd
League playing record (1988–89): P 10, W 6, D 1, L 3, F 177, A 104

ETON MANOR

Eastway Sports Centre, Quarter Mile Lane, Leyton. Tel: 01 519 0017. Clubhouse: Sidmouth Road, Leyton E10. Tel: 01 539 7218
Founded: 1928
President: Fred Spencer
Chairman: Frank Overland
Secretary: James Slough, 112 Copenhagen Place, London E14 7DE. Tel: 01 987 7216
League Contact: George Ford, Fairhaven, 36 Haynes Road, Billericay, Essex. Tel: 04024 57807
Fixtures Secretary: Martin Scott, 24 Preston Drive, Wanstead E11. Tel: 01 530 4451
Press Officer: Mark Farell, 25 Dorthwick Road, Stratford E15. Tel: 01 534 1790
Coach: Kevin Bevan
Club captain (1988–89): John Munro
Club captain (1989–90): John Munro
No. of teams: Senior 5, Youth 1, Minis Yes
Directions to ground: The Eastway Sports Centre, Quarter Mile Lane, Leyton E10 (Hackney Marsh). The Clubhouse is in Sidmouth Road off of Leyton High Road
Ground capacity: Standing 2000
Clubhouse facilities: Bar, lounge, kitchen facilities
Club colours: Dark blue, light blue hoop. (*Change colours:* Light blue and dark blue hoops)
Floodlights: Yes
League: London 2N
League position (1988–89): 1st
League playing record (1988–89): P 10, W 10, D 0, L 0, F 369, A 55
Competitions won: London 3NE – Season 1988-89. Essex Sevens Champions April 1989

FINCHLEY

Summers Lane, Finchley, London N12
President: S.F. Beard
Chairman: C. Elliott
Secretary: S. Clough, 91 Arcadian Gardens, London N22 5AG. Tel: 01 888 6526 (H). 472 1450 Ext 26234 (W)
League Contact: As Secretary
Fixtures Secretary: J. Devlin, 35 Richmond Road, New Barnet, London. Tel: 01 449 5898
Press Officer: Mike Clarke, Summers Lane, Finchley, London N12
Coach: Garnet Edwards
Club captain (1988–89): L. Gibbons
Club captain (1989–90): L. Gibbons
No. of teams: Senior 6, Youth 1
Directions to ground: Turn off North Circular (A406) at High Road Finchley heading north, take 1st right, Club 200 yards on right
Ground capacity: Seating 300, standing 1000
Clubhouse facilities: Bars, kitchen, stand, training lights, changing rooms, bath
Club colours: Red and white hoops. (*Change colours:* Navy blue)
Nickname: Finches
Floodlights: Training only
Membership fees: Playing £30, Social £9.50, Youth £15, Student £15
Local newspapers: Finchley Times, Barnet Advertiser
League: London 2N
League position (1988–89): 1st
League playing record (1988–89): P 34, W 26, D 0, L 8
Competitions won: London 3NW Winners

GRASSHOPPERS

MacFarlane Sports Ground
Founded: 1950
Secretary: G. Neve, 59 Meadow Road, Hanworth, Middx. Tel: 01-898 9388 (H), 01-741 2849 (W).
Fixtures Secretary: P. Welsh, 56 Crane Way, Whitton, Middx. Tel: 01-894 0446.
League: London 2N

IPSWICH

Humber Doucy Lane, Ipswich. Tel: 0473 724072
Founded: 1970
President: Ian Hepton
Chairman: John Spooner
Secretary: Bernard Rudland, 'Burostat', 9 Cavendish Street, Ipswich. Tel: 0473 216156
Fixtures Secretary: Alan Murray, Clematis Cottage, George Street, Hintlesham, Suffolk IP8 3NH. Tel: 0473 87448 (H), 251608 (W)
Press Officer: Stuart Jarrold, 46 Tuddenham Road, Ipswich. Tel: 0473 217189 (H), 218447 (W)
Coach: Terry Lock
Club captain (1988–89): Brian Caley
Club captain (1989–90): Karl King
No. of teams: Senior 5, Youth 5
Club colours: Black/amber stripe
League: London 2

NORWICH

Beeston Hyrne, North Walsham Road, Norwich. Tel: Norwich 426259
Founded: 1885
President: William Lusher
Chairman: William Lusher
Secretary: Christopher Gillham, Daynes Hill & Perks, Paston House, Princes Street, Norwich NR3 1BD. Tel: 0603 58439 (H). 660241 (W)
League Contact: Ted Searle, Mardon House, Ashby St. Mary, Norwich NR14 7BJ. Tel: Thurton 364 (H). 0603 53786 (W)
Fixtures Secretary: As League Contact
Press Officer: Roy Bishop, 29 Henby Way, Thorpe St. Andrew, Norwich NR7 0LD. Tel: 0603 36504 (H).

31122 (W)
Coach: David Everitt
Club captain (1988–89): Steve Henson
Club captain (1989–90): Chris Hogg
No. of teams: Senior 5, Youth 2, Minis 4
Directions to ground: Follow outer Ring Road and turn into B1150 (signposted Coltishall/North Walsham), over traffic lights within 800 yards, continue 1 mile, Ground on left
Ground capacity: Standing unlimited
Clubhouse facilities: Open Match days and most evenings
Club colours: Green, maroon and gold. (*Change colours:* White)
Floodlights: Yes
Membership fees: Full £20, Playing £27.50, Social £10, Youth £5.50, Student £5.50, OAP £10
Ground admission: Free
Programme: No. of editorial pages 8; No. of advertising pages 8; Price: Free
Programme editor: Alan Boswell, 17 Tunstead Road South, Hoveton, Wroxham, Norwich
Local newspapers: Eastern Daily Press, Evening News
League: London 2N
League position (1988–89): 3rd
League playing record (1988–89): P 10, W 6, D 1, L 3, F 182, A 120
Competitions won: Beccles Sevens

OLD ALBANIANS

Beech Bottom, Old Harpenden Road, St. Albans, Herts. Tel: 0727 64476/Stewart 0727 52082
Founded: 1922
President: I.F. Jennings
Secretary: P.G. Lipscomb, 35 Gurney Court Road, St. Albans, Herts. Tel: 0727 63621 (H), 01–784 5924 (W)
Fixtures Secretary: David C. Verdon, Pine Lodge, Hook Heath Road, Woking, Surrey GU22 0DP. Tel: 04862 64937 (H), 71812 (W)
Press Officer: Jeff Willis
Coach: Malcolm Evans
Club captain (1988–89): John Hibberd
Club captain (1989–90): Simon Henderson
No. of teams: Senior 5, Youth (Colts) 1, Minis 5
Directions to ground: 1 mile from centre of St. Albans on A1081 towards Luton, 150 yds from Ancient Briton P.H.
Clubhouse facilities: Single storey, 5 changing rooms, baths and showers
Club colours: Red blue and gold hooped shirts. (*Change colours:* Black)
Nickname: O.A's
Floodlights: Yes (training only)
Membership fees: Full £28, Playing £28, VPs £10, Youth Free, Student £12
Ground admission: 20p (with programme)
Programme: No. of editorial pages 8; No. of advertising pages 4; Price 20p
Programme editor: Peter Brazier
Local newspaper: Herts Advertiser
League: London N2
League position (1988–89): 4th
League playing record (1988–89): P 34, W 23, D 1, L 10, F 592, A 277
Competitions won: Colts (Youth) won the Herts County Sevens and Runners-Up in Herts County Cup

OLD MERCHANT TAYLORS'

'Durrants', Lincoln Drive, Croxley Green, Rickmansworth, Herts. Tel: 0923 773014
Founded: 1882
Chairman: David Andrews-Jones
Secretary: Mark Foster, The White House, 16 New Road, Croxley Green, Rickmansworth, Herts WD3 3EL. Tel: 0923 773014 (H), 01–257 3408 (W)
Fixtures Secretary: Geoff Shilling, The Lodge,

Wellingrove, Woodcock Hill, Rickmansworth, Herts WD3 1PT. Tel: 0923 774506 (H), 01–528 4444 (W)
Club captain (1988–89): David Wolff
Club captain (1989–90): David Wolff
No. of teams: Senior 5
Directions to ground: From A412 from Watford, right at Two Bridges P.H. into Baldwins Lane, right into Manor Way, right into Kenilworth Drive, left into Rochester Way, right at end. Ground entrance straight ahead
Ground capacity: Seating 500
Clubhouse facilities: Bar, snack bar, function rooms
Club colours: White Jerseys, black shorts. (*Change colours:* Black jerseys)
Nickname: OMTs
Floodlights: No
League: London N2
League position (1988–89): 7th
League playing record (1988–89): P 10, W 4, D 0, L 6, F 76, A 125

THURROCK

'Oakfield', Long Lane, Grays, Essex RM16 2PR. Tel: 0375 374877
Founded: 1928
President: Dr Alistair J.D. Farquharson
Chairman: Brian Godden
Secretary: Bob Burt, 105 Victoria Avenue, Grays Essex, RM16 2RN. Tel: 0375 371667 (H). 0836 733024 (W)
League Contact: As Secretary
Fixtures Secretary: Phillip James, 124 Lodge Lane, Grays, Essex. Tel: 0375 376848 (H). 671566 (W)
Press Officer: Duncan Evans, 80 Gordon Road, Grays, Essex RM16 4AW. Tel: 0375 378826 (H). 383944 (W)
Coach: T.B.A.
Club captain (1988–89): Steve Livermore
Club captain (1989–90): Graham Holbrook
No. of teams: Senior 7, Youth 4, Minis 5
Directions to ground: M25 to Junction 30/31. Take A13 towards Southend, first exit for Grays A1013, follow signs to next roundabout, first left to Stifford Clays via Long Lane; follow to crossroads, straight across, keep left of block of flats, 1st right after flats
Ground capacity: Seating 150, standing 1500
Clubhouse facilities: Bar open permitted licensing hours, gym, physio room, weights room, squash courts
Club colours: Black and white hooped shirts, black shorts, black socks. (*Change colours:* Black shirts)
Floodlights: Yes
Membership fees: Full £25 p.a., Playing £25 p.a., Social £25 p.a.
Local newspapers: Thurrock Gazette, Evening Echo, Yellow Advertiser
League: London 2N
League position (1988–89): 8th
League playing record (1988–89): P 10, W 3, D 1, L 6, F 107, A 122

WOODFORD

Highams, Woodford High Road, Woodford Green, Essex. Tel: 01 504 6764
Founded: 1926
President: Edward S. James
Chairman: Roger Clive Langdell
Secretary: Eric Beck, 20 Hollywood Way, Woodford Green, Essex. Tel: 01 527 2118 (H). 839 7766 (W)
League Contact: As Secretary
Fixtures Secretary: N. Hooper, Sheepcote Cottage, Clavering, Saffron Warden, Essex CB11 4SJ. Tel: 0799 550489
Press Officer: As Secretary
Coach: David McMahon and Paul Lees
Club captain (1988–89): Paul Grindley
Club captain (1989–90): Paul Grindley
No. of teams: Senior 7, Youth 2, Minis 6
Directions to ground: Woodford Tube Station, north

via Snakes Lane to Woodford High Road, thence left for 500 yards. Club entrance on right 25 yards off main road
Ground capacity: Seating 250, standing 1000
Club colours: White, lavender and black. (*Change colours:* Purple)
Floodlights: Training purposes only
Membership fees: Full £36.50, Playing £36.50, Social £16, Youth £15, Student £15, OAP £6
Ground admission: Free
Local newspapers: Wanstead & Woodford Guardian, Ilford Recorder
League: London 2N
League position (1988–89): 9th
League playing record (1988–89): P 10, W 3, D 0, L 7, F 146, A 162

LONDON 2 SOUTH

ALTON

Anstey Park, Alton, Hants. Tel: 0420 82076
Founded: 1924
President: Eddie Thomas
Chairman: Geoff Frith
Secretary: John Grace, 38 Grebe Close, Alton, Hants. Tel: 0420 87273
League Contact: Martin Hogwood, 1 Turnpike Cottages, Upper Froyle, Alton, Hants GU34 4JQ
Fixtures Secretary: Alan Brown, Three Beech Farm, Homestead Road, Medstead, Alton, Hants. Tel: 0420 63238
Press Officer: Ian Hogg, Braemar, Anstey Lane, Alton, Hants. Tel: 0420 83757
Coach: Martin Hodwood
Club captain (1988–89): Alan Fleetwood
Club captain (1989–90): Alan Fleetwood
No. of teams: Senior 4, Youth 3 (U14,16,19), Minis 6 (2×U12,2×U10,2×U5)
Directions to ground: Leave A31 at roundabout to NE of Alton Bypass, follow signs to Alton (A339). After mile turn right into Anstey Park
Ground capacity: Standing unlimited
Clubhouse facilities: Training nights (Tuesdays and Thursdays), Friday, Saturday, Sunday. Weight room opening summer '89
Club colours: Red shirts, black shorts. (*Change colours:* All black)
Nickname: The Reds
Floodlights: For training only
Membership fees: Playing £20, Social £5, Youth £10, Student £10
Ground admission: Nil
Programme: No. of editorial pages 2; No. of advertising pages 8; Price 50p
Programme editor: Geoff Frith, Gresham, Old Odiham Road, Alton, Hants. Tel: 0420 84732
Local newspapers: Alton Herald, Alton Gazette
League: London 2S
League position (1988–89): 1st in London 3SW
League playing record (1988–89): P 30, W 24, D 0, L 6, F 727, A 265
Competitions won: Winners London 3SW. Hants Cup Semi Finals

CAMBERLEY

'Watchetts', Park Road, Camberley, Surrey. Tel: 0276 25395
Founded: 1898
President: Tony Carter
Chairman: Steve Harvey
Secretary: John Pendleton, 'Serendipity', 11 Chaucer Road, Wellington Chase, Crowthorne, Berkshire RG11 7QN. Tel: 0344 777722 (H). 01 480 5152 (W)
League Contact: W.J. Fletcher, 63 Rookwood Ave, Owlsmoor, Camberley, Surrey GU15 4TY. Tel: 0344 777701 (H). 51555 Ext 234 (W)
Fixtures Secretary: As League Contact
Press Officer: As League Contact

Club captain (1988–89): Chris Gibson
Club captain (1989–90): Chris Gibson
No. of teams: Senior 6, Youth 6, Minis 5
Ground capacity: Standing 500
Clubhouse facilities: Open lunch time and evenings all week
Club colours: Black and amber. (*Change colours: Black*)
Floodlights: Yes
League: London 2S
League position (1988–89): 4th
League playing record (1988–89): P 33, W 24, D 1, L 8, F 649, A 308

DARTFORDIANS

Bourne End, Bexley, Kent. Tel: Crayford 524176.
Founded: 1924
Secretary: D. Stilling, 2 Brookfield, Kemsing, Near Sevenoaks, Kent TN15 6SQ. Tel: Otford 4468 (H), 01-629-4509 (B).
Fixtures Secretary: D. Rapley, 11 Felhampton Road, New Eltham, London SE19. Tel: 01-857-6198.
League: London 1

ESHER

369 Molesey Road, Hersham, Surrey
Founded: 1924
President: A.R. Prentice
Chairman: B.J. Holland
Secretary: A.R. Till, 25 Motspur Park, New Malden, Surrey KT3 6PS. Tel: 01–942 1380
Fixtures Secretary: J. Inerdale, 37 Borough Road, Kingston on Thames, Surrey. Tel: 01–546 6342
Coach: T.B.A.
Club captain (1988–89): C. Turner
Club captain (1989–90): A. Olsen
No. of teams: Senior 8, Youth and Minis 6
Directions to ground: 369 Molesey Road near Herssham BR Station – Walton-on-Thames – 15 mins from M25
Ground capacity: Standing 2000
Clubhouse facilities: Excellent clubhouse with bars and changing rooms
Club colours: Black and amber. (*Change colours: White*)
Floodlights: Yes
Membership fees: Full £30
Ground admission: Varies
Programme: No. of editorial pages varies; No. of advertising pages varies
Local newspapers: Surrey Herald, Surrey Comet
League: London 2 (S)
League position (1988–89): 7th
League playing record (1988–89): P 33, W 12, D 1, L 20

GRAVESEND

The Rectory Field, Milton Road, Gravesend, Kent. Tel: 0474 534840
Founded: 1921
President: Trevor A. Howard
Chairman: Brian T. Curtis
Secretary: John Moore, 375A Singlewell Road, Gravesend, Kent DA11 7RL. Tel: 0474 62998
League Contact: A.C. Panter, 21 Studley Crescent, New Barn, Kent DA3 7JL. Tel: 04747 2202
Fixtures Secretary: As Secretary
Press Officer: Richard and Jim Spackman, Dowland House, Cooling Street, Cliffe, Kent. Tel: 0634 221668
Coach: Peter Ford
Club captain (1988–89): Robert B. Bardell
Club captain (1989–90): Malcolm K. Willden
No. of teams: Senior 7, Youth 3, Minis 5
Directions to ground: Leave the M25 at the A2 intersection and head in the direction of Rochester/Dover. Leave the A2 at the 'Gravesend East' turn off (Valley Drive) and proceed to its end approx. 1 miles. Turn right into Old Road East. At the roundabout

take the first exit left, proceed for approx. mile. The entrance to the Ground is on the left
Ground capacity: Standing 3000+
Clubhouse facilities: Open lunchtime Wednesday–Sunday and every evening
Club colours: Shirts 4-inch black and white hoops. Socks black and white hoops. Shorts black. (*Change colours: Black*)
Nickname: G's
Floodlights: Yes
Membership fees: Full £25, Playing £25, Social £6, Youth £15, Student £8
Ground admission: Nil
Local newspapers: Gravesend Reporter, Evening Post, Leader
League: London 2S
League position (1988–89): 5th
League playing record (1988–89): P 10, W 5, D 0, L 5, F 127, A 115
Competitions won: Reporter Floodlite Sevens March 1989

GUILDFORD & GODALMING

Broadwater, Guildford Road, Godalming, Surrey. Tel: 048-68-6199
Founded: 1922
President: G.S. Howell
Chairman: J. Vivian
Coach: A. Roberts
Secretary: A.W. Bird, The Old Barn, Hog's Hill, Fernhurst, Haslemere, Surrey. Tel: 0428-53359
Fixtures Secretary: L. Bodill, 11 Briarway, Burpham, Guildford. Tel: 570580.
Club captain (1987–88): A.C. Sacha
Club captain (1988–89): A.C. Sacha
No. of teams: Senior 6. Youth & Minis 10.
Directions to Ground: A3100 Guildford to Godalming Road. 3 miles.
Ground capacity: 1,000
Colours: Green & white hoops
Change colours: Red or blue
Nickname: G & G
Floodlights: No
Membership: Players £30. Non-players £17.50.
Programme: 20p
Local newspaper: Surrey Advertiser
League: London I

OLD BROCKLEIANS

Eltham Palace Road, London SE9. Tel: 01 850 8650
Founded: 1924
President: A. Gearing
Chairman: A. Gearing
Secretary: R. Ellery, 13 Peacock Gardens, Selsdon CR2 8TE. Tel: 657 7973
League Contact: As Secretary
Fixtures Secretary: G. Wright, 3 Birling Avenue, Bearsted, Maidstone ME14 4DG. Tel: 0622 38396
Press Officer: Ian Tharby, 86 Amblecote Road, SE12 9TW. Tel: 01 857 4869
Club captain (1988–89): R. Cox
Club captain (1989–90): T.B.A.
No. of teams: Senior 5, Youth 1
Directions to ground: Near Junction A2-A21, South Circular Road (M25 exit 4)
Clubhouse facilities: Cosy
Club colours: Chocolate, emerald and old gold. (*Change colours: No*)
Floodlights: Training only
Membership fees: Full £30, Social £5, Youth reductions
Local newspapers: Kentish Times
League position (1988–89): 8th
League playing record (1988–89): P 10, W 3, D 1, L 6, F 84, A 157
Competitions won: Plate Winners, Kentish Times Sevens

OLD COLFEIANS

Horn Park, Eltham Road, Lee, London SE12. Tel:
01–852 1181
Founded: 1928
President: Patrick J. Paynter
Chairman: Martin Wale
Secretary: Dai Andrew, 80 Dallinger Road, Lee,
London SE12 0HT. Tel: 01–857 4036 (H), 01–318
7331 (W)
Fixtures Secretary: John Nunn, 'The Mount', 27
Westmount Road, Eltham, London SE9 1JB
Press Officer: Kevin Meekings, 30 Hook Lane,
Welling, Kent. Tel: 01–303 0295 (H), 0332 20836 (W)
Coach: Andy Smith
Club captain (1988–89): Martin Fenner
Club captain (1989–90): Martin Fenner
No. of teams: Senior 5, Youth (U19) 1
Directions to ground: On Eltham Road (A20) 400 m
from Lee Green and 600 m intersection of A20 and
A205 (South Circular Road)
Ground capacity: Standing 1000
Clubhouse facilities: 8 changing rooms, 3 bars and 2
squash courts
Club colours: Blue, black, maroon and old gold
bands. (*Change colours:* Scarlet)
Nickname: O.C.'s
Floodlights: Yes (training pitch only)
Membership fees: Full £40, Playing £40, Social £17,
Youth £10, Student £10 (these fees include
membership of Old Colfeians Ass. reduced by £12 or
£5 if life member)
Ground admission: Free
Programme: No. of editorial pages 4; No. of
advertising pages 6; Price 50p or Free
Programme editor: Kevin Meekings, 30 Hook Lane,
Welling, Kent
Local newspapers: Kentish Mercury and Kentish
Times
League: London 2S
League position (1988–89): 1st (promoted)
League playing record (1988–89): P 10, W 9, D 0,
L 1, F 185, A 81
Competitions won: London League 3SE, Kent Cup
(losing semi-finalists). Old Brockleians Best Seven in
Kent Winners. Old Caterhamians Sevens Winners

OLD MID-WHITGIFTIAN

Lime Meadow Avenue, Sanderstead, Surrey. Tel: 01
657 2014
President: Alan Sexton
Chairman: Chris Nunn
Secretary: Jeremy Glynn-Jones, 2 Elm Road, Purley,
Surrey CR2 2DR
League Contact: Andy Hillburn, 47A Foxearth Road,
Selsdon, South Croydon, Surrey CR2 8EL. Tel: 01
657 1825 (H). 686 8833 (W)
Fixtures Secretary: As League Contact
Press Officer: As Secretary
Club captain (1988–89): John Carey
Club captain (1989–90): Carl Wahlers
No. of teams: Senior 4, Youth 1
Directions to ground: Sanderstead roundbout.
Limpsfield Road towards Warlingham. mile past fire
station and garage, next left into Sanderstead Court
Avenue, 75 yards right into Lime Meadow Avenue.
Ground at end of road
Ground capacity: Seating Nil, standing 1000
Clubhouse facilities: Members bar and large club bar
Club colours: Dark blue. (*Change colours:* Green)
Nickname: Midwives
Floodlights: No
Membership fees: Playing £55, Social £12.50, Student
£25
Ground admission: Nil
Programme: To be revised for 1989/90 season
Programme editor: As Secretary
Local newspapers: Croydon Advertiser

League: London 2S
League position (1988–89): 3rd
League playing record (1988–89): P 33, W 24, D 1,
L 8, F 629, A 258
Competitions won: Winners Clob Merit Table – Kent
& East Surrey Division

TUNBRIDGE WELLS

St. Mark's, Frant Road, Tunbridge Wells, Kent. Tel:
0892 27448
Founded: 1933
President: J. Theobald
Chairman: Roger Clarke
Secretary: Joe Jones, 4 Wallace Close, Tunbridge
Wells, Kent TN2 5HW. Tel: 01 845 2345 (W)
League Contact: Roger Clarke, 4 Wallace Close,
Tunbridge Wells, Kent TN2 5HW. Tel: 01 845 2345
(W)
Fixtures Secretary: K. Bassi, 12 Richardson Road,
Tunbridge Wells. Tel: 0892 28542 (H). 515720 (W)
Press Officer: Christopher C. McCooey, 2 Wood
Cottages, Victoria Road, Southborough, Tunbridge
Wells, Kent. Tel: 0892 29228
Coach: Coordinator of coaches – David Moxon
Club captain (1988–89): Jimmy Hendley
Club captain (1989–90): Jimmy Hendley
No. of teams: Senior 5, Youth 4, Minis 4
Directions to ground: Proceed to the Pantiles
roundabout and take the A267 signposted
Eastbourne. 1 mile top of hill, ground of left 50 yards
from Forest Road intersection
Clubhouse facilities: Two-storey brick built 1983
Club colours: Royal blue and white hoops, white
shorts, royal blue socks. (*Change colours:* No)
Nickname: The Wells
Floodlights: No
Membership fees: Full £15, Playing £15, Social £15,
Youth £5, Student £5, OAP £5
Programme: No. of editorial pages 2; No. of
advertising pages 2; Price: Free
Programme editor: Peter Price, 15 Henwood Green
Road, Nr Tunbridge Wells, Kent. Tel: 0892 82 4333
Local newspapers: Kent and Sussex Courier
League: London 2S
League position (1988–89): 6th
League playing record (1988–89): P 10, W 5, D 0,
L 5, F 116, A 116
Competitions won: Under 12s Kent Mini Champions

WORTHING

The Rugby Park, Roundstone Lane, Angmering, West
Sussex. Tel: 0903 784706
Founded: 1920
President: Bob Rogers
Chairman: Alf Scringour
Secretary: Brian Vincent, 29 St Botolph's Road,
Worthing, W. Sussex. Tel: 0903 206516 (H). 36572
(W)
League Contact: Chris Saint, 39 Arlington Avenue,
Goring By Sea, West Worthing, Sussex BN12 4SU.
Tel: 0903 505534 (H). 42089 (W)
Fixtures Secretary: As League Contact
Press Officer: Ian Ferrey, 87 Offington Avenue,
Worthing, W. Sussex. Tel: 0903 60500
Coach: Colin Williams
Club captain (1988–89): Jon Forrest
Club captain (1989–90): Jon Forrest
No. of teams: Senior 5, Youth 3, Minis 4
Directions to ground: Roundstone Lane, Angmering.
mile north of Roundstone Corner, Littlehampton
Road (A259)
Ground capacity: Seating 100, standing unlimited
Clubhouse facilities: Open Match days. Tuesday,
Wednesday, Thursday training evenings
Club colours: Royal blue with chocolate and gold
hoops. (*Change colours:* Yellow)
Floodlights: Under construction
Membership fees: Playing £39, Social £10, Youth £8,
Student £8, OAP £10, Family £21, Country £5, Life

£150
Local newspapers: Worthing Herald, Evening Argus
League: London 2S
League position (1988–89): 2nd
League playing record (1988–89): P 10, W 7, D 1, L 2, F 186, A 66
Competitions won: Sussex Counts Cup 9th April, Final won against Lewes 15–3. Winners of Middlesex Sevens Counts Clubs Championship at Twickenham o 6th May, Crawley Sevens Winners 12th April. Qualified for Pilkington Cup 89/90

LONDON 3 NORTH WEST

BACAVIANS

Bragbury House, Bragbury End, Stevenage, Herts. Tel: 0438 812985
Founded: 1958
President: Daryl Hayler
Chairman: Graham Hamilton
Secretary: Howard Crompton, 22 York Road, Stevenage, Herts. SG1 4HE. Tel: 0438 354904 (H). 0462 686500 Ext 3237 (W)
League Contact: As Secretary
Fixtures Secretary: Fred McCarthy, 10 Lismore, Stevenage, Herts. Tel: 0438 316372 (H). 312422 Ext 2049 (W)
Press Officer: Richard Stephens, 18 Russell Close, Stevenage, Herts. Tel: 0438 351971 (H). 355751 (W)
Coach: T.B.A.
Club captain (1988–89): Frank Richardson
Club captain (1989–90): Frank Richardson
No. of teams: Senior 5, Youth 1
Directions to ground: From A1(M) Stevenage South East follow A602 towards Hertford. Ground on left hand side just past golf course
Clubhouse facilities: Large sports and social club
Club colours: Green shirts with amber hoop, white shorts, green socks. (*Change colours:* Blue shirts, white shorts, green socks)
Floodlights: No
Membership fees: Full £19, Playing £19, Social £5, Youth £5, Student £5
Local newspapers: North Herts. Gazette, Comet, Herald
League: London 3NW
League position (1988–89): 7th
League playing record (1988–89): P 10, W 3, D 2, L 5, F 110, A 140

FULLERIANS

Conningsby Drive, (off Parkside Drive), Watford, Herts. Tel: 0923 224483
Founded: 1925
President: R.E. Seymour
Chairman: J. Vain
Secretary: R.E. Seymour, 41 Ashlyns Road, Berkhamsted, Herts. HP4 3BL. Tel: 0442 866475 (H). 01 582 9238 (W)
League Contact: John Ayres, 9 Church Grove, Little Chalfont, Bucks. HP6 6SH. Tel: 02404 3266 (H). 01 361 1617 (W)
Fixtures Secretary: As League Contact
Press Officer: A. Thewlis, 39 Yarmouth Road, Watford, Herts. Tel: 0923 50017
Coach: Richard Gravestock
Club captain (1988–89): Spencer Craze
Club captain (1989–90): Spencer Craze
No. of teams: Senior 6, Youth 1
Directions to ground: South off A411, North West of Watford, into Langley Way. Turn right at end into Conningsby Drive
Clubhouse facilities: All mod cons
Club colours: Black/red/green hoops, white shorts. (*Change colours:* No)
Nickname: Fullers
Floodlights: No
Membership fees: Playing £20, Social £10

Local newspapers: Watford Observer
League: London 3NW
League position (1988–89): 8th
League playing record (1988–89): P 10, W 4, D 0, L 6, F 127, A 169

HEMEL HEMPSTEAD (CAMELOT)

Founded:
President:
Chairman:
Secretary: J.M. Clapham
Fixtures Secretary: A.J. Wakefield, 23 Riverside Court, Riverreach, Broomwater, Teddington, Middx. Tel: 01–977 0746 (H), 01–930 2399 (W)
Press Officer: Bob Woodard, 18 Pulleys Close, Warners End, Hemel Hempstead, Herts. Tel: 0442 43758
Coach: Tony Yorath
Club captain (1988–89): Tony Impey
Club captain (1989–90): Brian Clancy
No. of teams: Senior 5, Youth 2, Minis 2–3 (intend to start)
Directions to ground:
Ground capacity: Standing 000
Clubhouse facilities:
Club colours:
Nickname: Camelot
Floodlights: Yes (training only)
Membership fees: Full £25, Playing £25, Social £12.50, Colt £10, Junior £5
Ground admission: Nil
Local newspapers:
League: London 3NW
League position (1988–89): 6th
League playing record (1988–89): P 32, W 16, D 2, L 14, F 490, A 356
Competitions won: Herts Sevens Winners, April 1989

HERTFORD

'Highfields', Hoe Lane, Ware, Herts SG12 9NZ. Tel: 0920 462975
Founded: 1931
President: John Reginald Herbert Creasey
Chairman: John Stuart Atkinson
Secretary: Derek Williamson, 33 Hertford Road, Hoddesdon, Herts. Tel: 0992 441541
League Contact: Don Olsen, 22 Oak Grove, Hertford, Herts. Tel: 0992 550501
Fixtures Secretary: David J. Williams, 7 Sadlers Way, Hertford SG14 2DZ. Tel: 0992 586744
Press Officer: As Fixtures Secretary
Coach: Peter Cadle
Club captain (1988–89): Graeme Walters
Club captain (1989–90): Graeme Walters
No. of teams: Senior 8, Youth 4, Minis 5
Directions to ground: From London A10, come off at A414 junction signposted Harlow/Chelmsford. At Stansted roundabout turn immediately left onto B1502. Ground in Hoe Lane, 3 miles on right. From the west take A414 to Hertford. At Gallows Hill roundabout take B1502 and Ground is in Hoe Lane, 500 yards on left
Ground capacity: Seating 20, standing 500
Clubhouse facilities: 2 bars, kitchen and catering facilities, function room for dining and/or dancing, committee room, bath/showers, 2 squash courts, 5 pitches, adequate parking
Club colours: Black, royal blue and gold. (*Change colours:* Light blue)
Floodlights: Yes
Membership fees: Full £35, Playing £35, Social £5, Youth £10, Student £5
Ground admission: 30p
Programme: 8 pages; Price 30p
Programme editor: John Atkinson, 86 Winterscroft Road, Hoddesdon, Herts. EN11 8RJ
Local newspapers: Hertfordshire Mercury, 'This

Week' (free sheet inc. Rugby Report)
League position (1988–89): 11th in London 2N
League playing record (1988–89): P 38, W 14, D 1, L 23, F 306, A 629

KINGSBURIANS

Northwick Park Pavilion, The Fairway, Kenton, Middlesex. Tel: 01 904 4414
Founded: 1961
Chairman: Dave Hollings
Secretary: Brian J. Jones, 46 Woodcock Hill, Kenton, Harrow, Middlesex. Tel: 01 907 8220
League Contact: Bruce Bland, 10 Clitheroe Avenue, Rayners Lane, Harrow HA2 9UX. Tel: 01 868 5244 (H). 204 4442 (W)
Fixtures Secretary: As League Contact
Press Officer: Steve Dudmish, 20 Tintagel Drive, Stanmore, Middlesex. Tel: 01 958 4572 (H). 205 6237 (W)
Coach: Steve Hancock
Club captain (1988–89): Warren Jones
Club captain (1989–90): Steve Hancock
No. of teams: Senior 4
Directions to ground: Met. Line to Northwick Park Station, pavilion/pitches visible from station, proceed via footpath. Bus to John Lyon Pub in Watford Road (A404), take Norval Road off the green opposite pub. 400 yards to first left (Ground entrance)
Ground capacity: Standing – Pitch-side!
Clubhouse facilities: Bar open Tuesday/Thursday evenings (training) and Match days
Club colours: Black/amber hoops, black shorts. (*Change colours:* All black)
Nickname: Kings
Floodlights: Training only
Membership fees: Full £25, Playing £25, Social £5, Youth £5, Student £5, OAP £5
Local newspaper: Harrow Observer
League: London 3NW
League position (1988–89): 4th
League playing record (1988–89): P 10, W 7, D 0, L 3, F 122, A 81
Competitions won: Promoted to Fullers Brewery Middx County Clubs Merit Table from Associate Table. Loosing finalists at Berkshire Plate Sevens Tournament

MILL HILL

Page Street, Mill Hill, London NW7. Tel: 01 203 0685
Founded: 1937
President: T.A.C. Fletcher
Chairman: Ian Webster
Secretary: Francis Illing, 129 Farm Road, Edgware, Middlesex. Tel: 01 958 9267
League Contact: Peter J. Braddock, 43 Winstre Road, Borehamwood, Herts. WD6 5DR. Tel: 01 953 6500 (H). 587 7012 (W)
Fixtures Secretary: As League Contact
Press Officer: D.F. Munro, 103 Woodcote Avenue, London NW7. Tel: 01 906 0327
Club captain (1988–89): Mike Reed
No. of teams: Senior 6
Directions to ground: Page Street is at the Junction of Five Ways Corner. A1-A41 and Junction 2 of the M1 Motorway
Ground capacity: Seating Nil, standing 2000
Clubhouse facilities: Open Match days and evenings. Dining area, lounge bar, ladies lounge
Club colours: Chocolate and old gold hooped shirts and socks. (*Change colours:* Plain chocolate shirts, club crest on L/H breast)
Nickname: The Millers
Floodlights: Training area only
Membership fees: Playing £20, Social £5
Ground admission: Free
Programme: No. of editorial pages – special editions only; No. of advertising pages 4; Price 50p
Programme editor: As League Contact
Local newspapers: Hendon & Mill Times

League: London 3NW
League position (1988–89): 3rd
League playing record (1988–89): P 10, W 6, D 2, L 2, F 144, A 85
Competitions won: Runners Up: Middlesex Merit Table. Winners: Mill Hill & The Finchley XV 'A' Side Tournaments. Winners: Berlin 7 'A' Side Tournament

ST MARY'S HOSPITAL

St. Mary's Hospital Athletic Ground, Udney Park Road, Teddington. Tel: 01 088 3100
Founded: 1866
President: D. Rosen FRCS, FRCS(Ed), MS
Secretary: R.A.L. Young FRCS, West Middlesex Hospital, Twickenham Road, Middlesex
League Contact: John Mallinson, 70 Park Road, London W4 3HL. Tel: 994 6540
Fixtures Secretary: Prof. Peter Sever PhD, FRCP, c/o Mrs Gerry McArthy, 6 Ripley Road, Hampton, Middlesex TW12 2JH. Tel: 01 783 0810
Club captain (1988–89): A. Ellery
Club captain (1989–90): D.P. Gillen
No. of teams: Senior 4
Directions to ground: St. Mary's Hospital Athletic Ground, Udney Park Road, Teddington, Middlesex
Ground capacity: Standing 3000
Clubhouse facilities: Open Match days
Club colours: Blue shirts, blue shorts and socks. (*Change colours:* White shirts, blue shorts and socks)
Nickname: Mary's
Floodlights: No
Membership fees: Student £10, Post Graduate £20
League: London 3NW
League position (1988–89): 5th
League playing record (1988–89): P 10, W 6, D 1, L 3, F 131, A 114
Competitions won: United Hospitals Challenge Cup 1989 (1st and 2nd XV). United Hospitals 7-a-sides 1988

TABARD

Cobden Hill, Radlett, Herts. Tel: 09274 5561
Founded: 1951
President: W. Fullerlove
Chairman: B. Brennan
Secretary: R. Hopcroft, 100 Manor Road, Barton-le-Clay, Beds. MK45 4NS
Fixtures Secretary: C. Carmichael, 10 Chandos Road, Borehamwood, Herts. Tel: 01 953 9006
Coach: T.B.A.
Club captain (1988–89): Tim Smithers
Club captain (1989–90): Tim Smithers
No. of teams: Senior 4, Youth & Minis 1
Directions to ground: Off the A5, opposite 'Cat & Fiddle' PH in Radlett
Club colours: Navy, broad yellow band, edged red. (*Change colours:* Various (to suit))
Nickname: Tabs
Floodlights: No
Membership fees: £20
Ground admission: Free
Local newspapers: Herts Adviser
League: London 3NW
Competitions won: Hertfordshire Merit Table

TWICKENHAM

'Parkfields', South Road, Hampton, Middlesex. Tel: 01–979 2427
President: Peter Harvey
Chairman: Peter Harvey
Secretary: Simon Weathers, 41 Silver Crescent, London W4 5SF. Tel: 01–747 1127 (H), 01–995 1441 (W)
Fixtures Secretary: Ray Bairstow, 20 Tudor Avenue, Hampton, Middlesex. Tel: 01–979 1401 (H), 01–831 6781 (W)
Press Officer: John Samuels, 33 Manor Road,

Teddington, Middlesex. Tel: 01–9777 6835 (H),
01–567 3060 (W)
Coach: Shaun Rusk
Club captain (1988–89): Ray Dudman
Club captain (1989–90): David Basley
No. of teams: Senior 6, Youth and Minis 10
Directions to ground: On request
Ground capacity: Standing Ample
Clubhouse facilities: Beer, food, kit and hot water
Club colours: Red and black irregular hoops. (*Change
colours:* Light blue)
Floodlights: Yes (training only)
Membership fees: Full £20, Playing £20, Social £10,
Youth £5, Student £8.50, OAP £10
Ground admission: Nil
Programme: No. of editorial pages 12; No. of
advertising pages Several; Price 50p
Programme editor: David Lawrenson (Sunday Times),
11 Abbott Close, Hampton, Middlesex
Local newspapers: Middlesex Chronicle, Richmond &
Twickenham Times
League: Middlesex 1
League position (1988–89): 1st (promoted)
League playing record (1988–89): P 34, W 28, D 2,
L 4, F 827, A 309
Competitions won: Middlesex Division 1 Winners,
1988/89

UPPER CLAPTON

The Clubhouse, Upland Road, Thornwood Common,
Nr Epping, Essex CM16 7NL. Tel: 0378 72588
Founded: 1879
President: Terry Martin
Secretary: David Miller, 13 Rushfield,
Sawbridgeworth, Herts. CM21 9NF. Tel: 0279 724849
(H). 01 480 7629 (0860 427651) (W)
League Contact: As Secretary
Fixtures Secretary: Frank Harding, 32 Grangewood,
Little Heath, Nr Potters Bar, Herts. Tel: 0707 57814
(H). 0992 767340 (W)
Press Officer: David Tomlinson, 16 Little Pynchons,
Harlow, Essex. Tel: 0279 30379 (H). 726990 (W)
Coach: Mike Lovett
Club captain (1988–89): Jim O'Shea
Club captain (1989–90): Spencer Elmer
No. of teams: Senior 5, Youth 1
Directions to ground: Take Mqq north to Junction 7
(Harlow exit). Turn south to Epping on B1393 (old
A11). Approx. 1 mile, Upland Road on right,
signposted Epping Green, just before Texaco petrol
station
Ground capacity: Standing 500+
Clubhouse facilities: Changing facilities for 8 sides,
mini gym, plunge bath, showers, large bar
Club colours: Red and white 7″ hoops. (*Change
colours:* All white)
Nickname: The Club
Floodlights: Training lights
Membership fees: Playing £30, Social £7, Youth £3,
Student £3
Ground admission: Nil
Programme: No. of editorial pages 2; No. of
advertising pages 6; Price 50p
Programme editor: Marcus Tobin
Local newspapers: Guardian Gazette Group (Harlow
and Epping editions)
League: London 2N
League position (1988–89): 10th

WELWYN

Hobbs Way, Welwyn Garden City, Hertfordshire.
Tel: 0707 329116
Founded: 1931
President: K.A. Chivers
Chairman: H.D. Harris
Secretary: J.M. Sargeant, 67 Woodhall Lane, Welwyn
Garden City, Herts. AL7 3TG. Tel: 0707 331186 (H).
326318 (W)
League Contact: As Secretary

Fixtures Secretary: Nigel Mercer, 20 Parkside,
Welwyn, Herts. Tel: 043 871 7759
Press Officer: As Secretary
Coach: S. Hardy
Club captain (1988–89): Peter Emsden
Club captain (1989–90): Peter Emsden
No. of teams: Senior 5, Youth 1, Minis 4
Directions to ground: Turn left off Parkway in
Welwyn Garden City into Turnore Dale, turn left into
Colgrove and sharp right into Hobbs Way
Clubhouse facilities: Five changing rooms, showers,
bath
Club colours: Maroon and white hoops, white shorts,
maroon socks. (*Change colours:* Black shirts, black
shorts, black socks)
Floodlights: No
Membership fees: Playing £20, Social £7.50, Youth
£3.50, Student £7.50
Local newspapers: Welwyn/Hatfield Review
League: London 3NW
League position (1988–89): 1st in Herts League
Division 1
League playing record (1988–89): P 35, W 18, D 3,
L 14, F 597, A 447
Competitions won: Herts League Division 1

LONDON 3 NORTH EAST

BRENTWOOD

King Georges Playing Fields, Ingrave Road,
Brentwood, Essex. tel: 0277 210267
Founded: 1935
President: Mike Fleming
Chairman: Tony Broom
Secretary: Clive Gildersleeves, 19 Further Meadow,
Writtle, Chelmsford, Essex CM1 3LE. Tel: 0245
420679 (H). 267111 Ext 2440 (W)
League Contact: As Secretary
Fixtures Secretary: Clive Gower, 11 The Oakes,
Great Burstead, Essex CM11 2RP. Tel: 0277 659373
(H). 01 504 9602 (W)
Press Officer: Rick Rush, 9 Cecil Avenue,
Hornchurch, Essex RM11 2NA. Tel: 04024 72226
Coach: Scott Milne
Club captain (1988–89): Peter Cook
Club captain (1989–90): Peter Cook
No. of teams: Senior 5, Youth 4, Minis 4
Directions to ground: Opposite Fountains Head Public
House on A128 in centre of Brentwood
Clubhouse facilities: Open Match days (Saturday
p.m., Sunday noon), occasional evenings
Club colours: Maroon, grey and white hoops. (*Change
colours:* No)
Floodlights: No
Membership fees: Full £40, Playing £40, Social £20,
Youth £20, Student £10
Local newspapers: Brentwood Gazette
League: London 3NE
League position (1988–89): 8th
League playing record (1988–89): P 34, W 15, D 0,
L 19, F 535, A 610
Competitions won: Romford U24 Competition.
Maldon Veterans (over 35) Competition. Brentwood
Golden Boot (U16) Competition

CAMBRIDGE

Granchester Road, Cambridge
Founded: 1923
President: John Ashley
Chairman: David Beck
Coach: Russell Jones
Secretary: David Martin, 45 York Street, Cambridge.
Tel: 0223 314705.
Fixtures Secretary: Alan Curtis, Kendal Lodge,
Coton, Cambridge.
Club captain (1987–88): Stuart Gibbons
Club captain (1988–89): Kenny Isbister
No. of teams: Senior 5.

Directions to Ground: Take junction 12 off of M11 to towards Cambridge about one mile – turn right into Grantchester Road.
Ground capacity: 3000 if need be
Clubhouse: 5 changing rooms, large bar, lounge bar, 2 large baths, 8 showers.
Colours: Blood & sand. (*Change colours:* Cambridge blue
Floodlights: No
Membership: £23
Local newspaper: Cambridge Evening News
League: London 3NE

CANTABRIGIAN

Sedley Taylor Road, Cambridge CB2 2PW. Tel: 0223 213061
Founded: 1945
President: C.W. Gifford
Chairman: G.C. Cresswell
Secretary: B.J. Wakefield, The Old Manse, 27 High Street, Ramsey, Huntingdon, Cambs. PE17 1AE. Tel: 0487 812146 (H). 01 822 5737 (W)
League Contact: N.J. Seaber, 5 Ross Street, Cambridge, CB1 3BP. Tel: 0223 210145 (H). 423307 (W)
Fixtures Secretary: S. Barrett, 42 Melvin Way, Histon, Cambridge. Tel: 0223 237040 (H). 315315 (W)
Press Officer: As League Contact
Club captain (1988–89): M.C. Cracknell
Club captain (1989–90): N.J. Seaber
No. of teams: Senior 5, Youth 1
Directions to ground: M11, Junction 11, right at second set of traffic lights (Long Road). Near Addenbrookes Hospital
Clubhouse facilities: Open Match days, bar, lounge, open fire. Training facilities: floodlights, multi-gym, indoor training
Club colours: Navy blue, white hoops. (*Change colours:* No)
Nickname: Cantabs
Floodlights: No
Membership fees: Full £25, Playing £25, Social £10, Youth £10
Programme: No. of editorial pages 3; No. of advertising pages 2
Programme editor: M. Hargreaves, 11 Stockwell Street, Cambridge
Local newspapers: Cambridge Evening News
League: London 3NE
League position (1988–89): 7th
League playing record (1988–89): P 10, W 5, D 0, L 5, F 147, A 116

CHINGFORD

Lea Valley Playing Fields, Waltham Way, Chingford E4. Tel: 01 529 4879
Founded: 1928
President: Howard Hartley
Secretary: Jeffrey Carratt, 24 Alpha Road, Chingford E4 6TB. Tel: 01 524 2005 (H). 0727 66277 (W)
Fixtures Secretary: Raz Hales, 24 Moreland Way, Chingford, London E4. Tel: 01 524 0351
Coach: Steve Slowik
Club captain (1988–89): Ian Rabey
Club captain (1989–90): Paul Spencer
No. of teams: Senior 5, Youth 3, Minis 4
Directions to ground: Turn off North Circular Road (A406) by B&Q warehouse (A1009–Chingford). Ground mile along on left (next to Golf Driving Range)
Ground capacity: Standing unlimited
Clubhouse facilities: One large bar, hall, kitchen, showers, refs room, medical room, large changing room with 2 separate team rooms
Club colours: Black jersey, blue and white hoops, white shorts, blue socks. (*Change colours:* Red and black hooped shirts, llight blue shorts)
Nickname: Ching

Floodlights: Training only
Membership fees: Full £20, Playing £20, Social £15, Youth £5, Student £5, OAP £5
Ground admission: Nil
Local newspapers: Waltham Forest Guardian
League: London 3NE
League position (1988–89): 2nd
League playing record (1988–89): P 10, W 8, D 0, L 2, F 200, A 104
Competitions won: Runners-up Essex Colts. Runners-up Cheshunt Sevens. Winners Essex Sevens Plate

COLCHESTER

Mill Road, Mile End, Colchester, Essex CO4 5JF. Tel: 0206 851610
Founded: 1925
President: Don Reid
Chairman: Tim Wright
Secretary: Ron Hatch, 99 Ernest Road, Wivenhoe, Essex CO7 9LJ. Tel: 0206 22 3548
League Contact: George Ford, 36 Haynes Road, Hornchurch, Essex
Fixtures Secretary: John Roberts, 5 Spencer Close, Maldon, Essex. Tel: Maldon 54043
Press Officer: Gino Debiase, 3 South Street, Colchester, Essex CO2 7BL. Tel: 0206 863335 (H). 0245 267111 (W)
Coach: Vivyan Davies
Club captain (1988–89): Clive Bentley
Club captain (1989–90): Chris Yeats
No. of teams: Senior 6, Youth & Minis 11
Directions to ground: A12 from London. Colchester turn off to Station. A134 as far as 'Dog & Pheasant', turn right into Mill Road, club on left after mile
Clubhouse facilities: 2 storey. 6 changing rooms
Club colours: Black. (*Change colours:* Red and gold hoops)
Floodlights: Yes
Membership fees: Full £25
Ground admission: Free
Programme: Free
Programme editor: Gino Debiase
Local newspapers: Essex Standard
League: London 3N
League position (1988–89): 9th
League playing record (1988–89): P 10, W 3, D 0, L 7, F 190, A 125

HARLOW

Elizabeth Way, Harlow. Tel: 0279 29750
Founded: 1955
President: Ronald E. Bracewell
Chairman: Mike Ryland
Secretary: Brian Holgarth, 40 Purford Green, Harlow, Essex CM18 6HL. Tel: 0279 21249 (H). 0378 73518 (W)
League Contact: As Secretary
Fixtures Secretary: John Pendleton, 29 Priory Court, Harlow. Tel: 0279 39265
Press Officer: Jim Beaven, 14 Mark Hall Moors, Harlow. Tel: 0279 411401
Coach: Ray Harris
Club captain (1988–89): Simon Cook
Club captain (1989–90): Richard Drage
No. of teams: Senior 6, Youth 5
Directions to ground: Left at ski-slope roundabout when approaching from town centre. Ground mile on right, down Elizabeth Way
Ground capacity: Standing 400
Clubhouse facilities: Bar and lounge open every evening
Club colours: Red shirts with green collars, white shorts, red socks. (*Change colours:* Bottle green)
Nickname: Rams
Floodlights: Training standard only
Local newspapers: Harlow Gazette, Harlow Star
League: London 3NE
League position (1988–89): 1st in Eastern Counties 1
League playing record (1988–89): P 10, W 9, D 0,

L 1, F 247, A 55
Competitions won: Winners Eastern Counties League
One 1988/89

METROPOLITAN POLICE CHIGWELL

Metropolitan Police Sports Club, Chigwell Hall,
Chigwell Road, Chigwell, Essex. Tel: 01 500 2735
Founded: 1943
President: Commissioner of Pollice for the Metropolis
Chairman: Michael Lawrence
Secretary: Peter Ingham, 68 Gelsthorpe Road, Collier
Row, Romford, Essex RM5 2LX. Tel: 0708 28582
League Contact: As Secretary
Fixtures Secretary: James Harding, 30 Buxton House,
Buxton Drive, London E11. Tel: 01 989 2991
Press Officer: Andrew Hunter, D.I.'s office. Barking
Police Station, 6 Ripple Road, Barking Essex. Tel:
02774 450819 (H). 0708 29514 (W)
Coach: Cam Burnell
Club captain (1988–89): Cam Burnell
Club captain (1989–90): Cam Burnell
No. of teams: Senior 3
Directions to ground: By tube to Chigwell. Out of
Station, turn right. Ground 1 ile on left. 1 mile from
M11 in Chigwell village using Loughton turn off
Ground capacity: Seating 100, standing unlimited
Clubhouse facilities: Old Manor House converted to 3
bars and function rooms
Club colours: Royal blue shirts, navy shorts, red
socks. (*hange colours:* Red shirts)
Nickname: Chigwell Piggeries
Floodlights: No
Programme: No. of editorial pages 1–2; No. of
advertising pages 2; Price: Free
Programme editor: Ivor Smith
Local newspapers: Romford Recorder, Ilford Gazette
League: London 3NE
League position (1988–89): 6th
League playing record (1988–89): P 10, W 5, D 0,
L 5, F 168, A 131
Competitions won: Five League wins

ROMFORD & GIDEA PARK

Crow Lane, Romford, Essex. Tel: 0708 760068
Founded: 1930
President: Ron W. Johnson
Chairman: Anthony K. Richards
Secretary: David G.E. Davies, 25 Stanley Avenue,
Gidea Park, Romford, Essex RM2 5DL. Tel:
Romford 24870
League Contact: As Secretary
Fixtures Secretary: Ken Parry, 112 London Road,
Brentwood, Essex. Tel: Brentwod 224881 (H). 01 592
5623 (W)
Press Officer: As Secretary
Playing Committee Chairman: Andy McGill
Club captain (1988–89): David Duffus
Club captain (1989–90): David Duffus
No. of teams: Senior 5, Youth 3, Minis 2
Directions to ground: A12 to Moby Dick Public
House. From London right, or from East left, into
Whalebone Lane North, cross traffic lights to
Whalebone Lane South. 2nd left (immed. after
Railway Bridge). Ground 1 mile on right
Clubhouse facilities: Changing, showering, Clubroom
and bar (4 pitches)
Club colours: Black jerseys with alternate 2″ bands of
white/purple and white across chest and arms.
(*Change colours:* Alternate 2″ bands of
black/purple/white)
Floodlights: No
League: London 3NE
League position (1988–89): 2nd
League playing record (1988–89): P 37, W 31, D 0,
L 6, F 776, A 204

Competitions won: Brentwood Silver Ball Winners.
Losing Finalists in Essex County Cup

SAFFRON WALDEN

Springate, Henham, Bishops Stortford, Herts. Tel:
0279 850791
Founded: 1963
President: Dr Geoffrey Elcoat TD, MA
Chairman: Bryan Peachey
Secretary: Martin Curtis, New Barn Farm, Lindsell,
Dunmow, Essex CM6 3QH. Tel: 0371 84 461
League Contact: As Secretary
Fixtures Secretary: John Hamilton, Smiths Cottage,
Smiths Green, Takeley, Bishops Stortford, Herts. Tel:
0279 22107
Press Officer: Chris Edwards, 96 Radwinten Road,
Saffron Walden, Essex. Tel: 0799 22107
Coach: Frank Bennett
Club captain (1988–89): Ian McKernan
Club captain (1989–90): Julian Philips
No. of teams: Senior 4, Youth 2
Directions to ground: B1383 from Stumps Cross
roundabout to Bishops Stortford through Newport.
After 1.5 miles, left to Henham and Elsenham, signs
to Henham through village. Ground on left. From
M11 (Junction 8) turn off to Stanstead airport, A120
to Hertford to roundabout, take B1383 to Stanstead,
right in middle of village to railway station, at bottom
of hill left, then fork right to Elsenham. Through
village, after 1 mile left to Henham, right at Henham
crossroad. Ground 2 miles left
Ground capacity: Seating 80, standing 1000
Clubhouse facilities: Bar and clubrom, 4 changing
rooms, bath and showers
Club colours: Myrtle green shirts, white shorts.
(*Change colours:* Royal blue shirts)
Nickname: The Green Army
Floodlights: No
Membership fees: Full/VP £15, Playing £10, Social £5,
Youth £10, Student £10
Local newspapers: Saffron Walden Weekly News,
Saffron Walden Reporter
League: London 3NE
League position (1988–89): 10th
League playing record (1988–89): P 10, W 1, D 0,
L 9, F 65, A 375

WESTCLIFF

'The Gables', Aviation Way, Southend-on-Sea, Essex
SS2 6UN. Tel: 0702 541499
Founded: 1922
President: Howard P. Briggs
Chairman: Chris J. Sharples
Secretary: Nick J. Crowe, 68 Leighton Avenue,
Leigh-on-Sea, Essex SS9 1QA. Tel: 0702 711647 (H).
0268 756111 (W)
League Contact: As Secretary
Fixtures Secretary: Ian Dudley, 105 Eversley Road,
Benfleet, Essex. Tel: 0268 794112 (H). 0702 367818
(W)
Press Officer: Geoff C. Sawyer, 30 Lascelles Gardens,
Rochford, Essex. Tel: 0702 544434 (H). 01 227 3285
(W)
Club captain (1988–89): Jim P. Rafferty
Club captain (1989–90): Stuart N. Richmond
No. of teams: Senior 5, Youth 3, Minis 4
Directions to ground: A127 to Southend. Approx. 3
miles after Rayleigh Weir roundabout, turn left at
traffic lights by Perry's Garage. First right into Snakes
Lane, at end turn right, 4th left into Aviation Way,
sharp right at top of Aviation Way, Ground 50 yards
on left
Ground capacity: Standing – as many as will fit
Clubhouse facilities: Two bars, two squash courts,
mini-gymnasium
Club colours: maroon and gold hooped shirts, blue
shorts. (*Change colours:* No)
Floodlights: No
League: London 3NE

League position (1988–89): 5th
League playing record (1988–89): P 10, W 6, D 0,
L 4, F 158, A 98

WEST NORFOLK

Gatehouse Lane, North Wootton, Kings Lynn,
Norfolk. Tel: 0553 87307
Founded: 1923
President: Robert S. Fraulo
Chairman: Patrick W. Wakefield
Secretary: Mark Harold Ballman, 10 Shipdham Road,
Toftwood, Dereham, Norfolk NR19 1JJ. Tel: 0362
698289 (H). 0553 773393 (W)
League Contact: As Secretary
Fixtures Secretary: John Wittred, 48 Holcombe
Avenue, Kings Lynn, Norfolk. Tel: 0553 775386
Press Officer: Andrew Owen, 23 Burghley Road,
Kings Lynn, Norfolk. Tel: 0553 671017 (H). 773606
(W)
Coach: Robert Crome
Club captain (1988–89): John Moses
Club captain (1989–90): Stuart Haydon
No. of teams: Senior 4, Youth 4, Minis 4
Directions to ground: Approach Kings Lynn via A10,
A17 or A47 and follow A149 to Hunstanton/Cromer
and then left at Knights Hill roundabout. A148
signposted Docks. At lights right into Castle Rising
Road and after mile left into Priory Lane. Enter
30mph zone and left into Gatehouse Lane after Post
Office. Ground on right
Ground capacity: Standing 1000
Clubhouse facilities: Under construction
Club colours: French grey and cerise. (*Change
colours:* No)
Floodlights: No
Membership fees: Full £25, Playing £25, Social £12.50,
Youth £5, Student £25, OAP £12.50
Local newspapers: Eastern Daily Press, Kings Lynn
News and Advertiser
League: London 3NE
League position (1988–89): 4th
League playing record (1988–89): P 10, W 6, D 0,
L 4, F 215, A 138
Competitions won: Norfolk Cup 19.2.89. Holt Sevens
9.4.89

LONDON 3 SOUTH EAST

BECKENHAM

Balmoral Avenue, Elmers End, Beckenham, Kent.
Tel: 01 650 7176
Founded: 1894
President: Laurance Pinn
Chairman: Laurance Pinn
Secretary: William Guy Sumner, 19 Lakeside,
Beckenham, Kent BR3 2LX. Tel: 01 650 2230 (H).
0634 719122 (W)
League Contact: As Secretary
Fixtures Secretary: J.M. Arger, 15 Thatcher Road,
Staplehurst, Kent TN12 0ND. Tel: 0580 891550 (H).
01 388 3211 (W)
Press Officer: John Snelders, 87 Meadowview Road,
Catford SE6. Tel: 01 697 5563
Coach: Martin Parker
Club captain (1988–89): Paul Slattery
No. of teams: Senior 6, Youth 1, Minis 6
Directions to ground: Club entrance in Balmoral
Avenue which runs between Eden Park Avenue and
A214 Upper Elmers End Road. Turn off A222
Croydon Road into either of above roads
Ground capacity: Seating 300, standing 500
Clubhouse facilities: Bar, lounge bar, tea room, 6
showers, 2 baths, 6 changing rooms, kitchen
Club colours: Royal blue and old gold stripes.
(*Change colours:* Brown/purple)
Floodlights: Training only
Membership fees: Full £30, Playing £30, Social £10,

Student £10
Ground admission: Nil
Programme: No. of editorial pages 1; No. of
advertising pages 4
Programme editor: C. Stevens, 49 Harlescott Road,
London SE15 3DA. Tel: 01 732 9790
Local newspapers: Beckenham Times (Kentish
Times), Beckenham Advertiser, Bromley Advertiser
League: London 3SE
League position (1988–89): 4th
League playing record (1988–89): P 10, W 6, D 0,
L 4, F 129, A 102
Competitions won: Kentish Times Seven-a-side
Competition – April 1989

BOGNOR

Nyewood Lane, Bognor Regis, West Sussex. Tel:
0243 865462
Founded: 1964
President: Philip Mead
Chairman: Leighton Thomas
Secretary: J. Martin Eley, 23 Ilex Way, Middleton-on-
Sea, West Sussex PO22 6PQ. Tel: 0243 584588 (H).
864401 (W)
League Contact: As Secretary
Fixtures Secretary: Dean Dewey, 39 Carleton
Avenue, Rose Green, Bognor Regis. Tel: 0243
266185
Press Officer: A. Guiry, 27 Pinehurst Park, Aldwick,
Bognor Regis
Club captain (1988–89): R. Hine
Club captain (1989–90): R. Hine
No. of teams: Senior 4, Youth 2, Minis 3
Directions to ground: Turn off A259 Chichester Road
into Hawthorn Road, through lights, Ground 400m on
left
Clubhouse facilities: Large, upstairs bar, 3 squash
courts
Club colours: Maroon, green and white hoops.
(*Change colours:* Green)
Floodlights: Training only
Membership fees: Full £25, Playing £25, Social £5
Programme: No. of editorial pages: part of 1; No. of
advertising pages: 10; Price: free
Programme editor: As Press Officer
Local newspapers: Bognor Post, Bognor Observer
League: London 3SE
League position (1988–89): 9th
League playing record (1988–89): P 10, W 2, D 0,
L 7, F 94, A 121

CHARLTON PARK

Pippin Hall Sports Ground, Footscray Road, Eltham,
London SE9. Tel: 01 850 0408
President: Peter Budd
Chairman: Andy Potts
Secretary: Dennis Attwood, 6 Somerset Gardens, St
Johns, Lewisham, London SE13 7SY. Tel: 01 691
2820 (H). 856 9909 (W)
Fixtures Secretary: Roger Foxon, 245 McLeod Road,
Abbey Wood, London SE2 0XJ. Tel: 01 311 9580
(Day)
Press Officer: John Hughes, 115 Bexhill Road,
London SE4 1SH. Tel: 01 690 4148
Coach: Dave Collen
Club captain (1988–89): Anthony Penfold
Club captain (1989–90): Martin Haines
No. of teams: Senior 5
Directions to ground: Entrance at junction of
Footscray Road, Southend Crescent, Eltham, London
SE9
Club colours: Red, white shirts, navy shorts, red
socks. (*Change colours:* Navy)
Floodlights: No
Membership fees: Full £30
Programme editor: John Hughes, c/o Clubhouse
Local newspapers: SE London Mercury, Kentish
Times
League: London 3SE

League position (1988–89): Equal 3rd
League playing record (1988–89): P 33, W 21, D 0, L 12, F 666, A 384
Competitions won: Algarve Rugby Tournament. Ian Johns gained full County Honours, while P. Lambert-Williams, C. Taylor played for Kent Clubs

CRAWLEY

West Green, Crawley, Sussex. Tel: 0293 33995
Founded: 1923 (re-founded 1950)
President: Brian M. Roberts Esq.
Chairman: David F. Jenn Esq.
Secretary: Ray Lloyd, 105 Gales Drive, Three Bridges, Crawley, Sussex. Tel: 0293 36664 (H). 0737 768600 (W)
League Contact: Harry Townsend, 6 Manor Road, East Grinstead, Sussex RH19 1LR. Tel: 0342 322508
Fixtures Secretary: Kevin Stokes, 1 Rivermead, Ifield Green, Crawley, Sussex. Tel: 0293 547118 (H). 01 623 1010 (W)
Press Officer: As League Contact
Coach: Harry Townsend
Club captain (1988–89): Tim Donovan
Club captain (1989–90): Bruce Fisher
No. of teams: Senior 5, Youth 4, Minis 3, Ladies 1
Directions to ground: Exit 10 off M23. Follow A23 (Crawley Bypass) to 3rd roundabout. Turn left at sign for Hospital. Ground is 100 yards on left
Ground capacity: Standing 200
Clubhouse facilities: Bar, kitchen, toilets, etc
Club colours: Maroon and sky blue hoops. (Change colours: Navy and yellow hoops)
Nickname: The Bricklayers
Floodlights: Yes, full match floodlights
Membership fees: Full £35, Playing £35, Social £10, Youth £15, Student £15, OAP £10
Ground admission: £1 with programme
Programme: No. of editorial pages 4; No. of advertising pages 8; Price £1
Programme editor: As League Contact
Local newspapers: Crawley Observer, Crawley News, Newsbreak
League: London 3SE
League position (1988–89): 3rd
League playing record (1988–89): P 30, W 18, D 0, L 12, F 495, A 303

EAST GRINSTEAD

Saint Hill Road, East Grinstead, West Sussex RH19 4JU. Tel: 0342 322338
Founded: 1929
President: John R.P. Price
Chairman: Anthony (Pom) P. Marshall
Secretary: Christopher S.L. Williams, Woodhurst, Lewes Road, East Grinstead, W. Sussex RH19 3TA. Tel: 0342 325690 (H). 01 261 9253 (W)
League Contact: R.P. Russell, 1 Rose Cottages, Plaistow Street, Lingfield, Surrey RH7 6AU. Tel: 0342 834648
Fixtures Secretary: As League Contact
Press Officer: Mike J. Bardwell, 106 Charlwoods Road, East Grinstead, W. Sussex RH19 2JE
Club captain (1988–89): Alex Hunter
Club captain (1989–90): Robin Morgan
No. of teams: Senior 5, Youth 3, Minis 3
Directions to ground: Saint Hill on minor road to Horstead Keynes. From B2110 Turners Hill Road
Clubhouse facilities: Open Match days, Sunday lunchtime, evenings Tuesday–Friday inclusive
Club colours: Blue shirts with broad white hoops. (Change colours: No)
Floodlights: No
League: London 3SE
League position (1988–89): 8th
League playing record (1988–89): P 30, W 8, D 3, L 19
Competitions won: Brighton Sevens

GILLINGHAM ANCHORIANS

Dartland Avenue, Gillingham, Kent. Tel: 0634 51495
Founded: 1928
President: A.T.J. Harrington
Chairman: M. Masters
Secretary: J.C.B. Jennings, 49 Marshall Road, Rainham, Gillingham, Kent ME8 0AW. Tel: 0634 33431
Fixtures Secretary: B. Barker, 16 The Covert, Walderslade, Chatham, Kent ME5 9JJ. Tel: 0634 201159
Press Officer: Adrian Brooker, 271 Barnsole Road, Gillingham, Kent. Tel: 0634 53587
Coach: R.D. Fisher
Club captain (1988–89): C. Heather
No. of teams: Senior 6, Youth 1, Minis and Vets 1
Directions to ground: Darland Avenue joins the A2 at the Star Public House in Gillingham
Clubhouse facilities: Lounge, club bar, changing for 8 rugby + football + 6 hockey + ladies
Club colours: Purple, black and silver. (Change colours: Dark blue)
Nickname: Anchs
Floodlights: In near future
Membership fees: Full £15 Q £5 association sub
Local newspapers: Chatham, Rochester and Gillingham News; Evening Post
League: Kent 1
League position (1988–89): 1st
League playing record (1988–89): P 10, W 8, D 1, L 1, F 138, A 59
Competitions won: Runners-Up Canterbury 7's, 1989. Kent League Division 1 Champions, 1988/89

HORSHAM

Coolhurst, Hammer Pond Road, Horsham, Sussex. Tel: 0403 65027
Founded: 1928
President: John Price
Chairman: Mike Beckwith
Secretary: Barry Johnson, 5 Riverside, Storrington, Pulborough, W. Sussex RH20 4NN
League Contact: As Secretary
Fixtures Secretary: Geoff Curtis, The Bungalow, Church Road, Mannings Heath, W. Sussex. Tel: 0403 68262 (H). 0293 28744 (W)
Press Officer: Barry Wright
Coach: Mike Stigwood
Club captain (1988–89): Chris Pratt
Club captain (1989–90): Rob Merry
No. of teams: Senior 5, Youth 3, Minis 3
Directions to ground: Hammer Pond Road is signposted to Bucks Head off St Leonards Road, Horsham. St Leonards Road is between Horsham–Brighton Road (A281). Turn at St Leonards Arms Pub and Horsham–Crawley Road (A?), turn down Cromptons Lane also signposted Brighton
Ground capacity: Standing 1000
Clubhouse facilities: Open Match days, Tuesday, Thursday and Friday evenings, Sunday lunch
Club colours: Emerald green jersey, white collar, white shorts, emerald green socks. (Change colours: All white)
Floodlights: No
Membership fees: Playing £30, Non-playing £17.50, Social £10, U19 £10, U16 £7.50
Ground admission: Free
Programme editor: B. Wright
Local newspapers: W. Sussex County Times
League: London 3SE
League position (1988–89): 9th
League playing record (1988–89): P 10, W 2, D 0, L 8, F 123, A 128
Competitions won: Sussex U14 League, Eastbourne U14 Sevens, Horsham U14 Sevens

HOVE

Hove Park, Goldstone Crescent, Hove, East Sussex.
Tel: 0273 505103
Founded: 1933
President: Richard Lewis
Chairman: Richard Jenkins
Secretary: Nick Laurence, 128 Victoria Road,
Portslade, Brighton, East Sussex BN4 1XD. Tel: 0273
415214
Fixtures Secretary: Mike Richardson, 6 Waywide,
Westdene, Brighton, East Sussex BN1 5HL. Tel: 0273
500512 (H), 01–644 4388 ext. 219 (W)
Press Officer: Rick Walker, 21 Cabton Drive, Hove,
East Sussex. Tel: 0273 557790 (H), 770578 (W)
Coach: Geoff Atkinson.
Club captain (1988–89): Kevin Joy
Club captain (1989–90): Peter Allen
No. of teams: Senior 5, Youth 3, Minis 5
Directions to ground: Hove Park is on the A27
immediately opposite Brighton & Hove Albion F.C.
(the Goldstone Ground)
Ground capacity: Standing Unlimited
Clubhouse facilities: Open matchdays and training
evenings (Tues. and Thurs.)
Club colours: Maroon and sky blue hoops. (*Change
colours:* Dark blue)
Floodlights: No
Membership fees: Full £15, Playing £15, Social £10,
Youth £7, Student £7
Local newspapers: Evening Argus, Brighton & Hove
Leader
League: Sussex 1
League position (1988–89): 1st (promoted)
League playing record (1988–89): P 10, W 8, D 1,
L 1, F 249, A 107
Competitions won: Sussex League One Championship,
1988/89

OLD BECCEHAMIAN

Sparrows Den, CorkscrewHill, West Wickham, Kent.
Tel: 01 777 8105
Founded: 1933
President: Ian Douglas
Chairman: Ian Douglas
Secretary: Bill Gault, 45 Bushey Way, Beckenham,
Kent BR3 3PS. Tel: 01 650 2994 (H). 658 7211 (W)
League Contact: As Secretary
Fixtures Secretary: David Skidmore, 16 Surrey Road,
West Wickham, Kent. Tel: 01 777 4287
Press Officer: Nick Brooks, 36 Berrylands, Orpington,
Kent. 0689 75120
Coach: Ron Beveridge
Club captain (1988–89): Les Simpson
Club captain (1989–90): Les Simpson
No. of teams: Senior 6, Youth 2, Minis 9
Directions to ground: Near Croydon/Bromley junction
A2022 and A232
Ground capacity: Standing – lots
Clubhouse facilities: Members bar, function hall and
bar. Open Saturdays, Sundays, Tuesday evenings
Club colours: Black/white/maroon. (*Change colours:*
Maroon)
Nickname: Beccs or Bees
Floodlights: No
Membership fees: Full £20 + match fee, Playing as
Full, Social £5, Student £8 (U21)
Ground admission: Nil
Programme: League and cup games sponsored
Programme editor: As Secretary
Local newspapers: Kentish Times Group, Croydon
Advertiser Group
League: London 3SE
League position (1988–89): 5th
League playing record (1988–89): P 10, W 6, D 0,
L 4, F 117, A 113
Competitions won: Kent Colts Cup. Kent Veterans
Sevens Cup

OLD JUDDIAN

The Slade, Tonbridge, Kent TN9 1HR. (Postal items
except clubs championship material to secretary.) Tel:
0732 358548
Founded: 1928
President: Keith Starling MA(Cantab)
Chairman: Christopher Wickham
Secretary: Steve Davey, 35 Dowgate Close,
Tonbridge, Kent TN9 2EH. Tel: 0732 357429 (H).
Edenbridge 866066 (W)
League Contact: A.B. Russell, 28 Whistler Road,
Tonbridge, Kent TN10 4RD. Tel: 0732 355582 (H).
01 227 3284 (W)
Fixtures Secretary: As League Contact
Press Officer: As League Contact
Coach: Nick Colyer/Justin Hams (joint responsibility)
Club captain (1988–89): Steve Rees
Club captain (1989–90): Andy Young
No. of teams: Senior 5
Directions to ground: OJRFC play on Tonbridge
Sports Ground. Turn from Tonbridge High Street into
Castle Street (opposite Rose & Crown Hotel); bear
right, left and right again through sweeping bend.
Take next left turn (The Slade) and fork right at end
into clubhouse car park
Ground capacity: Seating Nil, standing – as many as
can crowd the touchlines
Clubhouse facilities: Bar, lounge area, dining area,
light snacks area
Club colours: Claret and light blue hooped jerseys;
blue shorts. (*Change colours:* Variable – usually red/
white quarters)
Nickname: The Js
Floodlights: No
Membership fees: Full £30, Playing £30, Social £15
(non-playing), Student £15
Ground admission: Nil
Programme: T.B.A.
Programme editor: T.B.A.
Local newspapers: Kent & Sussex Courier, Kent
Messenger
League: London 3SE
League position (1988–89): 6th
League playing record (1988–89): P 10, W 5, D 2,
L 3, F 131, A 132

WESTCOMBE PARK

Craven Road, Orpington, Kent BR6 7RT. Tel: 0689
26422
Founded: 1904
President: John E. Yeates
Chairman: Michael Payne
Secretary: Robin I. Taylor, 24 Pinchbeck Road,
Green Street, Green, Orpington, Kent BR6 4DR.
Tel: 0689 55052 (H), 01–310 9868 (W)
Fixtures Secretary: Peter Pinner, 3 Raleigh Mews,
Orpington, Kent BR6 6NR. Tel: 0689 51747
Press Officer: Ralph Sharratt, 22 Lila Place, Swanley,
Kent BR8 8JB. Tel: 0322 64607
Coach: Chas G. Chapman
Club captain (1988–89): Fraser Thomson
Club captain (1989–90): Fraser Thomson
No. of teams: Senior 6, Youth 6, Minis 5
Directions to ground: Turn into Avalon Road,
Orpington, of A224 Court Road (Orpington bypass).
Craven Rod is off Avalon Road
Club colours: Navy/white hoops, navy shorts. (*Change
colours:* Red, navy shorts)
Nickname: 'Combe
Floodlights: Yes (training only)
Membership fees: Playing £28, Non-Playing £5, Youth
£7.50, Student £7.50, OAP £2.50 (min)
Ground admission: Nil
Programme: No. of editorial pages 3–3; No. of
advertising pages 2–3 ; Price 20p
Programme editor: Stewart Robinson, 5 Dryland
Avenue, Berkwood Park, Orpington, Kent BR6 3S2
Local newspapers: Kentish Times, News Shopper,
Leader

League: London 3SE
League position (1988–89): 2nd
League playing record (1988–89): P 30, W 17, D 1, L 12, F 502, A 404
Competitions won: Kent County 7's Plate Winners, K7 Sevens Plate Runner-Up

LONDON 3 SOUTH WEST

DORKING

DORKING

The Pavilion, Big Field, Kiln Lane, Brockham, Surrey. Tel: Betchworth 3928.
Founded: 1921
Chairman: John Milner
Secretary: Robnert Brigham, 12 Clyde Road, Sutton, SM1 2RR. Tel: 01 661 0338 (H) 01 661 0321 (W)
Fixtures Secretary: James Beardmore, 7 Riverside, Dorking. Tel: 036 884049 (H) 0306 885055 (W)
Club captain (1988–89): J.A. Evans
No. of teams: Senior 5, youth & Minis 5
Directions to ground: Take signposted road to Brockham off A215 between Dorking and Reigate (Dorking 1 mile). Ground on right.
Club colours: Red and white hoops, blue shorts. (*Change colours:* blue.
Floodlights: No
Membership: £25 + VAT
Local newspaper: Dorking Advertiser

GUY'S HOSPITAL

Guy's Hospital Clubs Union Ground, Brockley Rise, Honor Oak Park, London SE23 1NW. Tel: 01 690 1612
Founded: 1843
President: Dr. T. Gibson MD, FRCP
Chairman: Dr T. Gibson MD, FRCP
Secretary: J.R. Barwell, Boland House, Guy's Hospital, London SE1 9RT
League Contact: P.A.E. Rosell, Boland House, Guy's Hospital London SE1 9RT. Tel: 01 955 5000 Ext 5202
Fixtures Secretary: As League Contact
Press Officer: Mr C. Eraint Thomason, 100 Harleyford Road, Kennington. Tel: 01 582 4852 (H). 928 6677 Ext 6299 (W)
Coach: Neil Davies
Club captain (1988–89): Wayne Llewellyn
Club captain (1989–90): Neil Davies
No. of teams: Senior 4
Directions to ground: Honor Oak Park Station (S. Region BR). Crofton Park (S. Region BR)
Ground capacity: Seating 1000, standing 5000
Clubhouse facilities: Bar/lounge, 3 large changing rooms
Club colours: Navy blue and gold hoops. (*Change colours:* Navy Blue)
Floodlights: No
Programme: No. of editorial pages 2; No. of advertising pages 4; Price 20p
Programme editor: Mr T. Gibson, Guy's Hospital
League: London 3SW
League position (1988–89): 7th
League playing record (1988–89): P 10, W 4, D 0, L 6
Competitions won: Winners of Gutteridge Plate (University of London Competition)

KCS OLD BOYS

Robin Hood Way, Kingston Avenue, London SW15. Tel: 01 546 5461
Founded: 1907
President: John D.E. Hamilton
Chairman: Darryl M. Druckman
Secretary: Michael E. Bruce, 40 Prince's Road, Kingston-Upon-Thames, Surrey KT2 6AZ. Tel: 01 549 5118
League Contact: J.D.E. Hamilton, 1 Conway Road,

Wimbledon, London SW20 8PB. Tel: 01 946 7009 (H). 680 4647 (W)
Fixtures Secretary: Andrew B. Todd, 5 Wendover Drive, New Malden, Surrey KT3 5RN. Tel: 01 942 0048
Press Officer: Richard L.S. Shinn, 88 Alric Avenue, New Malden, Surrey KT3 4JW. Tel: 01 942 5796
Club captain (1988–89): Richard L.S. Shinn
Club captain (1989–90): Richard L.S. Shinn
No. of teams: Senior 5
Directions to ground: A3 from Putney, Ground on left past Robin Hood roundabout
Ground capacity: Standing 1500
Clubhouse facilities: Basic
Club colours: Red, blue and old gold. (*Change colours:* No)
Nickname: Kings
Floodlights: No
Membership fees: Full £20, Playing £20, Social £5, Student £5
Local newspapers: Wimbledon News, Surrey Comet
League: London 2S
League position (1988–89): 10th
League playing record (1988–89): P 10, W 2, D 2, L 6, F 96, A 147

OLD REIGATIAN

Park Lane, Reigate, Surrey. Tel: 0737 245634
Founded: 1927
President: John Hamlyn
Chairman: John Rowlands
Secretary: Tony Walker, 43 Yorke Road, Reigate, Surey RH2 9HH. Tel: 0737 247172 (H). 242477 Ext 42 (W)
League Contact: As Fixtures Secretary
Fixtures Secretary: Keith Ireland, 36 Barrow Green Road, Oxted, Surrey RH8 0NN. Tel: 0883 712713 (H). 01 651 6321 (W)
Club captain (1988–89): Ian Kirk
Club captain (1989–90): Graham Price
No. of teams: Senior 6, Minis 4
Directions to ground: Enter Reigate town one-way system on A25 and go through centre of the town East–West. At west end turn left into Park Lane. Ground on right after 500 yards
Ground capacity: Standing 1000
Club colours: Green/blue hoops. **Nickname:** OR's
Floodlights: No
Membership fees: Playing £35, Social £10, Youth £10, Student £10
Local newspapers: Surrey Mirror
League: London 3SW
League position (1988–89): 10th
League playing record (1988–89): P 9, W 2, D 0, L 7, F 64, A 106

OLD GUILDFORDIANS

The Pavilion, Stoke Park, London Road, Guildford, Surrey
Founded: 1931
President: John Daniel MA
Chairman: Dr Douglas Keir
Secretary: Ian Newton, 36 Ambleside Road, Lightwater, Surrey GU18 5TA. Tel: 0276 74367 (H). 0734 583626 Ext 2978 (W)
League Contact: As Secretary
Fixtures Secretary: Gerry Hills, 28 Bannister Close, Wheeler Lane, Witley, Surrey. Tel: 042879 4337 (H). 01 623 4600 (W)
Press Officer: Alan Harding, 3 Bryanstone Close, Guildford, Surrey. Tel: 0483 68945 (H). 67879 (W)
Coach: Russell Burton/Philip Townsend
Club captain (1988–89): Philip Townsend
Club captain (1989–90): Russell Burton
No. of teams: Senior 5, Youth 1
Directions to ground: Take London Road from centre of Guildford towards A3. Pavilion is at north end of Stoke Park, close to old 'AA' roundabout, about 5 minutes drive from town centre

Clubhouse facilities: New Pavilion opening July 1989
Club colours: Green shirts with narrow maroon and white hoops, white shorts, red socks. (*Change colours:* No)
Floodlights: Training only
Membership fees: Full £5
Local newspapers: Surrey Advertiser, Guildford (Contact Richard Spillar)
League: London 3SW
League position (1988–89): Runners Up
League playing record (1988–89): P 31, W 25, D 0, L 6, F 819, A 117
Competitions won: 9 League wins, quarter finalists Surrey Cup. Winners University Vandals Sevens (11.9.88) and Lensbury Sevens (25.9.88 – third successive year)

OLD EMANUEL

Blagdons, New Malden, Surrey. Tel: 01 942 3857
Founded: 1910
President: Alan Booth
Chairman: Vic Dodds
Secretary: Ian Blair, 28 Hunters Road, Chessington, Surrey KT9 1RU. Tel: 01 397 1272 (H). 872 3003 (W)
League Contact: As Secretary
Fixtures Secretary: John Monkhouse, 'Chenies', 26 Oriental Road, Woking, Surrey GU22 7AN. Tel: 04862 64114 (H). 09323 55144 (W)
Press Officer: As Secretary
Club captain (1988–89): Brian Cassidy
Club captain (1989–90): Keith Agutter
No. of teams: Senior 4
Directions to ground: Shannon Corner, New Malden on London-bound slip road to A3
Ground capacity: Standing 1500
Clubhouse facilities: 2 Bars, dining facilities
Club colours: White. (*Change colours:* Royal blue)
Floodlights: No
Membership fees: Varies £3 – £26
Programme: No. of editorial pages 0; No. of advertising pages 6; Price: Free
Programme editor: John Evans, c/o Clubhouse
Local newspapers: Surrey Comet
League: London 3SW
League position (1988–89): 4th
League playing record (1988–89): P 31, W 18, D 1, L 11, F 396, A 348

OLD WALCOUNTIANS

The Clockhouse Ground, Carshalton Road, Woodmansterne, Surrey. Tel: 07373 54348
Founded: 1927
President: W.J. Ireland
Chairman: Roger Phillips
Secretary: G. Jones, 3 Braemer Avenue, Purley, Surrey CR2 0QA. Tel: 01–660 7892 (H), 01–680 2638 (W)
Fixtures Secretary: R. McDowell, 56 Hillside Gardens, Wallington, Surrey SM6 9NY. Tel: 01–669 6801
Press Officer: M. Clarke, 29 Vernow Walk, Tadworth, Surrey. Tel: 07373 58196
Coach: Benny Jones
Club captain (1988–89): Neil Smith
Club captain (1989–90): Neil Smith
No. of teams: Senior 6, Youth 1
Directions to ground: Off A2022 Purley Banstead Road
Clubhouse facilities: Bar, showers, bath, 5 changing rooms
Club colours: Blue, black, gold hoops. (*Change colours:* Red)
Floodlights: Yes (training only)
Membership fees: Full £35, Social £15
Programme: No. of editorial pages Varies; No. of advertising pages Varies
Programme editor: As Secretary (special games only)
Local newspaper: Croydon Advertiser Group
League: London & SE: SW3

League position (1988–89): 3rd
League playing record (1988–89): P 10, W 6, D 0, L 4, F 152, A 102
Competitions won: Surrey Colts Cup

OLD WHITGIFTIAN

Croham Manor Road, South Croydon, Surrey CR2 7BG. Tel: 01 688 3248 and 686 2127 (answerphone)
Founded: 1876
President: Rear Admiral Peter La Niece CB, CBE
Chairman: Michael Spanswick
Secretary: Geoff Austin, Flat 8, Nicoll Court, 48 Nicoll Road, Harlesden, London NW10 9AD. Tel: 01 965 0498 (H). 761 1911 (W)
League Contact: As Secretary
Fixtures Secretary: Andrew Stone, 86 Greenacres, Oxted, Surrey 4H8 0PB. Tel: 088 371 2857 (H). 01 648 6699 (W)
Press Officer: As Secretary
Coach: Stuart Hardie
Club captain (1988–89): Nigel Cooper
Club captain (1989–90): T.B.A.
No. of teams: Senior 4, Minis 3
Directions to ground: From South Croydon BR Station turn left down steps into Croham Road, and turn left. ground is mile on right. Bus 64 (264 on Suns) from either East or West passes ground
Ground capacity: Seating 25 on Clubhouse roof. Standing capacity never tested!
Clubhouse facilities: Well appointed clubhouse on ground, open evenings and match days
Club colours: Red, black and blue hooped shirts, white shorts. (*Change colours:* Royal blue shirts, white shorts)
Floodlights: Training only
Membership fees: Playing member £43 (under 21 £21), Non-playing member £23(under 21 £12)
Ground admission: No charge, voluntary donations only)
Programme: No. of editorial pages 8; No. of advertising pages 8; Price 30p
Programme editor: As Secretary
Local newspapers: Croydon Advertiser
Club sponsor: Goddard & Jones
League: London 3SW
League position (1988–89): 6th
League playing record (1988–89): P 10, W 5, D 0, L 5, F 85, A 166
Competitions won: East Grinstead RFC 'Sunshine Sevens' Plate Winners (April 1989)

PORTSMOUTH

Rugby Camp, Norway Road, Hilsea, Portsmouth. Tel: 0705 660610
Founded: 1886
President: George Ebdon-Hussey
Chairman: Dr Peter Golding
Secretary: John Collins, 4 Neelands Grove, Paulsgrove, Portsmouth, Hants. Tel: 0705 380859 (H). 0703 330229 (W)
League Contact: John Smith, 23 East Field Close, Southbourne, Emsworth, Hants. PO10 8NJ. Tel: 0243 374222 (H). 0705 264466 Ext 3678 (W)
Fixtures Secretary: As League Contact
Press Officer: Roger T. Hollis, 69 Blackbrook Road, Fareham, Hants. PO15 5DE. Tel: 0329 236506
Coach: Nigel Morgan and Michael Beveridge
Club captain (1988–89): Ian 'Beano' Chandler
Club captain (1989–90): Steve Cameron
No. of teams: Senior 6, Youth U14,U16,U19, Minis U8,U10,U12
Directions to ground: Enter Portsmouth by A3. At Coach & Horses take left fork, then 1st left (Norway Road), Ground 200 yards on right
Clubhouse facilities: Open Match days, lunchtime except Saturdays, Tuesday and Thursday evenings
Club colours: Black with 2 amber or white hooped shirts, black shorts, black/amber socks. (*Change colours:* Plain amber or plain red)

Floodlights: No
Membership fees: Playing £25, Social £10, Youth £12.50, Student £12.50
Ground admission: via tax office car park – free
Local newspapers: The News – Portsmouth, Evening Echo – Southampton
League: London 3SW
League position (1988–89): 5th
League playing record (1988–89): P 9, W 6, D 0, L 3, F 109, A 109

PURLEY

'Parsons Pightle', Coulsdon Road, Old Coulsdon, Surrey. Tel: 07375 53042
Founded: 1926
President: Mansel Barnes
Secretary: Ian Martin, 41 Court Road, Caterham, Surrey. Tel: 0883 48509 (H). 01 799 2121 (W)
League Contact: Graham Brooks, 47 Woodcote Grove Road, Coulsdon, Surrey CR3 2AJ. Tel: 01 668 8024 (H). 0737 764419 (W)
Fixtures Secretary: As League Contact
Press Officer: Jay Gravette, 1 Shirley Avenue, Old Coulsdon, Surrey. Tel: 01 660 1290
Club captain (1988–89): Brian Johnson
Club captain (1989–90): Brian Johnson
No. of teams: Senior 5, Youth 1
Directions to ground: Train to Purley: Bus 409, 411 to Lacy Green, Ground opposite. By road: M25 to M23 to Croydon (A23) to Coulsdon, take B276 (and B2030) to Caterham, 600 yards past Tudor Rose Pub, Ground on right
Clubhouse facilities: Open Match days and evenings
Club colours: Black/white hoops. (*Change colours:* Green/blue/white hoops)
Floodlights: Yes
Membership fees: Full £30, Playing £30, Social £15, Youth £15, Student £15
Ground admission: Nil
Programme: No. of editorial pages 4; No. of advertising pages 4; Price 25p
Programme editor: As Press Officer

Local newspapers: Surrey Mirror, Croydon Advertiser
League: London 3SW
League position (1988–89): 9th in London 2SW
League playing record (1988–89): P 10, W 3, D 0, L 7, F 99, A 139

SOUTHAMPTON

Test Playing Fields, Millbrook, Southampton. Tel: 0703 737777
Founded: 1964
President: Bill Massey
Chairman: Doug Rose
Secretary: Steve Edge, 15 Bangor Road, Millbrook, Southampton. Tel: 0703 786758
League Contact: George Materna, 539 Romsey Road, Maybush, Southampton. Tel: 0703 784409 (H). 0489 886611 (W)
Fixtures Secretary: As League Contact
Press Officer: As League Contact
Club captain (1988–89): Rob Swain
Club captain (1989–90): Kevin Boault
No. of teams: Senior 3
Directions to ground: M27 to the M271 turning to Lordshill. 50 yards after the turning turn right, Club 200 yards on right
Clubhouse facilities: Bar, kitchen, darts, skittle alley, open fire
Club colours: Red/white hoops, navy shorts, red socks. (*Change colours:* Navy blue)
Nickname: Saints
Floodlights: No
Membership fees: Full £20, Playing £20, Social £10
Local newspapers: Southern Evening Echo
League: London 3SW
League position (1988–89): 1st in Hampshire 1
League playing record (1988–89): P 10, W 9, D 1, L 0, F 236, A 77
Competitions won: Southampton Sevens Tournament. Hampshire League Division 1

Worthing of London 1 – 1988–89. Photo: Warwick Baker

MIDDLESEX LEAGUES

AFTER an initial competition of four leagues Middlesex now had five covering 52 teams, an increase of eight on last season. The fifth division consists of nine teams and the fourth division had 10, with the others all fielding 11 sides. St. Mary's Hospital return in Division 5 next season.

Twickenham – relegated from London 3NW last time out – suffered only one draw in their 10 outings and won by two points from London New Zealand in the top division's keenly contested title fight, but three teams were relegated from the division – all old boys clubs. Down go Haberdashers, Paulines (a second successive descent for them) and Abbotstonians, whose stay at the top was curtailed to just the one term.

Two old boys teams replace them with the famous Millhillians gaining reward for only one defeat and a 286–37 points differential being joined in the ascent by Meadonians, but again three teams are demoted from this league and the "chopper" fell on three sides all with six points – Richmond Thamesians, Old Hamptonians and Hammersmith & Fulham.

Going up from a tight Division 3 competition (four points separated the top six clubs) are Old Grammarians and Osterley, but once again three sides descend – Pinner & Grammarians, Northolt and Belsize Park. To replace them come Bank of England, robbed only once in nine outings, and Meadhurst, whilst at the foot of the table Hayes and S.T. & C. are demoted. Hayes were last in their league campaign, when Pinner & Grammarians also suffered relegation.

H.A.C. (champions and winners of all their eight matches for an amazing 347–17 points differential) and Royal Free Hospital are the first teams to be promoted from the new fifth division, but the sad table-proppers are G.W.R., losers of their eight matches for a differential of 19–311. One hopes they will not be discouraged by the disasters.

MIDDLESEX LEAGUE ONE:

D. Gershlick,
20A The Avenue,
Potters Bar,   (H) 0707 44433
Hertfordshire EN6 1EB   (O) 01 453 1047

MIDDLESEX LEAGUE TWO:

G. Sykes,
11 Ivy Close,
Eastcote,
Pinner, Middlesex   (H) 01 866 5430

MIDDLESEX LEAGUE THREE:

P. Astbury,
32 Kneller Gardens,
Isleworth,
Middlesex   (H) 01 898 5372

MIDDLESEX LEAGUE FOUR:

A. Rabjohn,
52 Central Avenue,
Hounslow,
Middlesex   (H) 01 894 1850

MIDDLESEX LEAGUE FIVE:

B. East,
17 Waterlow Road,   (H) 01 272 5686
London N19 5NJ   (O) 01 485 4100 Ext. 287

TABLES 1987–88

MIDDLESEX 1

	P	W	D	L	F	A	PTS
Finchley	10	8	1	1	130	38	17
Staines	10	7	0	3	129	87	14
O Haberdashers	10	6	0	4	110	77	14
Sudbury Ct	10	6	0	4	110	77	12
Uxbridge	10	6	0	4	78	91	12
Lensbury	10	5	0	5	114	89	10
London NZ	10	4	1	5	114	123	9
Hampstead	10	4	0	6	115	152	8
O Meadonians	10	3	0	7	82	105	6
Orleans FP	10	2	0	8	65	131	4
O Millhillians	10	2	0	8	63	130	4

MIDDLESEX 2

	P	W	D	L	F	A	PTS
O Abbotsonians	11	11	0	0	19	63	22
Centaurs	11	7	0	4	209	116	14
Civ Service	11	6	0	5	167	106	12
Hackney	11	5	2	4	136	101	12
O Hamptonians	11	6	0	5	104	106	12
Richmond Ts	11	6	0	5	104	106	12
Barclays Bk	11	4	1	6	90	124	9
St. Bart's Hos	11	4	1	6	90	124	9
London Cor	11	4	0	7	127	218	8
Osterley	11	4	0	7	147	218	8
Antlers	11	3	1	7	83	156	7
Pinner & Gs	11	3	1	7	54	158	7

MIDDLESEX 3N

	P	W	D	L	F	A	PTS
Haringey	10	10	0	0	279	35	20
Wembley	10	8	0	2	202	50	16
O Tottonians	10	6	1	3	168	85	13
Belsize Pk	10	6	1	3	123	103	13
O Grammarians	10	6	0	4	182	75	12
Roxeth Man OB	10	5	0	5	99	88	10
UCS OB	10	5	0	5	99	88	10
Old Ignatians	10	4	0	6	101	106	8
ST and C	10	2	0	8	70	235	4
Enfield O G	10	1	0	9	41	245	2
Kodak	10	0	0	10	28	351	0

MIDDLESEX 3S

	P	W	D	L	F	A	PTS
Hamm & Ful	9	7	1	1	163	73	15
CAV	9	6	1	2	82	57	13
O Isleworthians	9	6	0	3	109	77	12
Quintin	9	5	1	3	94	81	11
Bank of Eng	9	4	1	4	98	53	9
O Actonians	9	4	1	4	88	84	9
London French	9	4	0	5	134	102	8
Feltham	9	3	0	6	54	117	6
Meadhurst	9	24	0	7	64	127	6
Hayes	9	1	1	7	229	135	3

Brunel University (withdrawn – all matches void).
St. Mary's College (withdrawn – all matches void).

TABLES 1988-89

MIDDLESEX 1

	P	W	D	L	F	A	PTS
Twickenham	10	9	0	1	186	79	19
London NZ	10	8	1	1	188	93	17
Uxbridge	10	5	2	3	150	98	12
Centaurs	10	5	2	3	136	118	12
Lensbury	10	5	1	4	120	101	11
Staines	10	3	4	3	93	88	10
Hampstead	10	4	2	4	138	144	10
Sudbury Ct	10	3	0	7	110	125	6
O Haberdashers	10	2	2	6	67	176	6
O Paulines	10	1	2	7	83	162	4
O Abbotstonians	10	1	1	8	88	175	3

MIDDLESEX 2

	P	W	D	L	F	A	PTS
O Millhillians	10	9	0	1	286	37	18
O Meadonians	10	7	0	3	130	80	14
Barclays Bk	10	6	0	4	114	137	12
Haringey	10	5	1	4	140	77	11
Hackney	10	5	1	4	145	101	11
Orleans F.P.	10	4	1	5	71	124	9
Civ Service	10	4	1	5	67	123	9
St. Bart's Hos	10	4	0	6	98	167	8
Richmond Ts	10	3	0	7	98	145	6
O Hamptonians	10	3	0	7	86	158	6
Hamm & Ful	10	3	0	7	132	218	6

MIDDLESEX 3

	P	W	D	L	F	A	PTS
O Grammarians	10	7	1	2	126	82	15
Osterley	10	6	2	2	176	82	14
London Cor	10	7	0	3	141	94	14
Wembley	10	6	1	3	158	105	13
Quintin	10	6	1	3	102	64	13
Antlers	10	5	1	4	147	106	11
O Tottonians	10	3	2	5	108	118	8
O Isleworthians	10	4	0	6	71	100	8
Pinner & Gs	10	3	0	7	68	162	6
Northolt	10	2	0	8	63	143	4
Belsize Pk	10	2	0	8	77	181	4

MIDDLESEX 4

	P	W	D	L	F	A	PTS
Bank of Eng	9	8	0	1	182	70	16
Meadhurst	9	7	0	2	160	65	14
Enfield Igs	9	6	1	2	137	43	13
Roxeth M OB	9	6	0	3	126	71	12
Old Actonians	9	4	1	4	90	100	9
London French	9	3	2	4	98	86	8
Feltham	9	4	0	5	105	104	8
U.C.S. O.B.	9	2	2	5	85	106	6
Hayes	9	2	0	7	102	157	4
S.T. & C.	9	0	0	9	27	310	0

MIDDLESEX 5

	P	W	D	L	F	A	PTS
H.A.C.	8	8	0	0	347	17	16
Roy Free Hos	8	7	0	1	161	47	14
Brunel Univ	8	6	0	2	225	69	12
St. Nich O.B.	8	5	0	3	131	125	10
Middx Hos	8	3	1	4	136	125	7
Brit Airways	8	3	0	5	129	134	6
Kodak	8	2	0	6	71	233	4
Southall T Col	8	11	1	6	114	272	3
G.W.R.	8	0	0	8	19	311	0

Millfield Old Boys withdrawn. St. Mary's College withdrawn.

LONDON & SOUTH EAST DIVISION FIXTURES 1989/90

MIDDLESEX LEAGUE ONE

Sat. 23rd September (Week 4)
Harrow v Hampstead
Old Meadonians v Old Millhillians
Staines v Hendon
Sudbury Court v London New Zealand
Uxbridge v Lensbury

Sat. 14th October (Week 6)
Lensbury v Harrow
London New Zealand v Uxbridge
Hendon v Sudbury Court
Old Millhillians v Staines
Centaurs v Old Meadonians

Sat. 28th October (Week 8)
Harrow v London New Zealand
Hampstead v Lensbury
Staines v Centaurs
Sudbury Court v Old Millhillians
Uxbridge v Hendon

Sat. 11th November (Week 10)
London New Zealand v Hampstead
Hendon v Harrow
Old Millhillians v Uxbridge
Centaurs v Sudbury Court
Old Meadonians v Staines

Sat 18th November (Week 11)
Harrow v Old Millhillians
Hampstead v Hendon
Lensbury v London New Zealand
Sudbury Court v Old Meadonians
Uxbridge v Centaurs

Sat. 25th November (Week 12)
Hendon v Lensbury
Old Millhillians v Hampstead
Centaurs v Harrow
Old Meadonians v Uxbridge
Staines v Sudbury Court

Sat. 13th January (Week 18)
Harrow v Old Meadonians
Hampstead v Centaurs
Lensbury v Old Millhillians
London New Zealand v Hendon
Uxbridge v Staines

Sat. 27th January (Week 20)
Old Millhillians v London New Zealand
Centaurs v Lensbury
Old Meadonians v Hampstead
Staines v Harrow
Sudbury Court v Uxbridge

Sat. 10th February (Week 22)
Harrow v Sudbury Court
Hampstead v Staines
Lensbury v Old Meadonians
London New Zealand v Centaurs
Hendon v Old Millhillians

Sat. 24th February (Week 24)
Centaurs v Hendon
Old Meadonians v London New Zealand
Staines v Lensbury
Sudbury Court v Hampstead
Uxbridge v Harrow

Sat. 10th March (Week 26)
Hampstead v Uxbridge
Lensbury v Sudbury Court
London New Zealand v Staines
Hendon v Old Meadonians
Old Millhillians v Centaurs

LONDON & SOUTH EAST DIVISION FIXTURES 1989/90

MIDDLESEX LEAGUE TWO

Sat. 23rd September (Week 4)
St. Bart's Hospital v Barclays Bank
Old Paulines v Old Abbotstonians
Old Grammarians v Old Haberdashers
Orleans F.P. v Civil Service
Osterley v Haringey

Sat. 14th October (Week 6)
Haringey v St. Bart's Hospital
Civil Service v Osterley
Old Haberdashers v Orleans F.P.
Old Abbotstonians v Old Grammarians
Hackney v Old Paulines

Sat. 28th October (Week 8)
St. Bart's Hospital v Civil Service
Barclays Bank v Haringey
Old Grammarians v Hackney
Orleans F.P. v Old Abbotstonians
Osterley v Old Haberdashers

Sat. 11th November (Week 10)
Civil Service v Barclays Bank
Old Haberdashers v St. Bart's Hospital
Old Abbotstonians v Osterley
Hackney v Orleans F.P.
Old Paulines v Old Grammarians

Sat 18th November (Week 11)
St. Bart's Hospital v Old Abbotstonians
Barclays Bank v Old Haberdashers
Haringey v Civil Service
Orleans F.P. v Old Paulines
Osterley v Hackney

Sat. 25th November (Week 12)
Old Haberdashers v Haringey
Old Abbotstonians v Barclays Bank
Hackney v St. Bart's Hospital
Old Paulines v Osterley
Old Grammarians v Orleans F.P.

Sat. 13th January (Week 18)
St. Bart's Hospital v Old Paulines
Barclays Bank v Hackney
Haringey v Old Abbotstonians
Civil Service v Old Haberdashers
Osterley v Old Grammarians

Sat. 27th January (Week 20)
Old Abbotstonians v Civil Service
Hackney v Haringey
Old Paulines v Barclays Bank
Old Grammarians v St. Bart's Hospital
Orleans F.P. v Osterley

Sat. 10th February (Week 22)
St. Bart's Hospital v Orleans F.P.
Barclays Bank v Old Grammarians
Haringey v Old Paulines
Civil Service v Hackney
Old Haberdashers v Old Abbotstonians

Sat. 24th February (Week 24)
Hackney v Old Haberdashers
Old Paulines v Civil Service
Old Grammarians v Haringey
Orleans F.P. v Barclays Bank
Osterley v St. Bart's Hospital

Sat. 10th March (Week 26)
Barclays Bank v Osterley
Haringey v Orleans F.P.
Civil Service v Old Grammarians
Old Haberdashers v Old Paulines
Old Abbotstonians v Hackney

LONDON & SOUTH EAST DIVISION FIXTURES 1989/90

MIDDLESEX LEAGUE THREE

Sat. 23rd September (Week 4)
Meadhurst v London Cornish
Antlers v Wembley
Old Hamptonians v Hammersmith & Fulham
Richmond Thamesians v Old Isleworthians
Quinton v Bank of England

Sat. 14th October (Week 6)
Bank of England v Meadhurst
Old Isleworthians v Quinton
Hammersmith & Fulham v Richmond Thamesians
Wembley v Old Hamptonians
Old Tottonians v Antlers

Sat. 28th October (Week 8)
Meadhurst v Old Isleworthians
London Cornish v Bank of England
Old Hamptonians v Old Tottonians
Richmond Thamesians v Wembley
Quinton v Hammersmith & Fulham

Sat. 11th November (Week 10)
Old Isleworthians v London Cornish
Hammersmith & Fulham v Meadhurst
Wembley v Quinton
Old Tottonians v Richmond Thamesians
Antlers v Old Hamptonians

Sat 18th November (Week 11)
Meadhurst v Wembley
London Cornish v Hammersmith & Fulham
Bank of England v Old Isleworthians
Richmond Thamesians v Antlers
Quinton v Old Tottonians

Sat. 25th November (Week 12)
Hammersmith & Fulham v Bank of England
Wembley v London Cornish
Old Tottonians v Meadhurst
Antlers v Quinton
Old Hamptonians v Richmond Thamesians

Sat. 13th January (Week 18)
Meadhurst v Antlers
London Cornish v Old Tottonians
Bank of England v Wembley
Old Isleworthians v Hammersmith & Fulham
Quinton v Old Hamptonians

Sat. 27th January (Week 20)
Wembley v Old Isleworthians
Old Tottonians v Bank of England
Antlers v London Cornish
Old Hamptonians v Meadhurst
Richmond Thamesians v Quinton

Sat. 10th February (Week 22)
Meadhurst v Richmond Thamesians
London Cornish v Old Hamptonians
Bank of England v Antlers
Old Isleworthians v Old Tottonians
Hammersmith & Fulham v Wembley

Sat. 24th February (Week 24)
Old Tottonians v Hammersmith & Fulham
Antlers v Old Isleworthians
Old Hamptonians v Bank of England
Richmond Thamesians v London Cornish
Quinton v Meadhurst

Sat. 10th March (Week 26)
London Cornish v Quinton
Bank of England v Richmond Thamesians
Old Isleworthians v Old Hamptonians
Hammersmith & Fulham v Antlers
Wembley v Old Tottonians

LONDON & SOUTH EAST DIVISION FIXTURES 1989/90

MIDDLESEX LEAGUE FOUR

Sat. 23rd September (Week 4)
Belsize Park v Roxeth Manor O.B.
H.A.C. v Royal Free Hospital
Old Actonians v Enfield Ignatians
Pinner & Grammarians v Feltham
Northolt v U.C.S. O.B.

Sat. 14th October (Week 6)
U.C.S. O.B. v Belsize Park
Feltham v Northolt
Enfield Ignatians v Pinner & Grammarians
Royal Free Hospital v Old Actonians
London French v H.A.C.

Sat. 28th October (Week 8)
Belsize Park v Feltham
Roxeth Manor O.B. v U.C.S. O.B.
Old Actonians v London French
Pinner & Grammarians v Royal Free Hospital
Northolt v Enfield Ignatians

Sat. 11th November (Week 10)
Feltham v Roxeth Manor O.B.
Enfield Ignatians v Belsize Park
Royal Free Hospital v Northolt
London French v Pinner & Grammarians
H.A.C. v Old Actonians

Sat 18th November (Week 11)
Belsize Park v Royal Free Hospital
Roxeth Manor O.B. v Enfield Ignatians
U.C.S. O.B. v Feltham
Pinner & Grammarians v H.A.C.
Northolt v London French

Sat. 25th November (Week 12)
Enfield Ignatians v U.C.S. O.B.
Royal Free Hospital v Roxeth Manor O.B.
London French v Belsize Park
H.A.C. v Northolt
Old Actonians v Pinner & Grammarians

Sat. 13th January (Week 18)
Belsize Park v H.A.C.
Roxeth Manor O.B. v London French
U.C.S. O.B. v Royal Free Hospital
Feltham v Enfield Ignatians
Northolt v Old Actonians

Sat. 27th January (Week 20)
Royal Free Hospital v Feltham
London French v U.C.S. O.B.
H.A.C. v Roxeth Manor O.B.
Old Actonians v Belsize Park
Pinner & Grammarians v Northolt

Sat. 10th February (Week 22)
Belsize Park v Pinner & Grammarians
Roxeth Manor O.B. v Old Actonians
U.C.S. O.B. v H.A.C.
Feltham v London French
Enfield Ignatians v Royal Free Hospital

Sat. 24th February (Week 24)
London French v Enfield Ignatians
H.A.C. v Feltham
Old Actonians v U.C.S. O.B.
Pinner & Grammarians v Roxeth Manor O.B.
Northolt v Belsize Park

Sat. 10th March (Week 26)
Roxeth Manor O.B. v Northolt
U.C.S. O.B. v Pinner & Grammarians
Feltham v Old Actonians
Enfield Ignatians v H.A.C.
Royal Free Hospital v London French

LONDON & SOUTH EAST DIVISION FIXTURES 1989/90

MIDDLESEX LEAGUE FIVE

Sat. 23rd September (Week 4)
G.W.R. v Middlesex Hospital
New Southgate v Brunel University
Hayes v British Airways
St. Nicholas O.B. v Kodak

Sat. 14th October (Week 6)
St. Mary's College v G.W.R.
British Airways v St. Nicholas O.B.
Brunel University v Hayes
Southall Tech. Coll. v New Southgate

Sat. 28th October (Week 8)
G.W.R. v Kodak
Middlesex Hospital v St. Mary's College
Hayes v Southall Tech. Coll.
St. Nicholas O.B. v Brunel University

Sat. 11th November (Week 10)
Kodak v Middlesex Hospital
British Airways v G.W.R.
Southall Tech. Coll. v St. Nicholas O.B.
New Southgate v Hayes

Sat 18th November (Week 11)
G.W.R. v Brunel University
Middlesex Hospital v British Airways
St. Mary's College v Kodak
St. Nicholas O.B. v New Southgate

Sat. 25th November (Week 12)
British Airways v St. Mary's College
Brunel University v Middlesex Hospital
Southall Tech. Coll. v G.W.R.
Hayes v St. Nicholas O.B.

Sat. 13th January (Week 18)
G.W.R. v New Southgate
Middlesex Hospital v Southall Tech. Coll.
St. Mary's College v Brunel University
Kodak v British Airways

Sat. 27th January (Week 20)
Brunel University v Kodak
Southall Tech. Coll. v St. Mary's College
New Southgate v v Middlesex Hospital
Hayes v G.W.R.

Sat. 10th February (Week 22)
G.W.R. v St. Nicholas O.B.
Middlesex Hospital v Hayes
St. Mary's College v New Southgate
Kodak v Southall Tech. Coll.
British Airways v Brunel University

Sat. 24th February (Week 24)
Southall Tech. Coll. v British Airways
New Southgate v Kodak
Hayes v St. Mary's College
St. Nicholas O.B. v Middlesex Hospital

Sat. 10th March (Week 26)
St. Mary's College v St. Nicholas O.B.
Kodak v Hayes
British Airways v New Southgate
Brunel University v Southall Tech.. Coll.

MIDDLESEX 1

CENTAURS

Centaur Sports Ground, Gower Road, Syon Lane, Osterley, Middlesex. Tel: 01–560 4500
Founded: 1923
President: Rob L. Clubb
Chairman: Mike O'Donnell
Secretary: Robert D. Charon, c/o Centaurs Sports Ground (as above)
Fixtures Secretary: Paul N. Astbury, 32 Kneller Gardens, Isleworth, Middlesex TW7 7NW. Tel: 01–898 5372
Press Officer: As Fixtures Secretary
Coach: Ian Jones/Bob Myhill
Club captain (1988–89): Ian Jones
Club captain (1989–90): Nick Lambert
No. of teams: Senior 6
Directions to ground: A4 Great West Road to Gillette Corner. From Heathrom → London turn left, London → Heathrow turn right into Syon Lane. Gower Road approx. 400 yds on right
Ground capacity: Seating 250
Clubhouse facilities: Changing/showers/baths. Bar/function room
Club colours: Sky blue/navy blue hoops, dark blue shorts and socks. (*Change colours:* Red shirts)
Floodlights: Yes (training only)
Membership fees: Full £25, Playing £25, Social £5, Youth Nil, Student Reduced
Ground admission: Nil
League: Middlesex 1
League position (1988–89): 4th
League playing record (1988–89): P 10, W 5, D 2, L 3, F 136, A 118

HAMPSTEAD

Heath Extension, Hampstead Way, London NW11. Tel: 01–455 5183
Founded: 1968
President: Roger Dearling
Chairman: Peter Boucher
Secretary: Stephen Loffler, 29 Kingsley Way, London N2 0EM. Tel: 01–458 6512 (H), 01–759 4822 (W)
Fixtures Secretary: Danny Harrison, Flat 3, Benson Court, 172 Junction Road, London N19. Tel: 01–281 7357 (H), 01–263 0163 (W)
Press Officer: Roger Dearling, 90 Durham Road, London N2 9QS. Tel: 01–883 4504 (H), 01–586 9483 (W)
Coach: Terry Skyrme
Club captain (1988–89): Simon Peacock
Club captain (1989–90): Simon Peacock
No. of teams: Senior 6
Directions to ground: Hampstead Heath extension, Hampstead Way, Hampstead Garden suburb, London NW11
Ground capacity: Standing Infinite
Clubhouse facilities: The Washington, Englands Lane, Hampstead NW3
Club colours: Gold, claret, white. (*Change colours:* Yellow)
Floodlights: No
Membership fees: Full £25, Playing £25, Social £10, Youth £10, Student £10
Local newspaper: Hampstead & Highgate Express
League: Middlesex 1
League position (1988–89): 7th
League playing record (1988–89): P 33, W 15, D 2, L 16, F 455, A 475

HARROW

Grovefield Wood Lane, Stanmore, Middx. Tel: 01-954 2615.
Founded: 1891
Secretary: A. Wheeler, 55 Whippendell Road, Watford, Herts. Tel: 0923 228184 (H). 01-954 2311. Extn 4123 (W)

Fixtures Secretary: P.R. Pope, 16 Kenilworth Drive, Croxley Green, Herts. Tel: Watford 41504 (H)
League: London 3NW

HENDON

Copthall Playing Fields, Great North Way, Hendon NW4. Tel: 01 203 1737
Founded: 1932
President: David Gershlick
Chairman: John Brown
Secretary: Tom Brownsell, 16 Floriston Gardens, Stanmore, Middlesex. Tel: 01 907 3247
League Contact: John Brown, 61 Cartmel Drive, Dunstable, Bedfordshire LU6 3PT. Tel: 0582 600004
Fixtures Secretary: Craig Silver, 15 Hartfield Avenue, Elstree, Herts. Tel: 01 953 6587
Press Officer: Mick Wood, 38 Calvort Road, Barnet, Herts. Tel: 01 440 9496
Club captain (1988–89): John Ryan
Club captain (1989–90): Joe Walsh
No. of teams: Senior 5, Youth 1
Directions to ground: From M1 travelling South – leave at Junction 2, ground 200 yards on left. 113 bus from Hendon Central to Page Street (5 Ways Corner), Ground 500 yards along Great North Way on left hand side
Clubhouse facilities: Open Match days
Club colours: Bottle green, black and white.
Floodlights: No
Membership fees: Full £30, Playing £30, Social £10, Youth £5, Student £5
Programme: No. of editorial pages 5; No. of advertising pages 8; Price 50p
Local newspapers: Hendon Times, Hampstead & Highgate Express
League: London 3NW
League position (1988–89): 10th

LENSBURY

Lensbury Club, Broom Road, Teddington, Middlesex. Tel: 01–977 8821
Founded: 1920
President: Peter G. Yarranton
Chairman: David O. Spyer
Secretary: Ronald G. Golding, 1 Christchurch Avenue, Teddington, Middlesex TW11 9AB. Tel: 01–977 4014 (H), 01–934 6859 (W)
Fixtures Secretary: Charles Gibson, 12 Wolsey Road, Hampton Hill, Middlesex TU12 1QV. Tel: 01–979 0822 (H), 01–302 2636 (W)
Press Officer: As Secretary
Club captain (1988–89): Ian Grocott
Club captain (1989–90): Ian Grocott
No. of teams: Senior 5
Clubhouse facilities: Residential, swimming pool, sauna, tennis, squash, etc.
Club colours: Purple/gold/black. (*Change colours:* Black)
Floodlights: Yes (partial)
Membership fees: Full £1, Playing £1, Social £1, Youth £1, Student £1, OAP £1
Local newspapers: Surrey Comet and Richmond & Twickenham Times
League: Middlesex 1

LONDON NEW ZEALAND

St. Pauls Playing Fields, Jersey Road, Osterley, Middlesex. Tel: 01–577 6420
Founded: 1926
President: Ted Sturmer
Secretary: Miss W. Whitechurch, 25 Canbury Avenue, Kingston, Surrey. Tel: 01–546 3647 (H), 01–976 5869 (W)
Fixtures Secretary: Richard Peacock, 'Oakfell', Downley Common, High Wycombe, Bucks HP13 5YL. Tel: 0494 488 157 (H), 01–583 0200 (W)

Press Officer: As Fixtures Secretary
Coach: Ray Francis
Club captain (1988–89): Jamie White
Directions to ground: At Gillette Corner on Great West Road (A4), turn north onto Syon Lane (B454). After mile turn left into Jersey Road, entrance mile on right
Club colours: All black
Floodlights: No
League: Middlesex 1
League position (1988–89): 2nd
League playing record (1988–89): P 10, W 8, D 1, L 1, F 188, A 93

OLD MEADONIANS

Riverside Lands, Chiswick, London W4. Tel: 01-994 6956.
Founded: 1958
Secretary: T.D. Smith, 2 Sandford cottages, Kingsclere, Newbury, Berks. Tel: 0635 298231 (H), 9628 39255 (W).
Fixtures Secretary: R. Willingace, Fairmile Farm Cottage, Denbyrd, Cobham, Surrey. Tel: 0932 66927 (H). 0932 45599 (W).
League Contact: B. F. Martin, 8 Burlington Road, Isleworth, Middlesex TW7 4LY**League:** Middlesex 1

OLD MILLHILLIANS

Headstone Lane, Harrow, Middlesex. Tel: 01–428 2281
Founded: 1878
President: John Bolton
Chairman: Andrew Mortimer
Secretary: Michael Leon, Wildacre, Bushfield Road, Bovingdon, Herts HPB 0DR. Tel: 0442 833665
Fixtures Secretary: David Rodda, 1 The Chestnuts, Walton-on-Thames, Surrey KT12 1EE. Tel: 09322 20318 (H), 01–276 8689 (W)
Club captain (1988–89): David Coakley
Club captain (1989–90): Simon Englander
No. of teams: Senior 4, Youth 1
Directions to ground: Opposite Headstone Lane Station
Ground capacity: Seating 50, Standing 1000
Clubhouse facilities: Bar, tearoom, baths, etc. Open matchdays only
Club colours: Chocolate and white
Nickname: OMs
Floodlights: No
Membership fees: Full £150, Playing £60, Social £25, Student £10
Programme: No. of editorial pages 2; No. of advertising pages 14
Programme editor: Robert Hudgell, Collingwood, Baskerville Lane, Lower Shiplake, Henley-on-Thames, Oxon RG9 3JY
Local newspapers: Mill Hill Times, Harrow Observer
League: Middlesex 2
League position (1988–89): 1st (promoted)
League playing record (1988–89): P 35, W 23, D 2, L 11, F 669, A 333
Competitions won: Middlesex 2, 1988/89. Hendon 7s, April 1989

STAINES

The Reeves', Feltham Hill Road, Hanworth, Middlesex TW13 7WB. Tel: 01–890 3051
Founded: 1926
President: Eric J. Devou
Chairman: Warren Lee
Secretary: Graham M. Clark, 38 Shepherds Close, Shepperton, Middlesex TW17 9AL. Tel: 0932 242045 (H), 01–941 4131 (W)
Fixtures Secretary: Eric J. Devou, 94 Groveley Road, Sunbury-on-Thames, Middlesex TW16 7LB. Tel: 01–890 6643 (H), 01–248 1117 (W)
Press Officer: Dave Hoade, 26 Denman Drive, Ashford, Middlesex. Tel: 0784 250353 (H), 01–562

6347 (W)
Coach: Bob Lawless
Club captain (1988–89): Chris Smith
Club captain (1989–90): Jeff Smith
No. of teams: Senior 6, Youth 6, Minis (All ages) 10
Directions to ground: Off A316 signposted Hanworth/ Lower Feltham, left at Jobs Dairy (Unigate) into Feltham Hill road, keep leftm ground is 500 yds on left
Clubhouse facilities: New Aug '89. Open 7 days a week
Club colours: Red and blue hoops. (*Change colours:* Light blue and red)
Nickname: Swans
Floodlights: Yes
Membership fees: Full £30, Playing £30, Social £15, Youth £15, Student £15, OAP Half
Local newspapers: Staines & Egham Middlesex Chronicle
League: Middlesex 1
League position (1988–89): 6th
League playing record (1988–89): P 35, W 13, D 4, L 18, F 409, A 485

SUDBURY COURT

The Pavilion, East Lane, North Wembley, Middx. Tel: 01–904 8485
Founded: 1958
President: Tony McCann
Chairman: Paul Wilkinson
Secretary: Derek Gray, 33 Northwick Park Road, Harrow, Middx. Tel: 01–427 4155
Fixtures Secretary: David Keeling, 17 Nunnery Lane, Luton, Beds LU3 1XA. Tel: 0582 507602
Press Officer: Simon Mitchell, 168A Bilton Road, Perivale, Middx. Tel: 01–998 9203 (H), 01–523 3261 (W)
Coach: Adrian Lewis
Club captain (1988–89): Andy stitson
Club captain (1989–90): Mick Broderick
No. of teams: Senior 5
Directions to ground: Train to North Wembley Station, turn left on leaving and ground is 600 yds on left. Or train to Sudbury Town Station and No. 245 bus to East Lane School. Ground is opposite bus stop
Clubhouse facilities: 4 changing rooms, modern bath and shower facilities, two bars
Club colours: Dark blue, red and white. (*Change colours:* Yellow)
Floodlights: Yes (training only)
Membership fees: Full £15, Playing £15, Social £9, Student £8
Ground admission: Nil
Local newspapers: Wembley Observer, Willesden & Brent Chronicle
League: Middlesex 1
League position (1988–89): 8th
League playing record (1988–89): P 34, W 12, D 0, L 22, F 396, A 512

UXBRIDGE

Belfry Avenue, Harefield, Middx. Tel: Harefield 3281
Founded: 1948
President: John French
Chairman: Colin Whiting
Secretary: Chris Webb, 124 Whitby Road, South Ruislip, Middx HA4 9DR. Tel: 0895 631746 (H), 01–864 5373 (W)
Fixtures Secretary: Peter John, 3 Parkview Chase, Burnham, Slough, Berks. Tel: 0628 602010 (H), 0895 832323 (W)
Press Officer: Sue Park, 33 Braunston Drive, Yeading, Hayes, Middx. Tel: 01–841 7850
Club captain (1988–89): Mark Parry
Club captain (1989–90): Richard Jones
No. of teams: Senior 4, Youth 1
Directions to ground: Travel to Harefield, at mini roundabout in the centre of Harefield follow sign to

Uxbridge R.F.C. down lane. Belfry Avenue is 3rd road on your right
Clubhouse facilities: Bar, pool table, darts, TV
Club colours: Red, black and white
Floodlights: No
Membership fees: Full £10, Playing £10, Social £10, Youth £5
League: Middlesex 1
League position (1988–89): 3rd
League playing record (1988–89): P 29, W 17, D 3, L 9, F 514, A 220

MIDDLESEX 2

BARCLAYS BANK

Park View Road, Ealing, London W5 2JF
Founded: 1921
President: D.C. Mann
Chairman: D. Hooper
Secretary: B.D. Stevenson, 89 Oyster Lane, Byfleet, Surrey KT14 7JF. Tel: 09323-44937.
Fixtures Secretary: D.M. Bevan-Jones, 23 Cypress Avenue, Whitton, Middx. Tel: 01-898 4107.
Club captain (1987–88): D.J.J. Lavery
Club captain (1988–89): D.J.J. Lavery
No. of teams: Senior 5.
Directions to Ground: Off the North Circular on the western side of Hanger Lane.
Clubhouse: Adjacent to pitches
Colours: Maroon with gold and silver band. (*Change colours:* Navy blue).
Floodlights: No
Membership: Closed Club. Barclays staff only.
League: Middx. Div II.

CIVIL SERVICE

Dukes Meadows, Riverside Drive, Chiswick, W4. Tel: 01-993 1202 (office) (H), 01-994 2343 (Members)
Founded: 1863
President: Martin Creasy
Chairman: Gavin Bleakley
Secretary: Nick Alway, 14 Freshford Street, London SW18 3TF. Tel: 01-946 3082 (H), 01-836 8333 (W)
Fixtures Secretary: Ralph Hulme, 64 Walmington Fold, London N12. Tel: 01-346 1557
Press Officer: Steve Barry, 149 Village Way, Beckenham BR3 3WL. Tel: 01-650 2945
Coach: Dave Moore
Club captain (1988–89): Chris Bishop
Club captain (1989–90): T.B.A.
No. of teams: Senior 4
Directions to ground: A4 to the Hogarth roundabout, take the A316 signposted Richmond. After approx. mile turn left at first traffic lights into Riverside Drive. The entrance to the ground is at the bottom of the Drive on the right
Ground capacity: Standing Ample
Clubhouse facilities: Open Saturdays, Sundays and Mondays to Thursdays
Club colours: White shirts with red tudor crown, blue shorts, blue and white socks. (*Change colours:*)
Floodlights: Yes (training only)
Membership fees: Full £20, Playing £15
Ground admission: Free

HACKNEY

Spring Hill Ground, Spring Hill, Hackney, London. Tel: 01-806 5289
Secretary: A. Leader, 4 Wilbury Way, London N18. Tel: 01-803 9413 (W)
League Contact: J. K. grimmer, 189 Winchmore Hillroad, Winchmore Hill, London N21 1ZN
Colours: Navy Blue/Sky Blue/Gold
League: Middlesex 2.

HARINGEY

New River Sports Centre, White Hart Lane, Wood Green N22 5QW. Tel: 01-881 1926 (Reception), 01-881 2310 (Office)

Founded: 1963
Chairman: Ken Williams
Secretary: Glynne Jones, 44 Park Hall Road, East Finchley, London N2 9PX. Tel: 01-883 8091 (H), 01-348 4506 (Fax)
Fixtures Secretary: Colin Field, 4 Highview Close, Potters Bar, Herts. Tel: 0707-45557 (H), 01-340 1771 (W)
Press Officer: As Secretary
Coach: Alan Richards/Michael Brock
Club captain (1988–89): Lyndon Morris
Club captain (1989–90): Lyndon Morris
No. of teams: Senior 5
Directions to ground: A406 (North Circular Road) to junction with A10 (Great Cambridge Road), along A10 in direction of Central London, White Hart Lane 6th right, ground mile
Ground capacity: Standing 2000+
Clubhouse facilities: Under Athletics spectator stand
Club colours: Green, scarlet, white. (*Change colours:* Red)
Nickname: 'The Rhinos'
Floodlights: Yes (training only)
Membership fees: Full £20, Playing £20, VPs £25
Programme editor: Secretary: (Weekly Club Newsletter 'Rhino Rumblings'), address as Secretary (above)
Local newspapers: The Hornsey Journal
League: Middlesex 2
League position (1988–89): 4th
League playing record (1988–89): P 33, W 22, D 1, L 10, F 515, A 343

OLD ABBOTSTONIANS

Polehill Open Spaces, Gainsborough Road, Hayes, Middx. Tel: 01-845 1452
Founded: 1957
Chairman: Frank Holder
Secretary: Glen Baptista, 2 Denecroft Crescent, Hillington UB10 9HU. Tel: 0895 71100 (H), 01-798 7045 (W)
Fixtures Secretary: David Wiggins, 49 Petworth Gardens, Hillingdon UB10 9HQ. Tel: 0895 51585
Coach: Derek Harper
Club captain (1988–89): Derek Harper
Club captain (1989–90): Ken Homer
No. of teams: Senior 4, Youth 1, Vets 1
Directions to ground: Junction of Raeburn Road and Gainsborough Road off Charville Lane, Hayes
Club facilities: Full clubhouse and changing facilities
Club colours: Red and blue hoops. (*Change colours:* Royal blue)
Nickname: Abbotts
Floodlights: Yes (training)
Membership fees: Full £30, Playing £30, Social £25, Youth £5, Student £5, Ladies £5
Local newspapers: Gazette
League: Middlesex 2
League position (1988–89): Bottom (relegated)
League playing record (1988–89): P 26, W 6, D 1, L 19
Competitions won: Final Slough Floodlit

OLD GRAMMARIANS

Ground: Queen Street, Tottenham, London N17.
Clubhouse: Corner of Manor Road/Denmark Street, Tottenham, London N17. Tel: 01-898 7697
Founded: 1929
President: Keith McGuinness
Secretary: Brian Calderwood, 17 Birch Crescent, Aylesford, Maidstone, Kent ME20 7QE. Tel: 0622 718350 (H), 01-831 7171 ext. 4903 (W)
Fixtures Secretary: Mike Holt, 64 Chandos Road,

London N2 9AP. Tel: 01–883 4016
Press Officer: John Crouch, 21 Salmons Road,
Edmonton, London N9 7JT
Coach: David Kaplan
Club captain (1988–89): John Wing
Club captain (1989–90): Chris Izzard
No. of teams: Senior 4
Directions to ground: Approached via Great
Cambridge Road (A10) or High Road (A1010) or
from North Circular Road (Sterling Way) (A406) via
Bull Lane
Clubhouse facilities: Open weekends and training
nights. Weight training and table tennis facilities
Club colours: Navy blue, light blue and red
Floodlights: No
League: Middlesex 3
League position (1988–89): 1st
League playing record (1988–89): P 33, W 22, D 2,
L 9, F 397, A 300
Competitions won: Middlesex League 3 Champions.
Combined London Old Boys Merit Table, NE
London, Runners-Up

OLD HABERDASHERS

Croxdale Road, Theobald Street, Boreham Wood,
herts WD6 4PY. Tel: 01–953 1987
Founded: 1923
President: Antony J.S. Alexander
Chairman: Martin S. Baker
Secretary: Malcolm Tappin, 10 Woodway, Holtspur,
Beaconsfield, Bucks HP9 1DH. Tel: 0494 672459 (H),
01–449 5501 (W)
Fixtures Secretary: John J. Hanson, The Castle,
School Lane, Old Bricket Wood, St. Albans, Hants
AL2 3XS. Tel: 0923 673263 (H), 01–953 2178 (W)
Press Officer: Antony J.S. Alexander, 80 Oxhey
Avenue, Watford, Hants. Tel: 0923 248458
Coach: T.B.A.
Club captain (1988–89): Andy Charles
Club captain (1989–90): Ian D. McCarthy
No. of teams: Senior 3, Youth 1
Directions to ground: From Elstree Station proceed
north along Theobalds Street. Croxdale Road is a
turning on the right after about mile
Ground capacity: Seating 40
Clubhouse facilities: Bar, dining, pool, darts
Club colours: Blue, white, magenta. (*Change colours:*
Navy, blue)
Floodlights: No
Membership fees: Full £20, Playing £20, Social £10
Local newspaper: Borehamwood Post
League position (1988–89): 9th (relegated)
League playing record (1988–89): P 10, W 2, D 2,
L 6, F 67, A 176

OLD PAULINE

Speer Road, Thames Ditton, Surrey. Tel: 01–398 1858
Founded: 1871
President: High Master St. Paul's School
Chairman: N.J. Downie
Secretary: A.M. Boardman, (N.J. Downie), 85
Teddington Park Road, Teddington, Middx TW11
8NG. Tel: 943 0091 (H), 749 3842 (W)
Fixtures Secretary: Brian Jones, 27 Montrose Avenue,
Whitton, Twickenham, Midd. Tel: 898 6408
Club captain (1989–90): Paul Redstone
No. of teams: Senior 4, Youth 1
Directions to ground: Thames Ditton Station
Club colours: Red, black and white hoops. (*Change
colours:* White)
Nickname: OP's
Floodlights: No
Membership fees: Full £10, Playing £10, Youth £10
League position (1988–89): 10th
League playing record (1988–89): P 10, W 1, D 2,
L 7, F 83, A 162

ORLEANS FORMER PUPILS

Orleans Park, Richmond Road, Twickenham, Middx.
Tel: 01–892 5743
Founded: 1963
President: Denis Davidson
Chairman: Anthony Squire
Secretary: Anthony Squire, 3 Lyndhurst Avenue,
Twickenham, Middx TW2 6BG. Tel: 01–894 4100
Fixtures Secretary: Vince Tullett, 8 Douglas House,
The Avenue, St. Margarets, Twickenham, Middx.
Tel: 01–894 0554 (H), 01–890 3600 ext. 2086 (W)
Press Officer: Len Masters, 1 Broadway Avenue,
Twickenham, Middx TW1 1RH. Tel: 01–891 1135
Club captain (1988–89): Hans Formella
Club captain (1989–90): Richard Hoyland
No. of teams: Senior 3
Directions to ground: A316 to St. Margarets turn
down towards Station, just past Station take right fork
down Crown Road, at road junction opposite is
Crown P.H., right just past Orleans Road entrance
gates on left
Clubhouse facilities: Open matchday, Sunday lunch
and Monday evening
Club colours: Maroon gold and white hoops. (*Change
colours:* All gold)
Nickname: O's
Floodlights: No
Membership fees: Full £25, Social £10, Youth £50,
Student £10
Local newspaper: Richmond & Twickenham Times
League position (1988–89): 6th
League playing record (1988–89): P 10, W 4, D 1,
L 5, F 71, A 124

OSTERLEY

Tentelow Lane, Norwood Green, Southall,
Middlesex. Tel: 01-574 3774.
Founded: 1922
Secretary: D.R. Shepherd, 34 Chandos Avenue,
Ealing, London W5. Tel: 01-847 2759 (H), 01-560
5151 (W).
Fixtures Secretary: J. Green, 92 Roxborough Avenue,
Isleworth, Middlesex. Tel: 01-568 5557.

ST BART'S HOSPITAL

West Smithfield, London EC1
Founded: 1873
President: J. Gilmore
Secretary: G.C. Cloud, Medical College, St Barts
Hospital, Charterhouse Square, London EC1. Tel: 01-
987 5129.
Fixtures Secretary: G.C. Cloud. As above.
League Contact: M. Juniper, MSCR, St. Barts
Hospital, London EC1. Tel: 01–251 5826
Club captain (1988–89): D. Clarke
No. of teams: Senior 1.
Directions to Ground: Perry Street, Foxbury,
Chislehurst, Kent. (By train from London Bridge).
Ground capacity: Fair. Stand 2–300.
Clubhouse: Bar & dining facilities and changing rooms
for 6-4 teams.
Colours: Black and white. (*Change colours:* White
and black).
Nickname: Barts
Floodlights: No

ANTLERS

Bushy Park, Teddington, Middlsex. Tel: 01–977 4989
Founded: 1966

Chairman: Steve Croft
Secretary: Peter Woolgar, 114 Elgin Avenue,
Ashford, Middlesex TW15 1QG. Tel: 0784 259734
(H), 01–223 1271 (W)
Fixtures Secretary: Rod Bromfield, 104 Station Road,
Hampton, Middx. Tel: 0979 5635
Press Officer: Andy Rogers, 62 More Lane, Esher,
Surrey. Tel: 0372 63447 (H), 437 4774 (W)
Coach: T.B.A.
Club captain (1988–89): Paul Rattenbury
Club captain (1989–90): Taffy Jones
No. of teams: Senior 4 Women 1
Directions to ground: Trains from Waterloo to
Teddington Station. Out of main entrance of station,
down Adelaide Road and straight across the road –
first left down Park Lane. Turn right down Queens
Road, then first left down Coleshill Road, through the
road in N.P.L., pavilion on right inside Park Gates.
By road: through Kingston and over Kingston Bridge,
take the left fork to Hampton Court. Approx. one
mile turn right at 'The Greyhound' into Bushy Park.
Past the roundabout take the first on the left marked
'To Car Park'. Pass the sign marked 'No unauthorised
vehicles' and turn right at Bartons Cottage to
Teddington Town Sports Club (not Teddington
Cricket Club)
Clubhouse facilities: Bar
Club colours: Dark blue. (*Change colours:* Various)
Floodlights: Yes (training only)
Membership fees: Full £25, Playing £25, Social £10,
Youth £5, Student £5
Local newspapers: Richmond & Twickenham Times,
Surrey Comet, Middlesex Chronicle
League: Middlesex 2
League position (1988–89): 6th
League playing record (1988–89): P 10, W 5, D 1,
L 4, F 147, A 106

HAMMERSMITH & FULHAM

Hurlingham Stadium, Hurlingham Park, London
SW6. Tel: 01–736 5186
Founded: 1978
President: Cliff Morgan
Chairman: Terry Alleyne
Secretary: Chris Cuthbertson, 17 Wheatsheaf Wharf,
Wheatsheaf Lane, London SW6 6LS. Tel: 01–381
6054 (H), 0252 875075 (W)
Fixtures Secretary: Lyndon Walters, 32 Chapel Road,
Hounslow TW3 1JL. Tel: 01–572 3853 (H), 01–228
6454 ext. 267 (W)
Press Officer: Fred Mundy, 265 Westway, London
W12 7AW. Tel: 01–743 5927 (H), 01–221 2340 (W)
Coach: Dave Higgins
Club captain (1988–89): Steffan Francis
Club captain (1989–90): Pete Tolput
No. of teams: Senior 4
Directions to ground: From Hammersmith Broadway
take the Fulham Palace Road (A219) towards Putney
Bridge. Just before the bridge turn left at the traffic
lights into the New Kings Road (A308). Take the first
right, under the railway bridge, into Hurlingham
Road. The ground is 300 yds on the right
Ground capacity: Seating 3000, Standing 1000
Clubhouse facilities: The Alma pub in Parsons Green
Lane, SW6
Club colours: Red shirt with two white and one blue
band. (*Change colours:* Sky blue or white)
Floodlights: No
Membership fees: Full £20
Local newspaper: Fulham Chronicle
League: Middlesex 3
League position (1988–89): 10th (relegated)
League playing record (1988–89): P 10, W 3, D 0,
L 7, F 132, A 218

LONDON CORNISH

Richardson-Evans Memorial Ground, by Robinhood

Roundabout, roehampton Vale, Kingston upon
Thames. Tel: 01–788 3638
President: Ross A.L. Brown
Chairman: Mike Herring
Secretary: Steve Lang, 31 Coleshill Road,
Teddington, Middx TW11 0LL. Tel: 01–943 0931 (H),
01–874 3922 (W)
Fixtures Secretary: Philip Silby, 10 Cobold Road,
London W12 9LW. Tel: 01–749 8817 (H), 01–409
2666 (W)
Press Officer: Steve Floyd, 332 Carr Road, Northolt,
Middx UB5 4RN. Tel: 01–422 2828 (H), 01–920 8351
(W)
Club captain (1988–89): Tim Evans
Club captain (1989–90): Tim Evans
No. of teams: Senior 4
Directions to ground: 75 yds on left before Robin
Hood Roundabout at junction with Kingston bypass
(A3) heading out of London. Large car park
Ground capacity: Standing Ample
Clubhouse facilities: Cross Keys, Black Lion Lane,
W6
Club colours: Black with narrow gold hoops
(Cornwall County colours). (*Change colours:* Black)
Floodlights: No
Membership fees: Full £30, Playing £30, Social £10,
Student £10
League: Middlesex 3
League position (1988–89): 3rd
League playing record (1988–89): P 10, W 7, D 0,
L 3, F 141, A 94
Competitions won: Harrodian Sevens, April 1989

MEADHURST

Meadhurst Club, Sunbury-on-Thames, Middx. Tel:
09327 63502
Founded: 1952/53
President: R. Malpas
Chairman: R. Corbett
Secretary: Julian Norley, BP Research Centre,
Chertsey Road, Sunbury-on-Thames, Middx TW16
7LN. Tel: 09327 64038 (W)
Fixtures Secretary: Dr. I. Little, 151/202 BP Research
Centre, Chertsey Road, Sunbury-on-Thames,
Middlesex TW16 7LN. Tel: 01–979 6661 (H), 0932
762770 (W)
Coach: T. Fearn
Club captain (1988–89): Ian Somerville
Club captain (1989–90): Neil McCracken
No. of teams: Senior 2–3
Directions to ground: From Richmond (A316) or
Kingston (A308) to Sunbury Cross roundabout. Exit
along A308 to Staines. In mile turn right at lights by
Shears pub into Cadbury Road. Continue for mile.
Club is on right just beyond lights
Ground capacity: Standing 200
Clubhouse facilities: Large bar area/restaurant. Own
ground. 10 changing rooms and showers. 2 pitches
Club colours: Green and yellow reverse quarters.
(*Change colours:* Maroon)
Floodlights: No
Membership fees: Closed club
Local newspaper: Staines Informer
League: Middlesex 3
League position (1988–89): 2nd
League playing record (1988–89): P 9, W 7, D 0, L 2,
F 160, A 65
Competitions won: Oil Company 7's

OLD HAMPTONIANS

Dean Road, Hampton, Middx. Tel: 979 2784
Founded: 1957
President: Kevin Bell
Chairman: Kevin Bell
Secretary: Nicholas J.G. Bugler, 3 Walpole Place,
Teddington, Middx. Tel: 977 1380 (H), 327 6702 (W)
Fixtures Secretary: Robert Hudson, 29 Undine Rod,
Clippers Quay, London E14. Tel: 538 5140 (H), 283
2474 ext. 2113 (W)

Press Officer: As Secretary
Coach: Pete Davidson
Club captain (1988–89): David Jacob
Club captain (1989–90): Kevin Bell
No. of teams: Senior 3
Directions to ground: Coming west from London on the A316 turn left at Apex Corner, on to the A312. After approx. mile turn right into Hanworth Road, travel past 3 schools and turn right into Dean Road. Entrance on right
Ground capacity: Standing Touchline
Clubhouse facilities: Open all weekends, weekday evenings except Mondays
Club colours: Black, gold, silver hoops. (*Change colours:* Dark blue, plain)
Floodlights: No
Membership fees: Full £30, Playing £30, Social £7.50, Youth £15, Student £15, OAP £15
Local newspapers: Richmond and Twickenham Times, Surrey Comet, Middlesex Chronicle
League: Middlesex 3
League position (1988–89): 10th
League playing record (1988–89): P 29, W 10, D 16, L 3, F 309, A 315

OLD ISLEWORTHIANS

Wood Lane, Isleworth, Middlesex. Tel: 01-560 7949.
Founded: 1957
Secretary: K. Tighe, 40 Douglas Lane, Wraysbury, Berks. Tel: 078481 2622 (H), 01-626 0566. Extn. 3417 (W).
League: Middlesex 3S

OLD TOTTONIANS

Tottenham School, Selby Road, London N17.
Founded: 1931
Secretary: T.W. De La Salle, 25 Penton Drive, Cheshunt, Herts EN8 9RS. Tel: 0992 38492 (H). 0494 444816 (W).
League: Middlesex 3
Final position (1987–88): 3rd

THE QUINTIN

Hartington Road, Chiswick, London W4. Tel: 01–994 0476/1554
Founded: 1885
President: Colin Smith
Chairman: Ernie Deacy
Secretary: Nigel Smith, Ruskin Hall, 16 Church Road, Acton, London W3 8PP. Tel: 992 5614 (H), 242 9050 ext. 3582 (W)
Fixtures Secretary: Ernie Deacy, 98 Portland Road, Bromley, Kent. Tel: 851 0105
Club captain (1988–89): Mark Southern
Club captain (1989–90): Mark Southern
No. of teams: Senior 3
Club colours: Red and green hoops, blue shorts
Floodlights: No
League: Middx 3

RICHMOND THAMESIANS

Richmond College, Egerton Road, Twickenham, Middlesex (formerly Richmond Thamesians)
President: Clive Morley
Chairman: Dave Brook
Secretary: Kevin Patrick, 11 Cedar Road, Teddington, Middlesex TW11 9AN. Tel: 01–977 7845 (H), 01–847 4803 (W)
Fixtures Secretary: Jerry Wright, 5 Kathleen Road, London SW11 2JR. Tel: 01–228 0830 (H), 01–541 8359 (W)
Press Officer: Simon Calver, 60 Kingston Road, Teddington, Middlesex. Tel: 01–943 2854 (H), 01–541 8397 (W)

Coach: Nigel Botherway
Club captain (1988–89): Nigel Botherway
Club captain (1989–90): Dave Curry
No. of teams: Senior 3 + Vets
Directions to ground: From A316 (Chertsey Road) Currie Motors Garage roundabout, head towards M3 motorway. Approx. 200 yds turn first left into Egerton Road, ground immediately on right
Clubhouse facilities: Showers on site. Bar facilities 1 mile (will have on site new clubhouse during 1989–90 season)
Club colours: Maroon and green shirts, white shorts
Nickname: The T's
Floodlights: No
Membership fees: Full £24
Local newspapers: Surrey Comet, Richmond & Twickenham Times
League: Middlesex 1
League position (1988–89): 9th

WEMBLEY LM

Broadfields, Headstone Lane, North Harrow, Middx. Tel: 01–428 0286
Founded: 1927
President: M. Southgate
Chairman: David Jones
Secretary: Noreen Conlon, 62 Canterbury Way, Croxley Green, Rickmansworth, Herts WD3 3SS. Tel: 0923 30640
Fixtures Secretary: Chris Green, 26 Anmersh Grove, Stanmore, Middx. Tel: 01–952 4850
Press Officer: Kevin Instance, c/o Secretary's address. Tel: 01–578 9743
Club captain (1988–89): Mark Reeves
Club captain (1989–90): Gary Skirton
No. of teams: Senior 3
Directions to ground: Headstone Lane Station at top of Broadfields, Harrow Town. Take Pinner Road to Headstone Lane, right at lights, through 6.6 gap, next turn on left. From Uxbridge Road watch end Headstone Lane, turn 1st right, over bridge into Broadfields
Clubhouse facilities: Bar
Club colours: Maroon/amber band. (*Change colours:* Yellow/green band)
Floodlights: Yes (for training)
Membership fees: Full £20, Playing £20, Social £2
Local newspaper: Harrow Observer
League: Middlesex 3
League position (1988–89): 4th
League playing record (1988–89): P 28, W 13, D 4, L 11, F 421, A 339

MIDDLESEX 4

BELSIZE PARK

c/o Copthall Sports Centre, Great North Way, London NW4 (shared with Hendon R.F.C.)
Founded: 1972
President: John Connelly
Chairman: Giles Lenton
Secretary: Terry Campbell, 2 Orpington Gardens, Enfield, London N18. Tel: 807 0806 (H), 794 8912 (W)
Fixtures Secretary: Brian East, 17 Waterlow Road, London N19 5NJ. Tel: 272 5686 (H), 485 4100 ext. 287 (W)
Press Officer: Trevor Barnes, 19 Mansfield Heights, Great North Road, London N2 0NY. Tel: 341 7779 (H), 725 3642 (W)
Coach: Keith Price
Club captain (1988–89): John Roche
Club captain (1989–90): Mark Batchelor
No. of teams: Senior 3
Directions to ground: A41 from London to Five Ways Intersection. Ground 300 yds up A1 (behind Chevron Garage)
Clubhouse facilities: Shared facilities with Hendon

R.F.C.
Club colours: Black and purple. (*Change colours:* Black and red)
Floodlights: No
Membership fees: Full £20, Playing £20, Social £10, Student £10
Local newspaper: Hampstead & Highgate Express
League: Middlesex 4
League position (1988–89): 11th (relegated)
League playing record (1988–89): P 10, W 2, D 0, L 8, F 77, A 181

ENFIELD IGNATIANS

The Clubhouse, Donkey Lane, Enfield, Middx. Tel: 01-363 2877.
Founded: 1951
Chairman: K.G. Jones
Coach: J. Cooper
Secretary: D. Wills, 81 Eastbrook Road, Waltham Abbey, Essex. Tel: 0992 715541.
Fixtures Secretary: T. Ryan, 72 Gt Bushey Drive, Totteridge, London N20. Tel: 01-445 5372.
League Contact: K. G. Jones, 45 Halifax Road, Enfield, Middlesex. Tel: 01–366 3207
Press Officer: J. Cooper. Tel: 01–360 9561
Club captain(1987–88): P. Poulain
Club captain (1988–89): T. Fenn
No. of teams: Senior 4.
Directions to Ground: South of M25 on A20 at Queen Elizabeth Stadium.
Clubhouse: Own clubhouse, bar and changing facilities.
Colours: Gold and blue. (*Change colours:* Red).
Nickname: Old I's
Floodlights: Yes
Membership: £25 season
Local newspaper: Enfield Gazette
League: Middx. 4
Final position (1987–88): 6th
Playing record (1987–88): P 29, W 11, D 1, L 17. F 439, A 400.

FELTHAM

Clubhouse, Hanworth Park, Park Road, Hanworth, Middlesex. Tel: 01-894 3609
Founded: 1947
President: John Soper
Chairman: Ian Carne
Secretary: Mel Plumpton, 4 Sandown Close, Blackwater, Camberley, Surrey GU17 0EL. Tel: 0252 872853
Fixtures Secretary: John Butler, 155 Uxbridge Road, Feltham, Middlesex TW13 5EJ. Tel: 01–898 9253
Press Officer: Derek Pearson, 84 Manor Lane, Sunbury-on-Thames, Middlesex TW16 6JB. Tel: Sunbury 82192
Club captain (1988–89): Chris Deakin
Club captain (1989–90): Duncan Wright
No. of teams: Senior 5, Youth 1
Directions to ground: Off the Hounslow Road (A314) just by A316 (end of M3), Park Road is by the Jolly Sailor pub, take the right turn just before Park Road takes a sharp left bend
Clubhouse facilities: Bar open matchdays, weekends and most evenings
Club colours: Light blue/dark blue/gold hoops, navy shorts, light blue/dark blue socks. (*Change colours:* Red shirts, blue shorts)
Floodlights: Yes (training only)
Membership fees: Full £10, Playing £10, Social £5, Youth £3, Student £3, OAP £5
Ground admission: Free
Programme: No. of editorial pages Varies; No. of advertising pages Varies; Price Free (when printed)
Programme editor: Derek Pearson/Alan Keen, 80 Worple Road, Staines, Middlesex
Local newspapers: Middlesex Chronicle, The Informer, Leader
League: Middlesex 4

League position (1988–89): 7th
League playing record (1988–89): P 9, W 4, D 0, L 5, F 105, A 104

HAC

Armoury House, City Road, London EC1. Tel: 01 606 4644
League Contact: M. Fiddes, 26 Upper Grotto Road, Twickenham, Middlesex. Tel: 01 891 5726
Club colours: Dark blue/red
League: Middlesex 4

LONDON FRENCH

Prince Georges Playing Fields, Bushey Road, Raynes Park, London SW20. Tel: 949 5569
Founded: 1959
Chairman: Andrew Byrd
Secretary: André James, 2B Priory Road, London W4. Tel: 994 1090 (H), 236 3611 (W)
Fixtures Secretary: Bob Dudley, 72 Elm Road, New Malden Surrey KT3 3HH. Tel: 949 5569 (H), 0602 504645 (W)
Press Officer: As Fixtures Secretary
Club captain (1988–89): Ed Will
Club captain (1989–90): Geoff Leaver-Heaton
No. of teams: Senior 3 + Vets
Directions to ground: From London on A3. After Robin Hood Roundabout take second exit onto Bushey Road Flyover. Car park is right after 1st lights into grand drive
Clubhouse facilities: None
Club colours: French blue. (*Change colours:* White)
Floodlights: No
Membership fees: Full £20, Student £10
League: Middlesex 4
League position (1988–89): 6th
League playing record (1988–89): P 9, W 3, D 2, L 4, F 98, A 86

NORTHOLT

Kensington and Chelsea Playing Fields, Dolphin Road, Northolt, Middlesex (off Kensington Road). Tel: 01–841 3088
Founded: 1960
President: Thomas Lynham
Chairman: Stuart Knight
Secretary: Colin Nicholl, 20B Northolt Avenue, South Ruislip, Middlesex HA4 6ST. Tel: 01–841 1410
Fixtures Secretary: Geoff Payne, 16 Brackenbridge Drive, South Ruislip, Middlesex HA5 0NG. Tel: 01–845 0874 (H), 01–937 5464 ext. 2846 (W)
Press Officer: As Fixtures Secretary
Coach: Alan Ross
Club captain (1988–89): Mike Cooke
Club captain (1989–90): Tony Jones
No. of teams: Senior 3–4
Directions to ground: Take A40 (Western Avenue) to Northolt turn-off (A312 Target Roundabout). Exit roundabout in easterly direction as if joining A40 towards London, but remain in left-hand lane signposted to Southall, avoiding joining A40. Turn right at T-junction (Kensington Road) and go under A40. After slip-road back towards Northolt take 1st turning right (Dolphin Road). The clubhouse and ground entrance are approx. 400 yds ahead of you
Clubhouse facilities: 2 bars (one exclusively for use by Northolt R.F.C.) on second floor level above changing rooms and showers. 2nd floor also includes extensive balcony (with barbecue area) overlooking pitches. Club open nightly plus weekends. Floodlit training area (training on Tuesday nights)
Club colours: Navy and sky blue hoops, black shorts, navy and sky blue hooped socks. (*Change colours:* White)
Floodlights: Yes (training only)
Membership fees: Playing £30, Social £10
Programme editor: See Fixtures Secretary
Local newspapers: The Gazette (Ealing), The Leader

(Ealing), Ruislip & Northwood, Hayes & Harmondsworth, West Drayton, Hillingdon Gazettes
League: Middlesex 3
League position (1988–89): 10th
League playing record (1988–89): P 10, W 2, D 0, L 8, F 63, A 143
Competitions won: British Airways Sevens Runners-Up, September 1988. Hayes Sevens (Plate) Runners-Up, April 1989

OLD ACTONIANS

Gunnersbury Drive, London W5. Tel: 01-567 4556.
Founded: 1968
Secretary: A. Hart, 60 St Mary's Road, Harlesden, London NW10 4AX. Tel: 01-961 7578 (H), 01-353 8000. Extn. 4088 (W)
League Contact: P. Grove-'white, Alexandra Road, London N6. Tel: 01–881 0167
Colours: Royal Blue/White
League: Middlesex 4

PINNER & GRAMMARIANS

Shaftesbury Playing Fields, Grimsdyke Road, Hatch End, Pinner, Middx. Tel: 01–428 3136
President: Bill North
Chairman: Steve Woad
Secretary: Dave Hiles, 31 Lulworth Close, South Harrow, Middx HA2 9NR. Tel: 01–864 0787 (H), 01–954 7776 ext. 242 (College)
Fixtures Secretary: Barry Whitcombe, 2 Letchworth Terrace, Headstone Lane, Harrow, Middx. Tel: 01–421 0509 (H), 01–922 3987 (W)
Press Officer: Phil Martin, 76 Evelyn Drive, Pinner, Middx. Tel: 428 120 (H), 846 9933 (W)
Coach: Club captains
Club captain (1988–89): Phil Skelton
Club captain (1989–90): Phil Skelton
No. of teams: Senior 4 + Vets
Directions to ground: Road: Uxbridge Road, Hatch End, turn into Grimsdyke Road (opposite Railway Pub), then 2nd right, 1st left (Coburn Avenue). Playing field entrance and car park on left. Rail: BR/Bakerloo to Hatch End then as above
Clubhouse facilities: Clubhouse, bar, kitchen, 4 changing rooms, bath and showers, ladies cloaks
Club colours: Scarlet and navy hoops (4″)
Nickname: Pelicans
Floodlights: No
Membership fees: Full £30, Playing £30, Social £15, Youth £5, Student £5
Local newspapers: Harrow Observer and Freebies: Leader, Independent, Review, Informer, Focus
League: Middlesex 4
League position (1988–89): 9th (relegated)
League playing record (1988–89): P 10, W 3, D 0, L 7, F 68, A 162

ROYAL FREE HOSPITAL

Myddleton House, Bulls Cross, Enfield. Tel: 01 976 1553
League Contact: Fixtures Secretary, Rugby Football Club, RFH School of Medicine, Rowland Hill Street, Hampstead, London NW3. Tel: 01 794 0500
Club colours: Gold/black
League: Middlesex 4

ROXETH MANOR OLD BOYS

Polytechnic of North London Sports Ground, Honey Pot Lane, Stanmore, Middx HA7 1AR. Tel: 01–952 1893

Founded: 1961
President: Dennis Holliday
Chairman: Roger Meek
Secretary: John Holland, 25 Rayners Lane, South Harrow, Middx HA2 0UD. Tel: 01–864 1333 (H), 01–965 5787 ext. 5240 (W)
Fixtures Secretary: Phil Noot, 18 Glebe Road, Chalfont St. Peter, Bucks. Tel: 0753 886702
Press Officer: Peter Tenconi, 65 Francis Road, Harrow, Middx HA1 2RA. Tel: 01–861 1265 (H), 01–422 3434 (W)
Club captain (1988–89): Laurence Seabridge
Club captain (1989–90): Andy Miller
No. of teams: Senior 5
Directions to ground: Close to A4140, Marsh Lane, Stanmore
Clubhouse facilities: Open matchday and evenings
Club colours: Black. (*Change colours:* Amber)
Floodlights: No
Membership fees: Full £15, Playing £15, Social £15, Youth Nil
Local newspaper: Harrow Gazette
League: Middlesex 4
League position (1988–89): 4th
League playing record (1988–89): P 30, W 16, D 2, L 12, F 431, A 342

UCS OLD BOYS

UCS Playing Fields, off Ranulf Road, London NW2. Tel: 01–452 4337
Founded: 1892
Chairman: Philippe Bobroff
Secretary: Adrian G.B. Paterson, 29 Nicholas Way, Northwood, Middlesex HA6 2TR. Tel: 09274 21417 (H), 01–260 9746 (W)
Fixtures Secretary: Frank Butterworth, 74A Alexandra Road, London NW4 2RY. Tel: 01–203 4819 (H), 01–203 4819 (W)
Press Officer: Geoffrey Boxer, 19 Queens Road, Finchley N3 2AG. Tel: 01–346 7189 (H), 01–846 1402 (W)
Coach: Geoffrey Boxer/Tim Lewis
Club captain (1988–89): John Lawrence
Club captain (1989–90): T.B.A.
No. of teams: Senior 3
Directions to ground: Turn off Hendry Way into Lyndale. Ground opposite end of Lyndale in Ranulf Road (alternative access by foot at end of Farm Avenue/Hocroft Road)
Ground capacity: Standing Perimeter
Clubhouse facilities: Bar and other standard facilities
Club colours: Maroon, black and white hoops. (*Change colours:* White)
Nickname: Old Gowers (School formerly in Gower Street, London)
Floodlights: Yes (mobile ones for training)
Membership fees: Full £18, Playing £18, Social £8, Youth £4, Student £9, OAP £8 (all inclusive of Old Boys' main club sub.)
Ground admission: Nil
Local newspaper: Hampstead & Highgate Express
League: Middlesex 4
League position (1988–89): 8th
League playing record (1988–89): P 9, W 2, D 0, L 7, F 85, A 106

MIDDLESEX 5

BRITISH AIRWAYS

Concorde Centre, Crane Lodge Road, off High Street, Cranford. Tel: 01–562 0291
Chairman: James Wheeler
Secretary: Terry Bennett, 120 The Gardens, Bedfont, Middx. Tel: 01–890 2337 (H), 01–562 7123 (W)
Fixtures Secretary: Brian Gorman, 15 Gibson Court, Ditton Road, Langley, Slough. Tel: 0753 47165 (H), 01–562 7772 (W)
Press Officer: As Secretary

Coach: Phil Robert
Club captain (1988–89): Derek Marshall
Club captain (1989–90): Steve Savage
No. of teams: Senior 2
Directions to ground: Off High Street, Cranford
Club colours: Red, white, blue hoops. (*Change colours:* White)
Floodlights: No
League: Middlesex 4
League position (1988–89): 6th
League playing record (1988–89): P 8, W 3, D 0, L 5, F 129, A 134

BRUNEL UNIVERSITY

University Playing Fields, Kingston Lane, Uxbridge, Middx. Tel: Uxbridge 360558 35955.
Founded: 1959
Secretary: Hon. Secretary, RFC, Brunel University, Kingston Lane, Uxbridge, Middlesex. Tel: Uxbridge 39125.
League: Middlesex 5

GWR

Castle Bar Park, Wollisway, West Ealing, London. Tel: 01 998 7928
League Contact: Roy Sullivan, 100 Westcott Crescent, Hanwell, Middlesex. Tel: 01 575 6074
Club colours: Cardinal/black
League: Middlesex 5

HAYES (MIDDX.)

Grosvenor Playing Fields, Kingshill Avenue, Hayes, Middx. Tel: 01–845 4963
Founded: 1965
President: Andrew Murphy
Chairman: Jack Collins
Secretary: M. (Reg) Hall, 2 Fulwood Close, Church Road, Hayes, Middx. Tel: 573 7133
Fixtures Secretary: As Secretary
Club captain (1988–89): Adrian Wilkes
Club captain (1989–90): Grant Lewis
No. of teams: Senior 3, Youth 1
Directions to ground: From London via the A40 (Western Avenue) turn off at Target. Proceed down Church Road to roundabout. Cross over heading for Hayes. Turn right at first set traffic lights (Kingshill Avenue). Ground 1 mile on right
Clubhouse facilities: Includes 2 bars, large function hall plus members bar. Size 30 m × 13 m. Separate building 6 changing rooms, showers
Club colours: navy. (*Change colours:* Yellow with blue band)
Floodlights: Yes (training)
Membership fees: Full £15, Playing £15, Social £17, Youth Nil, Student Nil, OAP Nil
Programme editor: As Secretary
Local newspaper: Hayes Gazette
League: Middlesex 4
League position (1988–89): 8th
League playing record (1988–89): P 9, W 2, D 0, L 7, F 104, A 156

KODAK

The Sports Ground, Kodak Ltd., Harrow View, Harrow, Middx. Tel: 01–247 2642
Founded: 1937
President: Micheal Simmonds
Chairman: Neville Davis
Secretary: Dave Jackson, 82 Langley Way, Watford, WD7 3EF. Tel: 0923 37087 (H), 01–427 4370 ext. 22366 (W)
Fixtures Secretary: Peter Summers, 63 Ridge Lea, Hemel Hempstead, Herts. Tel: 0442 68097 (H), 01–427 4380 ext. 55634 (W)
Press Officer: Bruce Haynes, 17 Exmouth Road, S Ruislip, Middx. Tel: 01–841 4545 (H), 01–501 2266 (W)

Coach: Graham Buckingham
Club captain (1988–89): Paul Childs
Club captain (1989–90): Paul Childs
No. of teams: Senior 2
Directions to ground: Adjacent to the Kodak Factory in Harrow View, which is between the A410 and A404, running parallel to the A409 in the borough of Harrow. Nearest railway stations for British Rail and Bakerloo is Harrow & Wealdstone. Metropolitan is Harrow-on-Hill
Clubhouse facilities: Bar, shower, restaurant, multigym, sports hall
Club colours: Gold and green. (*Change colours:* Green and gold or blue)
Floodlights: Yes (partial)
League: Middlesex 5
League position (1988–89): 7th
League playing record (1988–89): P 8, W 2, D 0, L 6, F 71, A 233
Competitions won: Idris White Cup

UCH & MIDDLESEX HOSPITAL

League Contact: c/o Students Union, University College Hospital, 43-49 Huntley Street, London WC1. Tel: 01 580 7518
League: Middlesex 5

NEW SOUTHGATE

Oakleigh Road South, New Southgate, London N11 1HB. Tel: 01–368 1234 ext. 2655 or ask for Pavilion (previously Standard Telephones (New Southgate) S.T.C. R.F.C.
Founded: 1927
President: Sean Curran
Chairman: Geoffrey Anthony Potter
Secretary: David Hockey, 107 Hazelwood Lane, Palmers Green, London, N13. Tel: 01–882 5080 (H), 01–606 7321 ext. 42 (W)
Fixtures Secretary: Geoffrey Anthony Potter, 1 Arlow Road, Winchmore Hill, London N21 3JS. Tel: 01–882 1107 (H), 01–945 2722 (W)
Press Officer: Simon Stormer, 106 Mount Pleasant, Cockfosters, Barnet, Herts EN4 9HQ. Tel: 01–449 8066 (H), 01–945 4000 (W)
Coach: Stephen Oliver
Club captain (1988–89): Stephen Oliver
Club captain (1989–90): David Priddle
No. of teams: Senior 3
Directions to ground: North Circular Road to New Southgate, turn north at traffic lights into High Road, at roundabout at Turrets P.H. turn right. At next roundabout take first left, factory approx. 6 mile
Ground capacity: Standing Perimeter
Clubhouse facilities: Part of social club
Club colours: Light blue, dark blue and gold hoops. (*Change colours:* Red)
Floodlights: No
Membership fees: Full £10, Playing £10, Social £10
League: Middlesex 5
League position (1988–89): Bottom
League playing record (1988–89): P 9, W 0, D 0, L 9, F 24, A 310

ST MARYS COLLEGE

No further information available.

SOUTHALL TECHNICAL COLLEGE

Warren Park, Carlyon Road, Hayes, Middlesex. (01 573 2889)
League Contact: c/o Students Union, University College Hospital, 43-49 Huntley Street, London WC1.

Tel: 01 580 7518
Colours: Black'Orange
League: Middlesex 5

ST. NICHOLAS OLD BOYS

Either Hillingdon House Farm, Hillingdon or c/o
Ickenham Cricket Club, Ickenham
President: Oan Dothie
Chairman: Paul Brown
Secretary: Simon Byrne, 10 Savay Close, Denham,
Uxbridge, Middx. Tel: 0895 834903 (H), 0932 788888
(W)
Fixtures Secretary: Duncan Sykes, 113 Hallowell
Road, Northwood, Middx. Tel: 09274 25400 (H),
01–427 4345 (W)

Press Officer: As Secretary
Club captain (1988–89): Nick Rudd
Club captain (1989–90): Nick Rudd
No. of teams: Senior 2
Ground capacity: Standing Perimeter touchline
Clubhouse facilities: T.B.A.
Club colours: Scarlet shirts, white shorts
Nickname: 'Saints'
Floodlights: No
Membership fees: Full £20, Playing £20, Social £7.50,
Youth £7.50, Student £7.50, OAP £7.50
Ground admission: Nil
Local newspapers: Ruislip/Northwood Gazette, The
Informer, Ruislip/Pinner Recorder
League: Middlesex 5
League position (1988–89): 4th
League playing record (1988–89): P 8, W 5, D 0, L 3,
F 131, A 125

*Haringey 29 Haberdashers 7 – Middlesex 2 on 29.10.88. Max Casini (Haringey) wins
line-out ball. Photo: Mark Moody, Hornsey Journal.*

HERTFORDSHIRE LEAGUES

ONE of the country's smallest league "set-ups" sees only a total of 14 teams compete in two divisions of eight and six sides respectively and the top sections was won by Welwyn, who drew two of their seven matches and won the rest. Down go Old Ashmoleans and Royston, the former having been promoted only 12 months earlier. Hitchin (winners of all their five games) and Tring replace them, but spare a thought for De Havilland, who lost all their five games, scored only nine points and conceded 123. For Tring it was a swift rise after relegation the previous season, but it was won on points difference from St. Albans, whose differential was only two adrift of Tring!

HERTFORDSHIRE all Leagues OFFICIAL:

C. Pool, Esq.,
24 Firs Walk,
Tewin Wood,
Welwyn,
Hertfordshire   (H) 043879
AL6 0NZ   (O) 01 609 8004

TABLES 1987–88

HERTFORDSHIRE 1

	P	W	D	L	F	A	PTS
Hemel Hempstead	7	5	0	2	124	5	10
O Elizabethans	7	5	0	2	79	53	10
Barnet	7	5	0	2	85	68	10
O Verulamians	7	5	0	2	78	63	10
Welwyn	7	3	0	4	83	69	6
Harpenden	7	3	0	4	91	83	6
Stevenage	7	2	0	5	62	82	4
Traing	7	0	0	7	39	174	0

HERTFORDSHIRE 2

	P	W	D	L	F	A	PTS
O Ashmolians	6	5	0	1	95	43	10
Royston	6	5	0	1	64	41	10
St. Albans	6	4	0	2	90	54	8
Hitchin	6	3	0	3	49	82	6
Watford	6	3	0	3	49	82	6
Datchworth	6	1	0	5	33	82	2
East Herts Coll	6	0	0	6	19	87	0

Hatfield Poly withdrawn – all matches void

TABLES 1988–89

HERTFORDSHIRE 1

Welwyn	7	5	2	0	112	45	12
Barnet	7	5	0	2	99	43	10
Harpenden	7	4	1	2	105	31	9
O Verulamians	7	4	1	2	81	54	9
Stevenage	7	3	1	3	73	79	7
O Elizabethans	7	2	1	4	44	34	5
O Ashmolians	7	2	0	5	43	104	4
Royston	7	0	0	7	46	212	0

HERTFORDSHIRE 2

	P	W	D	L	F	A	PTS
Hitchin	5	5	0	0	86	30	10
Tring	5	3	0	2	72	46	6
St. Albans	5	3	0	2	66	42	6
Datchworth	5	2	0	3	60	36	4
Watford	5	2	0	3	58	74	4
De Havilland	5	0	0	5	9	123	06

LONDON & SOUTH EAST DIVISION FIXTURES 1989/90

HERTFORDSHIRE LEAGUE ONE

Sat. 14th October (Week 6)
Barnet v Tring
Hitchin v Old Elizabethans
Old Verulamians v Letchworth
Stevenage v Harpenden

Sat. 28th October (Week 8)
Barnet v Old Elizabethans
Old Verulamians v Hitchin
Letchworth v Stevenage
Tring v Harpenden

Sat. 11th November (Week 10)
Old Elizabethans v Tring
Hitchin v Barnet
Stevenage v Old Verulamians
Letchworth v Harpenden

Sat. 25th November (Week 12)
Old Verulamians v Old Elizabethans
Letchworth v Hitchin
Tring v Stevenage
Harpenden v Barnet

Sat. 27th January (Week 20)
Hitchin v Tring
Old Elizabethans v Letchworth
Barnet v Stevenage
Harpenden v Old Verulamians

Sat. 10th February (Week 22)
Barnet v Old Verulamians
Stevenage v Hitchin
Tring v Letchworth
Old Elizabethans v Harpenden

Sat. 24th February (Week 24)
Old Verulamians v Tring
Letchworth v Barnet
Stevenage v Old Elizabethans
Harpenden v Hitchin

HERTFORDSHIRE LEAGUE TWO 1989/90

Sat. 14th October (Week 6)
Old Ashmoleans v Royston
Watford v St. Albans

Sat. 28th October (Week 8)
St. Albans v Old Ashmoleans
Watford v Datchworth

Sat. 11th November (Week 10)
Royston v St. Albans
Old Ashmoleans v Datchworth

Sat. 18th November (Week 11)
Watford v Old Ashmoleans
Datchworth v Royston

Sat. 25th November (Week 12)
St. Albans v Datchworth
Royston v Watford

Sat. 13th January (Week 18)
Royston v Old Ashmoleans
St. Albans v Watford
De Havilland v Datchworth

Sat. 27th January (Week 20)
Old Ashmoleans v St. Albans
Datchworth v Watford

Sat. 10th February (Week 22)
St. Albans v Royston
Datchworth v Old Ashmoleans

Sat. 24th February (Week 24)
Old Ashmoleans v Watford
Royston v Datchworth

Sat. 10th March (Week 26)
Datchworth v St. Albans
Watford v Royston

BARNET
Byng Road, Barnet, Herts. Tel: 01–449 0040
Founded: 1919
President: Michael Tant
Chairman: Christopher Pool
Secretary: Maurice Martin, 20 North Mount, 1147/61
High Road, Whetstone, London N20 0PH. Tel:
01–446 4401 (H), 01–359 0242 (W)
Fixtures Secretary: Peter Glenister, 47 Bury Lane,
Codicote, Herts. Tel: 0438 820 692 (H)
Press Officer: Peter Ingram, 12 Birch Tree Walk,
Nascot Wood, Watford, Herts. Tel: 0923 36887
Club captain (1988–89): Nick Allen
Club captain (1989–90): Nick Allen
Clubhouse facilities: Bar
Club colours: Navy blue and claret. (*Change colours:*
Claret)
Nickname: B's
Floodlights: Yes (training only)
Membership fees: Playing £30, VPs £5, Youth £12.50,
Student £12.50
Local newspapers: Barnet Press, Barnet Borough
Times
League: London/Herts 1
League position (1988–89): 2nd

HARPENDEN
Redbourn Lane, Harpenden, Herts. Tel: 0582 460711
Founded: 1921
President: Vivian Jenkins
Chairman: Peter Danby
Secretary: Mike Aldous-Ball, 4 Wells Close,
Harpenden, Herts. Tel: 0582 461527
Fixtures Secretary: Geoff Dignum, 5 Linden Court,
Milton Road, Harpenden, Herts. Tel: 05827 62623
Press Officer: Andy Kiff, 12 Old School Walk, Slip
End, Beds. Tel: Luton 457143 (H), 0442 230033 (W)
Coach: John Kirby
Club captain (1988–89): Alistair Crick
Club captain (1989–90): Colin Hiom
No. of teams: Senior 5, Youth 4, Minis 5
Directions to ground: B487 off A1081 (was A6) to
Redbourn. Club 1 mile from A1081. B487 off A5183
(was A5) to Harpenden. Club mile from A5183
Ground capacity: Seating 250, Standing 2000
Clubhouse facilities: Bar, TV room, snug bar, main
clubroom
Club colours: Brown shirts, white shorts
Nickname: Harps
Floodlights: Yes
Membership fees: Playing £31.80, Social £5 min.,
Student £7.20
Local newspapers: S. Harpenden Herald, Harpenden
Review
League: Herts 1
League position (1988–89): 3rd
League playing record (1988–89): P 7, W 4, D 1, L 2,
F 105, A 32

HITCHIN
King George V Fields, Old Hale Way, Hitchin, Herts.
Tel: Hitchin 32679
Founded: 1954
President: H. Sanderson
Chairman: J. Drew
Secretary: C. McDonald, 9 Claymore Drive,
Ickleford, Hitchin, Herts. Tel: Hitchin 55595 (H),
Stevenage 754313 (W)
Fixtures Secretary: J. Humphries, 32 West Hill,
Hitchin, Herts. Tel: Hitchin 32994
Press Officer: T.B.A.
Coach: T.B.A.
Club captain (1988–89): P. Newman
Club captain (1989–90): T.B.A.
No. of teams: Senior 5, Minis 3
Directions to ground: At Angels Reply PH on A600
north side of Hitchin, turn into Bearton Road, second

left into Old Hale Way, turn into ground by phonebox
Clubhouse facilities: Open matchdays, Sunday lunch,
Tuesday and Thursday evenings
Club colours: Maroon and white shorts. (*Change
colours:* Blue with red band)
Nickname: Hedgehogs
Floodlights: No
Membership fees: Playing £25, Social £5, Youth £5,
Match Fee £3
Local newspapers: Hitchin Gazette, Herald, Comet,
Express
League: Herts 1
League position (1988–89): 1st (promoted)
League playing record (1988–89): P 8, W 8, D 0, L 0
Competitions won: Herts Division 2 Winners. St.
Albans 15-a-Side

LETCHWORTH GARDEN CITY
Baldock Road, Letchworth, Herts. Tel: 0462 682554
Founded: 1924
President: J.M. Procter
Chairman: Roger Firth
Secretary: R.K. Howman, 21 London Road, Hitchin,
Herts SG4 9ET. Tel: 0462 33113 (H), 0462 52655 (W)
Fixtures Secretary: Chris Priestley, 88 Cowslip Hill,
Letchworth, Herts. Tel: 01–629 0209 (W)
Press Officer: As Secretary
Coach: T.B.A.
Club captain (1988–89): Rupert Howman
Club captain (1989–90): Graham Walker
No. of teams: Senior 5, Youth 4, Minis 4
Directions to ground: Turn off A1 to Letchworth, turn
right at A505 to Baldock, turn right at mini
roundabout
Ground capacity: Standing 2000
Clubhouse facilities: Open matchdays and Thursdays
Club colours: Black and amber. (*Change colours:*
Black)
Floodlights: No
Membership fees: Full £15, Playing £35, Junior £4
Ground admission: Nil
Local newspapers: Herts Gazette, The Comet
League: Herts 1
League position (1988–89): 9th (relegated)
League playing record (1988–89): P 10, W 3, D 1,
L 6, F 117, A 171

OLD ELIZABETHANS (BARNET)
Gipsy Corner, Mays Lane, Barnet, Tel: 01-449 9481
Founded:1935
President: R.D. Parker
Chairman: P.G. Yates (0707 44046)
Coach: I. Whitefield
Secretary: N.A. Ward, 82 Barnet Road, Potters Bar,
Herts. Tel: 0707 58066.
Fixtures Secretary: B.J. Fuller, 109 Margaret Road,
New Barnet, Herts. Tel: 04 449 0590.
Club captain (1988–89): K. Watt
Club captain (1989–90): K. Watt
No. of teams: Senior 4. Youth 1.
Directions to ground: From A1 take A411 towards
Barnet Ground on left 1 mile.
Club colours: Light and dark blue hooped shirts.
Nickname: O E's
Floodlights: Yes, training only
Membership fees: £22.50
Programme editor: As Fixtures Secretary
Local newspapers: Barnet Press

OLD VERULAMIAN
Cotlandswick, A405 St. Albans, Herts. Tel: 0727
22929
Founded: 1948
President: Douglas V. Hobbs
Chairman: Alan Radford

Secretary: Max C.D. Schroeder, 15 Hopground Close, St. Albans, Herts AL1 5TA. Tel: 0727 67791 (H), 01–726 4050 (W)
Fixtures Secretary: H. Grey, 48 Parkfield Crescent, Kimpton, Herts SG4 8EQ. Tel: 0438 832714 (H), 01–377 8644 (W)
Press Officer: Nigel Nicholls, 34 Colney Heath Lane, St. Albans, Herts AL4 0TY. Tel: 0727 41710 (H), 0727 41710 (W)
Coach: I.R. Graham
Club captain (1988–89): P. Halford
Club captain (1989–90): A. Merrifield
No. of teams: Senior 6, Youth 1, Minis 1
Directions to ground: On A405 200 m on left from London Colney roundabout towards M10 beginning on the south side of St. Albans
Clubhouse facilities: Main room, bar, snug, bath/showers/changing facilities
Club colours: Royal blue, yellow 'V', white shorts. (*Change colours:* Red or white)
Nickname: Old Vees
Floodlights: No
Membership fees: Full £30, Playing £30, Social £7.50, Student £10, Schoolboys Nil
Programme: No. of editorial pages 4; No. of advertising pages 17; Price Nil
Programme editor: Nigel Nicholls/Max Schroeder, 34 Colney Heath Lane, St. Albans, Herts AL4 0TY. Tel: 0727 41710 (H), 0727 41710 (W)
Local newspapers: Herts Advertiser, Review, Observer, Herald
League: Herts 1
League position (1988–89): 4th
League playing record (1988–89): P 7, W 4, D 1, L 2, F 81, A 55
Competitions won: Herts Over-35 Champions, March '89. Bedfordshire Over-35 Runners-Up, April '89

STEVENAGE
North Road, Stevenage, Hertfordshire. Tel: 0438 359788
Founded: 1955
President: Malcolm Gomm
Chairman: Paul Cowley
Secretary: Mike Curtin, 212 Chertsey Rise, Stevenage, Hertfordshire ST2 9JD. Tel: 0438 359605 (H), 312981 (W)
Fixtures Secretary: Robert Howe, 64 Hillcrest, Baldock, Hertfordshire. Tel: 0462 893834 (H), 0860 274380 (W)
Press Officer: David Aylett, 127 Lonsdale Road, Stevenage. Tel: 0438 316547 (H), 01–276 6875 (W)
Coach: David Jancey
Club captain (1988–89): David Parry
Club captain (1989–90): David Parry
No. of teams: Senior 4, Youth 1
Directions to ground: Leave A1(M) at Stevenage North roundabout, take Graveley Road, turn right 50 yds past entrance to garden centre. Rugby Club ¼ mile on right
Ground capacity: Standing 500
Clubhouse facilities: Lounge bar, hall and bar, kitchen, meeting room, changing rooms
Club colours: Broad green hoops with narrow gold hoops, green socks, black shorts. (*Change colours:* Red shirts)
Floodlights: Yes (full pitch)
League: Herts 1
League position (1988–89): 5th
League playing record (1988–89): P 3, W 3, D 1, L 3, F 73, A 79

TRING
Pendley, Cow Lane, Tring, Herts. Tel: Tring 5710.
Founded: 1965
President: S. Wallis
Chairman: C. Armstrong
Coach: M. Walters
Secretary: K. Boniface, 36 Millview Road, Tring. Tel: Tring 5053.

Fixtures Secretary: D. Clarke, 39 Chiltern Way, Tring. Tel: Tring 3753
Club captain (1987–88): M. Fountain
Club captain (1988–89): M. Fountain
No. of teams: Senior 5. Youth & Minis 9.
Directions to Ground: Cow Lane off A41 south side of Tring.
Clubhouse: New clubhouse opened 1986.
Colours: Black and gold hoops. (*Change colours:* Black).
Floodlights: No
Membership: £25 Playing, £5 Social
Local newspaper: Tring & Berkhamsted Gazette
League: Herts 2

DATCHWORTH
Datchworth Green, Datchworth, Herts. Tel: 0438 812490
President: David Clark
Chairman: David Clark
Secretary: Anthony James Woodward, 4 The Cottages, Lemsford, Nr. W.G.C., Herts. Tel: 0707 372336 (H), 0438 356101 (W)
Fixtures Secretary: Philip Nightingale. Tel: 0438 820500
Press Officer: angus Waft, 25 Deards End Lane, Knebworth, Herts. Tel: 0438 813240
Coach: Dick Stabler
Club captain (1988–89): Graham Smith
Club captain (1989–90): Richard Holt
No. of teams: Senior 4, Youth 4, Minis 6
Directions to ground: From south A1(M) to Welwyn exit. Take B194 towards Knebworth, at Woolmer Green turn right to Datchworth
Club colours: Green shirts and socks, black shorts
Floodlights: Yes
League: London & SE/Herts 2
League position (1988–89): 4th
League playing record (1988–89): P 33, W 18, D 2, L 13, F 475, A 370

DE HAVILLAND
(Hatfield)
The De Havilland (Hatfield) Sports & Social Club, British Aerospace, Comet Way, Hatfield, Herts. Tel: 07072 62665
League Contact: K.J. Tume, 100 Lords Wood, Welwyn Garden City, Herts. AL7 2HG. Tel: 0707 321655
Club colours: Black/amber/white
League: Herts 2

OLD ASHMOLEAN
Ashmole School, Burleigh Gardens, Southgate N14. Tel: 01–368 4984 (Sports Hall)
Founded: 1961
President: A. Seagroatt
Chairman: A. Seagroatt
Secretary: J. Byrne, 85A Burford Gardens, Palmers Green, London N13 4LR. Tel: 01–886 5995
Fixtures Secretary: As Secretary
Press Officer: F. Colborne, 15 Calton Road, Barnet, Hertfordshire. Tel: 01–449 1921
Coach: D. Perks
Club captain (1988–89): N. Harper
Club captain (1989–90): D. Perks
No. of teams: Senior 3
Directions to ground: At the roundabout at Southgate Underground Station turn into Ashfield Parade, bear right into Burleigh Gardens. School first left
Clubhouse facilities: Share with local tennis club. Open matchdays and training nights
Club colours: Scarlet/emerald hoops. (*Change colours:* Black)

Floodlights: Yes (training only)
Membership fees: Full £30, Playing £30, Social £6, Youth £6, Student £6
Local newspaper: Barnet Press
League: Herts 1
League position (1988–89): 7th
League playing record (1988–89): P 7, W 2, D 0, L 5, F 43, A 104

ROYSTON

Royston Sporting Club, Therfield Heath, Baldock Road, Royston. Tel: 0763 243613
Founded: 1961
President: Barry Dickins
Chairman: Eric Trim
Secretary: Keith Brown, 22 Walnut Tree Close, Bassingbourn, Royston, Herts. Tel: Royston 246057 (H), Letchworth 686500 ext. 2217 (W)
Fixtures Secretary: Godfrey Everett, 24 Clarkes Way, Bassingbourn, Royston Herts SG8 5LT. Tel: 0763 243846 (H), 255161 ext. 3445 (W)
Press Officer: Geoff Anderson, 8 Keats Close, Royston. Tel: Royston 244983
Coach: T.B.A.
Club captain (1988–89): Paul Pousland
Club captain (1989–90): Jamie Johnson
No. of teams: Senior 3–4, Youth 1
Directions to ground: On s. side of Baldock Road, mile w. of Royston town centre on Therfield Heath
Ground capacity: Standing Ample
Clubhouse facilities: Open evenings and lunchtime at weekends
Club colours: Black and white hoops
Floodlights: No
Membership fees: T.B.D.
Local newspapers: Royston Crow, Cambridge Evening News
League: Herts 2
League position (1988–89): 8th (relegated)
League playing record (1988–89): P 7, W 0, D 0, L 7, F 46, A 210

ST. ALBANS

Boggymead Spring, Oaklands Lane, Smallford, St.

Albans, Herts. Tel: 0727 69945
Chairman: Robin Foley
Secretary: Redmond Lee, 10 Harefield Place, St. Albans, Herts AL4 9JQ. Tel: 0727 53727 (H), 01–283 4311 ext. 250 (W)
Fixtures Secretary: Gerald Thomas, 176 Park Street Lane, Park Street, St. Albans, Herts. Tel: 0727 73004
Press Officer: Andy Donachie, 32 Seymour Road, St. Albans, Herts. Tel: 0727 39563 (H), 01–405 6994 (W)
Coach: Mike Humphries
Club captain (1988–89): Mile Millar
Club captain (1989–90): Mike Millar
No. of teams: Senior 5, Youth 1, Ladies 1
Directions to ground: Off A1 tkae A414 to St. Albans then right off A414 at the Smallford roundabout (nr. Notcutts). From St. Albans city centre take A414 to Hatfield, left at Smallford roundabout. Entrance to ground 200 yds on left
Club colours: Bolue/gold hoops, navy blue shorts. (*Change colours:* As appropriate)
Floodlights: No (planned for 1989/90
                Membership fees: Full £25, So
ial £10, Student £12.50 (In all cases there is a late payment fee of £5)
Programme: Price Free
Programme editor: As Press Officer
Local newspapers: St. Albans Review, St. Albans Herald, St. Albans & District Observer, Herts Advertiser, Welwyn & Hatfield Express & Gazette
League: Herts 2
League position (1988–89): 3rd
League playing record (1988–89): P 33, W 11, D 0, L 22

WATFORD

Knutsford Playing Fields, Radlett Road, Watford, Herts. Tel: 0923 43292.
Founded: 1973
Secretary: R.S. Tatford, 73 Buttermere Place, Linden Lea, Leavesden, Watford, Herts WD1 7DW. Tel: 0923 661088 (H). 0582 420613 (W).
League: Hertfordshire 2

EASTERN COUNTIES LEAGUES

AN EXTRA league was added for the season just ended and this meant that a total of 61 sides took part with a further four being admitted for the new season – Burnham, Essex Police, Broadland and Mistley.

From Eastern Counties 1 Harlow (champions) and Romford and Gidea Park ended on the same number of points having lost one match each with the former having a better goal difference, whilst at the foot of the table Lowestoft and Yarmouth could win only one game and are the only team to descend with Old Edwardians (a draw being their only blot in a 10 match programme) and Braintree being promoted; Old Edwardians also won promotion the previous season and have a draw from that season as their only other blemish, so when will they lose their first league match?

Thetford – with only a draw in their programme – go down for a second successive season and have yet to win a league match, but in Eastern Counties 4 Bancrofts did lose a first league game in two seasons without the set-back halting the promotion progress started last season; Old Brentwoods accompany them – albeit on points difference from Old Palmerians. Chigwell are the unlucky team to be relegated and their replacements from League 5 are The London Hospital and Loughton with Sawston descending.

The new Eastern Counties 6 sees three teams go up – Thames Sports, Ongar and Billericay – whilst Orwell – allocated to the new division at the start of the season – "broke their duck" and won their first game, but still ended up in last place. This is where the Olympic spirit of taking part must be invoked with best wishes for improved fortune.

EASTERN COUNTIES LEAGUES ONE, TWO & THREE: OFFICER

M.J. Stott, Esq.,
Brick Kiln Farm,
North Walsham,
Norfolk   (H) 0692 403096

TABLES 1987–88

EASTERN COUNTIES 1

	P	W	D	L	F	A	PTS
Met. Police, Chig	10	9	1	0	157	62	19
Cambridge	10	9	0	1	223	72	18
Romford & G Pk	10	8	1	1	167	46	17
Harlow	10	6	0	4	322	110	12
Rochford	10	5	0	5	99	87	10
Lowe & Yar	10	4	0	6	100	129	8
Crusaders	10	4	0	6	99	174	8
Shelford	10	3	0	7	111	150	6
Redbridge	10	3	0	7	102	175	6
Ely	10	3	0	7	69	202	6
Thetford	10	0	0	10	45	292	0

EASTERN COUNTIES 2

	P	W	D	L	F	A	PTS
Basildon	10	8	2	0	189	66	18
Canvey Is	10	8	0	2	140	107	16
Chelmsford	10	7	0	3	168	98	14
P.L.A.	10	5	3	2	105	90	13
Braintree	10	5	2	3	132	115	12
Upminster	10	4	2	4	99	94	10
Wanstead	10	5	0	5	87	117	10
Woodbridge	10	4	1	5	137	144	9
East London	10	3	0	7	92	85	6
Diss	10	1	0	9	65	171	0

EASTERN COUNTIES LEAGUES FOUR, FIVE & SIX:

M. Tuck, Esq.,
51 Highfield Road,
Billericay,
Essex CM11 2PE   (H) 0277 655483

TABLES 1988–89

EASTERN COUNTIES 1

	P	W	D	L	F	A	PTS
Harlow	10	9	0	1	247	55	18
Romford & G Pk	10	9	0	1	194	50	18
Canvey Is	10	7	0	3	314	61	14
Basildon	10	7	0	3	116	142	14
Shelford	10	6	0	4	150	113	12
Ely	10	5	0	5	106	131	10
Rochford	10	3	1	6	77	161	7
Crusaders	10	3	0	7	77	169	6
Redbridge	10	2	1	7	69	275	5
Bury St. Eds	10	2	0	8	81	132	4
Lowe & Yar	10	1	0	9	85	227	2

EASTERN COUNTIES 2

	P	W	D	L	F	A	PTS
O Edwardians	10	9	1	0	274	65	19
Braintree	10	8	1	1	232	61	17
Diss	10	6	0	4	111	138	12
Wanstead	10	5	1	4	91	112	11
Chelmsford	10	5	0	5	125	80	10
Port of Lon A	10	4	2	4	139	111	10
Upminster	10	5	0	5	119	168	10
Woodbridge	10	4	1	5	154	108	9
S Wood Ferrers	10	4	1	5	72	121	9
East London	10	1	0	9	70	189	2
Thetford	10	0	1	9	65	299	1

EASTERN COUNTIES 3

	P	W	D	L	F	A	PTS
O Edwardians	10	9	1	0	320	74	19
S Wood Ferrers	10	7	0	3	184	76	14
Holt	10	7	0	3	148	87	14
Newmarket	10	7	0	3	125	64	14
Maldon	10	6	0	4	163	102	12
Wymondham	10	4	9	6	142	125	8
Beccles	10	4	0	6	48	152	7
Wisbech	10	3	1	6	48	152	7
Harwich & Dov	10	3	0	7	83	145	6
Lakenham-Hew	10	3	0	7	99	179	6
Southwold	10	0	0	10	48	330	0

EASTERN COUNTIES 4

	P	W	D	L	F	A	PTS
Campion	10	9	0	1	421	34	18
O Bealonians	10	8	1	1	211	60	17
Stowmarket	10	8	0/				
			1N/				
			2	170	81	16	
O Palmerians	10	6	1	3	171	123	13
Gothic**	10	6	0	4	169	137	10
Fakenham	10	5	0	5	78	167	10
Felixstowe	10	3	1	6	141	165	7
NELPOB	10	2	1	7	56	251	5
Mayf'd OB*	9	3	0	6	121	184	4
Clacton	10	2	0	8	98	182	4
Rayleigh**	9	0	0	9	19	271	2

**2 championship points deducted – breach of rules.

EASTERN COUNTIES 5

	P	W	D	L	F	A	PTS
Bancroft	11	11	0	0	447	35	22
O Brentwoods	11	10	0	1	327	80	20
London Hos	11	9	0	2	408	75	18
Dereham	11	6	1	4	242	226	13
March	11	6	0	5	171	202	12
Haverhill	11	5	0	6	154	144	10
Thurston	11	4	1	6	135	189	9
Loughton	11	4	0	7	156	199	8
Swaffham	11	4	0	7	136	192	8
Norwich Union	11	3	0	8	106	263	6
Sawston	11	3	0	8	86	307	6
Orwell	11	0	0	11	42	498	0

EASTERN COUNTIES 3

	P	W	D	L	F	A	PTS
Campion	10	9	1	0	289	64	19
Maldon	10	8	1	1	201	88	17
O Bealonians	10	8	0	2	174	85	16
Wymondham	10	6	0	4	140	91	12
Beccles	10	5	0	5	138	108	10
Newmarket	10	5	0	5	125	102	10
Holt	10	5	0	5	123	119	10
Ilford Wand	10	5	0	5	89	119	10
Harwich & Dov	10	2	0	8	111	201	4
Lakenham Hew	10	1	0	9	33	156	2
Wisbech	10	0	0	10	20	310	0

EASTERN COUNTIES 4

	P	W	D	L	F	A	PTS
Bancroft	10	9	0	1	412	74	18
O Brentwoods	10	9	0	1	183	73	18
O Palmerians	10	8	0	2	190	121	16
Mayfield OB	10	6	0	4	171	135	12
Clacton	10	6	0	4	122	110	12
Felixstowe	10	6	0	4	153	160	12
Stowmarket	10	2	2	6	78	137	6
Fakenham	10	2	1	7	88	185	5
Southwold	10	2	1	7	111	253	3
Gothic	10	2	0	8	92	202	4
Chigwell**	10	1	0	9	34	184	0

** = 2 championship points deducted – rule violation.

EASTERN COUNTIES 5

	P	W	D	L	F	A	PTS
London Hos	8	7	0	1	282	604	14
Loughton	8	6	0	2	164	104	12
Dereham	8	6	0	2	132	93	12
March	8	5	0	3	97	89	10
Haverhill	8	4	0	4	138	109	8
Thurston	8	4	0	4	78	109	8
Swaffham	8	2	0	6	96	137	4
Norwich U	8	2	0	6	83	157	4
Sawston	8	0	0	8	26	238	0

Rayleigh Wyverns withdrew

EASTERN COUNTIES 6

	P	W	D	L	F	A	PTS
Thames Sports	7	6	1	0	203	49	13
Ongar	7	6	0	1	206	26	12
Billericay	7	5	0	2	124	50	10
O Cooperians	7	4	0	3	78	52	8
Witham	7	2	2	3	59	72	6
Hadleigh	7	1	1	5	57	120	3
Brightlingsea	7	1	0	6	40	143	2
Orwell	7	1	0	6	28	283	2

LONDON & SOUTH EAST DIVISION FIXTURES 1989/90

EASTERN COUNTIES LEAGUE ONE

Sat. 23rd September (Week 4)
Ipswich Y.M.C.A. v Bury St. Edmunds
Canvey Island v Braintree
Ely v Shelford
Old Edwardians v Crusaders
Basildon v Rochford

Sat. 14th October (Week 6)
Rochford v Ipswich Y.M.C.A.
Crusaders v Basildon
Shelford v Old Edwardians
Braintree v Ely
Redbridge v Canvey Island

Sat. 28th October (Week 8)
Ipswich Y.M.C.A. v Crusaders
Bury St. Edmunds v Rochford
Ely v Redbridge
Old Edwardians v Braintree
Basildon v Shelford

Sat. 11th November (Week 10)
Crusaders v Bury St. Edmunds
Shelford v Ipswich Y.M.C.A.
Braintree v Basildon
Redbridge v Old Edwardians
Canvey Island v Ely

Sat 18th November (Week 11)
Ipswich Y.M.C.A. v Braintree
Bury St. Edmunds v Shelford
Rochford v Crusaders
Old Edwardians v Canvey Island
Basildon v Redbridge

Sat. 25th November (Week 12)
Shelford v Rochford
Braintree v Bury St. Edmunds
Redbridge v Ipswich Y.M.C.A.
Canvey Island v Basildon
Ely v Old Edwardians

Sat. 13th January (Week 18)
Ipswich Y.M.C.A. v Canvey Island
Bury St. Edmunds v Redbridge
Rochford v Braintree
Crusaders v Shelford
Basildon v Ely

Sat. 27th January (Week 20)
Braintree v Crusaders
Redbridge v Rochford
Canvey Island v Bury St. Edmunds
Ely v Ipswich Y.M.C.A.
Old Edwardians v Basildon

Sat. 10th February (Week 22)
Ipswich Y.M.C.A. v Old Edwardians
Bury St. Edmunds v Ely
Rochford v Canvey Island
Crusaders v Redbridge
Shelford v Braintree

Sat. 24th February (Week 24)
Redbridge v Shelford
Canvey Island v Crusaders
Ely v Rochford
Old Edwardians v Bury St. Edmunds
Basildon v Ipswich Y.M.C.A.

Sat. 10th March (Week 26)
Bury St. Edmunds v Basildon
Rochford v Old Edwardians
Crusaders v Ely
Shelford v Canvey Island
Braintree v Redbridge

LONDON & SOUTH EAST DIVISION FIXTURES 1989/90

EASTERN COUNTIES LEAGUE TWO

Sat. 23rd September (Week 4)
Diss v Lowestoft & Yar.
Maldon v P.L.A.
East London v Upminster
Wanstead v South Woodham Ferrers
Campion v Woodbridge

Sat. 14th October (Week 6)
Woodbridge v Diss
South Woodham Ferrers v Campion
Upminster v Wanstead
P.L.A. v East London
Chelmsford v Maldon

Sat. 28th October (Week 8)
Diss v South Woodham Ferrers
Lowestoft & Yar. v Woodbridge
East London v Chelmsford
Wanstead v P.L.A.
Campion v Upminster

Sat. 11th November (Week 10)
South Woodham Ferrers v Lowestoft & Yar.
Upminster v Diss
P.L.A. v Campion
Chelmsford v Wanstead
Maldon v East London

Sat 18th November (Week 11)
Diss v P.L.A.
Lowestoft & Yar. v Upminster
Woodbridge v South Woodham Ferrers
Wanstead v Maldon
Campion v Chelmsford

Sat. 25th November (Week 12)
Upminster v Woodbridge
P.L.A. v Lowestoft & Yar.
Chelmsford v Diss
Maldon v Campion
East London v Wanstead

Sat. 13th January (Week 18)
Diss v Maldon
Lowestoft & Yar. v Chelmsford
Woodbridge v P.L.A.
South Woodham Ferrers v Upminster
Campion v East London

Sat. 27th January (Week 20)
P.L.A. v South Woodham Ferrers
Chelmsford v Woodbridge
Maldon v Lowestoft & Yar.
East London v Diss
Wanstead v Campion

Sat. 10th February (Week 22)
Diss v Wanstead
Lowestoft & Yar. v East London
Woodbridge v Maldon
South Woodham Ferrers v Chelmsford
Upminster v P.L.A.

Sat. 24th February (Week 24)
Chelmsford v Upminster
Maldon v South Woodham Ferrers
East London v Woodbridge
Wanstead v Lowestoft & Yar.
Campion v Diss

Sat. 10th March (Week 26)
Lowestoft & Yar. v Campion
Woodbridge v Wanstead
South Woodham Ferrers v East London
Upminster v Maldon
P.L.A. v Chelmsford

LONDON & SOUTH EAST DIVISION FIXTURES 1989/90

EASTERN COUNTIES LEAGUE THREE

Sat. 23rd September (Week 4)
Bancrofts v Old Brentwoods
Thetford v Harwich & Dover't
Wymondham v Lakenham Hewett
Holt v Ilford Wanderers
Beccles v Old Bealonians

Sat. 14th October (Week 6)
Old Bealonians v Bancrofts
Ilford Wanderers v Beccles
Lakenham Hewett v Holt
Harwich & Dover't v Wymondham
Newmarket v Thetford

Sat. 28th October (Week 8)
Bancrofts v Ilford Wanderers
Old Brentwoods v Old Bealonians
Wymondham v Newmarket
Holt v Harwich & Dover't
Beccles v Lakenham Hewett

Sat. 11th November (Week 10)
Ilford Wanderers v Old Brentwoods
Lakenham Hewett v Bancrofts
Harwich & Dover't v Beccles
Newmarket v Holt
Thetford v Wymondham

Sat 18th November (Week 11)
Bancrofts v Harwich & Dover't
Old Brentwoods v Lakenham Hewett
Old Bealonians v Ilford Wanderers
Holt v Thetford
Beccles v Newmarket

Sat. 25th November (Week 12)
Lakenham Hewett v Old Bealonians
Harwich & Dover't v Old Brentwoods
Newmarket v Bancrofts
Thetford v Beccles
Wymondham v Holt

Sat. 13th January (Week 18)
Bancrofts v Thetford
Old Brentwoods v Newmarket
Old Bealonians v Harwich & Dover't
Ilford Wanderers v Lakenham Hewett
Beccles v Wymondham

Sat. 27th January (Week 20)
Harwich & Dover't v Ilford Wanderers
Newmarket v Old Bealonians
Thetford v Old Brentwoods
Wymondham v Bancrofts
Holt v Beccles

Sat. 10th February (Week 22)
Bancrofts v Holt
Old Brentwoods v Wymondham
Old Bealonians v Thetford
Ilford Wanderers v Newmarket
Lakenham Hewett v Harwich & Dover't

Sat. 24th February (Week 24)
Newmarket v Lakenham Hewett
Thetford v Ilford Wanderers
Wymondham v Old Bealonians
Holt v Old Brentwoods
Beccles v Bancrofts

Sat. 10th March (Week 26)
Old Brentwoods v Beccles
Old Bealonians v Holt
Ilford Wanderers v Wymondham
Lakenham Hewett v Thetford
Harwich & Dover't v Newmarket

LONDON & SOUTH EAST DIVISION FIXTURES 1989/90

EASTERN COUNTIES LEAGUE FOUR

Sat. 23rd September (Week 4)
Wisbech v Southwold
Mayfield Old Boys v Felixstowe
Loughton v Stowmarket
London Hospital v Clacton

Sat. 14th October (Week 6)
Stowmarket v London Hospital
Felixstowe v Loughton
Southwold v Mayfield Old Boys
Old Palmerians v Wisbech

Sat. 28th October (Week 8)
Fakenham v Clacton
Mayfield Old Boys v Old Palmerians
Loughton v Southwold
London Hospital v Felixstowe

Sat. 11th November (Week 10)
Stowmarket v Fakenham
Southwold v London Hospital
Old Palmerians v Loughton
Wisbech v Mayfield Old Boys

Sat 18th November (Week 11)
Fakenham v Felixstowe
Clacton v Stowmarket
Loughton v Wisbech
London Hospital v Old Palmerians

Sat. 25th November (Week 12)
Felixstowe v Clacton
Southwold v Fakenham
Wisbech v London Hospital
Mayfield Old Boys v Loughton

Sat. 13th January (Week 18)
Fakenham v Old Palmerians
Clacton v Southwold
Stowmarket v Felixstowe
London Hospital v Mayfield Old Boys

Sat. 27th January (Week 20)
Southwold v Stowmarket
Old Palmerians v Clacton
Wisbech v Fakenham
Loughton v London Hospital

Sat. 10th February (Week 22)
Fakenham v Mayfield Old Boys
Clacton v Wisbech
Stowmarket v Old Palmerians
Felixstowe v Southwold

Sat. 24th February (Week 24)
Old Palmerians v Felixstowe
Wisbech v Stowmarket
Mayfield Old Boys v Clacton
Loughton v Fakenham

Sat. 10th March (Week 26)
Fakenham v London Hospital
Clacton v Loughton
Stowmarket v Mayfield Old Boys
Felixstowe v Wisbech
Southwold v Old Palmerians

LONDON & SOUTH EAST DIVISION FIXTURES 1989/90

EASTERN COUNTIES LEAGUE FIVE

Sat. 14th October (Week 6)
Norwich Union v Dereham
Thurston v Chigwell
Thames Sports v March
Ongar v Swaffham
Billericay v Haverhill

Sat. 28th October (Week 8)
Swaffham v Norwich Union
Haverhill v Thurston
Chigwell v Thames Sports
March v Ongar
Billericay v Dereham

Sat. 11th November (Week 10)
Thames Sports v Haverhill
Norwich Union v March
Dereham v Swaffham
Thurston v Billericay
Ongar v Chigwell

Sat 18th November (Week 11)
Haverhill v Ongar
Swaffham v Billericay
March v Dereham
Chigwell v Norwich Union
Thurston v Thames Sports

Sat. 25th November (Week 12)
Ongar v Thurston
Billericay v Thames Sports
Norwich Union v Haverhill
Dereham v Chigwell
Swaffham v March

Sat. 27th January (Week 20)
Billericay v March
Thames Sports v Ongar
Chigwell v Swaffham
Haverhill v Dereham
Thurston v Norwich Union

Sat. 10th February (Week 22)
Ongar v Billericay
Norwich Union v Thames Sports
Dereham v Thurston
Swaffham v Haverhill
March v Chigwell

Sat. 24th February (Week 24)
Chigwell v Billericay
Haverhill v March
Thurston v Swaffham
Thames Sports v Dereham
Ongar v Norwich Union

Sat. 10th March (Week 26)
Norwich Union v Billericay
Dereham v Ongar
Swaffham v Thames Sports
March v Thurston
Chigwell v Haverhill

LONDON & SOUTH EAST DIVISION FIXTURES 1989/90

EASTERN COUNTIES LEAGUE SIX

Sat. 14th October (Week 6)
Orwell v Witham
Old Cooperians v Sawston
Broadland v Burnham Sports
Mistley v Brightlingsea
Essex Police v Hadleigh

Sat. 28th October (Week 8)
Brightlingsea v Orwell
Hadleigh v Old Cooperians
Sawston v Broadland
Burnham Sports v Mistley
Essex Police v Witham

Sat. 11th November (Week 10)
Broadland v Hadleigh
Orwell v Burnham Sports
Witham v Brightlingsea
Old Cooperians v Essex Police
Mistley v Sawston

Sat 18th November (Week 11)
Hadleigh v Mistley
Brightlingsea v Essex Police
Burnham Sports v Witham
Sawston v Orwell
Old Cooperians v Broadland

Sat. 25th November (Week 12)
Mistley v Old Cooperians
Essex Police v Broadland
Orwell v Hadleigh
Witham v Sawston
Brightlingsea v Burnham Sports

Sat. 27th January (Week 20)
Essex Police v Burnham Sports
Broadland v Mistley
Sawston v Brightlingsea
Hadleigh v Witham
Old Cooperians v Orwell

Sat. 10th February (Week 22)
Mistley v Essex Police
Orwell v Broadland
Witham v Old Cooperians
Brightlingsea v Hadleigh
Burnham Sports v Sawston

Sat. 24th February (Week 24)
Sawston v Essex Police
Hadleigh v Burnham Sports
Old Cooperians v Brightlingsea
Broadland v Witham
Mistley v Orwell

Sat. 10th March (Week 26)
Orwell v Essex Police
Witham v Mistley
Brightlingsea v Broadland
Burnham Sports v Old Cooperians
Sawston v Hadleigh

EASTERN COUNTIES 1

BASILDON

The Clubhouse, Gardiner Close, Basildon, Essex.
Tel: 0268 3136
Founded: 1955
President: O.J. Knott
Chairman: S. Nash
Secretary: N. Searle, Address as above.
Fixtures Secretary: D. Dunn, 73 Brackendale
Avenue, Pitsea, Essex. Tel: 0268 554657.
Club captain (1988–89): D. Terrell
No. of teams: Senior 5. Youth & Minis 4.
Directions to Ground: Take A132 turning off the A127
in direction of Basildon. At first roundabout
turnright. Proceed to a set of traffic lights, turn right
into Gardiners Lane South. First left into Gardiners
Close and then right at the bottom of the road.
Clubhouse: Recently extended bar and clubhouse,
with 4 changing rooms and showers.
Colours: Bottle green with two white hoops.
Floodlights: Yes ⸱
Membership: £25 full membership
Local newspaper: Evening Echo
League: Eastern Counties Div 1

BRAINTREE

Recreation Field, Tabor Avenue, Braintree, Essex.
Tel: Braintree 22282.
Founded: 5th
Secretary: P. Carter, 11 Orchard Avenue, Halstead,
Essex. Tel: Halstead 473977 (H), Halstead 477261
(W).
League Contacts & Press Officer: 75 Thistley Green
Road, Braintree, Essex CM7 6SF. Tel: 0376 44334
Colours: Amber/Black
League: Eastern Counties 2

BURY ST EDMUNDS

The Haberden, Southgate Green, Bury St Edmunds.
Tel: 0284 753920
Founded: 1923
President: John Cousins
Chairman: Robert Fenner
Secretary: Peter Gair, 81A Guildhall Street, Bury St
Edmunds. Tel; 0284 767241 (H). 762331 (W)
Fixtures Secretary: Roy Lion, 2 The Gardens, Bury
Road, Beyton, Suffolk. Tel: 0359 71085
Press Officer: John Dunlea, 40 Harefield, Long
Melford, Suffolk. Tel: 0787 310701
Coach: Andrew Herlihy
Club captain (1988–89): Christopher Hamer
Club captain (1989–90): Christopher Hamer
No. of teams: Senior 4, Youth 3, Minis 3
Directions to ground: Leave A45 at Junction for Bury
South/Sudbury. Go towards town centre. Club on
right approx. 400 yards
Clubhouse facilities: Open Match days and most
evenings
Club colours: Green shirts, white shorts, green socks.
(*Change colours:* Yellow shirts)
Floodlights: Yes
Membership fees: Full £25, Playing £25, Social £5,
Youth £1, Student £1, OAP £25
Ground admission: Nil
Local newspapers: Bury Free Press, East Anglian
Daily Times
League: Eastern Counties 1
League position (1988–89): 10th
League playing record (1988–89): P 10, W 2, D 0,
L 8, F 81, A 132
Competitions won: Suffolk Plate

CANVEY ISLAND

Tewkes Creek, Dovervelt Road, Canvey Island,
Essex. Tel: 0268 681881
President: Donald Maclean

Chairman: Leonard Hymans
Secretary: Kevin Bennett, 31 South Parade, Canvey
Island, Essex SS8 7PG. Tel: 0268 684544
Fixtures Secretary: Len Hymans, 32 Devon Way,
Canvey Island, Essex. Tel: 0268 693899
Press Officer: Glen Hale, Beecroft Crescent, Canvey
Island, Essex
Club captain (1988–89): Micheal Norris
Club captain (1989–90): Micheal Norris
No. of teams: Senior 4, Youth 2
Directions to ground: A130 to Canvey from A13
Saddlers Farm second exit from roundabout past
sports centre, over small roundabout and take first left
after school
Clubhouse facilities: Bar, kitchen, showers, changing
rooms
Club colours: Scarlet and blue shirts, black shorts
Floodlights: No
Membership fees: Full £15, Playing £15, Social £9,
Youth £5, Student £5
Local newspapers: Evening Echo, Standard Recorder,
Yellow Advertiser
League: Eastern Counties 1
League position (1988–89): 3rd
League playing record (1988–89): P 10, W 7, D 0,
L 3, F 357, A 123

CRUSADERS

Beckhythe, Little Melton, Norwich, Norfolk. Tel:
0603 811157
Founded: 1962
President: Brian Wilde
Chairman: Mike Younger
Secretary: David Austin, 3 Albury Walk, Eaton,
Norwich NR4 6JE. Tel: 0603 506676 (H). 613750 (W)
Fixtures Secretary: David Williams, 6 St Johns Close,
Hethersett, Norwich, Norfolk. Tel: 0603 810679
Press Officer: Mike Bridgeman, 4 Bensley Road,
Norwich. Tel: 250926
Coach: David Lyon
Club captain (1988–89): Richard Richardson
Club captain (1989–90): Roy Watts
No. of teams: Senior 4, Youth 1
Directions to ground: Old A11 to Norwich, turn right
to Colney, going from Norwich towards Wymondham.
1st left, 1st right, 1st left, 1st left. Ground is on right
hand side
Ground capacity: Standing 400
Clubhouse facilities: Brick built, bar, 4 team changing
facilities, 2 pitches
Club colours: Green and yellow.
Nickname: Crus
Floodlights: Training
Membership fees: £25
Local newspaper: Eastern Daily Press
League: Eastern Counties 1
League position (1988–89): 8th
League playing record (1988–89): P 10, W 3, D 0,
L 7, F 77, A 169

ELY

Downham Road, Ely, Cambs. Tel: 0353 66 2156
Founded: 1967
President: Paul Leach
Chairman: Terry Moore
Coach: Terry Moore
Secretary: Peter Honess, 50 West End, Ely, Cambs
CB6 3AY. Tel: 0353 663042.
Fixtures Secretary: Andy Emery, 51 Mudenhall Road,
Littleport, Ely. Tel: Bunt Fen 224.
Club captain (1987–88): Ian O'Donnell
Club captain (1988–89): Chris Hughes
No. of teams: Senior 4. Youth & Minis 6. 1 womens
team.
Directions to Ground: Turn off the A10 at the Little
Downham/Ely staggered junction (A10 Ely bypass).
1st left. (Ground and club house very visible from
A10 Ely bypass).
Ground capacity: 1000+

Clubhouse: Two storey brick and tile building.
Lounge and main bar. Changing rooms (6)
overlooking 3 pitches. Squash club (2 courts).
Colours: Black and gold hoops.
Floodlights: No
Membership: £25
Local newspaper: Ely Standard, Cambridge Evening
News
League: Eastern Counties 1

IPSWICH YMCA

YMCA Sports Ground, The Street, Rushmere,
Ipswich.
Founded: 1926
President: D.L. Sanders
Chairman: Robin Hood
Secretary: Stephen Dunn, 7 Westwood Avenue,
Ipswich IP1 4EQ. Tel: 0473 211865 (H). 719565 (W)
Fixtures Secretary: Neil Andrews, Flat 4, Acar
Grove, Brookwood, Ipswich. Tel: 04073 691292 (H).
0394 380666 (W)
Press Officer: R. Daniels, 85 Weston Avenue,
Felixstowe. Tel: Felix. 283907 (H). 0473 221331 (W)
Club captain (1988–89): Mark Vaughan
Club captain (1989–90): T.B.A.
No. of teams: Senior 2
Directions to ground: Take turning off Ipswich bypass
for Rushmere, go through village, pass church.
YMCA sports ground on right
Ground capacity: Standing – quite a few
Clubhouse facilities: New Clubhouse with bar
Gold and Maroon hoops. (*Change colours:* No)
Floodlights: For training
Membership fees: Full £15 + YMCA subscription
Programme editor: As Secretary
Local newspapers: Ipswich Evening Star, East Anglia
Daily Times
League: London 3NE
League position (1988–89): 11th
League playing record (1988–89): P 10, W 0, D 0,
L 10, F 24, A 525

OLD EDWARDIANS

Westlands Playing Fields, London Road, Romford,
Essex.
Founded: 1967
Secretary: P.J. Hensher, 108 Stanley Avenue, Gidea
Park, Romford, Essex. Tel: Romford 64429 (H). 01-
593 7621 (W).
Colours: Navy Blue/White
League: Eastern Counties 1
Final position (1988–89): 1st (promoted)

REDBRIDGE

Founded: 1952
Secretary: M.D. Hornby, 22 Washington Avenue,
Laindon West, Basildon, Essex. Tel: Basildon 41430.
League contact: I. Lander, 6 Brias Close, Billericay,
Essex. Tel: 02277 655021.
Colours: Navy Blue
League: Eastern Counties 1

ROCHFORD HUNDRED

The Clubhouse, Magnolia Road, Hawkwell,
Rochford, Essex. Tel: 0702 544021
Founded: 1962
President: John Roden
Chairman: Mike Drinkwater
Secretary: Simon Wakefield, 54 Parklands Drive,
Springfield, Chelmsford, Essex CM1 5SP. Tel: 0245
266158 (H). 0702 541581 (W)
Fixtures Secretary: Mike Tuck, 51 Highfield Road,
Billericay, Essex CM11 2PE. Tel: 0277 55483 (H). 01
519 2588 (W)
Press Officer: Colin Chandler, 21 Durants Walk,
Wickford, Essex SS12 9DD. Tel: 0277 766748

Coach: David Hawes
Club captain (1988–89): Peter Pearce
Club captain (1989–90): Andrew Hawes
No. of teams: Senior 5, Youth 1, Minis 3
Directions to ground: A127 to Southend, follow signs
to Rochford. In Rochford follow sign to Ashingdon,
turn left into Rectory Road. After 800 yards turn right
into Magnolia Road, follow to Clubhouse
Ground capacity: Standing 200
Clubhouse facilities: Bar, catering, changing facilities
Club colours: Black shirts and shorts, black/white
socks.
Floodlights: No
Membership fees: Full £20, Playing £20, Social £5,
Youth £5, Student £5
Local newspaper: Evening Echo
League: Eastern Counties 1
League position (1988–89): 7th
League playing record (1988–89): P 10, W 3, D 1,
L 6, F 77, A 161

SHELFORD

Davey Field, Cambridge Road, Gt. Shelford,
Cambridge. Tel: 0223 843357
Founded: 1933
President: W. Bradford
Chairman: N. Kotschy
Secretary: J. Foreman, 20 Greenfield Close,
Stapleford, Cambridge. Tel: 0223 842486
League Contact: Peter Kennedy, 30 Princess Drive,
Sawston, Cambridge CB2 4DL. Tel: 0223 834918 (H).
836987 (W)
Fixtures Secretary: N. Woodgate, 43 High Street,
Balsham, Cambridge. Tel: 0223 893885 (H). 0533
555886
Press Officer: N. Kotschy, 10 stonehill Road, Gt.
Shelford, Cambs. Tel: 0223 842301 (H). 312639 (W)
Coach: Tim Cadman
Club captain (1988–89): Peter Kennedy
Club captain (1989–90): Peter Kennedy
No. of teams: Senior 4, Youth 1
Directions to ground: Leave M11 Exit 11, right at 1st
traffic lights, approx. 1 mile on right (opposite
Scotsdales Garden Centre)
Ground capacity: Standing 500 (1st XV pitch)
Clubhouse facilities: Open Match days, evenings.
Outside bookings taken
Club colours: Maroon/white irregular hoops.
Floodlights: Yes
Membership fees: Full £20, Social £2.50, Youth £10
Programme editor: Rob Stevens, 32 Queensway,
Sawston, Cambridge
Local newspapers: Cambridge Evening News,
Haverhill Echo
League: Eastern Counties 1
League position (1988–89): 5th
League playing record (1988–89): P 10, W 6, D 0,
L 4, F 150, A 113

EASTERN COUNTIES 2

CAMPION

Clubhouse, Cottons Park, Cottons Approach,
Romford, Essex. Tel: 0708 753209
Founded: 1977
President: Dr Rowbottom
Chairman: Peter O'Brien
Coach: Danny McCarthy
Secretary: Kelvin Wilson, 290 Southend Arterial
Road, Hornchurch, Essex RM11 2SG.. Tel: 04024
70587.
Fixtures Secretary: Kevin Marmion, 132 Warley Hill,
Brentwood, Essex CM14 5HB. Tel: 0277 211148.
Club captain (1987–88): Kevin O'Neill
Club captain (1988–89): Kevin O'Neill
No. of teams: Senior 4.
Directions to Ground: From Gallows Corner (junction
A127 and A12) proceed towards London. turn right at

3rd set lights. Right into Marks Road. First left into Cottons Approach.
Clubhouse: Recently refurbished.
Colours: Red and black hoops. (*Change colours:* Sky blue).
Floodlights: No
Membership: £30
Local newspaper: Romford Recorder
League: EC 2

CHELMSFORD

Coronation Park, Timson Lane, Chelmsford, Essex. Tel: 0245 261159
Founded: 1920
President: R. Gammie, J.P.
Chairman: M. Greenleafe
Secretary: J. Bacon, c/o I.D. Stuart, 49 Hillside Grove, Chelmsford, Essex. Tel: 0245 352790
Fixtures Secretary: I.D. Stuart, 49 Hillside Grove, Chelmsford, Essex. Tel: 0245 352790
Press Officer: P. Jordan
Coach: N. Eva
Club captain (1988–89): N. Pilgrim
Club captain (1989–90): A. Matthews
No. of teams: Senior 4, Youth 3, Minis 5
Directions to ground: Within Chelmsford
Clubhouse facilities: Bar, showers
Club colours: Navy blue. (*Change colours:* White)
Nickname: Chelm
Floodlights: No
Membership fees: Playing £25, Social £10
League: London & SE Eastern Counties 2
League position (1988–89): 5th
League playing record (1988–89): P 10, W 5, D 0, L 5, F 125, A 80

DISS

Bellrope Lane, Roydon, Diss, Norfolk. Tel: 0379 642891.
Founded: 1958
President: B.A.C. Gaze
Chairman: T.J. Childerhouse
Coach: K.J. Davies/H Lind
Secretary: S.R.W. Smith, 10 Waveney Road, Diss, Norfolk. Tel: 0379 651108 (H), 0379 651931 (W).
Fixtures Secretary: P. Whetter, 35 Fair Green, Diss Norfolk IP22 3BG. Tel: 0379 642077
Press Officer: S. J. Moore. Tel: 0379 84782
Club captain (1987–88): S.D. Middleton
Club captain (1988–89): T. Baldwin
No. of teams: Senior 5. Youth & Minis 7.
Directions to Ground: Travelling west on a1066 from diss, proceed through Roydon, turn right opposite White Hart PH. Club on left.
Colours: Royal Blue/White (*Change colours:* Blue, white hoops/pink)
Floodlights: Yes, training only.
Membership: £25 playing membership
Local newspaper: Diss Express/Eastern Daily Press
League: Eastern Counties 2
Final position (1988–89): 9th

EAST LONDON

Clubhouse and ground: Holland Road, West Ham, London E15. Tel: 01 474 6761
Founded: 1950
President: Not filled since death of first president
Chairman: O.N. Evans
Secretary: R.H. James, 84 Forest Approach, Wodford Green, Essex. Tel: 01 504 1477
Fixtures Secretary: A. Oldaker, 154 Amery Gardens, Romford, Essex. Tel: 0708 762900
Coach: T.B.A.
Club captain (1988–89): Ray Gladman
Club captain (1989–90): Ray Gladman
No. of teams: Senior 6, Youth & Minis 2
Directions to ground: From West Ham Tube Station (District Line) turn left into Memorial Avenue, follow

to end, turn right into Holland Road and club faces you
Club colours: Maroon and navy. (*Change colours:* Grey)
Floodlights: Training only
Membership fees: £25 (includes squash)
Local newspapers: Newnham Recorder and Stratford Press
League: Eastern Counties 2

LOWESTOFT & GREAT YARMOUTH

Gunton Park, Corton Long Lane, Corton, Lowestoft, Suffolk
Founded: 1879
President: Rodney Francis
Chairman: Keith Nelson
Secretary: Ian Walker, The White Cottage, Boat Dyke Road, Upton, Acle, Norwich, Norfolk NR13 6BG. Tel; 0493 750370 (H). 856122 (W)
Fixtures Secretary: Mark Ruffles, Eades Farm, Carlton Colville, Lowestoft, Suffolk. Tel: 9376 772
Press Officer: Keith Nelson, 70 Upper Cliff Road, Gorleston, Great Yarmouth, Norfolk. Tel: 0493 653095 (H). 856151 (W)
Coach: Mark Attenborough
Club captain (1988–89): Simon Titterington
Club captain (1989–90): Ian Castro
No. of teams: Senior 4, Youth 3
Directions to ground: From Great Yarmouth take A12 towards Lowestoft, at end of dual carriageway (approx. 10 miles) take 1st left to Corton (Pleasurewood Hills), then 1st right. From Lowestoft, A12 to Great Yarmouth, to dual carriageway
Ground capacity: Seating nil, standing 1000 (pitch-side)
Clubhouse facilities: Tennis, archery, cricket, squash, bar
Club colours: Royal blue and white hoops. (*Change colours:* White with red collars and cuffs)
Floodlights: No
Membership fees: Full £25, Playing £25, Social £5, Youth £10, Student £12.50, U16 £5
Ground admission: Nil
Programme editor: Hon. Secretary as required
Local newspapers: Lowestoft Journal, Great Yarmouth Mercury
League: Eastern Counties 2
League position (1988–89): Bottom of Eastern Counties 1
League playing record (1988–89): P 10, W 1, D 0, L 9

MALDON

Drapers Chase, Goldhanger Road, Heybridge, Maldon, Essex. Tel: 0621 852152
Founded: 1947
President: Richard Bright
Secretary: Neil Meadows, 23 Cedar Avenue, Tiptree, Essex CO5 0NR. Tel: 0621 818030 (H). 0223 844371 (W)
Fixtures Secretary: Norman Manning, 57 Larch Walk, Heybridge, Maldon, Essex. Tel: 0621 856073
Coach: David Redfern
Club captain (1988–89): Patrick Murphy
Club captain (1989–90): Jack Redfern
No. of teams: Senior 5, Youth 2, Minis 2
Directions to ground: Maldon to Colchester Road, turn right signposted Goldhanger. 1 mile on left, Drapers Farm Chase (next to phone box), Ground at end of lane
Clubhouse facilities: Bar
Club colours: Royal blue and white hoops.
Floodlights: No
League: Eastern Counties 3
League position (1988–89): 2nd
League playing record (1988–89): P 10, W 8, D 1, L 1, F 201, A 88

PORT OF LONDON AUTHORITY

PLA Sports and Social Club, The Drive, Ilford, Essex. Tel: 01 554 9156
Founded: 1875
President: John McNab
Chairman: Derek Platt
Secretary: Gerard Vallely, Flat 3, 18 Vernham Road, Plumstead, London SE18 3EZ. Tel: 01 855 8355 (H). 858 8001 (W)
Fixtures Secretary: Dave Westbrook, 91 Ashurst Avenue, Thorpe Bay, Essex. Tel: 0702 582440 (H). 01 534 6880 (W)
Club captain (1988–89): Gary Bishop
Club captain (1989–90): Gary Bishop
No. of teams: Senior 4, Youth 1
Directions to ground: To Gants Hill on A12 to London (Eastern Ave), 2nd left into The Drive. Entrance 500 yards on left
Club colours: Navy blue and gold.
Nickname: Ravens
Floodlights: No
Membership fees: Full £30, Playing £30, Social £16.75
League: Eastern Counties 2
League playing record (1988–89): P 10, W 4, D 2, L 4, F 139, A 11

SOUTH WOODHAM FERRERS

Saltcoats Park, Ferrers Road, South Woodham Ferrers, Essex. Tel: 0245 320041
Founded: 1981
President: Alan G. Woolmer
Chairman: James N. Moncrieff
Secretary: David Parkinson, 43 Clements Green Lane, South Woodham Ferrers, Essex CM3 5JS. Tel: 0245 321376 (H). 0702 345219 (W)
Fixtures Secretary: Gerwyn Turner, Fenn Fields, South Woodham Ferrers, Essex. Tel: 0245 322933
Press Officer: Timothy Cramphorn, 19 King Edwards Road, South Woodham Ferrers, Essex. Tel: 0245 325083
Coach: Alan B. Eaton
Club captain (1988–89): Robert E. Pitts
Club captain (1989–90): James Head
No. of teams: Senior 3, Minis 3
Directions to ground: From A127 take A130 to Chelmsford, at Rettenden Turnpike take A132 to SWF. Follow signs to Saltcoats Ind. Est. Ground on left after 3rd roundabout
Clubhouse facilities: SWF Sports Council Pavillion Bar, Saltcoats Park
Club colours: All black. (*Change colours:* Red jerseys, black shorts)
Floodlights: No
Membership fees: Full £25, Playing £25, Social £10, Youth £10, Student £10, OAP £10
Ground admission: Nil
Local newspapers: Southend Evening Echo, SWF Chronicle
League: Eastern Counties 2
League position (1988–89): 9th
League playing record (1988–89): P 10, W 4, D 1, L 5, F 72, A 121

UPMINSTER

Hall Lane Playing Fields, Upminster, Essex. Tel: 04022 20320.
Founded: 1964
Secretary: D. Hope, 115A Corbets Tey Road, Upminster, Essex RM14 2AA. Tel: 04022 24526 (H). 01-377 0660 (W).

Colours: Yellow/Blue
League: Eastern Counties 2

WANSTEAD RFC

Roding Lane North, Woodford Bridge, Ilford, Essex. Tel: 01 550 1561
Founded: 1892
President: Michael Adams
Chairman: Geoff Reeves
Secretary: Frank Houghton, 43 Addison Road, Wanstead E11 2RG
League Contact: As Secretary
Fixtures Secretary: Terry Elliott, 18 Highbury Gardens, Seven Kings, Ilford, Essex. Tel: 599 2743
Press Officer: Julian Greatrex, 15 Grange Avenue, Woodford Green, Essex. Tel: 01 504 0191
Coach: Ken Williams
Club captain (1988–89): Kevin Shuttlewood
Club captain (1989–90): Paul Lazarus
No. of teams: Senior 6, Youth 1
Clubhouse facilities: Open Match days, Monday, Wednesday and Thursday evenings, Sunday lunchtime
Club colours: Blue and white 2" hoops.
Nickname: Herons
Floodlights: No
Membership fees: Full £20, Playing £20, Social £5, Youth £5, Student £5
Local newspapers: Ilford Recorder, Redbridge Guardian
League: Eastern Counties 2
League position (1988–89): 4th
League playing record (1988–89): P 31, W 8, D 1, L 22, F 279, A 487

WOODBRIDGE

Hatchley Barn, Bromeswell, Woodbridge, Suffolk. Tel: 0394 460630
Founded: 1969
President: Michael G. Lubbock
Secretary: David M. Neal, Bradmere Lodge, Spring Lane, Wickham Market, Woodbridge, Suffolk. IP13 0SH. Tel: 0728 746442 (H). 03943 2263 Fax 03943 3030 (W)
League Contact: As Secretary
Fixtures Secretary: Bruce Harrington, 24 Bury Hill Close, Melton, Woodbridge, Suffolk IP12 1LE. Tel: 03943 6208 (H). 0394 385582 (W)
Press Officer: As Fixtures Secretary
Coach: Roger Coombs
Club captain (1988–89): John Cummings
Club captain (1989–90): Doug Inglis
No. of teams: Senior 4, Youth 2, Minis 2, and Veterans
Directions to ground: On A12 Woodbridge Bypass, at roundabout follow signs RAF Bentwaters. Straight on at traffic lights, cross railway and river, left at roundabout on B1084. Ignore left fork and follow signs for Orford. 1/3 mile turn right posted Hatchley Barn (WRUFC & Faith Baptist Church)
Clubhouse facilities: Modern clubhouse, large clubroom, bar, kitchen, stoves, 4 changing rooms, committee rooms, showers
Club colours: Sky blue.
Floodlights: Yes
Membership fees: Full £1, Playing £1, Social £5, Youth £1, Student £1
Ground admission: Match fees – £3 per game. Reductions for students, UB40s, etc.
Local newspapers: East Anglian Daily Times, Ipswich
League: Eastern Counties 2
League position (1988–89): 8th
League playing record (1988–89): P 10, W 4, D 1, L 5, F 154, A 108
Competitions won: County Colts Sevens Cup retained April '89. Runners up and third place in County Sevens (Guests/Winners – Blackheath)

EASTERN COUNTIES 3

BANCROFT

Buckhurst Way, Buckhurst Hill, Essex. Tel: 01–504 0429
Founded: 1894
President: Michael R. Stout
Chairman: John Thomas
Secretary: Stephen B. Thirsk, 4 Bentley Way, Woodford Green, Essex IG8 0SE. Tel: 01–504 1468 (H), 0378 561111 (W)
Fixtures Secretary: Richard J. Sewinnerton, 57 Grove Park Road, South Hornchurch, Essex. Tel: 04027 25217
Coach: Eric West
Club captain (1988–89): Bill Woollcott
Club captain (1989–90): Bill Woollcott
No. of teams: Senior 5, Youth 1, Minis 4
Directions to ground: A104 from M11/A406 junction to Woodford Green 'Castle', turn right at lights by 'Castle' P.H., down Broadmead Road, turn left at 2nd lights, follow road through 1 miles. Ground on right before railway bridge
Clubhouse facilities: Clubroom and bar, separate lounge, squash courts. Open all week
Club colours: Blue/black/claret/light blue hoops.
(*Change colours:* Various)
Floodlights: No
Membership fees: Full £20, Playing £35, Social £20, Squash £35
Ground admission: Nil
Local newspapers: Guardian/Gazette Group and Recorder Group
League: Eastern Counties 3
League position (1988–89): 1st

BECCLES

Beef Meadow, Common Lane, Beccles, Suffolk. Tel: 0502 712016
Founded: 1966
President: John Hipperson
Chairman: Ian Johnstone
Secretary: Willy Wells, Cliff Cottage, Pudding Moor, Beccles, Suffolk NR34 9PP. Tel: 0502 715509
Fixtures Secretary: David Smith, 17 Scales Stret, Bungay, Suffolk. Tel: 4606
Press Officer: Martin Summons, 17 Pine Tree Close, Worlingham, Beccles. Tel: 0502 712550
Coach: R. Grieve
Club captain (1988–89): N. Beese
Club captain (1989–90): N. Beese
No. of teams: Senior 3/4, Youth 3, Minis 5
Directions to ground: Turn to Beccles off Bypass, past station, over railway line, turn left into Common Lane
Clubhouse facilities: Council owned, shared
Club colours: Emerald green.
Floodlights: No
Membership fees: Full £20, Playing £20, Youth £10, Student £5
Local newspapers: Beccles and Bungay Journal, Eastern Daily Press
League: Eastern Counties 3
League position (1988–89): 5th
Competitions won: Norfolk League Div. 3. Woodbridge Floodlite Cup. Norwich Union Sevens

HARWICH & DOVERCOURT

The Pavilion, Low Road Playing Fields, Dovercourt, Suffolk. Tel: 0255 506571.
Secretary: G. Brazier, 10 Main Road, Great Oakley, Harwich, Essex. CO12 5AZ. Tel: 0255 886233 (H). 0255 428231 (W).
Colours: Black/White.
League: Eastern Counties 3
Final position (1988–89): 9th

HOLT

Bridge Road, High Kelling, Holt, Norfolk. Tel: 0263 712191
Founded: 1961
President: Canon D. Maurice
Chairman: Billy Ritchie
Secretary: M.D. Bush, The Warren, Sir Williams Lane, Aylsham, Norwich NR11 6AW. Tel: 0263 732051
Fixtures Secretary: R. Harrison, Hall Farm, Metton, Norwich. Tel: 0263 761255
Club captain (1988–89): Roger K. Day
Club captain (1989–90): Mark Simmons
No. of teams: Senior 4, Youth 1
Directions to ground: Approx. 1 mile from Holt on Cromer Road, A148
Clubhouse facilities: Single storey brick building with pitched roof
Club colours: All black shirts, shorts and socks.
(*Change colours:* White shirts, black shorts and socks)
Nickname: The Owls
Floodlights: No
Membership fees: Playing £22, Social £10, Youth £5, Student £5
Local newspapers: Eastern Daily Press, North Norfolk News
League position (1988–89): 7th
League playing record (1988–89): P 10, W 5, D 0, L 5, F 123, A 119

ILFORD WANDERERS

Forest Road, Barkingside, Ilford, Essex. Tel: 01 500 4622
Founded: 1896
President: Dr. B. Cronin
Chairman: L.T.G. Kirwan
Secretary: T.J. Kneeshaw, 103 Kinfauns Road, Goodmayes, Ilford, Essex IG3 9QJ. Tel: 01 599 3505 (H). 534 7601 (W)
League Contact: As Secretary
Fixtures Secretary: J. Dixon, 19 Thriftwood, Bickenacre, Danbury, Chelmsford, Essex. Tel: 0245 414968
Press Officer: D.J. Cutter, 45 Rose Valley, Brentwood, Essex CM14 4HT. Tel: 0277 222209
Club captain (1988–89): T. Gunyon
Club captain (1989–90): A. Beeston
No. of teams: Senior 5
Directions to ground: LRT Central Line to Hainault Station, 5 minutes walk. Bus 150 or 247 from Ilford BR Station to Hainault via Barkingside. Car A12 to Gants Hill to Barkingside High Street into Forest Road at Fulwell Cross
Clubhouse facilities: Excellent, new members welcome
Club colours: Red, white, green hoops.
Nickname: Wanderers
Floodlights: Training area only
Membership fees: Full £30, Playing £30
Local newspapers: Ilford Recorder, Redbridge Guardian, Barking and Dagenham Post
League position (1988–89): 8th
League playing record (1988–89): P 10, W 5, D 0, L 5, F 89, A 119

LAKENHAM-HEWETT

Hilltop Sports Centre, Norwich Road, Swardeston, Norwich, Norfolk. Tel: 0508 78826
Founded: 1962
President: Ian Forton
Chairman: Rob Jenkinson
Secretary: David Key, Burnaby, Mill Road, Hempnall, Norwich, Norfolk. Tel: Hempnall 342
League Contact: Bruce Ridgeway, 130 Abinger Way, Eaton, Norwich, Norfolk NR4 6NA. Tel: 0603 53076 (H). 628333 Ext 451 (W)
Fixtures Secretary: As League Contact
Press Officer: Michael Browne, 174 Links Avenue, Norwich. Tel: 0603 412488 (H). 628333 Ext 453 (W)

Coach: Phil Boyce
Club captain (1988–89): Gary Brown
Club captain (1989–90): Mick Edwards
No. of teams: Senior 3, Youth 1
Directions to ground: Take A140 out of Norwich, after 3 miles turn right onto B1113, clubhouse 1 miles on right before Swardeston
Ground capacity: Standing 1000
Clubhouse facilities: Clubhouse, open Match days, Tuesday and Thursday evenings, and Sundays
Club colours: Red shirt, socks, white shorts. (*Change colours:* Red and white quarters shirt, red socks, white shorts)
Floodlights: No
Membership fees: Full £25, Playing £3.50, Social £12.50, Youth £12.50, Student £12.50
Local newspaper: Eastern Daily Press
League: Eastern Counties 3
League position (1988–89): 10th
League playing record (1988–89): P 10, W 1, D 0, L 9, F 33, A 156

OLD BEALONIANS

Clubhouse: Wards Road, Ilford, Essex. Ground: Beal High School, Woodford Bridge Road, Redbridge
Founded: 1964
Chairman: J. Sims
Secretary: M.P. March, 22 Landview Gardens, Marden Ash, Ongar, Essex CM5 9EQ
Fixtures Secretary: M. Venables, 36 Rothbury Avenue, Rainham, Essex RM13 9HZ. Tel: 04027 24824
Coach: P. Morrison
Club captain (1988–89): Paul Morrison
Club captain (1989–90): Paul Morrison
No. of teams: Senior 3, Youth 2
Directions to ground: M11 to Redbridge, A12 to Gants Hill. A4306 from Gants Hill and ground is in Woodford Bridge Road, about 2 miles from Gants Hill
Clubhouse facilities: Open Match days
Club colours: Scarlet. (*Change colours:* Red, yellow and black hoops)
Floodlights: No
Local newspaper: Ilford Recorder
League: Eastern Counties 3
League position (1988–89): 3rd

OLD BRENTWOODS

Ashwells Road, Kelvedon Hatch, Brentwood, Essex. Tel: 0277 74070
Founded: 1967
President: G.N. Kingston
Chairman: D.J. Oldham
Coach: G. Waite
Secretary: T.M.B. Kerrigan, c/o 20 Wormwood Street, London EC21 M1RQ. Tel: 0277 223044 (H), 01-588 4304 (W).
Fixtures Secretary: D.K. Hatton, 13 Regent Square, Bruce Road, London E3 3HQ. Tel: 01-981 0421.

NEWMARKET

Scaltback Middle School, Exning Road, Newmarket, Suffolk. Tel: 0638 663082
Founded: 1956
President: N.O. Martin
Chairman: I. Melvin
Secretary: M. Stone, 41 Drinkwater Close, Newmarket, Suffolk CB8 0QN. Tel: 0638 660000 (H). 01 891 4383 (W)
League Contact: John Taylor, 32 High Street, Stetchworth, Newmarket CB8 9TJ. Tel: 0638 76483
Fixtures Secretary: As League Contact
Press Officer: Andy Downing, 3 Collings Place, Newmarket. Tel: 0638 669363
Coach: T.B.A.
Club captain (1988–89): Kevin Mosedale
Club captain (1989–90): T.B.A.

No. of teams: Senior 4, Youth 3
Directions to ground: Newmarket, clock tower, off the traffic flow towards Exning B1063 (B1103), follow road past Hospital, sign 'Industrial Estate', off left into Elizabeth Avenue, opposite Depot Road, 100 yards, left into Scaltback Middle School. Follow road to Sports Pavilion
Clubhouse facilities: Bar and changing
Club colours: Emerald green and black hoops. (*Change colours:* Black)
Floodlights: No
Membership fees: Playing £25, Social £7, Youth £11, Student £6
Local newspapers: Newmarket Journal, Cambridge Evening News, East Anglian Daily Times
League: Eastern Counties 3
League position (1988–89): 6th
League playing record (1988–89): P 10, W 5, D 0, L 5, F 125, A 102
Competitions won: Newmarket 2nd XV Winners Cambridgeshire Junior Cup 13-6. Sunday 5 March 1989. Runners Up, Old Cantabrigians 2nd XV

THETFORD

Two Mile Bottom, Mungford Road, Thetford. Tel: 0842 755176
Founded: 1959
President: Andrew Luckhurst
Chairman: Ken Ellis
Secretary: Tom Tumath, Gael Cottage, The Avenue, Brookville, Norfolk IP26 4RF. Tel: 0366 728633 (H). 0842 819769
League Contact: As Secretary
Fixtures Secretary: As Secretary
Press Officer: Tony Faulconbridge, 49 Ethel Colman Way, Thetford. Tel: 0842 764930
Coach: Ken Ellis
Club captain (1988–89): Joe Hanson
Club captain (1989–90): Nigel Goodhall
No. of teams: Senior 3
Directions to ground: From Thetford A134 to King's Lynn. Ground 1200 yards past last factory on right, Club entrance almost opposite 'Thermalite' sign. When the Thetford Bypass (A11) opens at end of year, use this road and turn left at roundabout for A134
Ground capacity: Seating nil, standing 2000
Clubhouse facilities: Open Match days, Monday and Thursday evenings, Sunday lunchtime
Club colours: Red and white hoops.
Floodlights: No
League: Eastern Counties 2
League position (1988–89): 11th
League playing record (1988–89): P 33, W 11, D 1, L 21

WYMONDHAM

Tutles Lane East, Wymondham, Norfolk. Tel; 0953 607332
Founded: 1971
President: Robert Sutton
Chairman: Martin Crook
Secretary: Martin Warren, 67 Hawkes Lane, Beacon Ash, Norfolk NR14 8EW. Tel: 0508 70669 (H). 0603 616112 (W)
Fixtures Secretary: Shaemus Good, 9 Poplar Way, Attleborough, Norfolk. Tel: 0953 453006
Press Officer: S. Dinneen, 108 West End, Old Costessey, Norwich, Norfolk NR8 5AJ. Tel: 0603 742324 (H). 622233 Ext 2368 (W)
Coach: John Kelly
Club captain (1988–89): Christopher Dinneen
Club captain (1989–90): Christopher Dinneen
No. of teams: Senior 3, Youth 1, Minis 4
Directions to ground: A11 to north of Wymondham, off roundabout signpost Dereham, straight over second roundabout, 400 yards on right
Clubhouse facilities: Bar, kitchen, changing rooms
Club colours: Red and black.

Floodlights: No
Membership fees: Full £25, Playing £25, Social £5, Youth £5, Student £15
Local newspaper: Eastern Daily Press
League: Eastern Counties 3
League position (1988–89): 4th
League playing record (1988–89): P 30, W 21, D 1, L 8, F 648, A 260
Competitions won: Norwich Union Norfolk League Champions

EASTERN COUNTIES 4

CLACTON

Recreation Ground, Valley Road, Clacton-On-Sea. Tel: 0255 421602
Founded: 1935
President: Steve Gage
Chairman: Tony Cook
Secretary: Graham Barney, 80 Vista Road, Clacton-On-Sea, Essex. Tel: 0255 432270
League Contact: As Press Officer
Fixtures Secretary: Chris White, 87 Old Road, Finton On Sea. Tel: 02556 71884
Press Officer: Brian White, 80 Vista Road, Clacton-On-Sea. Tel: 0255 432270
Coach: Barry Smith
Club captain (1988–89): Mark Pickett
Club captain (1989–90): Mark Pickett
No. of teams: Senior 3, Youth 1/2
Clubhouse facilities: Changing, bar, social area, floodlit training area
Club colours: Maroon shirts, navy shorts.
Nickname: Seasiders
Floodlights: Training only
Membership fees: Playing £15, Social £5, Youth £5, Student £5, VP £10
Local newspapers: Evening Gazette, East Essex Gazette
League: Eastern Counties 4
League position (1988–89): 5th
League playing record (1988–89): P 10, W 6, D 0, L 4, F 122, A 110

FAKENHAM

Old Wells Road, Fakenham, Norfolk
Founded: 1982
President: L. Hogston
Chairman: Terry Bishop
Secretary: Nicola Stewart, 18 North Park, Fakenham, Norfolk NR21 9RQ. Tel: 0328 51974 (H). 0553 766266 Ext 462/463 (W)
Fixtures Secretary: Alan Young, 9 Copperbeach Close, Fakenham, Norfolk NR21 8JZ. Tel: 0328 55285
Coach: David Swift
Club captain (1988–89): Steve Finn
Club captain (1989–90): Vince Stewart
No. of teams: Senior 3, Youth 4, Minis 3
Directions to ground: From Swaffham, to roundabout, turn right to town centre, first left into Old Wells Road, follow to end, Clubhouse down lane to right
Ground capacity: Standing unlimited
Clubhouse facilities: Open Match days and evenings
Club colours: Light blue/black quarters, black shorts and socks. (Change colours: All light blue shirt, black shorts and socks)
Nickname: 2nd XV – The Griffins
Floodlights: No
Membership fees: Full £138 (life), Playing £26, Social £6, Youth £7
Ground admission: Nil
Local newspapers: Fakenham & Wells Times
League: Eastern Counties 4
League position (1988–89): 8th
League playing record (1988–89): P 10, W 2, D 1, L 7, F 88, A 185
Competitions won: North Walsham Sevens

FELIXSTOWE

Coronation Park, Mill Lane, Felixstowe, Suffolk. Tel: 0394 270150
Founded: 1930
President: Terry Butler
Chairman: Colin Bentley
Secretary: Robert Woodward, The Well House, 86 Grange Road, Felixstowe, Suffolk. Tel: 0394 284562
Fixtures Secretary: Terry Butler, 9 Gainsborough Road, Felixstowe, Suffolk. Tel: 0394 277360 (H). 674021 (W)
Club captain (1988–89): Richard Smith
Club captain (1989–90): Chris Summers
No. of teams: Senior 3, Youth 1
Directions to ground: A45 from Ipswich to Felixstowe, through to 2nd roundabout. Take exit to right (Garrison Lane), follow to 2nd traffic lights. Mill Lane is right turn, Ground at bottom
Clubhouse facilities: Open Match days and Sunday lunchtime
Club colours: Black and white hoops, black shorts. (Change colours: Red)
Floodlights: No
Membership fees: Full £17.50, Playing £17.50, Social £12.50, Youth £5, Student £5
Local newspapers: East Anglian Daily Times, Ipswich
League: Eastern Counties 4
League position (1988–89): 6th
League playing record (1988–89): P 10, W 6, D 0, L 4, F 153, A 160

GOTHIC

Earlham School, Earlham, Norwich. –Tel: 0603 51611.
Founded: 1979
Secretary: T. Stubbs, 94 Dover Street, Norwich. Tel: 0603 611370 (H)
League: Eastern Counties 4

LONDON HOSPITAL

Wadham Road, Hale End, Walthamstow (North Circular Road). Tel: 01–527 5724
Founded: 1865
President: Dr. Colin Barnes
Secretary: Gary Constable, London Hospital Clubs Union, Stepney Way, Whitechapel, London E1 2AD. Tel: 01–407 1677 (H), 01–257 3185 (W)
Fixtures Secretary: P. Jameson, address As Secretary. Tel: 01–790 7958 (H), 01–247 3185 (W)
Press Officer: As Secretary
Club captain (1988–89): Dick Baker
Club captain (1989–90): Sean Curry
No. of teams: Senior 3
Directions to ground: From Central London (Victoria Line Underground) or from Bethnal Green and Liverpool Street (BR) take a train to Walthamstow Central, then any bus from Stand C in the bus station outside, alighting at Crooked Billet roundabout. Ground is 150 yds east of roundabout
Club colours: Navy blue and white chequers. (Change colours: Blue and white hoops)
Floodlights: No
League: London & SE/Eastern Counties 4
League position (1988–89): 1st
League playing record (1988–89): P 8, W 7, D 0, L 1, F 282, A 60
Competitions won: Eastern Counties 5 Champions

LOUGHTON

Squirrels Lane, Hornbeam Road, Buckhurst Hill, Essex. Tel: 01 504 0065
Founded: 1955
Fixtures Secretary: Brian Westley, 30 The Avenue, St Pauls Cray, Orpington, Kent. Tel: 01 302 0755 (H).

932 3129 (W)
Press Officer: Mathiew Baldwin, 72A Pyrles Lane,
Loughton, Essex. Tel: 01 508 8518 (H). 508 8665 (W)
Coach: Russell Stock
Club captain (1988–89): Michael Carter
Club captain (1989–90): Michael Walker
No. of teams: Senior 3
Directions to ground: Squirrels Lane, off Hornbeam
Road opposite 'The Monkhams' Pub, in Buckhurst
Way, Buckhurst Hill, Essex
Clubhouse facilities: Changing rooms, showers, bar
and club room, weights room
Club colours: White with one wide green and two
narrow black hoops. (*Change colours:* Green)
Floodlights: No
League: Eastern Counties 5
League position (1988–89): 2nd
League playing record (1988–89): P 8, W 6, D 0, L 2,
F 164, A 104

MAYFIELD OLD BOYS

Whitbread Sports Ground, Durham Avenue,
Buckhurst Hill, Essex.
Founded: 1971
President: P. Harvey
Chairman: B. Jones
Secretary: Mrs P. Willcocks, 59 Felbrigge Road,
Ilford, Essex IG3 8DN. Tel: 01 599-6672.
Fixtures Secretary: J. Holland, 72 Park Avenue,
Barking, Essex. Tel: 01 591-0410.
Press Officer: M. Hilton, 117 Marlborough Way,
Billericay, Essex CM12 0YH. Tel: 0277 650337.
Club captain (1988–89): M. Feild
No. of teams: Senior 2
Directions to Ground: North Circular to Charlie
Browns roundabout Chigwell Road to Snakes Lane
East Prospect Road to Durham Avenue.
Ground capacity: Plenty of standing room.
Clubhouse: We use local pub.
Colours: Green & white hoops.
Nickname: The Feild
Floodlights: No
Membership: £20.00
Local newspaper: Ilford Recorder
League: Eastern Counties 4

OLD PALMERIANS

c/o Palmers College, Grays, Essex. Tel: 0375 370121
Founded: 1977
President: A.K. Smetham
Chairman: P. Clarke
Secretary: R.O. Heapy, 48 Nutberry Avenue, Grays,
Essex RM16 2TL. Tel: 0375 379359 (H). 383061 (W)
League Contact: As Secretary
Fixtures Secretary: As Secretary
Press Officer: A. Hutchinson, 5 Browns Cottage,
High Road, North Stifford, Grays, Essex. Tel: 0375
390801
Coach: Phil Burnett
Club captain (1988–89): A. Baylis
Club captain (1989–90): A. Baylis
No. of teams: Senior 3, (Youth & Minis run by
College)
Directions to ground: M25 junctions 30/31. A13
Eastbound, 1st turnoff Grays. 1st roundabout, 2nd
exit Lodge Lane to Chadwell St Mary. 1st roundabout
3rd exit Woodview. Bear left at fork, College on right
next to traffic lights
Clubhouse facilities: c/o Rook Hall Club, Dell Road,
Grays. (Own Club under development)
Club colours: Sky/navy. (*Change colours:* Black)
Floodlights: Training only
Membership fees: Full £15, Playing £15, Social £15,
Youth £5, Student £5, OAP free
Local newspaper: Thurrock Gazette
League: Eastern Counties 4
League position (1988–89): 3rd
League playing record (1988–89): P 10, W 8, D 0,
L 2, F 190, A 121

SOUTHWOLD

The Pavilion, The Common, Southwold, Suffolk
Founded: 1964/65
President: Tony P. Kelk
Chairman: Roger Middleditch
Secretary: Andrew S. Toone, 17 Portsch Close,
Carlton Colville, Lowestoft, Suffolk NR33 8TY. Tel:
0502 515649
League Contact: As Secretary
Fixtures Secretary: Bob Stephenson, Woodside Farm,
Holton, Halesworth, Suffolk. Tel: 722907
Press Officer: As Secretary
Coach: Roy Excell
Club captain (1988–89): Robert Temple
Club captain (1989–90): Rob Dawson
No. of teams: Senior 2
Directions to ground: Turn right at Kings Head Hotel
and proceed straight towards water tower
Clubhouse facilities: Bar, changing rooms, showers
(due for redevelopment)
Club colours: Black with old gold chest hoop.
(*Change colours:* Maroon)
Nickname: Southwold Jacks
Floodlights: No
Membership fees: Playing £15, Social £10, Youth
£12.50, Student £12.50, OAP £10, VP £10
Local newspaper: Lowestoft Journal
League: Eastern Counties 4
League position (1988–89): 9th
League playing record (1988–89): P 10, W 2, D 1,
L 7, F 111, A 253

STOWMARKET

Chilton Field Sports Club, Chilton Way, Stowmarket,
Suffolk. Tel: 0449 613181
Founded: 1962
President: R. Cresswell
Chairman: R. Cresswell
Secretary: R. Dakin, 2 Creeting Hall Cottages,
Creeting St Peter, Nr Stowmarket, Suffolk. Tel: 0449
720645
League Contact: As Secretary
Fixtures Secretary: T.B.A.
Press Officer: T. Green, 7 Gilbert Close, Needham
Market, Nr Ipswich, Suffolk. Tel: 0449 721881
Coach: C. Manning
Club captain (1988–89): P. Relf
Club captain (1989–90): C. Manning
No. of teams: Senior 4, Youth 1
Directions to ground: From town centre traffic lights,
follow sign to Mid-Suffolk Leisure Centre, approx.
mile turn right into Onehouse Road, follow road past
high school, turn right into Chilton Way
Clubhouse facilities: Clubroom, 4 changing rooms
Club colours: Navy with 1 red hoop and 2 small white
hoops. (*Change colours:* Yellow and black hoops)
Nickname: Vultures
Floodlights: No
Membership fees: Full £20, Playing £20, Social £10,
Youth £10, Student £10
Local newspapers: East Anglian Daily Times, The
Bury Free Press
League: Eastern Counties 4
League position (1988–89): 7th
League playing record (1988–89): P 10, W 2, D 2,
L 6, F 78, A 137
Competitions won: Suffolk Sevens Plate Competition
Winners

WISBECH

Chapel Road, Wisbech. Tel: 0945 63666
Founded: 1947
President: Gordon Timm
Chairman: Tony Maris
Secretary: Peter Sheldrick, 36 Tavistock Road,
Wisbech. Tel: 0945 63829 (H). 585161 (W)
League Contact: As Secretary

Fixtures Secretary: Cliff Humphries, Chesnas, Corporation Road, Wisbech. Tel: 0945 587316 (H). 63017 (W)
Press Officer: Tony Leach, 54 Elm Road, Wisbech. Tel: 0945 581302
Coach: Dave Debson
Club captain (1988–89): Les Vassall
Club captain (1989–90): Ben Harrington
No. of teams: Senior 2, Minis 4
Directions to ground: From Police Station roundabout follow signs to Wisbech St Mary, 300 yards on right
Ground capacity: Standing – several
Clubhouse facilities: Bar/lounge, etc
Club colours: Scarlet shirts, navy shorts, red socks. (*Change colours:* Green)
Floodlights: Yes
Membership fees: Full £25, Playing £25, Social £25, Youth free, Student £15
Local newspapers: Wisbech Standard, Fenland Advertiser
League: Eastern Counties 3
League position (1988–89): 11th
League playing record (1988–89): P 10, W 0, D 0, L10, F 20, A 310

EASTERN COUNTIES 5

BILLERICAY

Willowbrook, Stock Road, Billericay, Essex. Tel: 0277 841442
President: R. Gatehouse
Chairman: J. Henshaw
Secretary: G. Buggle, 96 Norsey View Drive, Billericay, Essex CM12 0QU. Tel: 0277 650249 (H). 677777 (W)
League Contact: As Secretary
Fixtures Secretary: N. Cline, 16 Holbrook Close, South Woodham Ferrers, Essex CM3 5ST. Tel: 0245 325530
Press Officer: R. Ross, 14 Brock Hill, Wickford, Essex SS11 7NJ. Tel: 0268 766881
Coach: L. Moore
Club captain (1988–89): M. Garwood
Club captain (1989–90): P. Driver
No. of teams: Senior 3, Youth 1
Directions to ground: Proceed north along Stock Road from Billericay for 1 miles approx. – ground is on right hand side
Clubhouse facilities: Bar and changing rooms
Club colours: Black and gold.
Floodlights: No
Membership fees: Full £25, Playing £25, Social £5
League: Eastern Counties 5
League position (1988–89): 3rd in EC6
League playing record (1988–89): P 7, W 5, D 0, L 2, F 124, A 50

CHIGWELL

'High View', Lambourne Road, Chigwell, Essex. Tel: 01 500 8574
President: James Hagger
Chairman: David George
Secretary: James Hagger, 17 Halsham Crescent, Barking, Essex IG11 9HG. Tel: 01 594 4576 (H). 555 5437 (W)
Fixtures Secretary: Eric McLaughlan, 17 Halsham Crescent, Barking, Essex. Tel: 01 594 4576 (H). 555 5437 (W)
Press Officer: David Pritchard, 10 Lake Avenue, Dagenham, Essex
Club captain (1988–89): Mark Collins
Club captain (1989–90): Mark Collins
No. of teams: Senior 2
Directions to ground: A12 to A127, turn right at Moby Dick PH, carry on approx. 3 miles to Maypole PH. Turn left at lights. Ground 500 yards along on left hand side, opposite 'Shillibeer Walk'
Clubhouse facilities: Bar

Club colours: Maroon/black.
Floodlights: No
League: Eastern Counties 5
League position (1988–89): Bottom of EC4
League playing record (1988–89): P 9, W 1, D 0, L 8

DEREHAM

Moorgate, Dereham, Norfolk
Founded: 1974
President: I. Walker
Chairman: P. Gorham
Coach: J. Vaughan
Secretary: W. Parfitt, 41 Windmill Avenue, Dereham, Norfolk. Tel: (0362) 693450.
Fixtures Secretary: L. Grauwiler, Daleview House, Dereham Road, Scarning, Dereham, Norfolk. Tel: (0362) 694141.
League Contact & Press Officer: P. Gorham, 19 The Cresaur, Toftwood, Dereham, Norfolk. Tel: 0362 695052.
Club captain (1988–89): F. Savage
No. of teams: Senior 2. Youth & Minis 1.
Directions to Ground: Dereham turning off A47 through Moorgate Housing Estate.
Colours: Maroon, black, white. (*Change colours:* Pale blue
Floodlights: No
Membership: £20 playing member
Local newspaper: Dereham & Fakenham Times
League: Eastern Counties 5

HAVERHILL & DISTRICT

Castle Hill Playing Fields, Haverhill, Suffolk. Tel: Haverhill 702871
Founded: 1964
President: Dai Nicholas
Chairman: Henry McCauley
Secretary: Stuart Parry, 10 Pavilion Court, Manor Road, Haverhill, Suffolk. Tel: 0440 705411 Ext 2224 (W)
Fixtures Secretary: Andrew Mudway, 19 Butley Court, Haverhill, Suffolk. Tel: Hav. 704085 (H). 61131 (W)
Press Officer: Christopher Spencer, 12 Exeter Court, Haverhill, Suffolk. Tel: Hav. 703472 (H). 704444 Ext 348 (W)
Coach: Anthony Hope, Paul Raffell, Ricky Green, Paul Marper
Club captain (1988–89): Kevin Pullen
Club captain (1989–90): Anthony Hope
No. of teams: Senior 2, Youth 1
Directions to ground: Into town centre, up Camps Road, 5th turning on right, School Lane, go to top and Rugby Club is across the field
Ground capacity: Standing 2500
Clubhouse facilities: Wooden Clubhouse, bar, showers and changing rooms
Club colours: 1st XV, Maroon and blue quarters with black collars and cuffs. (*Change colours:* Maroon and blue hoops)
Floodlights: No
Membership fees: Playing £20, Social £5, Youth £3, Student £3, OAP free
Local newspapers: Haverhill Echo, Cambridge Free Paper
League: Eastern Counties 5
League position (1988–89): 5th
League playing record (1988–89): P 8, W 4, D 0, L 4, F 138, A 109
Competitions won: Runners Up Suffolk Merit Table. Bury St Edmunds Invitation XV Plate Winners

MARCH BRSA

Neale-Wade Community College, Wimblington Road, March
Founded: 1968

President: Vivian M. Allen
Chairman: Terry Stevens
Secretary: Barry Fleetham, 13 Cherrywood Avenue, March, Cambs. PE15 9ST. Tel: 0354 56703
Fixtures Secretary: Andrew Stimson, 66 Westfield Road, Manea, Cambs. Tel: 035478 549
Press Officer: T. Robinson, 34 Borrowmoor Road, March, Cambs. PE15 9RP. Tel: 0354 53142
Coach: Chris Amps
Club captain (1988–89): Dave Emmerton
Club captain (1989–90): Chris Amps
No. of teams: Senior 2
Directions to ground: A141 to March, turn right B1101 at roundabout, Neale-Wade Community College on right approx. 1 miles, opposite side Seven Stars PH
Clubhouse facilities: Open Match days and training evenings
Club colours: 1st XV, maroon, white hoops. 2nd XV, all maroon. (*Change colours:* Black)
Nickname: Bears
Floodlights: Yes
Membership fees: Playing £10, Student £5
Local newspapers: Cambridgeshire Times, Fenland Advertiser, Peterborough Evening Telegraph
League: Eastern Counties 5
League position (1988–89): 4th
League playing record (1988–89): P 8, W 5, D 0, L 3, F 97, A 89
Competitions won: Jack Arch Trophy, April 23, 1989

NORWICH UNION

Pinebanks, White Farm Lane, Harvey Lane, Norwich. Tel: 0603 33752
Founded: 1931
President: Robin J. Miles
Secretary: David K. Johnson, c/o CSYSLIFE 3 Department, Norwich Union Insurance Group, Norwich, Norfolk NR1 3NG
League Contact: Mark L. Howell, c/o CSYSLIFE 4, Norwich Union Insurance Group, Surrey Street, Norwich, Norfolk NR1 3NG. Tel: 0603 614280 (H). 680755 (W)
Fixtures Secretary: Mark L. Howell, 45 Belvoir Street, Norwich, Norfolk NR2 3AY. Tel: 0603 614280 (H). 680755 (W)
Press Officer: Ian Purdy, c/o CSYSLIFE 3 Department, Norwich Union Insurance Group, Norwich, Norfolk NR1 3NG. Tel: 0603 417040 (H). 683824 (W)
Club captain (1988–89): Mark Penton
Club captain (1989–90): Mark Penton
No. of teams: Senior 2
Directions to ground: From the south – follow the Ring Road signed A47 Great Yarmouth. After the football ground stay on the Ring Road and follow the one way system past the AA building (on your left). At the traffic lights after the Mustard Pot PH (on your right) turn left – now signposted to Cromer. At the top of the hill opposite the Morrison Lodge PH turn right into White Farm Lane. The ground is at the end. From the west – follow the Ring Road to the Heartsease PH roundabout. Take the third exit (PH will be on immediate right). White Farm Lane is about half a mile on the left
Clubhouse facilities: 2 Bars, ballroom, 4 squash courts, 2 badminton courts, sauna, solarium
Club colours: Green and white hoops, white shorts, green socks.
Floodlights: No
Local newspapers: Eastern Daily Press, Eastern Evening News
League: Eastern Counties 5
League position (1988–89): 8th
League playing record (1988–89): P 8, W 2, D 0, L 6, F 83, A 157

ONGAR

Ongar Sports & Social Club, Love Lane, Ongar,
Essex. Tel: 0277 363838
League Contact: N.D. McCarthy, 33 Granville Road, South Woodford, London E18 1LD. Tel: 01 989 8956
Press Officer: Alfred Jones. Tel: 0277 363846
Club colours: Blue/amber
League: Eastern Counties 5

SWAFFHAM

North Pickenham Road, Swaffham, Norfolk. Tel: 0760 24829
Founded: 1981
President: Mervyn Gribbon
Chairman: Michael Pond
Secretary: Robert Woodwards, 5 The Pightle, Swaffham, Norfolk. Tel: 0760 23821 (H). 721480 (W)
League Contact: As Secretary
Fixtures Secretary: Eric Nye, 7 Warstade Way, Swaffham, Norfolk. Tel: 0760 23377
Press Officer: As League Contact
Club captain (1988–89): Ian Mason
Club captain (1989–90): Ian Mason
No. of teams: Senior 2, Minis 1
Directions to ground: Into Swaffham town centre, take A47 towards E. Dereham, take North Pickenham Road at Grady's Hotel, ground 400 metres on right
Clubhouse facilities: Lounge bar, 2 changing rooms, kitchen, showers
Club colours: Amber shirts, black shorts. (*Change colours:* White shirts)
Floodlights: No
Membership fees: Full £15, Playing £15, Social £5, Student £5, OAP £5
Local newspapers: Eastern Daily Press, Swaffham and Watton Times, Kings Lynn News and Advertiser
League: Eastern Counties 5
League position (1988–89): 7th
League playing record (1988–89): P 8, W 2, D 0, L 6, F 96, A 138

THAMES

Thurrock Management Centre, Love Lane, Aveley, South Ockendon, Essex
President: Gordon Jones
Chairman: Paul Brett
Secretary: Kelvin Carter, 49A Hall Road, Aveley, South Ockendon, Essex RM15 4HJ. Tel: 0708 867865 (H). 01 934 2243 (W)
League Contact: As Secretary
Fixtures Secretary: As Secretary
Coach: W.E. Thomas
Club captain (1988–89): Kevin Lyons
Club captain (1989–90): Kevin Lyons
No. of teams: Senior 3
Directions to ground: From M25 Junction 30/31, take 2nd exit to A1306 roundabout, take 5th exit to Aveley. Follow road into Aveley Village, take 1st turn left into Hall Road. Proceed to top of road and right into Love Lane
Clubhouse facilities: The Tophouse, Aveley
Club colours: Emerald and black hoops. (*Change colours:* Purple, emerald, black irregular hoops)
Nickname: Toucans
Floodlights: No
Membership fees: Full £25, Playing £25, Social £10
Local newspaper: Thurrock Gazette
League: Eastern Counties 6
League position (1988–89): 1st
League playing record (1988–89): P 7, W 6, D 1, L 0, F 203, A 49
Competitions won: Eastern Counties League 6. BL Office Centre Merit Table

THURSTON

Thurston Upper School, Thurston, Bury St Edmonds, Suffolk.
Founded: 1973
Secretary: R. Tully, Seletar, Hepworth Road,

Stanton, Bury St Edmonds, Suffolk. Tel: 0359 50160 (H).
Fixtures Secretary: R. Wyatt, Stone Cottage, The Green, Beyton, Suffolk. Tel: 0359 70410 (H).
League Contact: C. Lawrence, 8 Rowen Drive, Brandon, Suffolk. Tel: 0842 812768.
League: Eastern Counties 5

EASTERN COUNTIES 6

BRIGHTLINGSEA RC

Colne High School, Church Road, Brightlingsea, Colchester
President: Ernest Oliver
Chairman: Kevin Chell
Secretary: Alan Howlett, 6 Tudor Close, Brightlingsea, Essex CO7 0QW. Tel: 0206 30 3827
League Contact: As Secretary
Fixtures Secretary: Russell Griffs, 2 Kirkhurst Close, Brightlingsea, Essex CO7 0EY
Press Officer: As Secretary
Coach: T.B.A.
Club captain (1988–89): Chris Payne
Club captain (1989–90): Mark Hexley
No. of teams: Senior 2
Directions to ground: Turn onto B1029, off B1027 at Thorrington (Colchester/Clacton Road), Colne High School approx. 2 miles along road into town
Ground capacity: Standing 100-200
Clubhouse facilities: Public House
Club colours: Red shirts, black shorts and socks. (*Change colours:* Red and black hooped shirts, black shorts and socks)
Nickname: 'Sea, Reds
Floodlights: No
Membership fees: Full £15, Playing £15, Social £15, Youth £5, Student £5, OAP £5
Local newspapers: Essex County Standard, Colchester Evening Gazette, East Essex Gazette, Brightlingsea Chronical, East Anglian Daily Times, Coastal Expresses, Yellow Advertiser
League: Eastern Counties 6
League position (1988–89): 7th
League playing record (1988–89): P 7, W 1, D 0, L 6, F 40, A 143

BROADLAND

Cobholm Playing Fields, Nr. Gt. Yarmouth
President: Robert Jones
Chairman: Andrew Ruddick
Secretary: Hazel Goff, 5 Humberstone Road, Gorleston, Gt. Yarmouth, Norfolk. Tel: 0493 653808 (H), 844380 (W)
Fixtures Secretary: David Oliver, 178 Alderson Road, Gt. Yarmouth, Norfolk. Tel: 0493 853585 (H), 650528 (W)
Press Officer: Susan Watson, Cow Trott Cottage, Cow Trott Lane, Off Back Lane, Rollesby, Gt. Yarmouth. Tel: 0493 748775 (H), 657052 (W)
Coach: Cliff Horobin
Club captain (1988–89): David Joseph
Club captain (1989–90): David Joseph
No. of teams: Senior 2, Youth 3
Directions to ground: From Norwich: (A47) 1st roundabout 3rd exit, over new bridge. Ground 400 yds on right. From Lowestoft: (A12) follow A12 main route through Gorleston then follo signposts for A47 (Norwich). Ground on left 400 yds before new bridge
Club colours: Red, white blue hoops. (*Change colours:* Gold)
Floodlights: No
Membership fees: Full £12, Playing £20, Social £6, Youth £2.50, Student £2.50, OAP £6
Ground admission: Nil
Local newspapers: Gt. Yarmouth Mercury, Eastern Daily Press, Local Advertiser
League: Eastern Counties 6

League position (1988–89): 6th
Competitions won: Southwold Sevens Trophy

BURHAM-SPURS

Recreation Ground, Millfields, Station Road, Burham-on-Crouch, Essex. Tel: 0621 784633
President: Aubrey Brabon
Chairman: Warwick Harold Bridge
Secretary: Matthew Barr, 18, Lilian Road, Burnham-on-Crouch, Essex CM0 8EH. Tel: 0621 783944 (H), 0621 784858 (W)
League Contact W. H. Bridge, 12 Glendale Road, Burham-on-Crouch, Essex CM0 8LY. Tel: 0621 783807 (H), 01–022 4904 (W)
Press Officer: Alan Stone, Eastlands Cottage, East End Road, Bradwell-on-Sea, Nr Southminster, Essex. CM0 7PW. Tel: 0621 76466 (H), 0621 76466 (W)
Coach: Shaun McCloud-Jones
Club captain (1988–89): Andrew Charles Wade
Club captain (1989–90): Andrew Charles wade
No. of teams: Senior 2, Youth 1, Minis 1
Direction to ground: East direction (North of River Crouch). Pick up BIOIO to Burnham. Turn right at T-junct (large tree) to town centre. Over railway bridge to library on right. Entrance immediately on right. (Dengie Hundred Sports Centre 150 yds)
Ground capacity: Seating none, Standing 1000
Clubhouse facilities: Bar, Social Area, Changing Facilities
Colours: Amber/Blue Stripes
Membership fees: Full £25.00, Playing £25.00, Social £20.00, Youth £5.00, Student £10.00, OAP £00p
Ground admission: Nil
Local newspaper: Maldon and Burham Standard

ESSEX POLICE

Witham R.F.C., Spa Road, Witham, Essex. Tel: 0376 511066
President: Dep. Ch. Con. Peter Simpson, Q.P.M.
Chairman: Michael Hall
Secretary: William Clark, Force Support Unit, Police Headquarters, Chelmsford, Essex. Tel: 0245 542429 (direct line)
Fixtures Secretary: R.C. Shakespeare, Essex Police CID, Police Station, Southway, Colechester, Essex. Tel: 0206 751068 (H), 762212 (W)
Press Officer: Douglas Bedford, Force Support Unit, Police Headquarters, Chelmsford, Essex. Tel: 0376 513041 (H), 0245 452429 (W)
Coach: Michael Hall
Club captain (1988–89): David Crighton-Smith
Club captain (1989–90): David Crighton-Smith
No. of teams: Senior 2
Directions to ground: From A12 into Witham, to Spinks Lane by Bridge Hospital, turn left/right. To the T-junction, turn right into Highfield (this then becomes Spa Road), under rail bridge, immediate left
Ground capacity: Standing 2000 approx.
Clubhouse facilities: 2 changing rooms, players bar and lounge bar
Club colours: Royal blue/white
League: NL/Eastern Counties 6
Competitions won: B.L. Merit Table Sevens

HADLEIGH

Layham Road Sports Ground, Lower Layham, Hadleigh, Suffolk. Contact No. Match days: 047333 272
President: Raymond Law
Chairman: Arthur Bell
Secretary: Jim Ashe (RAF Police RAF Wattisham Suffolk), c/o 4 Birch Road, Onehouse, Stowmarket, Suffolk IP14 3EZ. Tel: 0449 741529
League Contact: T.E. Sands, 4 Birch Road, Onehouse, Stowmarket, Suffolk. Tel: 0449 677995 (H). 0473 33 287 (W)
Fixtures Secretary: As League Contact
Press Officer: Jim Ashe, 23 Elder Crescent, RAF

Wattisham, Suffolk. Tel: 0449 741529
Coach: Andrew Cummings
Club captain (1988–89): Terry Sands
Club captain (1989–90): Eamon Hogan
No. of teams: Senior 2
Directions to ground: Follow A12 towards Ipswich, take the Hadleigh turn off, approx. 7 miles into Hadleigh High Street, 2nd left (Chemist on corner), Ground 1 mile on left
Ground capacity: Standing 750
Clubhouse facilities: Local Public House (Brewers Arms)
Club colours: Maroon and white quarters. (*Change colours:* White)
Floodlights: No
Membership fees: Full £15, Playing £15, Social £10, Youth £7, Student £7, OAP £5
Ground admission: Nil
Programme: No. of editorial pages 8; No. of advertising pages 21; Price F.O.C.
Programme editor: T.E. Sands, address as League Contact. (Assistant A. Cummings)
Local newspaper: East Anglian Daily Times
League: Eastern Counties 6
League position (1988–89): 6th
League playing record (1988–89): P 7, W 1, D 1, L 5, F 57, A 120

MISTLEY

Furze Hill, Mistley, Manningtree, Essex (new club)
President: Marie Reid
Chairman: Roger Wright
Secretary: Paul Game, 2 Woodview Cottages, Duke Street, Hintlesham, Ipswich IP8 3QP. Tel: 0463 87456
Fixtures Secretary: Steve Rose, The Brambles, Wix Road, Bradfield. Tel: 0255 870010
Coach: Ronald West
Club captain (1988–89): John Tweddle
Club captain (1989–90): Roger Sparling
No. of teams: Senior 2, Youth 2, Minis 1
Directions to ground: From Mistley main street, up hill towards Harwich, round right-hand bend by Anchor pub, turn right by sharp left-hand bend, follow signs to Recreation ground
Clubhouse facilities: Changing rooms and bar only
Club colours: Red shirts, black shorts. (*Change colours:* Black shirts, black shorts)
Floodlights: No
Membership fees: Full £20, Playing £20, Social £10
Local newspapers: Eastern Counties Newspaper Group, East Anglian Daily Times
League: Eastern Counties 6

OLD COOPERIANS

Salisbury Hall, North Circular Road, Crooked Billet Roundabout, Walthamstow, London E17. Tel: 01 527 3346
President: Geoffrey George Brown
Chairman: Alan Aldsworth
Secretary: John Green, 146 St Johns Road, Walthamstow, London E17 4JJ. Tel: 01 523 0790 (H). 0279 21166 (W)
Fixtures Secretary: Dave Russell, 51 Perth Road, Leyton, London E10. Tel: 01 539 0794 (H). 729 3535 (W)
Press Officer: Geoffrey George Brown, 12A Balgores Square, Gidea Park, Essex RM2 6AU. Tel: 0708 752456 (H). 01 257 3734 (W)
Coach: Peter Mathews
Club captain (1988–89): Danny Dawes
Club captain (1989–90): Danny Dawes
No. of teams: Senior 4, Youth 1
Directions to ground: 150 yards west of Crooked Billet Roundabout, Walthamstow E17. Leyton on Central Line or Walthamstow Central on Victoria Line and then bus to Crooked Billett
Ground capacity: Standing 200
Clubhouse facilities: The Lord Brooke, Shernhall Street, Walthamstow, London E17

Club colours: Dark blue with thin gold and light blue hoops. (*Change colours:* Red)
Nickname: Coops
Floodlights: No
Membership fees: Full £10, Playing £10, Social £5, Youth £2.50, Student £2.50, OAP £2.50
Ground admission: Nil
Local newspaper: Romford Recorder
League: Eastern Counties 6
League position (1988–89): 4th
League playing record (1988–89): P 7, W 4, D 0, L 3, F 70, A 54

ORWELL

Gainsborough Sports Centre, Manyon Road, Ipswich, Suffolk. Tel: 0473 713088.
Founded: 1964
President: B. Kinsey
Chairman: P. Gardner
Coach: S. Bevan
Secretary: R. Knowles, Felixstowe 284350
Fixtures Secretary: D. Bothwright, 12 Vermont Road, Ipswich, Suffolk. Tel: 0473 215866.
Club captain (1987–88): M. Ferguson
Club captain (1988–89): M. Ferguson
No. of teams: Seniors 2.
Directions to Ground: A45 bypass to Felixstowe. 1st left after Orwell Bridge. Follow signs to airport.
Colours: Red, black. (*Change colours:* Black, red.)
Floodlights: No
Membership: £15
Local newspaper: Evening Star

SAWSTON

Sawston Village College, Sawston, Cambridge. Tel: 0223 836615
Founded: 1978
President: J. Marven
Chairman: M.P. Tomlinson
Coach: G. McMillan
Secretary: Ms K. Elbrow, 5 Rawlyn Close, Cambridge CB5 8NN. Tel: (0223) 244486
Fixtures Secretary: D. Cox, 9 Westmoore Avenue, Sawston, Cambridge. Tel: Cambridge (0223) 836011.
Club captain (1987–88): S. Cox
Club captain (1988–89): S. Cox
No. of teams: Senior 2.
Directions to Ground: Sawston High Street, turn left down New Road, college on right. Ground and clubhouse on the edge of playing fields.
Clubhouse: Brick built.
Colours: Navy, black with one white stripe. (*Change colours:* Red/white hoops.)
Nickname: "Qupnis Hora Temulenti!"
Floodlights: No
Admission: Free
Membership: £15
Local newspaper: Sawston Reporter, Cambridge Evening News.

WITHAM

Spa Road, Witham, Essex. Tel: 0376 511066
President: Edward Gilbert
Chairman: Malcolm Gentle
Secretary: Tom Whelan, 79 Keable Road, Marks Tey, Essex CO6 1XR
Fixtures Secretary: Keith Hennahane, 79 Keable Road, Marks Tey, Essex CO6 1XR. Tel: 0206 210596 (H). 01 325 3160 (W)
Club captain (1988–89): Gareth Farmer
Club captain (1989–90): Nicholas Redfearn
No. of teams: Senior 3
Directions to ground: A12 to Witham, from Witham High Street turn into Spinks Lane, at end of road turn right at T-junction. Follow road round and under

railway bridge, Spa Road is first left
Clubhouse facilities: Open Tuesdays, Fridays, Saturdays and Sundays
Club colours: Brown/white hoop shirts, navy blue shorts and socks. (*Change colours:* All white)

Floodlights: No
League: Eastern Counties 6
League position (1988–89): 5th
League playing record (1988–89): P 7, W 2, D 2, L 3, F 59, A 72

Catch them young! Wisbech set an example even though the young enthusiast here may not be an immediate prospect for the First XV.

KENT LEAGUES

KENT again had four divisions and 42 clubs in them this time – an increase of two on last time. Gillingham Anchorians took the top section narrowly from Betteshanger and Park House, leaving Tonbridge and Old Elthamians to prop up the table and go down a league with Sevenoaks and Dover replacing them in differing circumstances – the former winning all 10 matches and the latter go up on points difference from New Ash Green and Folkestone.

Greenwich and Lloyds Bank drop down into League 3 with Metropolitan Police (Hayes), who won all their 10 matches and had a tremendous points difference of 239–24 after being relegated the previous campaign, and Sittingbourne go up. Thames Polytechnic go down for a second successive season in League 3 along with Orpington, who also take a second plunge in two seasons and have still to win a league match.

From League 4 Citizens (only one draw in eight undefeated matches and a points difference of 247–47) and Darenth Valley ascend, the former being a new team in the competition. Well done! Poor East Peckham managed just one draw in an otherwise disastrous campaign. Someone has to be last.

KENT LEAGUE ONE: OFFICER

K. Prior, Esq.,
29 GoldsmiD Road,
Tonbridge,
Kent   (H) 0732 354836
TN9 2BX   (O) 01 588 2787

KENT LEAGUE TWO: OFFICER

J. Carley, Esq.,
Trinity Court,
Easole Street,
Nonnington,
Kent CT15 4HE   (H) 0304 841066

KENT LEAGUES THREE & FOUR: OFFICER

R. Fisher, Esq.,
7 Manwood Close,
Sittingbourne,
Kent   (H) 0795 71433
ME10 4QL   (O) 0634 388765

TABLES 1987–88

KENT 1

	P	W	D	L	F	A	PTS
Charlton Park	10	9	1	0	266	57	19
Erith	10	9	0	1	234	78	18
Medway	10	6	1	3	151	94	13
Park House	10	6	0	4	151	126	12
Thanet Wand	10	6	0	4	151	126	12
Bromley	10	4	0	6	132	128	8
Tonbridge	10	3	2	5	84	131	8
O Elthamians	10	3	1	6	88	112	7
Sevenoaks	10	3	0	7	83	301	6
Nat West Bank	10	3	0	7	83	301	6
O Shootershill's	10	0	0	10	57	179	0

KENT 2

	P	W	D	L	F	A	PTS
Betteshanger	10	9	0	1	211	81	18
Snowdowns	10	8	0	2	191	75	16
Folkestone	10	8	0	2	182	104	16
Dover	10	7	0	3	197	133	14
Ashford	10	6	0	4	208	114	12
Greenwich	10	5	0	5	114	109	10
Midland Bank	10	5	0	5	136	153	10
Lloyds Bank	10	4	0	6	138	154	8
Thames Poly	10	2	0	8	104	223	4
Met Police Hayes	9	0	0	9	78	202	0
Orpington	9	0	0	9	43	254	0

KENT 3

	P	W	D	L	F	A	PTS
New Ash Green	8	8	0	0	156	34	16
Linton	8	6	0	2	154	83	12
Vigo	8	6	0	2	103	30	12
Sittingbourne	8	4	1	3	65	58	9
Deal Wand	8	3	2	3	68	72	8
O Gravesend's	8	3	0	5	70	86	6
Sheppey	8	2	1	5	58	79	5
Cranbrook	8	1	2	5	52	90	4
Bexley	8	0	0	8	22	236	0

KENT 4

	P	W	D	L	F	A	PTS
Williamsonians	8	7	1	0	153	28	15
O Olavians	8	7	0	1	145	18	14
STC Footscray	8	6	1	1	70	26	13
Edenbridge	8	4	0	4	69	58	8
Darenth Valley	8	3	0	5	103	51	6
Univ of Kent	8	3	0	5	100	74	6
Whitstable	8	3	0	5	122	113	6
East Peckham	8	2	0	6	55	169	4
Lordswood	8	0	0	8	22	302	0

TABLES 1988–89

KENT 1

	P	W	D	L	F	A	PTS
Gill'ham Anch	10	8	1	1	138	59	17
Betteshanger	10	8	0	2	121	84	16
Park House	10	7	1	2	143	83	15
Medway	10	6	0	4	165	105	12
Bromley	10	6	0	4	117	112	12
Snowdown C.W.	10	5	0	5	122	104	10
Thanet Wand	10	4	1	5	91	103	9
Erith	10	4	0	6	98	105	8
Canterbury	10	3	0	7	68	143	6
Tonbridge	10	1	1	8	43	117	3
O Elthamians	10	1	0	9	67	158	2

KENT 2

	P	W	D	L	F	A	PTS
Sevenoaks	10	10	0	0	261	56	20
Dover	10	7	0	3	164	62	14
New Ash Green	10	6	2	2	115	83	14
Folkestone	10	6	2	2	139	109	14
Linton	10	6	0	4	167	84	12
O Shooters'ians	10	5	1	4	111	100	11
Nat West Bank	10	4	1	5	111	149	9
Midland Bank	10	4	0	6	105	144	8
Ashford	10	2	0	8	95	142	4
Greenwich	10	1	0	9	65	181	2
Lloyds Bank	10	1	0	9	40	263	2

KENT 3

	P	W	D	L	F	A	PTS
Met Pol Hayes	10	10	0	0	239	24	20
Sittingbourne	10	8	0	2	166	40	16
Vigo	10	7	0	3	164	68	14
Sheppey	10	5	1	4	155	130	11
O Will'sonians	10	5	0	5	148	132	10
Deal	10	4	1	5	155	124	9
Cranbrook	10	4	0	6	114	139	8
O Olavians	10	3	2	5	100	151	8
O Graves'ians	10	3	1	6	101	178	7
Thames Poly	10	3	0	7	119	165	6
Orpington	10	0	1	9	33	343	1

KENT 4

	P	W	D	L	F	A	PTS
Citizens	8	7	1	0	247	47	15
Darenth Valley	8	6	1	1	144	64	13
STC Footscray	8	6	0	2	131	75	12
Edenbridge**	7	3	2	2	85	48	8
Bexley	8	3	1	4	77	72	7
Whitstable**	7	2	1	4	52	76	5
Univ Of Kent**	7	2	1	4	71	115	5
Lordswood**	7	1	0	6	18	165	2
East Peckham	8	0	1	7	30	193	1

** = Matches not played with permission of League Committee.

LONDON & SOUTH EAST DIVISION FIXTURES 1989/90

KENT LEAGUE ONE

Sat. 23rd September (Week 4)
Park House v Betteshanger
Sevenoaks v Dover
Old Dunstonians v Canterbury
Medway v Bromley
Thanet Wanderers v Snowdon Colliery

Sat. 14th October (Week 6)
Snowdon Colliery v Park House
Bromley v Thanet Wanderers
Canterbury v Medway
Dover v Old Dunstonians
Erith v Sevenoaks

Sat. 28th October (Week 8)
Park House v Bromley
Betteshanger v Snowdon Colliery
Old Dunstonians v Erith
Medway v Dover
Thanet Wanderers v Canterbury

Sat. 11th November (Week 10)
Bromley v Betteshanger
Canterbury v Park House
Dover v Thanet Wanderers
Erith v Medway
Sevenoaks v Old Dunstonians

Sat 18th November (Week 11)
Park House v Dover
Betteshanger v Canterbury
Snowdon Colliery v Bromley
Medway v Sevenoaks
Thanet Wanderers v Erith

Sat. 25th November (Week 12)
Canterbury v Snowdon Colliery
Dover v Betteshanger
Erith v Park House
Sevenoaks v Thanet Wanderers
Old Dunstonians v Medway

Sat. 13th January (Week 18)
Park House v Sevenoaks
Betteshanger v Erith
Snowdon Colliery v Dover
Bromley v Canterbury
Thanet Wanderers v Old Dunstonians

Sat. 27th January (Week 20)
Dover v Bromley
Erith v Snowdon Colliery
Sevenoaks v Betteshanger
Old Dunstonians v Park House
Medway v Thanet Wanderers

Sat. 10th February (Week 22)
Park House v Medway
Betteshanger v Old Dunstonians
Snowdon Colliery v Sevenoaks
Bromley v Erith
Canterbury v Dover

Sat. 24th February (Week 24)
Erith v Canterbury
Sevenoaks v Bromley
Old Dunstonians v Snowdon Colliery
Medway v Betteshanger
Thanet Wanderers v Park House

Sat. 10th March (Week 26)
Betteshanger v Thanet Wanderers
Snowdon Colliery v Medway
Bromley v Old Dunstonians
Canterbury v Sevenoaks
Dover v Erith

LONDON & SOUTH EAST DIVISION FIXTURES 1989/90

KENT LEAGUE TWO

Sat. 23rd September (Week 4)
Met. Police, Hayes v Nat. West. Bank
New Ash Green v Old Shootershillians
Old Elthamians v Midland Bank
Linton v Tonbridge
Folkestone v Sittingbourne

Sat. 14th October (Week 6)
Sittingbourne v Met. Police, Hayes
Tonbridge v Folkestone
Midland Bank v Linton
Old Shootershillians v Old Elthamians
Ashford v New Ash Green

Sat. 28th October (Week 8)
Met. Police, Hayes v Tonbridge
Nat. West. Bank v Sittingbourne
Old Elthamians v Ashford
Linton v Old Shootershillians
Folkestone v Midland Bank

Sat. 11th November (Week 10)
Tonbridge v Nat. West. Bank
Midland Bank v Met. Police, Hayes
Old Shootershillians v Folkestone
Ashford v Linton
New Ash Green v Old Elthamians

Sat 18th November (Week 11)
Met. Police, Hayes v Old Shootershillians
Nat. West. Bank v Midland Bank
Sittingbourne v Tonbridge
Linton v New Ash Green
Folkestone v Ashford

Sat. 25th November (Week 12)
Midland Bank v Sittingbourne
Old Shootershillians v Nat. West. Bank
Ashford v Met. Police, Hayes
New Ash Green v Folkestone
Old Elthamians v Linton

Sat. 13th January (Week 18)
Met. Police, Hayes v New Ash Green
Nat. West. Bank v Ashford
Sittingbourne v Old Shootershillians
Tonbridge v Midland Bank
Folkestone v Old Elthamians

Sat. 27th January (Week 20)
Old Shootershillians v Tonbridge
Ashford v Sittingbourne
New Ash Green v Nat. West. Bank
Old Elthamians v Met. Police, Hayes
Linton v Folkestone

Sat. 10th February (Week 22)
Met. Police, Hayes v Linton
Nat. West. Bank v Old Elthamians
Sittingbourne v New Ash Green
Tonbridge v Ashford
Midland Bank v Old Shootershillians

Sat. 24th February (Week 24)
Ashford v Midland Bank
New Ash Green v Tonbridge
Old Elthamians v Sittingbourne
Linton v Nat. West. Bank
Folkestone v Met. Police, Hayes

Sat. 10th March (Week 26)
Nat. West. Bank v Folkestone
Sittingbourne v Linton
Tonbridge v Old Elthamians
Midland Bank v New Ash Green
Old Shootershillians v Ashford

LONDON & SOUTH EAST DIVISION FIXTURES 1989/90

KENT LEAGUE THREE

Sat. 23rd September (Week 4)
Lloyds Bank v Vigo
Cranbrook v Deal
Citizens v Sheppey
Old Williamsonians v Old Gravesendians
Old Olavians v Darenth Valley

Sat. 14th October (Week 6)
Darenth Valley v Lloyds Bank
Old Gravesendians v Old Olavians
Sheppey v Old Williamsonians
Deal v Citizens
Greenwich v Cranbrook

Sat. 28th October (Week 8)
Lloyds Bank v Old Gravesendians
Vigo v Darenth Valley
Citizens v Greenwich
Old Williamsonians v Deal
Old Olavians v Sheppey

Sat. 11th November (Week 10)
Old Gravesendians v Vigo
Sheppey v Lloyds Bank
Deal v Old Olavians
Greenwich v Old Williamsonians
Cranbrook v Citizens

Sat 18th November (Week 11)
Lloyds Bank v Deal
Vigo v Sheppey
Darenth Valley v Old Gravesendians
Old Williamsonians v Cranbrook
Old Olavians v Greenwich

Sat. 25th November (Week 12)
Sheppey v Darenth Valley
Deal v Vigo
Greenwich v Lloyds Bank
Cranbrook v Old Olavians
Citizens v Old Williamsonians

Sat. 13th January (Week 18)
Lloyds Bank v Cranbrook
Vigo v Greenwich
Darenth Valley v Deal
Old Gravesendians v Sheppey
Old Olavians v Citizens

Sat. 27th January (Week 20)
Deal v Old Gravesendians
Greenwich v Darenth Valley
Cranbrook v Vigo
Citizens v Lloyds Bank
Old Williamsonians v Old Olavians

Sat. 10th February (Week 22)
Lloyds Bank v Old Williamsonians
Vigo v Citizens
Darenth Valley v Cranbrook
Old Gravesendians v Greenwich
Sheppey v Deal

Sat. 24th February (Week 24)
Greenwich v Sheppey
Cranbrook v Old Gravesendians
Citizens v Darenth Valley
Old Williamsonians v Vigo
Old Olavians v Lloyds Bank

Sat. 10th March (Week 26)
Vigo v Old Olavians
Darenth Valley v Old Williamsonians
Old Gravesendians v Citizens
Sheppey v Cranbrook
Deal v Greenwich

LONDON & SOUTH EAST DIVISION FIXTURES 1989/90

KENT LEAGUE FOUR

Sat. 23rd September (Week 4)
STC Footscray v Thames Polytechnic
Lordswood v East Peckham
Orpington v Edenbrige
Westerham v University of Kent
Centurians v Bexley

Sat. 14th October (Week 6)
Bexley v STC Footscray
University of Kent v Centurians
Edenbrige v Westerham
East Peckham v Orpington
Whitstable v Lordswood

Sat. 28th October (Week 8)
STC Footscray v University of Kent
Thames Polytechnic v Bexley
Orpington v Whitstable
Westerham v East Peckham
Centurians v Edenbrige

Sat. 11th November (Week 10)
University of Kent v Thames Polytechnic
Edenbrige v STC Footscray
East Peckham v Centurians
Whitstable v Westerham
Lordswood v Orpington

Sat 18th November (Week 11)
STC Footscray v East Peckham
Thames Polytechnic v Edenbrige
Bexley v University of Kent
Westerham v Lordswood
Centurians v Whitstable

Sat. 25th November (Week 12)
Edenbrige v Bexley
East Peckham v Thames Polytechnic
Whitstable v STC Footscray
Lordswood v Centurians
Orpington v Westerham

Sat. 13th January (Week 18)
STC Footscray v Lordswood
Thames Polytechnic v Whitstable
Bexley v East Peckham
University of Kent v Edenbrige
Centurians v Orpington

Sat. 27th January (Week 20)
East Peckham v University of Kent
Whitstable v Bexley
Lordswood v Thames Polytechnic
Orpington v STC Footscray
Westerham v Centurians

Sat. 10th February (Week 22)
STC Footscray v Westerham
Thames Polytechnic v Orpington
Bexley v Lordswood
University of Kent v Whitstable
Edenbrige v East Peckham

Sat. 24th February (Week 24)
Whitstable v Edenbrige
Lordswood v University of Kent
Orpington v Bexley
Westerham v Thames Polytechnic
Centurians v STC Footscray

Sat. 10th March (Week 26)
Thames Polytechnic v Centurians
Bexley v Westerham
University of Kent v Orpington
Edenbrige v Lordswood
East Peckham v Whitstable

KENT 1

BETTESHANGER COLLIERY WELFARE

Ground: Welfare Ground, Cavell Square, Mill Hill, Deal, Kent. Clubhouse: Welfare Club (1st Floor), Cowdrey Square, Mill Hill, Deal, Kent. Tel: 0304 365090
Founded: 1948
President: Gerald Griffiths
Chairman: Charles Burmister
Secretary: Hugh Fraser, 42 Quern Road, Deal CT14 9EQ. Tel: 0304 364297
Fixtures Secretary: Bob Pinnick, 65 Courtenay Road, Dunkirk, Faversham, Kent ME13 9LH. Tel: 0227 750530 (H), 750530 (W)
Press Officer: Gerald Griffiths, 51 Thornbridge Road, Deal, Kent. Tel: 0304 374249
Coach: Cliff Davies
Club captain (1988–89): Glyn Stone
Club captain (1989–90): Phil Johnson
No. of teams: Senior 4, Youth 1, Vets 1
Directions to ground: M2 Junction 7 → A2(T) Dover (20 miles) → A258 Deal (5 miles) → Upper Walmer (4th left Church Street) → 800 metres T-junction turn right (Court Road) → 100 metres T-junction turn left (St. Richards Road) 4th right (Mill Hill) 1st left (Redsal Avenue) 2nd left (Douglas Road) miniroundabout turn left into ground
Ground capacity: Standing 400
Clubhouse facilities: Bar matchdays Friday evenings and Sundays. Hot meals
Club colours: Red and white hoops, blue shorts, red socks. (*Change colours:* Green and white hoops)
Floodlights: No
Membership fees: Full £12.50, Playing £7.50, Social £5, Youth £4, Student £4, VPs £6.50
Ground admission: Free
Programme: No. of editorial pages 8; No. of advertising pages 2; Price Free
Programme editor: Jim Davies, 30 Mary Road, Deal, Kent
Local newspapers: East Kent Mercury
League position (1988–89): 2nd
League playing record (1988–89): P 10, W 8, D 0, L 2, F 121, A 84
Competitions won: Shepherd Neame Floodlight Tournament (Canterbury) XV's. Shepherd Neame 'Golden Oldies' XV's Tournament, Meadowside Leisure Centre, Kidbrooke, London

BROMLEY

Barnet Wood Road, Hayes, Bromley, Kent. Tel: 01-462 3430
Founded: 1886
President: D.J. Davies
Chairman: J.T.A. Bromage
Coach: E.C. Millar
Secretary: R.R. Thomas, 118 Ravensbourne Avenue, Shortlands, Bromley BR2 0AX. Tel: 01-460 2816 (H), 01-460 4661 (W).
Fixtures Secretary: J.T.A. Bromage, 4 Sunningdale Road, Bickley, Bromley. Tel: 01-467 4375 (H), 01-403 1171 (W).
No. of teams: Senior 6, Youth & Minis 6.
Directions to Ground: see London A–Z
Clubhouse: Small and perfectly formed.
Colours: Black and amber. (*Change colours:* Black or gold).
Floodlights: No.
Membership: £40
Local newspaper: Kentish Times

CANTERBURY

Merton Lane, Canterbury. Tel: 0227 68958
Founded: 1929
President: David Hallwood

Chairman: Dickie Ovenden
Coach: T.B.A.
Secretary: Steve Uglon, 98 Whitstable Road, Canterbury. Tel: 0227 61657
Fixtures Secretary: Eddy Hardy, Gentil Knight, Shipman Avenue, Canterbury. Tel: 0227 65891
Club captain (1987–88): Paul Coakley
Club captain (1988–89): Dave Pearson
No. of teams: Senior 6. Youth & Minis 8.
Directions to Ground: Enter Canterbury on A2, follow ring road to 4th roundabout – take 3rd exit (Old Dover Road), proceed over traffic lights, after 3/5 mile turn right on B2068, after 9/10 mile, turnright. Do not cross over by-pass.
Ground capacity: 1000. Stand 200
Clubhouse: Single storey, clubroom with bar/kitchen, VPs bar, large changing.
Colours: Black/amber hoops. (*Change colours:* White or red, white, blue hoops
Floodlights: Yes
Membership: £20 sub, £2.50 match fee
Programme: 25p. (Editor: Mike Inlester. Tel: 0227 450426)
Local newspaper: Kentish Gazette

DOVER

Crabble Athletic Ground, River, Dover, Kent. Tel: 0304 210296
Founded: 1925
President: Bernard H. Lock
Chairman: Maurice G. Sayers
Secretary: J. Derek Thomas, 'Karma', Minnis Lane, River, Dover, Kent CT17 0PT. Tel: 0304 822169
Fixtures Secretary: Roy Dixon, 2 Roman Way, St. Margaret's at Cliffe, Dover, Kent. Tel: 0304 852776
Press Officer: As Secretary
Club captain (1988–89): Alan Massey
Club captain (1989–90): Alan Massey
No. of teams: Senior 5, Youth 2, Minis 3
Directions to ground: From A2/M2 turn right at Whitfield and left at bottom of hill. At traffic lights turn right under bridge to entrance 300 m on left. From A20/M20 enter Dover and leave on A2. Turn left at traffic lights on Crabble Hill
Ground capacity: Seating 100, standing 500
Clubhouse facilities: Match days, Sundays, training nights
Club colours: Light blue and dark blue hoops. (*Change colours:* Plain light blue or white)
Nickname: Sharks
Floodlights: No
Membership fees: Full £10, Playing £10, Social £3, Youth £2, Student £1
Local newspaper: Dover Express
League position (1988–89): 2nd (promoted)
League playing record (1988–89): P 10, W 7, D 0, L 3, F 164, A 62
Competitions won: Medway Sevens, April 1989

ERITH

Northumberland Heath Playing Fields, Sussex Road, Erith, Kent. Tel: 03224 32295
Founded: 1927
President: Peter Thurston Green
Chairman: Norman Button
Secretary: Joseph N. McConville, 18 Buxton Road, Erith, Kent. Tel: 0322 337064 (H), 347831 (W)
Fixtures Secretary: Barry Fielder, 50 Holmesdale Hill, South Darenth, Kent. Tel: Farningham 864574
Coach: Christopher Shears
Club captain (1988–89): Stewart Button
Club captain (1989–90): Kevin Whittern
No. of teams: Senior 4, Youth 2, Minis 5
Directions to ground: Off A2 to Bexley, follow signs to Erith, follow Bexley Road to Brook Street. Travel down Brook Street to Duchess of Kent Pub, turn left into Sussex Road
Clubhouse facilities: Bar and clubhouse (capacity approx. 150)

Club colours: Dark blue and light blue hoops.
(*Change colours:* Navy blue or Maroon)
Nickname: Ees (pronounced 'ease')
Floodlights: Yes (training only)
Membership fees: Playing £18, Social £8, Youth £2,
Student £5, OAP £8
Local newspapers: Kentish Times, Mercury
League position (1988–89): 8th
League playing record (1988–89): P 10, W 4, D 0,
L 6, F 98, A 105

MEDWAY

Priestfields, Rochester, Kent. Tel: 0634 47737
Founded: 1931
President: Mayor of Rochester-upon-Medway
Chairman: Michael Dakers
Secretary: Robert Doyle, 57 Wheatcroft Grove,
Rainham, Kent. Tel: 0634 337934 (H), 01–253 1979
(W)
Fixtures Secretary: Jim Hillier, 9 Oxford Road,
Gillingham, Kent ME7 4BP. Tel: 0634 527400 (H),
0322 23488 ext. 2117 (W)
Press Officer: John Winson, 38 Elm Avenue,
Chatham, Kent. Tel: 0634 813805 (H), 0622 77524
(W)
Coach: Michael Cadmore
Club captain (1988–89): Ian Dance
Club captain (1989–90): Ian Dance
No. of teams: Senior 5, Youth 5, Minis 5
Directions to ground: From the M25 or the M2 take
the A229 Chatham Road. At roundabout signposted
Rochester take the B2097, turn left into Priestfields
off this road
Clubhouse facilities:
Club colours: Red/amber
Floodlights: No
Local newspapers: Evening Post, Chatham News
League position (1988–89): 4th
League playing record (1988–89): P 35, W 19, D 1,
L 15, F 555, A 373

OLD DUNSTONIAN

St Dunstan's lane, Langley Park, Beckenham, Kent.
Tel: 01-650 1779.
Founded: 1903
President: S.D. Kelly
Coach: R. Bodenham
Secretary: N.A. Rogers, "Aboyne", Pickhurst Lane,
West Wickham, Kent BR4 0HN. Tel: 01-402 3064 (H)
01-379 7383 (W).
Fixtures Secretary: P.W. France Esq., 5 The Mead,
West Wickham, Kent. Tel: 01-776 0872 (H) 01-261
3368 (W).
Club captain (1987–88): K. McNally
Club captain (1988–89): H.G. Evans
No. of teams: Senior 6.
Directions to Ground: St. Dunstan's Lane or
Hawksbrook Lane off Wickham Way, Beckenham,
Kent.
Ground capacity: 2000
Clubhouse: 6 changing rooms, showers/bath, 3 bars,
hall & kitchen, 2 car parks.
Colours: Navy blue and white. (*Change colours:* Navy
blue and pink quarters)
Nickname: Pink Elephants
Floodlights: Training only.
Membership: £30 (playing); £10 (honorary).
Local newspaper: Beckenham Journal/Bromley &
Kentish Times
League: London 3SE

PARK HOUSE

Barnet Wood Road, Hayes, Kent. Tel: 462 7318
Founded: 1883
President: William Chisholm
Secretary: John Cross, 85 Murrey Avenue, Bromley,
Kent BR1 3Dj. Tel: 464 6456 (H), 631 0101 (W)
Fixtures Secretary: James H. McGarey, 'Greenways',

5 Pondfield Road, Hayes, Kent BR2 7HS. Tel: 462
1130 (H), 283 3100 ext. 4217 (W)
Press Officer: Ivor Bigone, 83 Croydon Road, Keston,
Kent BR2 8HU. Tel: 0689 58527 (H), 930 6262 (W)
Coach: Patrick McCarthy
Club captain (1988–89): Andy Wakefield
Club captain (1989–90): Andy Wakefield
No. of teams: Senior 6, Youth 2, Minis 2
Directions to ground: A21 to Bromley, turn right at
second traffic lights after Bromley South Station.
B265 to Hayes (Hayes Lane), continue into Baston
Road. At Baston Girls School turn left into Barnet
Wood Road (ground on right side)
Clubhouse facilities: Open matchdays, training
Monday, Wednesday
Club colours: Red and black. (*Change colours:* Black)
Floodlights: Yes
Membership fees: Full £35, Playing £35, Social £20,
Youth £25, Student £25, OAP £15
Ground admission: Nil
Local newspapers: Bromley Times, News Shopper
League position (1988–89): 3rd
League playing record (1988–89): P 10, W 7, D 1,
L 2, F 143, A 83

SEVENOAKS

Knole Paddock, Plymouth Drive, Sevenoaks, Kent.
Tel: 0732 452027
Founded: 1925
President: Richard Shirtcliff
Chairman: Howard Pearl
Secretary: John Maslin, 198 Chesterfield Drive,
Chipstead, Sevenoaks, Kent. Tel: 0732 460910
Fixtures Secretary: Howard Pearl, 10 Barnfield Road,
Riverhead, Sevenoaks, Kent TN13 2AY
Press Officer: Trevor Nicholson, Gillhams Farm,
French Street, Westerham, Kent TN16 1pN. Tel: 0959
62027 (H), 0732 460840 (W)
Coach: Stephen Manley
Club captain (1988–89): Dave Cotterill
Club captain (1989–90): Dave Cotterill
No. of teams: Senior 6, Youth 3, Minis 5
Directions to ground: North end of High Street, fork
right at Conservative Association building, first right
Plymouth Drive
Ground capacity: Standing 1000
Clubhouse facilities: All mod. cons.
Club colours: Blue and yellow hoops. (*Change
colours:* Dark blue (2nd strip if necessary))
Nickname: Oaks
Floodlights: No
Membership fees: Playing £21.50, Social £8.50, Youth
Nil, Student £5
Ground admission: Nil
Local newspaper: Sevenoaks Chronicle
League: Kent 1
League position (1988–89): 1st (promoted)
League playing record (1988–89): P 10, W 10, D 0,
L 0, F 261, A 56
Competitions won: Kent Division 2 Champions

SNOWDOWN COLLIERY

Welfare Ground, Aylesham. Tel: 0304 840278.
Founded: 1931
President: L. Kingston
Chairman: C. Owen
Coach: Lester Powell
Secretary: E.J. Sullivan, 4 Burgess Road, Aylesham,
Canterbury, Kent. Tel: 0304 840052.
Fixtures Secretary: Les Powell. Tel: 0304 840103.
Club captain (1988–89): R. Hadfield
No. of teams: Senior 4. Youth & Minis 1.
Directions to Ground: Take left turning off A2 approx
half way between Canterbury and Dover 1 mile
further on.
Clubhouse: Small Clubhouse
Colours: Red and blue hoops. (*Change colours:*
Black).
Floodlights: No

Membership: Players £10, non-players £4.
Local newspaper: Dover Express

THANET WANDERERS

St. Peters Recreation Ground, Callis Court Road,
Broadstairs, Kent. Tel: 0843 61499
Founded: 1886
President: Roy T. Mercer
Chairman: John D. Treharne
Secretary: J.A. Challinor, 124 Dumpton Park Drive,
Ramsgate, Kent. Tel: 0843 595712
Fixtures Secretary: P.J. Hawkins, 51 Park Road,
Ramsgate Kent. Tel: 0843 593142
Press Officer: Julian Sowden, 164 Grange Road,
Ramsgate, Kent. Tel: 0843 590028
Coach: A. Williamson
Club captain (1988–89): Tom Carlier
Club captain (1989–90): Tom Carlier
No. of teams: Senior 6, Youth 2, Minis 4
Directions to ground: Follow signpost for Broadstairs.
Clubhouse is signposted off St. Peters Park Road
Clubhouse facilities: On groun, one bar, small lounge
area
Club colours: Blue, black and yellow. (*Change
colours:* Royal blue)
Nickname: Wanderers
Floodlights: No
Membership fees: Full £20, VPs £10
Programme: No. of editorial pages 4; No. of
advertising pages 8
Programme editor: As Fixtures Secretary
Local newspaper: Isle of Thanet Gazette
League position (1988–89): 7th
League playing record (1988–89): P 10, W 4, D 1,
L 5, F 91, A 103

KENT 2

ASHFORD (KENT)

Kinney's Field, Canterbury Road, Bybrook, Ashford,
Kent. Tel: 0233 624693
Founded: 1885
President: John Roblin
Chairman: Mike Barnes
Secretary: Martin R. Briscall, c/o Yule Cottage, Park
Road, Kennington, Ashford, Kent. Tel: 0233 37311
(W)
Fixtures Secretary: Dave Slawson, 21 Tadworth Road,
Kennington, Ashford, Kent TN24 9JJ. Tel: 0233
30986 (H), 812761 (W)
Press Officer: As Fixtures Secretary
Coach: Andy Barr
Club captain (1988–89): Tom Murray
Club captain (1989–90): Dave Slawson
No. of teams: Senior 5, Youth 2, Minis 4
Directions to ground: Take 2nd exit on roundabout on
A20 (Simon Weil Avenue) west of Ashford
(roundabout has access to M20 link road). At junction
with A28 by M20 bridge, turn left (signposted
Canterbury), single track to club 300 yds on right
opposite Fire Station
Clubhouse facilities: Open matchdays, Tuesday
evenings and Sunday lunchtime
Club colours: Red gold black
Floodlights: No
League position (1988–89): 9th
League playing record (1988–89): P 10, W 2, D 0,
L 8, F 95, A 142

FOLKESTONE

New Burlington Field, Bargrove, Newington,
Folkestone, Kent CT18 8BM. Tel: 0303 66887
Founded: 1974
President: Alan Frew
Chairman: John Kidson
Coach: Jim Nixon
Secretary: Paul Barber, 1 Ethelburga Drive, Lyminge,

Kent CT18 8JJ. Tel: 0303 863036.
Fixtures Secretary: Dave Gilbert, 113 Surrenden
Road, Folkestone CT19 4AC. Tel: 0303 76640.
Club captain (1988–89): Anton Phillips
No. of teams: Senior 4. Youth & Minis 8.
Directions to Ground: Take exit 12 on M20 and follow
signs to Newington. After 1·2 miles take 1st turning at
roundabout to Hythe. Ground mile on right.
Ground capacity: 2000
Clubhouse: Opened June 1988 after Eurotunnel took
over possession of previous clubhouse.
Colours: Green. (*Change colours:* Green and white
hoops.
Floodlights: Fundraising for them at present.
Membership: £21 players, £15 non-player, £5 social
Programme: Only on cup days. 20p. (Editor: D.
Gilbert)
Local newspaper: Folkestone Herald

LINTON

Mote Park, Maidstone, Kent. Tel: 0622 54770
Founded: 1977
President: Jack Williams
Chairman: Dave Enston
Secretary: Bob Wilson, 7 Westwood Road, Loose,
Maidstone, Kent ME15 6BB. Tel: 0622 744468 (H),
0634 684335 (W)
Fixtures Secretary: Dave Enston, 47 Hornbeam
Close, Larkfield, Maidstone, Kent ME20 6LZ. Tel:
0732 842666
Press Officer: Paul Brotherwood, 'Hillrise', 125 Heath
Road, Barming, Maidstone, Kent ME16 9JJ. Tel:
0622 27569
Coach: Norman Bateman
Club captain (1988–89): Nigel Baker
Club captain (1989–90): Graham Sutton
No. of teams: Senior 4
Directions to ground: Mote Road, Maidstone, into
Mote Park through main gates and follow directions
to Pavilion which is on high ground above the lake
Clubhouse facilities: Hospitality at the Rising Sun
Public House, Marsham Street, Maidstone
Club colours: Red shirts and socks, black shorts.
(*Change colours:* Blue shirts)
Nickname: 'The Bulls'
Floodlights: No
Membership fees: Full £25, Playing £25, Social £10,
Student £15, OAP £10
Programme editor: Roy Milne, 1 Shirley Way,
Bearsted, Maidstone, Kent ME15 8PP
Local newspaper: Kent Messenger
League position (1988–89): 5th
League playing record (1988–89): P 10, W 6, D 0,
L 4, F 167, A 84

METROPOLITAN
POLICE (HAYES)

The Warren, Croydon Road, Hayes Common, Kent.
Tel: 01–462 1266
Founded: 1948
Secretary: John Early, 30 The Crescent, West
Wickham, Kent BR4 0HE. Tel: 01–777 6828 (H),
01–697 9317 (W)
Fixtures Secretary: Nigel Yeo, 32 Abbotsbury Road,
Hayes, Kent. Tel: 01–462 5782 (H), 01–200 2163 (W)
Club captain (1988–89): Brian O'Rourke
Club captain (1989–90): Brian O'Rourke
No. of teams: Senior 3
Directions to ground: A21 Bromley to Farnborough,
turn right into Croydon Road, across Hayes
Common. Ground 1 mile on right
Clubhouse facilities: Police sports club
Club colours: Sky blue. (*Change colours:* Maroon)
Floodlights: No
Membership fees: Any police officer
Ground admission: Nil
Local newspaper: Kentish Times
League position (1988–89): 1st

League playing record (1988–89): P 10, W 10, D 0, L 0, F 240, A 24

MIDLAND BANK

Lennard Road, New Beckenham, Kent. Tel: 01-778 6885
Founded: 1911
President: J.A. Brooks
Secretary: C.J. Rouse, 59 Crantock Road, SE6. Tel: 01-698 4527.
Fixtures Secretary: J.R.D. Hayhow, Five Trees, 36 Holbrook Lane, Chislehurst BR7 6PF. Tel: 01-467 3314.
Club captain (1988–89): P.R. Ayling
No. of teams: Senior 4.
Directions to Ground: Adjoining New Beckenham Railway Station.
Colours: Green shirts, navy blue shorts. (*Change colours:* Red shirts).
Nickname: City
Floodlights: No

NATIONAL WESTMINSTER BANK

Copers Cope Road, Beckenham, Kent. Tel: 01-650 9217/4559
Founded: 1886
President: John Melbourn
Chairman: Roger Harding
Secretary: C.J. Longhurst, 64 Aviemore Way, Beckenham, Kent BR3 3RT. Tel: 01-658 3575 (H), 01-734 1274 (W)
Fixtures Secretary: George Teale, 129 Ellerdine Road, Hounslow, Middx. Tel: 01-568 2629 (H), 01-726 1271 (W)
Coach: Dave Cordery
Club captain (1988–89): Richard Orridge
Club captain (1989–90): Richard Orridge
No. of teams: Senior 4
Directions to ground: By railway: frequent trains from Charing Cross, Cannon Street or London Bridge to Lower Sydenham. Leave station by the downside, bear right into Worsley Bridge Road. The ground is the first on the right. Enter via Copes Cope Road (1st right). By road: Copes Cope Road adjoins Beckenham Junction Station. Proceed 1 mile and the entrance is on the left. No. 54 bus passes Beckenham end of Copes Cope Road
Ground capacity: Standing 200
Clubhouse facilities: Open weekends and evenings
Club colours: Light and dark blue hoops. (*Change colours:* Red)
Floodlights: Yes
League position (1988–89): 7th
League playing record (1988–89): P 30, W 6, D 1, L 23, F 300, A 700

NEW ASH GREEN

Punch Croft, New Ash Green, Dartford, Kent. Tel: 0474 874660.
Founded: 1974
Secretary: L. Ellard, 9 Lambardes, New Ash Green, Near Dartford, Kent DA3 H8X. Tel: 0474 873924 (H).
League Contact: K. Milner, 32 Lambardes, New Ash Green, Kent DA3 8HX. Tel: 0474 874531

OLD ELTHAMIANS

Founded: 1911
Chairman: John Mack
Secretary: David Bullman, 117 Raeburn Road, Sidcup, Kent. Tel: 0753 684011 (W)
Fixtures Secretary: David Shaw, 22 Abbots Green, Addington, Croydon, Surrey. Tel: 01-656 8973

Club captain (1988–89): Jim Scully
Club captain (1989–90): Jim Scully
No. of teams: Senior 4, Youth 5, Minis 5
Ground capacity: Seating 30
Clubhouse facilities: Squash, two bars, hall, etc.
Club colours: Old gold and blue hoops
Floodlights: Yes
Membership fees: Full £25, Playing £25, Social £5, Student £5
Local newspaper: Kentish Times
League position (1988–89): Bottom (relegated)
League playing record (1988–89): P 10, W 1, D 0, L 9, F 67, A 158

OLD SHOOTERHILLIANS

Ground: Avery Hill Park, Avery Hill, Eltham, London, SE9. Clubhouse: 72 Footscray Road, Eltham, London, SE9. Tel: 01-850 9500
Founded: 1929
President: Dennis A.J. Frampton
Chairman: Peter Holt
Secretary: Kevin J. Bailey, 13 Lindon Avenue, Dartford, Kent DA1 2RA. Tel: 0322 76129 (H), 01-568 911 (W)
Fixtures Secretary: Peter J. Hills, 66 Hartslock Drive, Thamesmead SE2 9UU. Tel: 01-310 6585
Press Officer: Neil Sharp, 17 Denver Road, Dartford, Kent
Club captain (1988–89): Clive Aldridge
Club captain (1989–90): Jeff Hale
No. of teams: Senior 3–4
Directions to ground: Meet at clubhouse. Turn into Southend Crescent from Footscray Road, turn right at lights, proceed down Bexley Road, enter park through brick arch entrance, turn right to changing rooms
Clubhouse facilities: Bar, etc.
Club colours: Green, red, blue, yellow
Nickname: 'Shoots'
Floodlights: No
Local newspapers: Kentish Times and Mercury
League position (1988–89): 6th
League playing record (1988–89): P 10, W 5, D 1, L 4, F 111, A 100

SITTINGBOURNE

U.K. Paper Leisure Club, Gore Court Road, Sittingbourne, Kent. Tel: 0795 77047
Founded: 1977
President: Fred Garwood
Chairman: Stuart Tatton
Secretary: Hedley Chapman, 4 Morris Court close, Bapchild, Sittingbourne, Kent ME9 9PL. Tel: 0795 75668 (H), 0634 271681 (W)
Fixtures Secretary: Geoff Marshall, 90 Borden Lane, Sittingbourne, Kent ME10 1DG. Tel: 0795 71707
Press Officer: Mark Reed, 64 Rock Road, Sittingbourne, Kent ME10 1JG. Tel: 0795 74787
Coach: T.B.A.
Club captain (1988–89): Glen Collins
Club captain (1989–90): Glen Collins
No. of teams: Senior 4, Youth 2, Minis 4
Directions to ground: From London into town on A2, follow small one-way system to town centre, join main A2, 1st right, Park Road follow round, club on left
Clubhouse facilities: Open matchdays and training evenings
Club colours: Amber with a single blue hoop. (*Change colours:* Blue with a single amber hoop)
Nickname: 'Bourne'
Floodlights: No
Membership fees: Full £14
Local newspaper: East Kent Gazette
League position (1988–89): 2nd
League playing record (1988–89): P 10, W 8, D 0, L 2, F 166, A 40

TONBRIDGE

The Clubhouse, Avebury Avenue, Tonbridge, Kent.
Tel: 0732 350067
Founded: 1904
President: Keith Prior
Chairman: Peter Mitchell
Secretary: Gordon John Wood, 181 Southwood Road,
Rusthall, Tunbridge Wells, Kent TN4 8TP. Tel: 0892
542622
Fixtures Secretary: David Carver, 50 Pennington
Place, Southborough, Tunbridge Wells, Kent. Tel:
0892 543736 (H), 01–439 4937 (W)
Press Officer: As Fixtures Secretary
Coach: Gordon John Wood
Club captain (1988–89): Declan Ward
Club captain (1989–90): Kevin Jenner
No. of teams: Senior 5, Youth 3, Minis 5
Directions to ground: Exit Tonbridge south from A21,
approach town after railway station, turn left into
Avebury Avenue immediately after island
Club colours: Chocolate and old gold hoops, black
shorts and socks
Floodlights: No
League position (1988–89): 10th (relegated)
League playing record (1988–89): P 31, W 10, D 4,
L 17, F 305, A 383

KENT 3

CITIZENS

UCL Athletic Ground, Perry Street, Chislehurst. Tel:
01–467 3859
Chairman: Gerry Bishop
Secretary: Chris Southgate, 122 The Ridgeway,
Enfield, Middx EN2 8JN. Tel: 01–366 5791 (H),
01–367 5840 (W)
Fixtures Secretary: Ray Mannell, 281 Green Lane,
New Eltham, London SE9 3TB. Tel: 01–857 3057
Press Officer: As Secretary
Club captain (1988–89): Adrian Moody
Club captain (1989–90): Adrian Moody
No. of teams: Senior 3
Directions to ground: Charing Cross (BR) to Sidcup
Station. Left from Station Approach to bus stop
adjacent traffic lights. Bus 228 or 269 to Old Perry
Street, 1st stop past Western Motor works. Entrance
to ground a further 250 yds on the opposite side of
road
Ground capacity: Standing 500
Clubhouse facilities: Open matchdays
Club colours: Black with maroon and white hoops
Floodlights: No
Membership fees: Full £40, Playing £30, Social £10,
Youth £15, Student £15, OAP £5
Ground admission: Free
Local newspaper: Kentish Town Group
League position (1988–89): 1st (promoted)
League playing record (1988–89): P 8, W 7, D 1, L 0,
F 247, A 47
Competitions won: Kent League Division 4

CRANBROOK

Tomlin Ground, Angley Road, Cranbrook, Kent. Tel:
0580 712777
Founded: .
President: M.I. McMinnies
Chairman: D.C. McMinnies
Secretary: D.L.J. Davies, Beeches Station Road,
Staplehurst, Kent TN12 0QG. Tel: 0580 891448.
Fixtures Secretary: M. Fitzsimons, 32 Jaggard Way,
Staplehurst. Tel: 0580 891178.
Club captain (1988–89): A. Alison
No. of teams: Senior 4. Youth & Minis 4.
Directions to Ground: North side of Cranbrook bypass
on A229.
Clubhouse: Licensed.
Colours: Magenta/white. (*Change colours:* White).

Nickname: Cranes
Floodlights: No
Membership: £0.50
Local newspaper: Kent & Sussex Courier

DARENTH VALLEY

Five Bells, Eynsford, Kent DA4 0AB
Founded: 1977
President: David Kerr
Chairman: Ian Macknelly
Secretary: George Macknelly, 68 Saint Martins Drive,
Eynsford, Kent DA4 0EZ.
Fixtures Secretary: David Wilson, 26 Ashen Drive,
Dartford, Kent DA1 3UI. Tel: 0322 70781.
League Contact: R. Daniel, Flat 2, Sunnyside, High
Street, Farningham, Kent DA4 0DT. Tel: 0322
864478
Club captain (1988–89): Steve Wood
No. of teams: Senior 2
Directions to Ground: Seeking permanent home
ground. Home features 88/9 at Hextable School. Go
to centre of Hextable and then down College Road to
Egerton Avenue.
Colours: Black – white V in front. (2nd XV black and
white hoops).
Nickname: Valley
Floodlights: No
Membership: Players £20 for season + £3 a game.
Local newspaper: Kent Newspapers – Swanley &
Dartford
League: Kent 4

DEAL WANDERERS

North Deal Playing Field, Western Road, Deal, Kent.
Tel: 0304 365892
Founded: 1958
President: Jack Hinkins
Chairman: Peter Ebden
Secretary: Michael Parker, 83 Western Road, Deal,
Kent CT14 6PT. Tel: 0304 369372
Fixtures Secretary: Alan Bentley, 22 William Pitt
Avenue, Deal, Kent CT14 9QF. Tel: 0304 367909
Press Officer: As Fixtures Secretary
Coach: Richard Twyman
Club captain (1988–89): Paul Connolly
Club captain (1989–90): Paul Connolly
No. of teams: Senior 3, Youth 2, Minis 2
Directions to ground: From Dover: Into Deal along
The Strand, follow on to one-way system to seafront,
at roundabout take 2nd left into Queen Street through
pelican crossing to traffic lights (Swan P.H. on right).
Turn right into West Street, proceed along West
Street to end, T-junction. Club right in front of you
Clubhouse facilities: Open matchdays and Wednesday
evening and Sunday lunchtimes
Club colours: Blue and amber shirts, blue shorts, blue
and amber socks. (*Change colours:* Black with red
and yellow stripes (1 all black strip))
Floodlights: No
Membership fees: Full £12, Playing £12, Student £4
Local newspapers: East Kent Mercury, Deal Express
League: Kent 3
League position (1988–89): 6th
League playing record (1988–89): P 10, W 4, D 1,
L 5, F 155, A 124

GREENWICH (formerly Bloomfield & Lewisham)

Old Mill Road, Plumpstead Common, Plumpstead,
London SE18. Tel: 01-854 8637.
Founded: 1986
Secretary: D.J. Bennett, 318 Plumpstead High Street,
Plumpstead, London SE18. Tel: 01-854 0898 (H),
0322 332612. Extn. 22 (W)

LLOYDS BANK

Lloyds Bank Sports Club, Copers Cope Road, Beckenham, Kent. Tel: 01–658 3818
Founded: 1913
President: Spencer Hoyles
Chairman: Tony Charlwood
Secretary: Bob Brazier, 2 Crushes Close, Hutton, Brentwood, Essex CM13 1PR. Tel: 0277 213626 (H), 01–741 4611 (W)
Fixtures Secretary: Alan Stow, 4 Silkham Road, Oxted, Surrey RH8 0NP. Tel: 0883 717565 (H), 01–922 3932 (W)
Club captain (1988–89): Brian McWhinnie
Club captain (1989–90): Brian McWhinnie
No. of teams: Senior 3
Directions to ground: Frequent trains from Charing Cross, Cannon Street or London Bridge to Lower Sydenham. Leave station on down side, bear right from station approach. Copers Cope Road first on right
Ground capacity: Standing 200
Clubhouse facilities: Open on match days
Club colours: White with broad maroon hoop, narrow black hoop either side. (*Change colours:* Yellow)
Floodlights: Yes
League: Kent 3
League position (1988–89): 11th (relegated)
League playing record (1988–89): P 10, W 1, D 0, L 9, F 40, A 263

OLD GRAVESENDIANS

Fleetway Sports Ground, Parrock Street, Gravesend, Kent. Tel: 0474 65503.
Founded: 1925
Secretary: J. Oxtoby, 43 The Old Yews, Longfield, Gravesend, Kent.
League Contact: D. A. Hill, 1 Old Road West, Gravesend, Kent. Tel: 0474 69284
Colours: Light Blue/Dark Blue

OLD OLAVIANS

St. Olav's School, Goddington Lane, Orpington, Kent. Tel: 0689 30744
Founded: 1952
President: F.D. Coulson
Chairman: George Snelgrove
Secretary: Chris Hudson, 30 Badgers Copse, Tower Road, Orpington Kent. Tel: 0689 75065 (H), 01–313 2621 (W)
Fixtures Secretary: Simon Lapham, 9 Thyme Close, Enfude Village, Chineham North, Basingstoke, Hants. Tel: 0256 51877
Coach: George Snelgrove
Club captain (1988–89): Peter Hinton
Club captain (1989–90): John Michaelis
No. of teams: Senior 4
Directions to ground: Junction 4 M25. Take A21 to next roundabout, take 3rd exit out (A224), continue for 2 miles to parade of shops on left, turn left into Goddington Lane. Ground is 200 yds along on right
Club colours: Purple, blank, white hoops
Floodlights: No
League: Kent 3
League position (1988–89): 7th
League playing record (1988–89): P 32, W 15, D 5, L 12, F 339, A 387

OLD WILLIAMSONIANS

Maidstone Road, Rochester, Kent. Tel: 0634 42883
Founded: 1930
President: K. Wilson
Chairman: Roy Webb
Secretary: Gerald Rush, 23 Bolner Close, Chatham, Kent ME5 9PJ. Tel: 0634 681736 (H), 290866 (W)
Fixtures Secretary: Mark Roper, 125 Borstal Street, Borstal, Rochester, Kent ME1 3JU. Tel: 0634 826328

(H), 01–930 7772 ext. 2114 (W)
Press Officer: Alan Brassell. Tel: 0424 714910
Coach: J. Sheath
Club captain (1988–89): Graham Richards
Club captain (1989–90): Ian Pettman
No. of teams: Senior 3
Directions to ground: From M2 take A229 to Chatham, 400 yds to roundabout take B2097 Borstal. Ground is 2 mils on the left. Sir Joseph Williamsons Mathematical School, Maidstone, Road, Rochester
Club colours: Navy with one gold hoop
Nickname: Old Willies
Floodlights: No
Membership fees: Full £13.50
Local newspapers: Chatham News, Evening Post
League: Kent 3
League position (1988–89): 5th
League playing record (1988–89): P 10, W 5, D 0, L 5, F 155, A 130

SHEPPEY

Lower Road, Minster, Sheerness, Kent. Tel: 0795 872082
Founded: 1892
President: Ken Cooper
Chairman: Richard Barson
Coach: John Clayton
Secretary: Linda Neal, 16 New Road, Minster, Sheerness, Kent ME12 3PX. Tel: 0795 873983.
Fixtures Secretary: Gerry Lawson, Merba, Minster Drive, Minster, Sheerness, Kent. Tel: 0795 876363.
Club captain (1987–88): Mike Wells
Club captain (1988–89): Mike Wells
No. of teams: Senior 4. Youth & Minis 2.
Directions to Ground: A249 to Sheerness. Once on the Island take 2nd exit at roundabout. mile on left side.
Clubhouse: Single storey.
Colours: White with single red hoop. (*Change colours:* Black).
Floodlights: No
Membership: £15
Local newspaper: Sheerness Times Guardian

VIGO

Swanswood Field, Harvel Road, Harvel, Kent. Tel: 0732 823830.
Founded: 1969
Secretary: J. Jarman, 21 Grove Park Avenue, Sittingbourne, Kent. Tel: 0795 77249 (H), 0795 77291 (W).
Fixtures Secretary: J. Taylor, Sandon, Burnt House Lane, Hawley, Dartford, Kent. Tel: Dartford 27363 (H). 01-320 1920 (W).
League: Kent 3
Colours: Red

KENT 4

BEXLEY

Hall Place Park, Bourne Road, Bexley, Kent
Founded: 1957
President: Rt. Hon. Edward Heath, M.B.E., M.P.
Chairman: A. Hammond
Secretary: Keith Rutter, 19 Lakeside Close, Sidcup, Kent DA15 9PW. Tel: 01–304 5453 (H), 0703 764011 (W)
Fixtures Secretary: Jim Butler, 39 Baldwins Road, Bexley, Kent DA5 2AB. Tel: 0322 522693 (H), 01–379 6334 (W)
Coach: John Brunton
Club captain (1988–89): Jim Butler
Club captain (1989–90): Steve Fry
No. of teams: Senior 4
Directions to ground: Take Black Prince Interchange on A2, 2nd exit on roundabout, ground on right, Hall Place

Club colours: Royal blue and white hoop shirts, blue shorts, blue stockings, white tops
Nickname: Hermits
Floodlights: No
Membership fees: Full £16
Local newspaper: Kentish Times
League: Kent 4
League position (1988–89): 5th
League playing record (1988–89): P 8, W 3, D 1, L 4, F 77, A 72

CENTURIONS

New Burlington Field, Bargrove, Newington, Folkestone, Kent CT18 8BH. Tel: 0303 266887 (new club)
President: Peter Hermitage
Chairman: Joseph Feeney
Secretary: Victor Towell, The Slips, Cricketers Close, Hawkinge, Folkestone, Kent CT19 7NH. Tel: 0303 893633 (H), 269446 (W)
Fixtures Secretary: Keith Howland, Horton Cottage, Mill Lane, Monks Horton, Sellindge, Ashford, Kent TN25 6AS. Tel: 0303 812114
Press Officer: As Secretary
Club captain (1988–89): Paul Ticehurst
Club captain (1989–90): Paul Ticehurst
No. of teams: Senior 1
Directions to ground: From M20 take junction and follow A20 to Ashford for 1 miles, left at first roundabout, clubhouse on right
Clubhouse facilities: 6 changing rooms, bar, showers, etc.
Club colours: Shirt dark blue, light blue quarters, black shorts. (*Change colours:* Shirt blue/white hoops, black shorts)
Floodlights: No
Membership fees: Full £ 0, Playing £ 0, Social £ 0, Youth £ 0, Student £ 0, OAP £ 0
Ground admission: Nil
Programme: No. of editorial pages ; No. of advertising pages ; Price p
Programme editor:
Local newspapers:
League: London & SE/Kent 4

EAST PECKHAM

Pippin Road, East Peckham, Tonbridge, Kent
Founded: 1977
President: Chris J. Chown
Chairman: Kim N.C. Masters
Secretary: Mike J. Bull, 10 Leney Road, Wateringbury, Kent. Tel: 0622 812386 (H), 01–626 1544 ext. 1166 (W)
Fixtures Secretary: Paul S. Tucker, 31 Medway Meadows, East Peckham, Kent. Tel: 0622 871994
Press Officer: Andy N. Bodle, 2 Woodlands, Paddock wood, Kent TN12 6AR. Tel: 089 283 2423 (H), 01–876 3444 ext. 2326 (W)
Coach: Andy N. Bodle
Club captain (1988–89): Barton Archibald
Club captain (1989–90): Barton Archibald
No. of teams: Senior 2
Directions to ground: From A20, take B2016 signposted Paddock Wood. Turn right onto B2015, take right into Old Road by Rose & Crown, take 4th right into Bramley Road and 1st left is Pippin Road
Clubhouse facilities: East Peckham Club, Freehold, East Peckham, Kent
Club colours: Red, white and blue quarters, blue shorts, white socks. (*Change colours:* Red shirts)
Nickname: The Villagers
Floodlights: Yes (for training)
Membership fees: Full £30, Student £15
Ground admission: Free
Programme: No. of editorial pages Varies ; No. of advertising pages varies; Price: Varies
Programme editor: Andy N. Bodle, 2 Woodlands, Paddock Wood, Kent TN12 6AR. Tel: 089 283 2423 (H), 01–876 3444 ext. 2326 (W)

Local newspapers: Kent Messenger, Kent & Sussex Courier
League: Kent 4
League position (1988–89): 9th (relegated)
League playing record (1988–89): P 8, W 0, D 1, L 7, F 30, A 193
Competitions won: John Wright Memorial Trophy, 1989

EDENBRIDGE

The Recreation Ground, Lingfield Road, Edenbridge, Kent
Founded: 1977
Chairman: Rosslyn Davies
Secretary: Matthew Linden, Water Garden House, Saxbys, Cowden, Edenbridge, Kent. Tel: 0342 86836 (H), 0689 38301 (W)
Fixtures Secretary: Ron Mitchell, Amberly, Crouch House Road, Edenbridge, Kent TN8 5EE. Tel: 0732 863078 (H), 0737 774177 (W)
Press Officer: As Fixtures Secretary
Club captain (1988–89): James Walker
Club captain (1989–90): James Walker
No. of teams: Senior 3, Minis 1
Directions to ground: Opposite entrance to Edenbridge Town Station. Turn into Stangrove Road, left at junction into Crouch House Road, 2nd right and immediately right again, 150 yds left into Coomb Lane
Clubhouse facilities: Large clubroom for functions, bar, pool table. Refreshments
Club colours: Amber and black hoops
Nickname: Bridge
Floodlights: Yes (subject to planning permission)
Membership fees: Full £20, Playing £20, Social £10, Youth £5, Student £5, OAP £5
Local newspapers: The Kent & Sussex Courier, The Edenbridge Chronicle
League: Kent 4
League position (1988–89): 4th
League playing record (1988–89): P 7, W 3, D 2, L 2, F 86, A 48
Competitions won: The Mammoth Cup, Easter 1989

LORDSWOOD

Martin Grove, North Dane Way, Lordswood, Chatham, Kent. Tel: 0634 669138
President: Grant Wilbur
Chairman: Steve Smith
Secretary: Dennis gibson, 343A Loose Road, Maidstone, Kent ME15 9PY. Tel: 0622 682650 (H), 0860 395882 (W)
Fixtures Secretary: Steve Smith, 24 Charlebury Crescent, Maidstone, Kent. Tel: 0622 20179
Press Officer: Sam Wellings, 167 Ballens Road, Lordswood, Chatham, Kent. Tel: 0634 61924
Coach: Mick Peter
Club captain (1988–89): Richard Kent
Club captain (1989–90): Richard Kent
No. of teams: Senior 2, Youth 1, Vets (charity) 1
Directions to ground: A229 exit from M2, follow signs to Lordswood then Lordswood Leisure Centre
Ground capacity: Standing Ample
Clubhouse facilities: Open standard licensing hours (inc. all day Saturday)
Club colours: Amber shirts, black shorts. (*Change colours:* Black shirts, black shorts)
Nickname: Lords
Floodlights: No
Membership fees: Full £26, Playing £26, Social £12, Youth £5, Student £5
Local newspapers: Kent Messenger, Evening Post
League: Kent 4
League position (1988–89): 7th

ORPINGTON

Founded: 1969
Secretary: Ross Campbell. Tel: 0634 374899

Fixtures Secretary: Warwick Marriner, 28 Patridge
Drive, Orpington, Kent BR6 8PE. Tel: 0689 57056
(H), 01–488 3351 (W)
Club captain (1988–89): Gary O'Day
Club captain (1989–90): Mark 'Sid' Christmas
No. of teams: Senior 2
Clubhouse facilities: Clubroom, kitchen and bar
Club colours: Black
Floodlights: Yes (training)
League: Kent 4
League position (1988–89): 10th (relegated)
League playing record (1988–89): P 10, W 0, D 1,
L 9, F 33, A 343

STC FOOTSCRAY

Maidstone Road, Sidcup, Kent
Founded: 1967
President: Harold (Johnnie) Stockton
Chairman: James Castle
Secretary: Gary Tomkins, 41 Edna Road, Maidstone,
Kent ME14 2QN. Tel: 0622 685662 (H), 01–300 3333
(W)
Fixtures Secretary: Tony Codd, 74 Felthampton
Road, New Eltham SE9 3NX. Tel: 01–857 6070 (H),
01–832 5484 (W)
Club captain (1988–89): Martin Raynor
Club captain (1989–90): Bob Bender
No. of teams: Senior 3
Directions to ground: Behind STC/LSI Factories
opposite Footscray Bus Station at the bottom of
Sidcup Hill
Ground capacity: Seating 4, standing 300
Clubhouse facilities: 3 Star
Club colours: Blue and gold hoops
Floodlights: No
Ground admission: Free
Local newspaper: Sidcup Times
League: Kent 4
League position (1988–89): 3rd
League playing record (1988–89): P 8, W 6, D 0, L 2,
F 131, A 75

THAMES POLYTECHNIC

Kidbrooke Lane, Eltham, London SE9 6TA. Tel:
01–850 1221
Founded: 1937
President: Peter Arscott
Chairman: Michael Doveston
Secretary: John Baker, 26 Capel Place, Wilmington,
Kent DA2 7PU. Tel: 0322 28162
Fixtures Secretary: Gordon Miller, 85 Earlshall Road,
Eltham, London SE9. Tel: 01–850 2794
Coach: Kevin Short
Club captain (1989–90): Bernie Barnett
No. of teams: Senior 4
Directions to ground: Adjacent to South Circular
Road (Westhorne Avenue)
Club colours: Green red gold
Floodlights: No
Membership fees: Full £30, Social £10
Local newspaper: Kentish Times
League: Kent 4
League position (1988–89): 9th (relegated)
League playing record (1988–89): P 10, W 3, D 0,
L 7, F 104 A 171

UNIVERSITY OF KENT

Sports Federation, Sports Centre, UKC, Canterbury
CT2 7NI. Tel: 0227 68027
Founded: 1967
Chairman: Jim Odoire
Secretary: David Shore, Sports Federation, Sports
Centre, UKC, Canterbury CT2 7N1. Tel: 0227 68027
Fixtures Secretary: As Secretary
Club captain (1988–89): Robbie Collins
Club captain (1989–90): Aaron Swain

No. of teams: Senior 3
Directions to ground: Follow directions to Canterbury
off A2. Don't go into Canterbury but turn left by
Bernie/Beefeater Restaurant on first roundabout, then
follow directions to University
Club colours: Red and blue hoops
Floodlights: No
Local newspaper: Kentish Gazette
League: Kent 4
League position (1988–89): 7th
League playing record (1988–89): P 7, W 2, D 1, L 4,
F 71, A 115

WESTERHAM

King George V Ground, Westerham (new club)
President: Paul Fletcher
Chairman: Tony Swinney
Secretary: Phil Gordon-Smith, 22 Milton Road,
Dunton Green, Sevenoaks, Kent TN13 2XJ. Tel: 0732
462128
Fixtures Secretary: Guy Robins, 3 Woodhurst Lane,
Oxted, Surrey RH8 9HN. Tel: 0833 713635 (H),
01–735 8922 ext. 222 (W)
Press Officer: Nick Ingram, Westward, 5 Wellers
Close, Westerham, Kent. Tel: 0959 62722
Coach: Carl Armitage
Club captain (1988–89): Keith Bishop
Club captain (1989–90): Keith Bishop
No. of teams: Senior 1
Directions to ground: A25 to centre of Westerham to
green, turn down B233 to Biggin Hill → 1st right into
Quebec Avenue → 1st left to end and car park
Clubhouse facilities: Just built. Bar, 6 changing rooms
Club colours: All black. (*Change colours:* Green/
white/black)
Floodlights: No
Membership fees: Playing £30, Social £15
League: Kent 4

WHITSTABLE

Church Street Playing Fields, Whitstable. Tel: 0227
272226
Founded: 1981
President: Tom Crowther
Chairman: Pat Todd
Secretary: Sue Millington, 41 The Meadows,
Broomfield, Herne Bay, Kent CT6 7XF. Tel: 027
368035
Fixtures Secretary: Tony Cunningham, 'The Punch',
Harbour Street, Whitstable, Kent CT5 1AG. Tel:
0227 264755
Press Officer: Pat Todd, 60 Sherwood Drive,
Whitstable, Kent CT5 4PH. Tel: 0227 266006 (H),
0227 762055 (W)
Club captain (1988–89): Peter Sparrow
Club captain (1989–90): Tom Sutton
No. of teams: Senior 3, Youth 2, Minis 4
Directions to ground: From M2 onto Thanet Way
(A299): straight on at first two roundabouts, then 1st
left. Ground on left. From Thanet: 2nd right after
Chestfield roundabout. Ground on left
Ground capacity: Standing Ample
Clubhouse facilities: Whitstable Cricket Club,
Belmont Road, Whitstable
Club colours: Blue/white hoops shirts, white shorts,
royal blue socks. (*Change colours:* White shirts)
Nickname: 2nd XV 'The Gremlins'
Floodlights: No
Membership fees: Full £15, VPs £10
Local newspapers: Whitstable Times, Kentish Gazette
League: Kent 4
League position (1988–89): 6th
League playing record (1988–89): P 7, W 2, D 1, L 4,
F 52, A 76

SUSSEX LEAGUES

AN EXTRA team in 1988–89 meant that 28 teams took part in the Sussex Leagues last season, but none of the divisions reported in-completion of fixtures in a mild winter almost free of disruptions from the weather. Hove took top spot in Sussex 1 comfortably enough without playing all their games and Hellingly – only promoted in 1987–88 – go straight back to Sussex 2 even though they did manage two wins during the season. Heathfield, who won all eight matches (163–39), and St. Francis go up to the top league and at the foot of that table British Caledonian (to be known as BA Wingspan this coming season) go down after losing the six matches they played (14–139). In the small Sussex 3 Old Brighto-nians (who won all six games for an astonishing 326–7 overall scoreline) and R.M.P. Chichester, who won the five matches they played, both ascend, whilst at the bottom of the table Azurians did manage one draw in their seven matches but conceded 226 points and scored only 19. Again, we must cite the Olympic spirit to encourage them to keep going.

SUSSEX All Leagues:

C. Ward,
26 Raleigh Crescent,
Goring by Sea,
Worthing   (H) 0903 501949
Sussex   (O) 0403 67214

TABLES 1987–88

SUSSEX 1

	P	W	D	L	F	A	PTS
Bognor	10	10	0	0	195	44	20
Chichester	10	7	0	3	146	103	14
Eastbourne	10	5	1	4	121	10	11
Seaford	10	5	0	5	129	121	10
Burgess Hill	10	4	1	5	69	94	9
Crowborough	10	4	1	5	82	131	9
Hove	10	4	0	6	156	97	8
Haywards Hth	10	4	0	6	76	119	8
Brighton	10	4	0	6	76	119	8
Sussex Pol	10	3	1	6	83	199	7
Hastings & B	10	3	0	7	107	164	6

SUSSEX 2

	P	W	D	L	F	A	PTS
Uckfield	7	7	0	0	252	25	14
Hellingly	7	5	1	1	127	48	11
St Francis	7	4	0	3	47	45	8
Heathfield	7	3	0	4	96	89	6
Plumpton	7	3	0	4	102	178	6
Brit Cale	7	2	0	5	58	91	4
Sussex Univ	7	2	1	4	103	83	3
Azurians	7	1	0	6	8	228	2
(W.I.S.H.E. void)							

SUSSEX 3

	P	W	D	L	F	A	PTS
Pulborough	7	7	0	0	189	22	14
Brighton Poly	7	6	0	1	141	55	12
Midhurst**	6	4	0	2	103	28	8
Robin Hood**	6	3	1	2	82	50	7
Arun**	6	2	0	4	42	107	4
Sunallon	7	2	0	5	35	132	4
Newick**	6	1	0	5	33	152	2
Ditchling	7	0	1	6	40	118	1

** Matches not played – Rule 10(c) applies.

TABLES 1988–89

SUSSEX 1

	P	W	D	L	F	A	PTS
Hove	10	8	1	1	249	107	17
Chichester	10	6	1	3	156	127	13
Crowborough	10	5	2	3	134	101	12
Burgess Hill	10	6	0	4	132	146	12
Brighton	10	5	0	5	146	117	10
Haywards Hth	10	5	0	5	108	148	10
Uckfield	10	4	1	5	53	76	9
Sussex Pol	10	4	0	6	90	122	8
Seaford	10	4	0	6	118	155	8
Eastbourne	10	3	1	6	138	143	7
Hellingly	10	2	0	8	84	166	6

SUSSEX 2

	P	W	D	L	F	A	PTS
Heathfield	8	8	0	0	163	39	16
St. Francis	8	7	0	1	113	46	14
Hastings & B**	7	5	0	2	280	47	10
Plumpton	8	4	0	4	108	87	8
Sussex Univ	8	3	1	4	85	113	7
Pulborough	8	3	0	5	86	107	6
Brighton Poly	8	3	0	5	104	152	6
Midhurst	8	1	1	6	39	226	3
British Caledonian	7	0	0	7	14	175	–1

** = Match not played – British Caledonian deducted 1 point.

SUSSEX 3

	P	W	D	L	F	A	PTS
O Brightonians	7	7	0	0	359	7	14
R.M.P. Chich	7	6	0	1	167	73	12
W Sus In of H.E.	7	4	0	3	169	142	8
Ditchling	7	4	0	3	124	100	8
Newick	7	4	0	3	101	106	8
Arun	7	1	1	5	37	250	3
Azurians	7	0	1	6	19	226	1

I.B.M. withdrew. Pegasus withdraw

LONDON & SOUTH EAST DIVISION FIXTURES 1989/90

SUSSEX LEAGUE ONE

Sat. 23rd September (Week 4)
Uckfield v Brighton
Sussex Police v Eastbourne
St. Francis v Crowborough
Heathfield v Chichester
Seaford v Burgess Hill

Sat. 14th October (Week 6)
Burgess Hill v Uckfield
Chichester v Seaford
Crowborough v Heathfield
Eastbourne v St. Francis
Haywards Heath v Sussex Police

Sat. 28th October (Week 8)
Uckfield v Chichester
Brighton v Burgess Hill
St. Francis v Haywards Heath
Heathfield v Eastbourne
Seaford v Crowborough

Sat. 11th November (Week 10)
Chichester v Brighton
Crowborough v Uckfield
Eastbourne v Seaford
Haywards Heath v Heathfield
Sussex Police v St. Francis

Sat 18th November (Week 11)
Uckfield v Eastbourne
Brighton v Crowborough
Burgess Hill v Chichester
Heathfield v Sussex Police
Seaford v Haywards Heath

Sat. 25th November (Week 12)
Crowborough v Burgess Hill
Eastbourne v Brighton
Haywards Heath v Uckfield
Sussex Police v Seaford
St. Francis v Heathfield

Sat. 13th January (Week 18)
Uckfield v Sussex Police
St. Francis v Haywards Heath
Burgess Hill v Eastbourne
Chichester v Crowborough
Seaford v St. Francis

Sat. 27th January (Week 20)
Eastbourne v Chichester
Haywards Heath v Burgess Hill
Sussex Police v Brighton
St. Francis v Uckfield
Heathfield v Seaford

Sat. 10th February (Week 22)
Uckfield v Heathfield
Brighton v St. Francis
Burgess Hill v Sussex Police
Chichester v Haywards Heath
Crowborough v Eastbourne

Sat. 24th February (Week 24)
Haywards Heath v Crowborough
Sussex Police v Chichester
St. Francis v Burgess Hill
Heathfield v Brighton
Seaford v Uckfield

Sat. 10th March (Week 26)
Brighton v Seaford
Burgess Hill v Heathfield
Chichester v St. Francis
Crowborough v Sussex Police
Eastbourne v Haywards Heath

LONDON & SOUTH EAST DIVISION FIXTURES 1989/90

SUSSEX LEAGUE TWO

Sat. 14th October (Week 6)
R.M.P. Chichester v Plumpton
Old Brightonians v Pulborough
Hellingly v Midhurst
Hastings & Bexhill v Brighton Polytechnic

Sat. 28th October (Week 8)
Brighton Polytechnic v R.M.P. Chichester
Midhurst v Hastings & Bexhill
Pulborough v Hellingly
Sussex University v Old Brightonians

Sat. 11th November (Week 10)
R.M.P. Chichester v Midhurst
Plumpton v Brighton Polytechnic
Hellingly v Sussex University
Hastings & Bexhill v Pulborough

Sat 18th November (Week 11)
Midhurst v Plumpton
Pulborough v R.M.P. Chichester
Sussex University v Hastings & Bexhill
Old Brightonians v Hellingly

Sat. 25th November (Week 12)
R.M.P. Chichester v Sussex University
Plumpton v Pulborough
Brighton Polytechnic v Midhurst
Hastings & Bexhill v Old Brightonians

Sat. 27th January (Week 20)
Pulborough v Brighton Polytechnic
Sussex University v Plumpton
Old Brightonians v R.M.P. Chichester
Hellingly v Hastings & Bexhill

Sat. 10th February (Week 22)
R.M.P. Chichester v Hellingly
Plumpton v Old Brightonians
Brighton Polytechnic v Sussex University
Midhurst v Pulborough

Sat. 24th February (Week 24)
Sussex University v Midhurst
Old Brightonians v Brighton Polytechnic
Hellingly v Plumpton
Hastings & Bexhill v R.M.P. Chichester

Sat. 10th March (Week 26)
Plumpton v Hastings & Bexhill
Brighton Polytechnic v Hellingly
Midhurst v Old Brightonians
Pulborough v Sussex University

SUSSEX LEAGUE THREE

Sat. 14th October (Week 6)
B.A. Wingspan v Arun
Newick v Sunallon

Sat. 28th October (Week 8)
Arun v Newick
Ditchling v West Sussex I.H.E.

Sat. 11th November (Week 10)
Newick v B.A. Wingspan
West Sussex I.H.E. v Sunallon

Sat. 25th November (Week 12)
Arun v West Sussex I.H.E.
Sunallon v Ditchling

Sat. 27th January (Week 20)
West Sussex I.H.E. v B.A. Wingspan
Ditchling v Arun

Sat. 10th February (Week 22)
Newick v West Sussex I.H.E.
Arun v Sunallon
B.A. Wingspan v Ditchling

Sat. 24th February (Week 24)
Ditchling v Newick
Sunallon v B.A. Wingspan

SUSSEX 1

BRIGHTON

Horsdean, Vale Avenue, Patcham, Brighton. (Moving to Wateerhall, BN1 8YR in '90/'91 season). Tel: 0273 506995
Founded: 1868
President: Pat Ward Lee
Chairman: David Malby
Secretary: Allan Bradley, 155 Ditchling Rise, Brighton BN1 4QQ. Tel: 0273 680876 (H), 676894 (W)
Fixtures Secretary: Ray Greenwood, 11 Lyminster Avenue, Brighton. Tel: 502898
Press Officer: Ken Vogwill, 9 Harrington Road, Brighton BN1 6RE. Tel: 0273 507333 (H), 01–217 3015 (W)
Coach: Chris Jones
Club captain (1988–89): Peter Thompson
Club captain (1989–90): Peter Thompson
No. of teams: Senior 6, Youth 1
Directions to ground: Follow A23 south to Patcham lights at Borough boundary. Turn left and follow road over hill, clubhouse and ground on left
Ground capacity: Standing 500
Clubhouse facilities: Changing facilities, bar area
Club colours: Royal blue shirts and shorts, red socks. (*Change colours:* White shirts)
Floodlights: Yes
Membership fees: Full £30, Playing £30, Social £10, Youth £5, Student £10, OAP £5
Programme: No. of editorial pages 2; No. of advertising pages 2
Programme editor: Myra Vogwill, 9 Harrington Road, Brighton BN1 6RE
Local newspaper: Evening Argus
League: Sussex 1
League position (1988–89): 5th
League playng record (1988–89): P 10, W 5, D 0, L 5, F 146, A 117

BURGESS HILL

Poveys Close, Burgess Hill, W. Sussex. Tel: 04446 2221
Founded: 1962
President: Tony Balsdon
Chairman: Peter Corcoran
Secretary: Reg Thomas, Old Mill Cottage, Highbridge, Cuckfield, W. Sussex RH17 5AE. Tel: 0444 455376
Fixtures Secretary: Ian Packham, 5 Condor Way, Burgess Hill, W. Sussex. Tel: 04446 871755
Press Officer: Mark Parsons, 69 Mill Road, Burgess Hill, W. Sussex. Tel: 04446 3629
Club captain (1988–89): Bob Shed
Club captain (1989–90): Bob Shed
No. of teams: Senior 4, Youth 3, Minis 3
Directions to ground: Turn off A23 at Hickstead towards Burgess Hill, at roundabout turn right into Royal George Road, 2nd right at South Close, 2nd right at Poveys Close
Ground capacity: Standing 300
Clubhouse facilities: Open matchdays, Sundays and Tuesday and Thurdays evenings and some social evenings
Club colours: Black. (*Change colours:* Red yellow green hoops)
Floodlights: No
Membership fees: Playing £30, Social £5
Local newspapers: Sussex Evening Argus, Mid Sussex Times
League: Sussex 1
League position (1988–89): 4th
League playing record (1988–89): P 10, W 6, D 0, L 4, F 132, A 146

CHICHESTER

Oaklands Park, Wellington Road, Chichester, West Sussex. Tel: Chichester 779820.
Founded: 1927
Secretary: S. Hill, Tidewell Cottage, Selsey, Near Chichester, West Sussex. Tel: 0234 602 598 (H), 0243 781000 (W).
league Contact: D. Seaman, 29 Florence Road, Chichester, West Sussex

CROWBOROUGH

Steel Cross, Crowborough. Tel: 0892 654832
Founded: 1937
President: Bryan Kain
Chairman: Michael Clark
Secretary: Michael Clark, Forest Lea, London Road, Crowborough, East Sussex TN6 1TA. Tel: 0892 653285 (H), 01–488 3200 ext. 6276 (W)
Fixtures Secretary: T.B.A.
Press Officer: T.B.A.
Coach: T.B.A.
Club captain (1988–89): Fred Simpson
Club captain (1989–90): T.B.A.o. of teams: Senior 4, Minis 3
Directions to ground: Turn off A26 halfway between Crowborough Cross and the Boars Head public house signposted Jarvis Brook
Clubhouse facilities: Matchdays and training nights, Wednesday
Club colours: Red with white hoops. (*Change colours:* Blue/cherry with white hoops)
Floodlights: No
Membership fees: Full £30, Playing £30, Social £5, Youth £6
Local newspaper: Courier
League: Sussex 1
League position (1988–89): 3rd
League playing record (1988–89): P 10, W 5, D 2, L 3

EASTBOURNE

Park Avenue, Hampden Park, Eastbourne, East Sussex BN22 9ON. Tel: 0323 503076
Founded: 1928
President: Alan Paul
Chairman: John Feakins
Secretary: David Johnson, 11 The Hoo, Church Street, Willingdon, Eastbourne, East Sussex BN21 9HR. Tel: 0323 506489
Fixtures Secretary: Mark Feeney, 14 Baldwin Avenue, Eastbourne, East Sussex. Tel: 0323 506489
Press Officer: David Baxter, Salthaven, The Promenade, Pevensey Bay, East Sussex. Tel: 0323 768581
Coach: David Baxter
Club captain (1988–89): Mark Jones
Club captain (1989–90): David Robertshaw
No. of teams: Senior 4, Youth 1, Minis 6
Directions to ground: A22 to Eastbourne, just north of Eastbourne follow directions to east of the town. The ground is near the District Hospital
Ground capacity: Standing 1000
Clubhouse facilities: 2 changing rooms and showers, kitchen, bar, clubroom
Club colours: Blue and gold stripes
Floodlights: No
League: Sussex 1
League position (1988–89): 10th
League playing record (1988–89): P 10, W 3, D 1, L 6, F 138, A 143

HAYWARDS HEATH

Whiteman's Green, Cuckfield, Haywards Heath, W. Sussex. Tel: 0444 413950
Founded: 1958
President: Roger Harris
Chairman: Irwin Taylor
Secretary: Mike Travis, 'Bowood', Bashurst Copse, Itching Field, West Sussex. Tel: Horsham 790282
Fixtures Secretary: Ian Beckett, 94 Sunnywood Drive, Haywards Heath, West Sussex. Tel: 0444 412576 (H),

0293 772622 (W)
Press Officer: Robin Probert, 2 Fern Cottages, Brainsmead, Cuckfield, Haywards Heath, West Sussex. Tel: 0444 450832
Coach: Steve Heaton
Club captain (1988–89): Nigel Richards
Club captain (1989–90): Nigel Richards
No. of teams: Senior 4, Youth 4, Minis 5
Directions to ground: From A23 turn east onto B2115 (signposted) Warninglid, turn right at T-junction onto B2114. Ground mile on right-hand side
Club colours: Shirts red and black hoops, black shorts
Floodlights: Yes (training only)
Local newspapers: Mid Sussex Times and Evening Argus
League: Sussex 1
League position (1988–89): 6th
League playing record (1988–89): P 10, W 5, D 0, L 5, F 108, A 148
Competitions won: Plumpton Sevens

HEATHFIELD & WALDRON

c/o Blackboys Inn, Blackboys, East Sussex.
Founded: 1980
Secretary: S.D. Leney, Mill Cottage, Cross-in-Hand, Heathfield, East Sussex. Tel: 04352 6401 (H), 0273 28833 (W).
League Contact: K. Bromley, Sandy Cross Cottage, Sandy Cross, Heathfield, East Sussex
Colours: Green/White
League: Sussex 2

ST. FRANCIS

Broadfields Playing Fields, Rathlin Road, Crawley, Sussex. Tel: Crawley 33071
Founded: 1961
President: John W. Wright
Chairman: John A. Richardson
Secretary: Ian Mitchell, 5 Gosden Close, Furnace Green, Crawley. Tel: 0293 516108 (H), 01–242 7475 (W)
Fixtures Secretary: Malcom Pavey, 110 Worth Road, Pound Hill, Crawley. Tel: 0293 2896
Press Officer: Jeremy Willett, 33 Loveletts, Gossops Green, Crawley RH11 8EG. Tel: 547572 (H), 572207 (W)
Coach: Andy Cushing
Club captain (1988–89): Martin A. Rivers
Club captain (1989–90): Martin A. Rivers
No. of teams: Senior 3
Directions to ground: Along A23 to Horsham roundabout (Chrals Nursery), turn west (signposted Horsham) 400 yds to roundabout, follow signs Broadfields 600 yds to roundabout, turn left into car park
Clubhouse facilities: Open matchdays and Sundays, Tuesday and Thursday night
Club colours: Black white and royal blue hoops
Nickname: Saints
Floodlights: No
Membership fees: Full £17.50, Playing £17.50, Social £1.5, Youth £5, Student £5, VPs £7.50
Local newspapers: Crawley Observer, Crawley Advertiser
League: Sussex 2
League position (1988–89): 2nd
League playing record (1988–89): P 8, W 7, D 0, L 1, F 113, A 46
Competitions won: Sussex K.O. Cup Plate Winners, April 1989

SEAFORD

The Salts, Seaford, E. Sussex. Tel: 0323 892355
Founded: 1938
President: Roger Hayes
Chairman: Dave Cleaton

Secretary: Antony Pugh, 19 Chyngton Road, Seaford, E. Sussex. Tel: 0323 892020
Fixtures Secretary: Chris Cole, 32 Park Drive Close, Newhaven, E. Sussex. Tel: 0273 516888
Press Officer: Colin Hill, 38 Salisbury Road, Seaford, E. Sussex. Tel: 0323 892834
Coach: Chris Taylor
Club captain (1988–89): Romould Debil
Club captain (1989–90): Romould Debil
No. of teams: Senior 3, Youth 1
Directions to ground: Drive along Seaford seafront
Club colours: Scarlet jerseys, blue shorts
Floodlights: No
Membership fees: Playing £15, Non-Playing £2
Ground admission: Free
Local newspapers: Seaford Gazette, Sussex Express
League: Sussex 1
League position (1988–89): 9th
League playing record (1988–89): P 10, W 4, D 0, L 6, F 118, A 155

SUSSEX POLICE

Brighton RFC, Horsdean Vale Avenue, Brighton, Sussex.
Founded: 1968
Secretary: Det. Insp G. Randle, Police Station, Chichester, Sussex. Tel: 0903 784468 (H). 0243 784433. Extn. 223 (W).
League: Sussex 1
League Contact: F. Edmonds, 87 Wardsworth Drive, Eastbourne, East Sussex BN23 7QP
Press Officer: Brian Sole. Tel: 0273 31274
Colours: Dark Blue

UCKFIELD

Hempstead Playing Fields, Manor Park, Uckfield, East Sussex. Tel: 0825 68956
Founded: 1967
President: R. MArtin
Chairman: B. Evan-Cook
Secretary: C. Rudolph, 89 Framfield Road, Uckfield, East Sussex TN22 5AT. Tel: 0925 5766 (H), 082581 2491 (W)
Fixtures Secretary: I. Poole, 9 Kelo Avenue, Uckfield, E. Sussex. Tel: Uckfield 61151
Press Officer: Mike Stobart, 9 Lashbrook Road, Uckfield, East Sussex. Tel: 0825 4938
Coach: A.A. Black/A. Gannon
Club captain (1988–89): Adrian Evans
Club captain (1989–90): Gary Cooper
No. of teams: Senior 4, Minis 4
Directions to ground: At north end of town turn east off London Road into Browns Lane, turn left into Neville Road and take next right to clubhouse
Clubhouse facilities: 2 storey with two changing rooms, bar and hall upstairs
Club colours: Amber, purple and white hoops. (*Change colours:* Black with amber and purple band)
Floodlights: Yes
Membership fees: Full £25, Playing £25, Social £5, Youth £5, Student £15
Local newspapers: Uckfield Courier, Sussex Express
League: Sussex 1
League position (1988–89): 7th
League playing record (1988–89): P 10, W 4, D 1, L 5, F 53, A 76
Competitions won: Uckfield Pub Sevens Winners, April '89

SUSSEX 2

BRIGHTON POLYTECHNIC

Brighton Polytechnic, Falmer Site, Brighton
Founded: 1966
President: Mark Leach

Chairman: Peter Swallow
Secretary: David Edward Lewis, c/o Student Union Office, Cockcroft Building, Brighton Poly BN2 4GJ. Tel: 0273 68126
Fixtures Secretary: As Secretary
Club captain (1989–90): John Walters
No. of teams: Senior 2
Directions to ground: A27 towards Lewis. From Brighton turn off by Sussex Uni, over flyover, then turn right (well signposted)
Club colours: 1sts Gold/blue squares. 2nds Red/black
Nickname: Dolphins
Floodlights: No
League: Sussex 2
League position (1988–89): 7th
League playing record (1988–89): P 8, W 3, D 0, L 5, F 104, A 152

CHICHESTER RED CAP

Roussillon Barracks, Chichester, West Sussex. Tel: Chichester 7863111
Founded: 1927
President: William Gordon Woodiwiss
Chairman: Stuart Rogers
Secretary: Gary Milton, Gymnasium, Roussillon Barracks, Chichester, West Sussex. Tel: 0243 533686 (H), 786311 ext. 273 (W)
Fixtures Secretary: As Secretary
Press Officer: Miss Alison Chesworth, HQ RMPTC, Roussillon Barracks, Chichester, W. Sussex. Tel: 0243 786311 ext. 209 (W)
Coach: Gary Milton
Club captain (1988–89): Martyn Bird
Club captain (1989–90): Lightowler
No. of teams: Senior 1
Directions to ground: All routes into Chichester, follow A286 Midhurst for 1 mile for Barracks on right
Ground capacity: Standing 1000
Clubhouse facilities: Open on matchdays
Club colours: Red/royal blue quarters. (*Change colours:* Red and white hoops)
Floodlights: Yes
Membership fees: Full £2.50
Local newspaper: Chichester Observer
League: Sussex 3
League position (1988–89): 1st (promoted)

HASTINGS & BEXHILL

The Polegrove, Bexhill, E. Sussex. Tel: 0424 210224
Founded: 1924
President: Robbie Hall
Chairman: Mike Donegan
Secretary: John Northern, 19 Feardon Road, Hastings. Tel: 0424 421162
Fixtures Secretary: Robert N. Hamilton, 1 Bluestone Close, St. Leonards, E. Sussex. Tel: 0424 51399 (H), 0424 442442 (W)
Coach: Kevin Swallow/Robert Hamilton
Club captain (1988–89): Dave Sprinks
Club captain (1989–90): Steve Pepper
No. of teams: Senior 3, Youth 3, Minis 3
Club colours: Royal blue and white hoops
Floodlights: No
League: Sussex 2
League position (1988–89): 3rd
League playing record (1988–89): P 7, W 5, D 0, L 2, F 282, A 47
Competitions won: Plate Winners Canterbury Sevens

MIDHURST

The Ruins, Cowdray Park, Midhurst, Sussex.
Founded: 1981
Secretary: L.S. Lloyd, 4 Guillards Oak, Midhurst, West Sussex GU29 9JZ. Tel: 073081 2025 (H).
League: Sussex 3
League Contact: S. Wishart, 2 harvey Lodge, Harvey Road, Guildford, Surrey GU1 3NS. Tel: 0483 502945
Press Officer: Secretary

Colours: Yellow/Blue.

HELLINGLY

Horsebridge Recreation Ground, Nr. Hailsham, East Sussex.
Founded: 1972
President: Peter Hainstock
Chairman: Steve Baily
Secretary: Andy Vince, 100 Upper Horsebrige, Hailsham, East Sussex BN27 1NY. Tel: 0323 844443 (H), 30468 (W)
Fixtures Secretary: Tim Bowler, Brook House, Lower Horsebridge, Hailsham, East Sussex. Tel: 0323 845838
Press Officer: As Secretary
Club captain (1988–89): Ron Francis
Club captain (1989–90): Paul Ripley
No. of teams: Senior 2, Minis 1
Directions to ground: A22 to Hailsham, take Bexhill exit off Boship roundabout, 800 yds on right opposite White Hart pub
Ground capacity: Standing 200
Clubhouse facilities: Bar open matchdays
Club colours: Black and amber hoops
Nickname: The Loonies
Floodlights: No
Local newspaper: Hailsham Gazette
League: Sussex 2
League position (1988–89): Bottom (relegated)
League playing record (1988–89): P 10, W 2, D 0, L 8, F 84, A 166

OLD BRIGHTONIAN

c/o Brighton College, Eastern Road, Brighton, Sussex, BN2 AL
President: Michael Campbell
Chairman: Mark Hudson
Secretary: Peter Russell Rumney, 17 Bennett Drive, Hove, Sussex BN3 6PL. Tel: 0273 504981
Fixtures Secretary: As Secretary
Press Officer: As Secretary
Coach: Robert Bourn
Club captain (1988–89): Glyn Adams
Club captain (1989–90): Ben Stott
No. of teams: Senior 1
Directions to ground: Brighton College, Eastern Road, Brighton BN2 2AL (also Nevill Recreation)
Ground capacity: Seating 50, Standing 500
Clubhouse facilities: Bar and sports hall
Club colours: Light blue and magenta hoops on navy
Nickname: OB's
Floodlights: No
Membership fees: Full £5, Playing £15, Youth Free, Student Free
Ground admission: Free
Programme: No. of editorial pages ?; No. of advertising pages 2; Price 25p (for Sussex K.O. Cup matches only)
Programme editor: Glyn Adams, 18 Rigden Road, Hove, Sussex
Local newspapers: Evening Argus
League: Sussex 3
League position (1988–89): 1st (promoted)
League playing record (1988–89): P 7, W 7, D 0, L 0, F 359, A 14
Competitions won: Sussex League 3. Brighton Sevens, April 1989, Plate Winners

PLUMPTON

Plumpton Racecourse, Plumpton Lane, Plumpton, East Sussex BN7. Tel: 0273 890383
Founded: 1967
President: Roy A. Ford
Chairman: David Beale
Secretary: Greg M. Rogers, 2 Hill Rise Cottages, Station Road, Plumpton Green, East sussex BN7 3DR. Tel: 0273 890560
Fixtures Secretary: Ian Towner, Charbrook, Paynesfield, The Street, Bolney, Sussex Rh17 5PU.

Tel: 0444 82455
Press Officer: Rod Bellringer-Jones, 2 Hardings, London Lane, Cuckfield, Sussex RH17. Tel: 0444 417140
Coach: Perry Cragg
Club captain (1988–89): Mike Johnstone
Club captain (1989–90): Mike Johnstone
No. of teams: Senior 1
Directions to ground: To Plumpton Station, ground opposite, via Plumpton Lane to Racecourse Main Entrance
Ground capacity: Standing 1500
Clubhouse facilities: Open matchdays
Club colours: Maroon and gold jerseys and stockings, black shorts. (*Change colours:* Blue and white hoops)
Nickname: Plums
Floodlights: No
Membership fees: Full £15, Playing £15, Social £6, Youth £6, Student £6, OAP £6
Ground admission: Free
Programme: Only produced for charity and 7's tournaments
Programme editor: Steve Cox, c/o Fountain Public House, Station Road, Plumpton Green, East sussex BN7
Local newspapers: Mid sussex Times, Sussex Express
League: Sussex 2
League position (1988–89): 4th
League playing record (1988–89): P 8, W 4, D 0, L 4, F 108, A 87

PULBOROUGH

Recreation Ground, Rectory Lane, Pulborough, West Sussex. Tel: 07982 3020
Founded: 1968
President: James S.H. North
Chairman: John Mason
Secretary: John Thompson, Chennies, London Road, Watersfield, Pulborough, West Sussex RH20 1ND. Tel: 0798 831338 (H), 0403 722271 (W)
Fixtures Secretary: Elaine mercer, 14 Cousins Way, Pulborough, West Sussex RH20 2TB. Tel: 07982 3651
Press Officer: T.B.A.
Coach: Clive Coulson
Club captain (1988–89): Andrew MacKinnon
Club captain (1989–90): Stuart Davis
No. of teams: Senior 3, Youth 1, Minis 5
Directions to ground: Turn opposite Red Lion up Rectory Lane
Ground capacity: Standing 300
Clubhouse facilities: Joint sports club. Open all weekend sessions and some weekday sessions
Club colours: Black and white hoops
Floodlights: Yes
Ground admission: Nil
Local newspapers: West Sussex County Times, West Sussex Gazette, Evening Argus
League: Sussex 2
League position (1988–89): 6th
League playing record (1988–89): P 8, W 3, D 0, L 5, F 86, A 107

UNIVERSITY OF SUSSEX

University Sports Pavilion, Ridge Road, Falmer. Tel: 0273 678155
Founded: 1963
President: T.B.A.
Chairman: T.B.A.
Secretary: Andrew Walters, c/o Sports Federation Office, Falmer House, Falmer, Brighton BN1 9QF. Tel: 0273 600230 (H), 606755 ext. 2753 (W)
Fixtures Secretary: As Secretary
Press Officer: Tom Lovering, c/o Sports Federation Office, Falmer House, Falmer, Brighton BN1 9QF. Tel: 0273 678155 (W)
Coach: Dave Bosley
Club captain (1988–89): Dominic Cotton

Club captain (1989–90): Dave Bosley
No. of teams: Senior 3, Ladies 1
Directions to ground: From Brighton follow A23 to Lewes for 3 miles, take exit to University of Sussex. Pitches are at the Sports Pavilion
Ground capacity: Seating 100
Clubhouse facilities: Bar, TV room. After match food by arrangement
Club colours: Blue/red hoops. (*Change colours:* Red/ white hoops)
Nickname: Dalai Lamas
Floodlights: No
Membership fees: Full £7
Local newspaper: Brighton Evening Argus
League: Sussex 3
League position (1988–89): 5th
League playing record (1988–89): P 8, W 3, D 1, L 4, F 85, A 113
Competitions won: Utrecht Challenge Cup. UAU 'Milk Round' Sevens Plate Runners-Up

SUSSEX 3

ARUN

Littlehampton School, Hill Road, Littlehampton, Sussex.
League: Sussex 3
League Contact: N. cousins, 39 Windward Close, Littlehampton, West Sussex BN17 6QX. Tel: 0903 713756

AZURIANS

Palatine Park, Palatine Road, Worthing, Sussex.
Founded: 1927
Secretary: C. Spratt, 61 Tarrant Street, Arundel, Sussex. Tel: Arundel 8836812 (H). Worthing 34343 (W).
Fixtures Secretary: D. Rogers, 69 Cokehamland, Sompting, Worthing, Sussex. Tel: Worthing 750877.
Pres Officer: C. Thomas. Tel: 0903 763616.

BRITISH AIRWAYS (WINGSPAN)

Cherry Lane, Langley Green. (Contact Wingspan Sports and Social Club, Astral Towers, Betts Way, Crawley, Sussex). Tel: 0293 54677 (formerly British Caledonian (Wingspan)
Founded: 1972
Chairman: John 'Taph' Jones
Secretary: Martin L. Palmer, 21 Park Way, Horley, Surrey RH6 7HX. Tel: 0293 773848 (H), 31211 ext. 2348 (W)
Fixtures Secretary: Kevin Parke, 31B New England Road, Haywards Heath, West Sussex. Tel: 0444 414793
Press Officer: Andrew Gochmanski. Tel: Horsham 560470
Club captain (1988–89): James Canavan
Club captain (1989–90): John Leach
No. of teams: Senior 2
Clubhouse facilities: Bar and bar snacks
Club colours: Amber/blue hoops. (*Change colours:* Yellow)
Floodlights: No
Local newspaper: Crawley Observer
League position (1988–89): 9th
League playing record (1988–89): P 7, W 0, D 0, L 7, F 14, A 175

DITCHLING

Lewes Road, Ditchling, East Sussex. Tel: 07918 3423
Founded: 1962
President: Godfrey Harker
Chairman: Brian Griffiths

Secretary: Adam Godfrey, 82 Clarence Road, Horsham, W. Sussex RH13 5SG. Tel: 0403 58604 (H), 0737 760926 (W)
Fixtures Secretary: Justin Wallden, Broxmead Cottage, Broxmead Lane, Cuckfield, W. Sussex. Tel: 04446 870587 (H), 04446 5665 (W)
Press Officer: As Secretary
Club captain (1988–89): Steve Booth
Club captain (1989–90): Peter White
No. of teams: Senior 2
Directions to ground: From the crossroads head east, about mile on left-hand side
Clubhouse facilities: Pavilion with ample showers and bar, lounge and kitchen facilities
Club colours: Green/white shorts
Nickname: Mothers
Floodlights: No
Membership fees: Full £15
Ground admission: £2.50
Local newspaper: Mid Sussex Times
League position (1988–89): =3rd
League playing record (1988–89): P 7, W 4, D 0, L 3, F 124, A 100

NEWICK

Rear of Crown Inn, Church Road, Newick, Lewes, E. Sussex BN8 4JX. Tel: Newick (082572) 3293
Founded: 1965
President: D.L. Manwaring-Robertson
Chairman: P. Burnie
Coach: C. Briggs
Secretary: G.H. Major, 19 Oldaker Road, Newick, Lewes, E. Sussex BN8 4LN.
Fixtures Secretary: M. Barling, 80 Ditchling Road, Brighton, E. Sussex. Tel: Brighton 687110
League Contact: L. Morgan, 3 Aspen Walk, Haywards Heath, West Sussex RH16 3RB
Club captain (1988–89): C. Briggs
No. of teams: Senior 1
Directions to Ground: Turn south off A272 in centre of village, keep left at the Bull Inn, into Church Road. The Crown Inn is 200 yards on right.
Clubhouse: At rear of Crown Inn.
Colours: Maroon and navy blue hoops
Floodlights: No
Membership: £15
Local newspaper: Mid Sussex Times

SUNALLON

North Heath Lane, Horsham, W. Sussex

Founded: 1971
Chairman: D.W. Fowler
Secretary: B.R. Lewis, 2 Wain End, Wimblehurst Park, Horsham, W. Sussex RH12 4TQ. Tel: 0403 66267 (H), 64141 ext. 4506 (W)
Fixtures Secretary: As Secretary
Press Officer: As Secretary
Coach: Ian Howard
Club captain (1988–89): S. Davis
Club captain (1989–90): A. Stephenson
No. of teams: Senior 1
Directions to ground: From A24, take Warnham Road, second left into Wimblehurst Road, leading into North Heath Lane
Clubhouse facilities: Large, 2 bars, 6 dressing rooms
Club colours: Yellow and blue. (*Change colours:* Blue)
Nickname: Sun
Floodlights: No
Membership fees: Full £9.60 Social £2.40
Local newspaper: West Sussex County Times
League position (1988–89): 7th
League playing record (1988–89): P 24, W 10, D 0, L 14, F 272, A 390

WEST SUSSEX INSTITUTE OF HIGHER EDUCATION

Bishop Otter College, College Lane, Chichester, West Sussex. Tel: Chichester 787137
President: Roger Allott
Chairman: Rhodri Jones
Secretary: Richard Howe, Student Union, Bishop Otter College, College Lane, West Sussex. Tel: Chichester 787137
Fixtures Secretary: As Secretary
Coach: Ian Maynard
Club captain (1988–89): Tim Stirrup
Club captain (1989–90): Steve Potter
No. of teams: Senior 1
Clubhouse facilities: Changing rooms, bar
Club colours: Yellow/blue. (*Change colours:* Blue)
Floodlights: No
League: Sussex 3
League position (1988–89): 3rd
League playing record (1988–89): P 7, W 4, D 0, L 3, F 169, A 142

HAMPSHIRE LEAGUES

LAST season 21 sides took part in the Hampshire Leagues and this time there was no change with Southampton succeeding Gosport at the top and they thus find themselves in London 3SW next season – with the unfortunate Gosport back down again. The winners only completed nine of their ten matches, but as they drew only one and won the rest they ended with a point in hand over Esso.

To accommodate teams relegated from London SW3 no less than five sides go down to the lower league including Trojans, who won five and lost five of their games. The others to descend are Isle of Wight, Rushmoor, Tottonians and Fordingbridge, although only the latter two could really be said to have had poor campaigns, the last-named having been promoted last time out. They are replaced by Petersfield and Andover, who both scored 16 points (having lost a game each) with the former (relegated last time) winning the title on points difference. Nomads at the foot of the table lost all nine games played for a sad differential of 38–245. They have now lost all their 17 league matches played so far – and we wish them better luck soon.

HAMPSHIRE all Leagues:

J.S. Sneezum, Esq.,
Bursledon Lodge,
Salterns Lane,
Old Bursledon,
Southampton,
Hampshire SO3 8DH   (H) 042121 2286

TABLES 1987–88

HAMPSHIRE 1

	P	W	D	L	F	A	PTS
Gosport	10	8	1	1	147	55	17
Southampton	10	57	0	3	158	72	14
Millbrook	10	6	1	3	182	89	13
Isle of Wight	10	6	0	4	109	106	12
Esso	10	5	0	5	129	115	10
Sandown & Shank	10	5	0	5	129	116	10
Rushmoor	10	5	0	5	87	101	10
Tottonians	10	3	0	7	68	119	6
Fareham Heath's	10	3	0	7	75	137	6
Petersfield	10	3	0	7	70	156	6
New Milton	10	3	0	7	64	165	6

HAMPSHIRE 2

	P	W	D	L	F	A	PTS
Fordingbridge	9	8	0	1	219	75	16
Guernsey	9	7	1	1	181	62	15
Romsey	9	6	1	2	147	57	13
Waterlooville	9	6	0	3	125	98	12
Andover**	8	4	0	4	123	117	8
Overton	9	4	0	5	63	92	8
Pegasus**	8	3	0	5	68	120	6
Ventnor**	8	2	0	6	70	79	4
Ellingham	9	2	0	7	97	138	4
Nomads**	8	0	0	8	9	264	0

** = IBM withdrawn – all matches void

TABLES 1988–89

HAMPSHIRE 1

	P	W	D	L	F	A	PTS
Southampton	10	9	1	0	236	77	19
Esso	10	8	0	2	192	87	16
Millbrook	10	6	0	4	219	92	12
Guernsey**	9	6	0	3	188	89	12
Fareham Heath	10	5	1	4	131	115	11
Sandown & Shank	10	4	3	3	121	108	11
Trojans	10	5	0	5	95	167	10
Isle of Wight	10	4	0	6	102	152	8
Rushmoor**	9	2	1	6	89	152	5
Tottonians	10	1	0	9	76	156	2
Fordingbridge	10	1	0	9	52	305	2

** = Match not played – subjected to appeal.

HAMPSHIRE 2

	P	W	D	L	F	A	PTS
Petersfield	9	8	0	1	243	50	16
Andover	9	8	0	1	206	44	16
Romsey	9	8	0	1	137	52	16
New Milton**	8	5	0	3	157	88	10
Jersey U Bs**	8	4	0	4	84	98	8
Overton	9	3	1	5	90	111	7
Ellingham	9	2	2	5	72	168	6
Waterlooville	9	2	1	6	63	176	5
Ventnor	9	1	2	6	48	106	4
Nomads	9	0	0	9	38	245	0

** = Match not played – subjected to appeal.

LONDON & SOUTH EAST DIVISION FIXTURES 1989/90

HAMPSHIRE LEAGUE ONE

Sat. 23rd September (Week 4)
Guernsey v Jersey
Petersfield v Fareham Heathens
Winchester v Millbrook
Eastleigh v Sandown & Shanklin
Gosport v Esso

Sat. 14th October (Week 6)
Esso v Guernsey
Sandown & Shanklin v Gosport
Millbrook v Eastleigh
Fareham Heathens v Winchester
Andover v Petersfield

Sat. 28th October (Week 8)
Guernsey v Sandown & Shanklin
Jersey v Esso
Winchester v Andover
Eastleigh v Fareham Heathens
Gosport v Millbrook

Sat. 11th November (Week 10)
Sandown & Shanklin v Jersey
Millbrook v Guernsey
Fareham Heathens v Gosport
Andover v Eastleigh
Petersfield v Winchester

Sat 18th November (Week 11)
Guernsey v Fareham Heathens
Jersey v Millbrook
Esso v Sandown & Shanklin
Eastleigh v Petersfield
Gosport v Andover

Sat. 25th November (Week 12)
Millbrook v Esso
Fareham Heathens v Jersey
Andover v Guernsey
Petersfield v Gosport
Winchester v Eastleigh

Sat. 13th January (Week 18)
Guernsey v Petersfield
Jersey v Andover
Esso v Fareham Heathens
Sandown & Shanklin v Millbrook
Gosport v Winchester

Sat. 27th January (Week 20)
Fareham Heathens v Sandown & Shanklin
Andover v Esso
Petersfield v Jersey
Winchester v Guernsey
Eastleigh v Gosport

Sat. 10th February (Week 22)
Guernsey v Eastleigh
Jersey v Winchester
Esso v Petersfield
Sandown & Shanklin v Andover
Millbrook v Fareham Heathens

Sat. 24th February (Week 24)
Andover v Millbrook
Petersfield v Sandown & Shanklin
Winchester v Esso
Eastleigh v Jersey
Gosport v Guernsey

Sat. 10th March (Week 26)
Jersey v Gosport
Esso v Eastleigh
Sandown & Shanklin v Winchester
Millbrook v Petersfield
Fareham Heathens v Andover

LONDON & SOUTH EAST DIVISION FIXTURES 1989/90

HAMPSHIRE LEAGUE TWO

Sat. 9th September (Week 2)
Nomads v New Milton
Farnborough v Overton
Romsey v Ellingham
Tottonians v Fordingbridge
Ventnor v I.O.W.
Trojans v Waterlooville

Sat. 23rd September (Week 4)
Fordingbridge v Waterlooville
Farnborough v Nomads
Romsey v Trojans
Tottonians v Ventnor
Jersey Utd Banks v I.O.W.
Ellingham v New Milton

Sat. 14th October (Week 6)
I.O.W. v Fordingbridge
New Milton v Overton
Ventnor v Jersey Utd Banks
Waterlooville v Ellingham
Trojans v Tottonians
Nomads v Romsey

Sat. 28th October (Week 8)
Romsey v Farnborough
Tottonians v Nomads
Jersey Utd Banks v Trojans
Ellingham v I.O.W.
Fordingbridge v Ventnor
Overton v Waterlooville

Sat. 11th November (Week 10)
Nomads v Jersey Utd Banks
Farnborough v Tottonians
I.O.W. v Overton
Waterlooville v New Milton
Ventnor v Ellingham
Trojans v Fordingbridge

Sat 18th November (Week 11)
Tottonians v Romsey
Jersey Utd Banks v Farnborough
Ellingham v Trojans
Fordingbridge v Nomads
Overton v Ventnor
New Milton v I.O.W.

Sat. 25th November (Week 12)
Nomads v Ellingham
Farnborough v Fordingbridge
Romsey v Jersey Utd Banks
I.O.W. v Waterlooville
Ventnor v New Milton
Trojans v Overton

Sat. 13th January (Week 18)
Waterlooville v Ventnor
Jersey Utd Banks v Tottonians
Ellingham v Farnborough
Fordingbridge v Romsey
Overton v Nomads
New Milton v Trojans

Sat. 27th January (Week 20)
Ellingham v Tottonians
I.O.W. v Trojans
Fordingbridge v Jersey Utd Banks
Overton v Romsey
New Milton v Farnborough
Waterlooville v Nomads

Sat. 10th February (Week 22)
Nomads v I.O.W.
Farnborough v Waterlooville
Romsey v New Milton
Trojans v Ventnor
Jersey Utd Banks v Ellingham
Tottonians v Overton

Sat. 24th February (Week 24)
Ellingham v Fordingbridge
I.O.W. v Farnborough
Overton v Jersey Utd Banks
New Milton v Tottonians
Waterlooville v Romsey
Ventnor v Nomads

Sat. 10th March (Week 26)
Nomads v Trojans
Farnborough v Ventnor
Romsey v I.O.W.
Fordingbridge v Overton
Jersey Utd Banks v New Milton
Tottonians v Waterlooville

Sat. 31st March (Week X7)
Trojans v Farnborough
Overton v Ellingham
I.O.W. v Tottonians
New Milton v Fordingbridge
Waterlooville v Jersey Utd Banks
Ventnor v Romsey

HAMPSHIRE 1

ANDOVER

Goodship Park, Southway, Walworth Industrial Estate, Andover, Hampshire. Tel: 0264 62578
Founded: 1959
President: David Griffiths
Chairman: Jim Howcroft
Secretary: Roderick Smith, as Ground Address (above). Tel: 0264 59491 (H), 0264 332299 (W)
Fixtures Secretary: Colin Reeves, as Ground Address (above)
Press Officer: As Fixtures Secretary
Coach: Jeffrey Thornton
Club captain (1988–89): Roy Maloney
Club captain (1989–90): Roy Maloney
No. of teams: Senior 3, Youth 3, Minis 3, Ladies 1
Directions to ground: Exit A303, at signpost A3093 Andover, 2nd exit off 1st roundabout onto Industrial Estate, 1st right on estate. Clubhouse mile on right
Clubhouse facilities: Open matchdays and evenings
Club colours: All black. (*Change colours:* Green shirts, black shorts)
Floodlights: No
Membership fees: Full £20, Playing £20, Social £4, Youth £7.50, Student £7.50
Ground admission: Nil
Local newspapers: Andover Advertiser, Southern Evening Echo
League position (1988–89): 2nd (promoted)
League playing record (1988–89): P 9, W 8, D 0, L 1, F 276, A 44

EASTLEIGH

Bishopstoke Playing Fields, Bishopstoke Road, Eastleigh, Hants. Tel: 0703 641312
Founded: 1931
President: W.H.J. Saffery
Chairman: E.T. Lynch
Secretary: H.T. Coulter, 16 Burnham Beeches, Chandlers Ford, Eastleigh, Hants S?5 3QS. Tel: 0703 252535 (H), 0703 823795 (W)
Fixtures Secretary: J.S. Sneezum, Bursledon Lodge, Salterns Lane, Old Bursledon, Southampton SO3 8DH. Tel: 042121 2286
Press Officer: As Secretary
Coach: T.B.A.
Club captain (1988–89): Clive Rennison
Club captain (1989–90): Andy Cartwright
No. of teams: Senior 4, Minis Yes
Directions to ground: Leave M27 at Junction 1, through Eastleigh town centre to Bishopstoke Road B3037, over railway bridge and it is mile on left
Club colours: Black, amber, red
Floodlights: No
Membership fees: VPs £10, Playing £20, Social £3
Programme editor: As Secretary
Local newspapers: Eastleigh Weekly News, Southern Evening Echo
League position (1988–89): 9th (relegated)
League playing record (1988–89): P 10, W 3, D 0, L 7, F 72, A 141
Competitions won: County Cup Semi-Finalists

ESSO (FAWLEY)

Esso Recreation Ground, Long Lane, Holbury, Southampton. Tel: 0703 89375
Founded: 1935
President: Bill C. Davies
Chairman: Roger Maxwell
Secretary: Jeremy E. Tombs, 16 Hayley Close, Hythe, Hampshire. Tel: 0703 895450
Fixtures Secretary: Rob I. Tarbard, Mumbles, Blackfield Road, Fawley, Southampton SO4 IE9. Tel: 0703 899067 (H), 895127 (W)
Press Officer: As Fixtures Secretary
Club captain (1988–89): G. Barry Walker
Club captain (1989–90): David Gooch

No. of teams: Senior 3, Youth 1, Minis 3
Directions to ground: M27 (to Southampton) then M271, then A326 (to Fawley). Ground on right in Holbury adjacent to Cinema
Clubhouse facilities: Pub hours
Club colours: Red shirts, blue shorts, red socks. (*Change colours:* Blue shirts)
Floodlights: Yes
Local newspaper: Southern Evening Echo
League position (1988–89): 2nd
League playing record (1988–89): P 10, W 8, D 0, L 2, F 191, A 87

FAREHAM HEATHENS

Cams Alders Recreation Centre, Highfield Avenue, Farham, Hants. Tel: 0329 221793
Founded: 1975
President: Gerry Neighbour
Chairman: Mike Blow
Secretary: David Payne, 10 Abshot Close, Titchfield, Fareham PO10 4LZ. Tel: 0489 584290
Fixtures Secretary: Cyril turner, 4 Walberton Avenue, E. Cosham, Portsmouth PO6 2JH. Tel: 0705 370139
Press Officer: As Fixtures Secretary
Coach: Roger Evans/Gerald Laker
Club captain (1988–89): James Black
Club captain (1989–90): James Black
No. of teams: Senior 4
Directions to ground: Take A27 from Fareham town centre towards Southampton. Cross roundabout by Fareham railway station. Take 2nd left then right into Highfield Avenue
Clubhouse facilities: Council owned. Own bar, four changing rooms
Club colours: Red and black. (*Change colours:* Green, black)
Nickname: The Heathens
Floodlights: No
Membership fees: Full £10, Youth £1, Student £1
Ground admission: Nil
Local newspapers: Solent Reporter, Southampton Evening Echo, Portsmouth Evening News
League position (1988–89): 5th
Competitions won: 4 Nations Invitation at Pulheim, Germany, March 1989

GOSPORT & FAREHAM

Gosport Park, Park Road, Gosport, Hants. Tel: 0705 589852.
Founded: 1946
Secretary: M.T. Edmonds, 30 Meadow Walk, Gosport, Hants. Tel: 0329 283084 (H), 0329 224189 (W).
Fixtures secretary: K. O'Toole, 20 Rowalian Avenue, Gosport, Hants. Tel: 0705 587926.

GUERNSEY

Footes Lane, St. Peter Port, Guernsey. Tel: 0481 54590
Founded: 1928
President: M.K. Duquemin
Chairman: B.A. Mansell
Secretary: B.J. Mildon, P.O. Box 181, St. Peter Port, Guernsey. Tel: 0481 65493 (H), 28321 (W)
Fixtures Secretary: M. Boot, Gorey Villa Private Hotel, Route Des Coutoures, St. Sampsons, Guernsey. Tel: 044377
Press Officer: R. WArlow, 5 Guildown Close, Le Villocq, Castel, Guernsey. Tel: 0481 53251 (H), 26268 (W)
Coach: J. Good
Club captain (1988–89): D. Wadley
Club captain (1989–90): T.B.A.
No. of teams: Senior 3, Youth and Minis 2
Ground capacity: Standing 1000
Club colours: Green. (*Change colours:* Blue)
Floodlights: No
League position (1988–89): 4th

League playing record (1988–89): P 9, W 6, D 0, L 3, F 188, A 39

JERSEY

Airport Road, St. Peter, Jersey C1. Tel: 0534 42255
Founded: 1879
President: Victor Hanby
Chairman: Sid Simkin
Secretary: Tony Pitcher, P.O. Box 141, St. Helier, Jersey C1. Tel: 0534 77101(H), 33700 (W)
Fixtures Secretary: Tom Hart, Rose Farm, Mont a L'Abbe, St. Helier, Jersey C1(H), 0000 000000 (W) 534 63064 (H), 36201 (W)
Press Officer: Max Hewitt, Jersey Evening Post, P.O. Box 582, Five Oaks, St. Saviour. Tel: 0534 73333 (W)
Coach: Ed Sharpe
Club captain (1988–89): Adrian Cordell
Club captain (1989–90): Adrian Cordell
No. of teams: Senior 4, Minis 3
Directions to ground: Adjacent to airport
Ground capacity: Seating 120, standing 2000
Clubhouse facilities: Weights room, squash courts, sauna
Club colours: Blue shirts, white hoops, white shorts. (*Change colours:* Red shirts, white shorts)
Floodlights: No
Membership fees: Playing £35, Social £35, Youth £1, Student £1
Ground admission: Usually Nil
Programme: No. of editorial pages 4; No. of advertising pages 4; Price 50p
Programme editor: Peter Nowell, P.O. Box 141, St. Helier, Jersey
Local newspaper: Jersey Evening Post
League position (1988–89): 11th (relegated)
League playing record (1988–89): P 9, W 1, D 0, L 8, F 42, A 166
Competitions won: Siam Cup (v. Guernsey)

MILLBROOK

WSSC, Redbridge Lane, Nursling, Southampton, Hants. Tel: 0703 739759
Founded: 1971
President: Fred Lowry, B.A.
Chairman: Glen Joyce
Secretary: Tony Allan, 3 Marls Road, Botley, Soton, Hants. Tel: 0703 787337
Fixtures Secretary: Robert Prowting, 'Methven', Chinham Road, Bartley, Hants SO4 2LF. Tel: 0703 813742 (H), 780911 ext. 227 (W)
Press Officer: Kevin Byatt, 18 Ethelred Gardens, Totton, Hants SO4 3UA. Tel: 0703 663374
Coach: Tony Moss
Club captain (1988–89): Robert Prowting
Club captain (1989–90): T.B.A.
No. of teams: Senior 3, Youth 2
Clubhouse facilities: Open matchdays and evenings
Club colours: Red and green hooped shirts, white shorts, green socks
Floodlights: Yes (fixed and portable – for training only)
Membership fees: Full £12.50, Social £10, Youth £5
Local newspaper: Southern Evening Echo
League position (1988–89): 3rd
League playing record (1988–89): P 10, W 6, D 0, L 4, F 219, A 92

PETERSFIELD

Penns Place, Petersfield, Hants. Tel: Petersfield 64588
Founded: 1927
President: Aubrey Sayer
Chairman: Cliff Fairley
Secretary: John Holden, 1 Heather Mount, Stoney bottom, Grayshott, Hindhead, Surrey Gu26 6HN. Tel: 0428 736592 (H), 01–248 3939 ext. 280 (W)
Fixtures Secretary: Mike Rapley, 83 Bell Hill, Petersfield, Hants. Tel: Petersfield 63818 (H), 63180 (W)

Press Officer: Andy Millar, 31 Moggs Mead, Herne Farm, Petersfield GU31 4PO. Tel: Petersfield 65468 (H), 0730 894449 (W)
Coach: Dave Palethorpe
Club captain (1988–89): Mick Longley
Club captain (1989–90): Mick Longley
No. of teams: Senior 5, Youth 1, Minis 7
Directions to ground: From A3 just north of town, turn east into Pulens Lane by garage, follow signposts to Sports Centre
Ground capacity: Standing Ample
Clubhouse facilities: Bar/lounge, changing rooms, first floor balcony
Club colours: Red shirts with broad white hoop. (*Change colours:* Royal blue)
Floodlights: No
Membership fees: Full £30, Playing £30, Social £15, Youth £10, Student £10, Mini £7.50
Programme editor: As Fixtures Secretary
Local newspapers: Petersfield Herald, East Hants Post
League position (1988–89): 1st (promoted)
League playing record (1988–89): P 11, W 10, D 0, L 1, F 354, A 53
Competitions won: Champions Hampshire Division 2

SANDOWN AND SHANKLIN

The Clubhouse, The Fairway, Lake, Nr. Sandown, Isle of Wight. Tel: 0983 404707
Founded: 1961
President: M. Renouf
Chairman: G. Thomas
Secretary: R. Simpson, Tudor Lodge, 21 Beachfield Road, Sandown, I.O.W. PO36 8LT. Tel: 0983 402430
Fixtures Secretary: Colin Bond, Basement Flat, Green Knot, Cliff Path, Lake, Isle of Wight. Tel: 0403396
Coach: David Ball
Club captain (1988–89): Mark Whyndham-Jones
Club captain (1989–90): Mark Whyndham-Jones
No. of teams: Senior 3–4, Youth 1, Minis 3
Directions to ground: Ferry to Ryde, Isle of Wight, then train to Sandown. Walk under the subway to The Fairway
Clubhouse facilities: Two bars
Club colours: Blue and white hoops. (*Change colours:* Plain blue)
Floodlights: No
League position (1988–89): 6th
League playing record (1988–89): P 10, W 4, D 3, L 3, F 121, A 108

WINCHESTER

Beverley Meads, Barham Road, Copse Hill, Wimbledon, London SW19 Tel: 01 946 3156.
Founded: 1929
Secretary: P. Walder, Pedlars Cottage, Gunville Hill, Winterslow, Salisbury, Wilts SP5 1PJ. Tel: 0980 862315 (H), 0722 26128 (W)
Fixtures Secretary: D. Walters, "Conkers", The Pastures, Kingsworthy, Winchester, Hants. Tel: 0962 880659 (H)

ELLINGHAM

Picket Post, Picket Hill, Ringwood, Hampshire. Tel: 0425 476668
Founded: 1966
President: Roger Pitcher
Chairman: Terry Gauden
Secretary: Howard Neale, Plas-Bryn-Carw, Harthill Drove, Redlynch, Wiltshire. Tel: 0725 21621(H), 0703 701801 (W)
Fixtures Secretary: Steve Benson, 22 Fairlie, Poulner,

Ringwood, Hampshire. Tel: 0425 474991 (H), 0264 64144 ext. 377 (W)
Press Officer: As Fixtures Secretary
Club captain (1988–89): Julian Chiari
Club captain (1989–90): Julian Chiari
No. of teams: Senior 3
Directions to ground: At Picket Post on the A31 coming out of Ringwood in the direction of Southampton
Clubhouse facilities: Bar. Open matchdays
Club colours: Navy blue with yellow hoop. (*Change colours:* Red)
Floodlights: No
League: Hampshire 2
League position (1988–89): 8th
League playing record (1988–89): P 10, W 3, D 2, L 5

FARNBOROUGH

Tile Barn Close, Cove, Farnborough, Hants. Tel: 0252 514750
President: Keith Perry
Chairman: Lyn Davies
Secretary: Adrian Hathaway, 12 Queensbury Close, Blackwater, Camberley, Surrey. Tel: Camberley 35935
Fixtures Secretary: Barry McKay, 43 The Grove, Farnborough, Hants. Tel: 0252 512363 (H), Camberley 63377 ext. 4471 (W)
Coach: Peter Ludlow
Club captain (1988–89): John Shaler
Club captain (1989–90): Jeff Cadogan
No. of teams: Senior 4, Youth 1, Minis 4
Directions to ground: From M3 take Junction 4, after Ship public house on A325 turn right to Cove. At end of road turn left, Tile Barn Close is 3rd right
Ground capacity: Standing 1000
Clubhouse facilities: 4 changing rooms, 2 pitches, bar
Club colours: Light and dark blue. (*Change colours:* Red/white hoops)
Floodlights: No
Ground admission: Free
Local newspaper: Aldershot News
League: Hampshire 2
League position (1988–89): 8th
League playing record (1988–89): P 9, W 2, D 1, L 6

FORDINGBRIDGE

Recreation Ground, Fordingbridge, Hants. Tel: 0425 52047
Founded: 1983
President: S. Howard
Chairman: M. Noke
Secretary: S. Goddon, 157 Station Road, Fordingbridge, Hants SP6 1DF. Tel: 0425 54069
Fixtures Secretary: J. Trim, 'Trees', Fryern Court Road, Fordingbridge, Hants. Tel: 0425 55156
No. of teams: Senior 2, Minis 1
Directions to ground: Recreation Ground, Ringwood Road, Fordingbridge
Clubhouse facilities: Mixed sports club
Club colours: Sky blue. (*Change colours:* Black)
Floodlights: No
Membership fees: Full £12.50
Local newspaper: Fordingbridge Journal
League: Hampshire 1
League position (1988–89): Bottom

ISLE OF WIGHT

Wootton Recreation Ground, Wootton. Tel: 0983 883240
Founded: 1924
President: Stewart Peters
Chairman: Mike Farr
Secretary: Nick Carger, 114 Station Road, Wootton, I.O.W. PO33 4RQ. Tel: 0983 883537
Fixtures Secretary: Steve Lucy, The Paddocks, Morecon Road, Brading, I.O.W.. Tel: 0983 406801
Club captain (1988–89): Dave Bibby

Club captain (1989–90): Dave Bibby
No. of teams: Senior 2, Youth 1
Directions to ground: 1 or 1A Bus from Ryde Esplanade
Clubhouse facilities: Bar, changing
Club colours: Dark blue/gold hoops
Floodlights: No
League: Hampshire 1

JERSEY UNITED BANKS

Les Quennevais, St. Brelade, Jersey
President: Terry Bell
Chairman: Michael Stayte
Secretary: Michael Stayte, Lomon, Rue de Causie, St. Clement, Jersey. Tel: 0534 84782 (H), 72093 (W)
Fixtures Secretary: David Kaye, 2 Mont es Croix Cottages, St. Brelade, Jersey. Tel: 0534 42713 (H), 79111 ext. 121 (W)
Coach: James Richardson
Club captain (1988–89): Leonard McAvinney
Club captain (1989–90): Colin Goodfellow
No. of teams: Senior 2
Clubhouse facilities: Bar
Club colours: White/red trim, green socks. (*Change colours:* Black/green hoops, red/yellow hoops, green socks)
Nickname: The Banks
Floodlights: No
Membership fees: Full £40, Playing £40, Social £10
Local newspaper: Jersey Evening Post
League: Hampshire 1
League position (1988–89): 4th(?)
League playing record (1988–89): P 8
Competitions won: Sugden Cup

NEW MILTON & DISTRICT

Ashley Sports Ground, New Milton, Hants. Tel: 0425 610401
Founded: 1925
President: Robin Jackson
Chairman: Nicholas Musset
Secretary: Duncan Conacher, 20 Park Road, Milford on Sea, Lymington, Hants. Tel: 0590 45286
Fixtures Secretary: Gerald Holley, 19 Albert Road, New Milton, Hants BH25 6SP. Tel: 0425 621126 (H), 620124 (W)
Press Officer: As Secretary
Coach: Norman Cracknell
Club captain (1988–89): David Bradley
Club captain (1989–90): David Bradley
No. of teams: Senior 3, Youth 2, Minis 3
Directions to ground: Turn off M27 at Cadnam to Lyndhurst, then A35 for 6 miles, turn left on B3058 to New Milton town centre. Turn left at traffic lights, NMRFC mile on right (before Ashley Hotel)
Ground capacity: Standing 200
Clubhouse facilities: Changing rooms, showers, bar. Open match or training days
Club colours: Green and white squares. (*Change colours:* Blue quarters)
Floodlights: Yes
Membership fees: Full £16, Playing £16, Social £5, Youth £7.50 (no match fee), Student £5, OAP £5
Ground admission: Free
Local newspapers: New Milton Advertiser, Southern Echo
League: Hampshire 2
League position (1988–89): 4th
League playing record (1988–89): P 8, W 5, D 0, L 3, F 157, A 88

NOMADS

Farlington Recreation Ground, Eastern Road, Portsmouth
Founded: 1978
President: Colin A. Few

Chairman: Barry Bridgman
Secretary: Richard J. Woodward, 14 Weyhill Close, Porchester, Fareham, Hants PO16 8EL. Tel: 0705 382060
Fixtures Secretary: As Secretary
Press Officer: As Secretary
Coach: Ian Headon
Club captain (1988–89): Alan Cole
Club captain (1989–90): Michael Furse
No. of teams: Senior 2
Ground capacity: Standing Infinite
Clubhouse facilities: Bar, telephone, television
Club colours: Scarlet and black hoops, black shorts, red socks. (*Change colours:* Maroon)
Floodlights: No
Membership fees: Full £10, Playing £10, Student £5
Local newspaper: The News
League: Hampshire 2
League position (1988–89): 9th
League playing record (1988–89): P 10, W 1, D 0, L 9, F 53, A 245

OVERTON

Town Meadow, High Street, Overton, Hants
Founded: 1971
President: Mike Williams
Chairman: Paul Phillips
Secretary: Peter J. Williams, 8 The Greenways, St. John's Road, Oakley, Nr. Basingstoke, Hants. Tel: 0256 780874
Fixtures Secretary: Alec Malcolm Coles, 15 Rochford Road, Basingstoke, Hants RG21 1TQ. Tel: 0256 462827
Club captain (1988–89): Keith Coomber
Club captain (1989–90): John Spaul
No. of teams: Senior 2
Directions to ground: Basingstoke 3400 to Overton, through village, 50 yds on right
Ground capacity: Seating 3500
Clubhouse facilities: Open matchdays
Club colours: Royal Blue. (*Change colours:* Red)
Floodlights: No
Local newspapers: Basingstoke Gazette and Andover Advertiser
League: Hampshire 2
League position (1988–89): 6th
League playing record (1988–89): P 9, W 4, D 1, L 4, F 93, A 111

ROMSEY

Romsey Sports Centre, Southampton Road, Romsey. Tel: 0794 515103
President: Dr. John E. White, M.D., F.R.C.P.
Chairman: Robert W. Broomhall
Secretary: Nick J. Twyman, Tudor Cottage, Hillview Road, Michelmersh, Romsey SO51 0NN. Tel: 0794 68150 (H), 0256 56233 ext. 6172 (W)
Fixtures Secretary: Nigel D.Y. Mayor, 2 Love Lane, Romsey, Hants, SO51 8DE. Tel: 0794 523184 (H), 0703 252088 (W)
Press Officer: Robert Walker, 9 Chapelside, Titchfield, Nr. Fareham, Hants PO14 4AP. Tel: 0329 45425 (H), 0705 461034 (W)
Coach: Kevin R. Gregory
Club captain (1988–89): Mike Evans
Club captain (1989–90): Simon Peace
No. of teams: Senior 2
Directions to ground: Turn off M27 (Junc. 3) onto M271, follow A3057 towards Romsey until road meets A27. Turn left and sports centre situated approx. 1 miles on left before reaching town
Clubhouse facilities: The Abbey Hotel, Church Street, Romsey. Tel: 0794 513360
Club colours: Gold and royal blue hoops. (*Change colours:* Red)
Nickname: Royal Tobys
Floodlights: No
Membership fees: Full £15, Playing £15, Social £7.50, Student £7.50

Local newspapers: Romsey Advertiser and Southern Evening Echo
League: Hampshire 2
League position (1988–89): 3rd
League playing record (1988–89): P 10, W 9, D 0, L 1, F 167, A 65

TOTTONIANS

c/o Totton College, Water Lane, totton, Southampton, Hants
Founded: 1960
President: K. Johnson
Chairman: A. Woodhouse
Secretary: Adrian Hamilton, 4 Myrtle Avenue, Totton, Southampton SO4 37X. Tel: 0703 860085
Fixtures Secretary: S. Anderson, 35 Corriander Drive, Totton, Southampton. Tel: 0703 860085
Press Officer: As Secretary
Coach: Kevin Cleary
Club captain (1988–89): M. Townsend
Club captain (1989–90): M. Townsend
No. of teams: Senior 3, Youth 1, Minis 3
Directions to ground: M27 Junction 3. Turn south M271 signpost Totton. In Totton take the Ringwood Road, turn right at Calmore Road. Water Lane on right (college on corner)
Clubhouse facilities: King George 5th Playing Fields
Club colours: Green, black, white hoops
Nickname: 'Totts'
Floodlights: No
Membership fees: Full £18, Playing £18, Youth £6
Local newspaper: Southern Evening Echo
League: Hampshire 2
League position (1988–89): Bottom (relegated)
League playing record (1988–89): P 8, W 2, D 1, L 5

TROJANS

No further information

VENTNOR

Watcombe Bottom, Whitwell Road, Ventnor.
Founded: 1936
Secretary: R. Bayliss, Medina House, Church road, Northwood, Cowes, Isle of Wight. Tel: 0983 298448 (H), 0983 525121 (W).
League Contact: T. Flower, "Stonebow", Rectory Road, Niton, Isle of Wight PO38 2AU. Tel: 0983 730567.
Press Officer: David Ball. Tel: 0983 821000.
Colours: Navy Blue/White.
League: Hampshire 2

WATERLOOVILLE

Rowlands Avenue, Waterlooville, Portsmouth, Hampshire. Groundsman: Waterlooville 262492
Founded: 1981
President: Cmdr. Robins
Chairman: Christopher Powell
Secretary: Antony John McDowell, 69 Folkestone Road, Copnor, Portsmouth PO3 6LP. Tel: Portsmouth 671887 (H), 0329 285616 (W)
Fixtures Secretary: As Secretary
Press Officer: David Murphy, 69 Folkestone road, Copnor, Portsmouth PO3 6LP. Tel: Portsmouth 669351
Club captain (1988–89): James Furmedge
Club captain (1989–90): T.B.A.
No. of teams: Senior 1
Club colours: Sky blue shirts, black shorts, blue stockings
Floodlights: No
Membership fees: Playing £15, Social £10
Local newspaper: Portsmouth Evening News
League: Hampshire 2
League position (1988–89): 7th

SURREY LEAGUES

A TOTAL of 51 teams took part in the Surrey Leagues last season with 11 in both Surrey 1 and Surrey 2A, 12 in Surrey 2B, 10 in Surrey 3, and another seven in Surrey 4. This coming season teams will be organised into five consecutive leagues. Last time out 46 teams took part.

Leading the way in the top division was Dorking, whose sole blemish in a 10-game programme was a draw; they go up. Only one team is relegated from the division, Old Surbitonians with their single win being edged down by Effingham's superior points difference although in a similar one-win situation. Up come Harrodians (from 2A and promoted from League 3 last season) and John Fisher Old Boys (whose last effort was relegation from Surrey 1) with only one defeat and a points difference of 296–50.

With the leagues being re-adjusted several teams will find themselves in Surrey 3 next season and they are Old Reedonians, Old Freemans, Kingston, Farnham, Chobham, Old Pelhamians, Shirley Wanderers, Chipstead, King's College Hospital and Old Suttonians. Old Epsomians – at the foot of Surrey 2B – drop to Surrey 4. Also in Division 3 Battersea Ironsides' reward for losing only once in nine starts is inclusion in their numbers. The rest of Surrey 3 are in Surrey 4 now.

Surrey 4 was won in spectacular fashion by Surrey University with all 12 games won (teams met each other twice here) for a points differential of 303–60, but they along with Royal Holloway start the new season in the revised Surrey 4. The rest of that league will start in Surrey 5, where one would like to wish good luck to British Aerospace, who lost all 11 matches in the old Surrey 4 and scored 30 points against 319 conceded.

Complicated? By next season the whole large Surrey organisation will be easy to understand and, in any case, the increasing numbers show healthy competition.

SURREY GENERAL:

A.P. Titheridge, Esq.,
Treave House,
Beech Hill,
Mayford,Woking,   (H) 04862 69902
Surrey GU22 0SB   (O) 01 580 4528

SURREY ONE:

R. Greer Kirkwood, Esq.,
63 Shaftsbury Way,
Strawberry Hill,
Twickenham   (H) 01 898 1767
TW2 4RW   (O) 01 924 2464

SURREY TWO:

J.S. Laidman, Esq.,
2 West Dene,
Park Lane,
Cheam,   (H) 01 643 2919
Surrey   (O) 01 245 9411

SURREY THREE:

Miss E. Morris,
29 Mullens House,
Chartfield Avenue,
Putney,
London
SW15 6DA   (H) 01 788 5738

SURREY FOUR & FIVE:

A. Manly, Esq.,
7 Burgoyne Road,
South Norwood,
London   (H) 01 653 4585
SE25 6JT   (O) 01 760 0200

TABLES 1987–88

SURREY 1

	P	W	D	L	F	A	PTS
O Guilfordians	9	8	1	0	199	37	17
Dorking	9	7	1	1	141	54	15
Old Blues	9	5	2	2	128	80	12
O Rutlishian	9	6	0	3	95	103	12
Cranleigh	9	4	2	3			10
O Wimbledonians	9	4	1	4	87	72	9
O Tiffinians	9	2	2	5	109	116	6
O Surbitonians	9	1	2	6	51	139	4
O Cranleighans	9	1	1	7	53	191	3
J. Fisher OB's	9	1	0	8	73	151	2

St. Thomas Hospital (withdrawn – all matches void).

SURREY 2A

	P	W	D	L	F	A	PTS
Effingham	11	10	1	0	201	80	21
Wimbledon	11	9	0	2	216	93	18
Raynes Park	11	8	0	3	227	67	16
Univ Vandals	11	6	1	4	193	129	13
O Freemans	11	6	0	5	163	119	12
Kingston	11	4	1	6	110	158	9
Ch X/W Hosp	11	4	0	7	144	140	8
O Haleyburians	10	5	0	5	97	129	8
O Reedonians	10	4	0	6		150	7
Chobham	11	2	0	9			4
Shene OG's	11	2	1	8	74	255	2

** 2 championship points deducted – breach of rules.

SURREY 2B

	P	W	D	L	F	A	PTS
Merton	11	11	0	0	227	46	22
Mitcham	11	9	0	2	243	42	18
O Pelhamians	11	7	0	4	101	60	14
O Wandsworth's	11	6	1	4	150	83	13
O Joohnians	11	6	1	4	144	125	13
Bee Old Boys	11	6	0	5	117	124	12
Kings Coll Hos	11	5	2	4	110	158	12
Shirley Wand	11	4	1	6	129	117	9
O Suttonians	11	3	3	5	111	133	9
Chipstead	11	2	1	8	51	208	5
O Epsomians	11	2	0	9	40	221	4
O Bevonians	11	0	1	10	62	174	1

SURREY 3

	P	W	D	L	F	A	PTS
Harrodians	11	11	0	0	373	46	22
Law Society	11	8	1	2	242	55	17
Reigate & R	11	8	1	2	226	77	17
Surrey Pol	11	8	0	3	275	102	16
O Croydonians	11	6	0	5	186	98	12
Battersea Ir	11	5	0	6	164	147	10
London Fire B	11	5	0	6	109	182	10
Haslemere	11	5	0	6	58	196	10
BBC	11	4	0	7	129	180	8
O Caterhamians	11	4	0	7	129	180	8
Racal Decca**	11	1	0	10	74	364	0
Lightwater	11	0	0	11	35	379	0

Oxted (withdrawn – all matches void).

** 2 championship points deducted – rule violation.

TABLES 1988-89

SURREY 1

	P	W	D	L	F	A	PTS
Dorking	10	1	9	0	149	73	19
Old Blues	10	7	1	2	161	107	15
O Rutlishians	10	7	0	3	185	116	14
Cranleigh	10	6	2	2	121	74	14
Warlingham	10	5	1	4	120	89	11
O Cranleighans	10	5	0	5	111	122	10
O Tiffinians	10	4	1	5	145	134	9
O Wimbledonians	10	4	0	6	124	112	8
Merton	10	3	0	7	91	128	6
Effingham	10	1	0	9	84	161	2
O Surbitonians	10	1	0	9	66	241	2

SURREY 2A

	P	W	D	L	F	A	PTS
Harrodians	10	9	0	1	261	80	18
Wimbledon	10	9	0	1	211	54	18
Univ Vandals	10	6	0	4	120	125	12
Raynes Pk	10	5	0	5	141	116	10
Char X W Hosp	10	5	0	5	138	129	10
O Haileyburians	10	5	0	5	140	136	10
O Reedonians	10	5	0	5	123	152	10
O Freemans	10	4	1	5	125	97	9
Kingston	10	3	0	7	95	183	6
Farnham	10	2	1	7	92	148	5
Chobham	10	1	0	9	81	307	2

St. Thomas' Hospital withdrawn.

SURREY 2B

	P	W	D	L	F	A	PTS
J. Fisher O.B.	11	10	0	1	318	50	20
O Wandsworthians	11	10	0	1	207	74	20
Bec Old Boys	11	8	0	3	193	84	16
Mitcham	11	7	1	3	180	97	15
Law Society	11	7	1	3	151	113	15
O Johnians	11	5	0	6	136	183	10
O Pelhamians	11	4	0	7	134	97	8
Shirley Wand	11	4	0	7	100	144	8
Chipstead	11	3	1	7	69	139	7
K. Coll Hosp	11	2	1	8	69	239	5
O Suttonians	11	2	0	9	98	195	4
O Epsomians	11	2	0	9	55	295	4

SURREY 3

	P	W	D	L	F	A	PTS
Battersea Ir	9	8	0	1	204	46	16
O Caterhamians	9	7	0	2	178	68	14
Reigate & R	9	6	1	2	182	60	13
Surrey Pol	9	6	1	2	129	81	13
BBC	9	5	0	4	87	55	10
O Bevonians	9	5	0	4	95	91	10
O Croydonians	9	3	2	4	72	78	8
Shene OG's	9	1	1	7	76	194	3
London Fire B	9	1	1	7	56	183	3
Haslemere	9	0	0	9	409	263	0

SURREY 4

	P	W	D	L	F	A	PTS
Surrey Univ	12	12	0	0	365	63	24
Roy Holloway**	11	9	0	2	321	93	18
Oxted**	11	6	0	5	205	122	12
Economicals**	11	5	1	5	147	169	11
Racal Decca**	11	4	0	7	101	193	8
Lightwater	12	3	1	8	89	265	7
Brit Aerospace	12	0	0	2	30	353	0

** = Matches not played – with permission of League Committee.

LONDON & SOUTH EAST DIVISION FIXTURES 1989/90

SURREY LEAGUE ONE

Sat. 23rd September (Week 4)
Old Blues v Harrodians
Warlingham v Old Tiffinians
John Fisher O.B. v Effingham
Old Wimbledonians v Old Rutlishians
Cranleigh v Merton

Sat. 14th October (Week 6)
Merton v Old Blues
Old Rutlishians v Cranleigh
Effingham v Old Wimbledonians
Old Tiffinians v John Fisher O.B.
Old Cranleighans v Warlingham

Sat. 28th October (Week 8)
Old Blues v Old Rutlishians
Harrodians v Merton
John Fisher O.B. v Old Cranleighans
Old Wimbledonians v Old Tiffinians
Cranleigh v Effingham

Sat. 11th November (Week 10)
Old Rutlishians v Harrodians
Effingham v Old Blues
Old Tiffinians v Cranleigh
Old Cranleighans v Old Wimbledonians
Warlingham v John Fisher O.B.

Sat 18th November (Week 11)
Old Blues v Old Tiffinians
Harrodians v Effingham
Merton v Old Rutlishians
Old Wimbledonians v Warlingham
Cranleigh v Old Cranleighans

Sat. 25th November (Week 12)
Effingham v Merton
Old Tiffinians v Harrodians
Old Cranleighans v Old Blues
Warlingham v Cranleigh
John Fisher O.B. v Old Wimbledonians

Sat. 13th January (Week 18)
Old Blues v Warlingham
Harrodians v Old Cranleighans
Merton v Old Tiffinians
Old Rutlishians v Effingham
Cranleigh v John Fisher O.B.

Sat. 27th January (Week 20)
Old Tiffinians v Old Rutlishians
Old Cranleighans v Merton
Warlingham v Harrodians
John Fisher O.B. v Old Blues
Old Wimbledonians v Cranleigh

Sat. 10th February (Week 22)
Old Blues v Old Wimbledonians
Harrodians v John Fisher O.B.
Merton v Warlingham
Old Rutlishians v Old Cranleighans
Effingham v Old Tiffinians

Sat. 24th February (Week 24)
Old Cranleighans v Effingham
Warlingham v Old Rutlishians
John Fisher O.B. v Merton
Old Wimbledonians v Harrodians
Cranleigh v Old Blues

Sat. 10th March (Week 26)
Harrodians v Cranleigh
Merton v Old Wimbledonians
Old Rutlishians v John Fisher O.B.
Effingham v Warlingham
Old Tiffinians v Old Cranleighans

LONDON & SOUTH EAST DIVISION FIXTURES 1989/90

SURREY TWO

Sat. 23rd September (Week 4)
Old Wandsworthians v Cobham
University Vandals v Wimbledon
Bec Old Boys v Raynes Park
Old Haileyburians v Law Society
Old Johnians v Mitcham

Sat. 14th October (Week 6)
Mitcham v Old Wandsworthians
Law Society v Old Johnians
Raynes Park v Old Haileyburians
Wimbledon v Bec Old Boys
Charing X/West. Hosp. v U. Vandals

Sat. 28th October (Week 8)
Old Wandsworthians v Law Society
Cobham v Mitcham
Bec Old Boys v Charing X/W Hos.
Old Haileyburians v Wimbledon
Old Johnians v Raynes Park

Sat. 11th November (Week 10)
Law Society v Old Surbitonians
Raynes Park v Old Wandsworthians
Wimbledon v Old Johnians
Charing X/W Hos v O Haileyburians
University Vandals v Bec Old Boys

Sat 18th November (Week 11)
Old Wandsworthians v Wimbledon
Cobham v Raynes Park
Mitcham v Law Society
Old Haileyburians v University Vandals
Old Johnians v Charing X/West. Hosp.

Sat. 25th November (Week 12)
Raynes Park v Mitcham
Wimbledon v Old Surbitonians
Charing X/W Hos v Old Wandsworthians
University Vandals v Old Johnians
Bec Old Boys v Old Haileyburians

Sat. 13th January (Week 18)
Old Wandsworthians v University Vandals
Cobham v Charing X/W. Hosp.
Mitcham v Wimbledon
Law Society v Raynes Park
Old Johnians v Bec Old Boys

Sat. 27th January (Week 20)
Wimbledon v Law Society
Charing X/West. Hosp. v Mitcham
University Vandals v Cobham
Bec Old Boys v Old Wandsworthians
Old Haileyburians v Old Johnians

Sat. 10th February (Week 22)
Old Wandsworthians v Old Haileyburians
Cobham v Bec Old Boys
Mitcham v University Vandals
Law Society v Charing X/West. Hosp.
Raynes Park v Wimbledon

Sat. 24th February (Week 24)
Charing X/West. Hosp. v Raynes Park
University Vandals v Law Society
Bec Old Boys v Mitcham
Old Haileyburians v Cobham
Old Johnians v Old Wandsworthians

Sat. 10th March (Week 26)
Cobham v Old Johnians
Mitcham v Old Haileyburians
Law Society v Bec Old Boys
Raynes Park v University Vandals
Wimbledon v Charing X/West. Hosp.

LONDON & SOUTH EAST DIVISION FIXTURES 1989/90

SURREY LEAGUE THREE

Sat. 23rd September (Week 4)
Battersea Ironsides v Shirley Wanderers
Farnham v Old Suttonians
Old Pelhamians v Chobham
King's College Hosp. v Kingston
Old Reedonians v Old Freemans

Sat. 14th October (Week 6)
Old Freemans v Battersea Ironsides
Kingston v Old Reedonians
Chobham v King's College Hosp.
Old Suttonians v Old Pelhamians
Chipstead v Farnham

Sat. 28th October (Week 8)
Battersea Ironsides v Kingston
Shirley Wanderers v Old Freemans
Old Pelhamians v Chipstead
King's College Hosp. v Old Suttonians
Old Reedonians v Chobham

Sat. 11th November (Week 10)
Kingston v Shirley Wanderers
Chobham v Battersea Ironsides
Old Suttonians v Old Reedonians
Chipstead v King's College Hosp.
Farnham v Old Pelhamians

Sat 18th November (Week 11)
Battersea Ironsides v Old Suttonians
Shirley Wanderers v Chobham
Old Freemans v Kingston
King's College Hosp. v Farnham
Old Reedonians v Chipstead

Sat. 25th November (Week 12)
Chobham v Old Freemans
Old Suttonians v Shirley Wanderers
Chipstead v Battersea Ironsides
Farnham v Old Reedonians
Old Pelhamians v King's College Hosp.

Sat. 13th January (Week 18)
Battersea Ironsides v Farnham
Shirley Wanderers v Chipstead
Old Freemans v Old Suttonians
Kingston v Chobham
Old Reedonians v Old Pelhamians

Sat. 27th January (Week 20)
Old Suttonians v Kingston
Chipstead v Old Freemans
Farnham v Shirley Wanderers
Old Pelhamians v Battersea Ironsides
King's College Hosp. v Old Reedonians

Sat. 10th February (Week 22)
Battersea Ironsides v King's College Hosp.
Shirley Wanderers v Old Pelhamians
Old Freemans v Farnham
Kingston v Chipstead
Chobham v Old Suttonians

Sat. 24th February (Week 24)
Chipstead v Chobham
Farnham v Kingston
Old Pelhamians v Old Freemans
King's College Hosp. v Shirley Wanderers
Old Reedonians v Battersea Ironsides

Sat. 10th March (Week 26)
Shirley Wanderers v Old Reedonians
Old Freemans v King's College Hosp.
Kingston v Old Pelhamians
Chobham v Farnham
Old Suttonians v Chipstead

LONDON & SOUTH EAST DIVISION FIXTURES 1989/90

SURREY LEAGUE FOUR

Sat. 23rd September (Week 4)
B.B.C. v Old Epsomians
Reigate & Redhill v Surrey University
Shene Old Gramms. v Old Croydonians
Surrey Police v Old Caterhamians
Royal Holloway Coll. v Old Bevonians

Sat. 14th October (Week 6)
Old Bevonians v B.B.C.
Old Caterhamians v Royal Holloway Coll.
Old Croydonians v Surrey Police
Surrey University v Shene Old Gramms.
London Fire Brigade v Reigate & Redhill

Sat. 28th October (Week 8)
B.B.C. v Old Caterhamians
Old Epsomians v Old Bevonians
Shene Old Gramms. v London Fire Brigade
Surrey Police v Surrey University
Royal Holloway Coll. v Old Croydonians

Sat. 11th November (Week 10)
Old Caterhamians v Old Epsomians
Old Croydonians v B.B.C.
Surrey University v Royal Holloway Coll.
London Fire Brigade v Surrey Police
Reigate & Redhill v Shene Old Gramms.

Sat 18th November (Week 11)
B.B.C. v Surrey University
Old Epsomians v Old Croydonians
Old Bevonians v Old Caterhamians
Surrey Police v Reigate & Redhill
Royal Holloway Coll. v London Fire Brigade

Sat. 25th November (Week 12)
Old Croydonians v Old Bevonians
Surrey University v Old Epsomians
London Fire Brigade v B.B.C.
Reigate & Redhill v Royal Holloway Coll.
Shene Old Gramms. v Surrey Police

Sat. 13th January (Week 18)
B.B.C. v Reigate & Redhill
Old Epsomians v London Fire Brigade
Old Bevonians v Surrey University
Old Caterhamians v Old Croydonians
Royal Holloway Coll. v Shene Old Gramms.

Sat. 27th January (Week 20)
Surrey University v Old Caterhamians
London Fire Brigade v Old Bevonians
Reigate & Redhill v Old Epsomians
Shene Old Gramms. v B.B.C.
Surrey Police v Royal Holloway Coll.

Sat. 10th February (Week 22)
B.B.C. v Surrey Police
Old Epsomians v Shene Old Gramms.
Old Bevonians v Reigate & Redhill
Old Caterhamians v London Fire Brigade
Old Croydonians v Surrey University

Sat. 24th February (Week 24)
London Fire Brigade v Old Croydonians
Reigate & Redhill v Old Caterhamians
Shene Old Gramms. v Old Bevonians
Surrey Police v Old Epsomians
Royal Holloway Coll. v B.B.C.

Sat. 10th March (Week 26)
Old Epsomians v Royal Holloway Coll.
Old Bevonians v Surrey Police
Old Caterhamians v Shene Old Gramms.
Old Croydonians v Reigate & Redhill
Surrey University v London Fire Brigade

LONDON & SOUTH EAST DIVISION FIXTURES 1989/90

SURREY LEAGUE FIVE

Sat. 14th October (Week 6)
Woking v Economicals
Racal Decca v Gibraltar Eng.
Haslemere v Oxted
Nordic v Lightwater

Sat. 28th October (Week 8)
Lightwater v Woking
Oxted v Nordic
Racal Decca v Haslemere
Gibraltar Eng. v Economicals

Sat. 11th November (Week 10)
Woking v Oxted
Economicals v Lightwater
Nordic v Racal Decca
Gibraltar Eng. v Haslemere

Sat. 25th November (Week 12)
Lightwater v Gibraltar Eng.
Oxted v Economicals
Racal Decca v Woking
Haslemere v Nordic

Sat. 27th January (Week 20)
Woking v Haslemere
Economicals v Racal Decca
Lightwater v Oxted
Nordic v Gibraltar Eng.

Sat. 10th February (Week 22)
Racal Decca v Lightwater
Haslemere v Economicals
Nordic v Woking
Gibraltar Eng. v Oxted

Sat. 24th February (Week 24)
Woking v Gibraltar Eng.
Economicals v Nordic
Lightwater v Haslemere
Oxted v Racal Decca

CRANLEIGH

Wildwood Lane, Off Knowle Lane, Cranleigh, Surrey. Tel: 0483 275843
Founded: 1967
President: W. Ron Thomas
Chairman: Nigel Spong
Secretary: Jan Sherriff, 2 Waldy Rise, Cranleigh, Surrey. Tel: 0483 272808 (H), 0483 275376 (W)
Fixtures Secretary: Colston Herbert, 15 Lilyfields Chase, Ewhurst. Tel: 0483 272945 (H), 0483 505515 (W)
Press Officer: Hadyn Jones, 14 Orhcard Hill, Rudgwick, W. Sussex. Tel: 040372 3163
Coach: Colston Herbert
Club captain (1988–89): Chris Williams, 1st XV T. Newson
Club captain (1989–90): Chris Williams, 1st XV Toby Newson
No. of teams: Senior 5, Youth 5, Minis 5
Directions to ground: From Horsham to Guildford via A281 past Alfold Barn Pub (on right), past Alfold turning (on left), first right (Wildwood Lane). Ground 200 yds on left
Ground capacity: Standing 1000
Clubhouse facilities: Bar, 6 changing rooms, gymnasium
Club colours: Red/navy quarters, blue shorts, red socks
Nickname: Cranes
Floodlights: Yes (training only)
Membership fees: Full £25, Playing £25, Social £10, Youth £10, Student £15
Local newspapers: Surrey Advertiser, West Sussex County Times
League: Surrey 1
League position (1988–89): 3rd
League playing record (1988–89): P 10, W 6, D 2, L 2, F 121, A 67
Competitions won: Under 17 Surrey Cup Winners

EFFINGHAM

Brown's Lane, Effingham, Surrey. Tel: 0372 58845
Founded: 1966
President: David Hughes-Hallett
Chairman: Graham Hill
Secretary: Nicholas Webster, 'Glenside', 154 Connaught Road, Brookwood, Woking, Surrey GU24 0AL. Tel: 048 67 80477 (H), 0483 757555 ext. 2511 (W)
Fixtures Secretary: Ed Newton, 42 Milner Road, Kingston-upon-Thames, Surrey. Tel: 01–549 8213 (H), 01–434 1533 (W)
Press Officer: Gary Walters, 22 Old Lane, Cobham, Surrey. Tel: 04865 2437
Club captain (1988–89): N. Firth
Club captain (1989–90): G. Walters
No. of teams: Senior 4, Youth 3, Minis 6
Directions to ground: By car: the A246 between Guildford and Leatherhead. Entrance from Brown's Lane 100 yds on Leatherhead side of Effingham traffic lights
Clubhouse facilities: Bar
Club colours: Green and gold hoops
Floodlights: Yes (training only)
Membership fees: Full £30, Playing £30, Social £12.50, Youth £7.50, Student £7.50
Local newspapers: Leatherhead Advertiser, Surrey Advertiser
League: Surrey 1
League position (1988–89): 10th
League playing record (1988–89): P 10, W 1, D 0, L 9, F 84, A 161
Competitions won: Effingham Sevens

HARRODIAN

Harrodian Club, Mill Lodge, Lonsdale Road, Barnes,
London SW13 9QN. Tel: 01–748 5535
Founded: 1912
President: Colin Brown
Chairman: Paul Kirby
Secretary: Paul Kirby, 53 Stanhope Gardens, London SW7 5RF. Tel: 01–373 0120 (H), 01–602 4671 (W)
Fixtures Secretary: Jeremy Halse, 13 Ribstone Road, Cox Green, Maidenhead SL6 3HJ. Tel: 0628 36781 (H), 01–745 4643 (W)
Press Officer: Nicholas Goodwin, 11B Thorneyhedge Road, London W4. Tel: 01–747 0543 (H), 0494 31385 (W)
Coach: Charles Panton
Club captain (1988–89): Peter Walker
Club captain (1989–90): Dave Doonan
No. of teams: Senior 4
Directions to ground: Over Hammersmith Bridge towards Barnes, take first right into Lonsdale Road. The club is located mile on left
Clubhouse facilities: Private Sports/Social Club. Open lunchtime/evenings all days
Club colours: Green/gold hoops, white shorts. (*Change colours:* Black jerseys/black shorts)
Nickname: 'The Store'
Floodlights: No
Membership fees: Full £100, Playing £100, Social £100
Ground admission: £2 (inc. programme)
Programme: Price £2
Programme editor: David Doonan, 5 Elland Road, Walton, Surrey
Local newspapers Richmond & Twickenham Times
League: Surrey 1
League position (1988–89): 1st (promoted)
League playing record (1988–89): P 11, W 10, D 0, L 1
Competitions won: Surrey Division 2A Winners

JOHN FISHER OLD BOYS

198 Limpsfield Road, Hamsey Green, Warlingham, Surrey. Tel: 08832 5149.
Founded: 1959
President: T. King (Headmaster of John Fisher School)
Chairman: Bryan Whicher
Secretary: Niel Kenny, 20 Leith Road, Epsom, Surrey KT17 1DA. Tel: 03727 40831 (H), 01-582 5344 (W).
Fixtures Secretary: Tim Walkden, 24 Hyde Road, Sanderstead. Tel: 01-651 4686.
Club captain (1987–88): Steve Brown
Club captain (1988–89): Richard Wood
No. of teams: Senior 4.
Directions to Ground: Take the A2022, which is the first left on the Godstone Road after Purley railway station. Continue on the A2022 to the first roundabout. Turn right at the roundabout into the Limpsfield Road. The ground is approx 1 mile down on the right hand side.
Colours: Royal blue, white, gold hoops. (*Change colours:* Gold)
Floodlights: No
Membership: £23.50
Local newspaper: Croydon Advertiser
League: Surrey 1

MERTON

Faversham Road, Morden. Tel: 01-648 3239.
Founded: 1957
Secretary: M. Flood, 29 Parsons Field Road, Banstead, Surrey. Tel: 01-247 4321 (W).
Fixtures Secretary: A.P. Rees, 40 Braxted Park, Streatham, London SW16. Tel: 01-764 6014.
Colts Secretary: K. Phelps, 99 Tennyson Avenue, New Malden, Surrey. Tel: 01-942 8035.
League Contact: J. Caniff, 38 Hitchisson Road, Nunhead, London SE15 3AL. Tel: 01-732 4900.
Colours: Gold/White/Black.
League: Surrey 1

OLD BLUES

Founded: 1873
Secretary: Ian Hoskins, 1 Oak Tree Drive, Englefield Green, Surrey TW20 0NR. Tel: 0784 436707 (H), 01–930 1200 (W)
Fixtures Secretary: Matthew Fagan, 107 Stapleton Hall Road, London N4 4RH. Tel: 01–341 3361 (H), 01–387 3340 (W)
Press Officer: J.D. Williams, 9 Lion Gate Gardens, Richmond, Surrey. Tel: 01–940 5579 (H), 01–684 0011 (W)
Coach: Duncan Percy
Club captain (1988–89): John Simpson
Club captain (1989–90): John Simpson
No. of teams: Senior 4
Membership fees: Playing £45, Social £10, Student £15
League: Surrey 1
League position (1988–89): 2nd
League playing record (1988–89): P 33, W 18, D 4, L 11, F 474, A 496

OLD CRANLEIGHLIANS

Portsmouth Road, Thames Ditton, Surrey. Tel: 398 3092
Founded: 1928
President: Howard Cowley
Chairman: Mike Bacon
Secretary: Andrew Williams, St. Michaels, Ashwood Road, Woking, Surrey. Tel: 04862 20644 (H), 01–438 0665 (W)
Fixtures Secretary: Alex Rodrigues, 11 Spring Gardens, East Molesey, Surrey KT5 0JA. Tel: 01–783 0114 (H), 01–402 4200 (W)
Coach: Terry Hill
Club captain (1988–89): Nigel Griffiths
Club captain (1989–90): Tim Edwards
League: Surrey 1
League position (1988–89): 6th
League playing record (1988–89): P 10, W 5, D 0, L 5, F 111, A 122

OLD RUTLISHIANS

The Clubhouse, Poplar Road, Merton Park, London SW19 3JS. Tel: 01–542 3678
Founded: 1923
President: J. Gilby
Chairman: G.D. Aldis
Secretary: W.H. Griffin, 68 Love Lane, Morden, Surrey SM4 6LP. Tel: 01–644 9299 (H), 01–405 4377 ext. 2517 (W)
Fixtures Secretary: S.A. Bryant, 418 Kingston Road, Raynes Park, London SW20 8LL. Tel: 01-543 0629
Press Officer: As Secretary
Coach: Geoff Aldis
Club captain (1988–89): B. Cochrane
Club captain (1989–90): B. Cochrane
No. of teams: Senior 4, Youth 2
Clubhouse facilities: Open weekends and evenings
Club colours: Gold, silver, azure and black. (*Change colours:* Blue)
Floodlights: Yes
League: Surrey 1
League position (1988–89): 3rd
League playing record (1988–89): P 10, W 7, D 0, L 3, F 185, A 116

OLD TIFFINIANS

Grist Memorial Ground, Summer Road, East Molesey, Surrey. Tel: 01-398 1391.
Founded: 1924
Secretary: B.A. Bench, 70 Trinity Road, Wimbledon, London sW19., Tel: 01-543 1645 (H), 01-549 9222 (W).
Fixtures Secretary: R.G. Kirkwood, 63 Shaftesbury Avenue, Strawberry Hill, Twickenham, Middlesex. Tel: 01-898 1767.

League: Surrey 1
Colours: Violet/White/Navy

OLD WIMBLEDONIANS

104 Cottenham Park Road, West Wimbledon, London SW20. Tel: 01–879 0700
Founded: 1923
President: David Laundy
Chairman: David Laundy
Secretary: Edward Gardner, 22 Oakway, Raynes Park, London SW20 9JE. Tel: 01–542 4325 (H), 01–793 1121 (W)
Fixtures Secretary: Harry Groenen, 91 Merton Hall Road, Wimbledon SW19. Tel: 01–543 8903 (H), 0322 23320 (W)
Press Officer: Charles O'Rourke, 103 Cannon Hill Lane, Merton Park, London SW20 9LE. Tel: 01–540 6615 (H), 0293 511166 (W)
Coach: Bill Doherty
Club captain (1988–89): Patrick Ward
Club captain (1989–90): Roger Brosch
No. of teams: Senior 4, Youth 1
Directions to ground: A3 to Coombe Lane (East) signposted to Raynes Park, turn 5th left into Cambridge Road then 1st left to end, turn right. Ground on left
Ground capacity: Standing 1000
Clubhouse facilities: Open matchdays and evenings (4–11 p.m.)
Club colours: Maroon green gold hoops
Nickname: The Rams – Old Wombles
Floodlights: Yes (training only)
Local newspapers: Wimbledon News, Wimbledon Guardian, Surrey Comet
League: Surrey 1
League position (1988–89): 8th
League playing record (1988–89): P 10, W 4, D 0, L 6, F 118, A 112
Competitions won: Raynes Park Invitation Sevens Winners, April '89. Effingham Invitation Sevens Runners-Up, Sept. '88. Surrey County Sevens, Semi-Finalists, April '89

WARLINGHAM

Hamsey Green, Limpsfield Road, Warlingham, Surrey. Tel: 08832 2825
Founded: 1922
President: David Gray
Chairman: Paul Lunn
Secretary: John Desbottes, 167 Hillbury Road, Warlingham, Surrey. Tel: 08832 6118 (H), 2992 (W)
Fixtures Secretary: Paul Fettes, 63 Mitchley Hill, Sanderstead, Surrey. Tel: 01–657 7628 (H), 01–686 5611 (W)
Press Officer: Jonathon Chatfield
Club captain (1988–89): Pat Belton
Club captain (1989–90): Eddie Walker
No. of teams: Senior 6, Colts, Minis All age ranges
Club colours: Light blue and white
Nickname: 'Hammers'
Floodlights: Yes (training only)
Membership fees: Full £35, Playing £35, Social £7.50, Colts £15, Student £15
Local newspapers: Croydon Advertiser, Surrey Mirror
League: Surrey 1
League position (1988–89): 5th
League playing record (1988–89): P 10, W 5, D 1, L 4, F 120, A 89

SURREY 2

BEC OLD BOYS

Openview Sports and Social Club, Openview, Earlsfield, London SW18. Tel: 01–874 5411
Founded: 1930
President: Norman Gillis
Chairman: James Farmer

Secretary: Ron Bigden, 28 Woodland Road, Thornton Heath, Surrey. Tel: 0684 2894
Fixtures Secretary: Stefan Skrzynski, 54 Moffat Road, Thornton Heath, Surrey. Tel: 771 0205
Press Officer: Eddie Sanders, Charlwood Mansions, 2 Weir Road, London SW2
Club captain (1988–89): Mike Chapman
Club captain (1989–90): T.B.A.
No. of teams: Senior 4
Clubhouse facilities: Open every evening and all day Sunday and Saturday
Club colours: Blue, one gold and white. (*Change colours:*)
Floodlights: No
Membership fees: Full £15
Local newspaper: Wandsworth Borough News
League: Surrey 2B
League position (1988–89): 3rd
League playing record (1988–89): P 11, W 8, D 0, L 3, F 193, A 84

CHARING CROSS & WESTMINSTER HOSPITALS

CXW Athletics Union, Stoke D'Abernon, Cobham, Surrey. Tel: 0932 62013.
Founded: 1984
Secretary: The Hon. Secretary, Westminster Medical School, Horseferry Road, London, SW1P 2AR. Tel: 01-828 9811. Extn. 2289 (W)
League Contact: J. Griffiths, Srodent Union, Charing Cross/Westminister Hospital, St. Dunstan's Road, London W6 8RP. Tel: 01–748 2040.
League: Surrey 2A

COBHAM

Fairmile Lane, Cobham Surrey. Tel: 0932 63245 (previously Old Surbitonians)
Founded: 1930
President: Richard Blackman
Chairman: David Lofting
Secretary: Ian Johnson, 209 Portsmouth Road, Cobham, Surrey. Tel: 0932 62694 (H), 01–942 1033 (W)
Fixtures Secretary: Graham Finch, 23 Arlington Road, Surbiton, Surrey. Tel: 01–399 3049 (H), 01–673 7777 (W)
Press Officer: Tony Maddocks, 18 Clayton Drive, Rydes Hill, Guildford, Surrey. Tel: 0483 576792
Coach: David Doughty
Club captain (1988–89): Steve Coleman
Club captain (1989–90): Andrew Harburn
No. of teams: Senior 4, Youth 1, Minis 6
Directions to ground: Ground is at the junction of Fairmile Lane and Portsmouth Road (old A3), 2 miles from Esher, 1 mile from Cobham
Clubhouse facilities: 4 changing rooms, bar, dining area
Club colours: Blue maroon and gold
Floodlights: Yes (partial)
League: Surrey 2
League position (1988–89): 11th (relegated)
League playing record (1988–89): P 35, W 10, D 1, L 24, F 334, A 748

LAW SOCIETY

c/o Old Wimbledonians Cricket Club, Clayton Road, Hook, surrey. Tel: 01–397 1962
Founded: 1964
Chairman: Andrew Beer
Secretary: Adam Signy, 61 Ferntower Road, London N5 2JE. Tel: 01–226 8654 (H), 01–600 0808 (W)
Fixtures Secretary: John Smith, 55 Turney Road, Dulwich, London SE21 7JB. Tel: 01–733 8828 (H), 01–727 0581 (W)
Club captain (1988–89): Tim Richards

Club captain (1989–90): Richard Hale
No. of teams: Senior 4
Directions to ground: TAke A3 and come off at Hooks roundabout, take Hook Road and ground is 300 yds on right along Clayton Road
Clubhouse facilities: Bar and tearooms open on matchdays
Club colours: Black with purple and white hoops, black shorts
Floodlights: No
Membership fees: Full £35, Playing £35, Social £5, Student £20
League: Surrey 2B
League position (1988–89): 5th
League playing record (1988–89): P 11, W 7, D 1, L 3, F 151, A 113

MITCHAM

Wandle Valley Hospital Grounds, Middleton Road, Carshalton, Surrey. Tel: 648 4626
Founded: 1934
President: Richard King
Chairman: Mike Kelly
Secretary: Tony Simmons, 45 Derek Avenue, Wallington, Surrey. Tel: 01–773 0535
Fixtures Secretary: Gary Ashburn, 142 Northwood Road, Thornton Heath, Surrey. Tel: 01–771 0791
Club captain (1988–89): Paul Keery
Club captain (1989–90): Barry Drinkwater
No. of teams: Senior 4, Youth 6
Directions to ground: Turn left out of Mitcham Junction Station and then right at Goat pub. Ground is on the left (entrance to Wandle Valley Hospital)
Clubhouse facilities: Since July 1987 we have been on a month to month basis with local Health Authority that own our ground. It is in the process of being sold off for redevelopment. Once this is finalised we will be without a home and no where to go
Club colours: Green and lavender hoops, white shorts. (*Change colours:* Green shirts)
Floodlights: Yes (training only)
League: Surrey 2B
League position (1988–89): 4th
League playing record (1988–89): P 11, W 7, D 1, L 3, F 180, A 97

OLD HAILEYBURIANS & ISC

27 Ruxley Lane, Kingston Road, Ewell, Surrey. Tel: 01-393 3901.
Founded: 1903
Secretary: P.J.F. Whyte, 49 Wandsworth Common, Westside London SW18 2EE. Tel: 01-874 4745 (H), 01-930 7571 (W).
Fixtures Secretary: S.N. Hill, Willowtree Cottage, Early Dene, Sunninghill, Berks. Tel: 01-390 5646.
Leaue Contact: S. Clarke, 56 The Chase, London SW4. Tel: 01–720 6593.
League: Surrey 2A

OLD JOHNIANS

Oaken Lane, Claygate, Surrey. Tel: 01–398 0535
Founded: 1960
President: A.E.T. Stroud
Chairman: S.E. Dunsford
Secretary: R.S.T. Gunter, 69 Narbonne Avenue, London SW4 9JP. Tel: 01–675 1801 (H), 01–626 0155 (W)
Fixtures Secretary: Gordon Caporn, 16C Harwood Road, Fulham, London SW6 4PH. Tel: 01–736 3990 (H), 01–488 2488 (W)
Press Officer: As Fixtures Secretary
Club captain (1988–89): Steve Parrott
Club captain (1989–90): T.B.A.
No. of teams: Senior 4
Directions to ground: By rail: Hindley Wood Station from Waterloo. By road: From Eshers' Scilly Isles at

end of Kingston bypass take Littleworth Road which
runs into Oaken Lane
Clubhouse facilities: 4 changing rooms
Club colours: Green and white quarters
Floodlights: No
Membership fees: Full £30, Playing £30, Student £1.50
per game
Local newspaper: Esher News
League: Surrey 2B
League position (1988–89): 6th
League playing record (1988–89): P 11, W 5, D 0,
L 6, F 136, A 183

RAYNES PARK

Taunton Avenue, Raynes Park SW20. Tel: 946 8385
Founded: 1923
President: Alistair Ritchie
Chairman: David Tuffin
Secretary: Russell Price, 11 Claremont Avenue, New
Malden KT3 6QL. Tel: 949 2448
Fixtures Secretary: Peter Perrin, 33 Hanover Road,
Wimbledon SW19. Tel: 543 5333
Club captain (1988–89): Mark Muncer
Club captain (1989–90): Mark Muncer
No. of teams: Senior 4
Directions to ground: From Raynes Park Station
proceed along Coombe Lane to West Barnes Lane,
turn left at traffic lights then first right into Taunton
Avenue
Club colours: Blue and gold shirts, navy shorts and
socks
Floodlights: Yes
Local newspapers: Wimbledon News, Guardian,
Surrey Comet
League: Surrey 2
League position (1988–89): 4th

UNIVERSITY VANDALS

Brownacres, Tow Path, Walton-on-Thames, Surrey.
Tel: 0932 229610/227659
Founded: 1932
President: Peter A. Annett
Chairman: Rex
Secretary: Anthony E. Dudman, Long Cottage, 21
Crescent Road, Shepperton, Middx TW17 8BL. Tel:
0932 228655 (H), 0272 693831 ext. 4699 (W)
Fixtures Secretary: C. Cockrean, 94 Albany Road,
Hersham, Walton-on-Thames, Surrey. Tel: 0932
226837
Coach: R. Montgomery
Club captain (1988–89): Martin Dorsett
Club captain (1989–90): Steve Gulliver
No. of teams: Senior 5, Youth 4, Minis 6
Directions to ground: At Walton Bridge turn along
Thames towpath (Walton Lane and Coweysale)
upstream and cross bridge on right-hand side over
Desborough Cut. Proceed to ground, keeping river on
right-hand side and Water Works Reservoir on left
Clubhouse facilities: Bar, changing rooms, shower,
bath, tearoom
Club colours: Black, green, maroon
Nickname: Vandals
Floodlights: Yes (training only)
Membership fees: Full £40, Playing £40, Social £10,
Youth £5, Student £15, OAP £10
Local newspapers: Herald, Esher News
League: Surrey 2
League position (1988–89): 3rd
League playing record (1988–89): P 10, W 6, D 0,
L 4, F 120, A 125

WANDWORTHIANS

The Memorial Ground, Woodstock Lane,
Chessington, Surrey. Tel: 01–398 3720 (previously Old
Wandsworthians)
Founded: 1929
President: John Saunders
Chairman: Denis Norgan

Secretary: Elizabeth Morris, 29 Mullens House,
Chartfield Avenue, Putney, London SW15 6DA. Tel:
01–788 5738 (H), 01–589 5111 ext. 5585 (W)
Fixtures Secretary: Martin Smith, 61 Khama Road,
Tooting, London SW17 0EN. Tel: 01–767 3957
Press Officer: Leslie Herbert, 70 Thorndon Gardens,
Ewell, Surrey. Tel: 01–393 5708 (H), 0784 451400 ext.
3521 (W)
Coach: Terry Mackie
Club captain (1988–89): Denis Norgan
Club captain (1989–90): Christopher Wren
No. of teams: Senior 3
Directions to ground: A3 Hook underpass
Ground capacity: Standing 200
Clubhouse facilities: Bar
Club colours: Maroon, gold and white
Floodlights: No
League: Surrey 2B
League position (1988–89): 2nd
League playing record (1988–89): P 11, W 10, D 0,
L 1, F 207, A 74

WIMBLEDON

Beverley Meads, Barham Road, Copse Hill,
Wimbledon. Tel: 01-946 3156.
Founded: 1865
Secretary: A. Blows, 121 Stoneleigh Park Road,
Ewell, Surrey KT19 0RF. Tel: 01-393 7416 (H). 01-
828 9777 (W).
Fixtures Secretary: B. Thomas, 10 Sycamore Lodge,
Gipsy Lane, Barnes, London SW15. Tel: 01-878 6088.
League Contact: M. J. Keane, 30 Kenross Avenue,
Worcester Park, Surrey KT4 7AF. Tel: 01–337 6036.
Colours: Maroon/Cambridge Blue
League: Surrey 2A
Final position (1988–89): 2nd

SURREY 3

BATTERSEA IRONSIDES

Burntwood Lane, London SW17. Tel: 01-874 9913
Founded: 1943
President: J. Dickeson
Chairman: D. Wright
Secretary: M.P. Tanner, 38 Victory Road,
Wimbledon SW19. Tel: 01-540 5784.
Fixtures Secretary: T. O'Shea, 37 Headington Road,
London SW18. Tel: 01–947 3924.
No. of teams: Senior 4. Youth & Minis 2.
Directions to Ground: BR to Earlsfield Station. Turn
left out of station in Magdalen road. Openview 3rd
right ground at end on left.
Colours: Emerald green with white band.
Floodlights: No
Membership: £20
Local newspaper: Wandsworth Borough News/
Wimbledon Borough News
League: Surrey 3

CHIPSTEAD

The Heads, High Road, Chipstead, Surrey. Tel:
07375 53035
Founded: 1959
President: Colin Vaughan
Chairman: David Barber
Secretary: Peter Thornton, 10 Windsor Avenue,
North Cheam, Sutton, Surrey SM3 9RR. Tel: 01–644
4632 (H), 288 1917 (W).
Fixtures Secretary: Peter Sidebotham. Tel: 07373
56314
Press Officer: Richard Shreeve. Tel: 01–688 2569
No. of teams: Senior 4. Youth & Minis 8.
Colours: Blue/gold. (*Change colours:* Black).
Nickname: Chips
Floodlights: No
Membership: £30

CHOBHAM

Fowlers Wells, Windsor Road, Chobham, Surrey
GU24 8NA. Tel: 09905 8616
Founded: 1968
President: Alan Pinfold
Chairman: Christopher Whiting
Secretary: Brian Moore, 123 Hermitage Woods
Crescent, St. Johns, Woking, Surrey GU21 1UL. Tel:
04867 89225 (H), 01–430 6805 (W)
Fixtures Secretary: Wallace Hooper, 'Dunster',
Fowlers Mead, Chobham, Surrey. Tel: 09905 8661
Press Officer: Bruce Dimelow, 20 Waterers Rise,
Knaphill, Surrey. Tel: 04867 5459 (H), 04862 76155
(W)
Coach: Jonathan Smalley
Club captain (1988–89): Mike Meadway
Club captain (1989–90): Roger McConnell
No. of teams: Senior 4, Youth 4, Minis 4, Over 35s
(Maxis) 1
Directions to ground: M3 Junction 3, A322 towards
Guildford, A319 to Chobham and Woking, left at first
roundabout in Chobham, 2nd right after 600 yds
Ground capacity: Standing Ample
Clubhouse facilities: Open Sat., Sun. and Tues. and
Thurs. evenings
Club colours: Scarlet and gold hooper jerseys, white
shorts, scarlet and gold socks. (*Change colours:* Sky
blue jerseys)
Floodlights: Yes (for training only)
Membership fees: Playing £30, Social £6, Youth £7.50
Local newspaper: Woking News and Mail
League position (1988–89): 11th (relegated)
League playing record (1988–89): P 10, W 1, D 0,
L 9, F 81, A 307

FARNHAM

Westfield Lane, Wrecllesham, Farnham. Tel: 0252
721138
Chairman: D. Rimmer
Secretary: G. Robins, 60 Lower Weybourne Lane,
Farnham, Surrey. Tel: 0252 22106 (H), 711414 (W)
Fixtures Secretary: P. Barnsley, Timberstead, Gone
Hill Drive, Lower Bourne, Farnham, Surrey. Tel:
025125 2352
Coach: T.B.A.
Club captain (1988–89): T.J. Whitear
Club captain (1989–90): E. Van Dongen
No. of teams: Senior 4, Youth 2, Minis 4
Directions to ground: Proceed along Farnham bypass
(A31) towards Alton, turn left at roundabout onto
A325 towards Peterfield. After 1 mile Westfield Lane
on right, ground 50 yds on right
Club colours: Black and white hoops, black shorts,
black socks with white hoops. (*Change colours:* Green
with yellow and red band)
Floodlights: No
League position (1988–89): 10th (relegated)
League playing record (1988–89): P 10, W 2, D 1,
L 6, F 58, A 90
Competitions won:

KING'S COLLEGE HOSPITAL

KCH Playing Fields, Dog Kennel Hill, East Dulwich.
Tel: 01-274 3976.
Founded: 1869
Secretary: A. Padgett, KCHS Students Union, King's
College Hospital, Denmark Hill, London SE5. Tel:
01-274 6222 Extn. 2059.
League Contact: M. Jarvis, 48A Camberwell Church
Street, Camberwell, London SE5 8QZ. Tel: 01–701
9740.

KINGSTON

The Clubhouse, King Edward Recreation Ground,

Hook Road, Kingston, Surrey
Founded: 1887
President: J. Dove
Chairman: P. Stovell
Coach: G. Pickering/A. Hardy
Secretary: D. Wills, Brookwood, Weare Street,
Ockley, Surrey RH5 5NA. Tel: 0306-79222.
Fixtures Secretary: I. Ockendon, 88 Charter Ct,
Lindon Grove, New Malden, Surrey. Tel: 01-949
5828.
League Contact: I. M. Barnes, 18 Osborne Road,
Kingston, Surrey KT2 5HB. Tel: 01-549 2687.
Club captain (1988–89): I. Barnes
No. of teams: Senior 4. Youth & Minis 8.
Directions to Ground: Turn off A3 at Hook
Underpass towards Chessington. Ground 200 yds on
right.
Clubhouse: 2 bars, kitchen, showers, 4 changing
rooms.
Colours: Marron and white hoops, blue shorts.
(*Change colours:* black shirts, amber collar/cuffs.
Floodlights: Yes
Membership: £25
Local newspaper: Surrey Advertiser

OLD FREEMANS

Ashtead Park, Ashtead, Surrey. Tel: Ashtead 74158
Founded: 1931
President: N.H. Barnett
Chairman: J.G. Wild
Coach: H. Carter
Secretary: J.A.V. Maddock, Beech Cottage, Elms
Drive, Leatherhead, Surrey. Tel: L'head (0372)
373148
Fixtures Secretary: J.M. Mason, 30 Ryefield Road,
Upper Norwood, SE19 3QU. Tel: 01-771 5815.
Club captain (1987–88): R. Cox
Club captain (1988–89): M.F. Sims
No. of teams: Senior 5. Youth 1
Directions to Ground: In the grounds of the City of
London Freemen's School, Ashtead Park, Ashtead,
Surrey.
Clubhouse: Licenced!
Colours: Shirts dark blue, maroon and gold. Shorts
dark blue. (*Change colours:* Gold).
Floodlights: Yes, training only.
Membership: £20
Local newspaper: Leatherhead Advertiser

OLD PELHAMIANS

Poulter Park, Bishopsford Road, Mitcham, London.
Tel: 01-648 3755.
Founded: 1969
Secretary: M. Dines, Floor 1, 44 Chatsworth Avenue,
Wimbledon Chase, London SW20. Tel: 01-549 3840
(H), 01-836 9975 (W), 06284 75881 (W).
League Contact: C. Mitchell, 26 Spencer Court,
Spencer Road, London SW20. Tel: 01–944 1394.
Press Officer: John Nicholis. Tel: 01–734 0511.
Colours: Black/Amber.

OLD REEDONIANS

Whiteley Village, Burwood Road, Walton-on-
Thames, Surrey. Tel: 09328 49616
Founded: 1931
Chairman: David McElhiney
Secretary: Simon Bailey, 12 Annett Road, Walton,
Surrey KT12 2JR. Tel: 0932 231130 (H), 01–891 4565
(W)
Fixtures Secretary: Jeremy Isaacs, 39 Rydens Grove,
Hersham, Walton-on-Thames, Surrey KT12 5RU.
Tel: 0932 243021 (H), 01–481 2110 (W)
Press Officer: George Spinks, 47 Quintlis, Roman
Hill, Bracknell, Berkshire RG12 4QQ. Tel: 0344
429786 (H), 0883 46464 (W)
Club captain (1988–89): Roger Deane
Club captain (1989–90): Nicholas Savill
No. of teams: Senior 4

Directions to ground: A3 to Cobham, Surrey, turn off at intersection to Weybridge, down Seven Hills Road to Burwood Road, Whiteley village on right
Clubhouse facilities: Open match days
Club colours: Light blue, dark blue, white and red
Nickname: O.R.'s
Floodlights: Yes
Membership fees: Full £20, Playing £20
Local newspaper: Cobham and Esher News and Mail
League: Surrey 2A
League position (1988–89): 7th
League playing record (1988–89): P 10, W 5, D 0, L 5, F 123, A 152

OLD SUTTONIANS

Old Suttonians Association, Priest Hill Playing Fields, Banstead Road, Ewell, Surrey. Tel: 01 393 7427
Founded: 1970
President: Lt. Col. J.H. Wall
Chairman: Cliff Ford
Secretary: Stuart Udall, 4 Brunswick Manor, Brunswick Road, Sutton, Surrey
League Contact: Ian Moore, 10 Rothesay Avenue, Merton, London SW20 8JU. tel: 01 543 4986 (H). 408 6619 (W)
Fixtures Secretary: As League Contact
Club captain (1988–89): Richard Vernon Burkard
Club captain (1989–90): Richard Vernon Burkard
No. of teams: Senior 3
Club colours: Red, white and black hoops, black shorts. (*Change colours:* No)
Floodlights: No
League: Surrey 2B
League position (1988–89): 11th
League playing record (1988–89): P 31, W 9 D 0, L 22, F 270, A 552

SHIRLEY WANDERERS

Kent Gate, Kent Gate Way, Surrey. Tel: 01–777 5298
Founded: 1956
President: Alan Jenkins
Chairman: Trevor Coles
Secretary: Simon Reed, 40B Church Road, Paddock Wood, Kent. Tel: 089283 6074 (H), 0732 458202 (W)
Fixtures Secretary: David Brown, 'Rams Nest Inn', Ramsnest Common, Chiddingfold, Surrey. Tel: 0428 4460 (H), 4460 (W)
Press Officer: Kevin O'Connell, 62B Maberley Road, London SE19. Tel: 01–771 6804 (H), 0732 458202 (W)
Club captain (1988–89): Martin Stone
Club captain (1989–90): Ian Evans
No. of teams: Senior 5
Clubhouse facilities: Bar, function, changing
Club colours: White
Floodlights: No
Membership fees: Playing £30
Ground admission: Nil
League: Surrey 3
League position (1988–89): 8th
League playing record (1988–89): P 11, W 4, D 0, L 7, F 100, A 144

SURREY 4

BRITISH BROADCASTING CORPORATION

96 Motspur Park, New Malden, Surrey KT3 6PT
Founded: 1924
President: Mrs Muriel Fox
Chairman: Tom Palmer
Secretary: Ian Eggs, 86A Bilton Road, Perivale, Middlesex. Tel: 01 997 4805 (H). 743 8000 (W)
League Contact: As Fixtures Secretary
Fixtures Secretary: Alan O'Halloran, Flat 2, 17

Gordon Place, Kensington, London W8 4JD. Tel: 01 938 1171 (H). 580 4468 Ext 6491 (W)
Press Officer: James Shapland, 40 Tregarvon Road, London SW11. Tel: 01 223 4865 (H). 240 3456 Ext 2688 (W)
Club captain (1988–89): Julian Stewart
Club captain (1989–90): Julian Stewart
No. of teams: Senior 3
Directions to ground: By road: from London travel south on A3. Leave at Malden Underpass, follow directions to Worcester Park, turn left into road called Motspur Park, Ground is on right. By rail: from Waterloo to Motspur Park
Clubhouse facilities: Squash, tennis, multi-gym, sauna, snooker, bar open every day
Club colours: blue, black, gold and silver equal hoops. (*Change colours:* Black)
Nickname: The Beeb
Floodlights: Yes
Membership fees: Closed Club
League: Surrey 3
League position (1988–89): 5th
League playing record (1988–89): P 9, W 5, D 0, L 4, F 87, A 55

LONDON FIRE BRIGADE

Banstead Road, Ewell, Surrey. Tel: 01-394 1946. 01 393 0046.
Founded: 1947
President: G. Clarkson, Chief Officer
Chairman: B. Barklamb
Coach: TBA
Secretary: C. Down, 14 St Botolph Road, Northfleet, Kent DA11 8ES. Tel: 0474 363410.
Fixtures Secretary: B. Barklamb, 20 Northcroft Road, West Ewell, Surrey.
Club captain (1987–88): I. Brunning
Club captain (1988–89): I. Brunning
No. of teams: Senior 3.
Colours: Flame, ember, charcoal. (*Change colours:* Red).
Floodlights: No

OLD BEVONIANS

Ballard Coombe, Robin Hood Way, london SW15 3QX. Tel: 01 942 2907
League contact: M. Hobbs, 121 Tollers Lane, Old Coulsdon, Surrey CR3 1BG. Tel: 0737 555338
Press Officer: Michael Nunney. Tel: 01 949 7564
Club colours: Green/Black/Yellow

OLD CATERHAMIANS

Park Avenue, Caterham-on-the-Hill, Surrey. Tel: 0883 43488
Founded: 1924
President: S.R. Smith
Chairman: W. Broadhead
Secretary: S. Verral, 10 Hillacre, Underwood Road, Caterham, Surrey. Tel: 0883 47211 (H), 01–480 7200 (W)
Fixtures Secretary: A.W. Manly, 404 Brighton Road, South Croydon, Surrey CR2 6AN. Tel: 01–635 4585 (H), 01–681 8226 (W)
Press Officer: C. Haynes, 18 Bourne Street, Old Town, Croydon, Surrey
Club captain (1988–89): M.J. Baxendell
Club captain (1989–90): M.J. Baxendell (prov.)
No. of teams: Senior 4
Directions to ground: From M25 Godstone Junction (6) turn north towards Croydon, signs to Caterham 1 mile (left). Town centre, keep BR station on right go uphill. First left into Stanstead RL, 100 yds on right into Park Avenue. Ground 50 yds on left
Clubhouse facilities: Open matchdays
Club colours: Black with amber, silver, mauve bands. (*Change colours:* yellow and black hoops)

Nickname: Old Cats
Floodlights: Yes
Membership fees: Full £25, Playing £25, Social £10, Student £5
Local newspapers: Croydon Advertiser Series, Surrey Advertiser Series
League: Surrey 4
League position (1988–89): 2nd
League playing record (1988–89): P 9, W 7, D 0, L 2, F 178, A 68

OLD CROYDONIANS

Layhams Road, Keston, Bromley, Kent. Tel: 0959 73409.
Founded: 1924
Secretary: J. Matthews, 12 Birdwood Close, Selsdon, Croydon CA2 8QG. Tel: 01-621 1010. (W)
Colours: Magenta/White/Navy

OLD EPSOMIAN

Big Field Pavilion, Kiln Lane, Brockham, Betchworth, Surrey. Tel: 0737 843942
Founded: 1963
President: Dr. C.A. Hill
Chairman: I. Stewart-Hunter
Secretary: D.C. Kingham, Posterns Farm, Henfold Lane, South Holmwood, Dorking, Surrey RH5 4NX. Tel: 0306 888184 (H), 0737 245757 (W)
Fixtures Secretary: S. Schlaefli, 40 Broadhurst Gardens, Reigate, Surrey RH2 8AW. Tel: 0737 244983 (H), 01–542 6225 (W)
Club captain (1988–89): S. Burgess
Club captain (1989–90): D. Snedden
No. of teams: Senior 3
Directions to ground: A25 from Dorking eastbound for 2 miles, right towards Brockham, after 800 yds turn left. Ground is on left
Club colours: Navy blue shirts, white shorts. (*Change colours:* Navy blue and white narrow hoops)
Floodlights: No
Membership fees: Playing £25, Students & Non-Playing 6
League: Surrey 4
League position (1988–89): 12th (relegated)
League playing record (1988–89): P 26, W 4, D 2, L 20

REIGATE AND REDHILL

Eric Hodgkins Memorial Ground, Colley Lane, Reigate, Surrey. Tel: Reigate 221110
Founded: 1934
President: Mike Tobitt
Chairman: Neil Frederickson
Secretary: Richard Cattaneo, 2 Trindles Road, South Nutfield, Surrey. Tel: 0797 823451 (H), 0306 740521 (W)
Fixtures Secretary: Chris Gamber, 14 Barfields, Bletchley, Godstone, Surrey. Tel: Godstone 843868 (H), 01–488 2131 (W)
Press Officer: Anne St. John Hall, 62 Nutley Lane, Reigate, Surrey. Tel: Reigate 245938
Coach: John Cogbill
Club captain (1988–89): R.A.F. Mattar
Club captain (1989–90): Richard Ekloff
No. of teams: Senior 3, Youth 1
Directions to ground: From Dorking A25 turn into Colley Lane opposite Black Horse Inn
Ground capacity: Standing 5000
Clubhouse facilities: Clubhouse, bar, etc. Rebuilt 1986
Club colours: Royal blue. (*Change colours:* Red)
Nickname: Blues
Floodlights: Yes
Membership fees: Full £35, Playing £4, Social £5, Student £10
Ground admission: Nil
Local newspaper: Surrey Mirror
League: Surrey 3
League position (1988–89): 3rd

League playing record (1988–89): P 37, W 18, D 2, L 17, F 523, A 556
Competitions won: Quins Plate 7's

ROYAL HOLLOWAY AND BEDFORD NEW COLLEGE

Nobles Field, Royal Holloway and Bedford College, Egham Hill, Egham, Surrey TW20 0EX. Tel: 0784 35035
Chairman: Martin Duff
Secretary: Roderick Murchison, as Ground Address (above)
Fixtures Secretary: Andrew Jones, as Ground Address (above)
Club captain (1988–89): David Williams
Club captain (1989–90): Clive Evans
No. of teams: Senior 3
Directions to ground: Junction 13 M25. Follow signs for Egham & Staines, follow route of A30 through Egham to College on Egham Hill
Ground capacity: Standing Unlimited
Clubhouse facilities: Showers, separate changing rooms, bars
Club colours: Myrtle green and purple. (*Change colours:* All purple)
Nickname: The Buddy Hollys
Floodlights: No
Membership fees: Full £10
Ground admission: Nil
League: Surrey 4
League position (1988–89): 2nd
League playing record (1988–89): P 12, W 10, D 0, L 2, F 352, A 85

SHENE OLD GRAMMARIANS

Queen Elizabeth Walk, (off Rocks Lane), Barnes. Tel: 01–876 2059
Founded: 1962
President: Bill Holmes
Chairman: Brian Clymer
Secretary: R. Church, 44 South Street, Epsom, Surrey KT18 7PQ. Tel: Epsom 40907
Fixtures Secretary: Peter Winnicki, 24 Lillian Road, Barnes SW13. Tel: 741 0371
Press Officer: Brian White, 118 Sutton Court, Chiswick W4. Tel: 0747 0846
Coach: Keith Brown
Club captain (1988–89): Martin Smith
Club captain (1989–90): Duncan Green
No. of teams: Senior 2
Directions to ground: Barn Elms Sports Ground (behind Red Lion public house), Queen Elizabeth Walk (off Rocks Lane), Barnes
Clubhouse facilities: Bar, changing rooms. Food
Club colours: Sky blue. (*Change colours:* Red)
Floodlights: No
Membership fees: Full £15
League: Surrey 3
League position (1988–89): 8th

SURREY POLICE

Police H.Q., Sandy Lane, Guildford, Surrey. Tel: 0483 571212
Founded: 1963
President: Chief Con. B. Hayes, Q.P.M.
Chairman: Insp. Geoff Langley
Secretary: C.I. Shane Burrows, 4 Junewood Close, Woodham, Weybridge, Surrey. Tel: 09323 44607
Fixtures Secretary: Bob Miller, Flat 3, 127 Barnet Wood Lane, Ashtead, Surrey KT21 2LR. Tel: 0372 278486 (H), 0306 882284 ext. 6344 (W)
Press Officer: As Secretary
Coach: Gary Steadman

Club captain (1988–89): Paul Palmer
Club captain (1989–90): Geoffrey Brookes
No. of teams: Senior 3
Directions to ground: From Guildford town centre
A3100 toward Godalming, turn right opposite The
Ship P/H, then to Police H.Q. Reception mile on left
Ground capacity: Standing 100
Clubhouse facilities: At H.Q.
Club colours: Black shirts/shorts, red socks. (*Change
colours:* Blue shirts)
Nickname: 'Death Warmed Up'
Floodlights: No
League: Surrey 3
League position (1988–89): 3rd
League playing record (1988–89): P 9, W 6, D 1, L 2,
F 129, A 81
Competitions won: Police Athletic Association 7's
Plate

UNIVERSITY OF SURREY

Manor Farm Sports Pavilion, Egerton, Guildford.
Tel: Guildford 505271
President: P.J. Wheeler
Chairman: Andrew Symmonds
Secretary: Darren Williams, c/0 The Student Union,
Surrey University, Guildford, Surrey GU2 5XH. Tel:
0483 509223
Fixtures Secretary: Glyn Billinghurst, as Student
Union (above)
Coach: John Perrin
Club captain (1988–89): Andrew MacInnes
Club captain (1989–90): Prys Jenkins
No. of teams: Senior 3
Directions to ground: Come off the A3 at Guildford,
follow the signs for the hospital. At the roundabout
before turning off for the hospital, ground is on the
left
Clubhouse facilities: Open matchdays, lunchtimes and
evenings
Club colours: Black with blue, red and gold hoops.
(*Change colours:* White with blue, red and gold
hoops)
Floodlights: No
League: Surrey 4
League position (1988–89): 1st (promoted)
League playing record (1988–89): P 12, W 12, D 0,
L 0, F 368, A 64
Competitions won: Surrey League Four Winners

SURREY 5

GIBRALTAR ENGINEERS

No further information available.

HASLEMERE

Sports Ground, Woolmer Hill, Haslemere, Surrey.
Tel: 00428 3072
Founded: 1953
President: John S. Pearce
Chairman: David Mussell
Secretary: c/o Mark Daly, 3 Springfield Court, Copse
Road, Hammer, Haslemere, Surrey GU27 3QQ. Tel:
0483 570608
Fixtures Secretary: Coral Brodie, Mallaig House,
Passfield, Nr. Liphook, Hants GU30 7RH. Tel:
042877 481 (H), 042873 7030 (W)
Club captain (1988–89): Douglas Horne
Club captain (1989–90): T.B.A.
Directions to ground: A3 south to Hindhead traffic
lights, continue for 1 mile approx. at start of dual
carriageway turn left, 400 yds on turn left, ground 200
yds on left
Clubhouse facilities: Hot showers, warm beer, good

company
Club colours: Royal blue and white hoops. (*Change
colours:* Plain blue)
Nickname: 'Mere
Floodlights: Yes (for training only)
Membership fees: Full £15, Playing £15, Social £10
Local newspaper: Haslemere Herald
League: Surrey 3
League position (1988–89): (relegated)

LIGHTWATER

Lightwater Leisure Centre, The Avenue, Lightwater,
Surrey.
Founded: 1975
President: J.D. Barnett
Chairman: J.D. Barnett
Coach: J. Russell
Secretary: A. Sharp, 65 Cedar Close, Bagshot, Surrey
GU19 5AB. Tel: 0276-72994.
Fixtures Secretary: M. Hobson.
League Contact: R. A. Jams, 52 Bedfordshire Way,
Whoose Hiill, Wokingham, Berkshire.
Press Officer: Julian Barnett. Tel: 0276 74834.
Club captain (1988–89): D. Garrett
No. of teams: Senior 2
Directions to Ground: Junction 3 off M3 – head
towards Guildford – first right off dual carriageway –
2nd right up Avenue.
Ground capacity: 500
Clubhouse: Modern bar
Colours: White/green quarters. (*Change colours:*
Blue)
Floodlights: No
Membership: £20
Local newspaper: Camberley News

NORDIC

Thameside Sports & Social Club, Longmead Road,
Weston Green, Thames Ditton, Surrey (new club)
Chairman: David Richards
Secretary: Tony Smith, 88 Bridge Way, Whitton,
Twickenham TW2 7JJ. Tel: 01–894 4065 (H), 01–943
5144 ext. 4598 (W)
Fixtures Secretary: Dave Nicholson, 130 Waldergrave
Road, Teddington, Middx TW11 8NA. Tel: 01–977
7887 (H), 01–943 5144 (W)
Club captain (1988–89): Peter Churchill
Club captain (1989–90): Peter Churchill
No. of teams: Senior 1
Ground capacity: Standing 200
Clubhouse facilities: Showers/changing rooms (4), bar,
snooker, pool hall, etc.
Club colours: Amber/black hoops. (*Change colours:*
Green)
Floodlights: Yes
Membership fees: Full £20, Playing £15, Social £5,
Youth £2, Student £2, OAP £2
Local newspapers: Richmond & Twickenham Times,
Guardian, Informer, Star
League: Surrey County 5

OXTED

Holland Field, Holland Road, Hurst Green, Oxted,
Surrey
Founded: 1984
President: Martin Turner
Chairman: Chris Evamy
Secretary: G.A. Metcalfe, Staffend, Icehouse Wood,
Oxted, Surrey. Tel: 0883 714609
Fixtures Secretary: P. Budge, 18 Orhcard Way, Hurst
Green, Oxted, Surrey. Tel: 0883 713575 (H), 0883
217466 (W)
Club captain (1988–89): Richard Peed
Club captain (1989–90): T.B.A.
No. of teams: Senior 2
Directions to ground: At Oxted turn south on A25
under viaduct into Woodhurst Lane, proceed along
road for 1 miles. Ground on right 100 yds past 'The

Diamond' pub
Clubhouse facilities: Fully licensed facilities.
Weekends and evenings
Club colours: White jersey, red hoop, blue shorts, red
stockings
Nickname: The Oaks
Floodlights: No
Membership fees: Full £30, Playing £30, Social £15,
Youth £15, Student £15, OAP £15
Ground admission: Nil
Local newspapers: County Border News, Surrey
Mirror
League: Surrey 4
League position (1988–89): 3rd
League playing record (1988–89): P 23, W 12, D 1,
L 10, F 324, A 321

RACAL DECCA

Racal Decca Sports & Social Club, Kingston Road,
Tolworth, Surrey. Tel: 01-337 0519.

Founded: 1978
Secretary: N. Charter, 155 Ellerdine Road,
Hounslow, Middlesex TW3 2PU. Tel: 0932 228851.
Extn. 3486 (W).
League Contact: C. Finney, 118 Pinewood Park,
Cove, Farnborough, Hants. GU14 9LF. Tel: 0252
540054.
Colours: Blue/White

WOKING (formerly British Aerospace)

King's Head Lane, Byfleet, Surrey KT14 7AT. Tel:
09323 43601
League Contact: J. Keay, 52 Eden Grove Road,
Byfleet, Surrey. Tel: 09323 49840
Club colours: Blue/gold
League: Surrey 5

TOSHIBA DIVISIONAL CHAMPIONSHIP

1ST MATCHES. Saturday, 3rd December 1989. At Otley.

NORTH	27	MIDLANDS	6

Tries: Morris (1), Pears (1),
R. Underwood (1)
Penalty-Goals: Pears (5)
H.T. 13–3

Try: Cook
Penalty-Goal: Harris
Conversion: Harris

NORTH: S. Langford (Orrell); S. Burnhill (Sale), W. Carling (Harlequins), J. Buckton (Saracens), R. Underwood (Leicester); D. Pears (Sale), D. Morris (Liverpool St. Helens); M. Whitcombe (Sale), M. Fenwick (Durham City), P. Huntsman (Headingley), S. Hodgson (Vale of Lune), W. Dooley (Preston Grasshoppers), R. Kimmins (Orrell), P. Winterbottom (Harlequins) (captain), A. Macfarlane (Sale).

MIDLANDS (Nottingham unless stated): J. Harris (Leicester); B. Evans (Leicester), B. Musto, G. Hartley, S. Hackney; L. Cusworth (Leicester) (captain), S. Robson (Moseley); L. Johnson, B. Moore, G. Pearce (Northampton), J. Wells (Leicester), M. Reid (Leicester), M. Bayfield (Metropolitan Police), G. Rees, P. Cook. Replacements: B. Gabriel (Bedford) for Robson 75 minutes, M. Linnett (Moseley for Pearce 77 minutes.

Referee: B. Anderson, Scotland.

At Gloucester.

SOUTH-WEST	20	LONDON	13

Tries: Swift (2), Barnes (1), Teague (1)
Conversions: Barnes (2)
H.T. 10–9

Tries: Bailey (1), Thresher (1)
Penalty-Goal: Thresher
Conversion: Thresher

SOUTH-WEST (Bath unless stated): J. Webb (Bristol); A. Swift, J. Guscott, S. Hogg (Bristol), R. Knibbs (Bristol); S. Barnes (captain), R. Harding (Bristol); M. Preedy (Gloucester), K. Dunn (Gloucester), R. Pascall (Gloucester), J. Hall, J. Morrison, N. Redman, A. Robinson, M. Teague (Gloucester).

LONDON (Harlequins unless stated): S. Thresher; S. Smith (Wasps), J. Salmon, F. Clough (Wasps), M. Bailey (Wasps); A. Thompson, S. Bates (Wasps); P. Curtis, J. Olver, J. Probyn (Wasps), M. Skinner, N. Edwards, P. Ackford, D. Pegler (Wasps) (captain), J. Ellison (Wasps).

Referee: I. Bullerwell, East Midlands.

Neither game amounted to very much. The North had few problems in turning back the Midlands challenge without looking convincing, whilst in Gloucester the two sides played reasonable rugby after half-time when the South-West were lucky to win with there being an element of doubt about both their tries. Prior to half-time there had been a great deal of "niggle" and at least one England player could consider himself fortunate to be on the field when the teams changed ends.

2ND MATCHES. Saturday, 10th December 1989. At Imber Court.

| LONDON | 36 | NORTH | 4 |

Tries: Bailey (2), Clough (1), Try: R. Underwood
Salmon (1), Ellison (1), Edwards (1)
Penalty-Goals: Thresher (2)
Conversions: Thresher (3) H.T. 10–4

LONDON (Harlequins unless stated): S. Thresher; A. Harriman, F. Clough (Wasps), J. Salmon, M. Bailey (Wasps); A. Thompson, S. Bates (Wasps); P. Curtis, J. Olver, J. Probyn (Wasps), M. Skinner, N. Edwards, P. Ackford, D. Pegler (Wasps) (captain), J. Ellison (Wasps). Replacement: S. Pilgrim (Wasps) for Harriman 2 minutes, A. Mullins for Probyn 56 minutes.

NORTH: S. Langford (Orrell); A. Underwood (Leicester), J. Buckton (Saracens), W. Carling (Harlequins), R. Underwood (Leicester); D. Pears (Sale), D. Morris (Liverpool St. Helens); M. Whitcombe (Sale), M. Fenwick (Durham City), P. Huntsman (Headingley), S. Hodgson (Vale of Lune), R. Kimmins (Orrell), W. Dooley (Preston Grasshoppers), P. Winterbottom (Harlequins) (captain), A. Macfarlane (Sale).

Referee: L. Peard, Wales.

At Nottingham.

| MIDLANDS | 16 | SOUTH-WEST | 14 |

Try: Mosses Tries: Teague (1), Webb (1), Guscott (1)
Dropped-Goal: Dodge Conversion: Barnes
Penalty-Goals: Hodgkinson H.T. 6–10

MIDLANDS (Nottingham unless stated): S. Hodgkinson; B. Evans (Leicester), P. Dodge (Leicester), M. Stiles, S. Hackney; L. Cusworth (Leicester) (captain), S. Robson (Moseley); M. Linnett (Moseley), B. Moore, G. Mosses, J. Wells (Leicester), M. Bayfield (Metropolitan Police), M. Reid (Leicester), G. Rees, P. Cook.

SOUTH-WEST (Bath unless stated): J. Webb (Bristol); A. Swift, R. Knibbs (Bristol), J. Guscott, A. Lumsden; S. Barnes (captain), R. Hill; M. Preedy (Gloucester), G. Dawe, R. Pascall (Gloucester), J. Hall, J. Morrison, N. Redman, A. Robinson, M. Teague (Gloucester).

Referee: C. High, Manchester.

This was a far better day with the so-called "underdogs" winning in each case – Midlands perhaps fortuitously and London with conviction. The latter shrugged off an early Rory Underwood try to come back and outplay the Northerners, unbeaten in their previous eight divisional outings. By the end of the match the North had been completely demolished as two easy late London tries testified; a well drilled squad was just too much for the opposition. Midlands were outscored in terms of tries (3–1), but took their kicking chances against a tactically barren South-West side; Dodge won the match for them with a very late dropped-goal.

3RD MATCHES. Saturday, 17th December 1989. At Imber Court.

| LONDON | 27 | MIDLANDS | 9 |

Tries: Bates (1), Pegler (1), Try: Hackney
Thresher (1), Ackford (1), Conversion: Hodgkinson
Penalty-Goals: Thresher (3)
Conversion: Thresher H.T. 10–0

LONDON (Harlequins unless stated): S. Thresher; S. Smith (Wasps), J. Salmon, M. Bailey (Wasps); A. Thompson, S. Bates (Wasps); P. Curtis, J. Olver, J. Probyn (Wasps), M. Skinner, N. Edwards, P. Ackford, D. Pegler (Wasps) (captain), J. Ellison (Wasps).

MIDLANDS (Nottingham unless stated): S. Hodgkinson; B. Evans (Leicester), P. Dodge (Leicester), G. Hartley, S. Hackney; L. Cusworth (Leicester) (captain), S.

Robson (Moseley); L. Johnson, B. Moore, G. Mosses, J. Wells (Leicester), M. Reid (Leicester), M. Bayfield (Metropolitan Police), G. Rees, D. Richards (Leicester). Replacement: J. Harris (Leicester) for Cusworth 39 minutes.

Referee: O. Doyle, Ireland.

At Orrell.

NORTH	14	SOUTH-WEST	12
Tries: Dooley (1), R. Underwood (1)		Try: Swift	
Penalty-Goals: Carling (2)		Penalty-Goals: Barnes (2)	
H.T. 14–6		Conversion: Barnes	

NORTH: M. Lowther (Sale); T. Underwood (Leicester), W. Carling (Harlequins), B. Barley (Wakefield), R. Underwood (Leicester); S. Townend (Wakefield), D. Morris (Liverpool St. Helens); M. Whitcombe (Sale), N. Hitchen (Orrell), D. Southern (Orrell), S. Hodgson (Vale of Lune), W. Dooley (Preston Grasshoppers), R. Kimmins (Orrell), P. Winterbottom (Harlequins) (captain), P. Buckton (Liverpool St. Helens). Replacements: J. Buckton (Saracens) for T. Underwood 9 minutes, G. Doggart (Aspatria) for Lowther 80 minutes.

SOUTH-WEST (Bath unless stated): A. Buzza (Canbridge University); A. Swift, R. Knibbs (Bristol), J. Guscott, A. Lumsden; S. Barnes (captain), R. Hill; M. Preedy (Gloucester), K. Dunn (Gloucester), R. Pascall (Gloucester), J. Hall, J. Morrison, N. Redman, A. Robinson, M. Teague (Gloucester). Replacement: I. Smith (Gloucester) for Morrison 39 minutes.

Referee: R. Quittenton, London.

In keeping with the fact that the divisional matches had been of a better quality than in previous years the tournament ended with one good match and one which was exciting even though comparatively low-scoring by modern standards. London – usual back-markers – deservedly won the championship and deprived the North of their title after two seasons; although they did so only on points difference they were the most enterprising team amongst the divisions and played an all-round game which was not only attractive to watch but also effective. They had several players who advanced their England claims notably Stuart Thresher at full back, scrum-half Bates and all the forwards – Ellison and Curtis being noticeable examples. Their existing capped players did their chances of retention in the ranks no obvious harm.

The other divisions did less well although the South-West no. 8 from Gloucester, Mike Teague, had a fine tournament. Others did not really live up to expectations and injuries to important players such as South-West full back Jon Webb did the England cause no good at a time when national morale was very high.

However, for the first time the tournament did the impression that it had been a worthwhile exercise, from which the England selectors will have learned some useful pieces of information.

PILKINGTON CUP

Semi-Finals. Saturday, 25th March 1989. At Kingsholm, Gloucester.

GLOUCESTER	3	BATH	6

GLOUCESTER
Penalty-Goal: T. Smith
H.T. 3–6

BATH
Penalty-Goals: Barnes (2)

GLOUCESTER: T. Smith; J. Breeze, D. Cummins, R. Mogg, N. Price; M. Hamlin, M. Hannaford (captain); M. Preedy, K. Dunn, R. Pascall, J. Gadd, N. Scrivens, J. Etheridge, I. Smith, B. Clark.

BATH: A. Lumsden; A. Swift, S. Halliday, J. Guscott, B. Trevaskis; S. Barnes (captain), R. Hill; G. Chilcott, G. Dawe, R. Lee, A. Robinson, J. Morrison, N. Redman, J. Hall, D. Egerton.

Referee: R. Quittenton, London.

At the Stoop Memorial Ground, Twickenham.

HARLEQUINS   7   LEICESTER   16
Try: Cramb   Tries: Hare (1), Kardooni (1)
Penalty-Goal: S. Thresher   Dropped-Goal: Cusworth
                                                                    Penalty-Goal: Hare
H.T. 3–10   Conversion: Hare

HARLEQUINS: S. Thresher; J. Eagle, J. Salmon, A. Thompson, E. Davis; R. Cramb, C. Luxton; P. Curtis, J. Olver (captain), A. Mullins, M. Skinner, N. Edwards, P. Ackford, P. Winterbottom, D. Thresher.

LEICESTER: W. Hare; A. Underwood, P. Dodge (captain), I. Bates, R. Underwood; L. Cusworth, A. Kardooni; S. Redfern, T. Thacker, W. Richardson, J. Wells, M. Foulkes-Arnold, T. Smith, D. Richards.

Referee: I. Bullerwell, Midlands.

HARLEQUINS lost their crown and deserved to do so even though it needed the craft of the wily veterans Cusworth and Hare to do it for them. The home team had a poor first-half and also squandered numerous chances to keep themselves at least in touch with penalty attempts, whereas the Tigers took most of their chances with Hare even scoring their first try from a Cusworth cross-kick. Harlequins did well in the line-out, but were outplayed in the second phase and were perhaps fortunate not to lose Skinner, twice warned by the referee, before the end.

Bath just about earned their win at Gloucester in a poor game decided by penalties with all the scoring coming in the first-half, but who would bet against them in the final?

THE PILKINGTON CUP

1st Round
(Saturday 17th September 1988)
South

Barking	12	Ealing	7
Berry Hill	18	Askeans	7
Brixham	38	Okehampton	9
Combe Down	10	Havant	24
Exeter	40	Sudbury	12
Finchley	10	Lydney	9
Guildford & Godalming	12	Old Culverhaysians	20
Marlow	15	Maidstone	37
Medway	11	Old Mid's	9

Met. Police	13	Reading	11
North Walsham	38	Old Juddians	6
Oxford	17	Tabard	6
Redruth	21	Worthing	6
Swindon	22	Ruislip	0

North

Birkenhead Park	13	Bedworth	7
Fylde	17	Wolverhampton	6
Harrogate	10	West Hartlepool	22
Hereford	18	Leighton Buzzard	12
Matlock	12	Aspatria	34
Middlesbrough	30	West Park	21
Newark	6	Winnington Park	12
Plymouth Albion	60	Stoke Old Boys	3
Rugby	27	Vale of Lune	6
Sandal	0	Durham City	3
Sheffield	3	Wakefield	16
Stoneygate	9	Nuneaton	30
Tynedale	15	Stockwood Park	0
Widnes	16	Bromsgrove	13

Result of the round: Finchley 10, Lydney 9.

2nd Round

Bedford	16	Nuneaton	0
Berry Hill	24	London Welsh	9
Birkenhead Park	3	Tynedale	38
Coventry	7	Plymouth Albion	12
Durham City	19	Sale	10
Exeter	18	Redruth	3
Finchley	6	Richmond	40
Gosforth	31	Fylde	10
Headingley	7	Wakefield	10
Hereford	28	Widnes	9
London Irish	25	Met. Police	13
Maidstone	12	London Scottish	37
Medway	9	Havant	30
Middlesbrough	12	Aspatria	18
North Walsham	3	Saracens	31
Old Culverhaysians	3	Brixham	13
Oxford	28	Barking	0
Swindon	3	Blackheath	13
West Hartlepool	9	Rugby	30
Winnington Park	4	Northampton	37

Result of the round: Durham City 19, Sale 10.

3rd Round

Aspatria	6	Moseley	3
Bath	82	Oxford	9
Bedford	3	Nottingham	6
Blackheath	6	Waterloo	13
Bristol	13	Orrell	7
Brixham	4	Gloucester	28
Gosforth	9	Wakefield	29
Havant	9	Exeter	3
Hereford	10	Tynedale	6
Liverpool St. Helens	6	Leicester	37
London Irish	14	Berry Hill	3

London Scottish	16	Saracens	0
Richmond	6	Northampton	0
Rosslyn Park	18	Plymouth	0
Rugby	3	Harlequins	25
Wasps	33	Durham City	3

Result of the round: Aspatria 6, Moseley 3.

4th Round

Bath	48	Hereford	0
Bristol	45	London Irish	16
Gloucester	19	Waterloo	16
Harlequins	22	London Scottish	6
Richmond	9	Nottingham	12
Rosslyn Park	9	Leicester	23
Wakefield	18	Havant	10
Wasps	39	Aspatria	7

Match of the round: Gloucester 19, Waterloo 16.

Semi-Finals

| Gloucester | 3 | Bath | 6 |
| Harlequins | 7 | Leicester | 16 |

(Saturday, 25th March 1989)

Final

| Bath | 10 | Leicester | 6 |

(Saturday, 29th April 1989 at Twickenham)

ACKNOWLEDGEMENTS

ONCE AGAIN it is our pleasure to acknowledge all the help we have been given in producing this second Directory – starting appropriately with Courage Ltd. and the Executive Director of Public Affairs, Michael Reynolds.

In our Editorial the tremendous efforts of Michael Humphreys and his company's team have been acknowledged, but the thanks can well be repeated, whilst we could not possibly have produced the book on time without the extraordinary dedication and energy shown by Ken and May Culver and their very efficient team at MC Typeset Ltd. From Harmsworth Publications there was the support and help of Sally Cartwright, the Managing Director, Ken Hole and their efficient staff.

Assembling a directory of this nature is a mammoth task and it can never be accomplished in a satisfactory manner wtihout the help of the clubs secretaries, whose task it is to send in information, all of which we try to print. As the years roll on not only will this process become much easier for all concerned, but also as clubs realise how potentially good the book must be for their own prestige and publicity they will themselves insist on supplying more and more information and pictures, which will go into each succeeding publication.

We are most grateful to all those secretaries and press officers, who replied to our requests for information (and this year they were in a vast majority), and we would suggest that next year you not only supply us with as much information and photographic material that you can, but also bombard us with constructive ideas which would help us to make this a better book. It is your directory and you have a right to the best.

PILKINGTON CUP FINAL

Saturday, 29th April 1989. At Twickenham.

BATH	10	LEICESTER	6

BATH 10   LEICESTER 6
Fry: Barnes   Penalty-Goals Hare (2)
Penalty-Goals: Barnes (2)   H.T. 0–6

BATH: J. Palmer; A. Swift, S.Halliday, J. Guscott, F. Sagoe; S. Barnes (captain), R. Hill; G. Chilcott, G. Dawe, M. Lee, J. Hall, J. Morrison, D. Cronin, A. Robinson, D. Egerton. Replacement: P. Simpson for Egerton 52 minutes.

LEICESTER: W. Hare; B. Evans, P. Dodge (captain), I. Bates, R. Underwood; L. Cusworth, A. Kardooni; S. Redfern, T. Thacker, W. Richardson, J. Wells, M. Foulkes-Arnold, T. Smith, I. Smith, D. Richards.

Referee: F. Howard, Liverpool.

A CROWD of 58,000, which was a club record attendance for the whole world, came to see the country's two most charismatic teams and also – for the uncommitted and Leicester fans – to witness a triumphant finale to the great career of the much loved full back Dusty Hare.

In the event Hare did not let anyone down by putting over two penalties to give his side a first half lead, which was only caught by the determined favourites from Bath with some 11 minutes of the game left. Then the intensive pressure from the West Country side finally paid off in injury time as Stuart Barnes, their captain and score leveller with his own two penalties, forced his way over from a scrum and the gallant "Tigers" were buried.

It was a game of emotion rather than incident with the play – although absorbing – more notable for effort and commitment than for brilliant rugby with forwards mostly the heroes – especially Chilcott and Cronin for Bath. Barnes took his chances well and was an inspiring captain.

Leicester defended bravely when Bath applied the pressure, but their inability to force any serious attacks of their own in the second half was their eventual undoing. It was a game for the conoisseur.

SEVENS TOURNAMENTS

ENGLAND
OXFORDSHIRE
Sunday, 16th April 1989, at Iffley Road, Oxfordshire
London Scot 16 Blackheath 12

WIMPEY HOMES
Wednesday, 26th April 1989, at Rosslyn Park
London Scot 22 Public SW 6

IRELAND
OLD BELVEDERE
Sunday, 23rd April 1989, at Donnybrook, Dublin
Harlequins 24 London Irish 6

SCOTLAND
GALA
Saturday, 1st April 1989
Saltires 24 Jed-Forest 22

MELROSE
Saturday, 8th April 1989
Kelso 28 Ayr 22

HAWICK
Saturday, 15th April 1989
Jed-Forest 34 Melrose 6

EARLSTON
Sunday, 16th April 1989
Gala 32 St. Boswells 12

JED-FOREST
Saturday, 22nd April 1989
Selkirk 12 Hawick 6

LANGHOLM
Saturday, 29th April 1989
Jed-Forest 32 Selkirk 8

SAVE & PROSPER MIDDLESEX SEVENS

Finals: Saturday, 6th May 1989, at Twickenham

6th Round: Bristol 6 London Irish 4; Blackheath 26 Richmond 6; Rosslyn Park I 16 Old Alleynians 0; Loughborough Students 16 Hawick 8; London Scottish I 26 Rugby 6; Rosslyn Park II 18 London Scottish II 12; Wasps 22 Saracens 0; Harlequins 24 West London Institute 10.

Quarter-Finals: Bristol 20 Blackheath; Rosslyn Park I 14 Loughborough Students 12; London Scottish I 34 Rosslyn Park II 6; Harlequins 16; Wasps 10.

Semi-Finals: Rosslyn Park I 20 Bristol 16 (aet); Harlequins 16 London Scottish 12.

Final: Harlequins 18 Rosslyn Park I 12.

Teams in Final: Harlequins: J. Johnston, J. Eagle (capt.), A. Thompson, R. Glenister; C. Sheasby, P. Winterbottom, S. Thresher. Rosslyn Park I: K. Wyles, S. Hunter, M. Jermyn, A. Woodhouse (capt.); T. Hyde, D. Barnett, A. Dent. Referee: F. Howard. Scorers in Final: Harlequins: Sheasby 1 try, Glenister 1 try, Eagle 1 try, Thresher 3 cons. Rosslyn Park I: Wyles 1 try, Jermyn 1 try, 2 cons.

THE Harlequin wagon rolls on and this was a fourth consecutive success achieved with a greatly depleted side compared to the one which overwhelmed Wasps in the Wang National Sevens final. Even so the combination was just good enough to make it despite the calls of England 'B' and others but there were no easy matches this time enroute to victory with Wasps, London Scottish and finalists Rosslyn Park I all giving them a hard time.

OTHER RESULTS 1988–89

TABLE

	P	W	L	F	A	Pts
North	3	3	0	51	28	6
Midlands	3	1	2	49	44	2
South-West	3	1	2	28	30	2
London	3	1	2	15	41	2

UNIVERSITY MATCH
(at Twickenham)
Oxford v Cambridge 27–7

INTER-SERVICES CHAMPIONSHIP
(at Twickenham)

Royal Navy v The Army	3–35
Royal Navy v Royal Air Force	23–30
The Army v Royal Air Force	43–10

KNOCK-OUT CUP
Results of finals to date

1972	Gloucester v Moseley	17–6
1973	Coventry v Bristol	27–15
1974	Coventry v London Scottish	26–6
1975	Bedford v Rosslyn Park	28–12
1976	Gosforth v Rosslyn Park	23–14
1977	Gosforth v Waterloo	27–11
1978	Gloucester v Leicester	6–3
1979	Leicester v Moseley	15–12
1980	Leicester v London Irish	21–9
1981	Leicester v Gosforth	22–15
1982	Glucester v Moseley	12–12
	(Title shared)	
1983	Bristol v Leicester	28–22
1984	Bath v Bristol	10–9
1985	Bath v London Welsh	24–15
1986	Bath v Wasps	25–17
1987	Bath v Wasps	19–12
1988	Harlequins v Bristol	28–22
1989	Bath v Leicester	10–6

ENGLAND COUNTY CUP FINALS 1988–89

NORTH DIVISION
Cheshire: Lymm 25 West Cheshire College 3
Cumbria: Aspatria 21 Carlisle 3
Durham: West Hartlepool 19 Hartlepool Rovers 6 (at Hartlepool Rovers)
Lancashire: Orrell 48, Broughton Park 6
Northumberland: Northern 24 Tynedale 16 (after 12–12 draw)
Yorkshire: Headingley 48 Otley 9

MIDLANDS DIVISION
Bedfordshire*: Stockwood Park 16 Leighton Buzzard 6
Leicestershire: Vipers 12 Ston'gate 6
North Midlands: Dudley Kingswinford 11 Old Yardleians 6
Notts., Lincs. & Derbys.: Mansfield 7 Newark 6
Nottinghamshire*: Newark 111 Mansfield 6
Staffordshire: Stafford 6 Lichfield 3
Warwickshire: Bedworth 12 Old Leamingtonians 11

WEST & SOUTH WEST DIVISION
Berkshire: Reading 8 Maidenhead 4
Buckingham: High Wycombe 21 Marlow 3
Cornwall: Camborne 12 Redruth 3
Devon: Exeter 17 Barnstaple 9
Dorset & Wiltshire: Swanage & Wareham 12 Swindon 6
Gloucestershire: Berry Hill 37 Drybrook 6
Somerset: Taunton 12 Combe Down OB 10

LONDON & SOUTH EAST DIVISION
Eastern Counties: North Walsham 3 Barking 0
Hampshire: Havant 15 Basingstoke 13
Hertfordshire: Cheshunt 15 Tabard 7
Kent: Askeans 16 Sidcup 6
Middlesex: Ealing 7 Ruislip 6
Surrey: Old Alleynians 16 Streatham-Croydon 3
Sussex: Worthing 15 Lewes 3
* Winners do not qualify for Pilkington Cup.

INDEX

DIVISIONS & LEAGUES INDEX

When three page numbers are shown they indicate the start of that league's section, its fixture page and the start of the club section. When only one number is given, that league's section runs concurrently.

When three page numbers are shown they indicate the start of that league's section, its fixture page and the start of the club section. When only one number is given, that league's section runs concurrently.

INDEX OF CLUBS

P

MATCHES WATCHED – 1989–90

DATE	FIXTURE	VENUE	TEAM (HOME)
WED 13 SEP	CLUB MATCH	BOWER PARK	MET-POLICE
SAT 07 OCT		IMBER COURT	ASPATRIA
WED 13 SEP	CLUB MATCH	IMBER COURT	MET-POLICE
SAT 07 OCT		BOWER PARK	ASPATRIA
SAT 11 NOV	C-C-C NTH DIV-1	QUENDEN PARK	HALIFAX
SAT 25 NOV	C-C-C NAT DIV-3	CHANDOS PARK	ROUNDHAY
SAT 30 DEC	CLUB MATCH	OLD DEER PARK	LONDON WELSH
SAT 13 JAN	C-C-C DIV-3		LONDON WELSH

TEAM	RESULTS			
HARLEQUINS	13	26		
NEW BRIGHTON	21	15		
HARLEQUINS	13	26		
NEW BRIGHTON	21	15		
IRKENHEAD PK	12	10		
ONDON WELSH	22	6		
WASPS	8	25		
FYLDE	29	9		

608

NOTES

NOTES

NOTES

NOTES

NOTES

LEAGUE
STRUCTURE

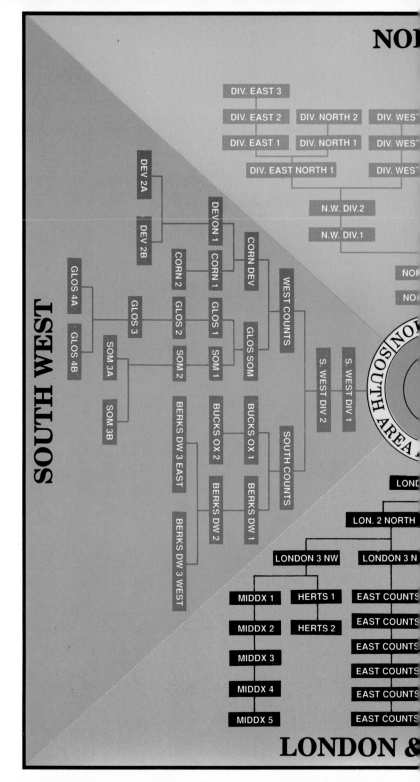

NO[RTH]

DIV. EAST 3

DIV. EAST 2   DIV. NORTH 2   DIV. WEST

DIV. EAST 1   DIV. NORTH 1   DIV. WEST

DIV. EAST NORTH 1   DIV. WES[T]

DEV 2A

DEV 2B

DEVON 1

CORN 2   CORN 1

GLOS 4A

GLOS 4B

GLOS 2   GLOS 1

GLOS 3

SOM 2   SOM 1

SOM 3A

SOM 3B

CORN DEV

GLOS SOM

WEST COUNTS

N.W. DIV.2

N.W. DIV.1

NO[RTH]

NO[RTH]

SOUTH WEST

S. WEST DIV 2   S. WEST DIV 1

BERKS DW 3 EAST

BUCKS OX 2   BUCKS OX 1

BUCKS OX   BERKS DW 1

BERKS DW 2

SOUTH COUNTS

BERKS DW 3 WEST

LONDON 3 NW

MIDDX 1   HERTS 1

MIDDX 2   HERTS 2

MIDDX 3

MIDDX 4

MIDDX 5

LON[DON]

LON. 2 NORTH

LONDON 3 N

EAST COUNTS

EAST COUNTS

EAST COUNTS

EAST COUNTS

EAST COUNTS

EAST COUNTS

LONDON &

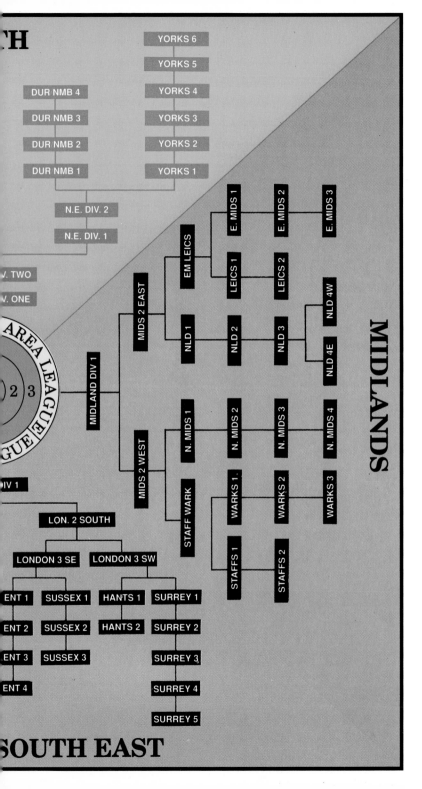